STANDARD MATHEMATICAL TABLES

TENTH EDITION

FORMERLY MATHEMATICAL TABLES
FROM HANDBOOK OF CHEMISTRY AND PHYSICS

Editor in Chief

Charles D. Hodgman, M.S.
Professor Emeritus, Case Institute of Technology

Associate Editor in Charge of Chemistry
Robert C. Weast, Ph.D.
Associate Professor of Chemistry at Case Institute of Technology

Associate Editor in Charge of Physics
Clarence W. Wallace, M.S.
Assistant Professor of Physics at Case Institute of Technology

Associate Editor in Charge of Mathematics
Samuel M. Selby, Ph.D.
Chairman, Mathematics Department at University of Akron

THREE DOLLARS IN UNITED STATES
THREE DOLLARS AND FIFTY CENTS OUTSIDE UNITED STATES

CHEMICAL RUBBER PUBLISHING COMPANY
2310 Superior Avenue, N. E. Cleveland, Ohio.

Preface

The collection of mathematical tables and formulae presented in this volume, although different in form, is similar in content with the mathematical section of the current edition of the Handbook of Chemistry and Physics.

Originally intended to provide adequate means for the ordinary computations of chemistry and physics the collection has been gradually enlarged and has for several years been published as a separate book. In response to the increasing demand for the small volume this desk size is offered as better suited to constant use. Modified type and spacing made possible by the larger page, very greatly increases legibility, and assists in avoiding fatigue.

Explanations of the nature and uses of the various tables have been considerably extended and collected at the front of the volume.

Every precaution has been used to insure accuracy in the numerical values, the proofs having been read against several sources. Notice of any errors which may be discovered will be sincerely appreciated.

The numerical table of former editions has been replaced by a new and improved form. It has been divided into two parts, the first of which gives the reciprocals and the circumference and area of circles to seven significant figures. The second section is devoted wholly to squares, cubes and roots. It is thus possible to give a much more complete and satisfactory table of these important values. The square and cube roots have been completely recomputed and are now given to seven significant figures. In addition, the values of the square roots of $10n$ and the cube roots of $10n$ and $100n$ are included.

In addition to suggestions from a large number of users of the book, we wish to acknowledge the valuable collaboration of the following persons:

Albert A. Bennett, Brown University
W. Bruce Ross, McGill University
B. H. Brown, Dartmouth College
D. A. Hill, The Ohio Public Service Company

CHEMICAL RUBBER PUBLISHING COMPANY

Cleveland, Ohio

Preface to the Tenth Edition

The tenth edition of the MATHEMATICAL TABLES FROM THE HANDBOOK OF CHEMISTRY AND PHYSICS is now being published under the title: C.R.C. STANDARD MATHEMATICAL TABLES. The independent status and change of title which this book now possesses resulted from the fact that the tenth edition contains considerably more information and tables than currently contained in the mathematical section of the HANDBOOK OF CHEMISTRY AND PHYSICS.

In preparing this book, it has been our aim to offer a balanced collection of information and still include information necessary for the changing technology of our times. It will continue to be the policy of the publishers to revise this book frequently in order to provide extensive and practical tables for both students and professional personnel in the fields of mathematics, physics, chemistry, engineering, science and statistics. It will continue to serve both as a teaching aid and reference book to its many users.

In order to meet the above objectives a thorough revision of the contents have been made. The tables for the hyperbolic functions of sinh x, cosh x, and tanh x have been extended to include a range of values to $x = 10$; and the exponential functions have been expanded in the values of x between 5 and 10. The integral tables have been revised and extensively enlarged to include an additional ninety-four formulas.

Among the new contents will be found tables with appropriate practical ranges of values for the following higher type of mathematical functions: Bessel functions of order zero and unity; Hyperbolic Bessel functions; Bessel Functions for Spherical Coordinates; the integral sine, the integral cosine, the integral exponential functions; and tables for elliptic integrals of the first and second kind.

Of particular benefit to the many interested in the solution of differential equations is included a table of Laplace Transforms, which should be of special convenience to them. For those interested in statistics and actuarial science there is now included a χ^2 Table, a special F and t table for 1% and 5% distributions, the Commissioner's 1941 Standard Ordinary Mortality Table, with an additional table based on it for the commutation symbols at $2\frac{1}{2}\%$. Other changes include minor revisions throughout the summary material with a new section added on vector analysis.

PREFACE TO THE TENTH EDITION

We are indebted to Doctor R. V. Churchill, author, and the McGraw-Hill Book Company for permission to use the table of Laplace Transforms as they appear in their book Modern Operational Mathematics in Engineering; to Doctor Ronald A. Fisher, author, and Oliver and Boyd Limited, publishers, Edinburgh, for permission to use the χ^2 and t tables from their book, Statistical Methods for Research Workers; to Doctor G. W. Snedecor, author, and the Iowa State College Press for permission to use the F tables for 5% and 1% distributions, as they appear in their Statistical Methods; and to Doctor Philip M. Morse, author, and McGraw-Hill Book Company, publishers, for permission to use the tables, Bessel Functions for Spherical Coordinates, and Hyperbolic Bessel Functions from their book, Vibrations and Sound; and to the American Actuarial Society for permission to use their CSO 1941 Mortality Tables.

We are also indebted to a large number of users of our tables for their many suggestions which have been incorporated into this new edition, and hereby acknowledge our appreciation for their valued assistance.

CHEMICAL RUBBER PUBLISHING COMPANY

Cleveland, Ohio
January 5, 1954.

Reprint September 1, 1954

CONTENTS

CONTENTS

CONTENTS

USE OF MATHEMATICAL TABLES

For a complete discussion of the principles and use of mathematical tables, textbooks on the subject should be consulted. The following brief statements are intended to give only sufficient information to make possible the intelligent use of the tables, omitting for the most part any attempt at treating the theory and principles.

Exponential Method of Expressing Numbers—For convenience in writing and manipulation, numbers are often expressed as factors of appropriate powers of 10. The following examples will illustrate:

2,380,000,000.	may be written	2.38×10^9
238.	may be written	2.38×10^2
.238	may be written	2.38×10^{-1}
.000000238	may be written	2.38×10^{-7}

Logarithms—The logarithm of a number is the exponent of that power to which another number, the base, must be raised to give the number first named. Any positive number greater than 1 might serve as a base. Two have been selected, yielding two systems of logarithms. One base, 2.718 . . . . usually indicated by the letter e, gives rise to a system of logarithms convenient in higher mathematics. These are called natural, Naperian, or hyperbolic logarithms. Reference will be made to their use in a subsequent paragraph.

The other base used is 10, giving logarithms particularly adapted to use in computation, called common or Briggian logarithms. Tables of logarithms given without designation are invariably of this latter type.

Since most numbers are incommensurable powers of ten, a common logarithm, in general, consists of an integer which is called the characteristic and an endless decimal, the mantissa.

It is to be observed that the common logarithms of all numbers expressed by the same figures in the same order with the decimal point in different positions have different characteristics but the same mantissa. To illustrate:—if the decimal point stand after the first figure of a number, counting from the left, the characteristic is 0; if after two figures, it is 1; if after three figures, it is 2, and so forth. If the decimal point stand before the first significant figure

1

the characteristic is −1, usually written $\bar{1}$; if there is one zero between the decimal point and the first significant figure it is $\bar{2}$ and so on. For example: log 256 = 2.40824, log 2.56 = 0.40824, log 0.256 = $\bar{1}$.40824, log 0.00256 = $\bar{3}$.40824. The two latter are often written log 0.256 = 9.40824−10, log 0.00256 = 7.40824−10.

A method of determining characteristics of logarithms is to write the number with one figure to the left of the decimal point multiplied by the appropriate power of 10. The characteristic is then the exponent used. For example:

$256,000,000 = 2.56 \times 10^8$ log = 8.40824
$0.000000256 = 2.56 \times 10^{-7}$ log = $\bar{7}$.40824 or 3.40824−10

Inasmuch as the characteristic may be determined by inspection the mantissas only are given in tables of common logarithms.

To find the logarithm of a number:

For a number of four figures, take out the tabular mantissa on a line with the first three figures of the number and under its fourth figure. The characteristic is determined as previously explained.

For a number of less than four figures, supply zeros to make a four figure number and take the value of the mantissa from the tables as before. For example: log 2 = log 2.000 = 0.30103.

For a number of more than four figures, take the tabular value of the mantissa for the first four figures; find the difference between this mantissa and the next greater tabular mantissa and multiply the difference so found by the remaining figures of the number as a decimal and add the product to the mantissa of the first four figures. For example: to find log 46.762.

$$\log 46.76 = 1.66987$$

Tabular difference between this mantissa and that for 4677 is .00010.

$$\therefore \log 46.762 = 1.66987 + .2 \times .00010$$
$$= 1.66987 + .00002$$
$$= 1.66989$$

To find the number corresponding to a given logarithm:

If the mantissa is found exactly in the table, join the figure at the top which is directly above the given mantissa to the three figures on the line at the left and place the decimal point according to the characteristic of the logarithm. For example, log^{-1} (antilogarithm) 3.39967 = 2510.

If the mantissa is not found exactly in the table it is necessary to interpolate. For example, $\log^{-1} 3.40028 = 2513. + \frac{9}{18} = 2513.5$.

The column of proportional parts at the right of each page of the table shows, under the heading of the various tabular differences, the parts of these differences which correspond to the digits from 1 to 9 in the fifth place. This makes it possible to take out a logarithm for a five figure number or to find an antilogarithm of the same number of significant figures with increased facility, usually by inspection.

The following formulae express the relations on which the use of logarithms is based:

$$\log ab = \log a + \log b$$

$$\log \frac{a}{b} = \log a - \log b$$

$$\log a^n = n \times \log a$$

$$\log \sqrt[n]{a} = \frac{\log a}{n}$$

The following examples will serve as illustrations:

1. $52600 \times 0.00381 \times 2.74 = 549.1$

$$\log 52600 = 4.72099$$
$$\log 0.00381 = \bar{3}.58092$$
$$\log 2.74 = 0.43775$$

Sum: $= 2.73966$
Antilogarithm $= 549.1$

The sum is the logarithm of the product, the mantissa of which is 73966. On looking up this mantissa in the logarithm tables we see that it corresponds to the digits 5491. The characteristic is 2, hence there are three figures before the decimal point. The number corresponding to the logarithm, called the antilogarithm, is 549.1.

2. $0.00123 \div 52.7 = 0.00002334$ An Alternative method:

$\log 0.00123 = \bar{3}.08991$ $\log 0.00123 = 7.08991 -10$
$\log \quad 52.7 = 1.72181$ $\log \quad 52.7 = 1.72181$

Subtracting $\bar{5}.36810$ $5.36810 -10$
Antilog $\quad 0.00002334$

The characteristic $\bar{5}$ (5. -10) shows four zeros after the decimal point before the first significant figure.

3. $\dfrac{273 \times 780}{292 \times 760} \times 15 \times 0.09 = 1.295$

log 273 = 2.43616	log 292	= 2.46538
log 780 = 2.89209	log 760	= 2.88081
log 15 = 1.17609		
log 0.09 = $\bar{2}$.95424	log denominator	= 5.34619

log sum = 5.45858

            log numerator   = 5.45858
            log denominator = 5.34619

            subtracting   = 0.11239
            antilogarithm = 1.295

As division may be accomplished by multiplying by the reciprocal of a number, the above may be considerably simplified. The logarithm of the reciprocal of a number, called the cologarithm, is readily obtained from the table by subtracting the logarithm of the number from zero. This may readily be read off from the table of mantissas. Change the sign of the characteristic algebraically adding to it -1, then mentally subtract each figure of the mantissa from 9 proceeding from left to right, the last figure being subtracted from 10. The example then is:

log	273	= 2.43616
log	780	= 2.89209
log	15	= 1.17609
log	0.09	= $\bar{2}$.95424
colog	292	= $\bar{3}$.53462
colog	760	= $\bar{3}$.11919

                  0.11239

4. $(0.00098)^4 = 9.224 \times 10^{-13}$

log 0.00098 = $\bar{4}$.99123

                        4

                    3.96492(a)
$\bar{4} \times 4$ $\bar{16}$.   (b)

log $(0.00098)^4$ = $\bar{13}$.96492(c)
antilog = 9.224×10^{-13}

An alternative method:

log $0.00098 = 6.99123 - 10$

                        4

                27.96492 -40
          or 7.96492 -20

          or $\bar{13}$.96492

antilog = 9.224×10^{-13}

In the above it will be noted that the mantissa is always positive hence the multiplication of the mantissa shown at (a) while (b) shows the multiplication of the characteristic. (c) is the algebraic sum.

5. $\sqrt[5]{492}$ = 3.455

    log 492 = 2.69197

Dividing the logarithm by 5 gives as the logarithm of the root 0.53839 the antilogarithm of which is 3.455 both characteristic and mantissa being positive. When the characteristic is negative and not evenly divisable by the root to be taken a modification of the logarithm is necessary.

6. $\sqrt[3]{0.000372}$ =

    log 3.72×10^{-4} = $\overline{4}.57054$ (a)

                 = $26.57054 - 30$(b)

dividing (b) by 3 gives $8.85685 - 10$ which may be written $\overline{2}.85685$ and is the logarithm of the root sought, the antilogarithm of which is 0.07192.

7. $0.000372^{1.2}$ = 0.000076674

  log 0.000372   = $\overline{4}.57054$

                or $6.57054 - 10$

                     1.2

              —————————

              $7.88465 - 12$

    antilogarithm 0.000076674

Four-Place Logarithms—This short table on two facing pages makes possible logarithmic computation precise to four significant figures, (three without interpolation). The mantissa is given complete and the proportional parts indicated for each line.

Four-Place Antilogarithms—Some computers prefer to use separate tables for determining antilogarithms; the table being entered from the margins with the logarithm and the number being found in the body of the table. Such a table is given to accompany the four-place logarithms.

Five-Place Logarithms—For computation involving five significant figures, (four without interpolation) the five-place table will be adequate. Since the first two figures will be the same for several lines of the table they are given in the first line only. The point at which these first two figures change is indicated by an asterisk.

5

While space does not permit the proportional parts for each line, tables will be found for each tabular difference.

The supplementary table following the five-place logarithms, giving seven-place logarithms for numbers of five significant figures from 10,000 to 12,000 will be found convenient to increase precision and avoid the inconvenience of interpolation where the differences are large.

Logarithms of the Trigonometric Functions—Logarithms of the functions are given for each minute from 0-360°.

The quantity -10 is to be appended to all logarithms of the sine and cosine, to logarithms of the tangent from 0-45° and of the cotangent from 45-90°.

With degrees indicated at either side of the top of the page use the column headings at the top. With degrees stated at the bottom of the page use the column designations at the bottom.

With degrees at the left (top or bottom) use the minute column at the left, and with degrees on the right side of the page use the minute column at the right.

To illustrate the proper employment of headings for angles in the four quadrants—

log sin $6° 24' = 9.04715 - 10$	log sin $186° 24' = 9.04715 - 10$
log sin $83° 15' = 9.99698 - 10$	log sin $263° 15' = 9.99698 - 10$
log cos $96° 41' = 9.06589 - 10$	log cos $276° 41' = 9.06589 - 10$
log cos $173° 49' = 9.99747 - 10$	log cos $353° 49' = 9.99747 - 10$

For the accurate determination of values where the tabular differences are large, the values of CS and CT are given. The following equations indicate their use.

To find the logarithm of the functions of an angle:

For angles 0–3°

$\log \sin \theta = \log \theta'' - CS$
$\log \tan \theta = \log \theta'' - CT$
$\log \cot \theta = \text{colog} \tan \theta$

For angles 87–90°

$\log \cos \theta = \log (90° - \theta)'' - CS$
$\log \cot \theta = \log (90° - \theta)'' - CT$
$\log \tan \theta = \text{colog} \cot \theta$

To find the angle:

For angles 0–3°

$\log \theta'' = \log \sin \theta + CS$
$\log \theta'' = \log \tan \theta + CT$

For angles 87–90°

$\log (90° - \theta)'' = \log \cos \theta + CS$
$\log (90° - \theta)'' = \log \cot \theta + CT$

In the above expressions, θ'' and $(90° - \theta)''$ are used to indicate the value of the angles expressed in seconds. The values in the body of the table are the cologarithms and should be used as indicated above.

The values of the logarithms S and T are also given in a separate table. For these the following relations hold:

To find the function of an angle.

$\log \sin \theta = \log \theta'' + S$ $\log \cos \theta = \log (90° - \theta)'' + S$

$\log \tan \theta = \log \theta'' + T$ $\log \cot \theta = \log (90° - \theta)'' + T$

To find the angle.

$\log \theta'' = \log \sin \theta - S$ $\log (90° - \theta)'' = \log \cos \theta - S$

$\log \theta'' = \log \tan \theta - T$ $\log (90° - \theta)'' = \log \cot \theta - T$

Where the values of CS and CT are given, the angles expressed in seconds are given in the supplementary column at the left.

The tabular differences are given under the headings "d" and "c.d.", the latter referring to the common difference for the tangent and cotangent. Tables of proportional parts ("P.P.") facilitate interpolation. At the bottom of each column will be found special proportional parts between the tabular differences for the tangent or cotangent and those for the sine or cosine. These are useful when one function is to be obtained directly from the other without determining the angle.

For example, suppose $\log \tan \theta$ is given as 9.67644 and $\log \cos \theta$ is required. The difference between the given logarithm and that given in the table, 9.67622, (opposite 25° 23'), is 22. The tabular differences of the two logarithmic functions at this place are 32 and 6. In the proportional table for $\frac{6}{32}$, 22 corresponds to 4; this, subtracted from the tabular logarithmic cosine 9.95591, gives the required $\log \cos \theta = 9.95587$.

The symbols $\bar{5}$ and $\dot{5}$ are used to indicate how the terminal 5 has been derived. For example, the logarithm 8.8307$\bar{5}$ is more fully given as 8.8307495 while the value 9.4082$\dot{5}$ is derived from 9.4082539.

Natural Trigonometric Functions—Values of the natural trigonometric functions of angles are given for each minute from 0-360°.

For degrees indicated at the top of the page use the column headings at the top. For degrees indicated at the bottom use the column indications at the bottom.

With degrees at the left of each block (top or bottom), use the minute column at the left and with degrees at the right of each block use the minute column at the right.

Natural Functions and their Logarithms are given for angles in degrees and tenths from 0 to 90 degrees.

Natural Functions and their Logarithms are given for angles in radians and hundredths, from 0 to 2 radians.

Haversines—Values of $(1 - \cos \theta)/2$ for angles between 0 and 180° are given to five significant figures. The five-place mantissas of the logarithms of the haversines are also given. The correct characteristic must be provided in each case.

The listed values of the haversines were derived from values which were computed to seven significant figures. The logarithms were independently derived from the more exact values of the haversines and are, therefore, in many cases not the exact value of the logarithm of the haversine as listed. This is notably true at the beginning of the table where the logarithm can be given with more exactness than the function.

Natural Logarithms—The natural logarithms of numbers from 0.000 to 999. are given in a group of four tables. The method of finding logarithms of numbers not included in the tables is indicated at the beginning of the third page. A convenient table of constants occurs at the top of the fourth page.

The first page gives the natural logarithms of numbers from 0.000 to 0.499. Since the characteristics change rapidly for the smaller numbers, they are indicated *above* the mantissa in the first line. In the second and following lines the characteristics are given at the left only. For example, $\log_e 0.004 = -5.52146$; $\log_e 0.014 = -4.26870$.

The succeeding pages give the natural logarithms of numbers up to 999.

Exponential Functions—Values of e^x, $\log e^x$ and e^{-x} where e is the base of the natural system of logarithms 2.71828...and x has values from 0 to 10. Facilitating the solution of exponential equations, these tables also serve as a table of natural or Naperian antilogarithms. For instance, if the logarithm or exponent $x = 3.26$, the corresponding number or value of e^x is 26.050. Its reciprocal e^{-x} is .038388.

Hyperbolic Functions—The table gives the values and logarithms of the hyperbolic sine x, cosine x, tangent x and cotangent x for values of x from 0 to 10.

Degrees-Radians—This table gives the value in radians to five significant figures; for each 10 minutes from 0° 0′ to 90° 0′; for each degree from 90 to 180; for each 10 degrees from 180 to 480. Values are also given for each minute from 0-60′ and for each second from 0-60″.

Tables are also provided to facilitate changing from degrees and decimal fractions to radians, from decimal fractions of a degree to minutes and seconds and the reverse operations.

Numerical Tables—The first section gives the reciprocals of numbers from 0 to 1000 and circumferences and areas of circles with diameters having these values. Reciprocals and circumferences for values not listed can be obtained by an appropriate shift of the decimal point.

The second section is devoted to squares, cubes and roots. The squares and cubes from 1 to 1000 are given exactly. The roots are given to seven significant figures. Since the square roots of $10n$ are given, values of the square roots from 1 to 10,000 may be found directly. For the square roots of numbers below and above this range, use may be made of the following relations: $\sqrt{100n} = 10\sqrt{n}$; $\sqrt{1000n} = 10\sqrt{10n}$; $\sqrt{\frac{1}{10}n} = \frac{1}{10}\sqrt{10n}$; $\sqrt{\frac{1}{100}n} = \frac{1}{10}\sqrt{n}$; $\sqrt{\frac{1}{1000}n} = \frac{1}{100}\sqrt{10n}$. For example, the square root of 0.268 may be found by using the form, $\sqrt{0.268} = \frac{1}{100}\sqrt{10 \times 268}$. The tabular value for the square root of $10n$ for 268 is 51.76872. Hence, the desired root is 0.5176872.

Values of cube roots for all numbers from 1 to 100,000 will be found directly in the table. Cube roots for numbers above or below this range will be found from the following relations: $\sqrt[3]{1000n} = 10\sqrt[3]{n}$; $\sqrt[3]{10,000n} = 10\sqrt[3]{10n}$; $\sqrt[3]{100,000n} = 10\sqrt[3]{100n}$; $\sqrt[3]{\frac{1}{10}n} = \frac{1}{10}\sqrt[3]{100n}$; $\sqrt[3]{\frac{1}{100}n} = \frac{1}{10}\sqrt[3]{10n}$; $\sqrt[3]{\frac{1}{1000}n} = \frac{1}{10}\sqrt[3]{n}$. For example, the cube root of 731,000 may be found by using the form, $\sqrt[3]{731,000} = 10\sqrt[3]{731}$. The tabular value of the root for 731 is 9.008223. The desired root is, therefore, 90.08223.

Powers of Numbers—This table is given to supplement the values of squares and cubes of numbers found in the preceding numerical table. The larger numbers are expressed exponentially to at least seven significant figures. The approximate value written as a whole number may be obtained by shifting the decimal point to the right by the number of places indicated in the exponent of 10 shown at the head of each group of values. For example: the approximate value of 33^8 is found in the table as 14.064086×10^{11}. Written as a whole number it is 1,406,408,600,000.

Factorials and their Logarithms—The product $n \times (n-1) \times (n-2) \times \ldots \times 1$ is called factorial n, expressed as $n!$ or $\lfloor n$. For example: factorial $5 = 5 \times 4 \times 3 \times 2 \times 1 = 120$. Factorials are very often met with in series. For purposes of computation in such cases the table giving the values of the factorials and of their logarithms for numbers from 1 to 100 is provided. The values of the factorials are expressed exponentially to 5 significant figures.

A brief table of exact values and reciprocals of factorials is to be found on page 190.

Factors for Computing Probable Errors—The probable error of a series of n measures $a_1, a_2, a_3 \ldots a_n$, the mean of which is m, is given by the expression,

$$e = \frac{0.6745}{\sqrt{n-1}} \sqrt{(m-a_1)^2 + (m-a_2)^2 + \ldots (m-a_n)^2}$$

The probable error of the mean is,

$$E = \frac{0.6745}{\sqrt{n(n-1)}} \sqrt{(m-a_1)^2 + (m-a_2)^2 + \ldots (m-a_n)^2}$$

The following approximate equations are convenient forms for computation,

$$e = 0.8453 \frac{\Sigma d}{\sqrt{n(n-1)}}$$

$$E = 0.8453 \frac{\Sigma d}{n \sqrt{n-1}}$$

The symbol Σd represents the arithmetical sum of the deviations.

For convenience in computing the probable error the value of several of the factors involved is given for values of n from 2 to 100.

Probability of Occurrence of Deviations—The significance of deviations is indicated by this table. The probability of occurrence of deviations as great as or greater than any specific value is given for various ratios of deviation to probable error and also with respect to the standard deviation. The probability of occurrence is stated in per cent or chances in 100. The odds against occurrence are also stated. The probable error is 0.6745 × the standard deviation.

Areas, Ordinates and Derivatives of the Normal Curve of Error—If, for a large number of observations, the frequency y, of the occurrence of an error of magnitude t be plotted, a curve results whose equation may be written,

$$y = \frac{1}{\sqrt{2\ \pi}}\ e^{-t^2/2}$$

The area, ordinates and derivatives for this curve given in the table are useful in the treatment of observational data. A text on statistical methods should be consulted for a complete explanation.

Factors and Primes—The table presents the prime factors of *all* factorable numbers and the logarithms of all prime numbers from 1 to 2000.

It should be noted that the third digit of the number is given at the top of the page and that the table runs across two facing pages. Thus, the factors of 258 are found, on the right hand page, on a line with 25 and under vertical column 8 to be 2·3·43.

Interest Tables—The equations involved in the computation and use of the interest tables are collected at the beginning of this section. For further explanation the reader is referred to a text-book of the mathematics of finance or investment. A much more complete set of interest tables is to be found in "Tables of Applied Mathematics in Finance, Insurance, Statistics," edited by James W. Glover.

CONVERSION TABLES
DECIMAL EQUIVALENTS OF COMMON FRACTIONS

		1/64 = 0.015625			11/32	22/64 = 0.34375		43/64 = 0.671875
	1/32	2/64 = .03125				23/64 = .359375	11/16 22/32	44/64 = .6875
		3/64 = .046875	3/8	12/32	24/64 = .375			45/64 = .703125
1/16	2/32	4/64 = .0625			25/64 = .390625		23/32	46/64 = .71875
		5/64 = .078125		13/32	26/64 = .40625			47/64 = .734375
	3/32	6/64 = .09375			27/64 = .421875	3/4	24/32	48/64 = .75
		7/64 = .109375	7/16	14/32	28/64 = .4375			49/64 = .765625
1/8	4/32	8/64 = .125			29/64 = .453125		25/32	50/64 = .78125
		9/64 = .140625		15/32	30/64 = .46875			51/64 = .796875
	5/32	10/64 = .15625			31/64 = .484375	13/16	26/32	52/64 = .8125
		11/64 = .171875	1/2	16/32	32/64 = .50			53/64 = .828125
3/16	6/32	12/64 = .1875			33/64 = .515625		27/32	54/64 = .84375
		13/64 = .203125		17/32	34/64 = .53125			55/64 = .859375
	7/32	14/64 = .21875			35/64 = .546875	7/8	28/32	56/64 = .875
		15/64 = .234375	9/16	18/32	36/64 = .5625			57/64 = .890625
1/4	8/32	16/64 = .25			37/64 = .578125		29/32	58/64 = .90625
		17/64 = .265625		19/32	38/64 = .59375			59/64 = .921875
	9/32	18/64 = .28125			39/64 = .609375	15/16	30/32	60/64 = .9375
		19/64 = .296875	5/8	20/32	40/64 = .625			61/64 = .953125
5/16	10/32	20/64 = .3125			41/64 = .640625		31/32	62/64 = .96875
		21/64 = .328125		21/32	42/64 = .65625			63/64 = .984375

Conversion Table

Inches		Centimeters	Centimeters		Inches
1	=	2.54001	1	=	0.39370
2	=	5.08001	2	=	0.78740
3	=	7.62002	3	=	1.1811
4	=	10.16002	4	=	1.5748
5	=	12.70003	5	=	1.9685
6	=	15.24003	6	=	2.3622
7	=	17.78004	7	=	2.7559
8	=	20.32004	8	=	3.1496
9	=	22.86005	9	=	3.5433

Feet		Meters	Meters		Feet
1	=	0.304801	1	=	3.28083
2	=	0.609601	2	=	6.56167
3	=	0.914402	3	=	9.84250
4	=	1.219202	4	=	13.12333
5	=	1.524003	5	=	16.40417
6	=	1.828804	6	=	19.68500
7	=	2.133604	7	=	22.96583
8	=	2.438405	8	=	26.24666
9	=	2.743205	9	=	29.52750

Yards		Meters	Meters		Yards
1	=	0.914402	1	=	1.093611
2	=	1.828804	2	=	2.187222
3	=	2.743205	3	=	3.280833
4	=	3.657607	4	=	4.374444
5	=	4.572009	5	=	5.468056
6	=	5.486411	6	=	6.561667
7	=	6.400813	7	=	7.655278
8	=	7.315215	8	=	8.748889
9	=	8.229616	9	=	9.842500

CONVERSION TABLES

Conversion Tables (Continued)

Miles	Kilometers	Kilometers	Miles
1	1.60935	1	0.62137
2	3.21869	2	1.24274
3	4.82804	3	1.86411
4	6.43739	4	2.48548
5	8.04674	5	3.10685
6	9.65608	6	3.72822
7	11.26543	7	4.34959
8	12.87478	8	4.97096
9	14.48412	9	5.59233

Pounds Av.	Kilograms	Kilograms	Pounds Av.
1	0.45359	1	2.20462
2	0.90718	2	4.40924
3	1.36078	3	6.61387
4	1.81437	4	8.81849
5	2.26796	5	11.02311
6	2.72155	6	13.22773
7	3.17514	7	15.43236
8	3.62874	8	17.63698
9	4.08233	9	19.84160

Conversion Factors

U. S. AND METRIC UNITS

Each unit in bold face type is followed by its equivalent in other units of the same quantity.

Acre—0.0015625 square mile; 4.3560 $\times 10^4$ square feet; 0.4046873 hectare

Bushel—1.2444 cubic feet; 2150.42 cubic inches; 0.035239 cubic meter; 35.238 liters

Centimeter—0.032808 foot; 0.39370 inch.

Circular Mil.—7.854 $\times 10^{-7}$ square inch; 5.0671 $\times 10^{-6}$ square centimeter

Cubic Centimeter—0.061023 cubic inch; 0.27051 dram; 16.231 minims; 0.99997 milliliter

Cubic Foot—0.80357 bushel; 7.481 gallon; 0.02831701 cubic meter; 28.316 liters

Cubic Inch—16.387162 cubic centimeters

Cubic Meter—35.314445 cubic feet; 264.173 gallons

Foot—0.3048006 meter

Gallon—0.13368 cubic foot; 0.83268 gallons (British); 231.00 cubic inches; 0.0037854 cubic meter; 3.7853 liters

Grain—0.064798918 gram

Gram—0.00220462 pound (avoirdupois); .0352740 ounce (avoirdupois); 15.4324 grains

Hectare—2.471044 acres; 1.0764 $\times 10^5$ square feet

Inch—2.540005 centimeter

Kilogram—2.2046223 pounds (avoirdupois)

Kilometer—0.62137 mile

Liter—0.26417762 gallon; 0.035316 cubic foot; 1.056710 quarts

Meter—1.093611 yards; 3.280833 feet; 39.3700 inches

Mile—1.60935 kilometers

Ounce (fluid)—1.80469 cubic inches; 29.5737 cubic centimeters

Ounce (avoirdupois)—28.349527 grams

Ounce (apothecary or troy)—31.103481 grams

Pint (liquid)—0.473167 liter; 473.-167 cubic centimeters

Pound (avoirdupois)—0.453592 kilogram, 453.5924 grams

Pound (apothecary or troy)—0.3732418 kilogram; 373.2418 grams

Quart—1.10120 liters

Quart (liquid)—.946333 liter

Radian—57.29578 degrees

Rod—5.029210 meters

Square Centimeter—0.15500 square inches

Square Foot—0.09290341 square meter

Square Inch—645.16258 square millimeters

Square Meter—10.76387 square feet

Square Yard—0.83613 square meter

Ton (short)—907.185 kilograms

Yard—0.91440183 meter

13

NUMERICAL CONSTANTS

NUMBERS CONTAINING π

$\pi = 3.14159\ 26536$ $\log_{10}\pi = 0.49714\ 98727$ $\log_e \pi = 1.14472\ 98858$

	Number	Logarithm		Number	Logarithm
π	3.1415 927	0.4971 499	$4\ \pi^2$	39.4784 176	1.5963 597
$2\ \pi$	6.2831 853	0.7981 799	$1/\ \pi^2$	0.1013 212	9.0057 003-10
$3\ \pi$	9.4247 780	0.9742 711	$1/(2\ \pi^2)$	0.0506 606	8.7046 703-10
$4\ \pi$	12.5663 706	1.0992 099	$1/(4\ \pi^2)$	0.0253 303	8.4036 403-10
$8\ \pi$	25.1327 412	1.4002 399	$\sqrt{\pi}$	1.7724 539	0.2485 749
$\pi/2$	1.5707 963	0.1961 199	$\sqrt{\pi/4}$ or		
$\pi/3$	1.0471 976	0.0200 286	$\sqrt{\pi}/2$	0.8862 269	9.9475 449-10
$\pi/4$	0.7853 982	9.8950 899-10			
$\pi/6$	0.5235 988	9.7189 986-10	$\sqrt{\pi/4}$	0.4431 135	9.6465 149-10
$\pi/8$	0.3926 991	9.5940 599-10	$\sqrt{\pi/2}$	1.2533 141	0.0980 599
$2\ \pi/3$	2.0943 951	0.3210 586			
$4\ \pi/3$	4.1887 902	0.6220 886	$\sqrt{2/\pi}$	0.7978 846	9.9019 401-10
$1/\ \pi$	0.3183 099	9.5028 501-10	π^3	31.0062 767	1.4914 496
$2/\ \pi$	0.6366 198	9.8038 801-10			
$4/\ \pi$	1.2732 395	0.1049 101	$\sqrt[3]{\pi}$	1.4645 919	0.1657 166
$1/(2\ \pi)$	0.1591 549	9.2018 201-10	$1/\sqrt[3]{\pi}$	0.6827 841	9.8342 834-10
$1/(4\ \pi)$	0.0795 775	8.9007 901-10	$\sqrt[3]{\pi^2}$	2.1450 294	0.3314 332
$1/(6\ \pi)$	0.0530 516	8.7246 989-10			
$1/(8\ \pi)$	0.0397 887	8.5997 601-10	$1/\sqrt{\pi}$	0.5641 896	9.7514 251-10
π^2	9.8696 044	0.9942 997	$2/\sqrt{\pi}$ or		
$2\ \pi^2$	19.7392 088	1.2953 297	$\sqrt{4/\pi}$	1.1283 792	0.0524 551

LOGARITHMIC CONSTANTS

$e = 2.71828\ 18284\ 59045$

$1/e = 0.36787\ 94412$

$\log_e 2 = 0.69314\ 71806$

$M = \log_{10} e = 0.43429\ 44819\ 03251\ 82765$

$1/M = \log_e 10 = 2.30258\ 50929\ 94045\ 68402$

$\log_{10} M = \log_{10} \log_{10} e = 9.63778\ 43113 - 10$

$\log_{10} 2 = 0.30102\ 99957$

CHANGE OF BASE

$$\log_a x = \log_b x / \log_b a$$

$$\log_{10} x = \log_e x / \log_e 10 \qquad \log_e x = \log_{10} x / \log_{10} e$$

$$\log_e x = 1/M \log_{10} x = 2.30258\ 50930\ \log_{10} x \qquad \log_{10} x = M \log_e x = 0.43429\ 44819\ \log_e x$$

Euler's Constant $\gamma = 0.57721\ 56649\ 01533$

Mean radius of the earth, 3959 miles = 6371 kilometers.

1 degree of latitude at 40° = 69 miles.

1 nautical mile = 1′ of arc on the earth's surface at the equator.

Mean density of the earth, 5.522 grams per cm³.

Constant of gravitation, $K = 6.670 \times 10^{-8}$ = the attraction in dynes between two gram masses one centimeter apart.

Acceleration due to gravity at sea level, lat. 45° = 980.616 cm. per sec. per sec. = 32.172 feet per sec. per sec.

Length of seconds pendulum at sea level, lat. 45° = 99.358 cm. = 39.117 in.

Density of mercury at 0° C. = 13.59509 g. per cm³.

Density of water, maximum at 3.98° C. = 0.999973 g. per cm³.

Density of dry air at 0° C. and 760 mm. = .001293 g. per cm³.

Velocity of sound in dry air at 0° C., 33,136 cm. per sec. = 1089 feet per sec.

Velocity of light in a vacuum = 2.99776×10^{10} cm. per sec. = 9.83514×10^8 feet per sec. = 186,272 mi./sec.

Heat equivalent of fusion of water 79.63 cal. per gram.

Heat equivalent of vaporization of water, 539.55 cal. per gram.

Coefficient of expansion of gases, .003665.

Specific heat of air, at constant pressure, 0.238.

Electrochemical equivalent of silver, 0.001118 g. per sec. per int. ampere.

Mean wave length of sodium light, .00005893 cm. or 5893. ångström units.

Absolute wave length of red cadmium line in air, 760 mm. pressure, 15° C.; 6438.4696 ångström units.

GREEK ALPHABET

Greek letter	Greek name	English equivalent	Greek letter	Greek name	English equivalent
A α	Alpha	a	N ν	Nu	n
B β	Beta	b	Ξ ξ	Xi	x
Γ γ	Gamma	g	O o	Omicron	ŏ
Δ δ	Delta	d	Π π	Pi	p
E ε	Epsilon	ĕ	P ρ	Rho	r
Z ζ	Zeta	z	Σ σ	Sigma	s
H η	Eta	ē	T τ	Tau	t
Θ θ	Theta	th	Υ υ	Upsilon	u
I ι	Iota	i	Φ φ	Phi	ph
K κ	Kappa	k	X χ	Chi	ch
Λ λ	Lambda	l	Ψ ψ	Psi	ps
M μ	Mu	m	Ω ω	Omega	ō

N	0	1	2	3	4	5	6	7	8	9	Proportional Parts								
											1	2	3	4	5	6	7	8	9
10	0000	0043	0086	0128	0170	0212	0253	0294	0334	0374	*4	8	12	17	21	25	29	33	37
11	0414	0453	0492	0531	0569	0607	0645	0682	0719	0755	4	8	11	15	19	23	26	30	34
12	0792	0828	0864	0899	0934	0969	1004	1038	1072	1106	3	7	10	14	17	21	24	28	31
13	1139	1173	1206	1239	1271	1303	1335	1367	1399	1430	3	6	10	13	16	19	23	26	29
14	1461	1492	1523	1553	1584	1614	1644	1673	1703	1732	3	6	9	12	15	18	21	24	27
15	1761	1790	1818	1847	1875	1903	1931	1959	1987	2014	*3	6	8	11	14	17	20	22	25
16	2041	2068	2095	2122	2148	2175	2201	2227	2253	2279	3	5	8	11	13	16	18	21	24
17	2304	2330	2355	2380	2405	2430	2455	2480	2504	2529	2	5	7	10	12	15	17	20	22
18	2553	2577	2601	2625	2648	2672	2695	2718	2742	2765	2	5	7	9	12	14	16	19	21
19	2788	2810	2833	2856	2878	2900	2923	2945	2967	2989	2	4	7	9	11	13	16	18	20
20	3010	3032	3054	3075	3096	3118	3139	3160	3181	3201	2	4	6	8	11	13	15	17	19
21	3222	3243	3263	3284	3304	3324	3345	3365	3385	3404	2	4	6	8	10	12	14	16	18
22	3424	3444	3464	3483	3502	3522	3541	3560	3579	3598	2	4	6	8	10	12	14	15	17
23	3617	3636	3655	3674	3692	3711	3729	3747	3766	3784	2	4	3	7	9	11	13	15	17
24	3802	3820	3838	3856	3874	3892	3909	3927	3945	3962	2	4	5	7	9	11	12	14	16
25	3979	3997	4014	4031	4048	4065	4082	4099	4116	4133	2	3	5	7	9	10	12	14	15
26	4150	4166	4183	4200	4216	4232	4249	4265	4281	4298	2	3	5	7	8	10	11	13	15
27	4314	4330	4346	4362	4378	4393	4409	4425	4440	4456	2	3	5	6	8	9	11	13	14
28	4472	4487	4502	4518	4533	4548	4564	4579	4594	4609	2	3	5	6	8	9	11	12	14
29	4624	4639	4654	4669	4683	4698	4713	4728	4742	4757	1	3	4	6	7	9	10	12	13
30	4771	4786	4800	4814	4829	4843	4857	4871	4886	4900	1	3	4	6	7	9	10	11	13
31	4914	4928	4942	4955	4969	4983	4997	5011	5024	5038	1	3	4	6	7	8	10	11	12
32	5051	5065	5079	5092	5105	5119	5132	5145	5159	5172	1	3	4	5	7	8	9	11	12
33	5185	5198	5211	5224	5237	5250	5263	5276	5289	5302	1	3	4	5	6	8	9	10	12
34	5315	5328	5340	5353	5366	5378	5391	5403	5416	5428	1	3	4	5	6	8	9	10	11
35	5441	5453	5465	5478	5490	5502	5514	5527	5539	5551	1	2	4	5	6	7	9	10	11
36	5563	5575	5587	5599	5611	5623	5635	5647	5658	5670	1	2	4	5	6	7	8	10	11
37	5682	5694	5705	5717	5729	5740	5752	5763	5775	5786	1	2	3	5	6	7	8	9	10
38	5798	5809	5821	5832	5843	5855	5866	5877	5888	5899	1	2	3	5	6	7	8	9	10
39	5911	5922	5933	5944	5955	5966	5977	5988	5999	6010	1	2	3	4	5	7	8	9	10
40	6021	6031	6042	6053	6064	6075	6085	6096	6107	6117	1	2	3	4	5	6	8	9	10
41	6128	6138	6149	6160	6170	6180	6191	6201	6212	6222	1	2	3	4	5	6	7	8	9
42	6232	6243	6253	6263	6274	6284	6294	6304	6314	6325	1	2	3	4	5	6	7	8	9
43	6335	6345	6355	6365	6375	6385	6395	6405	6415	6425	1	2	3	4	5	6	7	8	9
44	6435	6444	6454	6464	6474	6484	6493	6503	6513	6522	1	2	3	4	5	6	7	8	9
45	6532	6542	6551	6561	6571	6580	6590	6599	6609	6618	1	2	3	4	5	6	7	8	9
46	6628	6637	6646	6656	6665	6675	6684	6693	6702	6712	1	2	3	4	5	6	7	7	8
47	6721	6730	6739	6749	6758	6767	6776	6785	6794	6803	1	2	3	4	5	5	6	7	8
48	6812	6821	6830	6839	6848	6857	6866	6875	6884	6893	1	2	3	4	4	5	6	7	8
49	6902	6911	6920	6928	6937	6946	6955	6964	6972	6981	1	2	3	4	4	5	6	7	8
50	6990	6998	7007	7016	7024	7033	7042	7050	7059	7067	1	2	3	3	4	5	6	7	8
51	7076	7084	7093	7101	7110	7118	7126	7135	7143	7152	1	2	3	3	4	5	6	7	8
52	7160	7168	7177	7185	7193	7202	7210	7218	7226	7235	1	2	2	3	4	5	6	7	7
53	7243	7251	7259	7267	7275	7284	7292	7300	7308	7316	1	2	2	3	4	5	6	6	7
54	7324	7332	7340	7348	7356	7364	7372	7380	7388	7396	1	2	2	3	4	5	6	6	7
N	0	1	2	3	4	5	6	7	8	9	1	2	3	4	5	6	7	8	9

* Interpolation in this section of the table is inaccurate.

LOGARITHMS

N	0	1	2	3	4	5	6	7	8	9	Proportional Parts								
											1	2	3	4	5	6	7	8	9
55	7404	7412	7419	7427	7435	7443	7451	7459	7466	7474	1	2	2	3	4	5	5	6	7
56	7482	7490	7497	7505	7513	7520	7528	7536	7543	7551	1	2	2	3	4	5	5	6	7
57	7559	7566	7574	7582	7589	7597	7604	7612	7619	7627	1	2	2	3	4	5	5	6	7
58	7634	7642	7649	7657	7664	7672	7679	7686	7694	7701	1	1	2	3	4	4	5	6	7
59	7709	7716	7723	7731	7738	7745	7752	7760	7767	7774	1	1	2	3	4	4	5	6	7
60	7782	7789	7796	7803	7810	7818	7825	7832	7839	7846	1	1	2	3	4	4	5	6	6
61	7853	7860	7868	7875	7882	7889	7896	7903	7910	7917	1	1	2	3	4	4	5	6	6
62	7924	7931	7938	7945	7952	7959	7966	7973	7980	7987	1	1	2	3	3	4	5	6	6
63	7993	8000	8007	8014	8021	8028	8035	8041	8048	8055	1	1	2	3	3	4	5	5	6
64	8062	8069	8075	8082	8089	8096	8102	8109	8116	8122	1	1	2	3	3	4	5	5	6
65	8129	8136	8142	8149	8156	8162	8169	8176	8182	8189	1	1	2	3	3	4	5	5	6
66	8195	8202	8209	8215	8222	8228	8235	8241	8248	8254	1	1	2	3	3	4	5	5	6
67	8261	8267	8274	8280	8287	8293	8299	8306	8312	8319	1	1	2	3	3	4	5	5	6
68	8325	8331	8338	8344	8351	8357	8363	8370	8376	8382	1	1	2	3	3	4	4	5	6
69	8388	8395	8401	8407	8414	8420	8426	8432	8439	8445	1	1	2	2	3	4	4	5	6
70	8451	8457	8463	8470	8476	8482	8488	8494	8500	8506	1	1	2	2	3	4	4	5	6
71	8513	8519	8525	8531	8537	8543	8549	8555	8561	8567	1	1	2	2	3	4	4	5	5
72	8573	8579	8585	8591	8597	8603	8609	8615	8621	8627	1	1	2	2	3	4	4	5	5
73	8633	8639	8645	8651	8657	8663	8669	8675	8681	8686	1	1	2	2	3	4	4	5	5
74	8692	8698	8704	8710	8716	8722	8727	8733	8739	8745	1	1	2	2	3	4	4	5	5
75	8751	8756	8762	8768	8774	8779	8785	8791	8797	8802	1	1	2	2	3	3	4	5	5
76	8808	8814	8820	8825	8831	8837	8842	8848	8854	8859	1	1	2	2	3	3	4	5	5
77	8865	8871	8876	8882	8887	8893	8899	8904	8910	8915	1	1	2	2	3	3	4	4	5
78	8921	8927	8932	8938	8943	8949	8954	8960	8965	8971	1	1	2	2	3	3	4	4	5
79	8976	8982	8987	8993	8998	9004	9009	9015	9020	9025	1	1	2	2	3	3	4	4	5
80	9031	9036	9042	9047	9053	9058	9063	9069	9074	9079	1	1	2	2	3	3	4	4	5
81	9085	9090	9096	9101	9106	9112	9117	9122	9128	9133	1	1	2	2	3	3	4	4	5
82	9138	9143	9149	9154	9159	9165	9170	9175	9180	9186	1	1	2	2	3	3	4	4	5
83	9191	9196	9201	9206	9212	9217	9222	9227	9232	9238	1	1	2	2	3	3	4	4	5
84	9243	9248	9253	9258	9263	9269	9274	9279	9284	9289	1	1	2	2	3	3	4	4	5
85	9294	9299	9304	9309	9315	9320	9325	9330	9335	9340	1	1	2	2	3	3	4	4	5
86	9345	9350	9355	9360	9365	9370	9375	9380	9385	9390	1	1	2	2	3	3	4	4	5
87	9395	9400	9405	9410	9415	9420	9425	9430	9435	9440	0	1	1	2	2	3	3	4	4
88	9445	9450	9455	9460	9465	9469	9474	9479	9484	9489	0	1	1	2	2	3	3	4	4
89	9494	9499	9504	9509	9513	9518	9523	9528	9533	9538	0	1	1	2	2	3	3	4	4
90	9542	9547	9552	9557	9562	9566	9571	9576	9581	9586	0	1	1	2	2	3	3	4	4
91	9590	9595	9600	9605	9609	9614	9619	9624	9628	9633	0	1	1	2	2	3	3	4	4
92	9638	9643	9647	9652	9657	9661	9666	9671	9675	9680	0	1	1	2	2	3	3	4	4
93	9685	9689	9694	9699	9703	9708	9713	9717	9722	9727	0	1	1	2	2	3	3	4	4
94	9731	9736	9741	9745	9750	9754	9759	9763	9768	9773	0	1	1	2	2	3	3	4	4
95	9777	9782	9786	9791	9795	9800	9805	9809	9814	9818	0	1	1	2	2	3	3	4	4
96	9823	9827	9832	9836	9841	9845	9850	9854	9859	9863	0	1	1	2	2	3	3	4	4
97	9868	9872	9877	9881	9886	9890	9894	9899	9903	9908	0	1	1	2	2	3	3	4	4
98	9912	9917	9921	9926	9930	9934	9939	9943	9948	9952	0	1	1	2	2	3	3	4	4
99	9956	9961	9965	9969	9974	9978	9983	9987	9991	9996	0	1	1	2	2	3	3	3	4
N	0	1	2	3	4	5	6	7	8	9	1	2	3	4	5	6	7	8	9

N	0	1	2	3	4	5	6	7	8	9
.10	−1.000	−.9957	−.9914	−.9872	−.9830	−.9788	−.9747	−.9706	−.9666	−.9626
.11	−.9586	−.9547	−.9508	−.9469	−.9431	−.9393	−.9355	−.9318	−.9281	−.9245
.12	−.9208	−.9172	−.9136	−.9101	−.9066	−.9031	−.8996	−.8962	−.8928	−.8894
.13	−.8861	−.8827	−.8794	−.8761	−.8729	−.8697	−.8665	−.8633	−.8601	−.8570
.14	−.8539	−.8508	−.8477	−.8447	−.8416	−.8386	−.8356	−.8327	−.8297	−.8268
.15	−.8239	−.8210	−.8182	−.8153	−.8125	−.8097	−.8069	−.8041	−.8013	−.7986
.16	−.7959	−.7932	−.7905	−.7878	−.7852	−.7825	−.7799	−.7773	−.7747	−.7721
.17	−.7696	−.7670	−.7645	−.7620	−.7595	−.7570	−.7545	−.7520	−.7496	−.7471
.18	−.7447	−.7423	−.7399	−.7375	−.7352	−.7328	−.7305	−.7282	−.7258	−.7235
.19	−.7212	−.7190	−.7167	−.7144	−.7122	−.7100	−.7077	−.7055	−.7033	−.7011
.20	−.6990	−.6968	−.6946	−.6925	−.6904	−.6882	−.6861	−.6840	−.6819	−.6799
.21	−.6778	−.6757	−.6737	−.6716	−.6696	−.6676	−.6655	−.6635	−.6615	−.6596
.22	−.6576	−.6556	−.6536	−.6517	−.6498	−.6478	−.6459	−.6440	−.6421	−.6402
.23	−.6383	−.6364	−.6345	−.6326	−.6308	−.6289	−.6271	−.6253	−.6234	−.6216
.24	−.6198	−.6180	−.6162	−.6144	−.6126	−.6108	−.6091	−.6073	−.6055	−.6038
.25	−.6021	−.6003	−.5986	−.5969	−.5952	−.5935	−.5918	−.5901	−.5884	−.5867
.26	−.5850	−.5834	−.5817	−.5800	−.5784	−.5768	−.5751	−.5735	−.5719	−.5702
.27	−.5686	−.5670	−.5654	−.5638	−.5622	−.5607	−.5591	−.5575	−.5560	−.5544
.28	−.5528	−.5513	−.5498	−.5482	−.5467	−.5452	−.5436	−.5421	−.5406	−.5391
.29	−.5376	−.5361	−.5346	−.5331	−.5317	−.5302	−.5287	−.5272	−.5258	−.5243
.30	−.5229	−.5214	−.5200	−.5186	−.5171	−.5157	−.5143	−.5129	−.5114	−.5100
.31	−.5086	−.5072	−.5058	−.5045	−.5031	−.5017	−.5003	−.4989	−.4976	−.4962
.32	−.4949	−.4935	−.4921	−.4908	−.4895	−.4881	−.4868	−.4855	−.4841	−.4828
.33	−.4815	−.4802	−.4789	−.4776	−.4763	−.4750	−.4737	−.4724	−.4711	−.4698
.34	−.4685	−.4672	−.4660	−.4647	−.4634	−.4622	−.4609	−.4597	−.4584	−.4572
.35	−.4559	−.4547	−.4535	−.4522	−.4510	−.4498	−.4486	−.4473	−.4461	−.4449
.36	−.4437	−.4425	−.4413	−.4401	−.4389	−.4377	−.4365	−.4353	−.4342	−.4330
.37	−.4318	−.4306	−.4295	−.4283	−.4271	−.4260	−.4248	−.4237	−.4225	−.4214
.38	−.4202	−.4191	−.4179	−.4168	−.4157	−.4145	−.4134	−.4123	−.4112	−.4101
.39	−.4089	−.4078	−.4067	−.4056	−.4045	−.4034	−.4023	−.4012	−.4001	−.3990
.40	−.3979	−.3969	−.3958	−.3947	−.3936	−.3925	−.3915	−.3904	−.3893	−.3883
.41	−.3872	−.3862	−.3851	−.3840	−.3830	−.3820	−.3809	−.3799	−.3788	−.3778
.42	−.3768	−.3757	−.3747	−.3737	−.3726	−.3716	−.3706	−.3696	−.3686	−.3675
.43	−.3665	−.3655	−.3645	−.3635	−.3625	−.3615	−.3605	−.3595	−.3585	−.3575
.44	−.3565	−.3556	−.3546	−.3536	−.3526	−.3516	−.3507	−.3497	−.3487	−.3478
.45	−.3468	−.3458	−.3449	−.3439	−.3429	−.3420	−.3410	−.3401	−.3391	−.3382
.46	−.3372	−.3363	−.3354	−.3344	−.3335	−.3325	−.3316	−.3307	−.3298	−.3288
.47	−.3279	−.3270	−.3261	−.3251	−.3242	−.3233	−.3224	−.3215	−.3206	−.3197
.48	−.3188	−.3179	−.3170	−.3161	−.3152	−.3143	−.3134	−.3125	−.3116	−.3107
.49	−.3098	−.3089	−.3080	−.3072	−.3063	−.3054	−.3045	−.3036	−.3028	−.3019
.50	−.3010	−.3002	−.2993	−.2984	−.2976	−.2967	−.2958	−.2950	−.2941	−.2933
.51	−.2924	−.2916	−.2907	−.2899	−.2890	−.2882	−.2874	−.2865	−.2857	−.2848
.52	−.2840	−.2832	−.2823	−.2815	−.2807	−.2798	−.2790	−.2782	−.2774	−.2765
.53	−.2757	−.2749	−.2741	−.2733	−.2725	−.2716	−.2708	−.2700	−.2692	−.2684
.54	−.2676	−.2668	−.2660	−.2652	−.2644	−.2636	−.2628	−.2620	−.2612	−.2604

* This table can be used conveniently for finding the cologarithms of the decimal numbers, since the colog $N = -\log N$. For example, colog $0.61 = 0.2147$.

N	0	1	2	3	4	5	6	7	8	9
.55	−.2596	−.2588	−.2581	−.2573	−.2565	−.2557	−.2549	−.2541	−.2534	−.2526
.56	−.2518	−.2510	−.2503	−.2495	−.2487	−.2480	−.2472	−.2464	−.2457	−.2449
.57	−.2441	−.2434	−.2426	−.2418	−.2411	−.2403	−.2396	−.2388	−.2381	−.2373
.58	−.2366	−.2358	−.2351	−.2343	−.2336	−.2328	−.2321	−.2314	−.2306	−.2299
.59	−.2291	−.2284	−.2277	−.2269	−.2262	−.2255	−.2248	−.2240	−.2233	−.2226
.60	−.2218	−.2211	−.2204	−.2197	−.2190	−.2182	−.2175	−.2168	−.2161	−.2154
.61	−.2147	−.2140	−.2132	−.2125	−.2118	−.2111	−.2104	−.2097	−.2090	−.2083
.62	−.2076	−.2069	−.2062	−.2055	−.2048	−.2041	−.2034	−.2027	−.2020	−.2013
.63	−.2007	−.2000	−.1993	−.1986	−.1979	−.1972	−.1965	−.1959	−.1952	−.1945
.64	−.1938	−.1931	−.1925	−.1918	−.1911	−.1904	−.1898	−.1891	−.1884	−.1878
.65	−.1871	−.1864	−.1858	−.1851	−.1844	−.1838	−.1831	−.1824	−.1818	−.1811
.66	−.1805	−.1798	−.1791	−.1785	−.1778	−.1772	−.1765	−.1759	−.1752	−.1746
.67	−.1739	−.1733	−.1726	−.1720	−.1713	−.1707	−.1701	−.1694	−.1688	−.1681
.68	−.1675	−.1669	−.1662	−.1656	−.1649	−.1643	−.1637	−.1630	−.1624	−.1618
.69	−.1612	−.1605	−.1599	−.1593	−.1586	−.1580	−.1574	−.1568	−.1561	−.1555
.70	−.1549	−.1543	−.1537	−.1530	−.1524	−.1518	−.1512	−.1506	−.1500	−.1494
.71	−.1487	−.1481	−.1475	−.1469	−.1463	−.1457	−.1451	−.1445	−.1439	−.1433
.72	−.1427	−.1421	−.1415	−.1409	−.1403	−.1397	−.1391	−.1385	−.1379	−.1373
.73	−.1367	−.1361	−.1355	−.1349	−.1343	−.1337	−.1331	−.1325	−.1319	−.1314
.74	−.1308	−.1302	−.1296	−.1290	−.1284	−.1278	−.1273	−.1267	−.1261	−.1255
.75	−.1249	−.1244	−.1238	−.1232	−.1226	−.1221	−.1215	−.1209	−.1203	−.1198
.76	−.1192	−.1186	−.1180	−.1175	−.1169	−.1163	−.1158	−.1152	−.1146	−.1141
.77	−.1135	−.1129	−.1124	−.1118	−.1113	−.1107	−.1101	−.1096	−.1090	−.1085
.78	−.1079	−.1073	−.1068	−.1062	−.1057	−.1051	−.1046	−.1040	−.1035	−.1029
.79	−.1024	−.1018	−.1013	−.1007	−.1002	−.0996	−.0991	−.0985	−.0980	−.0975
.80	−.0969	−.0964	−.0958	−.0953	−.0947	−.0942	−.0937	−.0931	−.0926	−.0921
.81	−.0915	−.0910	−.0904	−.0899	−.0894	−.0888	−.0883	−.0878	−.0872	−.0867
.82	−.0862	−.0857	−.0851	−.0846	−.0841	−.0835	−.0830	−.0825	−.0820	−.0814
.83	−.0809	−.0804	−.0799	−.0794	−.0788	−.0783	−.0778	−.0773	−.0768	−.0762
.84	−.0757	−.0752	−.0747	−.0742	−.0737	−.0731	−.0726	−.0721	−.0716	−.0711
.85	−.0706	−.0701	−.0696	−.0691	−.0685	−.0680	−.0675	−.0670	−.0665	−.0660
.86	−.0655	−.0650	−.0645	−.0640	−.0635	−.0630	−.0625	−.0620	−.0615	−.0610
.87	−.0605	−.0600	−.0595	−.0590	−.0585	−.0580	−.0575	−.0570	−.0565	−.0560
.88	−.0555	−.0550	−.0545	−.0540	−.0535	−.0531	−.0526	−.0521	−.0516	−.0511
.89	−.0506	−.0501	−.0496	−.0491	−.0487	−.0482	−.0477	−.0472	−.0467	−.0462
.90	−.0458	−.0453	−.0448	−.0443	−.0438	−.0434	−.0429	−.0424	−.0419	−.0414
.91	−.0410	−.0405	−.0400	−.0395	−.0391	−.0386	−.0381	−.0376	−.0372	−.0367
.92	−.0362	−.0357	−.0353	−.0348	−.0343	−.0339	−.0334	−.0329	−.0325	−.0320
.93	−.0315	−.0311	−.0306	−.0301	−.0297	−.0292	−.0287	−.0283	−.0278	−.0273
.94	−.0269	−.0264	−.0259	−.0255	−.0250	−.0246	−.0241	−.0237	−.0232	−.0227
.95	−.0223	−.0218	−.0214	−.0209	−.0205	−.0200	−.0195	−.0191	−.0186	−.0182
.96	−.0177	−.0173	−.0168	−.0164	−.0159	−.0155	−.0150	−.0146	−.0141	−.0137
.97	−.0132	−.0128	−.0123	−.0119	−.0114	−.0110	−.0106	−.0101	−.0097	−.0092
.98	−.0088	−.0083	−.0079	−.0074	−.0070	−.0066	−.0061	−.0057	−.0052	−.0048
.99	−.0044	−.0039	−.0035	−.0031	−.0026	−.0022	−.0017	−.0013	−.0009	−.0004

ANTILOGARITHMS

<table>
<thead>
<tr><th></th><th>0</th><th>1</th><th>2</th><th>3</th><th>4</th><th>5</th><th>6</th><th>7</th><th>8</th><th>9</th><th colspan="9">Proportional Parts</th></tr>
<tr><th></th><th></th><th></th><th></th><th></th><th></th><th></th><th></th><th></th><th></th><th></th><th>1</th><th>2</th><th>3</th><th>4</th><th>5</th><th>6</th><th>7</th><th>8</th><th>9</th></tr>
</thead>
<tbody>
<tr><td>.00</td><td>1000</td><td>1002</td><td>1005</td><td>1007</td><td>1009</td><td>1012</td><td>1014</td><td>1016</td><td>1019</td><td>1021</td><td>0</td><td>0</td><td>1</td><td>1</td><td>1</td><td>1</td><td>2</td><td>2</td><td>2</td></tr>
<tr><td>.01</td><td>1023</td><td>1026</td><td>1028</td><td>1030</td><td>1033</td><td>1035</td><td>1038</td><td>1040</td><td>1042</td><td>1045</td><td>0</td><td>0</td><td>1</td><td>1</td><td>1</td><td>1</td><td>2</td><td>2</td><td>2</td></tr>
<tr><td>.02</td><td>1047</td><td>1050</td><td>1052</td><td>1054</td><td>1057</td><td>1059</td><td>1062</td><td>1064</td><td>1067</td><td>1069</td><td>0</td><td>0</td><td>1</td><td>1</td><td>1</td><td>1</td><td>2</td><td>2</td><td>2</td></tr>
<tr><td>.03</td><td>1072</td><td>1074</td><td>1076</td><td>1079</td><td>1081</td><td>1084</td><td>1086</td><td>1089</td><td>1091</td><td>1094</td><td>0</td><td>0</td><td>1</td><td>1</td><td>1</td><td>1</td><td>2</td><td>2</td><td>2</td></tr>
<tr><td>.04</td><td>1096</td><td>1099</td><td>1102</td><td>1104</td><td>1107</td><td>1109</td><td>1112</td><td>1114</td><td>1117</td><td>1119</td><td>0</td><td>1</td><td>1</td><td>1</td><td>1</td><td>2</td><td>2</td><td>2</td><td>2</td></tr>
<tr><td>.05</td><td>1122</td><td>1125</td><td>1127</td><td>1130</td><td>1132</td><td>1135</td><td>1138</td><td>1140</td><td>1143</td><td>1146</td><td>0</td><td>1</td><td>1</td><td>1</td><td>1</td><td>2</td><td>2</td><td>2</td><td>2</td></tr>
<tr><td>.06</td><td>1148</td><td>1151</td><td>1153</td><td>1156</td><td>1159</td><td>1161</td><td>1164</td><td>1167</td><td>1169</td><td>1172</td><td>0</td><td>1</td><td>1</td><td>1</td><td>1</td><td>2</td><td>2</td><td>2</td><td>2</td></tr>
<tr><td>.07</td><td>1175</td><td>1178</td><td>1180</td><td>1183</td><td>1186</td><td>1189</td><td>1191</td><td>1194</td><td>1197</td><td>1199</td><td>0</td><td>1</td><td>1</td><td>1</td><td>1</td><td>2</td><td>2</td><td>2</td><td>2</td></tr>
<tr><td>.08</td><td>1202</td><td>1205</td><td>1208</td><td>1211</td><td>1213</td><td>1216</td><td>1219</td><td>1222</td><td>1225</td><td>1227</td><td>0</td><td>1</td><td>1</td><td>1</td><td>1</td><td>2</td><td>2</td><td>2</td><td>3</td></tr>
<tr><td>.09</td><td>1230</td><td>1233</td><td>1236</td><td>1239</td><td>1242</td><td>1245</td><td>1247</td><td>1250</td><td>1253</td><td>1256</td><td>0</td><td>1</td><td>1</td><td>1</td><td>1</td><td>2</td><td>2</td><td>2</td><td>3</td></tr>
<tr><td>.10</td><td>1259</td><td>1262</td><td>1265</td><td>1268</td><td>1271</td><td>1274</td><td>1276</td><td>1279</td><td>1282</td><td>1285</td><td>0</td><td>1</td><td>1</td><td>1</td><td>1</td><td>2</td><td>2</td><td>2</td><td>3</td></tr>
<tr><td>.11</td><td>1288</td><td>1291</td><td>1294</td><td>1297</td><td>1300</td><td>1303</td><td>1306</td><td>1309</td><td>1312</td><td>1315</td><td>0</td><td>1</td><td>1</td><td>1</td><td>2</td><td>2</td><td>2</td><td>2</td><td>3</td></tr>
<tr><td>.12</td><td>1318</td><td>1321</td><td>1324</td><td>1327</td><td>1330</td><td>1334</td><td>1337</td><td>1340</td><td>1343</td><td>1346</td><td>0</td><td>1</td><td>1</td><td>1</td><td>2</td><td>2</td><td>2</td><td>2</td><td>3</td></tr>
<tr><td>.13</td><td>1349</td><td>1352</td><td>1355</td><td>1358</td><td>1361</td><td>1365</td><td>1368</td><td>1371</td><td>1374</td><td>1377</td><td>0</td><td>1</td><td>1</td><td>1</td><td>2</td><td>2</td><td>2</td><td>3</td><td>3</td></tr>
<tr><td>.14</td><td>1380</td><td>1384</td><td>1387</td><td>1390</td><td>1393</td><td>1396</td><td>1400</td><td>1403</td><td>1406</td><td>1409</td><td>0</td><td>1</td><td>1</td><td>1</td><td>2</td><td>2</td><td>2</td><td>3</td><td>3</td></tr>
<tr><td>.15</td><td>1413</td><td>1416</td><td>1419</td><td>1422</td><td>1426</td><td>1429</td><td>1432</td><td>1435</td><td>1439</td><td>1442</td><td>0</td><td>1</td><td>1</td><td>1</td><td>2</td><td>2</td><td>2</td><td>3</td><td>3</td></tr>
<tr><td>.16</td><td>1445</td><td>1449</td><td>1452</td><td>1455</td><td>1459</td><td>1462</td><td>1466</td><td>1469</td><td>1472</td><td>1476</td><td>0</td><td>1</td><td>1</td><td>1</td><td>2</td><td>2</td><td>2</td><td>3</td><td>3</td></tr>
<tr><td>.17</td><td>1479</td><td>1483</td><td>1486</td><td>1489</td><td>1493</td><td>1496</td><td>1500</td><td>1503</td><td>1507</td><td>1510</td><td>0</td><td>1</td><td>1</td><td>1</td><td>2</td><td>2</td><td>2</td><td>3</td><td>3</td></tr>
<tr><td>.18</td><td>1514</td><td>1517</td><td>1521</td><td>1524</td><td>1528</td><td>1531</td><td>1535</td><td>1538</td><td>1542</td><td>1545</td><td>0</td><td>1</td><td>1</td><td>1</td><td>2</td><td>2</td><td>2</td><td>3</td><td>3</td></tr>
<tr><td>.19</td><td>1549</td><td>1552</td><td>1556</td><td>1560</td><td>1563</td><td>1567</td><td>1570</td><td>1574</td><td>1578</td><td>1581</td><td>0</td><td>1</td><td>1</td><td>1</td><td>2</td><td>2</td><td>3</td><td>3</td><td>3</td></tr>
<tr><td>.20</td><td>1585</td><td>1589</td><td>1592</td><td>1596</td><td>1600</td><td>1603</td><td>1607</td><td>1611</td><td>1614</td><td>1618</td><td>0</td><td>1</td><td>1</td><td>1</td><td>2</td><td>2</td><td>3</td><td>3</td><td>3</td></tr>
<tr><td>.21</td><td>1622</td><td>1626</td><td>1629</td><td>1633</td><td>1637</td><td>1641</td><td>1644</td><td>1648</td><td>1652</td><td>1656</td><td>0</td><td>1</td><td>1</td><td>2</td><td>2</td><td>2</td><td>3</td><td>3</td><td>3</td></tr>
<tr><td>.22</td><td>1660</td><td>1663</td><td>1667</td><td>1671</td><td>1675</td><td>1679</td><td>1683</td><td>1687</td><td>1690</td><td>1694</td><td>0</td><td>1</td><td>1</td><td>2</td><td>2</td><td>2</td><td>3</td><td>3</td><td>3</td></tr>
<tr><td>.23</td><td>1698</td><td>1702</td><td>1706</td><td>1710</td><td>1714</td><td>1718</td><td>1722</td><td>1726</td><td>1730</td><td>1734</td><td>0</td><td>1</td><td>1</td><td>2</td><td>2</td><td>2</td><td>3</td><td>3</td><td>4</td></tr>
<tr><td>.24</td><td>1738</td><td>1742</td><td>1746</td><td>1750</td><td>1754</td><td>1758</td><td>1762</td><td>1766</td><td>1770</td><td>1774</td><td>0</td><td>1</td><td>1</td><td>2</td><td>2</td><td>2</td><td>3</td><td>3</td><td>4</td></tr>
<tr><td>.25</td><td>1778</td><td>1782</td><td>1786</td><td>1791</td><td>1795</td><td>1799</td><td>1803</td><td>1807</td><td>1811</td><td>1816</td><td>0</td><td>1</td><td>1</td><td>2</td><td>2</td><td>2</td><td>3</td><td>3</td><td>4</td></tr>
<tr><td>.26</td><td>1820</td><td>1824</td><td>1828</td><td>1832</td><td>1837</td><td>1841</td><td>1845</td><td>1849</td><td>1854</td><td>1858</td><td>0</td><td>1</td><td>1</td><td>2</td><td>2</td><td>3</td><td>3</td><td>3</td><td>4</td></tr>
<tr><td>.27</td><td>1862</td><td>1866</td><td>1871</td><td>1875</td><td>1879</td><td>1884</td><td>1888</td><td>1892</td><td>1897</td><td>1901</td><td>0</td><td>1</td><td>1</td><td>2</td><td>2</td><td>3</td><td>3</td><td>3</td><td>4</td></tr>
<tr><td>.28</td><td>1905</td><td>1910</td><td>1914</td><td>1919</td><td>1923</td><td>1928</td><td>1932</td><td>1936</td><td>1941</td><td>1945</td><td>0</td><td>1</td><td>1</td><td>2</td><td>2</td><td>3</td><td>3</td><td>4</td><td>4</td></tr>
<tr><td>.29</td><td>1950</td><td>1954</td><td>1959</td><td>1963</td><td>1968</td><td>1972</td><td>1977</td><td>1982</td><td>1986</td><td>1991</td><td>0</td><td>1</td><td>1</td><td>2</td><td>2</td><td>3</td><td>3</td><td>4</td><td>4</td></tr>
<tr><td>.30</td><td>1995</td><td>2000</td><td>2004</td><td>2009</td><td>2014</td><td>2018</td><td>2023</td><td>2028</td><td>2032</td><td>2037</td><td>0</td><td>1</td><td>1</td><td>2</td><td>2</td><td>3</td><td>3</td><td>4</td><td>4</td></tr>
<tr><td>.31</td><td>2042</td><td>2046</td><td>2051</td><td>2056</td><td>2061</td><td>2065</td><td>2070</td><td>2075</td><td>2080</td><td>2084</td><td>0</td><td>1</td><td>1</td><td>2</td><td>2</td><td>3</td><td>3</td><td>4</td><td>4</td></tr>
<tr><td>.32</td><td>2089</td><td>2094</td><td>2099</td><td>2104</td><td>2109</td><td>2113</td><td>2118</td><td>2123</td><td>2128</td><td>2133</td><td>0</td><td>1</td><td>1</td><td>2</td><td>2</td><td>3</td><td>3</td><td>4</td><td>4</td></tr>
<tr><td>.33</td><td>2138</td><td>2143</td><td>2148</td><td>2153</td><td>2158</td><td>2163</td><td>2168</td><td>2173</td><td>2178</td><td>2183</td><td>0</td><td>1</td><td>1</td><td>2</td><td>2</td><td>3</td><td>3</td><td>4</td><td>4</td></tr>
<tr><td>.34</td><td>2188</td><td>2193</td><td>2198</td><td>2203</td><td>2208</td><td>2213</td><td>2218</td><td>2223</td><td>2228</td><td>2234</td><td>1</td><td>1</td><td>2</td><td>2</td><td>3</td><td>3</td><td>4</td><td>4</td><td>5</td></tr>
<tr><td>.35</td><td>2239</td><td>2244</td><td>2249</td><td>2254</td><td>2259</td><td>2265</td><td>2270</td><td>2275</td><td>2280</td><td>2286</td><td>1</td><td>1</td><td>2</td><td>2</td><td>3</td><td>3</td><td>4</td><td>4</td><td>5</td></tr>
<tr><td>.36</td><td>2291</td><td>2296</td><td>2301</td><td>2307</td><td>2312</td><td>2317</td><td>2323</td><td>2328</td><td>2333</td><td>2339</td><td>1</td><td>1</td><td>2</td><td>2</td><td>3</td><td>3</td><td>4</td><td>4</td><td>5</td></tr>
<tr><td>.37</td><td>2344</td><td>2350</td><td>2355</td><td>2360</td><td>2366</td><td>2371</td><td>2377</td><td>2382</td><td>2388</td><td>2393</td><td>1</td><td>1</td><td>2</td><td>2</td><td>3</td><td>3</td><td>4</td><td>4</td><td>5</td></tr>
<tr><td>.38</td><td>2399</td><td>2404</td><td>2410</td><td>2415</td><td>2421</td><td>2427</td><td>2432</td><td>2438</td><td>2443</td><td>2449</td><td>1</td><td>1</td><td>2</td><td>2</td><td>3</td><td>3</td><td>4</td><td>4</td><td>5</td></tr>
<tr><td>.39</td><td>2455</td><td>2460</td><td>2466</td><td>2472</td><td>2477</td><td>2483</td><td>2489</td><td>2495</td><td>2500</td><td>2506</td><td>1</td><td>1</td><td>2</td><td>2</td><td>3</td><td>3</td><td>4</td><td>5</td><td>5</td></tr>
<tr><td>.40</td><td>2512</td><td>2518</td><td>2523</td><td>2529</td><td>2535</td><td>2541</td><td>2547</td><td>2553</td><td>2559</td><td>2564</td><td>1</td><td>1</td><td>2</td><td>2</td><td>3</td><td>4</td><td>4</td><td>5</td><td>5</td></tr>
<tr><td>.41</td><td>2570</td><td>2576</td><td>2582</td><td>2588</td><td>2594</td><td>2600</td><td>2606</td><td>2612</td><td>2618</td><td>2624</td><td>1</td><td>1</td><td>2</td><td>2</td><td>3</td><td>4</td><td>4</td><td>5</td><td>5</td></tr>
<tr><td>.42</td><td>2630</td><td>2636</td><td>2642</td><td>2649</td><td>2655</td><td>2661</td><td>2667</td><td>2673</td><td>2679</td><td>2685</td><td>1</td><td>1</td><td>2</td><td>2</td><td>3</td><td>4</td><td>4</td><td>5</td><td>6</td></tr>
<tr><td>.43</td><td>2692</td><td>2698</td><td>2704</td><td>2710</td><td>2716</td><td>2723</td><td>2729</td><td>2735</td><td>2742</td><td>2748</td><td>1</td><td>1</td><td>2</td><td>3</td><td>3</td><td>4</td><td>4</td><td>5</td><td>6</td></tr>
<tr><td>.44</td><td>2754</td><td>2761</td><td>2767</td><td>2773</td><td>2780</td><td>2786</td><td>2793</td><td>2799</td><td>2805</td><td>2812</td><td>1</td><td>1</td><td>2</td><td>3</td><td>3</td><td>4</td><td>4</td><td>5</td><td>6</td></tr>
<tr><td>.45</td><td>2818</td><td>2825</td><td>2831</td><td>2838</td><td>2844</td><td>2851</td><td>2858</td><td>2864</td><td>2871</td><td>2877</td><td>1</td><td>1</td><td>2</td><td>3</td><td>3</td><td>4</td><td>5</td><td>5</td><td>6</td></tr>
<tr><td>.46</td><td>2884</td><td>2891</td><td>2897</td><td>2904</td><td>2911</td><td>2917</td><td>2924</td><td>2931</td><td>2938</td><td>2944</td><td>1</td><td>1</td><td>2</td><td>3</td><td>3</td><td>4</td><td>5</td><td>5</td><td>6</td></tr>
<tr><td>.47</td><td>2951</td><td>2958</td><td>2965</td><td>2972</td><td>2979</td><td>2985</td><td>2992</td><td>2999</td><td>3006</td><td>3013</td><td>1</td><td>1</td><td>2</td><td>3</td><td>3</td><td>4</td><td>5</td><td>5</td><td>6</td></tr>
<tr><td>.48</td><td>3020</td><td>3027</td><td>3034</td><td>3041</td><td>3048</td><td>3055</td><td>3062</td><td>3069</td><td>3076</td><td>3083</td><td>1</td><td>1</td><td>2</td><td>3</td><td>4</td><td>4</td><td>5</td><td>6</td><td>6</td></tr>
<tr><td>.49</td><td>3090</td><td>3097</td><td>3105</td><td>3112</td><td>3119</td><td>3126</td><td>3133</td><td>3141</td><td>3148</td><td>3155</td><td>1</td><td>1</td><td>2</td><td>3</td><td>4</td><td>4</td><td>5</td><td>6</td><td>6</td></tr>
<tr><td></td><td>0</td><td>1</td><td>2</td><td>3</td><td>4</td><td>5</td><td>6</td><td>7</td><td>8</td><td>9</td><td>1</td><td>2</td><td>3</td><td>4</td><td>5</td><td>6</td><td>7</td><td>8</td><td>9</td></tr>
</tbody>
</table>

ANTILOGARITHMS

	0	1	2	3	4	5	6	7	8	9	Proportional Parts								
											1	2	3	4	5	6	7	8	9
.50	3162	3170	3177	3184	3192	3199	3206	3214	3221	3228	1	1	2	3	4	4	5	6	7
.51	3236	3243	3251	3258	3266	3273	3281	3289	3296	3304	1	2	2	3	4	5	5	6	7
.52	3311	3319	3327	3334	3342	3350	3357	3365	3373	3381	1	2	2	3	4	5	5	6	7
.53	3388	3396	3404	3412	3420	3428	3436	3443	3451	3459	1	2	2	3	4	5	6	6	7
.54	3467	3475	3483	3491	3499	3508	3516	3524	3532	3540	1	2	2	3	4	5	6	6	7
.55	3548	3556	3565	3573	3581	3589	3597	3606	3614	3622	1	2	2	3	4	5	6	7	7
.56	3631	3639	3648	3656	3664	3673	3681	3690	3698	3707	1	2	3	3	4	5	6	7	8
.57	3715	3724	3733	3741	3750	3758	3767	3776	3784	3793	1	2	3	3	4	5	6	7	8
.58	3802	3811	3819	3828	3837	3846	3855	3864	3873	3882	1	2	3	4	4	5	6	7	8
.59	3890	3899	3908	3917	3926	3936	3945	3954	3963	3972	1	2	3	4	5	5	6	7	8
.60	3981	3990	3999	4009	4018	4027	4036	4046	4055	4064	1	2	3	4	5	6	6	7	8
.61	4074	4083	4093	4102	4111	4121	4130	4140	4150	4159	1	2	3	4	5	6	7	8	9
.62	4169	4178	4188	4198	4207	4217	4227	4236	4246	4256	1	2	3	4	5	6	7	8	9
.63	4266	4276	4285	4295	4305	4315	4325	4335	4345	4355	1	2	3	4	5	6	7	8	9
.64	4365	4375	4385	4395	4406	4416	4426	4436	4446	4457	1	2	3	4	5	6	7	8	9
.65	4467	4477	4487	4498	4508	4519	4529	4539	4550	4560	1	2	3	4	5	6	7	8	9
.66	4571	4581	4592	4603	4613	4624	4634	4645	4656	4667	1	2	3	4	5	6	7	9	10
.67	4677	4688	4699	4710	4721	4732	4742	4753	4764	4775	1	2	3	4	5	7	8	9	10
.68	4786	4797	4808	4819	4831	4842	4853	4864	4875	4887	1	2	3	4	6	7	8	9	10
.69	4898	4909	4920	4932	4943	4955	4966	4977	4989	5000	1	2	3	5	6	7	8	9	10
.70	5012	5023	5035	5047	5058	5070	5082	5093	5105	5117	1	2	4	5	6	7	8	9	11
.71	5129	5140	5152	5164	5176	5188	5200	5212	5224	5236	1	2	4	5	6	7	8	10	11
.72	5248	5260	5272	5284	5297	5309	5321	5333	5346	5358	1	2	4	5	6	7	9	10	11
.73	5370	5383	5395	5408	5420	5433	5445	5458	5470	5483	1	3	4	5	6	8	9	10	11
.74	5495	5508	5521	5534	5546	5559	5572	5585	5598	5610	1	3	4	5	6	8	9	10	12
.75	5623	5636	5649	5662	5675	5689	5702	5715	5728	5741	1	3	4	5	7	8	9	10	12
.76	5754	5768	5781	5794	5808	5821	5834	5848	5861	5875	1	3	4	5	7	8	9	11	12
.77	5888	5902	5916	5929	5943	5957	5970	5984	5998	6012	1	3	4	5	7	8	10	11	12
.78	6026	6039	6053	6067	6081	6095	6109	6124	6138	6152	1	3	4	6	7	8	10	11	13
.79	6166	6180	6194	6209	6223	6237	6252	6266	6281	6295	1	3	4	6	7	9	10	11	13
.80	6310	6324	6339	6353	6368	6383	6397	6412	6427	6442	1	3	4	6	7	9	10	12	13
.81	6457	6471	6486	6501	6516	6531	6546	6561	6577	6592	2	3	5	6	8	9	11	12	14
.82	6607	6622	6637	6653	6668	6683	6699	6714	6730	6745	2	3	5	6	8	9	11	12	14
.83	6761	6776	6792	6808	6823	6839	6855	6871	6887	6902	2	3	5	6	8	9	11	13	14
.84	6918	6934	6950	6966	6982	6998	7015	7031	7047	7063	2	3	5	6	8	10	11	13	15
.85	7079	7096	7112	7129	7145	7161	7178	7194	7211	7228	2	3	5	7	8	10	12	13	15
.86	7244	7261	7278	7295	7311	7328	7345	7362	7379	7396	2	3	5	7	8	10	12	13	15
.87	7413	7430	7447	7464	7482	7499	7516	7534	7551	7568	2	3	5	7	9	10	12	14	16
.88	7586	7603	7621	7638	7656	7674	7691	7709	7727	7745	2	4	5	7	9	11	12	14	16
.89	7762	7780	7798	7816	7834	7852	7870	7889	7907	7925	2	4	5	7	9	11	13	14	16
.90	7943	7962	7980	7998	8017	8035	8054	8072	8091	8110	2	4	6	7	9	11	13	15	17
.91	8128	8147	8166	8185	8204	8222	8241	8260	8279	8299	2	4	6	8	9	11	13	15	17
.92	8318	8337	8356	8375	8395	8414	8433	8453	8472	8492	2	4	6	8	10	12	14	15	17
.93	8511	8531	8551	8570	8590	8610	8630	8650	8670	8690	2	4	6	8	10	12	14	16	18
.94	8710	8730	8750	8770	8790	8810	8831	8851	8872	8892	2	4	6	8	10	12	14	16	18
.95	8913	8933	8954	8974	8995	9016	9036	9057	9078	9099	2	4	6	8	10	12	15	17	19
.96	9120	9141	9162	9183	9204	9226	9247	9268	9290	9311	2	4	6	8	11	13	15	17	19
.97	9333	9354	9376	9397	9419	9441	9462	9484	9506	9528	2	4	7	9	11	13	15	17	20
.98	9550	9572	9594	9616	9638	9661	9683	9705	9727	9750	2	4	7	9	11	13	16	18	20
.99	9772	9795	9817	9840	9863	9886	9908	9931	9954	9977	2	5	7	9	11	14	16	18	20
	0	1	2	3	4	5	6	7	8	9	1	2	3	4	5	6	7	8	9

FIVE-PLACE LOGARITHMS

N.	0	1	2	3	4	5	6	7	8	9
100	00 000	043	087	130	173	217	260	303	346	389
101	432	475	518	561	604	647	689	732	775	817
102	860	903	945	988	*030	*072	*115	*157	*199	*242
103	01 284	326	368	410	452	494	536	578	620	662
104	703	745	787	828	870	912	953	995	*036	*078
105	02 119	160	202	243	284	325	366	407	449	490
106	531	572	612	653	694	735	776	816	857	898
107	938	979	*019	*060	*100	*141	*181	*222	*262	*302
108	03 342	383	423	463	503	543	583	623	663	703
109	743	782	822	862	902	941	981	*021	*060	*100
110	04 139	179	218	258	297	336	376	415	454	493
111	532	571	610	650	689	727	766	805	844	883
112	922	961	999	*038	*077	*115	*154	*192	*231	*269
113	05 308	346	385	423	461	500	538	576	614	652
114	690	729	767	805	843	881	918	956	994	*032
115	06 070	108	145	183	221	258	296	333	371	408
116	446	483	521	558	595	633	670	707	744	781
117	819	856	893	930	967	*004	*041	*078	*115	*151
118	07 188	225	262	298	335	372	408	445	482	518
119	555	591	628	664	700	737	773	809	846	882
120	918	954	990	*027	*063	*099	*135	*171	*207	*243
121	08 279	314	350	386	422	458	493	529	565	600
122	636	672	707	743	778	814	849	884	920	955
123	991	*026	*061	*096	*132	*167	*202	*237	*272	*307
124	09 342	377	412	447	482	517	552	587	621	656
125	691	726	760	795	830	864	899	934	968	*003
126	10 037	072	106	140	175	209	243	278	312	346
127	380	415	449	483	517	551	585	619	653	687
128	721	755	789	823	857	890	924	958	992	*025
129	11 059	093	126	160	193	227	261	294	327	361
130	394	428	461	494	528	561	594	628	661	694
131	727	760	793	826	860	893	926	959	992	*024
132	12 057	090	123	156	189	222	254	287	320	352
133	385	418	450	483	516	548	581	613	646	678
134	710	743	775	808	840	872	905	937	969	*001
135	13 033	066	098	130	162	194	226	258	290	322
136	354	386	418	450	481	513	545	577	609	640
137	672	704	735	767	799	830	862	893	925	956
138	988	*019	*051	*082	*114	*145	*176	*208	*239	*270
139	14 301	333	364	395	426	457	489	520	551	582
140	613	644	675	706	737	768	799	829	860	891
141	922	953	983	*014	*045	*076	*106	*137	*168	*198
142	15 229	259	290	320	351	381	412	442	473	503
143	534	564	594	625	655	685	715	746	776	806
144	836	866	897	927	957	987	*017	*047	*077	*107
145	16 137	167	197	227	256	286	316	346	376	406
146	435	465	495	524	554	584	613	643	673	702
147	732	761	791	820	850	879	909	938	967	997
148	17 026	056	085	114	143	173	202	231	260	289
149	319	348	377	406	435	464	493	522	551	580
150	609	638	667	696	725	754	782	811	840	869
N.	0	1	2	3	4	5	6	7	8	9

Proportional Parts

	44	43	42
1	4.4	4.3	4.2
2	8.8	8.6	8.4
3	13.2	12.9	12.6
4	17.6	17.2	16.8
5	22.0	21.5	21.0
6	26.4	25.8	25.2
7	30.8	30.1	29.4
8	35.2	34.4	33.6
9	39.6	38.7	37.8

	41	40	39
1	4.1	4.0	3.9
2	8.2	8.0	7.8
3	12.3	12.0	11.7
4	16.4	16.0	15.6
5	20.5	20.0	19.5
6	24.6	24.0	23.4
7	28.7	28.0	27.3
8	32.8	32.0	31.2
9	36.9	36.0	35.1

	38	37	36
1	3.8	3.7	3.6
2	7.6	7.4	7.2
3	11.4	11.1	10.8
4	15.2	14.8	14.4
5	19.0	18.5	18.0
6	22.8	22.2	21.6
7	26.6	25.9	25.2
8	30.4	29.6	28.8
9	34.2	33.3	32.4

	35	34	33
1	3.5	3.4	3.3
2	7.0	6.8	6.6
3	10.5	10.2	9.9
4	14.0	13.6	13.2
5	17.5	17.0	16.5
6	21.0	20.4	19.8
7	24.5	23.8	23.1
8	28.0	27.2	26.4
9	31.5	30.6	29.7

	32	31	30
1	3.2	3.1	3.0
2	6.4	6.2	6.0
3	9.6	9.3	9.0
4	12.8	12.4	12.0
5	16.0	15.5	15.0
6	19.2	18.6	18.0
7	22.4	21.7	21.0
8	25.6	24.8	24.0
9	28.8	27.9	27.0

FIVE-PLACE LOGARITHMS

N.	0	1	2	3	4	5	6	7	8	9
150	17 609	638	667	696	725	754	782	811	840	869
151	898	926	955	984	*013	*041	*070	*099	*127	*156
152	18 184	213	241	270	298	327	355	384	412	441
153	469	498	526	554	583	611	639	667	696	724
154	752	780	808	837	865	893	921	949	977	*005
155	19 033	061	089	117	145	173	201	229	257	285
156	312	340	368	396	424	451	479	507	535	562
157	590	618	645	673	700	728	756	783	811	838
158	866	893	921	948	976	*003	*030	*058	*085	*112
159	20 140	167	194	222	249	276	303	330	358	385
160	412	439	466	493	520	548	575	602	629	656
161	683	710	737	763	790	817	844	871	898	925
162	952	978	*005	*032	*059	*085	*112	*139	*165	*192
163	21 219	245	272	299	325	352	378	405	431	458
164	484	511	537	564	590	617	643	669	696	722
165	748	775	801	827	854	880	906	932	958	985
166	22 011	037	063	089	115	141	167	194	220	246
167	272	298	324	350	376	401	427	453	479	505
168	531	557	583	608	634	660	686	712	737	763
169	789	814	840	866	891	917	943	968	994	*019
170	23 045	070	096	121	147	172	198	223	249	274
171	300	325	350	376	401	426	452	477	502	528
172	553	578	603	629	654	679	704	729	754	779
173	805	830	855	880	905	930	955	980	*005	*030
174	24 055	080	105	130	155	180	204	229	254	279
175	304	329	353	378	403	428	452	477	502	527
176	551	576	601	625	650	674	699	724	748	773
177	797	822	846	871	895	920	944	969	993	*018
178	25 042	066	091	115	139	164	188	212	237	261
179	285	310	334	358	382	406	431	455	479	503
180	527	551	575	600	624	648	672	696	720	744
181	768	792	816	840	864	888	912	935	959	983
182	26 007	031	055	079	102	126	150	174	198	221
183	245	269	293	316	340	364	387	411	435	458
184	482	505	529	553	576	600	623	647	670	694
185	717	741	764	788	811	834	858	881	905	928
186	951	975	998	*021	*045	*068	*091	*114	*138	*161
187	27 184	207	231	254	277	300	323	346	370	393
188	416	439	462	485	508	531	554	577	600	623
189	646	669	692	715	738	761	784	807	830	852
190	875	898	921	944	967	989	*012	*035	*058	*081
191	28 103	126	149	171	194	217	240	262	285	307
192	330	353	375	398	421	443	466	488	511	533
193	556	578	601	623	646	668	691	713	735	758
194	780	803	825	847	870	892	914	937	959	981
195	29 003	026	048	070	092	115	137	159	181	203
196	226	248	270	292	314	336	358	380	403	425
197	447	469	491	513	535	557	579	601	623	645
198	667	688	710	732	754	776	798	820	842	863
199	885	907	929	951	973	994	*016	*038	*060	*081
200	30 103	125	146	168	190	211	233	255	276	298

Proportional parts

	29	28
1	2.9	2.8
2	5.8	5.6
3	8.7	8.4
4	11.6	11.2
5	14.5	14.0
6	17.4	16.8
7	20.3	19.6
8	23.2	22.4
9	26.1	25.2

	27	26
1	2.7	2.6
2	5.4	5.2
3	8.1	7.8
4	10.8	10.4
5	13.5	13.0
6	16.2	15.6
7	18.9	18.2
8	21.6	20.8
9	24.3	23.4

	25
1	2.5
2	5.0
3	7.5
4	10.0
5	12.5
6	15.0
7	17.5
8	20.0
9	22.5

	24	23
1	2.4	2.3
2	4.8	4.6
3	7.2	6.9
4	9.6	9.2
5	12.0	11.5
6	14.4	13.8
7	16.8	16.1
8	19.2	18.4
9	21.6	20.7

	22	21
1	2.2	2.1
2	4.4	4.2
3	6.6	6.3
4	8.8	8.4
5	11.0	10.5
6	13.2	12.6
7	15.4	14.7
8	17.6	16.8
9	19.8	18.9

N.	0	1	2	3	4	5	6	7	8	9	Proportional parts

FIVE-PLACE LOGARITHMS

N.	0	1	2	3	4	5	6	7	8	9
200	30 103	125	146	168	190	211	233	255	276	298
201	320	341	363	384	406	428	449	471	492	514
202	535	557	578	600	621	643	664	685	707	728
203	750	771	792	814	835	856	878	899	920	942
204	963	984	*006	*027	*048	*069	*091	*112	*133	*154
205	31 175	197	218	239	260	281	302	323	345	366
206	387	408	429	450	471	492	513	534	555	576
207	597	618	639	660	681	702	723	744	765	785
208	806	827	848	869	890	911	931	952	973	994
209	32 015	035	056	077	098	118	139	160	181	201
210	222	243	263	284	305	325	346	366	387	408
211	428	449	469	490	510	531	552	572	593	613
212	634	654	675	695	715	736	756	777	797	818
213	838	858	879	899	919	940	960	980	*001	*021
214	33 041	062	082	102	122	143	163	183	203	224
215	244	264	284	304	325	345	365	385	405	425
216	445	465	486	506	526	546	566	586	606	626
217	646	666	686	706	726	746	766	786	806	826
218	846	866	885	905	925	945	965	985	*005	*025
219	34 044	064	084	104	124	143	163	183	203	223
220	242	262	282	301	321	341	361	380	400	420
221	439	459	479	498	518	537	557	577	596	616
222	635	655	674	694	713	733	753	772	792	811
223	830	850	869	889	908	928	947	967	986	*005
224	35 025	044	064	083	102	122	141	160	180	199
225	218	238	257	276	295	315	334	353	372	392
226	411	430	449	468	488	507	526	545	564	583
227	603	622	641	660	679	698	717	736	755	774
228	793	813	832	851	870	889	908	927	946	965
229	984	*003	*021	*040	*059	*078	*097	*116	*135	*154
230	36 173	192	211	229	248	267	286	305	324	342
231	361	380	399	418	436	455	474	493	511	530
232	549	568	586	605	624	642	661	680	698	717
233	736	754	773	791	810	829	847	866	884	903
234	922	940	959	977	996	*014	*033	*051	*070	*088
235	37 107	125	144	162	181	199	218	236	254	273
236	291	310	328	346	365	383	401	420	438	457
237	475	493	511	530	548	566	585	603	621	639
238	658	676	694	712	731	749	767	785	803	822
239	840	858	876	894	912	931	949	967	985	*003
240	38 021	039	057	075	093	112	130	148	166	184
241	202	220	238	256	274	292	310	328	346	364
242	382	399	417	435	453	471	489	507	525	543
243	561	578	596	614	632	650	668	686	703	721
244	739	757	775	792	810	828	846	863	881	899
245	917	934	952	970	987	*005	*023	*041	*058	*076
246	39 094	111	129	146	164	182	199	217	235	252
247	270	287	305	322	340	358	375	393	410	428
248	445	463	480	498	515	533	550	568	585	602
249	620	637	655	672	690	707	724	742	759	777
250	794	811	829	846	863	881	898	915	933	950

Proportional parts

	22	21
1	2.2	2.1
2	4.4	4.2
3	6.6	6.3
4	8.8	8.4
5	11.0	10.5
6	13.2	12.6
7	15.4	14.7
8	17.6	16.8
9	19.8	18.9

	20
1	2.0
2	4.0
3	6.0
4	8.0
5	10.0
6	12.0
7	14.0
8	16.0
9	18.0

	19
1	1.9
2	3.8
3	5.7
4	7.6
5	9.5
6	11.4
7	13.3
8	15.2
9	17.1

	18
1	1.8
2	3.6
3	5.4
4	7.2
5	9.0
6	10.8
7	12.6
8	14.4
9	16.2

	17
1	1.7
2	3.4
3	5.1
4	6.8
5	8.5
6	10.2
7	11.9
8	13.6
9	15.3

N.	0	1	2	3	4	5	6	7	8	9	Proportional parts

FIVE-PLACE LOGARITHMS

N.	0	1	2	3	4	5	6	7	8	9
250	39 794	811	829	846	863	881	898	915	933	950
251	967	985	*002	*019	*037	*054	*071	*088	*106	*123
252	40 140	157	175	192	209	226	243	261	278	295
253	312	329	346	364	381	398	415	432	449	466
254	483	500	518	535	552	569	586	603	620	637
255	654	671	688	705	722	739	756	773	790	807
256	824	841	858	875	892	909	926	943	960	976
257	993	*010	*027	*044	*061	*078	*095	*111	*128	*145
258	41 162	179	196	212	229	246	263	280	296	313
259	330	347	363	380	397	414	430	447	464	481
260	497	514	531	547	564	581	597	614	631	647
261	664	681	697	714	731	747	764	780	797	814
262	830	847	863	880	896	913	929	946	963	979
263	996	*012	*029	*045	*062	*078	*095	*111	*127	*144
264	42 160	177	193	210	226	243	259	275	292	308
265	325	341	357	374	390	406	423	439	455	472
266	488	504	521	537	553	570	586	602	619	635
267	651	667	684	700	716	732	749	765	781	797
268	813	830	846	862	878	894	911	927	943	959
269	975	991	*008	*024	*040	*056	*072	*088	*104	*120
270	43 136	152	169	185	201	217	233	249	265	281
271	297	313	329	345	361	377	393	409	425	441
272	457	473	489	505	521	537	553	569	584	600
273	616	632	648	664	680	696	712	727	743	759
274	775	791	807	823	838	854	870	886	902	917
275	933	949	965	981	996	*012	*028	*044	*059	*075
276	44 091	107	122	138	154	170	185	201	217	232
277	248	264	279	295	311	326	342	358	373	389
278	404	420	436	451	467	483	498	514	529	545
279	560	576	592	607	623	638	654	669	685	700
280	716	731	747	762	778	793	809	824	840	855
281	871	886	902	917	932	948	963	979	994	*010
282	45 025	040	056	071	086	102	117	133	148	163
283	179	194	209	225	240	255	271	286	301	317
284	332	347	362	378	393	408	423	439	454	469
285	484	500	515	530	545	561	576	591	606	621
286	637	652	667	682	697	712	728	743	758	773
287	788	803	818	834	849	864	879	894	909	924
288	939	954	969	984	*000	*015	*030	*045	*060	*075
289	46 090	105	120	135	150	165	180	195	210	225
290	240	255	270	285	300	315	330	345	359	374
291	389	404	419	434	449	464	479	494	509	523
292	538	553	568	583	598	613	627	642	657	672
293	687	702	716	731	746	761	776	790	805	820
294	835	850	864	879	894	909	923	938	953	967
295	982	997	*012	*026	*041	*056	*070	*085	*100	*114
296	47 129	144	159	173	188	202	217	232	246	261
297	276	290	305	319	334	349	363	378	392	407
298	422	436	451	465	480	494	509	524	538	553
299	567	582	596	611	625	640	654	669	683	698
300	712	727	741	756	770	784	799	813	828	842

N.	0	1	2	3	4	5	6	7	8	9

Proportional parts

	18	17	16	15	14
1	1.8	1.7	1.6	1.5	1.4
2	3.6	3.4	3.2	3.0	2.8
3	5.4	5.1	4.8	4.5	4.2
4	7.2	6.8	6.4	6.0	5.6
5	9.0	8.5	8.0	7.5	7.0
6	10.8	10.2	9.6	9.0	8.4
7	12.6	11.9	11.2	10.5	9.8
8	14.4	13.6	12.8	12.0	11.2
9	16.2	15.3	14.4	13.5	12.6

N.	0	1	2	3	4	5	6	7	8	9
300	47 712	727	741	756	770	784	799	813	828	842
301	857	871	885	900	914	929	943	958	972	986
302	48 001	015	029	044	058	073	087	101	116	130
303	144	159	173	187	202	216	230	244	259	273
304	287	302	316	330	344	359	373	387	401	416
305	430	444	458	473	487	501	515	530	544	558
306	572	586	601	615	629	643	657	671	686	700
307	714	728	742	756	770	785	799	813	827	841
308	855	869	883	897	911	926	940	954	968	982
309	996	*010	*024	*038	*052	*066	*080	*094	*108	*122
310	49 136	150	164	178	192	206	220	234	248	262
311	276	290	304	318	332	346	360	374	388	402
312	415	429	443	457	471	485	499	513	527	541
313	554	568	582	596	610	624	638	651	665	679
314	693	707	721	734	748	762	776	790	803	817
315	831	845	859	872	886	900	914	927	941	955
316	969	982	996	*010	*024	*037	*051	*065	*079	*092
317	50 106	120	133	147	161	174	188	202	215	229
318	243	256	270	284	297	311	325	338	352	365
319	379	393	406	420	433	447	461	474	488	501
320	515	529	542	556	569	583	596	610	623	637
321	651	664	678	691	705	718	732	745	759	772
322	786	799	813	826	840	853	866	880	893	907
323	920	934	947	961	974	987	*001	*014	*028	*041
324	51 055	068	081	095	108	121	135	148	162	175
325	188	202	215	228	242	255	268	282	295	308
326	322	335	348	362	375	388	402	415	428	441
327	455	468	481	495	508	521	534	548	561	574
328	587	601	614	627	640	654	667	680	693	706
329	720	733	746	759	772	786	799	812	825	838
330	851	865	878	891	904	917	930	943	957	970
331	983	996	*009	*022	*035	*048	*061	*075	*088	*101
332	52 114	127	140	153	166	179	192	205	218	231
333	244	257	270	284	297	310	323	336	349	362
334	375	388	401	414	427	440	453	466	479	492
335	504	517	530	543	556	569	582	595	608	621
336	634	647	660	673	686	699	711	724	737	750
337	763	776	789	802	815	827	840	853	866	879
338	892	905	917	930	943	956	969	982	994	*007
339	53 020	033	046	058	071	084	097	110	122	135
340	148	161	173	186	199	212	224	237	250	263
341	275	288	301	314	326	339	352	364	377	390
342	403	415	428	441	453	466	479	491	504	517
343	529	542	555	567	580	593	605	618	631	643
344	656	668	681	694	706	719	732	744	757	769
345	782	794	807	820	832	845	857	870	882	895
346	908	920	933	945	958	970	983	995	*008	*020
347	54 033	045	058	070	083	095	108	120	133	145
348	158	170	183	195	208	220	233	245	258	270
349	283	295	307	320	332	345	357	370	382	394
350	407	419	432	444	456	469	481	494	506	518

Proportional parts

15
1	1.5
2	3.0
3	4.5
4	6.0
5	7.5
6	9.0
7	10.5
8	12.0
9	13.5

14
1	1.4
2	2.8
3	4.2
4	5.6
5	7.0
6	8.4
7	9.8
8	11.2
9	12.6

13
1	1.3
2	2.6
3	3.9
4	5.2
5	6.5
6	7.8
7	9.1
8	10.4
9	11.7

12
1	1.2
2	2.4
3	3.6
4	4.8
5	6.0
6	7.2
7	8.4
8	9.6
9	10.8

N.	0	1	2	3	4	5	6	7	8	9	Proportional parts

FIVE-PLACE LOGARITHMS

N.	0	1	2	3	4	5	6	7	8	9
350	54 407	419	432	444	456	469	481	494	506	518
351	531	543	555	568	580	593	605	617	630	642
352	654	667	679	691	704	716	728	741	753	765
353	777	790	802	814	827	839	851	864	876	888
354	900	913	925	937	949	962	974	986	998	*011
355	55 023	035	047	060	072	084	096	108	121	133
356	145	157	169	182	194	206	218	230	242	255
357	267	279	291	303	315	328	340	352	364	376
358	388	400	413	425	437	449	461	473	485	497
359	509	522	534	546	558	570	582	594	606	618
360	630	642	654	666	678	691	703	715	727	739
361	751	763	775	787	799	811	823	835	847	859
362	871	883	895	907	919	931	943	955	967	979
363	991	*003	*015	*027	*038	*050	*062	*074	*086	*098
364	56 110	122	134	146	158	170	182	194	205	217
365	229	241	253	265	277	289	301	312	324	336
366	348	360	372	384	396	407	419	431	443	455
367	467	478	490	502	514	526	538	549	561	573
368	585	597	608	620	632	644	656	667	679	691
369	703	714	726	738	750	761	773	785	797	808
370	820	832	844	855	867	879	891	902	914	926
371	937	949	961	972	984	996	*008	*019	*031	*043
372	57 054	066	078	089	101	113	124	136	148	159
373	171	183	194	206	217	229	241	252	264	276
374	287	299	310	322	334	345	357	368	380	392
375	403	415	426	438	449	461	473	484	496	507
376	519	530	542	553	565	576	588	600	611	623
377	634	646	657	669	680	692	703	715	726	738
378	749	761	772	784	795	807	818	830	841	852
379	864	875	887	898	910	921	933	944	955	967
380	978	990	*001	*013	*024	*035	*047	*058	*070	*081
381	58 092	104	115	127	138	149	161	172	184	195
382	206	218	229	240	252	263	274	286	297	309
383	320	331	343	354	365	377	388	399	410	422
384	433	444	456	467	478	490	501	512	524	535
385	546	557	569	580	591	602	614	625	636	647
386	659	670	681	692	704	715	726	737	749	760
387	771	782	794	805	816	827	838	850	861	872
388	883	894	906	917	928	939	950	961	973	984
389	995	*006	*017	*028	*040	*051	*062	*073	*084	*095
390	59 106	118	129	140	151	162	173	184	195	207
391	218	229	240	251	262	273	284	295	306	318
392	329	340	351	362	373	384	395	406	417	428
393	439	450	461	472	483	494	506	517	528	539
394	550	561	572	583	594	605	616	627	638	649
395	660	671	682	693	704	715	726	737	748	759
396	770	780	791	802	813	824	835	846	857	868
397	879	890	901	912	923	934	945	956	966	977
398	988	999	*010	*021	*032	*043	*054	*065	*076	*086
399	60 097	108	119	130	141	152	163	173	184	195
400	206	217	228	239	249	260	271	282	293	304

Proportional parts

	13		**12**		**11**		**10**
1	1.3	1	1.2	1	1.1	1	1.0
2	2.6	2	2.4	2	2.2	2	2.0
3	3.9	3	3.6	3	3.3	3	3.0
4	5.2	4	4.8	4	4.4	4	4.0
5	6.5	5	6.0	5	5.5	5	5.0
6	7.8	6	7.2	6	6.6	6	6.0
7	9.1	7	8.4	7	7.7	7	7.0
8	10.4	8	9.6	8	8.8	8	8.0
9	11.7	9	10.8	9	9.9	9	9.0

FIVE-PLACE LOGARITHMS

N.	0	1	2	3	4	5	6	7	8	9
400	60 206	217	228	239	249	260	271	282	293	304
401	314	325	336	347	358	369	379	390	401	412
402	423	433	444	455	466	477	487	498	509	520
403	531	541	552	563	574	584	595	606	617	627
404	638	649	660	670	681	692	703	713	724	735
405	746	756	767	778	788	799	810	821	831	842
406	853	863	874	885	895	906	917	927	938	949
407	959	970	981	991	*002	*013	*023	*034	*045	*055
408	61 066	077	087	098	109	119	130	140	151	162
409	172	183	194	204	215	225	236	247	257	268
410	278	289	300	310	321	331	342	352	363	374
411	384	395	405	416	426	437	448	458	469	479
412	490	500	511	521	532	542	553	563	574	584
413	595	606	616	627	637	648	658	669	679	690
414	700	711	721	731	742	752	763	773	784	794
415	805	815	826	836	847	857	868	878	888	899
416	909	920	930	941	951	962	972	982	993	*003
417	62 014	024	034	045	055	066	076	086	097	107
418	118	128	138	149	159	170	180	190	201	211
419	221	232	242	252	263	273	284	294	304	315
420	325	335	346	356	366	377	387	397	408	418
421	428	439	449	459	469	480	490	500	511	521
422	531	542	552	562	572	583	593	603	613	624
423	634	644	655	665	675	685	696	706	716	726
424	737	747	757	767	778	788	798	808	818	829
425	839	849	859	870	880	890	900	*910	921	931
426	941	951	961	972	982	992	*002	*012	*022	*033
427	63 043	053	063	073	083	094	104	114	124	134
428	144	155	165	175	185	195	205	215	225	236
429	246	256	266	276	286	296	306	317	327	337
430	347	357	367	377	387	397	407	417	428	438
431	448	458	468	478	488	498	508	518	528	538
432	548	558	568	579	589	599	609	619	629	639
433	649	659	669	679	689	699	709	719	729	739
434	749	759	769	779	789	799	809	819	829	839
435	849	859	869	879	889	899	909	919	929	939
436	949	959	969	979	988	998	*008	*018	*028	*038
437	64 048	058	068	078	088	098	108	118	128	137
438	147	157	167	177	187	197	207	217	227	237
439	246	256	266	276	286	296	306	316	326	335
440	345	355	365	375	385	395	404	414	424	434
441	444	454	464	473	483	493	503	513	523	532
442	542	552	562	572	582	591	601	611	621	631
443	640	650	660	670	680	689	699	709	719	729
444	738	748	758	768	777	787	797	807	816	826
445	836	846	856	865	875	885	895	904	914	924
446	933	943	953	963	972	982	992	*002	*011	*021
447	65 031	040	050	060	070	079	089	099	108	118
448	128	137	147	157	167	176	186	196	205	215
449	225	234	244	254	263	273	283	292	302	312
450	321	331	341	350	360	369	379	389	398	408

Proportional parts

	11		10		9
1	1.1	1	1.0	1	0.9
2	2.2	2	2.0	2	1.8
3	3.3	3	3.0	3	2.7
4	4.4	4	4.0	4	3.6
5	5.5	5	5.0	5	4.5
6	6.6	6	6.0	6	5.4
7	7.7	7	7.0	7	6.3
8	8.8	8	8.0	8	7.2
9	9.9	9	9.0	9	8.1

N.	0	1	2	3	4	5	6	7	8	9
450	65 321	331	341	350	360	369	379	389	398	408
451	418	427	437	447	456	466	475	485	495	504
452	514	523	533	543	552	562	571	581	591	600
453	610	619	629	639	648	658	667	677	686	696
454	706	715	725	734	744	753	763	772	782	792
455	801	811	820	830	839	849	858	868	877	887
456	896	906	916	925	935	944	954	963	973	982
457	992	*001	*011	*020	*030	*039	*049	*058	*068	*077
458	66 087	096	106	115	124	134	143	153	162	172
459	181	191	200	210	219	229	238	247	257	266
460	276	285	295	304	314	323	332	342	351	361
461	370	380	389	398	408	417	427	436	445	455
462	464	474	483	492	502	511	521	530	539	549
463	558	567	577	586	596	605	614	624	633	642
464	652	661	671	680	689	699	708	717	727	736
465	745	755	764	773	783	792	801	811	820	829
466	839	848	857	867	876	885	894	904	913	922
467	932	941	950	960	969	978	987	997	*006	*015
468	67 025	034	043	052	062	071	080	089	099	108
469	117	127	136	145	154	164	173	182	191	201
470	210	219	228	237	247	256	265	274	284	293
471	302	311	321	330	339	348	357	367	376	385
472	394	403	413	422	431	440	449	459	468	477
473	486	495	504	514	523	532	541	550	560	569
474	578	587	596	605	614	624	633	642	651	660
475	669	679	688	697	706	715	724	733	742	752
476	761	770	779	788	797	806	815	825	834	843
477	852	861	870	879	888	897	906	916	925	934
478	943	952	961	970	979	988	997	*006	*015	*024
479	68 034	043	052	061	070	079	088	097	106	115
480	124	133	142	151	160	169	178	187	196	205
481	215	224	233	242	251	260	269	278	287	296
482	305	314	323	332	341	350	359	368	377	386
483	395	404	413	422	431	440	449	458	467	476
484	485	494	502	511	520	529	538	547	556	565
485	574	583	592	601	610	619	628	637	646	655
486	664	673	681	690	699	708	717	726	735	744
487	753	762	771	780	789	797	806	815	824	833
488	842	851	860	869	878	886	895	904	913	922
489	931	940	949	958	966	975	984	993	*002	*011
490	69 020	028	037	046	055	064	073	082	090	099
491	108	117	126	135	144	152	161	170	179	188
492	197	205	214	223	232	241	249	258	267	276
493	285	294	302	311	320	329	338	346	355	364
494	373	381	390	399	408	417	425	434	443	452
495	461	469	478	487	496	504	513	522	531	539
496	548	557	566	574	583	592	601	609	618	627
497	636	644	653	662	671	679	688	697	705	714
498	723	732	740	749	758	767	775	784	793	801
499	810	819	827	836	845	854	862	871	880	888
500	897	906	914	923	932	940	949	958	966	975

| N. | 0 | 1 | 2 | 3 | 4 | 5 | 6 | 7 | 8 | 9 |

Proportional parts

10	9	8
1 1.0	1 0.9	1 0.8
2 2.0	2 1.8	2 1.6
3 3.0	3 2.7	3 2.4
4 4.0	4 3.6	4 3.2
5 5.0	5 4.5	5 4.0
6 6.0	6 5.4	6 4.8
7 7.0	7 6.3	7 5.6
8 8.0	8 7.2	8 6.4
9 9.0	9 8.1	9 7.2

FIVE-PLACE LOGARITHMS

N.	0	1	2	3	4	5	6	7	8	9
500	69 897	906	914	923	932	940	949	958	966	975
501	984	992	*001	*010	*018	*027	*036	*044	*053	*062
502	70 070	079	088	096	105	114	122	131	140	148
503	157	165	174	183	191	200	209	217	226	234
504	243	252	260	269	278	286	295	303	312	321
505	329	338	346	355	364	372	381	389	398	406
506	415	424	432	441	449	458	467	475	484	492
507	501	509	518	526	535	544	552	561	569	578
508	586	595	603	612	621	629	638	646	655	663
509	672	680	689	697	706	714	723	731	740	749
510	757	766	774	783	791	800	808	817	825	834
511	842	851	859	868	876	885	893	902	910	919
512	927	935	944	952	961	969	978	986	995	*003
513	71 012	020	029	037	046	054	063	071	079	088
514	096	105	113	122	130	139	147	155	164	172
515	181	189	198	206	214	223	231	240	248	257
516	265	273	282	290	299	307	315	324	332	341
517	349	357	366	374	383	391	399	408	416	425
518	433	441	450	458	466	475	483	492	500	508
519	517	525	533	542	550	559	567	575	584	592
520	600	609	617	625	634	642	650	659	667	675
521	684	692	700	709	717	725	734	742	750	759
522	767	775	784	792	800	809	817	825	834	842
523	850	858	867	875	883	892	900	908	917	925
524	933	941	950	958	966	975	983	991	999	*008
525	72 016	024	032	041	049	057	066	074	082	090
526	099	107	115	123	132	140	148	156	165	173
527	181	189	198	206	214	222	230	239	247	255
528	263	272	280	288	296	304	313	321	329	337
529	346	354	362	370	378	387	395	403	411	419
530	428	436	444	452	460	469	477	485	493	501
531	509	518	526	534	542	550	558	567	575	583
532	591	599	607	616	624	632	640	648	656	665
533	673	681	689	697	705	713	722	730	738	746
534	754	762	770	779	787	795	803	811	819	827
535	835	843	852	860	868	876	884	892	900	908
536	916	925	933	941	949	957	965	973	981	989
537	997	*006	*014	*022	*030	*038	*046	*054	*062	*070
538	73 078	086	094	102	111	119	127	135	143	151
539	159	167	175	183	191	199	207	215	223	231
540	239	247	255	263	272	280	288	296	304	312
541	320	328	336	344	352	360	368	376	384	392
542	400	408	416	424	432	440	448	456	464	472
543	480	488	496	504	512	520	528	536	544	552
544	560	568	576	584	592	600	608	616	624	632
545	640	648	656	664	672	679	687	695	703	711
546	719	727	735	743	751	759	767	775	783	791
547	799	807	815	823	830	838	846	854	862	870
548	878	886	894	902	910	918	926	933	941	949
549	957	965	973	981	989	997	*005	*013	*020	*028
550	74 036	044	052	060	068	076	084	092	099	107
N.	0	1	2	3	4	5	6	7	8	9

Proportional parts

	9
1	0.9
2	1.8
3	2.7
4	3.6
5	4.5
6	5.4
7	6.3
8	7.2
9	8.1

	8
1	0.8
2	1.6
3	2.4
4	3.2
5	4.0
6	4.8
7	5.6
8	6.4
9	7.2

	7
1	0.7
2	1.4
3	2.1
4	2.8
5	3.5
6	4.2
7	4.9
8	5.6
9	6.3

N.	0	1	2	3	4	5	6	7	8	9
550	74 036	044	052	060	068	076	084	092	099	107
551	115	123	131	139	147	155	162	170	178	186
552	194	202	210	218	225	233	241	249	257	265
553	273	280	288	296	304	312	320	327	335	343
554	351	359	367	374	382	390	398	406	414	421
555	429	437	445	453	461	468	476	484	492	500
556	507	515	523	531	539	547	554	562	570	578
557	586	593	601	609	617	624	632	640	648	656
558	663	671	679	687	695	702	710	718	726	733
559	741	749	757	764	772	780	788	796	803	811
560	819	827	834	842	850	858	865	873	881	889
561	896	904	912	920	927	935	943	950	958	966
562	974	981	989	997	*005	*012	*020	*028	*035	*043
563	75 051	059	066	074	082	089	097	105	113	120
564	128	136	143	151	159	166	174	182	189	197
565	205	213	220	228	236	243	251	259	266	274
566	282	289	297	305	312	320	328	335	343	351
567	358	366	374	381	389	397	404	412	420	427
568	435	442	450	458	465	473	481	488	496	504
569	511	519	526	534	542	549	557	565	572	580
570	587	595	603	610	618	626	633	641	648	656
571	664	671	679	686	694	702	709	717	724	732
572	740	747	755	762	770	778	785	793	800	808
573	815	823	831	838	846	853	861	868	876	884
574	891	899	906	914	921	929	937	944	952	959
575	967	974	982	989	997	*005	*012	*020	*027	*035
576	76 042	050	057	065	072	080	087	095	103	110
577	118	125	133	140	148	155	163	170	178	185
578	193	200	208	215	223	230	238	245	253	260
579	268	275	283	290	298	305	313	320	328	335
580	343	350	358	365	373	380	388	395	403	410
581	418	425	433	440	448	455	462	470	477	485
582	492	500	507	515	522	530	537	545	552	559
583	567	574	582	589	597	604	612	619	626	634
584	641	649	656	664	671	678	686	693	701	708
585	716	723	730	738	745	753	760	768	775	782
586	790	797	805	812	819	827	834	842	849	856
587	864	871	879	886	893	901	908	916	923	930
588	938	945	953	960	967	975	982	989	997	*004
589	77 012	019	026	034	041	048	056	063	070	078
590	085	093	100	107	115	122	129	137	144	151
591	159	166	173	181	188	195	203	210	217	225
592	232	240	247	254	262	269	276	283	291	298
593	305	313	320	327	335	342	349	357	364	371
594	379	386	393	401	408	415	422	430	437	444
595	452	459	466	474	481	488	495	503	510	517
596	525	532	539	546	554	561	568	576	583	590
597	597	605	612	619	627	634	641	648	656	663
598	670	677	685	692	699	706	714	721	728	735
599	743	750	757	764	772	779	786	793	801	808
600	815	822	830	837	844	851	859	866	873	880

Proportional parts

	8
1	0.8
2	1.6
3	2.4
4	3.2
5	4.0
6	4.8
7	5.6
8	6.4
9	7.2

	7
1	0.7
2	1.4
3	2.1
4	2.8
5	3.5
6	4.2
7	4.9
8	5.6
9	6.3

N.	0	1	2	3	4	5	6	7	8	9	Proportional parts

N.	0	1	2	3	4	5	6	7	8	9
600	77 815	822	830	837	844	851	859	866	873	880
601	887	895	902	909	916	924	931	938	945	952
602	960	967	974	981	988	996	*003	*010	*017	*025
603	78 032	039	046	053	061	068	075	082	089	097
604	104	111	118	125	132	140	147	154	161	168
605	176	183	190	197	204	211	219	226	233	240
606	247	254	262	269	276	283	290	297	305	312
607	319	326	333	340	347	355	362	369	376	383
608	390	398	405	412	419	426	433	440	447	455
609	462	469	476	483	490	497	504	512	519	526
610	533	540	547	554	561	569	576	583	590	597
611	604	611	618	625	633	640	647	654	661	668
612	675	682	689	696	704	711	718	725	732	739
613	746	753	760	767	774	781	789	796	803	810
614	817	824	831	838	845	852	859	866	873	880
615	888	895	902	909	916	923	930	937	944	951
616	958	965	972	979	986	993	*000	*007	*014	*021
617	79 029	036	043	050	057	064	071	078	085	092
618	099	106	113	120	127	134	141	148	155	162
619	169	176	183	190	197	204	211	218	225	232
620	239	246	253	260	267	274	281	288	295	302
621	309	316	323	330	337	344	351	358	365	372
622	379	386	393	400	407	414	421	428	435	442
623	449	456	463	470	477	484	491	498	505	511
624	518	525	532	539	546	553	560	567	574	581
625	588	595	602	609	616	623	630	637	644	650
626	657	664	671	678	685	692	699	706	713	720
627	727	734	741	748	754	761	768	775	782	789
628	796	803	810	817	824	831	837	844	851	858
629	865	872	879	886	893	900	906	913	920	927
630	934	941	948	955	962	969	975	982	989	996
631	80 003	010	017	024	030	037	044	051	058	065
632	072	079	085	092	099	106	113	120	127	134
633	140	147	154	161	168	175	182	188	195	202
634	209	216	223	229	236	243	250	257	264	271
635	277	284	291	298	305	312	318	325	332	339
636	346	353	359	366	373	380	387	393	400	407
637	414	421	428	434	441	448	455	462	468	475
638	482	489	496	502	509	516	523	530	536	543
639	550	557	564	570	577	584	591	598	604	611
640	618	625	632	638	645	652	659	665	672	679
641	686	693	699	706	713	720	726	733	740	747
642	754	760	767	774	781	787	794	801	808	814
643	821	828	835	841	848	855	862	868	875	882
644	889	895	902	909	916	922	929	936	943	949
645	956	963	969	976	983	990	996	*003	*010	*017
646	81 023	030	037	043	050	057	064	070	077	084
647	090	097	104	111	117	124	131	137	144	151
648	158	164	171	178	184	191	198	204	211	218
649	224	231	238	245	251	258	265	271	278	285
650	291	298	305	311	318	325	331	338	345	351
N.	0	1	2	3	4	5	6	7	8	9

Proportional parts

8
1 | 0.8
2 | 1.6
3 | 2.4
4 | 3.2
5 | 4.0
6 | 4.8
7 | 5.6
8 | 6.4
9 | 7.2

7
1 | 0.7
2 | 1.4
3 | 2.1
4 | 2.8
5 | 3.5
6 | 4.2
7 | 4.9
8 | 5.6
9 | 6.3

6
1 | 0.6
2 | 1.2
3 | 1.8
4 | 2.4
5 | 3.0
6 | 3.6
7 | 4.2
8 | 4.8
9 | 5.4

N.	0	1	2	3	4	5	6	7	8	9	Proportional parts
650	81 291	298	305	311	318	325	331	338	345	351	
651	358	365	371	378	385	391	398	405	411	418	
652	425	431	438	445	451	458	465	471	478	485	
653	491	498	505	511	518	525	531	538	544	551	
654	558	564	571	578	584	591	598	604	611	617	
655	624	631	637	644	651	657	664	671	677	684	
656	690	697	704	710	717	723	730	737	743	750	
657	757	763	770	776	783	790	796	803	809	816	
658	823	829	836	842	849	856	862	869	875	882	
659	889	895	902	908	915	921	928	935	941	948	
660	954	961	968	974	981	987	994	*000	*007	*014	**7**
661	82 020	027	033	040	046	053	060	066	073	079	1 0.7
662	086	092	099	105	112	119	125	132	138	145	2 1.4
663	151	158	164	171	178	184	191	197	204	210	3 2.1
664	217	223	230	236	243	249	256	263	269	276	4 2.8
665	282	289	295	302	308	315	321	328	334	341	5 3.5
666	347	354	360	367	373	380	387	393	400	406	6 4.2
667	413	419	426	432	439	445	452	458	465	471	7 4.9
668	478	484	491	497	504	510	517	523	530	536	8 5.6
669	543	549	556	562	569	575	582	588	595	601	9 6.3
670	607	614	620	627	633	640	646	653	659	666	
671	672	679	685	692	698	705	711	718	724	730	
672	737	743	750	756	763	769	776	782	789	795	
673	802	808	814	821	827	834	840	847	853	860	
674	866	872	879	885	892	898	905	911	918	924	
675	930	937	943	950	956	963	969	975	982	988	
676	995	*001	*008	*014	*020	*027	*033	*040	*046	*052	
677	83 059	065	072	078	085	091	097	104	110	117	
678	123	129	136	142	149	155	161	168	174	181	
679	187	193	200	206	213	219	225	232	238	245	
680	251	257	264	270	276	283	289	296	302	308	**6**
681	315	321	327	334	340	347	353	359	366	372	1 0.6
682	378	385	391	398	404	410	417	423	429	436	2 1.2
683	442	448	455	461	467	474	480	487	493	499	3 1.8
684	506	512	518	525	531	537	544	550	556	563	4 2.4
685	569	575	582	588	594	601	607	613	620	626	5 3.0
686	632	639	645	651	658	664	670	677	683	689	6 3.6
687	696	702	708	715	721	727	734	740	746	753	7 4.2
688	759	765	771	778	784	790	797	803	809	816	8 4.8
689	822	828	835	841	847	853	860	866	872	879	9 5.4
690	885	891	897	904	910	916	923	929	935	942	
691	948	954	960	967	973	979	985	992	998	*004	
692	84 011	017	023	029	036	042	048	055	061	067	
693	073	080	086	092	098	105	111	117	123	130	
694	136	142	148	155	161	167	173	180	186	192	
695	198	205	211	217	223	230	236	242	248	255	
696	261	267	273	280	286	292	298	305	311	317	
697	323	330	336	342	348	354	361	367	373	379	
698	386	392	398	404	410	417	423	429	435	442	
699	448	454	460	466	473	479	485	491	497	504	
700	510	516	522	528	535	541	547	553	559	566	

N.	0	1	2	3	4	5	6	7	8	9	Proportional parts

N.	0	1	2	3	4	5	6	7	8	9	Proportional parts
700	84 510	516	522	528	535	541	547	553	559	566	
701	572	578	584	590	597	603	609	615	621	628	
702	634	640	646	652	658	665	671	677	683	689	
703	696	702	708	714	720	726	733	739	745	751	
704	757	763	770	776	782	788	794	800	807	813	
705	819	825	831	837	844	850	856	862	868	874	
706	880	887	893	899	905	911	917	924	930	936	
707	942	948	954	960	967	973	979	985	991	997	
708	85 003	009	016	022	028	034	040	046	052	058	
709	065	071	077	083	089	095	101	107	114	120	

7
1 0.7
2 1.4
3 2.1
4 2.8
5 3.5
6 4.2
7 4.9
8 5.6
9 6.3

N.	0	1	2	3	4	5	6	7	8	9
710	126	132	138	144	150	156	163	169	175	181
711	187	193	199	205	211	217	224	230	236	242
712	248	254	260	266	272	278	285	291	297	303
713	309	315	321	327	333	339	345	352	358	364
714	370	376	382	388	394	400	406	412	418	425
715	431	437	443	449	455	461	467	473	479	485
716	491	497	503	509	516	522	528	534	540	546
717	552	558	564	570	576	582	588	594	600	606
718	612	618	625	631	637	643	649	655	661	667
719	673	679	685	691	697	703	709	715	721	727
720	733	739	745	751	757	763	769	775	781	788
721	794	800	806	812	818	824	830	836	842	848
722	854	860	866	872	878	884	890	896	902	908
723	914	920	926	932	938	944	950	956	962	968
724	974	980	986	992	998	*004	*010	*016	*022	*028

6
1 0.6
2 1.2
3 1.8
4 2.4
5 3.0
6 3.6
7 4.2
8 4.8
9 5.4

N.	0	1	2	3	4	5	6	7	8	9
725	86 034	040	046	052	058	064	070	076	082	088
726	094	100	106	112	118	124	130	136	141	147
727	153	159	165	171	177	183	189	195	201	207
728	213	219	225	231	237	243	249	255	261	267
729	273	279	285	291	297	303	308	314	320	326
730	332	338	344	350	356	362	368	374	380	386
731	392	398	404	410	415	421	427	433	439	445
732	451	457	463	469	475	481	487	493	499	504
733	510	516	522	528	534	540	546	552	558	564
734	570	576	581	587	593	599	605	611	617	623
735	629	635	641	646	652	658	664	670	676	682
736	688	694	700	705	711	717	723	729	735	741
737	747	753	759	764	770	776	782	788	794	800
738	806	812	817	823	829	835	841	847	853	859
739	864	870	876	882	888	894	900	906	911	917

5
1 0.5
2 1.0
3 1.5
4 2.0
5 2.5
6 3.0
7 3.5
8 4.0
9 4.5

N.	0	1	2	3	4	5	6	7	8	9
740	923	929	935	941	947	953	958	964	970	976
741	982	988	994	999	*005	*011	*017	*023	*029	*035
742	87 040	046	052	058	064	070	075	081	087	093
743	099	105	111	116	122	128	134	140	146	151
744	157	163	169	175	181	186	192	198	204	210
745	216	221	227	233	239	245	251	256	262	268
746	274	280	286	291	297	303	309	315	320	326
747	332	338	344	349	355	361	367	373	379	384
748	390	396	402	408	413	419	425	431	437	442
749	448	454	460	466	471	477	483	489	495	500
750	506	512	518	523	529	535	541	547	552	558

N.	0	1	2	3	4	5	6	7	8	9	Proportional parts

N.	0	1	2	3	4	5	6	7	8	9	Proportional parts
750	87 506	512	518	523	529	535	541	547	552	558	
751	564	570	576	581	587	593	599	604	610	616	
752	622	628	633	639	645	651	656	662	668	674	
753	679	685	691	697	703	708	714	720	726	731	
754	737	743	749	754	760	766	772	777	783	789	
755	795	800	806	812	818	823	829	835	841	846	
756	852	858	864	869	875	881	887	892	898	904	
757	910	915	921	927	933	938	944	950	955	961	
758	967	973	978	984	990	996	*001	*007	*013	*018	
759	88 024	030	036	041	047	053	058	064	070	076	
760	081	087	093	098	104	110	116	121	127	133	**6**
761	138	144	150	156	161	167	173	178	184	190	1 0.6
762	195	201	207	213	218	224	230	235	241	247	2 1.2
763	252	258	264	270	275	281	287	292	298	304	3 1.8
764	309	315	321	326	332	338	343	349	355	360	4 2.4
765	366	372	377	383	389	395	400	406	412	417	5 3.0
766	423	429	434	440	446	451	457	463	468	474	6 3.6
767	480	485	491	497	502	508	513	519	525	530	7 4.2
768	536	542	547	553	559	564	570	576	581	587	8 4.8
769	593	598	604	610	615	621	627	632	638	643	9 5.4
770	649	655	660	666	672	677	683	689	694	700	
771	705	711	717	722	728	734	739	745	750	756	
772	762	767	773	779	784	790	795	801	807	812	
773	818	824	829	835	840	846	852	857	863	868	
774	874	880	885	891	897	902	908	913	919	925	
775	930	936	941	947	953	958	964	969	975	981	
776	986	992	997	*003	*009	*014	*020	*025	*031	*037	
777	89 042	048	053	059	064	070	076	081	087	092	
778	098	104	109	115	120	126	131	137	143	148	
779	154	159	165	170	176	182	187	193	198	204	
780	209	215	221	226	232	237	243	248	254	260	**5**
781	265	271	276	282	287	293	298	304	310	315	1 0.5
782	321	326	332	337	343	348	354	360	365	371	2 1.0
783	376	382	387	393	398	404	409	415	421	426	3 1.5
784	432	437	443	448	454	459	465	470	476	481	4 2.0
785	487	492	498	504	509	515	520	526	531	537	5 2.5
786	542	548	553	559	564	570	575	581	586	592	6 3.0
787	597	603	609	614	620	625	631	636	642	647	7 3.5
788	653	658	664	669	675	680	686	691	697	702	8 4.0
789	708	713	719	724	730	735	741	746	752	757	9 4.5
790	763	768	774	779	785	790	796	801	807	812	
791	818	823	829	834	840	845	851	856	862	867	
792	873	878	883	889	894	900	905	911	916	922	
793	927	933	938	944	949	955	960	966	971	977	
794	982	988	993	998	*004	*009	*015	*020	*026	*031	
795	90 037	042	048	053	059	064	069	075	080	086	
796	091	097	102	108	113	119	124	129	135	140	
797	146	151	157	162	168	173	179	184	189	195	
798	200	206	211	217	222	227	233	238	244	249	
799	255	260	266	271	276	282	287	293	298	304	
800	309	314	320	325	331	336	342	347	352	358	

N.	0	1	2	3	4	5	6	7	8	9	Proportional parts

N.	0	1	2	3	4	5	6	7	8	9
800	90 309	314	320	325	331	336	342	347	352	358
801	363	369	374	380	385	390	396	401	407	412
802	417	423	428	434	439	445	450	455	461	466
803	472	477	482	488	493	499	504	509	515	520
804	526	531	536	542	547	553	558	563	569	574
805	580	585	590	596	601	607	612	617	623	628
806	634	639	644	650	655	660	666	671	677	682
807	687	693	698	703	709	714	720	725	730	736
808	741	747	752	757	763	768	773	779	784	789
809	795	800	806	811	816	822	827	832	838	843
810	849	854	859	865	870	875	881	886	891	897
811	902	907	913	918	924	929	934	940	945	950
812	956	961	966	972	977	982	988	993	998	*004
813	91 009	014	020	025	030	036	041	046	052	057
814	062	068	073	078	084	089	094	100	105	110
815	116	121	126	132	137	142	148	153	158	164
816	169	174	180	185	190	196	201	206	212	217
817	222	228	233	238	243	249	254	259	265	270
818	275	281	286	291	297	302	307	312	318	323
819	328	334	339	344	350	355	360	365	371	376
820	381	387	392	397	403	408	413	418	424	429
821	434	440	445	450	455	461	466	471	477	482
822	487	492	498	503	508	514	519	524	529	535
823	540	545	551	556	561	566	572	577	582	587
824	593	598	603	609	614	619	624	630	635	640
825	645	651	656	661	666	672	677	682	687	693
826	698	703	709	714	719	724	730	735	740	745
827	751	756	761	766	772	777	782	787	793	798
828	803	808	814	819	824	829	834	840	845	850
829	855	861	866	871	876	882	887	892	897	903
830	908	913	918	924	929	934	939	944	950	955
831	960	965	971	976	981	986	991	997	*002	*007
832	92 012	018	023	028	033	038	044	049	054	059
833	065	070	075	080	085	091	096	101	106	111
834	117	122	127	132	137	143	148	153	158	163
835	169	174	179	184	189	195	200	205	210	215
836	221	226	231	236	241	247	252	257	262	267
837	273	278	283	288	293	298	304	309	314	319
838	324	330	335	340	345	350	355	361	366	371
839	376	381	387	392	397	402	407	412	418	423
840	428	433	438	443	449	454	459	464	469	474
841	480	485	490	495	500	505	511	516	521	526
842	531	536	542	547	552	557	562	567	572	578
843	583	588	593	598	603	609	614	619	624	629
844	634	639	645	650	655	660	665	670	675	681
845	686	691	696	701	706	711	716	722	727	732
846	737	742	747	752	758	763	768	773	778	783
847	788	793	799	804	809	814	819	824	829	834
848	840	845	850	855	860	865	870	875	881	886
849	891	896	901	906	911	916	921	927	932	937
850	942	947	952	957	962	967	973	978	983	988
N.	0	1	2	3	4	5	6	7	8	9

Proportional parts

6

1	0.6
2	1.2
3	1.8
4	2.4
5	3.0
6	3.6
7	4.2
8	4.8
9	5.4

5

1	0.5
2	1.0
3	1.5
4	2.0
5	2.5
6	3.0
7	3.5
8	4.0
9	4.5

N.	0	1	2	3	4	5	6	7	8	9	Proportional parts
850	92 942	947	952	957	962	967	973	978	983	988	
851	993	998	*003	*008	*013	*018	*024	*029	*034	*039	
852	93 044	049	054	059	064	069	075	080	085	090	
853	095	100	105	110	115	120	125	131	136	141	
854	146	151	156	161	166	171	176	181	186	192	
855	197	202	207	212	217	222	227	232	237	242	
856	247	252	258	263	268	273	278	283	288	293	
857	298	303	308	313	318	323	328	334	339	344	
858	349	354	359	364	369	374	379	384	389	394	
859	399	404	409	414	420	425	430	435	440	445	
860	450	455	460	465	470	475	480	485	490	495	
861	500	505	510	515	520	526	531	536	541	546	
862	551	556	561	566	571	576	581	586	591	596	
863	601	606	611	616	621	626	631	636	641	646	
864	651	656	661	666	671	676	682	687	692	697	
865	702	707	712	717	722	727	732	737	742	747	
866	752	757	762	767	772	777	782	787	792	797	
867	802	807	812	817	822	827	832	837	842	847	
868	852	857	862	867	872	877	882	887	892	897	
869	902	907	912	917	922	927	932	937	942	947	
870	952	957	962	967	972	977	982	987	992	997	
871	94 002	007	012	017	022	027	032	037	042	047	
872	052	057	062	067	072	077	082	086	091	096	
873	101	106	111	116	121	126	131	136	141	146	
874	151	156	161	166	171	176	181	186	191	196	
875	201	206	211	216	221	226	231	236	240	245	
876	250	255	260	265	270	275	280	285	290	295	
877	300	305	310	315	320	325	330	335	340	345	
878	349	354	359	364	369	374	379	384	389	394	
879	399	404	409	414	419	424	429	433	438	443	
880	448	453	458	463	468	473	478	483	488	493	
881	498	503	507	512	517	522	527	532	537	542	
882	547	552	557	562	567	571	576	581	586	591	
883	596	601	606	611	616	621	626	630	635	640	
884	645	650	655	660	665	670	675	680	685	689	
885	694	699	704	709	714	719	724	729	734	738	
886	743	748	753	758	763	768	773	778	783	787	
887	792	797	802	807	812	817	822	827	832	836	
888	841	846	851	856	861	866	871	876	880	885	
889	890	895	900	905	910	915	919	924	929	934	
890	939	944	949	954	959	963	968	973	978	983	
891	988	993	998	*002	*007	*012	*017	*022	*027	*032	
892	95 036	041	046	051	056	061	066	071	075	080	
893	085	090	095	100	105	109	114	119	124	129	
894	134	139	143	148	153	158	163	168	173	177	
895	182	187	192	197	202	207	211	216	221	226	
896	231	236	240	245	250	255	260	265	270	274	
897	279	284	289	294	299	303	308	313	318	323	
898	328	332	337	342	347	352	357	361	366	371	
899	376	381	386	390	395	400	405	410	415	419	
900	424	429	434	439	444	448	453	458	463	468	

Proportional parts:

6
1 | 0.6
2 | 1.2
3 | 1.8
4 | 2.4
5 | 3.0
6 | 3.6
7 | 4.2
8 | 4.8
9 | 5.4

5
1 | 0.5
2 | 1.0
3 | 1.5
4 | 2.0
5 | 2.5
6 | 3.0
7 | 3.5
8 | 4.0
9 | 4.5

4
1 | 0.4
2 | 0.8
3 | 1.2
4 | 1.6
5 | 2.0
6 | 2.4
7 | 2.8
8 | 3.2
9 | 3.6

| N. | 0 | 1 | 2 | 3 | 4 | 5 | 6 | 7 | 8 | 9 | Proportional parts |

N.	0	1	2	3	4	5	6	7	8	9	Proportional parts	
900	95 424	429	434	439	444	448	453	458	463	468		
901	472	477	482	487	492	497	501	506	511	516		
902	521	525	530	535	540	545	550	554	559	564		
903	569	574	578	583	588	593	598	602	607	612		
904	617	622	626	631	636	641	646	650	655	660		
905	665	670	674	679	684	689	694	698	703	708		
906	713	718	722	727	732	737	742	746	751	756		
907	761	766	770	775	780	785	789	794	799	804		
908	809	813	818	823	828	832	837	842	847	852		
909	856	861	866	871	875	880	885	890	895	899		
910	904	909	914	918	923	928	933	938	942	947		**5**
911	952	957	961	966	971	976	980	985	990	995	1	0.5
912	999	*004	*009	*014	*019	*023	*028	*033	*038	*042	2	1.0
913	96 047	052	057	061	066	071	076	080	085	090	3	1.5
914	095	099	104	109	114	118	123	128	133	137	4	2.0
											5	2.5
915	142	147	152	156	161	166	171	175	180	185	6	3.0
916	190	194	199	204	209	213	218	223	227	232	7	3.5
917	237	242	246	251	256	261	265	270	275	280	8	4.0
918	284	289	294	298	303	308	313	317	322	327	9	4.5
919	332	336	341	346	350	355	360	365	369	374		
920	379	384	388	393	398	402	407	412	417	421		
921	426	431	435	440	445	450	454	459	464	468		
922	473	478	483	487	492	497	501	506	511	515		
923	520	525	530	534	539	544	548	553	558	562		
924	567	572	577	581	586	591	595	600	605	609		
925	614	619	624	628	633	638	642	647	652	656		
926	661	666	670	675	680	685	689	694	699	703		
927	708	713	717	722	727	731	736	741	745	750		
928	755	759	764	769	774	778	783	788	792	797		
929	802	806	811	816	820	825	830	834	839	844		
930	848	853	858	862	867	872	876	881	886	890		**4**
931	895	900	904	909	914	918	923	928	932	937	1	0.4
932	942	946	951	956	960	965	970	974	979	984	2	0.8
933	988	993	997	*002	*007	*011	*016	*021	*025	*030	3	1.2
934	97 035	039	044	049	053	058	063	067	072	077	4	1.6
											5	2.0
935	081	086	090	095	100	104	109	114	118	123	6	2.4
936	128	132	137	142	146	151	155	160	165	169	7	2.8
937	174	179	183	188	192	197	202	206	211	216	8	3.2
938	220	225	230	234	239	243	248	253	257	262	9	3.6
939	267	271	276	280	285	290	294	299	304	308		
940	313	317	322	327	331	336	340	345	350	354		
941	359	364	368	373	377	382	387	391	396	400		
942	405	410	414	419	424	428	433	437	442	447		
943	451	456	460	465	470	474	479	483	488	493		
944	497	502	506	511	516	520	525	529	534	539		
945	543	548	552	557	562	566	571	575	580	585		
946	589	594	598	603	607	612	617	621	626	630		
947	635	640	644	649	653	658	663	667	672	676		
948	681	685	690	695	699	704	708	713	717	722		
949	727	731	736	740	745	749	754	759	763	768		
950	772	777	782	786	791	795	800	804	809	813		
N.	0	1	2	3	4	5	6	7	8	9	Proportional parts	

FIVE-PLACE LOGARITHMS

N.	0	1	2	3	4	5	6	7	8	9	Proportional parts
950	97 772	777	782	786	791	795	800	804	809	813	
951	818	823	827	832	836	841	845	850	855	859	
952	864	868	873	877	882	886	891	896	900	905	
953	909	914	918	923	928	932	937	941	946	950	
954	955	959	964	968	973	978	982	987	991	996	
955	98 000	005	009	014	019	023	028	032	037	041	
956	046	050	055	059	064	068	073	078	082	087	
957	091	096	100	105	109	114	118	123	127	132	
958	137	141	146	150	155	159	164	168	173	177	
959	182	186	191	195	200	204	209	214	218	223	
960	227	232	236	241	245	250	254	259	263	268	**5**
961	272	277	281	286	290	295	299	304	308	313	1 0.5
962	318	322	327	331	336	340	345	349	354	358	2 1.0
963	363	367	372	376	381	385	390	394	399	403	3 1.5
964	408	412	417	421	426	430	435	439	444	448	4 2.0 / 5 2.5
965	453	457	462	466	471	475	480	484	489	493	6 3.0
966	498	502	507	511	516	520	525	529	534	538	7 3.5
967	543	547	552	556	561	565	570	574	579	583	8 4.0
968	588	592	597	601	605	610	614	619	623	628	9 4.5
969	632	637	641	646	650	655	659	664	668	673	
970	677	682	686	691	695	700	704	709	713	717	
971	722	726	731	735	740	744	749	753	758	762	
972	767	771	776	780	784	789	793	798	802	807	
973	811	816	820	825	829	834	838	843	847	851	
974	856	860	865	869	874	878	883	887	892	896	
975	900	905	909	914	918	923	927	932	936	941	
976	945	949	954	958	963	967	972	976	981	985	
977	989	994	998	*003	*007	*012	*016	*021	*025	*029	
978	99 034	038	043	047	052	056	061	065	069	074	
979	078	083	087	092	096	100	105	109	114	118	
980	123	127	131	136	140	145	149	154	158	162	**4**
981	167	171	176	180	185	189	193	198	202	207	1 0.4
982	211	216	220	224	229	233	238	242	247	251	2 0.8
983	255	260	264	269	273	277	282	286	291	295	3 1.2
984	300	304	308	313	317	322	326	330	335	339	4 1.6 / 5 2.0
985	344	348	352	357	361	366	370	374	379	383	6 2.4
986	388	392	396	401	405	410	414	419	423	427	7 2.8
987	432	436	441	445	449	454	458	463	467	471	8 3.2
988	476	480	484	489	493	498	502	506	511	515	9 3.6
989	520	524	528	533	537	542	546	550	555	559	
990	564	568	572	577	581	585	590	594	599	603	
991	607	612	616	621	625	629	634	638	642	647	
992	651	656	660	664	669	673	677	682	686	691	
993	695	699	704	708	712	717	721	726	730	734	
994	739	743	747	752	756	760	765	769	774	778	
995	782	787	791	795	800	804	808	813	817	822	
996	826	830	835	839	843	848	852	856	861	865	
997	870	874	878	883	887	891	896	900	904	909	
998	913	917	922	926	930	935	939	944	948	952	
999	957	961	965	970	974	978	983	987	991	996	
1000	00 000	004	009	013	017	022	026	030	035	039	
N.	0	1	2	3	4	5	6	7	8	9	Proportional parts

LOGARITHMS

N.	0	1	2	3	4	5	6	7	8	9	d.
1000	000 0000	0434	0869	1303	1737	2171	2605	3039	3473	3907	434
1001	4341	4775	5208	5642	6076	6510	6943	7377	7810	8244	434
1002	8677	9111	9544	9977	*0411	*0844	*1277	*1710	*2143	*2576	433
1003	001 3009	3442	3875	4308	4741	5174	5607	6039	6472	6905	433
1004	7337	7770	8202	8635	9067	9499	9932	*0364	*0796	*1228	432
1005	002 1661	2093	2525	2957	3389	3821	4253	4685	5116	5548	432
1006	5980	6411	6843	7275	7706	8138	8569	9001	9432	9863	431
1007	003 0295	0726	1157	1588	2019	2451	2882	3313	3744	4174	431
1008	4605	5036	5467	5898	6328	6759	7190	7620	8051	8481	431
1009	8912	9342	9772	*0203	*0633	*1063	*1493	*1924	*2354	*2784	430
1010	004 3214	3644	4074	4504	4933	5363	5793	6223	6652	7082	430
1011	7512	7941	8371	8800	9229	9659	*0088	*0517	*0947	*1376	429
1012	005 1805	2234	2663	3092	3521	3950	4379	4808	5237	5666	429
1013	6094	6523	6952	7380	7809	8238	8666	9094	9523	9951	429
1014	006 0380	0808	1236	1664	2092	2521	2949	3377	3805	4233	428
1015	4660	5088	5516	5944	6372	6799	7227	7655	8082	8510	428
1016	8937	9365	9792	*0219	*0647	*1074	*1501	*1928	*2355	*2782	427
1017	007 3210	3637	4064	4490	4917	5344	5771	6198	6624	7051	427
1018	7478	7904	8331	8757	9184	9610	*0037	*0463	*0889	*1316	426
1019	008 1742	2168	2594	3020	3446	3872	4298	4724	5150	5576	426
1020	6002	6427	6853	7279	7704	8130	8556	8981	9407	9832	426
1021	009 0257	0683	1108	1533	1959	2384	2809	3234	3659	4084	425
1022	4509	4934	5359	5784	6208	6633	7058	7483	7907	8332	425
1023	8756	9181	9605	*0030	*0454	*0878	*1303	*1727	*2151	*2575	424
1024	010 3000	3424	3848	4272	4696	5120	5544	5967	6391	6815	424
1025	7239	7662	8086	8510	8933	9357	9780	*0204	*0627	*1050	424
1026	011 1474	1897	2320	2743	3166	3590	4013	4436	4859	5282	423
1027	5704	6127	6550	6973	7396	7818	8241	8664	9086	9509	423
1028	9931	*0354	*0776	*1198	*1621	*2043	*2465	*2887	*3310	*3732	422
1029	012 4154	4576	4998	5420	5842	6264	6685	7107	7529	7951	422
1030	8372	8794	9215	9637	*0059	*0480	*0901	*1323	*1744	*2165	422
1031	013 2587	3008	3429	3850	4271	4692	5113	5534	5955	6376	421
1032	6797	7218	7639	8059	8480	8901	9321	9742	*0162	*0583	421
1033	014 1003	1424	1844	2264	2685	3105	3525	3945	4365	4785	420
1034	5205	5625	6045	6465	6885	7305	7725	8144	8564	8984	420
1035	9403	9823	*0243	*0662	*1082	*1501	*1920	*2340	*2759	*3178	420
1036	015 3598	4017	4436	4855	5274	5693	6112	6531	6950	7369	419
1037	7788	8206	8625	9044	9462	9881	*0300	*0718	*1137	*1555	419
1038	016 1974	2392	2810	3229	3647	4065	4483	4901	5319	5737	418
1039	6155	6573	6991	7409	7827	8245	8663	9080	9498	9916	418
1040	017 0333	0751	1168	1586	2003	2421	2838	3256	3673	4090	417
1041	4507	4924	5342	5759	6176	6593	7010	7427	7844	8260	417
1042	8677	9094	9511	9927	*0344	*0761	*1177	*1594	*2010	*2427	417
1043	018 2843	3259	3676	4092	4508	4925	5341	5757	6173	6589	416
1044	7005	7421	7837	8253	8669	9084	9500	9916	*0332	*0747	416
1045	019 1163	1578	1994	2410	2825	3240	3656	4071	4486	4902	415
1046	5317	5732	6147	6562	6977	7392	7807	8222	8637	9052	415
1047	9467	9882	*0296	*0711	*1126	*1540	*1955	*2369	*2784	*3198	415
1048	020 3613	4027	4442	4856	5270	5684	6099	6513	6927	7341	414
1049	7755	8169	8583	8997	9411	9824	*0238	*0652	*1066	*1479	414
1050	021 1893	2307	2720	3134	3547	3961	4374	4787	5201	5614	413
N.	0	1	2	3	4	5	6	7	8	9	d.

N.	0	1	2	3	4	5	6	7	8	9	d.
1050	021 1893	2307	2720	3134	3547	3961	4374	4787	5201	5614	413
1051	6027	6440	6854	7267	7680	8093	8506	8919	9332	9745	413
1052	022 0157	0570	0983	1396	1808	2221	2634	3046	3459	3871	413
1053	4284	4696	5109	5521	5933	6345	6758	7170	7582	7994	412
1054	8406	8818	9230	9642	*0054	*0466	*0878	*1289	*1701	*2113	412
1055	023 2525	2936	3348	3759	4171	4582	4994	5405	5817	6228	411
1056	6639	7050	7462	7873	8284	8695	9106	9517	9928	*0339	411
1057	024 0750	1161	1572	1982	2393	2804	3214	3625	4036	4446	411
1058	4857	5267	5678	6088	6498	6909	7319	7729	8139	8549	410
1059	8960	9370	9780	*0190	*0600	*1010	*1419	*1829	*2239	*2649	410
1060	025 3059	3468	3878	4288	4697	5107	5516	5926	6335	6744	410
1061	7154	7563	7972	8382	8791	9200	9609	*0018	*0427	*0836	409
1062	026 1245	1654	2063	2472	2881	3289	3698	4107	4515	4924	409
1063	5333	5741	6150	6558	6967	7375	7783	8192	8600	9008	408
1064	9416	9824	*0233	*0641	*1049	*1457	*1865	*2273	*2680	*3088	408
1065	027 3496	3904	4312	4719	5127	5535	5942	6350	6757	7165	408
1066	7572	7979	8387	8794	9201	9609	*0016	*0423	*0830	*1237	407
1067	028 1644	2051	2458	2865	3272	3679	4086	4492	4899	5306	407
1068	5713	6119	6526	6932	7339	7745	8152	8558	8964	9371	406
1069	9777	*0183	*0590	*0996	*1402	*1808	*2214	*2620	*3026	*3432	406
1070	029 3838	4244	4649	5055	5461	5867	6272	6678	7084	7489	406
1071	7895	8300	8706	9111	9516	9922	*0327	*0732	*1138	*1543	405
1072	030 1948	2353	2758	3163	3568	3973	4378	4783	5188	5592	405
1073	5997	6402	6807	7211	7616	8020	8425	8830	9234	9638	405
1074	031 0043	0447	0851	1256	1660	2064	2468	2872	3277	3681	404
1075	4085	4489	4893	5296	5700	6104	6508	6912	7315	7719	404
1076	8123	8526	8930	9333	9737	*0140	*0544	*0947	*1350	*1754	403
1077	032 2157	2560	2963	3367	3770	4173	4576	4979	5382	5785	403
1078	6188	6590	6993	7396	7799	8201	8604	9007	9409	9812	403
1079	033 0214	0617	1019	1422	1824	2226	2629	3031	3433	3835	402
1080	4238	4640	5042	5444	5846	6248	6650	7052	7453	7855	402
1081	8257	8659	9060	9462	9864	*0265	*0667	*1068	*1470	*1871	402
1082	034 2273	2674	3075	3477	3878	4279	4680	5081	5482	5884	401
1083	6285	6686	7087	7487	7888	8289	8690	9091	9491	9892	401
1084	035 0293	0693	1094	1495	1895	2296	2696	3096	3497	3897	400
1085	4297	4698	5098	5498	5898	6298	6698	7098	7498	7898	400
1086	8298	8698	9098	9498	9898	*0297	*0697	*1097	*1496	*1896	400
1087	036 2295	2695	3094	3494	3893	4293	4692	5091	5491	5890	399
1088	6289	6688	7087	7486	7885	8284	8683	9082	9481	9880	399
1089	037 0279	0678	1076	1475	1874	2272	2671	3070	3468	3867	399
1090	4265	4663	5062	5460	5858	6257	6655	7053	7451	7849	398
1091	8248	8646	9044	9442	9839	*0237	*0635	*1033	*1431	*1829	398
1092	038 2226	2624	3022	3419	3817	4214	4612	5009	5407	5804	398
1093	6202	6599	6996	7393	7791	8188	8585	8982	9379	9776	397
1094	039 0173	0570	0967	1364	1761	2158	2554	2951	3348	3745	397
1095	4141	4538	4934	5331	5727	6124	6520	6917	7313	7709	397
1096	8106	8502	8898	9294	9690	*0086	*0482	*0878	*1274	*1670	396
1097	040 2066	2462	2858	3254	3650	4045	4441	4837	5232	5628	396
1098	6023	6419	6814	7210	7605	8001	8396	8791	9187	9582	395
1099	9977	*0372	*0767	*1162	*1557	*1952	*2347	*2742	*3137	*3532	395
1100	041 3927	4322	4716	5111	5506	5900	6295	6690	7084	7479	395
N.	0	1	2	3	4	5	6	7	8	9	d.

LOGARITHMS

N.	0	1	2	3	4	5	6	7	8	9	d.
1100	041 3927	4322	4716	5111	5506	5900	6295	6690	7084	7479	395
1101	7873	8268	8662	9056	9451	9845	*0239	*0633	*1028	*1422	394
1102	042 1816	2210	2604	2998	3392	3786	4180	4574	4968	5361	394
1103	5755	6149	6543	6936	7330	7723	8117	8510	8904	9297	394
1104	9691	*0084	*0477	*0871	*1264	*1657	*2050	*2444	*2837	*3230	393
1105	043 3623	4016	4409	4802	5195	5587	5980	6373	6766	7159	393
1106	7551	7944	8337	8729	9122	9514	9907	*0299	*0692	*1084	393
1107	044 1476	1869	2261	2653	3045	3437	3829	4222	4614	5006	392
1108	5398	5790	6181	6573	6965	7357	7749	8140	8532	8924	392
1109	9315	9707	*0099	*0490	*0882	*1273	*1664	*2056	*2447	*2839	392
1110	045 3230	3621	4012	4403	4795	5186	5577	5968	6359	6750	391
1111	7141	7531	7922	8313	8704	9095	9485	9876	*0267	*0657	391
1112	046 1048	1438	1829	2219	2610	3000	3391	3781	4171	4561	390
1113	4952	5342	5732	6122	6512	6902	7292	7682	8072	8462	390
1114	8852	9242	9632	*0021	*0411	*0801	*1190	*1580	*1970	*2359	390
1115	047 2749	3138	3528	3917	4306	4696	5085	5474	5864	6253	389
1116	6642	7031	7420	7809	8198	8587	8976	9365	9754	*0143	389
1117	048 0532	0921	1309	1698	2087	2475	2864	3253	3641	4030	389
1118	4418	4806	5195	5583	5972	6360	6748	7136	7525	7913	388
1119	8301	8689	9077	9465	9853	*0241	*0629	*1017	*1405	*1792	388
1120	049 2180	2568	2956	3343	3731	4119	4506	4894	5281	5669	388
1121	6056	6444	6831	7218	7606	7993	8380	8767	9154	9541	387
1122	9929	*0316	*0703	*1090	*1477	*1863	*2250	*2637	*3024	*3411	387
1123	050 3798	4184	4571	4958	5344	5731	6117	6504	6890	7277	387
1124	7663	8049	8436	8822	9208	9595	9981	*0367	*0753	*1139	386
1125	051 1525	1911	2297	2683	3069	3455	3841	4227	4612	4998	386
1126	5384	5770	6155	6541	6926	7312	7697	8083	8468	8854	386
1127	9239	9624	*0010	*0395	*0780	*1166	*1551	*1936	*2321	*2706	385
1128	052 3091	3476	3861	4246	4631	5016	5400	5785	6170	6555	385
1129	6939	7324	7709	8093	8478	8862	9247	9631	*0016	*0400	385
1130	053 0784	1169	1553	1937	2321	2706	3090	3474	3858	4242	384
1131	4626	5010	5394	5778	6162	6546	6929	7313	7697	8081	384
1132	8464	8848	9232	9615	9999	*0382	*0766	*1149	*1532	*1916	384
1133	054 2299	2682	3066	3449	3832	4215	4598	4981	5365	5748	383
1134	6131	6514	6896	7279	7662	8045	8428	8811	9193	9576	383
1135	9959	*0341	*0724	*1106	*1489	*1871	*2254	*2636	*3019	*3401	382
1136	055 3783	4166	4548	4930	5312	5694	6077	6459	6841	7223	382
1137	7605	7987	8369	8750	9132	9514	9896	*0278	*0659	*1041	382
1138	056 1423	1804	2186	2567	2949	3330	3712	4093	4475	4856	381
1139	5237	5619	6000	6381	6762	7143	7524	7905	8287	8668	381
1140	9049	9429	9810	*0191	*0572	*0953	*1334	*1714	*2095	*2476	381
1141	057 2856	3237	3618	3998	4379	4759	5140	5520	5900	6281	381
1142	6661	7041	7422	7802	8182	8562	8942	9322	9702	*0082	380
1143	058 0462	0842	1222	1602	1982	2362	2741	3121	3501	3881	380
1144	4260	4640	5019	5399	5778	6158	6537	6917	7296	7676	380
1145	8055	8434	8813	9193	9572	9951	*0330	*0709	*1088	*1467	379
1146	059 1846	2225	2604	2983	3362	3741	4119	4498	4877	5256	379
1147	5634	6013	6391	6770	7148	7527	7905	8284	8662	9041	379
1148	9419	9797	*0175	*0554	*0932	*1310	*1688	*2066	*2444	*2822	378
1149	060 3200	3578	3956	4334	4712	5090	5468	5845	6223	6601	378
1150	6978	7356	7734	8111	8489	8866	9244	9621	9999	*0376	378
N	0	1	2	3	4	5	6	7	8	9	d.

N.	0	1	2	3	4	5	6	7	8	9	d.
1150	060 6978	7356	7734	8111	8489	8866	9244	9621	9999	*0376	378
1151	061 0753	1131	1508	1885	2262	2639	3017	3394	3771	4148	377
1152	4525	4902	5279	5656	6032	6409	6786	7163	7540	7916	377
1153	8293	8670	9046	9423	9799	*0176	*0552	*0929	*1305	*1682	377
1154	062 2058	2434	2811	3187	3563	3939	4316	4692	5068	5444	376
1155	5820	6196	6572	6948	7324	7699	8075	8451	8827	9203	376
1156	9578	9954	*0330	*0705	*1081	*1456	*1832	*2207	*2583	*2958	376
1157	063 3334	3709	4084	4460	4835	5210	5585	5960	6335	6711	375
1158	7086	7461	7836	8211	8585	8960	9335	9710	*0085	*0460	375
1159	064 0834	1209	1584	1958	2333	2708	3082	3457	3831	4205	375
1160	4580	4954	5329	5703	6077	6451	6826	7200	7574	7948	374
1161	8322	8696	9070	9444	9818	*0192	*0566	*0940	*1314	*1688	374
1162	065 2061	2435	2809	3182	3556	3930	4303	4677	5050	5424	374
1163	5797	6171	6544	6917	7291	7664	8037	8410	8784	9157	373
1164	9530	9903	*0276	*0649	*1022	*1395	*1768	*2141	*2514	*2886	373
1165	066 3259	3632	4005	4377	4750	5123	5495	5868	6241	6613	373
1166	6986	7358	7730	8103	8475	8847	9220	9592	9964	*0336	372
1167	067 0709	1081	1453	1825	2197	2569	2941	3313	3685	4057	372
1168	4428	4800	5172	5544	5915	6287	6659	7030	7402	7774	372
1169	8145	8517	8888	9259	9631	*0002	*0374	*0745	*1116	*1487	371
1170	068 1859	2230	2601	2972	3343	3714	4085	4456	4827	5198	371
1171	5569	5940	6311	6681	7052	7423	7794	8164	8535	8906	371
1172	9276	9647	*0017	*0388	*0758	*1129	*1499	*1869	*2240	*2610	370
1173	069 2980	3350	3721	4091	4461	4831	5201	5571	5941	6311	370
1174	6681	7051	7421	7791	8160	8530	8900	9270	9639	*0009	370
1175	070 0379	0748	1118	1487	1857	2226	2596	2965	3335	3704	369
1176	4073	4442	4812	5181	5550	5919	6288	6658	7027	7396	369
1177	7765	8134	8503	8871	9240	9609	9978	*0347	*0715	*1084	369
1178	071 1453	1822	2190	2559	2927	3296	3664	4033	4401	4770	369
1179	5138	5506	5875	6243	6611	6979	7348	7716	8084	8452	368
1180	8820	9188	9556	9924	*0292	*0660	*1028	*1396	*1763	*2131	368
1181	072 2499	2867	3234	3602	3970	4337	4705	5072	5440	5807	368
1182	6175	6542	6910	7277	7644	8011	8379	8746	9113	9480	367
1183	9847	*0215	*0582	*0949	*1316	*1683	*2050	*2416	*2783	*3150	367
1184	073 3517	3884	4251	4617	4984	5351	5717	6084	6450	6817	367
1185	7184	7550	7916	8283	8649	9016	9382	9748	*0114	*0481	366
1186	074 0847	1213	1579	1945	2311	2677	3043	3409	3775	4141	366
1187	4507	4873	5239	5605	5970	6336	6702	7068	7433	7799	366
1188	8164	8530	8895	9261	9626	9992	*0357	*0723	*1088	*1453	365
1189	075 1819	2184	2549	2914	3279	3644	4010	4375	4740	5105	365
1190	5470	5835	6199	6564	6929	7294	7659	8024	8388	8753	365
1191	9118	9482	9847	*0211	*0576	*0940	*1305	*1669	*2034	*2398	364
1192	076 2763	3127	3491	3855	4220	4584	4948	5312	5676	6040	364
1193	6404	6768	7132	7496	7860	8224	8588	8952	9316	9680	364
1194	077 0043	0407	0771	1134	1498	1862	2225	2589	2952	3316	364
1195	3679	4042	4406	4769	5133	5496	5859	6222	6585	6949	363
1196	7312	7675	8038	8401	8764	9127	9490	9853	*0216	*0579	363
1197	078 0942	1304	1667	2030	2393	2755	3118	3480	3843	4206	363
1198	4568	4931	5293	5656	6018	6380	6743	7105	7467	7830	362
1199	8192	8554	8916	9278	9640	*0003	*0365	*0727	*1089	*1451	362
1200	079 1812	2174	2536	2898	3260	3622	3983	4345	4707	5068	362
N.	0	1	2	3	4	5	6	7	8	9	d.

LOGARITHMS OF THE TRIGONOMETRIC FUNCTIONS

Logarithms of the functions are given for each minute from 0 – 360°.

The quantity − 10 is to be appended to all logarithms of the sine and cosine, to logarithms of the tangent from 0–45° and of the cotangent from 45 – 90°.

With degrees indicated at either side of the top of the page use the column headings at the top. With degrees stated at the bottom of the page use the column designations at the bottom.

With degrees at the left (top or bottom) use the minute column at the left, and with degrees on the right side of the page use the minute column at the right.

The method of determining the functions of small angles by the auxiliary quantities S and T is given in the section explaining the use of the Mathematical Tables at the front of the volume.

LOGARITHMS OF THE TRIGONOMETRIC FUNCTIONS
Values of S and T

Min.	Values of S, −10 to be appended					Values of T, −10 to be appended					Sec.
	0°	1°	2°	3°	4°	0°	1°	2°	3°	4°	
0′	4.68 557	555	549	538	522	4.68 557	562	575	597	628	0″
1	557	555	549	537	522	557	562	575	598	629	60
2	557	555	548	537	522	557	562	576	598	629	120
3	557	555	548	537	521	557	562	576	599	630	180
4	557	555	548	537	521	558	563	576	599	631	240
5	557	555	548	537	521	558	563	577	599	631	300
6	557	555	548	536	520	558	563	577	600	632	360
7	557	555	548	536	520	558	563	577	600	632	420
8	557	555	548	536	520	558	563	578	601	633	480
9	557	555	547	536	520	558	563	578	601	634	540
10	4.68 557	555	547	535	519	4.68 558	564	578	602	634	600
11	557	554	547	535	519	558	564	579	602	635	660
12	557	554	547	535	519	558	564	579	603	635	720
13	557	554	547	535	518	558	564	579	603	636	780
14	557	554	547	534	518	558	564	580	604	637	840
15	557	554	546	534	518	558	564	580	604	637	900
16	557	554	546	534	517	558	565	580	605	638	960
17	557	554	546	534	517	558	565	581	605	639	1020
18	557	554	546	534	517	558	565	581	606	639	1080
19	557	554	546	533	516	558	565	581	606	640	1140
20	4.68 557	554	546	533	516	4.68 558	565	582	607	640	1200
21	557	554	545	533	516	558	566	582	607	641	1260
22	557	553	545	533	515	558	566	582	608	642	1320
23	557	553	545	532	515	558	566	583	608	642	1380
24	557	553	545	532	515	558	566	583	609	643	1440
25	557	553	545	532	515	558	566	583	609	644	1500
26	557	553	544	532	514	558	567	584	610	644	1560
27	557	553	544	531	514	558	567	584	610	645	1620
28	557	553	544	531	514	558	567	584	611	646	1680
29	557	553	544	531	513	559	567	585	611	646	1740
30	4.68 557	553	544	531	513	4.68 559	567	585	612	647	1800
31	557	552	544	530	513	559	568	585	612	648	1860
32	557	552	543	530	512	559	568	586	613	648	1920
33	557	552	543	530	512	559	568	586	613	649	1980
34	557	552	543	529	512	559	568	587	614	650	2040
35	557	552	543	529	511	559	569	587	614	650	2100
36	557	552	543	529	511	559	569	587	615	651	2160
37	557	552	542	529	511	559	569	588	615	652	2220
38	557	552	542	528	510	559	569	588	616	652	2280
39	557	552	542	528	510	559	570	589	616	653	2340
40	4.68 557	551	542	528	510	4.68 559	570	589	617	654	2400
41	556	551	542	528	509	560	570	589	617	654	2460
42	556	551	541	527	509	560	570	590	618	655	2520
43	556	551	541	527	508	560	571	590	619	656	2580
44	556	551	541	527	508	560	571	591	619	656	2640
45	556	551	541	527	508	560	571	591	620	657	2700
46	556	551	541	526	507	560	571	591	620	658	2760
47	556	551	540	526	507	560	572	592	621	659	2820
48	556	550	540	526	507	560	572	592	621	659	2880
49	556	550	540	525	506	560	572	593	622	660	2940
50	4.68 556	550	540	525	506	4.68 561	572	593	622	661	3000
51	556	550	540	525	506	561	573	593	623	661	3060
52	556	550	539	525	505	561	573	594	624	662	3120
53	556	550	539	524	505	561	573	594	624	663	3180
54	556	550	539	524	505	561	573	595	625	664	3240
55	556	549	539	524	504	561	574	595	625	664	3300
56	556	549	539	523	504	561	574	596	626	665	3360
57	556	549	538	523	503	562	574	596	626	666	3420
58	555	549	538	523	503	562	575	596	627	666	3480
59	555	549	538	523	503	562	575	597	628	667	3540
60	4.68 555	549	538	522	502	4.68 562	575	597	628	668	3600

LOGARITHMS OF THE TRIGONOMETRIC FUNCTIONS

"	'	L. Sin.	d.	C. S.	C. T.	L. Tan	c.d.	L. Cot.	L. Cos.	'
0	0	6.46 373		—	—	6.46 373		—	0.00 000	60
60	1	6.76 476	30103	5.31 443	5.31 443	6.76 476	30103	3.53 627	0.00 000	59
120	2	6.94 085	17609	5.31 443	5.31 443	6.94 085	17609	3.23 524	0.00 000	58
180	3	6.94 085	12494	5.31 443	5.31 443	6.94 085	12494	3.05 915	0.00 000	57
240	4	7.06 579	9691	5.31 443	5.31 443	7.06 579	9691	2.93 421	0.00 000	56
300	5	7.16 270	7918	5.31 443	5.31 442	7.16 270	7918	2.83 730	0.00 000	55
360	6	7.24 188	6694	5.31 443	5.31 442	7.24 188	6694	2.75 812	0.00 000	54
420	7	7.30 882	5800	5.31 443	5.31 442	7.30 882	5800	2.69 118	0.00 000	53
480	8	7.36 682	5115	5.31 443	5.31 442	7.36 682	5115	2.63 318	0.00 000	52
540	9	7.41 797	4576	5.31 443	5.31 442	7.41 797	4576	2.58 203	0.00 000	51
600	10	7.46 373	4139	5.31 443	5.31 442	7.46 373	4139	2.53 627	0.00 000	50
660	11	7.50 512	3779	5.31 443	5.31 442	7.50 512	3779	2.49 488	0.00 000	49
720	12	7.54 291	3476	5.31 443	5.31 442	7.54 291	3476	2.45 709	0.00 000	48
780	13	7.57 767	3218	5.31 443	5.31 442	7.57 767	3219	2.42 233	0.00 000	47
840	14	7.60 985	2997	5.31 443	5.31 442	7.60 986	2996	2.39 014	0.00 000	46
900	15	7.63 982	2802	5.31 443	5.31 442	7.63 982	2803	2.36 018	0.00 000	45
960	16	7.66 784	2633	5.31 443	5.31 442	7.66 785	2633	2.33 215	0.00 000	44
1020	17	7.69 417	2483	5.31 443	5.31 442	7.69 418	2482	2.30 582	9.99 999	43
1080	18	7.71 900	2348	5.31 443	5.31 442	7.71 900	2348	2.28 100	9.99 999	42
1140	19	7.74 248	2227	5.31 443	5.31 442	7.74 248	2228	2.25 752	9.99 999	41
1200	20	7.76 475	2119	5.31 443	5.31 442	7.76 476	2119	2.23 524	9.99 999	40
1260	21	7.78 594	2021	5.31 443	5.31 442	7.78 595	2020	2.21 405	9.99 999	39
1320	22	7.80 615	1930	5.31 443	5.31 442	7.80 615	1931	2.19 385	9.99 999	38
1380	23	7.82 545	1848	5.31 443	5.31 442	7.82 546	1848	2.17 454	9.99 999	37
1440	24	7.84 393	1773	5.31 443	5.31 442	7.84 394	1773	2.15 606	9.99 999	36
1500	25	7.86 166	1704	5.31 443	5.31 442	7.86 167	1704	2.13 833	9.99 999	35
1560	26	7.87 870	1639	5.31 443	5.31 442	7.87 871	1639	2.12 129	9.99 999	34
1620	27	7.89 509	1579	5.31 443	5.31 442	7.89 510	1579	2.10 490	9.99 999	33
1680	28	7.91 088	1524	5.31 443	5.31 442	7.91 089	1524	2.08 911	9.99 999	32
1740	29	7.92 612	1472	5.31 443	5.31 441	7.92 613	1473	2.07 387	9.99 998	31
1800	30	7.94 084	1424	5.31 443	5.31 441	7.94 086	1424	2.05 914	9.99 998	30
1860	31	7.95 508	1379	5.31 443	5.31 441	7.95 510	1379	2.04 490	9.99 998	29
1920	32	7.96 887	1336	5.31 443	5.31 441	7.96 889	1336	2.03 111	9.99 998	28
1980	33	7.98 223	1297	5.31 443	5.31 441	7.98 225	1297	2.01 775	9.99 998	27
2040	34	7.99 520	1259	5.31 443	5.31 441	7.99 522	1259	2.00 478	9.99 998	26
2100	35	8.00 779	1223	5.31 443	5.31 441	8.00 781	1223	1.99 219	9.99 998	25
2160	36	8.02 002	1190	5.31 443	5.31 441	8.02 004	1190	1.97 996	9.99 998	24
2220	37	8.03 192	1158	5.31 443	5.31 441	8.03 194	1159	1.96 806	9.99 997	23
2280	38	8.04 350	1128	5.31 443	5.31 441	8.04 353	1128	1.95 647	9.99 997	22
2340	39	8.05 478	1100	5.31 443	5.31 441	8.05 481	1100	1.94 519	9.99 997	21
2400	40	8.06 578	1072	5.31 443	5.31 441	8.06 581	1072	1.93 419	9.99 997	20
2460	41	8.07 650	1046	5.31 444	5.31 440	8.07 653	1047	1.92 347	9.99 997	19
2520	42	8.08 696	1022	5.31 444	5.31 440	8.08 700	1022	1.91 300	9.99 997	18
2580	43	8.09 718	999	5.31 444	5.31 440	8.09 722	998	1.90 278	9.99 997	17
2640	44	8.10 717	976	5.31 444	5.31 440	8.10 720	976	1.89 280	9.99 996	16
2700	45	8.11 693	954	5.31 444	5.31 440	8.11 696	955	1.88 304	9.99 996	15
2760	46	8.12 647	934	5.31 444	5.31 440	8.12 651	934	1.87 349	9.99 996	14
2820	47	8.13 581	914	5.31 444	5.31 440	8.13 585	915	1.86 415	9.99 996	13
2880	48	8.14 495	896	5.31 444	5.31 440	8.14 500	895	1.85 500	9.99 996	12
2940	49	8.15 391	877	5.31 444	5.31 440	8.15 395	878	1.84 605	9.99 996	11
3000	50	8.16 268	860	5.31 444	5.31 439	8.16 273	860	1.83 727	9.99 995	10
3060	51	8.17 128	843	5.31 444	5.31 439	8.17 133	843	1.82 867	9.99 995	9
3120	52	8.17 971	827	5.31 444	5.31 439	8.17 976	828	1.82 024	9.99 995	8
3180	53	8.18 798	812	5.31 444	5.31 439	8.18 804	812	1.81 196	9.99 995	7
3240	54	8.19 610	797	5.31 444	5.31 439	8.19 616	797	1.80 384	9.99 995	6
3300	55	8.20 407	782	5.31 444	5.31 439	8.20 413	782	1.79 587	9.99 994	5
3360	56	8.21 189	769	5.31 444	5.31 439	8.21 195	769	1.78 805	9.99 994	4
3420	57	8.21 958	755	5.31 445	5.31 439	8.21 964	756	1.78 036	9.99 994	3
3480	58	8.22 713	743	5.31 445	5.31 438	8.22 720	742	1.77 280	9.99 994	2
3540	59	8.23 456	730	5.31 445	5.31 438	8.23 462	730	1.76 538	9.99 994	1
3600	60	8.24 186		5.31 445	5.31 438	8.24 192		1.75 808	9.99 993	0
"	'	L. Cos.	d.	C. S.	C. T.	L. Cot.	c.d.	L. Tan.	L. Sin.	'

LOGARITHMS OF THE TRIGONOMETRIC FUNCTIONS

"	'	L. Sin.	d.	C. S.	C. T.	L. Tan.	c.d.	L. Cot.	L. Cos.	'
3600	0	8.24 186	717	5.31 445	5.31 438	8.24 192	718	1.75 808	9.99 993	60
3660	1	8.24 903	706	5.31 445	5.31 438	8.24 910	706	1.75 090	9.99 993	59
3720	2	8.25 609	695	5.31 445	5.31 438	8.25 616	696	1.74 384	9.99 993	58
3780	3	8.26 304	684	5.31 445	5.31 438	8.26 312	684	1.73 688	9.99 993	57
3840	4	8.26 988	673	5.31 445	5.31 437	8.26 996	673	1.73 004	9.99 992	56
3900	5	8.27 661	663	5.31 445	5.31 437	8.27 669	663	1.72 331	9.99 992	55
3960	6	8.28 324	653	5.31 445	5.31 437	8.28 332	654	1.71 668	9.99 992	54
4020	7	8.28 977	644	5.31 445	5.31 437	8.28 986	643	1.71 014	9.99 992	53
4080	8	8.29 621	634	5.31 445	5.31 437	8.29 629	634	1.70 371	9.99 992	52
4140	9	8.30 255	624	5.31 445	5.31 437	8.30 263	625	1.69 737	9.99 991	51
4200	10	8.30 879	616	5.31 446	5.31 437	8.30 888	617	1.69 112	9.99 991	50
4260	11	8.31 495	608	5.31 446	5.31 436	8.31 505	607	1.68 495	9.99 991	49
4320	12	8.32 103	599	5.31 446	5.31 436	8.32 112	599	1.67 888	9.99 990	48
4380	13	8.32 702	590	5.31 446	5.31 436	8.32 711	591	1.67 289	9.99 990	47
4440	14	8.33 292	583	5.31 446	5.31 436	8.33 302	584	1.66 698	9.99 990	46
4500	15	8.33 875	575	5.31 446	5.31 436	8.33 886	575	1.66 114	9.99 990	45
4560	16	8.34 450	568	5.31 446	5.31 435	8.34 461	568	1.65 539	9.99 989	44
4620	17	8.35 018	560	5.31 446	5.31 435	8.35 029	561	1.64 971	9.99 989	43
4680	18	8.35 578	553	5.31 446	5.31 435	8.35 590	553	1.64 410	9.99 989	42
4740	19	8.36 131	547	5.31 446	5.31 435	8.36 143	546	1.63 857	9.99 989	41
4800	20	8.36 678	539	5.31 446	5.31 435	8.36 689	540	1.63 311	9.99 988	40
4860	21	8.37 217	533	5.31 447	5.31 434	8.37 229	533	1.62 771	9.99 988	39
4920	22	8.37 750	526	5.31 447	5.31 434	8.37 762	527	1.62 238	9.99 988	38
4980	23	8.38 276	520	5.31 447	5.31 434	8.38 289	520	1.61 711	9.99 987	37
5040	24	8.38 796	514	5.31 447	5.31 434	8.38 809	514	1.61 191	9.99 987	36
5100	25	8.39 310	508	5.31 447	5.31 434	8.39 323	509	1.60 677	9.99 987	35
5160	26	8.39 818	502	5.31 447	5.31 433	8.39 832	502	1.60 168	9.99 986	34
5220	27	8.40 320	496	5.31 447	5.31 433	8.40 334	496	1.59 666	9.99 986	33
5280	28	8.40 816	491	5.31 447	5.31 433	8.40 830	491	1.59 170	9.99 986	32
5340	29	8.41 307	485	5.31 447	5.31 433	8.41 321	486	1.58 679	9.99 985	31
5400	30	8.41 792	480	5.31 447	5.31 433	8.41 807	480	1.58 193	9.99 985	30
5460	31	8.42 272	474	5.31 448	5.31 432	8.42 287	475	1.57 713	9.99 985	29
5520	32	8.42 746	470	5.31 448	5.31 432	8.42 762	470	1.57 238	9.99 984	28
5580	33	8.43 216	464	5.31 448	5.31 432	8.43 232	464	1.56 768	9.99 984	27
5640	34	8.43 680	459	5.31 448	5.31 432	8.43 696	460	1.56 304	9.99 984	26
5700	35	8.44 139	455	5.31 448	5.31 431	8.44 156	455	1.55 844	9.99 983	25
5760	36	8.44 594	450	5.31 448	5.31 431	8.44 611	450	1.55 389	9.99 983	24
5820	37	8.45 044	445	5.31 448	5.31 431	8.45 061	446	1.54 939	9.99 983	23
5880	38	8.45 489	441	5.31 448	5.31 431	8.45 507	441	1.54 493	9.99 982	22
5940	39	8.45 930	436	5.31 449	5.31 431	8.45 948	437	1.54 052	9.99 982	21
6000	40	8.46 366	433	5.31 449	5.31 430	8.46 385	432	1.53 615	9.99 982	20
6060	41	8.46 799	427	5.31 449	5.31 430	8.46 817	428	1.53 183	9.99 981	19
6120	42	8.47 226	424	5.31 449	5.31 430	8.47 245	424	1.52 755	9.99 981	18
6180	43	8.47 650	419	5.31 449	5.31 430	8.47 669	420	1.52 331	9.99 981	17
6240	44	8.48 069	416	5.31 449	5.31 429	8.48 089	416	1.51 911	9.99 980	16
6300	45	8.48 485	411	5.31 449	5.31 429	8.48 505	412	1.51 495	9.99 980	15
6360	46	8.48 896	408	5.31 449	5.31 429	8.48 917	408	1.51 083	9.99 979	14
6420	47	8.49 304	404	5.31 450	5.31 428	8.49 325	404	1.50 675	9.99 979	13
6480	48	8.49 708	400	5.31 450	5.31 428	8.49 729	401	1.50 271	9.99 979	12
6540	49	8.50 108	396	5.31 450	5.31 428	8.50 130	397	1.49 870	9.99 978	11
6600	50	8.50 504	393	5.31 450	5.31 428	8.50 527	393	1.49 473	9.99 978	10
6660	51	8.50 897	390	5.31 450	5.31 427	8.50 920	390	1.49 080	9.99 977	9
6720	52	8.51 287	386	5.31 450	5.31 427	8.51 310	386	1.48 690	9.99 977	8
6780	53	8.51 673	382	5.31 450	5.31 427	8.51 696	383	1.48 304	9.99 977	7
6840	54	8.52 055	379	5.31 450	5.31 427	8.52 079	380	1.47 921	9.99 976	6
6900	55	8.52 434	376	5.31 451	5.31 426	8.52 459	376	1.47 541	9.99 976	5
6960	56	8.52 810	373	5.31 451	5.31 426	8.52 835	373	1.47 165	9.99 975	4
7020	57	8.53 183	369	5.31 451	5.31 426	8.53 208	370	1.46 792	9.99 975	3
7080	58	8.53 552	367	5.31 451	5.31 425	8.53 578	367	1.46 422	9.99 974	2
7140	59	8.53 919	363	5.31 451	5.31 425	8.53 945	363	1.46 055	9.99 974	1
7200	60	8.54 282		5.31 451	5.31 425	8.54 308		1.45 692	9.99 974	0

"	'	L. Cos.	d.	C. S.	C. T.	L. Cot.	c.d.	L. Tan.	L. Sin.	'

LOGARITHMS OF THE TRIGONOMETRIC FUNCTIONS

″	′	L. Sin.	d.	C. S.	C. T.	L. Tan.	c.d.	L. Cot.	L. Cos.	′
7200	0	8.54 282	360	5.31 451	5.31 425	8.54 308	361	1.45 692	9.99 974	60
7260	1	8.54 642	357	5.31 451	5.31 425	8.54 669	358	1.45 331	9.99 973	59
7320	2	8.54 999	355	5.31 452	5.31 424	8.55 027	355	1.44 973	9.99 973	58
7380	3	8.55 354	351	5.31 452	5.31 424	8.55 382	352	1.44 618	9.99 972	57
7440	4	8.55 705	349	5.31 452	5.31 424	8.55 734	349	1.44 266	9.99 972	56
7500	5	8.56 054	346	5.31 452	5.31 423	8.56 083	346	1.43 917	9.99 971	55
7560	6	8.56 400	343	5.31 452	5.31 423	8.56 429	344	1.43 571	9.99 971	54
7620	7	8.56 743	341	5.31 452	5.31 423	8.56 773	341	1.43 227	9.99 970	53
7680	8	8.57 084	337	5.31 453	5.31 422	8.57 114	338	1.42 886	9.99 970	52
7740	9	8.57 421	336	5.31 453	5.31 422	8.57 452	336	1.42 548	9.99 969	51
7800	10	8.57 757	332	5.31 453	5.31 422	8.57 788	333	1.42 212	9.99 969	50
7860	11	8.58 089	330	5.31 453	5.31 421	8.58 121	330	1.41 879	9.99 968	49
7920	12	8.58 419	328	5.31 453	5.31 421	8.58 451	328	1.41 549	9.99 968	48
7980	13	8.58 747	325	5.31 453	5.31 421	8.58 779	326	1.41 221	9.99 967	47
8040	14	8.59 072	323	5.31 454	5.31 421	8.59 105	323	1.40 895	9.99 967	46
8100	15	8.59 395	320	5.31 454	5.31 420	8.59 428	321	1.40 572	9.99 967	45
8160	16	8.59 715	318	5.31 454	5.31 420	8.59 749	319	1.40 251	9.99 966	44
8220	17	8.60 033	316	5.31 454	5.31 420	8.60 068	316	1.39 932	9.99 966	43
8280	18	8.60 349	313	5.31 454	5.31 419	8.60 384	314	1.39 616	9.99 965	42
8340	19	8.60 662	311	5.31 454	5.31 419	8.60 698	311	1.39 302	9.99 964	41
8400	20	8.60 973	309	5.31 455	5.31 418	8.61 009	310	1.38 991	9.99 964	40
8460	21	8.61 282	307	5.31 455	5.31 418	8.61 319	307	1.38 681	9.99 963	39
8520	22	8.61 589	305	5.31 455	5.31 418	8.61 626	305	1.38 374	9.99 963	38
8580	23	8.61 894	302	5.31 455	5.31 417	8.61 931	303	1.38 069	9.99 962	37
8640	24	8.62 196	301	5.31 455	5.31 417	8.62 234	301	1.37 766	9.99 962	36
8700	25	8.62 497	298	5.31 455	5.31 417	8.62 535	299	1.37 465	9.99 961	35
8760	26	8.62 795	296	5.31 456	5.31 416	8.62 834	297	1.37 166	9.99 961	34
8820	27	8.63 091	294	5.31 456	5.31 416	8.63 131	295	1.36 869	9.99 960	33
8880	28	8.63 385	293	5.31 456	5.31 416	8.63 426	292	1.36 574	9.99 960	32
8940	29	8.63 678	290	5.31 456	5.31 415	8.63 718	291	1.36 282	9.99 959	31
9000	30	8.63 968	288	5.31 456	5.31 415	8.64 009	289	1.35 991	9.99 959	30
9060	31	8.64 256	287	5.31 456	5.31 415	8.64 298	287	1.35 702	9.99 958	29
9120	32	8.64 543	284	5.31 457	5.31 414	8.64 585	285	1.35 415	9.99 958	28
9180	33	8.64 827	283	5.31 457	5.31 414	8.64 870	284	1.35 130	9.99 957	27
9240	34	8.65 110	281	5.31 457	5.31 413	8.65 154	281	1.34 846	9.99 956	26
9300	35	8.65 391	279	5.31 457	5.31 413	8.65 435	280	1.34 565	9.99 956	25
9360	36	8.65 670	277	5.31 457	5.31 413	8.65 715	278	1.34 285	9.99 955	24
9420	37	8.65 947	276	5.31 458	5.31 412	8.65 993	276	1.34 007	9.99 955	23
9480	38	8.66 223	274	5.31 458	5.31 412	8.66 269	274	1.33 731	9.99 954	22
9540	39	8.66 497	272	5.31 458	5.31 412	8.66 543	273	1.33 457	9.99 954	21
9600	40	8.66 769	270	5.31 458	5.31 411	8.66 816	271	1.33 184	9.99 953	20
9660	41	8.67 039	269	5.31 458	5.31 411	8.67 087	269	1.32 913	9.99 952	19
9720	42	8.67 308	267	5.31 459	5.31 410	8.67 356	268	1.32 644	9.99 952	18
9780	43	8.67 575	266	5.31 459	5.31 410	8.67 624	266	1.32 376	9.99 951	17
9840	44	8.67 841	263	5.31 459	5.31 410	8.67 890	264	1.32 110	9.99 951	16
9900	45	8.68 104	263	5.31 459	5.31 409	8.68 154	263	1.31 846	9.99 950	15
9960	46	8.68 367	260	5.31 459	5.31 409	8.68 417	261	1.31 583	9.99 949	14
10020	47	8.68 627	259	5.31 460	5.31 408	8.68 678	260	1.31 322	9.99 949	13
10080	48	8.68 886	258	5.31 460	5.31 408	8.68 938	258	1.31 062	9.99 948	12
10140	49	8.69 144	256	5.31 460	5.31 408	8.69 196	257	1.30 804	9.99 948	11
10200	50	8.69 400	254	5.31 460	5.31 407	8.69 453	255	1.30 547	9.99 947	10
10260	51	8.69 654	253	5.31 460	5.31 407	8.69 708	254	1.30 292	9.99 946	9
10320	52	8.69 907	252	5.31 461	5.31 406	8.69 962	252	1.30 038	9.99 946	8
10380	53	8.70 159	250	5.31 461	5.31 406	8.70 214	251	1.29 786	9.99 945	7
10440	54	8.70 409	249	5.31 461	5.31 405	8.70 465	249	1.29 535	9.99 944	6
10500	55	8.70 658	247	5.31 461	5.31 405	8.70 714	248	1.29 286	9.99 944	5
10560	56	8.70 905	246	5.31 461	5.31 405	8.70 962	246	1.29 038	9.99 943	4
10620	57	8.71 151	244	5.31 462	5.31 404	8.71 208	245	1.28 792	9.99 942	3
10680	58	8.71 395	243	5.31 462	5.31 404	8.71 453	244	1.28 547	9.99 942	2
10740	59	8.71 638	242	5.31 462	5.31 403	8.71 697	243	1.28 303	9.99 941	1
10800	60	8.71 880		5.31 462	5.31 403	8.71 940		1.28 060	9.99 940	0

|) ″ | ′ | L. Cos. | d. | C. S. | C. T. | L. Cot. | c.d. | L. Tan. | L. Sin. | |

LOGARITHMS OF THE TRIGONOMETRIC FUNCTIONS

3° (183°)   **(356°) 176°**

'	L. Sin.	d.	L. Tan.	c.d.	L. Cot.	L. Cos.	'	P. P.				
0	8.71 880		8.71 940		1.28 060	9.99 940	60	''	**241**	**239**	**237**	**235**	**234**
1	8.72 120	240	8.72 181	241	1.27 819	9.99 940	59	1	4.0	4.0	4.0	3.9	3.9
2	8.72 359	239	8.72 420	239	1.27 580	9.99 939	58	2	8.0	8.0	7.9	7.8	7.8
3	8.72 597	238	8.72 659	239	1.27 341	9.99 938	57	3	12.0	12.0	11.8	11.8	11.7
4	8.72 834	237	8.72 896	237	1.27 104	9.99 938	56	4	16.1	15.9	15.8	15.7	15.6
		235		236									
5	8.73 069		8.73 132		1.26 868	9.99 937	55	5	20.1	19.9	19.8	19.6	19.5
6	8.73 303	234	8.73 366	234	1.26 634	9.99 936	54	6	24.1	23.9	23.7	23.5	23.4
7	8.73 535	232	8.73 600	234	1.26 400	9.99 936	53	7	28.1	27.9	27.6	27.4	27.3
8	8.73 767	232	8.73 832	232	1.26 168	9.99 935	52	8	32.1	31.9	31.6	31.3	31.2
9	8.73 997	230	8.74 063	231	1.25 937	9.99 934	51	9	36.2	35.8	35.6	35.2	35.1
		229		229									
10	8.74 226		8.74 292		1.25 708	9.99 934	50	''	**232**	**229**	**227**	**225**	**223**
11	8.74 454	228	8.74 521	229	1.25 479	9.99 933	49	1	3.9	3.8	3.8	3.8	3.7
12	8.74 680	226	8.74 748	227	1.25 252	9.99 932	48	2	7.7	7.6	7.6	7.5	7.4
13	8.74 906	226	8.74 974	226	1.25 026	9.99 932	47	3	11.6	11.4	11.4	11.2	11.2
14	8.75 130	224	8.75 199	225	1.24 801	9.99 931	46	4	15.5	15.3	15.1	15.0	14.9
		223		224									
15	8.75 353		8.75 423		1.24 577	9.99 930	45	5	19.3	19.1	18.9	18.8	18.6
16	8.75 575	222	8.75 645	222	1.24 355	9.99 929	44	6	23.2	22.9	22.7	22.5	22.3
17	8.75 795	220	8.75 867	222	1.24 133	9.99 929	43	7	27.1	26.7	26.5	26.2	26.0
18	8.76 015	220	8.76 087	220	1.23 913	9.99 928	42	8	30.9	30.5	30.3	30.0	29.7
19	8.76 234	219	8.76 306	219	1.23 694	9.99 927	41	9	34.8	34.4	34.0	33.8	33.4
		217		219									
20	8.76 451		8.76 525		1.23 475	9.99 926	40	''	**222**	**220**	**217**	**215**	**213**
21	8.76 667	216	8.76 742	217	1.23 258	9.99 926	39	1	3.7	3.7	3.6	3.6	3.6
22	8.76 883	216	8.76 958	216	1.23 042	9.99 925	38	2	7.4	7.3	7.2	7.2	7.1
23	8.77 097	214	8.77 173	215	1.22 827	9.99 924	37	3	11.1	11.0	10.8	10.8	10.6
24	8.77 310	213	8.77 387	214	1.22 613	9.99 923	36	4	14.8	14.7	14.5	14.3	14.2
		212		213									
25	8.77 522		8.77 600		1.22 400	9.99 923	35	5	18.5	18.3	18.1	17.9	17.8
26	8.77 733	211	8.77 811	211	1.22 189	9.99 922	34	6	22.2	22.0	21.7	21.5	21.3
27	8.77 943	210	8.78 022	211	1.21 978	9.99 921	33	7	25.9	25.7	25.3	25.1	24.8
28	8.78 152	209	8.78 232	210	1.21 768	9.99 920	32	8	29.6	29.3	28.9	28.7	28.4
29	8.78 360	208	8.78 441	209	1.21 559	9.99 920	31	9	33.3	33.0	32.6	32.2	32.0
		208		208									
30	8.78 568		8.78 649		1.21 351	9.99 919	30	''	**211**	**208**	**206**	**203**	**201**
31	8.78 774	206	8.78 855	206	1.21 145	9.99 918	29	1	3.5	3.5	3.4	3.4	3.4
32	8.78 979	205	8.79 061	206	1.20 939	9.99 917	28	2	7.0	6.9	6.9	6.8	6.7
33	8.79 183	204	8.79 266	205	1.20 734	9.99 917	27	3	10.6	10.4	10.3	10.2	10.0
34	8.79 386	203	8.79 470	204	1.20 530	9.99 916	26	4	14.1	13.9	13.7	13.5	13.4
		202		203									
35	8.79 588		8.79 673		1.20 327	9.99 915	25	5	17.6	17.3	17.2	16.9	16.8
36	8.79 789	201	8.79 875	202	1.20 125	9.99 914	24	6	21.1	20.8	20.6	20.3	20.1
37	8.79 990	201	8.80 076	201	1.19 924	9.99 913	23	7	24.6	24.3	24.0	23.7	23.4
38	8.80 189	199	8.80 277	201	1.19 723	9.99 913	22	8	28.1	27.7	27.5	27.1	26.8
39	8.80 388	199	8.80 476	199	1.19 524	9.99 912	21	9	31.6	31.2	30.9	30.4	30.2
		197		198									
40	8.80 585		8.80 674		1.19 326	9.99 911	20	''	**199**	**197**	**195**	**193**	**192**
41	8.80 782	197	8.80 872	198	1.19 128	9.99 910	19	1	3.3	3.3	3.2	3.2	3.2
42	8.80 978	196	8.81 068	196	1.18 932	9.99 909	18	2	6.6	6.6	6.5	6.4	6.4
43	8.81 173	195	8.81 264	196	1.18 736	9.99 909	17	3	10.0	9.8	9.8	9.6	9.6
44	8.81 367	194	8.81 459	195	1.18 541	9.99 908	16	4	13.3	13.1	13.0	12.9	12.8
		193		194									
45	8.81 560		8.81 653		1.18 347	9.99 907	15	5	16.6	16.4	16.2	16.1	16.0
46	8.81 752	192	8.81 846	193	1.18 154	9.99 906	14	6	19.9	19.7	19.5	19.3	19.2
47	8.81 944	192	8.82 038	192	1.17 962	9.99 905	13	7	23.2	23.0	22.8	22.5	22.4
48	8.82 134	190	8.82 230	192	1.17 770	9.99 904	12	8	26.5	26.3	26.0	25.7	25.6
49	8.82 324	190	8.82 420	190	1.17 580	9.99 904	11	9	29.8	29.6	29.2	29.0	28.8
		189		190									
50	8.82 513		8.82 610		1.17 390	9.99 903	10	''	**189**	**187**	**185**	**183**	**181**
51	8.82 701	188	8.82 799	189	1.17 201	9.99 902	9	1	3.2	3.1	3.1	3.0	3.0
52	8.82 888	187	8.82 987	188	1.17 013	9.99 901	8	2	6.3	6.2	6.2	6.1	6.0
53	8.83 075	187	8.83 175	188	1.16 825	9.99 900	7	3	9.4	9.4	9.2	9.2	9.0
54	8.83 261	186	8.83 361	186	1.16 639	9.99 899	6	4	12.6	12.5	12.3	12.2	12.1
		185		186									
55	8.83 446		8.83 547		1.16 453	9.99 898	5	5	15.8	15.6	15.4	15.2	15.1
56	8.83 630	184	8.83 732	185	1.16 268	9.99 898	4	6	18.9	18.7	18.5	18.3	18.1
57	8.83 813	183	8.83 916	184	1.16 084	9.99 897	3	7	22.0	21.8	21.6	21.4	21.1
58	8.83 996	183	8.84 100	184	1.15 900	9.99 896	2	8	25.2	24.9	24.7	24.4	24.1
59	8.84 177	181	8.84 282	182	1.15 718	9.99 895	1	9	28.4	28.0	27.8	27.4	27.2
		181		182									
60	8.84 358		8.84 464		1.15 536	9.99 894	0	10	31.5	31.2	30.8	30.5	30.2

'	L. Cos.	d.	L. Cot.	c.d	L. Tan.	L. Sin.	'	P. P.

LOGARITHMS OF THE TRIGONOMETRIC FUNCTIONS

4° (184°) (355°) **175°**

′	L. Sin.	d.	L. Tan.	c.d.	L. Cot.	L. Cos.	′	P. P.				
0	8.84 358	181	8.84 464	182	1.15 536	9.99 894	60	**″**	**182**	**181**	**179**	**178**	**177**
1	8.84 539	179	8.84 646	180	1.15 354	9.99 893	59	1	3.0	3.0	3.0	3.0	3.0
2	8.84 718	179	8.84 826	180	1.15 174	9.99 892	58	2	6.1	6.0	6.0	5.9	5.9
3	8.84 897	178	8.85 006	179	1.14 994	9.99 891	57	3	9.1	9.0	9.0	8.9	8.8
4	8.85 075	177	8.85 185	178	1.14 815	9.99 891	56	4	12.1	12.1	11.9	11.9	11.8
5	8.85 252	177	8.85 363	177	1.14 637	9.99 890	55	5	15.2	15.1	14.9	14.8	14.8
6	8.85 429	176	8.85 540	177	1.14 460	9.99 889	54	6	18.2	18.1	17.9	17.8	17.7
7	8.85 605	175	8.85 717	176	1.14 283	9.99 888	53	7	21.2	21.1	20.9	20.8	20.6
8	8.85 780	175	8.85 893	176	1.14 107	9.99 887	52	8	24.3	24.1	23.9	23.7	23.6
9	8.85 955	173	8.86 069	174	1.13 931	9.99 886	51	9	27.3	27.2	26.8	26.7	26.6
10	8.86 128	173	8.86 243	174	1.13 757	9.99 885	50	**″**	**176**	**175**	**174**	**173**	**172**
11	8.86 301	173	8.86 417	174	1.13 583	9.99 884	49	1	2.9	2.9	2.9	2.9	2.9
12	8.86 474	171	8.86 591	172	1.13 409	9.99 883	48	2	5.9	5.8	5.8	5.8	5.7
13	8.86 645	171	8.86 763	172	1.13 237	9.99 882	47	3	8.8	8.8	8.7	8.6	8.6
14	8.86 816	171	8.86 935	171	1.13 065	9.99 881	46	4	11.7	11.7	11.6	11.5	11.5
15	8.86 987	169	8.87 106	171	1.12 894	9.99 880	45	5	14.7	14.6	14.5	14.4	14.3
16	8.87 156	169	8.87 277	170	1.12 723	9.99 879	44	6	17.6	17.5	17.4	17.3	17.2
17	8.87 325	169	8.87 447	169	1.12 553	9.99 879	43	7	20.5	20.4	20.3	20.2	20.1
18	8.87 494	167	8.87 616	169	1.12 384	9.99 878	42	8	23.5	23.3	23.2	23.1	22.9
19	8.87 661	168	8.87 785	168	1.12 215	9.99 877	41	9	26.4	26.2	26.1	26.0	25.8
20	8.87 829	166	8.87 953	167	1.12 047	9.99 876	40	**″**	**171**	**170**	**169**	**168**	**167**
21	8.87 995	166	8.88 120	167	1.11 880	9.99 875	39	1	2.8	2.8	2.8	2.8	2.8
22	8.88 161	165	8.88 287	166	1.11 713	9.99 874	38	2	5.7	5.7	5.6	5.6	5.6
23	8.88 326	164	8.88 453	165	1.11 547	9.99 873	37	3	8.6	8.5	8.4	8.4	8.4
24	8.88 490	164	8.88 618	165	1.11 382	9.99 872	36	4	11.4	11.3	11.3	11.2	11.1
25	8.88 654	163	8.88 783	165	1.11 217	9.99 871	35	5	14.2	14.2	14.1	14.0	13.9
26	8.88 817	163	8.88 948	163	1.11 052	9.99 870	34	6	17.1	17.0	16.9	16.8	16.7
27	8.88 980	162	8.89 111	163	1.10 889	9.99 869	33	7	20.0	19.8	19.7	19.6	19.5
28	8.89 142	162	8.89 274	163	1.10 726	9.99 868	32	8	22.8	22.7	22.5	22.4	22.3
29	8.89 304	160	8.89 437	161	1.10 563	9.99 867	31	9	25.6	25.5	25.4	25.2	25.0
30	8.89 464	161	8.89 598	162	1.10 402	9.99 866	30	**″**	**166**	**165**	**164**	**163**	**162**
31	8.89 625	159	8.89 760	160	1.10 240	9.99 865	29	1	2.8	2.8	2.7	2.7	2.7
32	8.89 784	159	8.89 920	160	1.10 080	9.99 864	28	2	5.5	5.5	5.5	5.4	5.4
33	8.89 943	159	8.90 080	160	1.09 920	9.99 863	27	3	8.3	8.2	8.2	8.2	8.1
34	8.90 102	158	8.90 240	159	1.09 760	9.99 862	26	4	11.1	11.0	10.9	10.9	10.8
35	8.90 260	157	8.90 399	158	1.09 601	9.99 861	25	5	13.8	13.8	13.7	13.6	13.5
36	8.90 417	157	8.90 557	158	1.09 443	9.99 860	24	6	16.6	16.5	16.4	16.3	16.2
37	8.90 574	156	8.90 715	157	1.09 285	9.99 859	23	7	19.4	19.2	19.1	19.0	18.9
38	8.90 730	155	8.90 872	157	1.09 128	9.99 858	22	8	22.1	22.0	21.9	21.7	21.6
39	8.90 885	155	8.91 029	156	1.08 971	9.99 857	21	9	24.9	24.8	24.6	24.4	24.3
40	8.91 040	155	8.91 185	155	1.08 815	9.99 856	20	**″**	**161**	**160**	**159**	**158**	**157**
41	8.91 195	154	8.91 340	155	1.08 660	9.99 855	19	1	2.7	2.7	2.6	2.6	2.6
42	8.91 349	153	8.91 495	155	1.08 505	9.99 854	18	2	5.4	5.3	5.3	5.3	5.2
43	8.91 502	153	8.91 650	153	1.08 350	9.99 853	17	3	8.0	8.0	8.0	7.9	7.8
44	8.91 655	152	8.91 803	154	1.08 197	9.99 852	16	4	10.7	10.7	10.6	10.5	10.5
45	8.91 807	152	8.91 957	153	1.08 043	9.99 851	15	5	13.4	13.3	13.2	13.2	13.1
46	8.91 959	151	8.92 110	152	1.07 890	9.99 850	14	6	16.1	16.0	15.9	15.8	15.7
47	8.92 110	151	8.92 262	152	1.07 738	9.99 848	13	7	18.8	18.7	18.6	18.4	18.3
48	8.92 261	150	8.92 414	151	1.07 586	9.99 847	12	8	21.5	21.3	21.2	21.1	20.9
49	8.92 411	150	8.92 565	151	1.07 435	9.99 846	11	9	24.2	24.0	23.8	23.7	23.6
50	8.92 561	149	8.92 716	150	1.07 284	9.99 845	10	**″**	**156**	**155**	**154**	**153**	**152**
51	8.92 710	149	8.92 866	150	1.07 134	9.99 844	9	1	2.6	2.6	2.6	2.6	2.5
52	8.92 859	148	8.93 016	149	1.06 984	9.99 843	8	2	5.2	5.2	5.1	5.1	5.1
53	8.93 007	147	8.93 165	148	1.06 835	9.99 842	7	3	7.8	7.8	7.7	7.6	7.6
54	8.93 154	147	8.93 313	149	1.06 687	9.99 841	6	4	10.4	10.3	10.3	10.2	10.1
55	8.93 301	147	8.93 462	147	1.06 538	9.99 840	5	5	13.0	12.9	12.8	12.8	12.7
56	8.93 448	146	8.93 609	147	1.06 391	9.99 839	4	6	15.6	15.5	15.4	15.3	15.2
57	8.93 594	146	8.93 756	147	1.06 244	9.99 838	3	7	18.2	18.1	18.0	17.8	17.7
58	8.93 740	145	8.93 903	146	1.06 097	9.99 837	2	8	20.8	20.7	20.5	20.4	20.3
59	8.93 885	145	8.94 049	146	1.05 951	9.99 836	1	9	23.4	23.2	23.1	23.0	22.8
60	8.94 030		8.94 195		1.05 805	9.99 834	0	10	26.0	25.8	25.7	25.5	25.3

| ′ | L. Cos. | d. | L. Cot. | c.d. | L. Tan. | L. Sin. | ′ | P. P. |

94° (274°) (265°) **85°**

50

LOGARITHMS OF THE TRIGONOMETRIC FUNCTIONS

5° (185°) (354°) **174°**

'	L. Sin.	d	L. Tan.	c.d.	L. Cot.	L. Cos.	'
0	8.94 030	144	8.94 195	145	1.05 805	9.99 834	60
1	8.94 174	143	8.94 340	145	1.05 660	9.99 833	59
2	8.94 317	144	8.94 485	145	1.05 515	9.99 832	58
3	8.94 461	142	8.94 630	143	1.05 370	9.99 831	57
4	8.94 603	143	8.94 773	144	1.05 227	9.99 830	56
5	8.94 746	141	8.94 917	143	1.05 083	9.99 829	55
6	8.94 887	142	8.95 060	142	1.04 940	9.99 828	54
7	8.95 029	141	8.95 202	142	1.04 798	9.99 827	53
8	8.95 170	140	8.95 344	142	1.04 656	9.99 825	52
9	8.95 310	140	8.95 486	141	1.04 514	9.99 824	51
10	8.95 450	139	8.95 627	140	1.04 373	9.99 823	50
11	8.95 589	139	8.95 767	141	1.04 233	9.99 822	49
12	8.95 728	139	8.95 908	139	1.04 092	9.99 821	48
13	8.95 867	138	8.96 047	140	1.03 953	9.99 820	47
14	8.96 005	138	8.96 187	138	1.03 813	9.99 819	46
15	8.96 143	137	8.96 325	139	1.03 675	9.99 817	45
16	8.96 280	137	8.96 464	138	1.03 536	9.99 816	44
17	8.96 417	136	8.96 602	137	1.03 398	9.99 815	43
18	8.96 553	136	8.96 739	138	1.03 261	9.99 814	42
19	8.96 689	136	8.96 877	136	1.03 123	9.99 813	41
20	8.96 825	135	8.97 013	137	1.02 987	9.99 812	40
21	8.96 960	135	8.97 150	135	1.02 850	9.99 810	39
22	8.97 095	134	8.97 285	136	1.02 715	9.99 809	38
23	8.97 229	134	8.97 421	135	1.02 579	9.99 808	37
24	8.97 363	133	8.97 556	135	1.02 444	9.99 807	36
25	8.97 496	133	8.97 691	134	1.02 309	9.99 806	35
26	8.97 629	133	8.97 825	134	1.02 175	9.99 804	34
27	8.97 762	132	8.97 959	133	1.02 041	9.99 803	33
28	8.97 894	132	8.98 092	133	1.01 908	9.99 802	32
29	8.98 026	131	8.98 225	133	1.01 775	9.99 801	31
30	8.98 157	131	8.98 358	132	1.01 642	9.99 800	30
31	8.98 288	131	8.98 490	132	1.01 510	9.99 798	29
32	8.98 419	130	8.98 622	131	1.01 378	9.99 797	28
33	8.98 549	130	8.98 753	131	1.01 247	9.99 796	27
34	8.98 679	129	8.98 884	131	1.01 116	9.99 795	26
35	8.98 808	129	8.99 015	130	1.00 985	9.99 793	25
36	8.98 937	129	8.99 145	130	1.00 855	9.99 792	24
37	8.99 066	128	8.99 275	130	1.00 725	9.99 791	23
38	8.99 194	128	8.99 405	129	1.00 595	9.99 790	22
39	8.99 322	128	8.99 534	128	1.00 466	9.99 788	21
40	8.99 450	127	8.99 662	129	1.00 338	9.99 787	20
41	8.99 577	127	8.99 791	128	1.00 209	9.99 786	19
42	8.99 704	126	8.99 919	127	1.00 081	9.99 785	18
43	8.99 830	126	9.00 046	128	0.99 954	9.99 783	17
44	8.99 956	126	9.00 174	127	0.99 826	9.99 782	16
45	9.00 082	125	9.00 301	126	0.99 699	9.99 781	15
46	9.00 207	125	9.00 427	126	0.99 573	9.99 780	14
47	9.00 332	124	9.00 553	126	0.99 447	9.99 778	13
48	9.00 456	125	9.00 679	126	0.99 321	9.99 777	12
49	9.00 581	123	9.00 805	125	0.99 195	9.99 776	11
50	9.00 704	124	9.00 930	125	0.99 070	9.99 775	10
51	9.00 828	123	9.01 055	124	0.98 945	9.99 773	9
52	9.00 951	123	9.01 179	124	0.98 821	9.99 772	8
53	9.01 074	122	9.01 303	124	0.98 697	9.99 771	7
54	9.01 196	122	9.01 427	123	0.98 573	9.99 769	6
55	9.01 318	122	9.01 550	123	0.98 450	9.99 768	5
56	9.01 440	121	9.01 673	123	0.98 327	9.99 767	4
57	9.01 561	121	9.01 796	122	0.98 204	9.99 765	3
58	9.01 682	121	9.01 918	122	0.98 082	9.99 764	2
59	9.01 803	120	9.02 040	122	0.97 960	9.99 763	1
60	9.01 923		9.02 162		0.97 838	9.99 761	0

'	L. Cos.	d.	L. Cot.	c.d.	L. Tan.	L. Sin.	'

P. P.

''	151	149	148	147	146
1	2.5	2.5	2.5	2.4	2.4
2	5.0	5.0	4.9	4.9	4.9
3	7.6	7.4	7.4	7.4	7.3
4	10.1	9.9	9.9	9.8	9.7
5	12.6	12.4	12.3	12.2	12.2
6	15.1	14.9	14.8	14.7	14.6
7	17.6	17.4	17.3	17.2	17.0
8	20.1	19.9	19.7	19.6	19.5
9	22.6	22.4	22.2	22.0	21.9

''	145	144	143	142	141
1	2.4	2.4	2.4	2.4	2.4
2	4.8	4.8	4.8	4.7	4.7
3	7.2	7.2	7.2	7.1	7.0
4	9.7	9.6	9.5	9.5	9.4
5	12.1	12.0	11.9	11.8	11.8
6	14.5	14.4	14.3	14.2	14.1
7	16.9	16.8	16.7	16.6	16.4
8	19.3	19.2	19.1	18.9	18.8
9	21.8	21.6	21.4	21.3	21.2

''	140	139	138	137	136
1	2.3	2.3	2.3	2.3	2.3
2	4.7	4.6	4.6	4.6	4.5
3	7.0	7.0	6.9	6.8	6.8
4	9.3	9.3	9.2	9.1	9.1
5	11.7	11.6	11.5	11.4	11.3
6	14.0	13.9	13.8	13.7	13.6
7	16.3	16.2	16.1	16.0	15.9
8	18.7	18.5	18.4	18.3	18.1
9	21.0	20.8	20.7	20.6	20.4

''	135	134	133	132	131
1	2.2	2.2	2.2	2.2	2.2
2	4.5	4.5	4.4	4.4	4.4
3	6.8	6.7	6.6	6.6	6.6
4	9.0	8.9	8.9	8.8	8.7
5	11.2	11.2	11.1	11.0	10.9
6	13.5	13.4	13.3	13.2	13.1
7	15.8	15.6	15.5	15.4	15.3
8	18.0	17.9	17.7	17.6	17.5
9	20.2	20.1	20.0	19.8	19.6

''	130	129	128	127	126
1	2.2	2.2	2.1	2.1	2.1
2	4.3	4.3	4.3	4.2	4.2
3	6.5	6.4	6.4	6.4	6.3
4	8.7	8.6	8.5	8.5	8.4
5	10.8	10.8	10.7	10.6	10.5
6	13.0	12.9	12.8	12.7	12.6
7	15.2	15.0	14.9	14.8	14.7
8	17.3	17.2	17.1	16.9	16.8
9	19.5	19.4	19.2	19.0	18.9

''	125	124	123	122	121
1	2.1	2.1	2.0	2.0	2.0
2	4.2	4.1	4.1	4.1	4.0
3	6.2	6.2	6.2	6.1	6.0
4	8.3	8.3	8.2	8.1	8.1
5	10.4	10.3	10.2	10.2	10.1
6	12.5	12.4	12.3	12.2	12.1
7	14.6	14.5	14.4	14.2	14.1
8	16.7	16.5	16.4	16.3	16.1
9	18.8	18.6	18.4	18.3	18.2
10	20.8	20.7	20.5	20.3	20.2

95° (275°) (264°) **84°**

LOGARITHMS OF THE TRIGONOMETRIC FUNCTIONS

6° (186°) (353°) **173°**

′	L. Sin.	d.	L. Tan.	c.d.	L. Cot.	L. Cos.	′
0	9.01 923	120	9.02 162	121	0.97 838	9.99 761	60
1	9.02 043	120	9.02 283	121	0.97 717	9.99 760	59
2	9.02 163	120	9.02 404	121	0.97 596	9.99 759	58
3	9.02 283	119	9.02 525	120	0.97 475	9.99 757	57
4	9.02 402	118	9.02 645	121	0.97 355	9.99 756	56
5	9.02 520	119	9.02 766	119	0.97 234	9.99 755	55
6	9.02 639	118	9.02 885	120	0.97 115	9.99 753	54
7	9.02 757	117	9.03 005	119	0.96 995	9.99 752	53
8	9.02 874	118	9.03 124	118	0.96 876	9.99 751	52
9	9.02 992	117	9.03 242	119	0.96 758	9.99 749	51
10	9.03 109	117	9.03 361	118	0.96 639	9.99 748	50
11	9.03 226	116	9.03 479	118	0.96 521	9.99 747	49
12	9.03 342	116	9.03 597	117	0.96 403	9.99 745	48
13	9.03 458	116	9.03 714	118	0.96 286	9.99 744	47
14	9.03 574	116	9.03 832	116	0.96 168	9.99 742	46
15	9.03 690	115	9.03 948	117	0.96 052	9.99 741	45
16	9.03 805	115	9.04 065	116	0.95 935	9.99 740	44
17	9.03 920	114	9.04 181	116	0.95 819	9.99 738	43
18	9.04 034	115	9.04 297	116	0.95 703	9.99 737	42
19	9.04 149	113	9.04 413	115	0.95 587	9.99 736	41
20	9.04 262	114	9.04 528	115	0.95 472	9.99 734	40
21	9.04 376	114	9.04 643	115	0.95 357	9.99 733	39
22	9.04 490	113	9.04 758	115	0.95 242	9.99 731	38
23	9.04 603	112	9.04 873	114	0.95 127	9.99 730	37
24	9.04 715	113	9.04 987	114	0.95 013	9.99 728	36
25	9.04 828	112	9.05 101	113	0.94 899	9.99 727	35
26	9.04 940	112	9.05 214	114	0.94 786	9.99 726	34
27	9.05 052	112	9.05 328	113	0.94 672	9.99 724	33
28	9.05 164	111	9.05 441	112	0.94 559	9.99 723	32
29	9.05 275	111	9.05 553	113	0.94 447	9.99 721	31
30	9.05 386	111	9.05 666	112	0.94 334	9.99 720	30
31	9.05 497	110	9.05 778	112	0.94 222	9.99 718	29
32	9.05 607	110	9.05 890	112	0.94 110	9.99 717	28
33	9.05 717	110	9.06 002	111	0.93 998	9.99 716	27
34	9.05 827	110	9.06 113	111	0.93 887	9.99 714	26
35	9.05 937	109	9.06 224	111	0.93 776	9.99 713	25
36	9.06 046	109	9.06 335	110	0.93 665	9.99 711	24
37	9.06 155	109	9.06 445	111	0.93 555	9.99 710	23
38	9.06 264	108	9.06 556	110	0.93 444	9.99 708	22
39	9.06 372	109	9.06 666	109	0.93 334	9.99 707	21
40	9.06 481	108	9.06 775	110	0.93 225	9.99 705	20
41	9.06 589	107	9.06 885	109	0.93 115	9.99 704	19
42	9.06 696	108	9.06 994	109	0.93 006	9.99 702	18
43	9.06 804	107	9.07 103	108	0.92 897	9.99 701	17
44	9.06 911	107	9.07 211	109	0.92 789	9.99 699	16
45	9.07 018	106	9.07 320	108	0.92 680	9.99 698	15
46	9.07 124	107	9.07 428	108	0.92 572	9.99 696	14
47	9.07 231	106	9.07 536	107	0.92 464	9.99 695	13
48	9.07 337	105	9.07 643	108	0.92 357	9.99 693	12
49	9.07 442	106	9.07 751	107	0.92 249	9.99 692	11
50	9.07 548	105	9.07 858	106	0.92 142	9.99 690	10
51	9.07 653	105	9.07 964	107	0.92 036	9.99 689	9
52	9.07 758	105	9.08 071	106	0.91 929	9.99 687	8
53	9.07 863	105	9.08 177	106	0.91 823	9.99 686	7
54	9.07 968	104	9.08 283	106	0.91 717	9.99 684	6
55	9.08 072	104	9.08 389	106	0.91 611	9.99 683	5
56	9.08 176	104	9.08 495	105	0.91 505	9.99 681	4
57	9.08 280	103	9.08 600	105	0.91 400	9.99 680	3
58	9.08 383	103	9.08 705	105	0.91 295	9.99 678	2
59	9.08 486	103	9.08 810	104	0.91 190	9.99 677	1
60	9.08 589		9.08 914		0.91 086	9.99 675	0

′	L. Cos.	d.	L. Cot.	c.d.	L. Tan.	L. Sin.	′

P. P.

″	121	120	119	118
1	2.0	2.0	2.0	2.0
2	4.0	4.0	4.0	3.9
3	6.0	6.0	6.0	5.9
4	8.1	8.0	7.9	7.9
5	10.1	10.0	9.9	9.8
6	12.1	12.0	11.9	11.8
7	14.1	14.0	13.9	13.8
8	16.1	16.0	15.9	15.7
9	18.2	18.0	17.8	17.7
10	20.2	20.0	19.8	19.7
20	40.3	40.0	39.7	39.3
30	60.5	60.0	59.5	59.0
40	80.7	80.0	79.3	78.7
50	100.8	100.0	99.2	98.3

″	117	116	115	114
1	2.0	1.9	1.9	1.9
2	3.9	3.9	3.8	3.8
3	5.8	5.8	5.8	5.7
4	7.8	7.7	7.7	7.6
5	9.8	9.7	9.6	9.5
6	11.7	11.6	11.5	11.4
7	13.6	13.5	13.4	13.3
8	15.6	15.5	15.3	15.2
9	17.6	17.4	17.2	17.1
10	19.5	19.3	19.2	19.0
20	39.0	38.7	38.3	38.0
30	58.5	58.0	57.5	57.0
40	78.0	77.3	76.7	76.0
50	97.5	96.7	95.8	95.0

″	113	112	111	110
1	1.9	1.9	1.8	1.8
2	3.8	3.7	3.7	3.7
3	5.6	5.6	5.6	5.5
4	7.5	7.5	7.4	7.3
5	9.4	9.3	9.2	9.2
6	11.3	11.2	11.1	11.0
7	13.2	13.1	13.0	12.8
8	15.1	14.9	14.8	14.7
9	17.0	16.8	16.6	16.5
10	18.8	18.7	18.5	18.3
20	37.7	37.3	37.0	36.7
30	56.5	56.0	55.5	55.0
40	75.3	74.7	74.0	73.3
50	94.2	93.3	92.5	91.7

″	109	108	107	106
1	1.8	1.8	1.8	1.8
2	3.6	3.6	3.6	3.5
3	5.4	5.4	5.4	5.3
4	7.3	7.2	7.1	7.1
5	9.1	9.0	8.9	8.8
6	10.9	10.8	10.7	10.6
7	12.7	12.6	12.5	12.4
8	14.5	14.4	14.3	14.1
9	16.4	16.2	16.0	15.9
10	18.2	18.0	17.8	17.7
20	36.3	36.0	35.7	35.3
30	54.5	54.0	53.5	53.0
40	72.7	72.0	71.3	70.7
50	90.8	90.0	89.2	88.3

7° (187°)　　　　　　　　　　　　　　　　　　　**(352°) 172°**

′	L. Sin.	d.	L. Tan.	c.d.	L. Cot.	L. Cos.	′	P. P.			
0	9.08 589	103	9.08 914	105	0.91 086	9.99 675	60	″	105	104	103	102
1	9.08 692	103	9.09 019	104	0.90 981	9.99 674	59	1	1.8	1.7	1.7	1.7
2	9.08 795	102	9.09 123	104	0.90 877	9.99 672	58	2	3.5	3.5	3.4	3.4
3	9.08 897	102	9.09 227	103	0.90 773	9.99 670	57	3	5.2	5.2	5.2	5.1
4	9.08 999	102	9.09 330	104	0.90 670	9.99 669	56	4	7.0	6.9	6.9	6.8
5	9.09 101	101	9.09 434	103	0.90 566	9.99 667	55	5	8.8	8.7	8.6	8.5
6	9.09 202	102	9.09 537	103	0.90 463	9.99 666	54	6	10.5	10.4	10.3	10.2
7	9.09 304	101	9.09 640	102	0.90 360	9.99 664	53	7	12.2	12.1	12.0	11.9
8	9.09 405	101	9.09 742	103	0.90 258	9.99 663	52	8	14.0	13.9	13.7	13.6
9	9.09 506	100	9.09 845	102	0.90 155	9.99 661	51	9	15.8	15.6	15.4	15.3
10	9.09 606	101	9.09 947	102	0.90 053	9.99 659	50	10	17.5	17.3	17.2	17.0
11	9.09 707	100	9.10 049	101	0.89 951	9.99 658	49	20	35.0	34.7	34.3	34.0
12	9.09 807	100	9.10 150	102	0.89 850	9.99 656	48	30	52.5	52.0	51.5	51.0
13	9.09 907	99	9.10 252	101	0.89 748	9.99 655	47	40	70.0	69.3	68.7	68.0
14	9.10 006	100	9.10 353	101	0.89 647	9.99 653	46	50	87.5	86.7	85.8	85.0
15	9.10 106	99	9.10 454	101	0.89 546	9.99 651	45	″	101	100	99	98
16	9.10 205	99	9.10 555	101	0.89 445	9.99 650	44	1	1.7	1.7	1.6	1.6
17	9.10 304	98	9.10 656	100	0.89 344	9.99 648	43	2	3.4	3.3	3.3	3.3
18	9.10 402	99	9.10 756	100	0.89 244	9.99 647	42	3	5.0	5.0	5.0	4.9
19	9.10 501	98	9.10 856	100	0.89 144	9.99 645	41	4	6.7	6.7	6.6	6.5
20	9.10 599	98	9.10 956	100	0.89 044	9.99 643	40	5	8.4	8.3	8.2	8.2
21	9.10 697	98	9.11 056	99	0.88 944	9.99 642	39	6	10.1	10.0	9.9	9.8
22	9.10 795	98	9.11 155	99	0.88 845	9.99 640	38	7	11.8	11.7	11.6	11.4
23	9.10 893	97	9.11 254	99	0.88 746	9.99 638	37	8	13.5	13.3	13.2	13.1
24	9.10 990	97	9.11 353	99	0.88 647	9.99 637	36	9	15.2	15.0	14.8	14.7
25	9.11 087	97	9.11 452	99	0.88 548	9.99 635	35	10	16.8	16.7	16.5	16.3
26	9.11 184	97	9.11 551	98	0.88 449	9.99 633	34	20	33.7	33.3	33.0	32.7
27	9.11 281	96	9.11 649	98	0.88 351	9.99 632	33	30	50.5	50.0	49.5	49.0
28	9.11 377	97	9.11 747	98	0.88 253	9.99 630	32	40	67.3	66.7	66.0	65.3
29	9.11 474	96	9.11 845	98	0.88 155	9.99 629	31	50	84.2	83.3	82.5	81.7
30	9.11 570	96	9.11 943	97	0.88 057	9.99 627	30	″	97	96	95	94
31	9.11 666	95	9.12 040	98	0.87 960	9.99 625	29	1	1.6	1.6	1.6	1.6
32	9.11 761	96	9.12 138	97	0.87 862	9.99 624	28	2	3.2	3.2	3.2	3.1
33	9.11 857	95	9.12 235	97	0.87 765	9.99 622	27	3	4.8	4.8	4.8	4.7
34	9.11 952	95	9.12 332	96	0.87 668	9.99 620	26	4	6.5	6.4	6.3	6.3
35	9.12 047	95	9.12 428	97	0.87 572	9.99 618	25	5	8.1	8.0	7.9	7.8
36	9.12 142	94	9.12 525	96	0.87 475	9.99 617	24	6	9.7	9.6	9.5	9.4
37	9.12 236	95	9.12 621	96	0.87 379	9.99 615	23	7	11.3	11.2	11.1	11.0
38	9.12 331	94	9.12 717	96	0.87 283	9.99 613	22	8	12.9	12.8	12.7	12.5
39	9.12 425	94	9.12 813	96	0.87 187	9.99 612	21	9	14.6	14.4	14.2	14.1
40	9.12 519	93	9.12 909	95	0.87 091	9.99 610	20	10	16.2	16.0	15.8	15.7
41	9.12 612	94	9.13 004	95	0.86 996	9.99 608	19	20	32.3	32.0	31.7	31.3
42	9.12 706	93	9.13 099	95	0.86 901	9.99 607	18	30	48.5	48.0	47.5	47.0
43	9.12 799	93	9.13 194	95	0.86 806	9.99 605	17	40	64.7	64.0	63.3	62.7
44	9.12 892	93	9.13 289	95	0.86 711	9.99 603	16	50	80.8	80.0	79.2	78.3
45	9.12 985	93	9.13 384	94	0.86 616	9.99 601	15	″	93	92	91	90
46	9.13 078	93	9.13 478	95	0.86 522	9.99 600	14	1	1.6	1.5	1.5	1.5
47	9.13 171	92	9.13 573	94	0.86 427	9.99 598	13	2	3.1	3.1	3.0	3.0
48	9.13 263	92	9.13 667	94	0.86 333	9.99 596	12	3	4.6	4.6	4.6	4.5
49	9.13 355	92	9.13 761	93	0.86 239	9.99 595	11	4	6.2	6.1	6.1	6.0
50	9.13 447	92	9.13 854	94	0.86 146	9.99 593	10	5	7.8	7.7	7.6	7.5
51	9.13 539	91	9.13 948	93	0.86 052	9.99 591	9	6	9.3	9.2	9.1	9.0
52	9.13 630	92	9.14 041	93	0.85 959	9.99 589	8	7	10.8	10.7	10.6	10.5
53	9.13 722	91	9.14 134	93	0.85 866	9.99 588	7	8	12.4	12.3	12.1	12.0
54	9.13 813	91	9.14 227	93	0.85 773	9.99 586	6	9	14.0	13.8	13.6	13.5
55	9.13 904	90	9.14 320	92	0.85 680	9.99 584	5	10	15.5	15.3	15.2	15.0
56	9.13 994	91	9.14 412	92	0.85 588	9.99 582	4	20	31.0	30.7	30.3	30.0
57	9.14 085	90	9.14 504	93	0.85 496	9.99 581	3	30	46.5	46.0	45.5	45.0
58	9.14 175	91	9.14 597	91	0.85 403	9.99 579	2	40	62.0	61.3	60.7	60.0
59	9.14 266	90	9.14 688	92	0.85 312	9.99 577	1	50	77.5	76.7	75.8	75.0
60	9.14 356		9.14 780		0.85 220	9.99 575	0					

′	L. Cos.	d.	L. Cot.	c.d.	L. Tan.	L. Sin.	′	P. P.			

LOGARITHMS OF THE TRIGONOMETRIC FUNCTIONS

'	L. Sin.	d.	L. Tan.	c.d.	L. Cot.	L. Cos.	'
0	9.14 356	89	9.14 780	92	0.85 220	9.99 575̄	60
1	9.14 445̄	90	9.14 872	91	0.85 128	9.99 574̄	59
2	9.14 535̄	89	9.14 963	91	0.85 037	9.99 572	58
3	9.14 624	90	9.15 054	91	0.84 946	9.99 570	57
4	9.14 714	89	9.15 145̄	91	0.84 855̄	9.99 568	56
5	9.14 803	88	9.15 236	91	0.84 764	9.99 566	55
6	9.14 891	89	9.15 327	90	0.84 673	9.99 565̄	54
7	9.14 980	89	9.15 417	91	0.84 583	9.99 563	53
8	9.15 069	88	9.15 508	90	0.84 492	9.99 561	52
9	9.15 157	88	9.15 598	90	0.84 402	9.99 559	51
10	9.15 245̄	88	9.15 688	89	0.84 312	9.99 557	50
11	9.15 333	88	9.15 777	90	0.84 223	9.99 556	49
12	9.15 421	87	9.15 867	89	0.84 133	9.99 554	48
13	9.15 508	88	9.15 956	90	0.84 044	9.99 552	47
14	9.15 596	87	9.16 046	89	0.83 954	9.99 550̄	46
15	9.15 683	87	9.16 135̄	89	0.83 865̄	9.99 548	45
16	9.15 770	87	9.16 224	88	0.83 776	9.99 546	44
17	9.15 857	87	9.16 312	89	0.83 688	9.99 545̄	43
18	9.15 944	86	9.16 401	88	0.83 599	9.99 543	42
19	9.16 030	86	9.16 489	88	0.83 511	9.99 541	41
20	9.16 116	87	9.16 577	88	0.83 423	9.99 539	40
21	9.16 203	86	9.16 665̄	88	0.83 335̄	9.99 537	39
22	9.16 289	85	9.16 753	88	0.83 247	9.99 535̄	38
23	9.16 374	86	9.16 841	87	0.83 159	9.99 533	37
24	9.16 460	85	9.16 928	88	0.83 072	9.99 532	36
25	9.16 545̄	86	9.17 016	87	0.82 984	9.99 530	35
26	9.16 631	85	9.17 103	87	0.82 897	9.99 528	34
27	9.16 716	85	9.17 190	87	0.82 810	9.99 526	33
28	9.16 801	85	9.17 277	86	0.82 723	9.99 524	32
29	9.16 886	84	9.17 363	87	0.82 637	9.99 522	31
30	9.16 970	85	9.17 450̄	86	0.82 550̄	9.99 520	30
31	9.17 055̄	84	9.17 536	86	0.82 464	9.99 518	29
32	9.17 139	84	9.17 622	86	0.82 378	9.99 515̄	28
33	9.17 223	84	9.17 708	86	0.82 292	9.99 515̄	27
34	9.17 307	84	9.17 794	86	0.82 206	9.99 513	26
35	9.17 391	83	9.17 880	85	0.82 120	9.99 511	25
36	9.17 474	84	9.17 965̄	85	0.82 035̄	9.99 509	24
37	9.17 558	83	9.18 051	85	0.81 949	9.99 507	23
38	9.17 641	83	9.18 136	85	0.81 864	9.99 506̄	22
39	9.17 724	83	9.18 221	85	0.81 779	9.99 503	21
40	9.17 807	83	9.18 306	85	0.81 694	9.99 501	20
41	9.17 890	83	9.18 391	84	0.81 609	9.99 499	19
42	9.17 973	82	9.18 475̄	85	0.81 525̄	9.99 497	18
43	9.18 055̄	82	9.18 560	84	0.81 440	9.99 495̄	17
44	9.18 137	83	9.18 644	84	0.81 356	9.99 494	16
45	9.18 220	82	9.18 728	84	0.81 272	9.99 492	15
46	9.18 302	81	9.18 812	84	0.81 188	9.99 490	14
47	9.18 383	82	9.18 896	83	0.81 104	9.99 488	13
48	9.18 465̄	82	9.18 979	84	0.81 021	9.99 486	12
49	9.18 547	81	9.19 063	83	0.80 937	9.99 484	11
50	9.18 628	81	9.19 146	83	0.80 854	9.99 482	10
51	9.18 709	81	9.19 229	83	0.80 771	9.99 480	9
52	9.18 790	81	9.19 312	83	0.80 688	9.99 478	8
53	9.18 871	81	9.19 395̄	83	0.80 605̄	9.99 476	7
54	9.18 952	81	9.19 478	83	0.80 522	9.99 474	6
55	9.19 033	80	9.19 561	82	0.80 439	9.99 472	5
56	9.19 113	80	9.19 643	82	0.80 357	9.99 470	4
57	9.19 193	80	9.19 725̄	82	0.80 275̄	9.99 468	3
58	9.19 273	80	9.19 807	82	0.80 193	9.99 466	2
59	9.19 353	80	9.19 889	82	0.80 111	9.99 464	1
60	9.19 433		9.19 971		0.80 029	9.99 462	0
'	L. Cos.	d.	L. Cot.	c.d.	L. Tan.	L. Sin.	'

P. P.

''	92	91	90
1	1.5	1.5	1.5
2	3.1	3.0	3.0
3	4.6	4.6	4.5
4	6.1	6.1	6.0
5	7.7	7.6	7.5
6	9.2	9.1	9.0
7	10.7	10.6	10.5
8	12.3	12.1	12.0
9	13.8	13.6	13.5
10	15.3	15.2	15.0
20	30.7	30.3	30.0
30	46.0	45.5̄	45.0
40	61.3	60.7	60.0
50	76.7	75.8	75.0

''	89	88	87
1	1.5	1.5	1.4
2	3.0	2.9	2.9
3	4.4	4.4	4.4
4	5.9	5.9	5.8
5	7.4	7.3	7.2
6	8.9	8.8	8.7
7	10.4	10.3	10.2
8	11.9	11.7	11.6
9	13.4	13.2	13.0
10	14.8	14.7	14.5̄
20	29.7	29.3	29.0
30	44.5̄	44.0	43.5̄
40	59.3	58.7	58.0
50	74.2	73.3	72.5̄

''	86	85	84
1	1.4	1.4	1.4
2	2.9	2.8	2.8
3	4.3	4.2	4.2
4	5.7	5.7	5.6
5	7.2	7.1	7.0
6	8.6	8.5̄	8.4
7	10.0	9.9	9.8
8	11.5̄	11.3	11.2
9	12.9	12.8	12.6
10	14.3	14.2	14.0
20	28.7	28.3	28.0
30	43.0	42.5̄	42.0
40	57.3	56.7	56.0
50	71.7	70.8	70.0

''	83	82	81
1	1.4	1.4	1.4
2	2.8	2.7	2.7
3	4.2	4.1	4.0
4	5.5̄	5.5̄	5.4
5	6.9	6.8	6.8
6	8.3	8.2	8.1
7	9.7	9.6	9.4
8	11.1	10.9	10.8
9	12.4	12.3	12.2
10	13.8	13.7	13.5̄
20	27.7	27.3	27.0
30	41.5̄	41.0	40.5̄
40	55.3	54.7	54.0
50	69.2	68.3	67.5̄

′	L. Sin.	d.	L. Tan.	c.d.	L. Cot.	L. Cos.	′
0	9.19 433	80	9.19 971	82	0.80 029	9.99 462	60
1	9.19 513	79	9.20 053	81	0.79 947	9.99 460	59
2	9.19 592	80	9.20 134	82	0.79 866	9.99 458	58
3	9.19 672	79	9.20 216	81	0.79 784	9.99 456	57
4	9.19 751	79	9.20 297	81	0.79 703	9.99 454	56
5	9.19 830	79	9.20 378	81	0.79 622	9.99 452	55
6	9.19 909	79	9.20 459	81	0.79 541	9.99 450	54
7	9.19 988	79	9.20 540	81	0.79 460	9.99 448	53
8	9.20 067	78	9.20 621	80	0.79 379	9.99 446	52
9	9.20 145	78	9.20 701	80	0.79 299	9.99 444	51
10	9.20 223	79	9.20 782	80	0.79 218	9.99 442	50
11	9.20 302	78	9.20 862	80	0.79 138	9.99 440	49
12	9.20 380	78	9.20 942	80	0.79 058	9.99 438	48
13	9.20 458	77	9.21 022	80	0.78 978	9.99 436	47
14	9.20 535	78	9.21 102	80	0.78 898	9.99 434	46
15	9.20 613	78	9.21 182	79	0.78 818	9.99 432	45
16	9.20 691	77	9.21 261	80	0.78 739	9.99 429	44
17	9.20 768	77	9.21 341	79	0.78 659	9.99 427	43
18	9.20 845	77	9.21 420	79	0.78 580	9.99 425	42
19	9.20 922	77	9.21 499	79	0.78 501	9.99 423	41
20	9.20 999	77	9.21 578	79	0.78 422	9.99 421	40
21	9.21 076	77	9.21 657	79	0.78 343	9.99 419	39
22	9.21 153	76	9.21 736	78	0.78 264	9.99 417	38
23	9.21 229	77	9.21 814	79	0.78 186	9.99 415	37
24	9.21 306	76	9.21 893	78	0.78 107	9.99 413	36
25	9.21 382	76	9.21 971	78	0.78 029	9.99 411	35
26	9.21 458	76	9.22 049	78	0.77 951	9.99 409	34
27	9.21 534	76	9.22 127	78	0.77 873	9.99 407	33
28	9.21 610	75	9.22 205	78	0.77 795	9.99 404	32
29	9.21 685	76	9.22 283	78	0.77 717	9.99 402	31
30	9.21 761	75	9.22 361	77	0.77 639	9.99 400	30
31	9.21 836	76	9.22 438	78	0.77 562	9.99 398	29
32	9.21 912	75	9.22 516	77	0.77 484	9.99 396	28
33	9.21 987	75	9.22 593	77	0.77 407	9.99 394	27
34	9.22 062	75	9.22 670	77	0.77 330	9.99 392	26
35	9.22 137	74	9.22 747	77	0.77 253	9.99 390	25
36	9.22 211	75	9.22 824	77	0.77 176	9.99 388	24
37	9.22 286	75	9.22 901	76	0.77 099	9.99 385	23
38	9.22 361	74	9.22 977	77	0.77 023	9.99 383	22
39	9.22 435	74	9.23 054	76	0.76 946	9.99 381	21
40	9.22 509	74	9.23 130	76	0.76 870	9.99 379	20
41	9.22 583	74	9.23 206	77	0.76 794	9.99 377	19
42	9.22 657	74	9.23 283	76	0.76 717	9.99 375	18
43	9.22 731	74	9.23 359	76	0.76 641	9.99 372	17
44	9.22 805	73	9.23 435	75	0.76 565	9.99 370	16
45	9.22 878	74	9.23 510	76	0.76 490	9.99 368	15
46	9.22 952	73	9.23 586	75	0.76 414	9.99 366	14
47	9.23 025	73	9.23 661	76	0.76 339	9.99 364	13
48	9.23 098	73	9.23 737	75	0.76 263	9.99 362	12
49	9.23 171	73	9.23 812	75	0.76 188	9.99 359	11
50	9.23 244	73	9.23 887	75	0.76 113	9.99 357	10
51	9.23 317	73	9.23 962	75	0.76 038	9.99 355	9
52	9.23 390	72	9.24 037	75	0.75 963	9.99 353	8
53	9.23 462	73	9.24 112	74	0.75 888	9.99 351	7
54	9.23 535	72	9.24 186	75	0.75 814	9.99 348	6
55	9.23 607	72	9.24 261	74	0.75 739	9.99 346	5
56	9.23 679	73	9.24 335	75	0.75 665	9.99 344	4
57	9.23 752	71	9.24 410	74	0.75 590	9.99 342	3
58	9.23 823	72	9.24 484	74	0.75 516	9.99 340	2
59	9.23 895	72	9.24 558	74	0.75 442	9.99 337	1
60	9.23 967		9.24 632		0.75 368	9.99 335	0

P. P.

	80	79	78	77
1	1.3	1.3	1.3	1.3
2	2.7	2.6	2.6	2.6
3	4.0	4.0	3.9	3.8
4	5.3	5.3	5.2	5.1
5	6.7	6.6	6.5	6.4
6	8.0	7.9	7.8	7.7
7	9.3	9.2	9.1	9.0
8	10.7	10.5	10.4	10.3
9	12.0	11.8	11.7	11.6
10	13.3	13.2	13.0	12.8
20	26.7	26.3	26.0	25.7
30	40.0	39.5	39.0	38.5
40	53.3	52.7	52.0	51.3
50	66.7	65.8	65.0	64.2

	76	75	74	73
1	1.3	1.2	1.2	1.2
2	2.5	2.5	2.5	2.4
3	3.8	3.8	3.7	3.6
4	5.1	5.0	4.9	4.9
5	6.3	6.2	6.2	6.1
6	7.6	7.5	7.4	7.3
7	8.9	8.8	8.6	8.5
8	10.1	10.0	9.9	9.7
9	11.4	11.2	11.1	11.0
10	12.7	12.5	12.3	12.2
20	25.3	25.0	24.7	24.3
30	38.0	37.5	37.0	36.5
40	50.7	50.0	49.3	48.7
50	63.3	62.5	61.7	60.8

	72	71	3	2
1	1.2	1.2	0.0	0.0
2	2.4	2.4	0.1	0.1
3	3.6	3.6	0.2	0.1
4	4.8	4.7	0.2	0.1
5	6.0	5.9	0.2	0.2
6	7.2	7.1	0.3	0.2
7	8.4	8.3	0.4	0.2
8	9.6	9.5	0.4	0.3
9	10.8	10.6	0.4	0.3
10	12.0	11.8	0.5	0.3
20	24.0	23.7	1.0	0.7
30	36.0	35.5	1.5	1.0
40	48.0	47.3	2.0	1.3
50	60.0	59.2	2.5	1.7

3	3	3
79	**78**	**77**
13.2	13.0	12.8
39.5	39.0	38.5
65.8	65.0	64.2

3	3	3
76	**75**	**74**
12.7	12.5	12.3
38.0	37.5	37.0
63.3	62.5	61.7

′	L. Cos.	d.	L. Cot.	c.d.	L. Tan.	L. Sin.	′	P. P.

LOGARITHMS OF THE TRIGONOMETRIC FUNCTIONS

′	L. Sin.	d.	L. Tan.	c.d.	L. Cot.	L. Cos.	d.	′
0	9.23 967	72	9.24 632	74	0.75 368	9.99 335	2	60
1	9.24 039	71	9.24 706	73	0.75 294	9.99 333	2	59
2	9.24 110	71	9.24 779	74	0.75 221	9.99 331	3	58
3	9.24 181	72	9.24 853	73	0.75 147	9.99 328	2	57
4	9.24 253	71	9.24 926	74	0.75 074	9.99 326	2	56
5	9.24 324	71	9.25 000	73	0.75 000	9.99 324	2	55
6	9.24 395	71	9.25 073	73	0.74 927	9.99 322	3	54
7	9.24 466	70	9.25 146	73	0.74 854	9.99 319	2	53
8	9.24 536	71	9.25 219	73	0.74 781	9.99 317	2	52
9	9.24 607	70	9.25 292	73	0.74 708	9.99 315	2	51
10	9.24 677	71	9.25 365	72	0.74 635	9.99 313	3	50
11	9.24 748	70	9.25 437	73	0.74 563	9.99 310	2	49
12	9.24 818	70	9.25 510	72	0.74 490	9.99 308	2	48
13	9.24 888	70	9.25 582	73	0.74 418	9.99 306	2	47
14	9.24 958	70	9.25 655	72	0.74 345	9.99 304	3	46
15	9.25 028	70	9.25 727	72	0.74 273	9.99 301	2	45
16	9.25 098	70	9.25 799	72	0.74 201	9.99 299	2	44
17	9.25 168	69	9.25 871	72	0.74 129	9.99 297	3	43
18	9.25 237	70	9.25 943	72	0.74 057	9.99 294	2	42
19	9.25 307	69	9.26 015	71	0.73 985	9.99 292	2	41
20	9.25 376	69	9.26 086	72	0.73 914	9.99 290	2	40
21	9.25 445	69	9.26 158	71	0.73 842	9.99 288	3	39
22	9.25 514	69	9.26 229	72	0.73 771	9.99 285	2	38
23	9.25 583	69	9.26 301	71	0.73 699	9.99 283	2	37
24	9.25 652	69	9.26 372	71	0.73 628	9.99 281	3	36
25	9.25 721	69	9.26 443	71	0.73 557	9.99 278	2	35
26	9.25 790	68	9.26 514	71	0.73 486	9.99 276	2	34
27	9.25 858	69	9.26 585	70	0.73 415	9.99 274	3	33
28	9.25 927	68	9.26 655	71	0.73 345	9.99 271	2	32
29	9.25 995	68	9.26 726	71	0.73 274	9.99 269	2	31
30	9.26 063	68	9.26 797	70	0.73 203	9.99 267	3	30
31	9.26 131	68	9.26 867	70	0.73 133	9.99 264	2	29
32	9.26 199	68	9.26 937	71	0.73 063	9.99 262	2	28
33	9.26 267	68	9.27 008	70	0.72 992	9.99 260	3	27
34	9.26 335	68	9.27 078	70	0.72 922	9.99 257	2	26
35	9.26 403	67	9.27 148	70	0.72 852	9.99 255	3	25
36	9.26 470	68	9.27 218	70	0.72 782	9.99 252	2	24
37	9.26 538	67	9.27 288	69	0.72 712	9.99 250	2	23
38	9.26 605	67	9.27 357	70	0.72 643	9.99 248	3	22
39	9.26 672	67	9.27 427	69	0.72 573	9.99 245	2	21
40	9.26 739	67	9.27 496	70	0.72 504	9.99 243	2	20
41	9.26 806	67	9.27 566	69	0.72 434	9.99 241	3	19
42	9.26 873	67	9.27 635	69	0.72 365	9.99 238	2	18
43	9.26 940	67	9.27 704	69	0.72 296	9.99 236	3	17
44	9.27 007	66	9.27 773	69	0.72 227	9.99 233	2	16
45	9.27 073	67	9.27 842	69	0.72 158	9.99 231	2	15
46	9.27 140	66	9.27 911	69	0.72 089	9.99 229	3	14
47	9.27 206	67	9.27 980	69	0.72 020	9.99 226	2	13
48	9.27 273	66	9.28 049	68	0.71 951	9.99 224	3	12
49	9.27 339	66	9.28 117	69	0.71 883	9.99 221	2	11
50	9.27 405	66	9.28 186	68	0.71 814	9.99 219	2	10
51	9.27 471	66	9.28 254	69	0.71 746	9.99 217	3	9
52	9.27 537	65	9.28 323	68	0.71 677	9.99 214	2	8
53	9.27 602	66	9.28 391	68	0.71 609	9.99 212	3	7
54	9.27 668	66	9.28 459	68	0.71 541	9.99 209	2	6
55	9.27 734	65	9.28 527	68	0.71 473	9.99 207	3	5
56	9.27 799	65	9.28 595	67	0.71 405	9.99 204	2	4
57	9.27 864	66	9.28 662	68	0.71 338	9.99 202	2	3
58	9.27 930	65	9.28 730	68	0.71 270	9.99 200	3	2
59	9.27 995	65	9.28 798	67	0.71 202	9.99 197	2	1
60	9.28 060		9.28 865		0.71 135	9.99 195		0

P. P.

″	74	73	72
1	1.2	1.2	1.2
2	2.5	2.4	2.4
3	3.7	3.6	3.6
4	4.9	4.9	4.8
5	6.2	6.1	6.0
6	7.4	7.3	7.2
7	8.6	8.5	8.4
8	9.9	9.7	9.6
9	11.1	11.0	10.8
10	12.3	12.2	12.0
20	24.7	24.3	24.0
30	37.0	36.5	36.0
40	49.3	48.7	48.0
50	61.7	60.8	60.0

″	71	70	69
1	1.2	1.2	1.2
2	2.4	2.3	2.3
3	3.6	3.5	3.4
4	4.7	4.7	4.6
5	5.9	5.8	5.8
6	7.1	7.0	6.9
7	8.3	8.2	8.0
8	9.5	9.3	9.2
9	10.6	10.5	10.4
10	11.8	11.7	11.5
20	23.7	23.3	23.0
30	35.5	35.0	34.5
40	47.3	46.7	46.0
50	59.2	58.3	57.5

″	68	67	66
1	1.1	1.1	1.1
2	2.3	2.2	2.2
3	3.4	3.4	3.3
4	4.5	4.5	4.4
5	5.7	5.6	5.5
6	6.8	6.7	6.6
7	7.9	7.8	7.7
8	9.1	8.9	8.8
9	10.2	10.0	9.9
10	11.3	11.2	11.0
20	22.7	22.3	22.0
30	34.0	33.5	33.0
40	45.3	44.7	44.0
50	56.7	55.8	55.0

	3	3	3
	74	73	72
0			
1	12.3	12.2	12.0
2	37.0	36.5	36.0
3	61.7	60.8	60.0

	3	3	3	3
	71	70	69	68
0				
1	11.8	11.7	11.5	11.3
2	35.5	35.0	34.5	34.0
3	59.2	58.3	57.5	56.7

′	L. Cos.	d.	L. Cot.	c.d.	L. Tan.	L. Sin.	d.	′	P. P.

LOGARITHMS OF THE TRIGONOMETRIC FUNCTIONS

′	L. Sin.	d.	L. Tan.	c.d.	L. Cot.	L. Cos.	d.	′
0	9.28 060	65	9.28 865	68	0.71 135	9.99 195	3	60
1	9.28 125	65	9.28 933	67	0.71 067	9.99 192	2	59
2	9.28 190	64	9.29 000	67	0.71 000	9.99 190	3	58
3	9.28 254	65	9.29 067	67	0.70 933	9.99 187	2	57
4	9.28 319	65	9.29 134	67	0.70 866	9.99 185	3	56
5	9.28 384	64	9.29 201	67	0.70 799	9.99 182	2	55
6	9.28 448	64	9.29 268	67	0.70 732	9.99 180	3	54
7	9.28 512	65	9.29 335	67	0.70 665	9.99 177	2	53
8	9.28 577	64	9.29 402	66	0.70 598	9.99 175	3	52
9	9.28 641	64	9.29 468	67	0.70 532	9.99 172	2	51
10	9.28 705	64	9.29 535	66	0.70 465	9.99 170	3	50
11	9.28 769	64	9.29 601	67	0.70 399	9.99 167	2	49
12	9.28 833	64	9.29 668	66	0.70 332	9.99 165	3	48
13	9.28 896	64	9.29 734	66	0.70 266	9.99 162	2	47
14	9.28 960	64	9.29 800	66	0.70 200	9.99 160	3	46
15	9.29 024	63	9.29 866	66	0.70 134	9.99 157	2	45
16	9.29 087	63	9.29 932	66	0.70 068	9.99 155	3	44
17	9.29 150	64	9.29 998	66	0.70 002	9.99 152	2	43
18	9.29 214	63	9.30 064	66	0.69 936	9.99 150	3	42
19	9.29 277	63	9.30 130	65	0.69 870	9.99 147	2	41
20	9.29 340	63	9.30 195	66	0.69 805	9.99 145	3	40
21	9.29 403	63	9.30 261	65	0.69 739	9.99 142	2	39
22	9.29 466	63	9.30 326	65	0.69 674	9.99 140	3	38
23	9.29 529	62	9.30 391	66	0.69 609	9.99 137	2	37
24	9.29 591	63	9.30 457	65	0.69 543	9.99 135	3	36
25	9.29 654	62	9.30 522	65	0.69 478	9.99 132	2	35
26	9.29 716	63	9.30 587	65	0.69 413	9.99 130	3	34
27	9.29 779	62	9.30 652	65	0.69 348	9.99 127	3	33
28	9.29 841	62	9.30 717	65	0.69 283	9.99 124	2	32
29	9.29 903	63	9.30 782	64	0.69 218	9.99 122	3	31
30	9.29 966	62	9.30 846	65	0.69 154	9.99 119	2	30
31	9.30 028	62	9.30 911	64	0.69 089	9.99 117	3	29
32	9.30 090	61	9.30 975	65	0.69 025	9.99 114	2	28
33	9.30 151	62	9.31 040	64	0.68 960	9.99 112	3	27
34	9.30 213	62	9.31 104	64	0.68 896	9.99 109	3	26
35	9.30 275	61	9.31 168	65	0.68 832	9.99 106	2	25
36	9.30 336	62	9.31 233	64	0.68 767	9.99 104	3	24
37	9.30 398	61	9.31 297	64	0.68 703	9.99 101	3	23
38	9.30 459	62	9.31 361	64	0.68 639	9.99 099	3	22
39	9.30 521	61	9.31 425	64	0.68 575	9.99 096	3	21
40	9.30 582	61	9.31 489	63	0.68 511	9.99 093	2	20
41	9.30 643	61	9.31 552	64	0.68 448	9.99 091	3	19
42	9.30 704	61	9.31 616	63	0.68 384	9.99 088	2	18
43	9.30 765	61	9.31 679	64	0.68 321	9.99 086	3	17
44	9.30 826	61	9.31 743	63	0.68 257	9.99 083	3	16
45	9.30 887	60	9.31 806	64	0.68 194	9.99 080	2	15
46	9.30 947	61	9.31 870	63	0.68 130	9.99 078	3	14
47	9.31 008	60	9.31 933	63	0.68 067	9.99 075	3	13
48	9.31 068	61	9.31 996	63	0.68 004	9.99 072	2	12
49	9.31 129	60	9.32 059	63	0.67 941	9.99 070	3	11
50	9.31 189	61	9.32 122	63	0.67 878	9.99 067	3	10
51	9.31 250	60	9.32 185	63	0.67 815	9.99 064	2	9
52	9.31 310	60	9.32 248	63	0.67 752	9.99 062	3	8
53	9.31 370	60	9.32 311	62	0.67 689	9.99 059	3	7
54	9.31 430	60	9.32 373	63	0.67 627	9.99 056	2	6
55	9.31 490	59	9.32 436	62	0.67 564	9.99 054	3	5
56	9.31 549	60	9.32 498	63	0.67 502	9.99 051	3	4
57	9.31 609	60	9.32 561	62	0.67 439	9.99 048	3	3
58	9.31 669	59	9.32 623	62	0.67 377	9.99 046	2	2
59	9.31 728	60	9.32 685	62	0.67 315	9.99 043	3	1
60	9.31 788		9.32 747		0.67 253	9.99 040		0

P. P.

″	65	64	63
1	1.1	1.1	1.0
2	2.2	2.1	2.1
3	3.2	3.2	3.2
4	4.3	4.3	4.2
5	5.4	5.3	5.2
6	6.5	6.4	6.3
7	7.6	7.5	7.4
8	8.7	8.5	8.4
9	9.8	9.6	9.4
10	10.8	10.7	10.5
20	21.7	21.3	21.0
30	32.5	32.0	31.5
40	43.3	42.7	42.0
50	54.2	53.3	52.5

″	62	61	60
1	1.0	1.0	1.0
2	2.1	2.0	2.0
3	3.1	3.0	3.0
4	4.1	4.1	4.0
5	5.2	5.1	5.0
6	6.2	6.1	6.0
7	7.2	7.1	7.0
8	8.3	8.1	8.0
9	9.3	9.2	9.0
10	10.3	10.2	10.0
20	20.7	20.3	20.0
30	31.0	30.5	30.0
40	41.3	40.7	40.0
50	51.7	50.8	50.0

″	59	3	2
1	1.0	0.0	0.0
2	2.0	0.1	0.1
3	3.0	0.2	0.1
4	3.9	0.2	0.1
5	4.9	0.2	0.2
6	5.9	0.3	0.2
7	6.9	0.4	0.2
8	7.9	0.4	0.3
9	8.8	0.4	0.3
10	9.8	0.5	0.3
20	19.7	1.0	0.7
30	29.5	1.5	1.0
40	39.3	2.0	1.3
50	49.2	2.5	1.7

	3	3	3
	67	66	65
0			
1	11.2	11.0	10.8
2	33.5	33.0	32.5
3	55.8	55.0	54.2

	3	3	3
	64	63	62
0			
1	10.7	10.5	10.3
2	32.0	31.5	31.0
3	53.3	52.5	51.7

| ′ | L. Cos. | d. | L. Cot. | c.d. | L. Tan. | L. Sin. | d. | ′ | P. P. |

LOGARITHMS OF THE TRIGONOMETRIC FUNCTIONS

'	L. Sin.	d.	L. Tan.	c.d.	L. Cot.	L. Cos.	d.	'
0	9.31 788	59	9.32 747	63	0.67 253	9.99 040	2	60
1	9.31 847	60	9.32 810	62	0.67 190	9.99 038	3	59
2	9.31 907	59	9.32 872	62	0.67 128	9.99 035	2	58
3	9.31 966	59	9.32 933	62	0.67 067	9.99 032	2	57
4	9.32 025	59	9.32 995	62	0.67 005	9.99 030	3	56
5	9.32 084	59	9.33 057	62	0.66 943	9.99 027	3	55
6	9.32 143	59	9.33 119	61	0.66 881	9.99 024	3	54
7	9.32 202	59	9.33 180	62	0.66 820	9.99 022	3	53
8	9.32 261	58	9.33 242	61	0.66 758	9.99 019	3	52
9	9.32 319	59	9.33 303	62	0.66 697	9.99 016	3	51
10	9.32 378	59	9.33 365	61	0.66 635	9.99 013	2	50
11	9.32 437	58	9.33 426	61	0.66 574	9.99 011	3	49
12	9.32 495	58	9.33 487	61	0.66 513	9.99 008	3	48
13	9.32 553	59	9.33 548	61	0.66 452	9.99 005	3	47
14	9.32 612	58	9.33 609	61	0.66 391	9.99 002	2	46
15	9.32 670	58	9.33 670	61	0.66 330	9.99 000	3	45
16	9.32 728	58	9.33 731	61	0.66 269	9.98 997	3	44
17	9.32 786	58	9.33 792	61	0.66 208	9.98 994	3	43
18	9.32 844	58	9.33 853	60	0.66 147	9.98 991	2	42
19	9.32 902	58	9.33 913	61	0.66 087	9.98 989	3	41
20	9.32 960	58	9.33 974	60	0.66 026	9.98 986	3	40
21	9.33 018	57	9.34 034	61	0.65 966	9.98 983	3	39
22	9.33 075	58	9.34 095	60	0.65 905	9.98 980	2	38
23	9.33 133	57	9.34 155	60	0.65 845	9.98 978	3	37
24	9.33 190	58	9.34 215	61	0.65 785	9.98 975	3	36
25	9.33 248	57	9.34 276	60	0.65 724	9.98 972	3	35
26	9.33 305	57	9.34 336	60	0.65 664	9.98 969	2	34
27	9.33 362	58	9.34 396	60	0.65 604	9.98 967	3	33
28	9.33 420	57	9.34 456	60	0.65 544	9.98 964	3	32
29	9.33 477	57	9.34 516	60	0.65 484	9.98 961	3	31
30	9.33 534	57	9.34 576	59	0.65 424	9.98 958	3	30
31	9.33 591	56	9.34 635	60	0.65 365	9.98 955	2	29
32	9.33 647	57	9.34 695	60	0.65 305	9.98 953	3	28
33	9.33 704	57	9.34 755	59	0.65 245	9.98 950	3	27
34	9.33 761	57	9.34 814	60	0.65 186	9.98 947	3	26
35	9.33 818	56	9.34 874	59	0.65 126	9.98 944	3	25
36	9.33 874	57	9.34 933	59	0.65 067	9.98 941	3	24
37	9.33 931	56	9.34 992	59	0.65 008	9.98 938	2	23
38	9.33 987	56	9.35 051	60	0.64 949	9.98 936	3	22
39	9.34 043	57	9.35 111	59	0.64 889	9.98 933	3	21
40	9.34 100	56	9.35 170	59	0.64 830	9.98 930	3	20
41	9.34 156	56	9.35 229	59	0.64 771	9.98 927	3	19
42	9.34 212	56	9.35 288	59	0.64 712	9.98 924	3	18
43	9.34 268	56	9.35 347	59	0.64 653	9.98 921	2	17
44	9.34 324	56	9.35 405	59	0.64 595	9.98 919	3	16
45	9.34 380	56	9.35 464	59	0.64 536	9.98 916	3	15
46	9.34 436	55	9.35 523	58	0.64 477	9.98 913	3	14
47	9.34 491	56	9.35 581	59	0.64 419	9.98 910	3	13
48	9.34 547	55	9.35 640	58	0.64 360	9.98 907	3	12
49	9.34 602	56	9.35 698	59	0.64 302	9.98 904	3	11
50	9.34 658	55	9.35 757	58	0.64 243	9.98 901	3	10
51	9.34 713	56	9.35 815	58	0.64 185	9.98 898	2	9
52	9.34 769	55	9.35 873	58	0.64 127	9.98 896	3	8
53	9.34 824	55	9.35 931	58	0.64 069	9.98 893	3	7
54	9.34 879	55	9.35 989	58	0.64 011	9.98 890	3	6
55	9.34 934	55	9.36 047	58	0.63 953	9.98 887	3	5
56	9.34 989	55	9.36 105	58	0.63 895	9.98 884	3	4
57	9.35 044	55	9.36 163	58	0.63 837	9.98 881	3	3
58	9.35 099	55	9.36 221	58	0.63 779	9.98 878	3	2
59	9.35 154	55	9.36 279	57	0.63 721	9.98 875	3	1
60	9.35 209		9.36 336		0.63 664	9.98 872		0

P. P.

	63	62	61
1	1.0	1.0	1.0
2	2.1	2.1	2.0
3	3.2	3.1	3.0
4	4.2	4.1	4.1
5	5.2	5.2	5.1
6	6.3	6.2	6.1
7	7.4	7.2	7.1
8	8.4	8.3	8.1
9	9.4	9.3	9.2
10	10.5	10.3	10.2
20	21.0	20.7	20.3
30	31.5	31.0	30.5
40	42.0	41.3	40.7
50	52.5	51.7	50.8

	60	59	58
1	1.0	1.0	1.0
2	2.0	2.0	1.9
3	3.0	3.0	2.9
4	4.0	3.9	3.9
5	5.0	4.9	4.8
6	6.0	5.9	5.8
7	7.0	6.9	6.8
8	8.0	7.9	7.7
9	9.0	8.8	8.7
10	10.0	9.8	9.7
20	20.0	19.7	19.3
30	30.0	29.5	29.0
40	40.0	39.3	38.7
50	50.0	49.2	48.3

	57	56	55
1	1.0	0.9	0.9
2	1.9	1.9	1.8
3	2.8	2.8	2.8
4	3.8	3.7	3.7
5	4.8	4.7	4.6
6	5.7	5.6	5.5
7	6.6	6.5	6.4
8	7.6	7.5	7.3
9	8.6	8.4	8.2
10	9.5	9.3	9.2
20	19.0	18.7	18.3
30	28.5	28.0	27.5
40	38.0	37.3	36.7
50	47.5	46.7	45.8

	3	3	3
	62	61	60
0	10.3	10.2	10.0
1	31.0	30.5	30.0
2	51.7	50.8	50.0

	3	3	3
	59	58	57
0	9.8	9.7	9.5
1	29.5	29.0	28.5
2	49.2	48.3	47.5

'	L. Cos.	d.	L. Cot.	c.d.	L. Tan.	L. Sin.	d.	'	P. P.

LOGARITHMS OF THE TRIGONOMETRIC FUNCTIONS

'	L. Sin.	d.	L. Tan.	c.d.	L. Cot.	L. Cos.	d.	'	P. P.
0	9.35 209	54	9.36 336	58	0.63 664	9.98 872	3	60	
1	9.35 263	55	9.36 394	58	0.63 606	9.98 869	2	59	**57** **56** **55**
2	9.35 318	55	9.36 452	57	0.63 548	9.98 867	3	58	1 1.0 0.9 0.9
3	9.35 373	54	9.36 509	57	0.63 491	9.98 864	3	57	2 1.9 1.9 1.8
4	9.35 427	54	9.36 566	58	0.63 434	9.98 861	3	56	3 2.8 2.8 2.8
									4 3.8 3.7 3.7
5	9.35 481	55	9.36 624	57	0.63 376	9.98 858	3	55	
6	9.35 536	54	9.36 681	57	0.63 319	9.98 855	3	54	5 4.8 4.7 4.6
7	9.35 590	54	9.36 738	57	0.63 262	9.98 852	3	53	6 5.7 5.6 5.5
8	9.35 644	54	9.36 795	57	0.63 205	9.98 849	3	52	7 6.6 6.5 6.4
9	9.35 698	54	9.36 852	57	0.63 148	9.98 846	3	51	8 7.6 7.5 7.3
									9 8.6 8.4 8.2
10	9.35 752	54	9.36 909	57	0.63 091	9.98 843	3	50	
11	9.35 806	54	9.36 966	57	0.63 034	9.98 840	3	49	10 9.5 9.3 9.2
12	9.35 860	54	9.37 023	57	0.62 977	9.98 837	3	48	20 19.0 18.7 18.3
13	9.35 914	54	9.37 080	57	0.62 920	9.98 834	3	47	30 28.5 28.0 27.5
14	9.35 968	54	9.37 137	56	0.62 863	9.98 831	3	46	40 38.0 37.3 36.7
									50 47.5 46.7 45.8
15	9.36 022	53	9.37 193	57	0.62 807	9.98 828	3	45	
16	9.36 075	54	9.37 250	56	0.62 750	9.98 825	3	44	**54** **53** **52**
17	9.36 129	53	9.37 306	57	0.62 694	9.98 822	3	43	1 0.9 0.9 0.9
18	9.36 182	54	9.37 363	56	0.62 637	9.98 819	3	42	2 1.8 1.8 1.7
19	9.36 236	53	9.37 419	57	0.62 581	9.98 816	3	41	3 2.7 2.6 2.6
									4 3.6 3.5 3.5
20	9.36 289	53	9.37 476	56	0.62 524	9.98 813	3	40	
21	9.36 342	53	9.37 532	56	0.62 468	9.98 810	3	39	5 4.5 4.4 4.3
22	9.36 395	54	9.37 588	56	0.62 412	9.98 807	3	38	6 5.4 5.3 5.2
23	9.36 449	53	9.37 644	56	0.62 356	9.98 804	3	37	7 6.3 6.2 6.1
24	9.36 502	53	9.37 700	56	0.62 300	9.98 801	3	36	8 7.2 7.1 6.9
									9 8.1 8.0 7.8
25	9.36 555	53	9.37 756	56	0.62 244	9.98 798	3	35	
26	9.36 608	52	9.37 812	56	0.62 188	9.98 795	3	34	10 9.0 8.8 8.7
27	9.36 660	53	9.37 868	56	0.62 132	9.98 792	3	33	20 18.0 17.7 17.3
28	9.36 713	53	9.37 924	56	0.62 076	9.98 789	3	32	30 27 0 26.5 26.0
29	9.36 766	53	9.37 980	55	0.62 020	9.98 786	3	31	40 36.0 35.3 34.7
									50 45.0 44.2 43.3
30	9.36 819	52	9.38 035	56	0.61 965	9.98 783	3	30	
31	9.36 871	53	9.38 091	56	0.61 909	9.98 780	3	29	**51** **4** **3** **2**
32	9.36 924	52	9.38 147	55	0.61 853	9.98 777	3	28	1 0.8 0.1 0.0 0.0
33	9.36 976	52	9.38 202	55	0.61 798	9.98 774	3	27	2 1.7 0.1 0.1 0.1
34	9.37 028	53	9.38 257	56	0.61 743	9.98 771	3	26	3 2.6 0.2 0.2 0.1
									4 3.4 0.3 0.2 0.1
35	9.37 081	52	9.38 313	55	0.61 687	9.98 768	3	25	
36	9.37 133	52	9.38 368	55	0.61 632	9.98 765	3	24	5 4.2 0.3 0.2 0.2
37	9.37 185	52	9.38 423	56	0.61 577	9.98 762	3	23	6 5.1 0.4 0.3 0.2
38	9.37 237	52	9.38 479	55	0.61 521	9.98 759	3	22	7 6.0 0.5 0.4 0.2
39	9.37 289	52	9.38 534	55	0.61 466	9.98 756	3	21	8 6.8 0.5 0.4 0.3
									9 7.6 0.6 0.4 0.3
40	9.37 341	52	9.38 589	55	0.61 411	9.98 753	3	20	
41	9.37 393	52	9.38 644	55	0.61 356	9.98 750	4	19	10 8.5 0.7 0.5 0.3
42	9.37 445	52	9.38 699	55	0.61 301	9.98 746	3	18	20 17.0 1.3 1.0 0.7
43	9.37 497	52	9.38 754	54	0.61 246	9.98 743	3	17	30 25.5 2.0 1.5 1.0
44	9.37 549	51	9.38 808	55	0.61 192	9.98 740	3	16	40 34.0 2.7 2.0 1.3
									50 42.5 3.3 2.5 1.7
45	9.37 600	52	9.38 863	55	0.61 137	9.98 737	3	15	
46	9.37 652	51	9.38 918	54	0.61 082	9.98 734	3	14	**4** **4** **3** **3**
47	9.37 703	52	9.38 972	55	0.61 028	9.98 731	3	13	**55** **54** **58** **57**
48	9.37 755	51	9.39 027	55	0.60 973	9.98 728	3	12	
49	9.37 806	52	9.39 082	54	0.60 918	9.98 725	3	11	0 6.9 6.8 9.7 9.5
									1 20.6 20.2 29.0 28.5
50	9.37 858	51	9.39 136	54	0.60 864	9.98 722	3	10	2 34.4 33.8 48.3 47.5
51	9.37 909	51	9.39 190	55	0.60 810	9.98 719	4	9	3 48.1 47.2 — —
52	9.37 960	51	9.39 245	54	0.60 755	9.98 715	3	8	4
53	9.38 011	51	9.39 299	54	0.60 701	9.98 712	3	7	**3** **3** **3**
54	9.38 062	51	9.39 353	54	0.60 647	9.98 709	3	6	**56** **55** **54**
55	9.38 113	51	9.39 407	54	0.60 593	9.98 706	3	5	
56	9.38 164	51	9.39 461	54	0.60 539	9.98 703	3	4	
57	9.38 215	51	9.39 515	54	0.60 485	9.98 700	3	3	0 9.3 9.2 9.0
58	9.38 266	51	9.39 569	54	0.60 431	9.98 697	3	2	1 28.0 27.5 27.0
59	9.38 317	51	9.39 623	54	0.60 377	9.98 694	4	1	2 46.7 45.8 45.0
									3
60	9.38 368		9.39 677		0.60 323	9.98 690		0	
'	L. Cos.	d.	L. Cot.	c.d.	L. Tan.	L. Sin.	d.	'	P P.

14° (194°)   **(345°) 165°**

′	L. Sin.	d.	L. Tan.	c.d.	L. Cot.	L. Cos.	d.	′
0	9.38 368	50	9.39 677	54	0.60 323	9.98 690	3	60
1	9.38 418	51	9.39 731	54	0.60 269	9.98 687	3	59
2	9.38 469	50	9.39 785	53	0.60 215	9.98 684	3	58
3	9.38 519	51	9.39 838	54	0.60 162	9.98 681	3	57
4	9.38 570	50	9.39 892	53	0.60 108	9.98 678	3	56
5	9.38 620	50	9.39 945	54	0.60 055	9.98 675	4	55
6	9.38 670	51	9.39 999	53	0.60 001	9.98 671	4	54
7	9.38 721	50	9.40 052	54	0 59 948	9.98 668	3	53
8	9.38 771	50	9.40 106	53	0.59 894	9.98 665	3	52
9	9.38 821	50	9.40 159	53	0.59 841	9.98 662	3	51
10	9.38 871	50	9.40 212	54	0.59 788	9.98 659	3	50
11	9.38 921	50	9.40 266	53	0.59 734	9.98 656	3	49
12	9.38 971	50	9.40 319	53	0.59 681	9.98 652	3	48
13	9.39 021	50	9.40 372	53	0.59 628	9.98 649	3	47
14	9.39 071	50	9.40 425	53	0.59 575	9.98 646	3	46
15	9.39 121	49	9.40 478	53	0.59 522	9.98 643	3	45
16	9.39 170	50	9.40 531	53	0.59 469	9.98 640	4	44
17	9.39 220	50	9.40 584	52	0.59 416	9.98 636	3	43
18	9.39 270	49	9.40 636	53	0.59 364	9.98 633	3	42
19	9.39 319	50	9.40 689	53	0.59 311	9.98 630	3	41
20	9.39 369	49	9.40 742	53	0.59 258	9.98 627	4	40
21	9.39 418	49	9.40 795	52	0.59 205	9.98 623	3	39
22	9.39 467	50	9.40 847	53	0.59 153	9.98 620	3	38
23	9.39 517	49	9.40 900	52	0.59 100	9.98 617	3	37
24	9.39 566	49	9.40 952	53	0.59 048	9.98 614	4	36
25	9.39 615	49	9.41 005	52	0.58 995	9.98 610	3	35
26	9.39 664	49	9.41 057	52	0.58 943	9.98 607	3	34
27	9.39 713	49	9.41 109	52	0.58 891	9.98 604	3	33
28	9.39 762	49	9.41 161	53	0.58 839	9.98 601	3	32
29	9.39 811	49	9.41 214	52	0.58 786	9.98 597	3	31
30	9.39 860	49	9.41 266	52	0.58 734	9.98 594	3	30
31	9.39 909	49	9.41 318	52	0.58 682	9.98 591	3	29
32	9.39 958	48	9.41 370	52	0.58 630	9.98 588	3	28
33	9.40 006	49	9.41 422	52	0.58 578	9.98 584	3	27
34	9.40 055	48	9.41 474	52	0.58 526	9.98 581	3	26
35	9.40 103	49	9.41 526	52	0.58 474	9.98 578	4	25
36	9.40 152	48	9.41 578	51	0.58 422	9.98 574	3	24
37	9.40 200	49	9.41 629	52	0.58 371	9.98 571	3	23
38	9.40 249	48	9.41 681	52	0.58 319	9.98 568	3	22
39	9.40 297	49	9.41 733	51	0.58 267	9.98 565	4	21
40	9.40 346	48	9.41 784	52	0.58 216	9.98 561	3	20
41	9.40 394	48	9.41 836	51	0.58 164	9.98 558	3	19
42	9.40 442	48	9.41 887	52	0.58 113	9.98 555	4	18
43	9.40 490	48	9.41 939	51	0.58 061	9.98 551	3	17
44	9.40 538	48	9.41 990	51	0.58 010	9.98 548	3	16
45	9.40 586	48	9.42 041	52	0.57 959	9.98 545	4	15
46	9.40 634	48	9.42 093	51	0.57 907	9.98 541	3	14
47	9.40 682	48	9.42 144	51	0.57 856	9.98 538	3	13
48	9.40 730	48	9.42 195	51	0.57 805	9.98 535	4	12
49	9.40 778	47	9.42 246	51	0.57 754	9.98 531	3	11
50	9.40 825	48	9.42 297	51	0.57 703	9.98 528	3	10
51	9.40 873	48	9.42 348	51	0.57 652	9.98 525	4	9
52	9.40 921	47	9.42 399	51	0.57 601	9.98 521	3	8
53	9.40 968	48	9.42 450	51	0.57 550	9.98 518	3	7
54	9.41 016	47	9.42 501	51	0.57 499	9.98 515	4	6
55	9.41 063	48	9.42 552	51	0.57 448	9.98 511	3	5
56	9.41 111	47	9.42 603	50	0.57 397	9.98 508	3	4
57	9.41 158	47	9.42 653	51	0.57 347	9.98 505	4	3
58	9.41 205	47	9.42 704	51	0.57 296	9.98 501	3	2
59	9.41 252	48	9.42 755	50	0.57 245	9.98 498	4	1
60	9.41 300		9.42 805		0.57 195	9.98 494		0
	L. Cos.	d.	L. Cot.	c.d.	L. Tan.	L. Sin.	d.	′

P. P.

″	54	53	52
1	0.9	0.9	0.9
2	1.8	1.8	1.7
3	2.7	2.6	2.6
4	3.6	3.5	3.5
5	4.5	4.4	4.3
6	5.4	5.3	5.2
7	6.3	6.2	6.1
8	7.2	7.1	6.9
9	8.1	8.0	7.8
10	9.0	8.8	8.7
20	18.0	17.7	17.3
30	27.0	26.5	26.0
40	36.0	35.3	34.7
50	45.0	44.2	43.3

″	51	50	49
1	0.8	0.8	0.8
2	1.7	1.7	1.6
3	2.6	2.5	2.4
4	3.4	3.3	3.3
5	4.2	4.2	4.1
6	5.1	5.0	4.9
7	6.0	5.8	5.7
8	6.8	6.7	6.5
9	7.6	7.5	7.4
10	8.5	8.3	8.2
20	17.0	16.7	16.3
30	25.5	25.0	24.5
40	34.0	33.3	32.7
50	42.5	41.7	40.8

″	48	47	4	3
1	0.8	0.8	0.1	0.0
2	1.6	1.6	0.1	0.1
3	2.4	2.4	0.2	0.2
4	3.2	3.1	0.3	0.2
5	4.0	3.9	0.3	0.2
6	4.8	4.7	0.4	0.3
7	5.6	5.5	0.5	0.4
8	6.4	6.3	0.5	0.4
9	7.2	7.0	0.6	0.4
10	8.0	7.8	0.7	0.5
20	16.0	15.7	1.3	1.0
30	24.0	23.5	2.0	1.5
40	32.0	31.3	2.7	2.0
50	40.0	39.2	3.3	2.5

	4	4	4	4
	54	53	52	51
0	6.8	6.6	6.5	6.4
1	20.2	19.9	19.5	19.1
2	33.8	33.1	32.5	31.9
3	47.2	46.4	45.5	44.6

	3	3	3	3
	54	53	52	51
0	9.0	8.8	8.7	8.5
1	27.0	26.5	26.0	25.5
2	45.0	44.2	43.3	42.5

LOGARITHMS OF THE TRIGONOMETRIC FUNCTIONS

′	L. Sin.	d.	L. Tan.	c.d.	L. Cot.	L. Cos.	d.	′
0	9.41 300	47	9.42 805	51	0.57 195	9.98 494	3	60
1	9.41 347	47	9.42 856	50	0.57 144	9.98 491	3	59
2	9.41 394	47	9.42 906	51	0.57 094	9.98 488	3	58
3	9.41 441	47	9.42 957	50	0.57 043	9.98 484	3	57
4	9.41 488	47	9.43 007	50	0.56 993	9.98 481	4	56
5	9.41 535	47	9.43 057	51	0.56 943	9.98 477	3	55
6	9.41 582	46	9.43 108	50	0.56 892	9.98 474	3	54
7	9.41 628	47	9.43 158	50	0.56 842	9.98 471	4	53
8	9.41 675	47	9.43 208	50	0.56 792	9.98 467	3	52
9	9.41 722	46	9.43 258	50	0.56 742	9.98 464	4	51
10	9.41 768	47	9.43 308	50	0.56 692	9.98 460	3	50
11	9.41 815	46	9.43 358	50	0.56 642	9.98 457	4	49
12	9.41 861	47	9.43 408	50	0.56 592	9.98 453	3	48
13	9.41 908	46	9.43 458	50	0.56 542	9.98 450	3	47
14	9.41 954	47	9.43 508	50	0.56 492	9.98 447	4	46
15	9.42 001	46	9.43 558	49	0.56 442	9.98 443	3	45
16	9.42 047	46	9.43 607	50	0.56 393	9.98 440	4	44
17	9.42 093	47	9.43 657	50	0.56 343	9.98 436	3	43
18	9.42 140	46	9.43 707	49	0.56 293	9.98 433	4	42
19	9.42 186	46	9.43 756	50	0.56 244	9.98 429	3	41
20	9.42 232	46	9.43 806	49	0.56 194	9.98 426	4	40
21	9.42 278	46	9.43 855	50	0.56 145	9.98 422	3	39
22	9.42 324	46	9.43 905	49	0.56 095	9.98 419	4	38
23	9.42 370	46	9.43 954	50	0.56 046	9.98 415	3	37
24	9.42 416	45	9.44 004	49	0.55 996	9.98 412	3	36
25	9.42 461	46	9.44 053	49	0.55 947	9.98 409	4	35
26	9.42 507	46	9.44 102	49	0.55 898	9.98 405	3	34
27	9.42 553	46	9.44 151	50	0.55 849	9.98 402	4	33
28	9.42 599	45	9.44 201	49	0.55 799	9.98 398	3	32
29	9.42 644	46	9.44 250	49	0.55 750	9.98 395	4	31
30	9.42 690	45	9.44 299	49	0.55 701	9.98 391	3	30
31	9.42 735	46	9.44 348	49	0.55 652	9.98 388	4	29
32	9.42 781	45	9.44 397	49	0.55 603	9.98 384	3	28
33	9.42 826	46	9.44 446	49	0.55 554	9.98 381	4	27
34	9.42 872	45	9.44 495	49	0.55 505	9.98 377	4	26
35	9.42 917	45	9.44 544	48	0.55 456	9.98 373	3	25
36	9.42 962	46	9.44 592	49	0.55 408	9.98 370	4	24
37	9.43 008	45	9.44 641	49	0.55 359	9.98 366	3	23
38	9.43 053	45	9.44 690	48	0.55 310	9.98 363	4	22
39	9.43 098	45	9.44 738	49	0.55 262	9.98 359	3	21
40	9.43 143	45	9.44 787	49	0.55 213	9.98 356	4	20
41	9.43 188	45	9.44 836	48	0.55 164	9.98 352	3	19
42	9.43 233	45	9.44 884	49	0.55 116	9.98 349	4	18
43	9.43 278	45	9.44 933	48	0.55 067	9.98 345	3	17
44	9.43 323	44	9.44 981	48	0.55 019	9.98 342	4	16
45	9.43 367	45	9.45 029	49	0.54 971	9.98 338	4	15
46	9.43 412	45	9.45 078	48	0.54 922	9.98 334	3	14
47	9.43 457	45	9.45 126	48	0.54 874	9.98 331	4	13
48	9.43 502	44	9.45 174	48	0.54 826	9.98 327	3	12
49	9.43 546	45	9.45 222	49	0.54 778	9.98 324	4	11
50	9.43 591	44	9.45 271	48	0.54 729	9.98 320	3	10
51	9.43 635	45	9.45 319	48	0.54 681	9.98 317	4	9
52	9.43 680	44	9.45 367	48	0.54 633	9.98 313	4	8
53	9.43 724	45	9.45 415	48	0.54 585	9.98 309	3	7
54	9.43 769	44	9.45 463	48	0.54 537	9.98 306	4	6
55	9.43 813	44	9.45 511	48	0.54 489	9.98 302	3	5
56	9.43 857	44	9.45 559	47	0.54 441	9.98 299	4	4
57	9.43 901	45	9.45 606	48	0.54 394	9.98 295	4	3
58	9.43 946	44	9.45 654	48	0.54 346	9.98 291	3	2
59	9.43 990	44	9.45 702	48	0.54 298	9.98 288	4	1
60	9.44 034		9.45 750		0.54 250	9.98 284		0
′	L. Cos.	d.	L. Cot.	c.d.	L. Tan.	L. Sin.	d.	′

P. P.

″	51	50	49
1	0.8	0.8	0.8
2	1.7	1.7	1.6
3	2.6	2.5	2.4
4	3.4	3.3	3.3
5	4.2	4.2	4.1
6	5.1	5.0	4.9
7	6.0	5.8	5.7
8	6.8	6.7	6.5
9	7.6	7.5	7.4
10	8.5	8.3	8.2
20	17.0	16.7	16.3
30	25.5	25.0	24.5
40	34.0	33.3	32.7
50	42.5	41.7	40.8

″	48	47	46
1	0.8	0.8	0.8
2	1.6	1.6	1.5
3	2.4	2.4	2.3
4	3.2	3.1	3.1
5	4.0	3.9	3.8
6	4.8	4.7	4.6
7	5.6	5.5	5.4
8	6.4	6.3	6.1
9	7.2	7.0	6.9
10	8.0	7.8	7.7
20	16.0	15.7	15.3
30	24.0	23.5	23.0
40	32.0	31.3	30.7
50	40.0	39.2	38.3

″	45	44	4	3
1	0.8	0.7	0.1	0.0
2	1.5	1.5	0.1	0.1
3	2.2	2.2	0.2	0.2
4	3.0	2.9	0.3	0.2
5	3.8	3.7	0.3	0.2
6	4.5	4.4	0.4	0.3
7	5.2	5.1	0.5	0.4
8	6.0	5.9	0.5	0.4
9	6.8	6.6	0.6	0.4
10	7.5	7.3	0.7	0.5
20	15.0	14.7	1.3	1.0
30	22.5	22.0	2.0	1.5
40	30.0	29.3	2.7	2.0
50	37.5	36.7	3.3	2.5

	4	4	4	4
	50	49	48	47
0	6.2	6.1	6.0	5.9
1	18.8	18.4	18.0	17.6
2	31.2	30.6	30.0	29.4
3	43.8	42.9	42.0	41.1
4				

	3	3	3	3
	51	50	49	48
0	8.5	8.3	8.2	8.0
1	25.5	25.0	24.5	24.0
2	42.5	41.7	40.8	40.0
3				

′	L. Sin.	d.	L. Tan.	c.d.	L. Cot.	L. Cos.	d.	′	P. P.		
0	9.44 034	44	9.45 750	47	0.54 250	9.98 284	3	**60**	″	**48**	**47**	**46**
1	9.44 078	44	9.45 797	48	0.54 203	9.98 281	4	59	1	0.8	0.8	0.8
2	9.44 122	44	9.45 845	47	0.54 155	9.98 277	4	58	2	1.6	1.6	1.5
3	9.44 166	44	9.45 892	48	0.54 108	9.98 273	4	57	3	2.4	2.4	2.3
4	9.44 210	43	9.45 940	47	0.54 060	9.98 270	4	56	4	3.2	3.1	3.1
5	9.44 253	44	9.45 987	48	0.54 013	9.98 266	4	55	5	4.0	3.9	3.8
6	9.44 297	44	9.46 035	47	0.53 965	9.98 262	3	54	6	4.8	4.7	4.6
7	9.44 341	44	9.46 082	48	0.53 918	9.98 259	4	53	7	5.6	5.5	5.4
8	9.44 385	43	9.46 130	47	0.53 870	9.98 255	4	52	8	6.4	6.3	6.1
9	9.44 428	44	9.46 177	47	0.53 823	9.98 251	3	51	9	7.2	7.0	6.9
10	9.44 472	44	9.46 224	47	0.53 776	9.98 248	4	**50**	10	8.0	7.8	7.7
11	9.44 516	43	9.46 271	48	0.53 729	9.98 244	4	49	20	16.0	15.7	15.3
12	9.44 559	43	9.46 319	47	0.53 681	9.98 240	3	48	30	24.0	23.5	23.0
13	9.44 602	44	9.46 366	47	0.53 634	9.98 237	4	47	40	32.0	31.3	30.7
14	9.44 646	43	9.46 413	47	0.53 587	9.98 233	4	46	50	40.0	39.2	38.3
15	9.44 689	44	9.46 460	47	0.53 540	9.98 229	3	**45**	″ ′	**45**	**44**	**43**
16	9.44 733	43	9.46 507	47	0.53 493	9.98 226	4	44	1	0.8	0.7	0.7
17	9.44 776	43	9.46 554	47	0.53 446	9.98 222	4	43	2	1.5	1.5	1.4
18	9.44 819	43	9.46 601	47	0.53 399	9.98 218	3	42	3	2.2	2.2	2.2
19	9.44 862	43	9.46 648	46	0.53 352	9.98 215	4	41	4	3.0	2.9	2.9
20	9.44 905	43	9.46 694	47	0.53 306	9.98 211	4	**40**	5	3.8	3.7	3.6
21	9.44 948	44	9.46 741	47	0.53 259	9.98 207	3	39	6	4.5	4.4	4.3
22	9.44 992	43	9.46 788	47	0.53 212	9.98 204	4	38	7	5.2	5.1	5.0
23	9.45 035	42	9.46 835	46	0.53 165	9.98 200	4	37	8	6.0	5.9	5.7
24	9.45 077	43	9.46 881	47	0.53 119	9.98 196	4	36	9	6.8	6.6	6.4
25	9.45 120	43	9.46 928	47	0.53 072	9.98 192	3	35	10	7.5	7.3	7.2
26	9.45 163	43	9.46 975	46	0.53 025	9.98 189	4	34	20	15.0	14.7	14.3
27	9.45 206	43	9.47 021	47	0.52 979	9.98 185	4	33	30	22.5	22.0	21.5
28	9.45 249	43	9.47 068	46	0.52 932	9.98 181	4	32	40	30.0	29.3	28.7
29	9.45 292	42	9.47 114	46	0.52 886	9.98 177	3	31	50	37.5	36.7	35.8
30	9.45 334	43	9.47 160	47	0.52 840	9.98 174	4	**30**	″	**42**	**41**	**4** **3**
31	9.45 377	42	9.47 207	46	0.52 793	9.98 170	4	29	1	0.7	0.7	0.1 0.0
32	9.45 419	43	9.47 253	46	0.52 747	9.98 166	4	28	2	1.4	1.4	0.1 0.1
33	9.45 462	42	9.47 299	47	0.52 701	9.98 162	3	27	3	2.1	2.0	0.2 0.2
34	9.45 504	43	9.47 346	46	0.52 654	9.98 159	4	26	4	2.8	2.7	0.3 0.2
35	9.45 547	42	9.47 392	46	0.52 608	9.98 155	4	25	5	3.5	3.4	0.3 0.2
36	9.45 589	43	9.47 438	46	0.52 562	9.98 151	4	24	6	4.2	4.1	0.4 0.3
37	9.45 632	42	9.47 484	46	0.52 516	9.98 147	3	23	7	4.9	4.8	0.5 0.4
38	9.45 674	42	9.47 530	46	0.52 470	9.98 144	4	22	8	5.6	5.5	0.5 0.4
39	9.45 716	42	9.47 576	46	0.52 424	9.98 140	4	21	9	6.3	6.2	0.6 0.4
40	9.45 758	43	9.47 622	46	0.52 378	9.98 136	4	**20**	10	7.0	6.8	0.7 0.5
41	9.45 801	42	9.47 668	46	0.52 332	9.98 132	3	19	20	14.0	13.7	1.3 1.0
42	9.45 843	42	9.47 714	46	0.52 286	9.98 129	4	18	30	21.0	20.5	2.0 1.5
43	9.45 885	42	9.47 760	46	0.52 240	9.98 125	4	17	40	28.0	27.3	2.7 2.0
44	9.45 927	42	9.47 806	46	0.52 194	9.98 121	4	16	50	35.0	34.2	3.3 2.5
45	9.45 969	42	9.47 852	45	0.52 148	9.98 117	4	15				
46	9.46 011	42	9.47 897	46	0.52 103	9.98 113	3	14		**4**	**4**	**4** **4**
47	9.46 053	42	9.47 943	46	0.52 057	9.98 110	4	13				
48	9.46 095	41	9.47 989	46	0.52 011	9.98 106	4	12		**48**	**47**	**46** **45**
49	9.46 136	42	9.48 035	45	0.51 965	9.98 102	4	11				
50	9.46 178	42	9.48 080	46	0.51 920	9.98 098	4	**10**	0	6.0	5.9	5.8 5.6
51	9.46 220	42	9.48 126	45	0.51 874	9.98 094	4	9	1	18.0	17.6	17.2 16.9
52	9.46 262	41	9.48 171	46	0.51 829	9.98 090	3	8	2	30.0	29.4	28.8 28.1
53	9.46 303	42	9.48 217	45	0.51 783	9.98 087	4	7	3	42.0	41.1	40.2 39.4
54	9.46 345	41	9.48 262	45	0.51 738	9.98 083	4	6		**3**	**3**	**3** **3**
55	9.46 386	42	9.48 307	46	0.51 693	9.98 079	4	5		**48**	**47**	**46** **45**
56	9.46 428	41	9.48 353	45	0.51 647	9.98 075	4	4				
57	9.46 469	42	9.48 398	45	0.51 602	9.98 071	4	3				
58	9.46 511	41	9.48 443	46	0.51 557	9.98 067	4	2	0	8.0	7.8	7.7 7.5
59	9.46 552	42	9.48 489	45	0.51 511	9.98 063	3	1	1	24.0	23.5	23.0 22.5
60	9.46 594		9.48 534		0.51 466	9.98 060		**0**	2 3	40.0	39.2	38.3 37.5
′	L. Cos.	d.	L. Cot.	c.d.	L. Tan.	L. Sin.	d.	′	P. P.		

LOGARITHMS OF THE TRIGONOMETRIC FUNCTIONS

′	L. Sin.	d.	L. Tan.	c.d.	L. Cot.	L. Cos.	d.	′
0	9.46 594	41	9.48 534	45	0.51 466	9.98 060	4	60
1	9.46 635	41	9.48 579	45	0.51 421	9.98 056	4	59
2	9.46 676	41	9.48 624	45	0.51 376	9.98 052	4	58
3	9.46 717	41	9.48 669	45	0.51 331	9.98 048	4	57
4	9.46 758	42	9.48 714	45	0.51 286	9.98 044	4	56
5	9.46 800	41	9.48 759	45	0.51 241	9.98 040	4	55
6	9.46 841	41	9.48 804	45	0.51 196	9.98 036	4	54
7	9.46 882	41	9.48 849	45	0.51 151	9.98 032	3	53
8	9.46 923	41	9.48 894	45	0.51 106	9.98 029	4	52
9	9.46 964	41	9.48 939	45	0.51 061	9.98 025	4	51
10	9.47 005	40	9.48 984	45	0.51 016	9.98 021	4	50
11	9.47 045	41	9.49 029	44	0.50 971	9.98 017	4	49
12	9.47 086	41	9.49 073	45	0.50 927	9.98 013	4	48
13	9.47 127	41	9.49 118	45	0.50 882	9.98 009	4	47
14	9.47 168	41	9.49 163	44	0.50 837	9.98 005	4	46
15	9.47 209	40	9.49 207	45	0.50 793	9.98 001	4	45
16	9.47 249	41	9.49 252	44	0.50 748	9.97 997	4	44
17	9.47 290	40	9.49 296	45	0.50 704	9.97 993	4	43
18	9.47 330	41	9.49 341	44	0.50 659	9.97 989	3	42
19	9.47 371	40	9.49 385	45	0.50 615	9.97 986	4	41
20	9.47 411	41	9.49 430	44	0.50 570	9.97 982	4	40
21	9.47 452	40	9.49 474	45	0.50 526	9.97 978	4	39
22	9.47 492	41	9.49 519	44	0.50 481	9.97 974	4	38
23	9.47 533	40	9.49 563	44	0.50 437	9.97 970	4	37
24	9.47 573	40	9.49 607	45	0.50 393	9.97 966	4	36
25	9.47 613	41	9.49 652	44	0.50 348	9.97 962	4	35
26	9.47 654	40	9.49 696	44	0.50 304	9.97 958	4	34
27	9.47 694	40	9.49 740	44	0.50 260	9.97 954	4	33
28	9.47 734	40	9.49 784	44	0.50 216	9.97 950	4	32
29	9.47 774	40	9.49 828	44	0.50 172	9.97 946	4	31
30	9.47 814	40	9.49 872	44	0.50 128	9.97 942	4	30
31	9.47 854	40	9.49 916	44	0.50 084	9.97 938	4	29
32	9.47 894	40	9.49 960	44	0.50 040	9.97 934	4	28
33	9.47 934	40	9.50 004	44	0.49 996	9.97 930	4	27
34	9.47 974	40	9.50 048	44	0.49 952	9.97 926	4	26
35	9.48 014	40	9.50 092	44	0.49 908	9.97 922	4	25
36	9.48 054	40	9.50 136	44	0.49 864	9.97 918	4	24
37	9.48 094	39	9.50 180	43	0.49 820	9.97 914	4	23
38	9.48 133	40	9.50 223	44	0.49 777	9.97 910	4	22
39	9.48 173	40	9.50 267	44	0.49 733	9.97 906	4	21
40	9.48 213	39	9.50 311	44	0.49 689	9.97 902	4	20
41	9.48 252	40	9.50 355	43	0.49 645	9.97 898	4	19
42	9.48 292	40	9.50 398	44	0.49 602	9.97 894	4	18
43	9.48 332	39	9.50 442	43	0.49 558	9.97 890	4	17
44	9.48 371	40	9.50 485	44	0.49 515	9.97 886	4	16
45	9.48 411	39	9.50 529	43	0.49 471	9.97 882	4	15
46	9.48 450	40	9.50 572	44	0.49 428	9.97 878	4	14
47	9.48 490	39	9.50 616	43	0.49 384	9.97 874	4	13
48	9.48 529	39	9.50 659	44	0.49 341	9.97 870	4	12
49	9.48 568	39	9.50 703	43	0.49 297	9.97 866	5	11
50	9.48 607	40	9.50 746	43	0.49 254	9.97 861	4	10
51	9.48 647	39	9.50 789	44	0.49 211	9.97 857	4	9
52	9.48 686	39	9.50 833	43	0.49 167	9.97 853	4	8
53	9.48 725	39	9.50 876	43	0.49 124	9.97 849	4	7
54	9.48 764	39	9.50 919	43	0.49 081	9.97 845	4	6
55	9.48 803	39	9.50 962	43	0.49 038	9.97 841	4	5
56	9.48 842	39	9.51 005	43	0.48 995	9.97 837	4	4
57	9.48 881	39	9.51 048	44	0.48 952	9.97 833	4	3
58	9.48 920	39	9.51 092	43	0.48 908	9.97 829	4	2
59	9.48 959	39	9.51 135	43	0.48 865	9.97 825	4	1
60	9.48 998		9.51 178		0.48 822	9.97 821		0

P. P.

″	45	44	43
1	0.8	0.7	0.7
2	1.5	1.5	1.4
3	2.2	2.2	2.2
4	3.0	2.9	2.9
5	3.8	3.7	3.6
6	4.5	4.4	4.3
7	5.2	5.1	5.0
8	6.0	5.9	5.7
9	6.8	6.6	6.4
10	7.5	7.3	7.2
20	15.0	14.7	14.3
30	22.5	22.0	21.5
40	30.0	29.3	28.7
50	37.5	36.7	35.8

″	42	41	40
1	0.7	0.7	0.7
2	1.4	1.4	1.3
3	2.1	2.0	2.0
4	2.8	2.7	2.7
5	3.5	3.4	3.3
6	4.2	4.1	4.0
7	4.9	4.8	4.7
8	5.6	5.5	5.3
9	6.3	6.2	6.0
10	7.0	6.8	6.7
20	14.0	13.7	13.3
30	21.0	20.5	20.0
40	28.0	27.3	26.7
50	35.0	34.2	33.3

″	39	5	4	3
1	0.6	0.1	0.1	0.0
2	1.3	0.2	0.1	0.1
3	2.0	0.2	0.2	0.2
4	2.6	0.3	0.3	0.2
5	3.2	0.4	0.3	0.2
6	3.9	0.5	0.4	0.3
7	4.6	0.6	0.5	0.4
8	5.2	0.7	0.5	0.4
9	5.8	0.8	0.6	0.4
10	6.5	0.8	0.7	0.5
20	13.0	1.7	1.3	1.0
30	19.5	2.5	2.0	1.5
40	26.0	3.3	2.7	2.0
50	32.5	4.2	3.3	2.5

	5	4	4
	—	—	—
	43	45	44
0			
1	4.3	5.6	5.5
2	12.9	16.9	16.5
3	21.5	28.1	27.5
4	30.1	39.4	38.5
5	38.7		

	4	3	3
	—	—	—
	43	45	44
0	5.4	7.5	7.3
1	16.1	22.5	22.0
2	26.9	37.5	36.7
3	37.6	—	—
4			

′	L. Cos.	d.	L. Cot.	c.d.	L. Tan.	L. Sin.	d.	′	P. P.

LOGARITHMS OF THE TRIGONOMETRIC FUNCTIONS

18° (198°) (341°) **161°**

′	L. Sin.	d.	L. Tan.	c.d.	L. Cot.	L. Cos.	d.	′	P. P.		
0	9.48 998	39	9.51 178	43	0.48 822	9.97 821	4	60	″	43	42	41
1	9.49 037	39	9.51 221	43	0.48 779	9.97 817	5	59	1	0.7	0.7	0.7
2	9.49 076	39	9.51 264	42	0.48 736	9.97 812	4	58	2	1.4	1.4	1.4
3	9.49 115	38	9.51 306	43	0.48 694	9.97 808	4	57	3	2.2	2.1	2.0
4	9.49 153	39	9.51 349	43	0.48 651	9.97 804	4	56	4	2.9	2.8	2.7
5	9.49 192	39	9.51 392	43	0.48 608	9.97 800	4	55	5	3.6	3.5	3.4
6	9.49 231	38	9.51 435	43	0.48 565	9.97 796	4	54	6	4.3	4.2	4.1
7	9.49 269	39	9.51 478	42	0.48 522	9.97 792	4	53	7	5.0	4.9	4.8
8	9.49 308	39	9.51 520	43	0.48 480	9.97 788	4	52	8	5.7	5.6	5.5
9	9.49 347	38	9.51 563	43	0.48 437	9.97 784	5	51	9	6.4	6.3	6.2
10	9.49 385	39	9.51 606	42	0.48 394	9.97 779	4	50	10	7.2	7.0	6.8
11	9.49 424	38	9.51 648	43	0.48 352	9.97 775	4	49	20	14.3	14.0	13.7
12	9.49 462	38	9.51 691	43	0.48 309	9.97 771	4	48	30	21.5	21.0	20.5
13	9.49 500	39	9.51 734	42	0.48 266	9.97 767	4	47	40	28.7	28.0	27.3
14	9.49 539	38	9.51 776	43	0.48 224	9.97 763	4	46	50	35.8	35.0	34.2
15	9.49 577	38	9.51 819	42	0.48 181	9.97 759	5	45	″	39	38	37
16	9.49 615	39	9.51 861	42	0.48 139	9.97 754	4	44	1	0.6	0.6	0.6
17	9.49 654	38	9.51 903	43	0.48 097	9.97 750	4	43	2	1.3	1.3	1.2
18	9.49 692	38	9.51 946	42	0.48 054	9.97 746	4	42	3	2.0	1.9	1.8
19	9.49 730	38	9.51 988	43	0.48 012	9.97 742	4	41	4	2.6	2.5	2.5
20	9.49 768	38	9.52 031	42	0.47 969	9.97 738	4	40	5	3.2	3.2	3.1
21	9.49 806	38	9.52 073	42	0.47 927	9.97 734	5	39	6	3.9	3.8	3.7
22	9.49 844	38	9.52 115	42	0.47 885	9.97 729	4	38	7	4.6	4.4	4.3
23	9.49 882	38	9.52 157	43	0.47 843	9.97 725	4	37	8	5.2	5.1	4.9
24	9.49 920	38	9.52 200	42	0.47 800	9.97 721	4	36	9	5.8	5.7	5.6
25	9.49 958	38	9.52 242	42	0.47 758	9.97 717	4	35	10	6.5	6.3	6.2
26	9.49 996	38	9.52 284	42	0.47 716	9.97 713	5	34	20	13.0	12.7	12.3
27	9.50 034	38	9.52 326	42	0.47 674	9.97 708	4	33	30	19.5	19.0	18.5
28	9.50 072	38	9.52 368	42	0.47 632	9.97 704	4	32	40	26.0	25.3	24.7
29	9.50 110	38	9.52 410	42	0.47 590	9.97 700	4	31	50	32.5	31.7	30.8
30	9.50 148	37	9.52 452	42	0.47 548	9.97 696	5	30	″	36	5	4
31	9.50 185	38	9.52 494	42	0.47 506	9.97 691	4	29	1	0.6	0.1	0.1
32	9.50 223	38	9.52 536	42	0.47 464	9.97 687	4	28	2	1.2	0.2	0.1
33	9.50 261	37	9.52 578	42	0.47 422	9.97 683	4	27	3	1.8	0.2	0.2
34	9.50 298	38	9.52 620	41	0.47 380	9.97 679	5	26	4	2.4	0.3	0.3
35	9.50 336	38	9.52 661	42	0.47 339	9.97 674	4	25	5	3.0	0.4	0.3
36	9.50 374	37	9.52 703	42	0.47 297	9.97 670	4	24	6	3.6	0.5	0.4
37	9.50 411	38	9.52 745	42	0.47 255	9.97 666	4	23	7	4.2	0.6	0.5
38	9.50 449	37	9.52 787	42	0.47 213	9.97 662	5	22	8	4.8	0.7	0.5
39	9.50 486	37	9.52 829	41	0.47 171	9.97 657	4	21	9	5.4	0.8	0.6
40	9.50 523	38	9.52 870	42	0.47 130	9.97 653	4	20	10	6.0	0.8	0.7
41	9.50 561	37	9.52 912	41	0.47 088	9.97 649	4	19	20	12.0	1.7	1.3
42	9.50 598	37	9.52 953	42	0.47 047	9.97 645	5	18	30	18.0	2.5	2.0
43	9.50 635	38	9.52 995	42	0.47 005	9.97 640	4	17	40	24.0	3.3	2.7
44	9.50 673	37	9.53 037	41	0.46 963	9.97 636	4	16	50	30.0	4.2	3.3
45	9.50 710	37	9.53 078	42	0.46 922	9.97 632	4	15		5	5	5
46	9.50 747	37	9.53 120	41	0.46 880	9.97 628	5	14				
47	9.50 784	37	9.53 161	41	0.46 839	9.97 623	4	13		43	42	41
48	9.50 821	37	9.53 202	42	0.46 798	9.97 619	4	12	0	4.3	4.2	4.1
49	9.50 858	38	9.53 244	41	0.46 756	9.97 615	5	11	1	12.9	12.6	12.3
50	9.50 896	37	9.53 285	42	0.46 715	9.97 610	4	10	2	21.5	21.0	20.5
51	9.50 933	37	9.53 327	41	0.46 673	9.97 606	4	9	3	30.1	29.4	28.7
52	9.50 970	37	9.53 368	41	0.46 632	9.97 602	5	8	4	38.7	37.8	36.9
53	9.51 007	36	9.53 409	41	0.46 591	9.97 597	4	7	5			
54	9.51 043	37	9.53 450	42	0.46 550	9.97 593	4	6		4	4	4
55	9.51 080	37	9.53 492	41	0.46 508	9.97 589	5	5		43	42	41
56	9.51 117	37	9.53 533	41	0.46 467	9.97 584	4	4	0			
57	9.51 154	37	9.53 574	41	0.46 426	9.97 580	4	3	1	5.4	5.2	5.1
58	9.51 191	36	9.53 615	41	0.46 385	9.97 576	5	2	2	16.1	15.8	15.4
59	9.51 227	37	9.53 656	41	0.46 344	9.97 571	4	1	3	26.9	26.2	25.6
60	9.51 264		9.53 697		0.46 303	9.97 567		0	4	37.6	36.8	35.9

| ′ | L. Cos. | d. | L. Cot. | c.d. | L. Tan. | L. Sin. | d. | ′ | P. P. |

19° (199°) (340°) **160°**

′	L. Sin.	d.	L. Tan.	c.d.	L. Cot.	L. Cos.	d.	′
0	9.51 264	37	9.53 697	41	0.46 303	9.97 567	4	60
1	9.51 301	37	9.53 738	41	0.46 262	9.97 563	5	59
2	9.51 338	36	9.53 779	41	0.46 221	9.97 558	4	58
3	9.51 374	37	9.53 820	41	0.46 180	9.97 554	4	57
4	9.51 411	36	9.53 861	41	0.46 139	9.97 550	5	56
5	9.51 447	37	9.53 902	41	0.46 098	9.97 545	4	55
6	9.51 484	36	9.53 943	41	0.46 057	9.97 541	5	54
7	9.51 520	37	9.53 984	41	0.46 016	9.97 536	4	53
8	9.51 557	36	9.54 025	40	0.45 975	9.97 532	4	52
9	9.51 593	36	9.54 065	41	0.45 935	9.97 528	5	51
10	9.51 629	37	9.54 106	41	0.45 894	9.97 523	4	50
11	9.51 666	36	9.54 147	40	0.45 853	9.97 519	4	49
12	9.51 702	36	9.54 187	41	0.45 813	9.97 515	5	48
13	9.51 738	36	9.54 228	41	0.45 772	9.97 510	4	47
14	9.51 774	37	9.54 269	40	0.45 731	9.97 506	5	46
15	9.51 811	36	9.54 309	41	0.45 691	9.97 501	4	45
16	9.51 847	36	9.54 350	40	0.45 650	9.97 497	5	44
17	9.51 883	36	9.54 390	41	0.45 610	9.97 492	4	43
18	9.51 919	36	9.54 431	40	0.45 569	9.97 488	4	42
19	9.51 955	36	9.54 471	41	0.45 529	9.97 484	5	41
20	9.51 991	36	9.54 512	40	0.45 488	9.97 479	4	40
21	9.52 027	36	9.54 552	41	0.45 448	9.97 475	5	39
22	9.52 063	36	9.54 593	40	0.45 407	9.97 470	4	38
23	9.52 099	36	9.54 633	40	0.45 367	9.97 466	5	37
24	9.52 135	36	9.54 673	41	0.45 327	9.97 461	4	36
25	9.52 171	36	9.54 714	40	0.45 286	9.97 457	4	35
26	9.52 207	35	9.54 754	40	0.45 246	9.97 453	5	34
27	9.52 242	36	9.54 794	41	0.45 206	9.97 448	4	33
28	9.52 278	36	9.54 835	40	0.45 165	9.97 444	5	32
29	9.52 314	36	9.54 875	40	0.45 125	9.97 439	4	31
30	9.52 350	35	9.54 915	40	0.45 085	9.97 435	5	30
31	9.52 385	36	9.54 955	40	0.45 045	9.97 430	4	29
32	9.52 421	35	9.54 995	40	0.45 005	9.97 426	5	28
33	9.52 456	36	9.55 035	40	0.44 965	9.97 421	4	27
34	9.52 492	35	9.55 075	40	0.44 925	9.97 417	5	26
35	9.52 527	36	9.55 115	40	0.44 885	9.97 412	4	25
36	9.52 563	35	9.55 155	40	0.44 845	9.97 408	5	24
37	9.52 598	36	9.55 195	40	0.44 805	9.97 403	4	23
38	9.52 634	35	9.55 235	40	0.44 765	9.97 399	5	22
39	9.52 669	36	9.55 275	40	0.44 725	9.97 394	4	21
40	9.52 705	35	9.55 315	40	0.44 685	9.97 390	5	20
41	9.52 740	35	9.55 355	40	0.44 645	9.97 385	4	19
42	9.52 775	36	9.55 395	39	0.44 605	9.97 381	5	18
43	9.52 811	35	9.55 434	40	0.44 566	9.97 376	4	17
44	9.52 846	35	9.55 474	40	0.44 526	9.97 372	5	16
45	9.52 881	35	9.55 514	40	0.44 486	9.97 367	4	15
46	9.52 916	35	9.55 554	39	0.44 446	9.97 363	5	14
47	9.52 951	35	9.55 593	40	0.44 407	9.97 358	5	13
48	9.52 986	35	9.55 633	40	0.44 367	9.97 353	5	12
49	9.53 021	35	9.55 673	39	0.44 327	9.97 349	5	11
50	9.53 056	36	9.55 712	40	0.44 288	9.97 344	4	10
51	9.53 092	34	9.55 752	39	0.44 248	9.97 340	5	9
52	9.53 126	35	9.55 791	40	0.44 209	9.97 335	4	8
53	9.53 161	35	9.55 831	39	0.44 169	9.97 331	5	7
54	9.53 196	35	9.55 870	40	0.44 130	9.97 326	4	6
55	9.53 231	35	9.55 910	39	0.44 090	9.97 322	5	5
56	9.53 266	35	9.55 949	40	0.44 051	9.97 317	5	4
57	9.53 301	35	9.55 989	39	0.44 011	9.97 312	4	3
58	9.53 336	34	9.56 028	39	0.43 972	9.97 308	5	2
59	9.53 370	35	9.56 067	40	0.43 933	9.97 303	4	1
60	9.53 405		9.56 107		0.43 893	9.97 299		0

P. P.

″	41	40	39
1	0.7	0.7	0.6
2	1.4	1.3	1.3
3	2.0	2.0	2.0
4	2.7	2.7	2.6
5	3.4	3.3	3.2
6	4.1	4.0	3.9
7	4.8	4.7	4.6
8	5.5	5.3	5.2
9	6.2	6.0	5.8
10	6.8	6.7	6.5
20	13.7	13.3	13.0
30	20.5	20.0	19.5
40	27.3	26.7	26.0
50	34.2	33.3	32.5

″	37	36	35
1	0.6	0.6	0.6
2	1.2	1.2	1.2
3	1.8	1.8	1.8
4	2.5	2.4	2.3
5	3.1	3.0	2.9
6	3.7	3.6	3.5
7	4.3	4.2	4.1
8	4.9	4.8	4.7
9	5.6	5.4	5.2
10	6.2	6.0	5.8
20	12.3	12.0	11.7
30	18.5	18.0	17.5
40	24.7	24.0	23.3
50	30.8	30.0	29.2

″	34	5	4
1	0.6	0.1	0.1
2	1.1	0.2	0.2
3	1.7	0.2	0.2
4	2.3	0.3	0.3
5	2.8	0.4	0.3
6	3.4	0.5	0.4
7	4.0	0.6	0.5
8	4.5	0.7	0.6
9	5.1	0.8	0.6
10	5.7	0.8	0.7
20	11.3	1.7	1.3
30	17.0	2.5	2.0
40	22.7	3.3	2.7
50	28.3	4.2	3.3

	5	5	5
	41	40	39
0			
1	4.1	4.0	3.9
2	12.3	12.0	11.7
3	20.5	20.0	19.5
4	28.7	28.0	27.3
5	36.9	36.0	35.1

	4	4	4
	41	40	39
0			
1	5.1	5.0	4.9
2	15.4	15.0	14.6
3	25.6	25.0	24.4
4	35.9	35.0	34.1

′	L. Cos.	d.	L. Cot.	c.d.	L. Tan.	L. Sin.	d.	′	P. P.

20° (200°)   (339°) **159°**

′	L. Sin.	d.	L. Tan.	c.d.	L. Cot.	L. Cos.	d.	′
0	9.53 405	35	9.56 107	39	0.43 893	9.97 299	5	60
1	9.53 440	35	9.56 146	39	0.43 854	9.97 294	5	59
2	9.53 475	34	9.56 185	39	0.43 815	9.97 289	4	58
3	9.53 509	35	9.56 224	40	0.43 776	9.97 285	5	57
4	9.53 544	34	9.56 264	39	0.43 736	9.97 280	4	56
5	9.53 578	35	9.56 303	39	0.43 697	9.97 276	5	55
6	9.53 613	34	9.56 342	39	0.43 658	9.97 271	5	54
7	9.53 647	35	9.56 381	39	0.43 619	9.97 266	4	53
8	9.53 682	34	9.56 420	39	0.43 580	9.97 262	5	52
9	9.53 716	35	9.56 459	39	0.43 541	9.97 257	5	51
10	9.53 751	34	9.56 498	39	0.43 502	9.97 252	4	50
11	9.53 785	34	9.56 537	39	0.43 463	9.97 248	5	49
12	9.53 819	35	9.56 576	39	0.43 424	9.97 243	5	48
13	9.53 854	34	9.56 615	39	0.43 385	9.97 238	4	47
14	9.53 888	34	9.56 654	39	0.43 346	9.97 234	5	46
15	9.53 922	35	9.56 693	39	0.43 307	9.97 229	5	45
16	9.53 957	34	9.56 732	39	0.43 268	9.97 224	4	44
17	9.53 991	34	9.56 771	39	0.43 229	9.97 220	5	43
18	9.54 025	34	9.56 810	39	0.43 190	9.97 215	5	42
19	9.54 059	34	9.56 849	38	0.43 151	9.97 210	4	41
20	9.54 093	34	9.56 887	39	0.43 113	9.97 206	5	40
21	9.54 127	34	9.56 926	39	0.43 074	9.97 201	5	39
22	9.54 161	34	9.56 965	39	0.43 035	9.97 196	4	38
23	9.54 195	34	9.57 004	38	0.42 996	9.97 192	5	37
24	9.54 229	34	9.57 042	39	0.42 958	9.97 187	5	36
25	9.54 263	34	9.57 081	39	0.42 919	9.97 182	4	35
26	9.54 297	34	9.57 120	38	0.42 880	9.97 178	5	34
27	9.54 331	34	9.57 158	39	0.42 842	9.97 173	5	33
28	9.54 365	34	9.57 197	38	0.42 803	9.97 168	5	32
29	9.54 399	34	9.57 235	39	0.42 765	9.97 163	4	31
30	9.54 433	33	9.57 274	38	0.42 726	9.97 159	5	30
31	9.54 466	34	9.57 312	39	0.42 688	9.97 154	5	29
32	9.54 500	34	9.57 351	38	0.42 649	9.97 149	4	28
33	9.54 534	33	9.57 389	39	0.42 611	9.97 145	5	27
34	9.54 567	34	9.57 428	38	0.42 572	9.97 140	5	26
35	9.54 601	34	9.57 466	38	0.42 534	9.97 135	5	25
36	9.54 635	33	9.57 504	39	0.42 496	9.97 130	4	24
37	9.54 668	34	9.57 543	38	0.42 457	9.97 126	5	23
38	9.54 702	33	9.57 581	38	0.42 419	9.97 121	5	22
39	9.54 735	34	9.57 619	39	0.42 381	9.97 116	5	21
40	9.54 769	33	9.57 658	38	0.42 342	9.97 111	4	20
41	9.54 802	34	9.57 696	38	0.42 304	9.97 107	5	19
42	9.54 836	33	9.57 734	38	0.42 266	9.97 102	5	18
43	9.54 869	34	9.57 772	38	0.42 228	9.97 097	5	17
44	9.54 903	33	9.57 810	38	0.42 190	9.97 092	5	16
45	9.54 936	33	9.57 849	38	0.42 151	9.97 087	4	15
46	9.54 969	34	9.57 887	38	0.42 113	9.97 083	5	14
47	9.55 003	33	9.57 925	38	0.42 075	9.97 078	5	13
48	9.55 036	33	9.57 963	38	0.42 037	9.97 073	5	12
49	9.55 069	33	9.58 001	38	0.41 999	9.97 068	5	11
50	9.55 102	34	9.58 039	38	0.41 961	9.97 063	4	10
51	9.55 136	33	9.58 077	38	0.41 923	9.97 059	5	9
52	9.55 169	33	9.58 115	38	0.41 885	9.97 054	5	8
53	9.55 202	33	9.58 153	38	0.41 847	9.97 049	5	7
54	9.55 235	33	9.58 191	38	0.41 809	9.97 044	5	6
55	9.55 268	33	9.58 229	38	0.41 771	9.97 039	4	5
56	9.55 301	33	9.58 267	37	0.41 733	9.97 035	5	4
57	9.55 334	33	9.58 304	38	0.41 696	9.97 030	5	3
58	9.55 367	33	9.58 342	38	0.41 658	9.97 025	5	2
59	9.55 400	33	9.58 380	38	0.41 620	9.97 020	5	1
60	9.55 433		9.58 418		0.41 582	9.97 015		0

′	L. Cos.	d.	L. Cot.	c.d.	L. Tan.	L. Sin.	d.	′

P. P.

″	40	39	38
1	0.7	0.6	0.6
2	1.3	1.3	1.3
3	2.0	2.0	1.9
4	2.7	2.6	2.5
5	3.3	3.2	3.2
6	4.0	3.9	3.8
7	4.7	4.6	4.4
8	5.3	5.2	5.1
9	6.0	5.8	5.7
10	6.7	6.5	6.3
20	13.3	13.0	12.7
30	20.0	19.5	19.0
40	26.7	26.0	25.3
50	33.3	32.5	31.7

″	37	35	34
1	0.6	0.6	0.6
2	1.2	1.2	1.1
3	1.8	1.8	1.7
4	2.5	2.3	2.3
5	3.1	2.9	2.8
6	3.7	3.5	3.4
7	4.3	4.1	4.0
8	4.9	4.7	4.5
9	5.6	5.2	5.1
10	6.2	5.8	5.7
20	12.3	11.7	11.3
30	18.5	17.5	17.0
40	24.7	23.3	22.7
50	30.8	29.2	28.3

″	33	5	4
1	0.6	0.1	0.1
2	1.1	0.2	0.1
3	1.6	0.2	0.2
4	2.2	0.3	0.3
5	2.8	0.4	0.3
6	3.3	0.5	0.4
7	3.8	0.6	0.5
8	4.4	0.7	0.5
9	5.0	0.8	0.6
10	5.5	0.8	0.7
20	11.0	1.7	1.3
30	16.5	2.5	2.0
40	22.0	3.3	2.7
50	27.5	4.2	3.3

	5	5	5
	40	39	38
0	4.0	3.9	3.8
1	12.0	11.7	11.4
2	20.0	19.5	19.0
3	28.0	27.3	26.6
4	36.0	35.1	34.2
5			

	5	4	4
	37	39	38
0	3.7	4.9	4.8
1	11.1	14.6	14.2
2	18.5	24.4	23.8
3	25.9	34.1	33.2
4	33.3	—	—
5			

110° (290°)   (249°) **69°**

21° (201°)   **(338°)158°**

′	L. Sin.	d.	L. Tan.	c.d.	L. Cot.	L. Cos.	d.	′		P. P.	
0	9.55 433	33	9.58 418	37	0.41 582	9.97 015	5	60	″	38	37	36
1	9.55 466	33	9.58 455	38	0.41 545	9.97 010	5	59	1	0.6	0.6	0.6
2	9.55 499	33	9.58 493	38	0.41 507	9.97 005	4	58	2	1.3	1.2	1.2
3	9.55 532	32	9.58 531	38	0.41 469	9.97 001	5	57	3	1.9	1.8	1.8
4	9.55 564	33	9.58 569	37	0.41 431	9.96 996	5	56	4	2.5	2.5	2.4
5	9.55 597	33	9.58 606	38	0.41 394	9.96 991	5	55	5	3.2	3.1	3.0
6	9.55 630	33	9.58 644	38	0.41 356	9.96 986	5	54	6	3.8	3.7	3.6
7	9.55 663	32	9.58 681	38	0.41 319	9.96 981	5	53	7	4.4	4.3	4.2
8	9.55 695	33	9.58 719	38	0.41 281	9.96 976	5	52	8	5.1	4.9	4.8
9	9.55 728	33	9.58 757	37	0.41 243	9.96 971	5	51	9	5.7	5.6	5.4
10	9.55 761	32	9.58 794	38	0.41 206	9.96 966	4	50	10	6.3	6.2	6.0
11	9.55 793	33	9.58 832	37	0.41 168	9.96 962	5	49	20	12.7	12.3	12.0
12	9.55 826	32	9.58 869	38	0.41 131	9.96 957	5	48	30	19.0	18.5	18.0
13	9.55 858	33	9.58 907	37	0.41 093	9.96 952	5	47	40	25.3	24.7	24.0
14	9.55 891	32	9.58 944	37	0.41 056	9.96 947	5	46	50	31.7	30.8	30.0
15	9.55 923	33	9.58 981	38	0.41 019	9.96 942	5	45	″	33	32	31
16	9.55 956	32	9.59 019	37	0.40 981	9.96 937	5	44	1	0.6	0.5	0.5
17	9.55 988	33	9.59 056	38	0.40 944	9.96 932	5	43	2	1.1	1.1	1.0
18	9.56 021	32	9.59 094	37	0.40 906	9.96 927	5	42	3	1.6	1.6	1.6
19	9.56 053	32	9.59 131	37	0.40 869	9.96 922	5	41	4	2.2	2.1	2.1
20	9.56 085	33	9.59 168	37	0.40 832	9.96 917	5	40	5	2.8	2.7	2.6
21	9.56 118	32	9.59 205	38	0.40 795	9.96 912	5	39	6	3.3	3.2	3.1
22	9.56 150	32	9.59 243	37	0.40 757	9.96 907	4	38	7	3.8	3.7	3.6
23	9.56 182	33	9.59 280	37	0.40 720	9.96 903	5	37	8	4.4	4.3	4.1
24	9.56 215	32	9.59 317	37	0.40 683	9.96 898	5	36	9	5.0	4.8	4.6
25	9.56 247	32	9.59 354	37	0.40 646	9.96 893	5	35	10	5.5	5.3	5.2
26	9.56 279	32	9.59 391	38	0.40 609	9.96 888	5	34	20	11.0	10.7	10.3
27	9.56 311	32	9.59 429	37	0.40 571	9.96 883	5	33	30	16.5	16.0	15.5
28	9.56 343	32	9.59 466	37	0.40 534	9.96 878	5	32	40	22.0	21.3	20.7
29	9.56 375	33	9.59 503	37	0.40 497	9.96 873	5	31	50	27.5	26.7	25.8
30	9.56 408	32	9.59 540	37	0.40 460	9.96 868	5	30	″	6	5	4
31	9.56 440	32	9.59 577	37	0.40 423	9.96 863	5	29	1	0.1	0.1	0.1
32	9.56 472	32	9.59 614	37	0.40 386	9.96 858	5	28	2	0.2	0.2	0.1
33	9.56 504	32	9.59 651	37	0.40 349	9.96 853	5	27	3	0.3	0.2	0.2
34	9.56 536	32	9.59 688	37	0.40 312	9.96 848	5	26	4	0.4	0.3	0.3
35	9.56 568	31	9.59 725	37	0.40 275	9.96 843	5	25	5	0.5	0.4	0.3
36	9.56 599	32	9.59 762	37	0.40 238	9.96 838	5	24	6	0.6	0.5	0.4
37	9.56 631	32	9.59 799	36	0.40 201	9.96 833	5	23	7	0.7	0.6	0.5
38	9.56 663	32	9.59 835	37	0.40 165	9.96 828	5	22	8	0.8	0.7	0.5
39	9.56 695	32	9.59 872	37	0.40 128	9.96 823	5	21	9	0.9	0.8	0.6
40	9.56 727	32	9.59 909	37	0.40 091	9.96 818	5	20	10	1.0	0.8	0.7
41	9.56 759	31	9.59 946	37	0.40 054	9.96 813	5	19	20	2.0	1.7	1.3
42	9.56 790	32	9.59 983	36	0.40 017	9.96 808	5	18	30	3.0	2.5	2.0
43	9.56 822	32	9.60 019	37	0.39 981	9.96 803	5	17	40	4.0	3.3	2.7
44	9.56 854	32	9.60 056	37	0.39 944	9.96 798	5	16	50	5.0	4.2	3.3
45	9.56 886	31	9.60 093	37	0.39 907	9.96 793	5	15		6	5	5
46	9.56 917	32	9.60 130	36	0.39 870	9.96 788	5	14		37	38	37
47	9.56 949	31	9.60 166	37	0.39 834	9.96 783	5	13	0			
48	9.56 980	32	9.60 203	37	0.39 797	9.96 778	6	12	1	3.1	3.8	3.7
49	9.57 012	32	9.60 240	36	0.39 760	9.96 772	5	11	2	9.2	11.4	11.1
50	9.57 044	31	9.60 276	37	0.39 724	9.96 767	5	10	3	15.4	19.0	18.5
51	9.57 075	32	9.60 313	36	0.39 687	9.96 762	5	9	4	21.6	26.6	25.9
52	9.57 107	31	9.60 349	37	0.39 651	9.96 757	5	8	5	27.8	34.2	33.3
53	9.57 138	31	9.60 386	36	0.39 614	9.96 752	5	7	6	33.9	—	—
54	9.57 169	32	9.60 422	37	0.39 578	9.96 747	5	6		5	4	4
55	9.57 201	31	9.60 459	36	0.39 541	9.96 742	5	5		36	38	37
56	9.57 232	32	9.60 495	37	0.39 505	9.96 737	5	4	0			
57	9.57 264	31	9.60 532	36	0.39 468	9.96 732	5	3	1	3.6	4.8	4.6
58	9.57 295	31	9.60 568	37	0.39 432	9.96 727	5	2	2	10.8	14.2	13.8
59	9.57 326	32	9.60 605	36	0.39 395	9.96 722	5	1	3	18.0	23.8	23.1
60	9.57 358		9.60 641		0.39 359	9.96 717		0	4	25.2	33.2	32.4
									5	32.4	—	—
′	L. Cos.	d.	L. Cot.	c.d.	L. Tan.	L. Sin.	d.	′		P. P.	

LOGARITHMS OF THE TRIGONOMETRIC FUNCTIONS

′	L. Sin.	d.	L. Tan.	c.d.	L. Cot.	L. Cos.	d.	′	P.P.		
0	9.57 358	31	9.60 641	36	0.39 359	9.96 717	6	60	″	37	36	35
1	9.57 389	31	9.60 677	37	0.39 323	9.96 711	5	59	1	0.6	0.6	0.6
2	9.57 420	31	9.60 714	36	0.39 286	9.96 706	5	58	2	1.2	1.2	1.2
3	9.57 451	31	9.60 750	36	0.39 250	9.96 701	5	57	3	1.8	1.8	1.8
4	9.57 482	32	9.60 786	37	0.39 214	9.96 696	5	56	4	2.5	2.4	2.3
5	9.57 514	31	9.60 823	36	0.39 177	9.96 691	5	55	5	3.1	3.0	2.9
6	9.57 545	31	9.60 859	36	0.39 141	9.96 686	5	54	6	3.7	3.6	3.5
7	9.57 576	31	9.60 895	36	0.39 105	9.96 681	5	53	7	4.3	4.2	4.1
8	9.57 607	31	9.60 931	36	0.39 069	9.96 676	6	52	8	4.9	4.8	4.7
9	9.57 638	31	9.60 967	37	0.39 033	9.96 670	5	51	9	5.6	5.4	5.2
10	9.57 669	31	9.61 004	36	0.38 996	9.96 665	5	50	10	6.2	6.0	5.8
11	9.57 700	31	9.61 040	36	0.38 960	9.96 660	5	49	20	12.3	12.0	11.7
12	9.57 731	31	9.61 076	36	0.38 924	9.96 655	5	48	30	18.5	18.0	17.5
13	9.57 762	31	9.61 112	36	0.38 888	9.96 650	5	47	40	24.7	24.0	23.3
14	9.57 793	31	9.61 148	36	0.38 852	9.96 645	5	46	50	30.8	30.0	29.2
15	9.57 824	31	9.61 184	36	0.38 816	9.96 640	6	45	″	32	31	30
16	9.57 855	31	9.61 220	36	0.38 780	9.96 634	5	44	1	0.5	0.5	0.5
17	9.57 885	31	9.61 256	36	0.38 744	9.96 629	5	43	2	1.1	1.0	1.0
18	9.57 916	31	9.61 292	36	0.38 708	9.96 624	5	42	3	1.6	1.6	1.5
19	9.57 947	31	9.61 328	36	0.38 672	9.96 619	5	41	4	2.1	2.1	2.0
20	9.57 978	30	9.61 364	36	0.38 636	9.96 614	6	40	5	2.7	2.6	2.5
21	9.58 008	31	9.61 400	36	0.38 600	9.96 608	5	39	6	3.2	3.1	3.0
22	9.58 039	31	9.61 436	36	0.38 564	9.96 603	5	38	7	3.7	3.6	3.5
23	9.58 070	31	9.61 472	36	0.38 528	9.96 598	5	37	8	4.3	4.1	4.0
24	9.58 101	30	9.61 508	36	0.38 492	9.96 593	5	36	9	4.8	4.6	4.5
25	9.58 131	31	9.61 544	35	0.38 456	9.96 588	6	35	10	5.3	5.2	5.0
26	9.58 162	31	9.61 579	36	0.38 421	9.96 582	5	34	20	10.7	10.3	10.0
27	9.58 192	31	9.61 615	36	0.38 385	9.96 577	5	33	30	16.0	15.5	15.0
28	9.58 223	31	9.61 651	36	0.38 349	9.96 572	5	32	40	21.3	20.7	20.0
29	9.58 253	31	9.61 687	35	0.38 313	9.96 567	5	31	50	26.7	25.8	25.0
30	9.58 284	30	9.61 722	36	0.38 278	9.96 562	6	30	″	29	6	5
31	9.58 314	31	9.61 758	36	0.38 242	9.96 556	5	29	1	0.5	0.1	0.1
32	9.58 345	30	9.61 794	36	0.38 206	9.96 551	5	28	2	1.0	0.2	0.2
33	9.58 375	31	9.61 830	35	0.38 170	9.96 546	5	27	3	1.4	0.3	0.2
34	9.58 406	30	9.61 865	36	0.38 135	9.96 541	6	26	4	1.9	0.4	0.3
35	9.58 436	31	9.61 901	36	0.38 099	9.96 535	5	25	5	2.4	0.5	0.4
36	9.58 467	30	9.61 936	36	0.38 064	9.96 530	5	24	6	2.9	0.6	0.5
37	9.58 497	30	9.61 972	36	0.38 028	9.96 525	5	23	7	3.4	0.7	0.6
38	9.58 527	30	9.62 008	35	0.37 992	9.96 520	6	22	8	3.9	0.8	0.7
39	9.58 557	31	9.62 043	36	0.37 957	9.96 514	5	21	9	4.4	0.9	0.8
40	9.58 588	30	9.62 079	35	0.37 921	9.96 509	5	20	10	4.8	1.0	0.8
41	9.58 618	30	9.62 114	36	0.37 886	9.96 504	6	19	20	9.7	2.0	1.7
42	9.58 648	30	9.62 150	35	0.37 850	9.96 498	5	18	30	14.5	3.0	2.5
43	9.58 678	31	9.62 185	36	0.37 815	9.96 493	5	17	40	19.3	4.0	3.3
44	9.58 709	30	9.62 221	35	0.37 779	9.96 488	5	16	50	24.2	5.0	4.2
45	9.58 739	30	9.62 256	36	0.37 744	9.96 483	6	15		6		6
46	9.58 769	30	9.62 292	35	0.37 708	9.96 477	5	14		36		35
47	9.58 799	30	9.62 327	35	0.37 673	9.96 472	5	13				
48	9.58 829	30	9.62 362	36	0.37 638	9.96 467	6	12	0	3.0		2.9
49	9.58 859	30	9.62 398	35	0.37 602	9.96 461	5	11	1	9.0		8.8
50	9.58 889	30	9.62 433	35	0.37 567	9.96 456	5	10	2	15.0		14.6
51	9.58 919	30	9.62 468	36	0.37 532	9.96 451	6	9	3	21.0		20.4
52	9.58 949	30	9.62 504	35	0.37 496	9.96 445	5	8	4	27.0		26.2
53	9.58 979	30	9.62 539	35	0.37 461	9.96 440	5	7	5	33.0		32.1
54	9.59 009	30	9.62 574	35	0.37 426	9.96 435	6	6		5	5	5
55	9.59 039	30	9.62 609	36	0.37 391	9.96 429	5	5		37	36	35
56	9.59 069	29	9.62 645	35	0.37 355	9.96 424	5	4	0	3.7	3.6	3.5
57	9.59 098	30	9.62 680	35	0.37 320	9.96 419	5	3	1	11.1	10.8	10.5
58	9.59 128	30	9.62 715	35	0.37 285	9.96 413	6	2	2	18.5	18.0	17.5
59	9.59 158	30	9.62 750	35	0.37 250	9.96 408	5	1	3	25.9	25.2	24.5
60	9.59 188		9.62 785		0.37 215	9.96 403		0	4	33.3	32.4	31.5
									5			

′	L. Cos.	d.	L. Cot.	c.d.	L. Tan.	L. Sin.	d.	′	P.P.		

LOGARITHMS OF THE TRIGONOMETRIC FUNCTIONS

23° (203°)   (336°) **156°**

′	L. Sin.	d.	L. Tan.	c.d.	L. Cot.	L. Cos.	d.	′
0	9.59 188	30	9.62 785	35	0.37 215	9.96 403	6	60
1	9.59 218	29	9.62 820	35	0.37 180	9.96 397	5	59
2	9.59 247	30	9.62 855	35	0.37 145	9.96 392	5	58
3	9.59 277	30	9.62 890	36	0.37 110	9.96 387	6	57
4	9.59 307	29	9.62 926	35	0.37 074	9.96 381	5	56
5	9.59 336	30	9.62 961	35	0.37 039	9.96 376	6	55
6	9.59 366	30	9.62 996	35	0.37 004	9.96 370	5	54
7	9.59 396	29	9.63 031	35	0.36 969	9.96 365	5	53
8	9.59 425	30	9.63 066	35	0.36 934	9.96 360	6	52
9	9.59 455	29	9.63 101	34	0.36 899	9.96 354	5	51
10	9.59 484	30	9.63 135	35	0.36 865	9.96 349	6	50
11	9.59 514	29	9.63 170	35	0.36 830	9.96 343	5	49
12	9.59 543	30	9.63 205	35	0.36 795	9.96 338	5	48
13	9.59 573	29	9.63 240	35	0.36 760	9.96 333	6	47
14	9.59 602	30	9.63 275	35	0.36 725	9.96 327	5	46
15	9.59 632	29	9.63 310	35	0.36 690	9.96 322	6	45
16	9.59 661	29	9.63 345	34	0.36 655	9.96 316	5	44
17	9.59 690	30	9.63 379	35	0.36 621	9.96 311	6	43
18	9.59 720	29	9.63 414	35	0.36 586	9.96 305	5	42
19	9.59 749	29	9.63 449	35	0.36 551	9.96 300	6	41
20	9.59 778	30	9.63 484	35	0.36 516	9.96 294	5	40
21	9.59 808	29	9.63 519	34	0.36 481	9.96 289	5	39
22	9.59 837	29	9.63 553	35	0.36 447	9.96 284	6	38
23	9.59 866	29	9.63 588	35	0.36 412	9.96 278	5	37
24	9.59 895	29	9.63 623	34	0.36 377	9.96 273	6	36
25	9.59 924	30	9.63 657	35	0.36 343	9.96 267	5	35
26	9.59 954	29	9.63 692	34	0.36 308	9.96 262	6	34
27	9.59 983	29	9.63 726	35	0.36 274	9.96 256	5	33
28	9.60 012	29	9.63 761	35	0.36 239	9.96 251	6	32
29	9.60 041	29	9.63 796	34	0.36 204	9.96 245	5	31
30	9.60 070	29	9.63 830	35	0.36 170	9.96 240	6	30
31	9.60 099	29	9.63 865	34	0.36 135	9.96 234	5	29
32	9.60 128	29	9.63 899	35	0.36 101	9.96 229	6	28
33	9.60 157	29	9.63 934	34	0.36 066	9.96 223	5	27
34	9.60 186	29	9.63 968	35	0.36 032	9.96 218	6	26
35	9.60 215	29	9.64 003	34	0.35 997	9.96 212	5	25
36	9.60 244	29	9.64 037	35	0.35 963	9.96 207	6	24
37	9.60 273	29	9.64 072	34	0.35 928	9.96 201	5	23
38	9.60 302	29	9.64 106	34	0.35 894	9.96 196	6	22
39	9.60 331	28	9.64 140	35	0.35 860	9.96 190	5	21
40	9.60 359	29	9.64 175	34	0.35 825	9.96 185	6	20
41	9.60 388	29	9.64 209	34	0.35 791	9.96 179	5	19
42	9.60 417	29	9.64 243	35	0.35 757	9.96 174	6	18
43	9.60 446	28	9.64 278	34	0.35 722	9.96 168	6	17
44	9.60 474	29	9.64 312	34	0.35 688	9.96 162	5	16
45	9.60 503	29	9.64 346	35	0.35 654	9.96 157	6	15
46	9.60 532	29	9.64 381	34	0.35 619	9.96 151	5	14
47	9.60 561	28	9.64 415	34	0.35 585	9.96 146	6	13
48	9.60 589	29	9.64 449	34	0.35 551	9.96 140	5	12
49	9.60 618	28	9.64 483	34	0.35 517	9.96 135	6	11
50	9.60 646	29	9.64 517	35	0.35 483	9.96 129	6	10
51	9.60 675	29	9.64 552	34	0.35 448	9.96 123	5	9
52	9.60 704	28	9.64 586	34	0.35 414	9.96 118	6	8
53	9.60 732	29	9.64 620	34	0.35 380	9.96 112	5	7
54	9.60 761	28	9.64 654	34	0.35 346	9.96 107	6	6
55	9.60 789	29	9.64 688	34	0.35 312	9.96 101	6	5
56	9.60 818	28	9.64 722	34	0.35 278	9.96 095	5	4
57	9.60 846	29	9.64 756	34	0.35 244	9.96 090	6	3
58	9.60 875	28	9.64 790	34	0.35 210	9.96 084	5	2
59	9.60 903	28	9.64 824	34	0.35 176	9.96 079	6	1
60	9.60 931		9.64 858		0.35 142	9.96 073		0

| ′ | L. Cos. | d. | L. Cot. | c.d. | L. Tan. | L. Sin. | d. | ′ |

P. P.

″	36	35	34
1	0.6	0.6	0.6
2	1.2	1.2	1.1
3	1.8	1.8	1.7
4	2.4	2.3	2.3
5	3.0	2.9	2.8
6	3.6	3.5	3.4
7	4.2	4.1	4.0
8	4.8	4.7	4.5
9	5.4	5.2	5.1
10	6.0	5.8	5.7
20	12.0	11.7	11.3
30	18.0	17.5	17.0
40	24.0	23.3	22.7
50	30.0	29.2	28.3

″	30	29	28
1	0.5	0.5	0.5
2	1.0	1.0	0.9
3	1.5	1.4	1.4
4	2.0	1.9	1.9
5	2.5	2.4	2.3
6	3.0	2.9	2.8
7	3.5	3.4	3.3
8	4.0	3.9	3.7
9	4.5	4.4	4.2
10	5.0	4.8	4.7
20	10.0	9.7	9.3
30	15.0	14.5	14.0
40	20.0	19.3	18.7
50	25.0	24.2	23.3

″	6	5
1	0.1	0.1
2	0.2	0.2
3	0.3	0.2
4	0.4	0.3
5	0.5	0.4
6	0.6	0.5
7	0.7	0.6
8	0.8	0.7
9	0.9	0.8
10	1.0	0.8
20	2.0	1.7
30	3.0	2.5
40	4.0	3.3
50	5.0	4.2

	6	6	6
	36	35	34
0	3.0	2.9	2.8
1	9.0	8.8	8.5
2	15.0	14.6	14.2
3	21.0	20.4	19.8
4	27.0	26.2	25.5
5	33.0	32.1	31.2
6			

	5	5
	35	34
0	3.5	3.4
1	10.5	10.2
2	17.5	17.0
3	24.5	23.8
4	31.5	30.6
5		

113° (293°)   (246°) **66°**

24° (204°)   (335°) **155°**

′	L. Sin.	d.	L. Tan.	c.d.	L. Cot.	L. Cos.	d.	′	P. P.		
0	9.60 931	29	9.64 858	34	0.35 142	9.96 073	6	60	″	34	33
1	9.60 960	28	9.64 892	34	0.35 108	9.96 067	5	59	1	0.6	0.6
2	9.60 988	28	9.64 926	34	0.35 074	9.96 062	6	58	2	1.1	1.1
3	9.61 016	29	9.64 960	34	0.35 040	9.96 056	6	57	3	1.7	1.6
4	9.61 045	28	9.64 994	34	0.35 006	9.96 050	5	56	4	2.3	2.2
5	9.61 073	28	9.65 028	34	0.34 972	9.96 045	6	55	5	2.8	2.8
6	9.61 101	28	9.65 062	34	0.34 938	9.96 039	5	54	6	3.4	3.3
7	9.61 129	29	9.65 096	34	0.34 904	9.96 034	6	53	7	4.0	3.8
8	9.61 158	28	9.65 130	34	0.34 870	9.96 028	6	52	8	4.5	4.4
9	9.61 186	28	9.65 164	33	0.34 836	9.96 022	5	51	9	5.1	5.0
10	9.61 214	28	9.65 197	34	0.34 803	9.96 017	6	50	10	5.7	5.5
11	9.61 242	28	9.65 231	34	0.34 769	9.96 011	6	49	20	11.3	11.0
12	9.61 270	28	9.65 265	34	0.34 735	9.96 005	5	48	30	17.0	16.5
13	9.61 298	28	9.65 299	34	0.34 701	9.96 000	6	47	40	22.7	22.0
14	9.61 326	28	9.65 333	33	0.34 667	9.95 994	6	46	50	28.3	27.5
15	9.61 354	28	9.65 366	34	0.34 634	9.95 988	6	45	″	29	28	27
16	9.61 382	29	9.65 400	34	0.34 600	9.95 982	5	44	1	0.5	0.5	0 4
17	9.61 411	27	9.65 434	33	0.34 566	9.95 977	6	43	2	1.0	0.9	0.9
18	9.61 438	28	9.65 467	34	0.34 533	9.95 971	6	42	3	1.4	1.4	1.4
19	9.61 466	28	9.65 501	34	0.34 499	9.95 965	5	41	4	1.9	1.9	1.8
20	9.61 494	28	9.65 535	33	0.34 465	9.95 960	6	40	5	2.4	2.3	2.2
21	9.61 522	28	9.65 568	34	0.34 432	9.95 954	6	39	6	2.9	2.8	2.7
22	9.61 550	28	9.65 602	34	0.34 398	9.95 948	6	38	7	3.4	3.3	3.2
23	9.61 578	28	9.65 636	33	0.34 364	9.95 942	5	37	8	3.9	3.7	3.6
24	9.61 606	28	9.65 669	34	0.34 331	9.95 937	6	36	9	4.4	4.2	4.0
25	9.61 634	28	9.65 703	33	0.34 297	9.95 931	6	35	10	4.8	4.7	4.5
26	9.61 662	27	9.65 736	34	0.34 264	9.95 925	5	34	20	9.7	9.3	9.0
27	9.61 689	28	9.65 770	33	0.34 230	9.95 920	6	33	30	14.5	14.0	13.5
28	9.61 717	28	9.65 803	34	0.34 197	9.95 914	6	32	40	19.3	18.7	18.0
29	9.61 745	28	9.65 837	33	0.34 163	9.95 908	6	31	50	24.2	23.3	22.5
30	9.61 773	27	9.65 870	34	0.34 130	9.95 902	5	30	″	6	5
31	9.61 800	28	9.65 904	33	0.34 096	9.95 897	6	29	1	0.1	0.1
32	9.61 828	28	9.65 937	34	0.34 063	9.95 891	6	28	2	0.2	0.2
33	9.61 856	27	9.65 971	33	0.34 029	9.95 885	6	27	3	0.3	0.2
34	9.61 883	28	9.66 004	34	0.33 996	9.95 879	6	26	4	0.4	0.3
35	9.61 911	28	9.66 038	33	0.33 962	9.95 873	5	25	5	0.5	0.4
36	9.61 939	27	9.66 071	33	0.33 929	9.95 868	6	24	6	0.6	0.5
37	9.61 966	28	9.66 104	34	0.33 896	9.95 862	6	23	7	0.7	0.6
38	9.61 994	27	9.66 138	33	0.33 862	9.95 856	6	22	8	0.8	0.7
39	9.62 021	28	9.66 171	33	0.33 829	9.95 850	6	21	9	0.9	0.8
40	9.62 049	27	9.66 204	34	0.33 796	9.95 844	5	20	10	1.0	0.8
41	9.62 076	28	9.66 238	33	0.33 762	9.95 839	6	19	20	2.0	1.7
42	9.62 104	27	9.66 271	33	0.33 729	9.95 833	6	18	30	3.0	2.5
43	9.62 131	28	9.66 304	33	0.33 696	9.95 827	6	17	40	4.0	3.3
44	9.62 159	27	9.66 337	34	0.33 663	9.95 821	6	16	50	5.0	4.2
45	9.62 186	28	9.66 371	33	0.33 629	9.95 815	5	15			
46	9.62 214	27	9.66 404	33	0.33 596	9.95 810	6	14			
47	9.62 241	27	9.66 437	33	0.33 563	9.95 804	6	13			
48	9.62 268	28	9.66 470	33	0.33 530	9.95 798	6	12			
49	9.62 296	27	9.66 503	34	0.33 497	9.95 792	6	11		6	6	5
50	9.62 323	27	9.66 537	33	0.33 463	9.95 786	6	10		34	33	34
51	9.62 350	27	9.66 570	33	0.33 430	9.95 780	5	9	0			
52	9.62 377	28	9.66 603	33	0.33 397	9.95 775	6	8	1	2.8	2.8	3.4
53	9.62 405	27	9.66 636	33	0.33 364	9.95 769	6	7	2	8.5	8.2	10.2
54	9.62 432	27	9.66 669	33	0.33 331	9.95 763	6	6	3	14.2	13.8	17.0
55	9.62 459	27	9.66 702	33	0.33 298	9.95 757	6	5	4	19.8	19.2	23.8
56	9.62 486	27	9.66 735	33	0.33 265	9.95 751	6	4	5	25.5	24.8	30.6
57	9.62 513	28	9.66 768	33	0.33 232	9.95 745	6	3	6	31.2	30.2	—
58	9.62 541	27	9.66 801	33	0.33 199	9.95 739	6	2			
59	9.62 568	27	9.66 834	33	0.33 166	9.95 733	5	1			
60	9.62 595		9.66 867		0.33 133	9.95 728		0			
′	L. Cos.	d.	L. Cot.	c.d.	L. Tan.	L. Sin.	d.	′	P. P.		

114° (294°)   (245°) **65°**

LOGARITHMS OF THE TRIGONOMETRIC FUNCTIONS

25° (205°) (334°) **154°**

′	L. Sin.	d.	L. Tan.	c.d.	L. Cot.	L. Cos.	d	′	P. P.		
0	9.62 59̄5	27	9.66 867	33	0.33 133	9.95 728	6	60			
1	9.62 622	27	9.66 900	33	0.33 100	9.95 722	6	59		**33**	**32**
2	9.62 649	27	9.66 933	33	0.33 067	9.95 71̄6	6	58	″		
3	9.62 676	27	9.66 966	33	0.33 034	9.95 710	6	57	1	0.6	0.5
4	9.62 703	27	9.66 999	33	0.33 001	9.95 704	6	56	2	1.1	1.1
									3	1.6	1.6
5	9.62 730	27	9.67 032	33	0.32 968	9.95 698	6	55	4	2.2	2.1
6	9.62 757	27	9.67 06̄5	33	0.32 93̄5	9.95 692	6	54			
7	9.62 784	27	9.67 098	33	0.32 902	9.95 686	6	53	5	2.8	2.7
8	9.62 811	27	9.67 131	32	0.32 869	9.95 680	6	52	6	3.3	3.2
9	9.62 838	27	9.67 163	33	0.32 837	9.95 674	6	51	7	3.8	3.7
									8	4.4	4.3
10	9.62 86̄5	27	9.67 196	33	0.32 804	9.95 668	5	50	9	5̄.0	4̄.8
11	9.62 892	26	9.67 229	33	0.32 771	9.95 66̄3	6	49	10	5.5	5.3
12	9.62 918	27	9.67 262	33	0.32 738	9.95 657	6	48	20	11.0	10.7
13	9.62 94̄5	27	9.67 29̄5	32	0.32 70̄5	9.95 651	6	47	30	16.5	16.0
14	9.62 972	27	9.67 327	33	0.32 673	9.95 64̄5	6	46	40	22.0	21.3
									50	27.5	26.7
15	9.62 999	27	9.67 360	33	0.32 640	9.95 639	6	45			
16	9.63 026	26	9.67 393	33	0.32 607	9.95 633	6	44		**27**	**26**
17	9.63 052	27	9.67 426	32	0.32 574	9.95 627	6	43	″		
18	9.63 079	27	9.67 458	33	0.32 542	9.95 621	6	42	1	0.4	0.4
19	9.63 106	27	9.67 491	33	0.32 509	9.95 61̄5	6	41	2	0.9	0.9
									3	1.4	1.3
20	9.63 133	26	9.67 524	32	0.32 476	9.95 609	6	40	4	1.8	1.7
21	9.63 159	27	9.67 556	33	0.32 444	9.95 603	6	39			
22	9.63 186	27	9.67 589	33	0.32 411	9.95 597	6	38	5	2.2	2.2
23	9.63 213	26	9.67 622	32	0.32 378	9.95 591	6	37	6	2.7	2.6
24	9.63 239	27	9.67 654	33	0.32 346	9.95 58̄5	6	36	7	3.2	3.0
									8	3.6	3.̄5
25	9.63 266	26	9.67 687	32	0.32 313	9.95 579	6	35	9	4.0	3.9
26	9.63 292	27	9.67 719	33	0.32 281	9.95 573	6	34			
27	9.63 319	26	9.67 752	33	0.32 248	9.95 567	6	33	10	4.5	4.3
28	9.63 34̄5	27	9.67 78̄5	32	0.32 21̄5	9.95 561	6	32	20	9.0	8.7
29	9.63 372	26	9.67 817	33	0.32 183	9.95 55̄5	6	31	30	13.5	13.0
									40	18.0	17.3
30	9.63 398	27	9.67 8̄50	32	0.32 1̄50	9.95 549	6	30	50	22.5	21.7
31	9.63 42̄5	26	9.67 882	33	0.32 118	9.95 543	6	29	″	**7**	**6**	**5**
32	9.63 451	27	9.67 91̄5	32	0.32 08̄5	9.95 537	6	28	1	0.1	0.1	0.1
33	9.63 478	26	9.67 947	33	0.32 053	9.95 531	6	27	2	0.2	0.2	0.2
34	9.63 504	27	9.67 980	32	0.32 020	9.95 52̄5	6	26	3	0.4	0.3	0.2
									4	0.̄5	0.4	0.3
35	9.63 531	26	9.68 012	32	0.31 988	9.95 519	6	25				
36	9.63 557	26	9.68 044	33	0.31 956	9.95 513	6	24	5	0.6	0.5	0.4
37	9.63 583	27	9.68 077	32	0.31 923	9.95 507	7	23	6	0.7	0.6	0.5
38	9.63 610	26	9.68 109	33	0.31 891	9.95 5̄00	6	22	7	0.8	0.7	0.6
39	9.63 636	26	9.68 142	32	0.31 858	9.95 494	6	21	8	0.9	0.8	0.̄7
									9	1.0	0.9	0.8
40	9.63 662	27	9.68 174	32	0.31 826	9.95 488	6	20	10	1.2	1.0	0.8
41	9.63 689	26	9.68 206	33	0.31 794	9.95 482	6	19	20	2.3	2.0	1.7
42	9.63 71̄5	26	9.68 239	32	0.31 761	9.95 476	6	18	30	3.̄5	3.0	2.5
43	9.63 741	26	9.68 271	32	0.31 729	9.95 470	6	17	40	4.7	4.0	3.3
44	9.63 767	27	9.68 203	33	0.31 697	9.95 464	6	16	50	5.8	5.0	4.2
45	9.63 794	26	9.68 336	32	0.31 664	9.95 458	6	15				
46	9.63 820	26	9.68 368	32	0.31 632	9.95 452	6	14				
47	9.63 846	26	9.68 400	32	0.31 600	9.95 446	6	13				
48	9.63 872	26	9.68 432	33	0.31 568	9.95 440	6	12				
49	9.63 898	26	9.68 46̄5	32	0.31 53̄5	9.95 434	7	11		**7**	**6**	**5**
50	9.63 924	26	9.68 497	32	0.31 503	9.95 427	6	10		**32**	**32**	**33**
51	9.63 9̄50	26	9.68 529	32	0 31 471	9.95 421	6	9				
52	9.63 976	26	9.68 561	32	0.31 43̄9	9.95 41̄5	6	8	0			
53	9.64 002	26	9.68 593	33	0.31 407	9.95 409	6	7	1	2.3	2.7	3.3
54	9.64 028	26	9.68 626	32	0.31 374	9.95 403	6	6	2	6.9	8.0	9.9
									3	11.4	13.3	16.5
55	9.64 054	26	9.68 658	32	0.31 342	9.95 397	6	5	4	16.0	18.7	23.1
56	9.64 080	26	9.68 690	32	0.31 310	9.95 391	7	4	5	20.6	24.0	29.7
57	9.64 106	26	9.68 722	32	0.31 278	9.95 384	6	3	6	25.1	29.3	—
58	9.64 132	26	9.68 754	32	0.31 246	9.95 378	6	2	7	29.7	—	—
59	9.64 158	26	9.68 786	32	0.31 214	9.95 372	6	1				
60	9.64 184		9.68 818		0.31 182	9.95 366		0				

′	L. Cos.	d.	L. Cot.	c.d.	L. Tan.	L. Sin.	d.	′	P. P.

115° (295°) (244°) **64°**

'	L. Sin.	d.	L. Tan.	c.d.	L. Cot.	L. Cos.	d.	'
0	9.64 184	26	9.68 818	32	0.31 182	9.95 366	6	60
1	9.64 210	26	9.68 850	32	0.31 150	9.95 360	6	59
2	9.64 236	26	9.68 882	32	0.31 118	9.95 354	6	58
3	9.64 262	26	9.68 914	32	0.31 086	9.95 348	7	57
4	9.64 288	25	9.68 946	32	0.31 054	9.95 341	6	56
5	9.64 313	26	9.68 978	32	0.31 022	9.95 335	6	55
6	9.64 339	26	9.69 010	32	0.30 990	9.95 329	6	54
7	9.64 365	26	9.69 042	32	0.30 958	9.95 323	6	53
8	9.64 391	26	9.69 074	32	0.30 926	9.95 317	7	52
9	9.64 417	25	9.69 106	32	0.30 894	9.95 310	6	51
10	9.64 442	26	9.69 138	32	0.30 862	9.95 304	6	50
11	9.64 468	26	9.69 170	32	0.30 830	9.95 298	6	49
12	9.64 494	25	9.69 202	32	0.30 798	9.95 292	6	48
13	9.64 519	26	9.69 234	32	0.30 766	9.95 286	7	47
14	9.64 545	26	9.69 266	32	0.30 734	9.95 279	6	46
15	9.64 571	25	9.69 298	31	0.30 702	9.95 273	6	45
16	9.64 596	26	9.69 329	32	0.30 671	9.95 267	6	44
17	9.64 622	25	9.69 361	32	0.30 639	9.95 261	6	43
18	9.64 647	26	9.69 393	32	0.30 607	9.95 254	6	42
19	9.64 673	25	9.69 425	32	0.30 575	9.95 248	6	41
20	9.64 698	26	9.69 457	31	0.30 543	9.95 242	6	40
21	9.64 724	25	9.69 488	32	0.30 512	9.95 236	7	39
22	9.64 749	26	9.69 520	32	0.30 480	9.95 229	6	38
23	9.64 775	25	9.69 552	32	0.30 448	9.95 223	6	37
24	9.64 800	26	9.69 584	31	0.30 416	9.95 217	6	36
25	9.64 826	25	9.69 615	32	0.30 385	9.95 211	7	35
26	9.64 851	26	9.69 647	32	0.30 353	9.95 204	6	34
27	9.64 877	25	9.69 679	31	0.30 321	9.95 198	6	33
28	9.64 902	25	9.69 710	32	0.30 290	9.95 192	7	32
29	9.64 927	26	9.69 742	32	0.30 258	9.95 185	6	31
30	9.64 953	25	9.69 774	31	0.30 226	9.95 179	6	30
31	9.64 978	25	9.69 805	32	0.30 195	9.95 173	6	29
32	9.65 003	26	9.69 837	31	0.30 163	9.95 167	7	28
33	9.65 029	25	9.69 868	32	0.30 132	9.95 160	6	27
34	9.65 054	25	9.69 900	32	0.30 100	9.95 154	6	26
35	9.65 079	25	9.69 932	31	0.30 068	9.95 148	7	25
36	9.65 104	26	9.69 963	32	0.30 037	9.95 141	6	24
37	9.65 130	25	9.69 995	31	0.30 005	9.95 135	6	23
38	9.65 155	25	9.70 026	32	0.29 974	9.95 129	7	22
39	9.65 180	25	9.70 058	31	0.29 942	9.95 122	6	21
40	9.65 205	25	9.70 089	32	0.29 911	9.95 116	6	20
41	9.65 230	25	9.70 121	32	0.29 879	9.95 110	7	19
42	9.65 255	26	9.70 152	32	0.29 848	9.95 103	6	18
43	9.65 281	25	9.70 184	31	0.29 816	9.95 097	7	17
44	9.65 306	25	9.70 215	32	0.29 785	9.95 090	6	16
45	9.65 331	25	9.70 247	31	0.29 753	9.95 084	6	15
46	9.65 356	25	9.70 278	31	0.29 722	9.95 078	7	14
47	9.65 381	25	9.70 309	32	0.29 691	9.95 071	6	13
48	9.65 406	25	9.70 341	31	0.29 659	9.95 065	6	12
49	9.65 431	25	9.70 372	32	0.29 628	9.95 059	7	11
50	9.65 456	25	9.70 404	31	0.29 596	9.95 052	6	10
51	9.65 481	25	9.70 435	31	0.29 565	9.95 046	7	9
52	9.65 506	25	9.70 466	32	0.29 534	9.95 039	6	8
53	9.65 531	25	9.70 498	31	0.29 502	9.95 033	6	7
54	9.65 556	24	9.70 529	31	0.29 471	9.95 027	7	6
55	9.65 580	25	9.70 560	32	0.29 440	9.95 020	6	5
56	9.65 605	25	9.70 592	31	0.29 408	9.95 014	7	4
57	9.65 630	25	9.70 623	31	0.29 377	9.95 007	6	3
58	9.65 655	25	9.70 654	31	0.29 346	9.95 001	6	2
59	9.65 680	25	9.70 685	32	0.29 315	9.94 995	7	1
60	9.65 705		9.70 717		0.29 283	9.94 988		0

P. P.

"	32	31
1	0.5	0.5
2	1.1	1.0
3	1.6	1.6
4	2.1	2.1
5	2.7	2.6
6	3.2	3.1
7	3.7	3.6
8	4.3	4.1
9	4.8	4.6
10	5.3	5.2
20	10.7	10.3
30	16.0	15.5
40	21.3	20.7
50	26.7	25.8

"	26	25	24
1	0.4	0.4	0.4
2	0.9	0.8	0.8
3	1.3	1.2	1.2
4	1.7	1.7	1.6
5	2.2	2.1	2.0
6	2.6	2.5	2.4
7	3.0	2.9	2.8
8	3.5	3.3	3.2
9	3.9	3.8	3.6
10	4.3	4.2	4.0
20	8.7	8.3	8.0
30	13.0	12.5	12.0
40	17.3	16.7	16.0
50	21.7	20.8	20.0

"	7	6
1	0.1	0.1
2	0.2	0.2
3	0.4	0.3
4	0.5	0.4
5	0.6	0.5
6	0.7	0.6
7	0.8	0.7
8	0.9	0.8
9	1.0	0.9
10	1.2	1.0
20	2.3	2.0
30	3.5	3.0
40	4.7	4.0
50	5.8	5.0

	7/32	7/31	6/32
0			
1	2.3	2.2	2.7
2	6.9	6.6	8.0
3	11.4	11.1	13.3
4	16.0	15.5	18.7
5	20.6	19.9	24.0
6	25.1	24.4	29.3
7	29.7	28.8	

'	L. Cos.	d.	L. Cot.	c.d.	L. Tan.	L. Sin.	d.	'	P. P.

LOGARITHMS OF THE TRIGONOMETRIC FUNCTIONS

′	L. Sin.	d.	L. Tan.	c.d.	L. Cot.	L. Cos.	d.	′
0	9.65 705	24	9.70 717	31	0.29 283	9.94 988	6	60
1	9.65 729	25	9.70 748	31	0.29 252	9.94 982	7	59
2	9.65 754	25	9.70 779	31	0.29 221	9.94 975	6	58
3	9.65 779	25	9.70 810	31	0.29 190	9.94 969	7	57
4	9.65 804	24	9.70 841	32	0.29 159	9.94 962	6	56
5	9.65 828	25	9.70 873	31	0.29 127	9.94 956	7	55
6	9.65 853	25	9.70 904	31	0.29 096	9.94 949	6	54
7	9.65 878	24	9.70 935	31	0.29 065	9.94 943	7	53
8	9.65 902	25	9.70 966	31	0.29 034	9.94 936	6	52
9	9.65 927	25	9.70 997	31	0.29 003	9.94 930	7	51
10	9.65 952	24	9.71 028	31	0.28 972	9.94 923	6	50
11	9.65 976	25	9.71 059	31	0.28 941	9.94 917	6	49
12	9.66 001	24	9.71 090	31	0.28 910	9.94 911	7	48
13	9.66 025	25	9.71 121	32	0.28 879	9.94 904	6	47
14	9.66 050	25	9.71 153	31	0.28 847	9.94 898	7	46
15	9.66 075	24	9.71 184	31	0.28 816	9.94 891	6	45
16	9.66 099	25	9.71 215	31	0.28 785	9.94 885	7	44
17	9.66 124	24	9.71 246	31	0.28 754	9.94 878	7	43
18	9.66 148	25	9.71 277	31	0.28 723	9.94 871	6	42
19	9.66 173	24	9.71 308	31	0.28 692	9.94 865	7	41
20	9.66 197	24	9.71 339	31	0.28 661	9.94 858	6	40
21	9.66 221	25	9.71 370	31	0.28 630	9.94 852	7	39
22	9.66 246	24	9.71 401	30	0.28 599	9.94 845	6	38
23	9.66 270	25	9.71 431	31	0.28 569	9.94 839	7	37
24	9.66 295	24	9.71 462	31	0.28 538	9.94 832	6	36
25	9.66 319	24	9.71 493	31	0.28 507	9.94 826	7	35
26	9.66 343	25	9.71 524	31	0.28 476	9.94 819	6	34
27	9.66 368	24	9.71 555	31	0.28 445	9.94 813	7	33
28	9.66 392	24	9.71 586	31	0.28 414	9.94 806	7	32
29	9.66 416	25	9.71 617	31	0.28 383	9.94 799	6	31
30	9.66 441	24	9.71 648	31	0.28 352	9.94 793	7	30
31	9.66 465	24	9.71 679	30	0.28 321	9.94 786	6	29
32	9.66 489	24	9.71 709	31	0.28 291	9.94 780	7	28
33	9.66 513	24	9.71 740	31	0.28 260	9.94 773	6	27
34	9.66 537	25	9.71 771	31	0.28 229	9.94 767	7	26
35	9.66 562	24	9.71 802	31	0.28 198	9.94 760	7	25
36	9.66 586	24	9.71 833	30	0.28 167	9.94 753	6	24
37	9.66 610	24	9.71 863	31	0.28 137	9.94 747	7	23
38	9.66 634	24	9.71 894	31	0.28 106	9.94 740	6	22
39	9.66 658	24	9.71 925	30	0.28 075	9.94 734	7	21
40	9.66 682	24	9.71 955	31	0.28 045	9.94 727	7	20
41	9.66 706	25	9.71 986	31	0.28 014	9.94 720	6	19
42	9.66 731	24	9.72 017	31	0.27 983	9.94 714	7	18
43	9.66 755	24	9.72 048	30	0.27 952	9.94 707	7	17
44	9.66 779	24	9.72 078	31	0.27 922	9.94 700	6	16
45	9.66 803	24	9.72 109	31	0.27 891	9.94 694	7	15
46	9.66 827	24	9.72 140	30	0.27 860	9.94 687	7	14
47	9.66 851	24	9.72 170	31	0.27 830	9.94 680	6	13
48	9.66 875	24	9.72 201	30	0.27 799	9.94 674	7	12
49	9.66 899	23	9.72 231	31	0.27 769	9.94 667	7	11
50	9.66 922	24	9.72 262	31	0.27 738	9.94 660	6	10
51	9.66 946	24	9.72 293	30	0.27 707	9.94 654	7	9
52	9.66 970	24	9.72 323	31	0.27 677	9.94 647	7	8
53	9.66 994	24	9.72 354	30	0.27 646	9.94 640	6	7
54	9.67 018	24	9.72 384	31	0.27 616	9.94 634	7	6
55	9.67 042	24	9.72 415	30	0.27 585	9.94 627	7	5
56	9.67 066	24	9.72 445	31	0.27 555	9.94 620	6	4
57	9.67 090	23	9.72 476	30	0.27 524	9.94 614	7	3
58	9.67 113	24	9.72 506	31	0.27 494	9.94 607	7	2
59	9.67 137	24	9.72 537	30	0.27 463	9.94 600	7	1
60	9.67 161		9.72 567		0.27 433	9.94 593		0

′	L. Cos.	d.	L. Cot.	c.d.	L. Tan.	L. Sin.	d.	′

P. P.

″	32	31	30
1	0.5	0.5	0.5
2	1.1	1.0	1.0
3	1.6	1.6	1.5
4	2.1	2.1	2.0
5	2.7	2.6	2.5
6	3.2	3.1	3.0
7	3.7	3.6	3.5
8	4.3	4.1	4.0
9	4.8	4.6	4.5
10	5.3	5.2	5.0
20	10.7	10.3	10.0
30	16.0	15.5	15.0
40	21.3	20.7	20.0
50	26.7	25.8	25.0

″	25	24	23
1	0.4	0.4	0.4
2	0.8	0.8	0.8
3	1.2	1.2	1.2
4	1.7	1.6	1.5
5	2.1	2.0	1.9
6	2.5	2.4	2.3
7	2.9	2.8	2.7
8	3.3	3.2	3.1
9	3.8	3.6	3.4
10	4.2	4.0	3.8
20	8.3	8.0	7.7
30	12.5	12.0	11.5
40	16.7	16.0	15.3
50	20.8	20.0	19.2

″	7	6
1	0.1	0.1
2	0.2	0.2
3	0.4	0.3
4	0.5	0.4
5	0.6	0.5
6	0.7	0.6
7	0.8	0.7
8	0.9	0.8
9	1.0	0.9
10	1.2	1.0
20	2.3	2.0
30	3.5	3.0
40	4.7	4.0
50	5.8	5.0

	7 / 30	6 / 31	6 / 30
0			
1	2.1	2.6	2.5
2	6.4	7.8	7.5
3	10.7	12.9	12.5
4	15.0	18.1	17.5
5	19.3	23.2	22.5
6	23.6	28.4	27.5
7	27.9	—	—

28° (208°) (331°) **151°**

′	L. Sin.	d.	L. Tan.	c.d.	L. Cot.	L. Cos.	d.	′	P. P.		
0	9.67 161	24	9.72 567	31	0.27 433	9.94 593	6	**60**	″	**31**	**30**	**29**
1	9.67 185	23	9.72 598	30	0.27 402	9.94 587	7	59	1	0.5	0.5	0.5
2	9.67 208	24	9.72 628	31	0.27 372	9.94 580	7	58	2	1.0	1.0	1.0
3	9.67 232	24	9.72 659	30	0.27 341	9.94 573	6	57	3	1.6	1.5	1.4
4	9.67 256	24	9.72 689	31	0.27 311	9.94 567	7	56	4	2.1	2.0	1.9
5	9.67 280	23	9.72 720	30	0.27 280	9.94 560	7	55	5	2.6	2.5	2.4
6	9.67 303	24	9.72 750	30	0.27 250	9.94 553	7	54	6	3.1	3.0	2.9
7	9.67 327	23	9.72 780	31	0.27 220	9.94 546	6	53	7	3.6	3.5	3.4
8	9.67 350	24	9.72 811	30	0.27 189	9.94 540	7	52	8	4.1	4.0	3.9
9	9.67 374	24	9.72 841	31	0.27 159	9.94 533	7	51	9	4.6	4.5	4.4
10	9.67 398	23	9.72 872	30	0.27 128	9.94 526	7	**50**	10	5.2	5.0	4.8
11	9.67 421	24	9.72 902	30	0.27 098	9.94 519	6	49	20	10.3	10.0	9.7
12	9.67 445	23	9.72 932	31	0.27 068	9.94 513	7	48	30	15.5	15.0	14.5
13	9.67 468	24	9.72 963	30	0.27 037	9.94 506	7	47	40	20.7	20.0	19.3
14	9.67 492	23	9.72 993	30	0.27 007	9.94 499	7	46	50	25.8	25.0	24.2
15	9.67 515	24	9.73 023	31	0.26 977	9.94 492	7	45	″	**24**	**23**	**22**
16	9.67 539	23	9.73 054	30	0.26 946	9.94 485	6	44	1	0.4	0.4	0.4
17	9.67 562	24	9.73 084	30	0.26 916	9.94 479	7	43	2	0.8	0.8	0.7
18	9.67 586	23	9.73 114	30	0.26 886	9.94 472	7	42	3	1.2	1.2	1.1
19	9.67 609	24	9.73 144	31	0.26 856	9.94 465	7	41	4	1.6	1.5	1.5
20	9.67 633	23	9.73 175	30	0.26 825	9.94 458	7	**40**	5	2.0	1.9	1.8
21	9.67 656	24	9.73 205	30	0.26 795	9.94 451	6	39	6	2.4	2.3	2.2
22	9.67 680	23	9.73 235	30	0.26 765	9.94 445	7	38	7	2.8	2.7	2.6
23	9.67 703	23	9.73 265	30	0.26 735	9.94 438	7	37	8	3.2	3.1	2.9
24	9.67 726	24	9.73 295	31	0.26 705	9.94 431	7	36	9	3.6	3.4	3.3
25	9.67 750	23	9.73 326	30	0.26 674	9.94 424	7	**35**	10	4.0	3.8	3.7
26	9.67 773	23	9.73 356	30	0.26 644	9.94 417	7	34	20	8.0	7.7	7.3
27	9.67 796	24	9.73 386	30	0.26 614	9.94 410	6	33	30	12.0	11.5	11.0
28	9.67 820	23	9.73 416	30	0.26 584	9.94 404	7	32	40	16.0	15.3	14.7
29	9.67 843	23	9.73 446	30	0.26 554	9.94 397	7	31	50	20.0	19.2	18.3
30	9.67 866	24	9.73 476	31	0.26 524	9.94 390	7	**30**	″	**7**	**6**	
31	9.67 890	23	9.73 507	30	0.26 493	9.94 383	7	29	1	0.1	0.1	
32	9.67 913	23	9.73 537	30	0.26 463	9.94 376	7	28	2	0.2	0.2	
33	9.67 936	23	9.73 567	30	0.26 433	9.94 369	7	27	3	0.4	0.3	
34	9.67 959	23	9.73 597	30	0.26 403	9.94 362	7	26	4	0.5	0.4	
35	9.67 982	24	9.73 627	30	0.26 373	9.94 355	6	**25**	5	0.6	0.5	
36	9.68 006	23	9.73 657	30	0.26 343	9.94 349	7	24	6	0.7	0.6	
37	9.68 029	23	9.73 687	30	0.26 313	9.94 342	7	23	7	0.8	0.7	
38	9.68 052	23	9.73 717	30	0.26 283	9.94 335	7	22	8	0.9	0.8	
39	9.68 075	23	9.73 747	30	0.26 253	9.94 328	7	21	9	1.0	0.9	
40	9.68 098	23	9.73 777	30	0.26 223	9.94 321	7	**20**	10	1.2	1.0	
41	9.68 121	23	9.73 807	30	0.26 193	9.94 314	7	19	20	2.3	2.0	
42	9.68 144	23	9.73 837	30	0.26 163	9.94 307	7	18	30	3.5	3.0	
43	9.68 167	23	9.73 867	30	0.26 133	9.94 300	7	17	40	4.7	4.0	
44	9.68 190	23	9.73 897	30	0.26 103	9.94 293	7	16	50	5.8	5.0	
45	9.68 213	24	9.73 927	30	0.26 073	9.94 286	7	**15**				
46	9.68 237	23	9.73 957	30	0.26 043	9.94 279	6	14				
47	9.68 260	23	9.73 987	30	0.26 013	9.94 273	7	13				
48	9.68 283	22	9.74 017	30	0.25 983	9.94 266	7	12				
49	9.68 305	23	9.74 047	30	0.25 953	9.94 259	7	11		**7**	**6**	**6**
50	9.68 328	23	9.74 077	30	0.25 923	9.94 252	7	**10**		**31**	**31**	**30**
51	9.68 351	23	9.74 107	30	0.25 893	9.94 245	7	9	0			
52	9.68 374	23	9.74 137	29	0.25 863	9.94 238	7	8	1	2.2	2.6	2.5
53	9.68 397	23	9.74 166	30	0.25 834	9.94 231	7	7	2	6.6	7.8	7.5
54	9.68 420	23	9.74 196	30	0.25 804	9.94 224	7	6	3	11.1	12.9	12.5
55	9.68 443	23	9.74 226	30	0.25 774	9.94 217	7	**5**	4	15.5	18.1	17.5
56	9.68 466	23	9.74 256	30	0.25 744	9.94 210	7	4	5	19.9	23.2	22.5
57	9.68 489	23	9.74 286	30	0.25 714	9.94 203	7	3	6	24.4	28.4	27.5
58	9.68 512	22	9.74 316	29	0.25 684	9.94 196	7	2	7	28.8	—	—
59	9.68 534	23	9.74 345	30	0.25 655	9.94 189	7	1				
60	9.68 557		9.74 375		0.25 625	9.94 182		**0**				

′	L. Cos.	d.	L. Cot.	c.d.	L. Tan.	L. Sin.	d.	′	P. P.		

118° (298°) (241°) **61°**

LOGARITHMS OF THE TRIGONOMETRIC FUNCTIONS

′	L. Sin.	d.	L. Tan.	c.d.	L. Cot.	L. Cos.	d.	′
0	9.68 557	23	9.74 375	30	0.25 625	9.94 182	7	60
1	9.68 580	23	9.74 405	30	0.25 595	9.94 175	7	59
2	9.68 603	22	9.74 435	30	0.25 565	9.94 168	7	58
3	9.68 625	23	9.74 465	29	0.25 535	9.94 161	7	57
4	9.68 648	23	9.74 494	30	0.25 506	9.94 154	7	56
5	9.68 671	23	9.74 524	30	0.25 476	9.94 147	7	55
6	9.68 694	22	9.74 554	29	0.25 446	9.94 140	7	54
7	9.68 716	23	9.74 583	30	0.25 417	9.94 133	7	53
8	9.68 739	23	9.74 613	30	0.25 387	9.94 126	7	52
9	9.68 762	22	9.74 643	30	0.25 357	9.94 119	7	51
10	9.68 784	23	9.74 673	29	0.25 327	9.94 112	7	50
11	9.68 807	22	9.74 702	30	0.25 298	9.94 105	7	49
12	9.68 829	23	9.74 732	30	0.25 268	9.94 098	8	48
13	9.68 852	23	9.74 762	29	0.25 238	9.94 090	7	47
14	9.68 875	22	9.74 791	30	0.25 209	9.94 083	7	46
15	9.68 897	23	9.74 821	30	0.25 179	9.94 076	7	45
16	9.68 920	22	9.74 851	29	0.25 149	9.94 069	7	44
17	9.68 942	23	9.74 880	30	0.25 120	9.94 062	7	43
18	9.68 965	22	9.74 910	29	0.25 090	9.94 055	7	42
19	9.68 987	23	9.74 939	30	0.25 061	9.94 048	7	41
20	9.69 010	22	9.74 969	29	0.25 031	9.94 041	7	40
21	9.69 032	23	9.74 998	30	0.25 002	9.94 034	7	39
22	9.69 055	22	9.75 028	30	0.24 972	9.94 027	7	38
23	9.69 077	23	9.75 058	29	0.24 942	9.94 020	8	37
24	9.69 100	22	9.75 087	30	0.24 913	9.94 012	7	36
25	9.69 122	22	9.75 117	29	0.24 883	9.94 005	7	35
26	9.69 144	23	9.75 146	30	0.24 854	9.93 998	7	34
27	9.69 167	22	9.75 176	29	0.24 824	9.93 991	7	33
28	9.69 189	23	9.75 205	30	0.24 795	9.93 984	7	32
29	9.69 212	22	9.75 235	29	0.24 765	9.93 977	7	31
30	9.69 234	22	9.75 264	30	0.24 736	9.93 970	7	30
31	9.69 256	23	9.75 294	29	0.24 706	9.93 963	8	29
32	9.69 279	22	9.75 323	30	0.24 677	9.93 955	7	28
33	9.69 301	22	9.75 353	29	0.24 647	9.93 948	7	27
34	9.69 323	22	9.75 382	29	0.24 618	9.93 941	7	26
35	9.69 345	23	9.75 411	30	0.24 589	9.93 934	7	25
36	9.69 368	22	9.75 441	29	0.24 559	9.93 927	7	24
37	9.69 390	22	9.75 470	30	0.24 530	9.93 920	8	23
38	9.69 412	22	9.75 500	29	0.24 500	9.93 912	7	22
39	9.69 434	22	9.75 529	29	0.24 471	9.93 905	7	21
40	9.69 456	23	9.75 558	30	0.24 442	9.93 898	7	20
41	9.69 479	22	9.75 588	29	0.24 412	9.93 891	7	19
42	9.69 501	22	9.75 617	30	0.24 383	9.93 884	8	18
43	9.69 523	22	9.75 647	29	0.24 353	9.93 876	7	17
44	9.69 545	22	9.75 676	29	0.24 324	9.93 869	7	16
45	9.69 567	22	9.75 705	30	0.24 295	9.93 862	7	15
46	9.69 589	22	9.75 735	29	0.24 265	9.93 855	8	14
47	9.69 611	22	9.75 764	29	0.24 236	9.93 847	7	13
48	9.69 633	22	9.75 793	29	0.24 207	9.93 840	7	12
49	9.69 655	22	9.75 822	30	0.24 178	9.93 833	7	11
50	9.69 677	22	9.75 852	29	0.24 148	9.93 826	7	10
51	9.69 699	22	9.75 881	29	0.24 119	9.93 819	8	9
52	9.69 721	22	9.75 910	29	0.24 090	9.93 811	7	8
53	9.69 743	22	9.75 939	30	0.24 061	9.93 804	7	7
54	9.69 765	22	9.75 969	29	0.24 031	9.93 797	8	6
55	9.69 787	22	9.75 998	29	0.24 002	9.93 789	7	5
56	9.69 809	22	9.76 027	29	0.23 973	9.93 782	7	4
57	9.69 831	22	9.76 056	30	0.23 944	9.93 775	7	3
58	9.69 853	22	9.76 086	29	0.23 914	9.93 768	8	2
59	9.69 875	22	9.76 115	29	0.23 885	9.93 760	7	1
60	9.69 897		9.76 144		0.23 856	9.93 753		0
′	L. Cos.	d.	L. Cot.	c.d.	L. Tan.	L. Sin.	d.	′

P. P.

″	30	29	23
1	0.5	0.5	0.4
2	1.0	1.0	0.8
3	1.5	1.4	1.2
4	2.0	1.9	1.5
5	2.5	2.4	1.9
6	3.0	2.9	2.3
7	3.5	3.4	2.7
8	4.0	3.9	3.1
9	4.5	4.4	3.4
10	5.0	4.8	3.8
20	10.0	9.7	7.7
30	15.0	14.5	11.5
40	20.0	19.3	15.3
50	25.0	24.2	19.2

″	22	8	7
1	0.4	0.1	0.1
2	0.7	0.3	0.2
3	1.1	0.4	0.4
4	1.5	0.5	0.5
5	1.8	0.7	0.6
6	2.2	0.8	0.7
7	2.6	0.9	0.8
8	2.9	1.1	0.9
9	3.3	1.2	1.0
10	3.7	1.3	1.2
20	7.3	2.7	2.3
30	11.0	4.0	3.5
40	14.7	5.3	4.7
50	18.3	6.7	5.8

	8 / 30	8 / 29
0		
1	1.9	1.8
2	5.6	5.4
3	9.4	9.1
4	13.1	12.7
5	16.9	16.3
6	20.6	19.9
7	24.4	23.6
8	28.1	27.2

	7 / 30	7 / 29
0		
1	2.1	2.1
2	6.4	6.2
3	10.7	10.4
4	15.0	14.5
5	19.3	18.6
6	23.6	22.8
7	27.9	26.9

LOGARITHMS OF THE TRIGONOMETRIC FUNCTIONS

′	L. Sin.	d.	L. Tan.	c.d.	L. Cot.	L. Cos.	d.	′
0	9.69 897	22	9.76 144	29	0.23 856	9.93 753	7	60
1	9.69 919	22	9.76 173	29	0.23 827	9.93 746	8	59
2	9.69 941	22	9.76 202	29	0.23 798	9.93 738	7	58
3	9.69 963	21	9.76 231	30	0.23 769	9.93 731	7	57
4	9.69 984	22	9.76 261	29	0.23 739	9.93 724	7	56
5	9.70 006	22	9.76 290	29	0.23 710	9.93 717	8	55
6	9.70 028	22	9.76 319	29	0.23 681	9.93 709	7	54
7	9.70 050	22	9.76 348	29	0.23 652	9.93 702	7	53
8	9.70 072	21	9.76 377	29	0.23 623	9.93 695	8	52
9	9.70 093	22	9.76 406	29	0.23 594	9.93 687	7	51
10	9.70 115	22	9.76 435	29	0.23 565	9.93 680	7	50
11	9.70 137	22	9.76 464	29	0.23 536	9.93 673	8	49
12	9.70 159	21	9.76 493	29	0.23 507	9.93 665	7	48
13	9.70 180	22	9.76 522	29	0.23 478	9.93 658	8	47
14	9.70 202	22	9.76 551	29	0.23 449	9.93 650	7	46
15	9.70 224	21	9.76 580	29	0.23 420	9.93 643	7	45
16	9.70 245	22	9.76 609	30	0.23 391	9.93 636	8	44
17	9.70 267	21	9.76 639	29	0.23 361	9.93 628	7	43
18	9.70 288	22	9.76 668	29	0.23 332	9.93 621	7	42
19	9.70 310	22	9.76 697	28	0.23 303	9.93 614	8	41
20	9.70 332	21	9.76 725	29	0.23 275	9.93 606	7	40
21	9.70 353	22	9.76 754	29	0.23 246	9.93 599	8	39
22	9.70 375	21	9.76 783	29	0.23 217	9.93 591	7	38
23	9.70 396	22	9.76 812	29	0.23 188	9.93 584	7	37
24	9.70 418	21	9.76 841	29	0.23 159	9.93 577	8	36
25	9.70 439	22	9.76 870	29	0.23 130	9.93 569	7	35
26	9.70 461	21	9.76 899	29	0.23 101	9.93 562	8	34
27	9.70 482	22	9.76 928	29	0.23 072	9.93 554	7	33
28	9.70 504	21	9.76 957	29	0.23 043	9.93 547	8	32
29	9.70 525	22	9.76 986	29	0.23 014	9.93 539	7	31
30	9.70 547	21	9.77 015	29	0.22 985	9.93 532	7	30
31	9.70 568	22	9.77 044	29	0.22 956	9.93 525	8	29
32	9.70 590	21	9.77 073	28	0.22 927	9.93 517	7	28
33	9.70 611	22	9.77 101	29	0.22 899	9.93 510	8	27
34	9.70 633	21	9.77 130	29	0.22 870	9.93 502	7	26
35	9.70 654	21	9.77 159	29	0.22 841	9.93 495	7	25
36	9.70 675	22	9.77 188	29	0.22 812	9.93 487	8	24
37	9.70 697	21	9.77 217	29	0.22 783	9.93 480	8	23
38	9.70 718	21	9.77 246	28	0.22 754	9.93 472	7	22
39	9.70 739	22	9.77 274	29	0.22 726	9.93 465	8	21
40	9.70 761	21	9.77 303	29	0.22 697	9.93 457	7	20
41	9.70 782	21	9.77 332	29	0.22 668	9.93 450	8	19
42	9.70 803	21	9.77 361	29	0.22 639	9.93 442	7	18
43	9.70 824	22	9.77 390	28	0.22 610	9.93 435	8	17
44	9.70 846	21	9.77 418	29	0.22 582	9.93 427	7	16
45	9.70 867	21	9.77 447	29	0.22 553	9.93 420	8	15
46	9.70 888	21	9.77 476	29	0.22 524	9.93 412	7	14
47	9.70 909	22	9.77 505	28	0.22 495	9.93 405	8	13
48	9.70 931	21	9.77 533	29	0.22 467	9.93 397	7	12
49	9.70 952	21	9.77 562	29	0.22 438	9.93 390	8	11
50	9.70 973	21	9.77 591	28	0.22 409	9.93 382	7	10
51	9.70 994	21	9.77 619	29	0.22 381	9.93 375	8	9
52	9.71 015	21	9.77 648	29	0.22 352	9.93 367	7	8
53	9.71 036	22	9.77 677	29	0.22 323	9.93 360	8	7
54	9.71 058	21	9.77 706	28	0.22 294	9.93 352	8	6
55	9.71 079	21	9.77 734	29	0.22 266	9.93 344	7	5
56	9.71 100	21	9.77 763	28	0.22 237	9.93 337	8	4
57	9.71 121	21	9.77 791	29	0.22 209	9.93 329	7	3
58	9.71 142	21	9.77 820	29	0.22 180	9.93 322	8	2
59	9.71 163	21	9.77 849	28	0.22 151	9.93 314	7	1
60	9.71 184		9.77 877		0.22 123	9.93 307		0
′	L. Cos.	d.	L. Cot.	c.d.	L. Tan.	L. Sin.	d.	′

P.P.

″	30	29	28
1	0.5	0.5	0.5
2	1.0	1.0	0.9
3	1.5	1.4	1.4
4	2.0	1.9	1.9
5	2.5	2.4	2.3
6	3.0	2.9	2.8
7	3.5	3.4	3.3
8	4.0	3.9	3.7
9	4.5	4.4	4.2
10	5.0	4.8	4.7
20	10.0	9.7	9.3
30	15.0	14.5	14.0
40	20.0	19.3	18.7
50	25.0	24.2	23.3

″	22	21
1	0.4	0.4
2	0.7	0.7
3	1.1	1.0
4	1.5	1.4
5	1.8	1.8
6	2.2	2.1
7	2.6	2.4
8	2.9	2.8
9	3.3	3.2
10	3.7	3.5
20	7.3	7.0
30	11.0	10.5
40	14.7	14.0
50	18.3	17.5

″	8	7
1	0.1	0.1
2	0.3	0.2
3	0.4	0.4
4	0.5	0.5
5	0.7	0.6
6	0.8	0.7
7	0.9	0.8
8	1.1	0.9
9	1.2	1.0
10	1.3	1.2
20	2.7	2.3
30	4.0	3.5
40	5.3	4.7
50	6.7	5.8

	7	7	7
	30	29	28
0			
1	2.1	2.1	2.0
2	6.4	6.2	6.0
3	10.7	10.4	10.0
4	15.0	14.5	14.0
5	19.3	18.6	18.0
6	23.6	22.8	22.0
7	27.9	26.9	26.0

LOGARITHMS OF THE TRIGONOMETRIC FUNCTIONS

′	L. Sin.	d.	L. Tan.	c.d.	L. Cot.	L. Cos.	d.	′	P. P.		
0	9.71 184	21	9.77 877	29	0.22 123	9.93 307	8	60			
1	9.71 205	21	9.77 906	29	0.22 094	9.93 299	8	59	″	29	28
2	9.71 226	21	9.77 935	28	0.22 065	9.93 291	8	58	1	0.5	0.5
3	9.71 247	21	9.77 963	29	0.22 037	9.93 284	7	57	2	1.0	0.9
4	9.71 268	21	9.77 992	28	0.22 008	9.93 276	8	56	3	1.4	1.4
							7		4	1.9	1.9
5	9.71 289	21	9.78 020	29	0.21 980	9.93 269	8	55			
6	9.71 310	21	9.78 049	28	0.21 951	9.93 261	8	54	5	2.4	2.3
7	9.71 331	21	9.78 077	29	0.21 923	9.93 253	7	53	6	2.9	2.8
8	9.71 352	21	9.78 106	29	0.21 894	9.93 246	8	52	7	3.4	3.3
9	9.71 373	20	9.78 135	28	0.21 865	9.93 238	8	51	8	3.9	3.7
									9	4.4	4.2
10	9.71 393	21	9.78 163	29	0.21 837	9.93 230	7	50			
11	9.71 414	21	9.78 192	28	0.21 808	9.93 223	8	49	10	4.8	4.7
12	9.71 435	21	9.78 220	29	0.21 780	9.93 215	8	48	20	9.7	9.3
13	9.71 456	21	9.78 249	28	0.21 751	9.93 207	7	47	30	14.5	14.0
14	9.71 477	21	9.78 277	29	0.21 723	9.93 200	8	46	40	19.3	18.7
									50	24.2	23.3
15	9.71 498	21	9.78 306	28	0.21 694	9.93 192	8	45			
16	9.71 519	20	9.78 334	29	0.21 666	9.93 184	7	44	″	21	20
17	9.71 539	21	9.78 363	28	0.21 637	9.93 177	8	43	1	0.4	0.3
18	9.71 560	21	9.78 391	28	0.21 609	9.93 169	8	42	2	0.7	0.7
19	9.71 581	21	9.78 419	29	0.21 581	9.93 161	7	41	3	1.0	1.0
									4	1.4	1.3
20	9.71 602	20	9.78 448	28	0.21 552	9.93 154	8	40	5	1.8	1.7
21	9.71 622	21	9.78 476	29	0.21 524	9.93 146	8	39	6	2.1	2.0
22	9.71 643	21	9.78 505	28	0.21 495	9.93 138	7	38	7	2.4	2.3
23	9.71 664	21	9.78 533	29	0.21 467	9.93 131	8	37	8	2.8	2.7
24	9.71 685	20	9.78 562	28	0.21 438	9.93 123	8	36	9	3.2	3.0
25	9.71 705	21	9.78 590	28	0.21 410	9.93 115	7	35			
26	9.71 726	21	9.78 618	29	0.21 382	9.93 108	8	34	10	3.5	3.3
27	9.71 747	20	9.78 647	28	0.21 353	9.93 100	8	33	20	7.0	6.7
28	9.71 767	21	9.78 675	29	0.21 325	9.93 092	8	32	30	10.5	10.0
29	9.71 788	21	9.78 704	28	0.21 296	9.93 084	7	31	40	14.0	13.3
									50	17.5	16.7
30	9.71 809	20	9.78 732	28	0.21 268	9.93 077	8	30			
31	9.71 829	21	9.78 760	29	0.21 240	9.93 069	8	29	″	8	7
32	9.71 850	20	9.78 789	28	0.21 211	9.93 061	8	28	1	0.1	0.1
33	9.71 870	21	9.78 817	28	0.21 183	9.93 053	7	27	2	0.3	0.2
34	9.71 891	20	9.78 845	29	0.21 155	9.93 046	8	26	3	0.4	0.4
									4	0.5	0.5
35	9.71 911	21	9.78 874	28	0.21 126	9.93 038	8	25			
36	9.71 932	20	9.78 902	28	0.21 098	9.93 030	8	24	5	0.7	0.6
37	9.71 952	21	9.78 930	29	0.21 070	9.93 022	8	23	6	0.8	0.7
38	9.71 973	21	9.78 959	28	0.21 041	9.93 014	7	22	7	0.9	0.8
39	9.71 994	20	9.78 987	28	0.21 013	9.93 007	8	21	8	1.1	0.9
									9	1.2	1.0
40	9.72 014	20	9.79 015	28	0.20 985	9.92 999	8	20	10	1.3	1.2
41	9.72 034	21	9.79 043	29	0.20 957	9.92 991	8	19	20	2.7	2.3
42	9.72 055	20	9.79 072	28	0.20 928	9.92 983	7	18	30	4.0	3.5
43	9.72 075	21	9.79 100	28	0.20 900	9.92 976	8	17	40	5.3	4.7
44	9.72 096	20	9.79 128	28	0.20 872	9.92 968	8	16	50	6.7	5.8
45	9.72 116	21	9.79 156	29	0.20 844	9.92 960	8	15			
46	9.72 137	20	9.79 185	28	0.20 815	9.92 952	8	14			
47	9.72 157	20	9.79 213	28	0.20 787	9.92 944	8	13			
48	9.72 177	21	9.79 241	28	0.20 759	9.92 936	7	12			
49	9.72 198	20	9.79 269	28	0.20 731	9.92 929	8	11			
50	9.72 218	20	9.79 297	29	0.20 703	9.92 921	8	10		8	8	8
51	9.72 238	21	9.79 326	28	0.20 674	9.92 913	8	9		30	29	28
52	9.72 259	20	9.79 354	28	0.20 646	9.92 905	8	8				
53	9.72 279	20	9.79 382	28	0.20 618	9.92 897	8	7	1	1.9	1.8	1.8
54	9.72 299	21	9.79 410	28	0.20 590	9.92 889	8	6	2	5.6	5.4	5.2
									3	9.4	9.1	8.8
55	9.72 320	20	9.79 438	28	0.20 562	9.92 881	7	5	4	13.1	12.7	12.2
56	9.72 340	20	9.79 466	29	0.20 534	9.92 874	8	4	5	16.9	16.3	15.8
57	9.72 360	21	9.79 495	28	0.20 505	9.92 866	8	3	6	20.6	19.9	19.2
58	9.72 381	20	9.79 523	28	0.20 477	9.92 858	8	2	7	24.4	23.6	22.8
59	9.72 401	20	9.79 551	28	0.20 449	9.92 850	8	1	8	28.1	27.2	26.2
60	9.72 421		9.79 579		0.20 421	9.92 842		0				
′	L. Cos.	d.	L. Cot.	c.d.	L. Tan.	L.Sin.	d.	′	P. P.		

LOGARITHMS OF THE TRIGONOMETRIC FUNCTIONS

32° (212°) (327°) **147°**

′	L. Sin.	d.	L. Tan.	c.d.	L. Cot.	L. Cos.	d.	′		P.P.		
0	9.72 421	20	9.79 579	28	0.20 421	9.92 842	8	60	″	**29**	**28**	**27**
1	9.72 441	20	9.79 607	28	0.20 393	9.92 834	8	59	1	0.5	0.5	0.4
2	9.72 461	21	9.79 635	28	0.20 365	9.92 826	8	58	2	1.0	0.9	0.9
3	9.72 482	20	9.79 663	28	0.20 337	9.92 818	8	57	3	1.4	1.4	1.4
4	9.72 502	20	9.79 691	28	0.20 309	9.92 810	7	56	4	1.9	1.9	1.8
5	9.72 522	20	9.79 719	28	0.20 281	9.92 803	8	55				
6	9.72 542	20	9.79 747	29	0.20 253	9.92 795	8	54	5	2.4	2.3	2.2
7	9.72 562	20	9.79 776	28	0.20 224	9.92 787	8	53	6	2.9	2.8	2.7
8	9.72 582	20	9.79 804	28	0.20 196	9.92 779	8	52	7	3.4	3.3	3.2
9	9.72 602	20	9.79 832	28	0.20 168	9.92 771	8	51	8	3.9	3.7	3.6
									9	4.4	4.2	4.0
10	9.72 622	21	9.79 860	28	0.20 140	9.92 763	8	50	10	4.8	4.7	4.5
11	9.72 643	20	9.79 888	28	0.20 112	9.92 755	8	49	20	9.7	9.3	9.0
12	9.72 663	20	9.79 916	28	0.20 084	9.92 747	8	48	30	14.5	14.0	13.5
13	9.72 683	20	9.79 944	28	0.20 056	9.92 739	8	47	40	19.3	18.7	18.0
14	9.72 703	20	9.79 972	28	0.20 028	9.92 731	8	46	50	24.2	23.3	22.5
15	9.72 723	20	9.80 000	28	0.20 000	9.92 723	8	45	″	**21**	**20**	**19**
16	9.72 743	20	9.80 028	28	0.19 972	9.92 715	8	44	1	0.4	0.3	0.3
17	9.72 763	20	9.80 056	28	0.19 944	9.92 707	8	43	2	0.7	0.7	0.6
18	9.72 783	20	9.80 084	28	0.19 916	9.92 699	8	42	3	1.0	1.0	1.0
19	9.72 803	20	9.80 112	28	0.19 888	9.92 691	8	41	4	1.4	1.3	1.3
20	9.72 823	20	9.80 140	28	0.19 860	9.92 683	8	40	5	1.8	1.7	1.6
21	9.72 843	20	9.80 168	27	0.19 832	9.92 675	8	39	6	2.1	2.0	1.9
22	9.72 863	20	9.80 195	28	0.19 805	9.92 667	8	38	7	2.4	2.3	2.2
23	9.72 883	19	9.80 223	28	0.19 777	9.92 659	8	37	8	2.8	2.7	2.5
24	9.72 902	20	9.80 251	28	0.19 749	9.92 651	8	36	9	3.2	3.0	2.8
25	9.72 922	20	9.80 279	28	0.19 721	9.92 643	8	35	10	3.5	3.3	3.2
26	9.72 942	20	9.80 307	28	0.19 693	9.92 635	8	34	20	7.0	6.7	6.3
27	9.72 962	20	9.80 335	28	0.19 665	9.92 627	8	33	30	10.5	10.0	9.5
28	9.72 982	20	9.80 363	28	0.19 637	9.92 619	8	32	40	14.0	13.3	12.7
29	9.73 002	20	9.80 391	28	0.19 609	9.92 611	8	31	50	17.5	16.7	15.8
30	9.73 022	19	9.80 419	28	0.19 581	9.92 603	8	30	″	**9**	**8**	**7**
31	9.73 041	20	9.80 447	27	0.19 553	9.92 595	8	29	1	0.2	0.1	0.1
32	9.73 061	20	9.80 474	28	0.19 526	9.92 587	8	28	2	0.3	0.3	0.2
33	9.73 081	20	9.80 502	28	0.19 498	9.92 579	8	27	3	0.4	0.4	0.4
34	9.73 101	20	9.80 530	28	0.19 470	9.92 571	8	26	4	0.6	0.5	0.5
35	9.73 121	19	9.80 558	28	0.19 442	9.92 563	8	25	5	0.8	0.7	0.6
36	9.73 140	20	9.80 586	28	0.19 414	9.92 555	9	24	6	0.9	0.8	0.7
37	9.73 160	20	9.80 614	28	0.19 386	9.92 546	8	23	7	1.0	0.9	0.8
38	9.73 180	20	9.80 642	27	0.19 358	9.92 538	8	22	8	1.2	1.1	0.9
39	9.73 200	19	9.80 669	28	0.19 331	9.92 530	8	21	9	1.4	1.2	1.0
40	9.73 219	20	9.80 697	28	0.19 303	9.92 522	8	20	10	1.5	1.3	1.2
41	9.73 239	20	9.80 725	28	0.19 275	9.92 514	8	19	20	3.0	2.7	2.3
42	9.73 259	19	9.80 753	28	0.19 247	9.92 506	8	18	30	4.5	4.0	3.5
43	9.73 278	20	9.80 781	27	0.19 219	9.92 498	8	17	40	6.0	5.3	4.7
44	9.73 298	20	9.80 808	28	0.19 192	9.92 490	8	16	50	7.5	6.7	5.8
45	9.73 318	19	9.80 836	28	0.19 164	9.92 482	9	15				
46	9.73 337	20	9.80 864	28	0.19 136	9.92 473	8	14				
47	9.73 357	20	9.80 892	27	0.19 108	9.92 465	8	13		**8**	**8**	**7**
48	9.73 377	19	9.80 919	28	0.19 081	9.92 457	8	12		—	—	—
49	9.73 396	20	9.80 947	28	0.19 053	9.92 449	8	11		**29**	**28**	**28**
50	9.73 416	19	9.80 975	28	0.19 025	9.92 441	8	10				
51	9.73 435	20	9.81 003	27	0.18 997	9.92 433	8	9	0	1.8	1.8	2.0
52	9.73 455	19	9.81 030	28	0.18 970	9.92 425	9	8	1	5.4	5.2	6.0
53	9.73 474	20	9.81 058	28	0.18 942	9.92 416	8	7	2	9.1	8.8	10.0
54	9.73 494	19	9.81 086	27	0.18 914	9.92 408	8	6	3	12.7	12.2	14.0
									4	16.3	15.8	18.0
55	9.73 513	20	9.81 113	28	0.18 887	9.92 400	8	5	5	19.9	19.2	22.0
56	9.73 533	19	9.81 141	28	0.18 859	9.92 392	8	4	6	23.6	22.8	26.0
57	9.73 552	20	9.81 169	27	0.18 831	9.92 384	8	3	7	27.2	26.2	—
58	9.73 572	19	9.81 196	28	0.18 804	9.92 376	9	2	8			
59	9.73 591	20	9.81 224	28	0.18 776	9.92 367	8	1				
60	9.73 611		9.81 252		0.18 748	9.92 359		0				
′	L. Cos.	d.	L. Cot.	c.d.	L. Tan.	L. Sin.	d.	′		P.P.		

122° (302°) (237°) **57°**

78

LOGARITHMS OF THE TRIGONOMETRIC FUNCTIONS

'	L. Sin.	d.	L. Tan.	c.d.	L. Cot.	L. Cos.	d.	'
0	9.73 611	19	9.81 252	27	0.18 748	9.92 359	8	60
1	9.73 630	20	9.81 279	28	0.18 721	9.92 351	8	59
2	9.73 650	19	9.81 307	28	0.18 693	9.92 343	8	58
3	9.73 669	20	9.81 335	27	0.18 665	9.92 335	9	57
4	9.73 689	19	9.81 362	28	0.18 638	9.92 326	8	56
5	9.73 708	19	9.81 390	28	0.18 610	9.92 318	8	55
6	9.73 727	20	9.81 418	27	0.18 582	9.92 310	8	54
7	9.73 747	19	9.81 445	28	0.18 555	9.92 302	9	53
8	9.73 766	19	9.81 473	27	0.18 527	9.92 293	8	52
9	9.73 785	20	9.81 500	28	0.18 500	9.92 285	8	51
10	9.73 805	19	9.81 528	28	0.18 472	9.92 277	8	50
11	9.73 824	19	9.81 556	27	0.18 444	9.92 269	9	49
12	9.73 843	20	9.81 583	28	0.18 417	9.92 260	8	48
13	9.73 863	19	9.81 611	27	0.18 389	9.92 252	8	47
14	9.73 882	19	9.81 638	28	0.18 362	9.92 244	9	46
15	9.73 901	20	9.81 666	27	0.18 334	9.92 235	8	45
16	9.73 921	19	9.81 693	28	0.18 307	9.92 227	8	44
17	9.73 940	19	9.81 721	27	0.18 279	9.92 219	8	43
18	9.73 959	19	9.81 748	28	0.18 252	9.92 211	9	42
19	9.73 978	19	9.81 776	27	0.18 224	9.92 202	8	41
20	9.73 997	20	9.81 803	28	0.18 197	9.92 194	8	40
21	9.74 017	19	9.81 831	27	0.18 169	9.92 186	9	39
22	9.74 036	19	9.81 858	28	0.18 142	9.92 177	8	38
23	9.74 055	19	9.81 886	27	0.18 114	9.92 169	8	37
24	9.74 074	19	9.81 913	28	0.18 087	9.92 160	9	36
25	9.74 093	20	9.81 941	27	0.18 059	9.92 152	8	35
26	9.74 113	19	9.81 968	28	0.18 032	9.92 144	8	34
27	9.74 132	19	9.81 996	27	0.18 004	9.92 136	9	33
28	9.74 151	19	9.82 023	28	0.17 977	9.92 127	8	32
29	9.74 170	19	9.82 051	27	0.17 949	9.92 119	8	31
30	9.74 189	19	9.82 078	28	0.17 922	9.92 111	9	30
31	9.74 208	19	9.82 106	27	0.17 894	9.92 102	8	29
32	9.74 227	19	9.82 133	28	0.17 867	9.92 094	8	28
33	9.74 246	19	9.82 161	27	0.17 839	9.92 086	9	27
34	9.74 265	19	9.82 188	27	0.17 812	9.92 077	8	26
35	9.74 284	19	9.82 215	28	0.17 785	9.92 069	9	25
36	9.74 303	19	9.82 243	27	0.17 757	9.92 060	8	24
37	9.74 322	19	9.82 270	28	0.17 730	9.92 052	8	23
38	9.74 341	19	9.82 298	27	0.17 702	9.92 044	9	22
39	9.74 360	19	9.82 325	27	0.17 675	9.92 035	8	21
40	9.74 379	19	9.82 352	28	0.17 648	9.92 027	9	20
41	9.74 398	19	9.82 380	27	0.17 620	9.92 018	8	19
42	9.74 417	19	9.82 407	28	0.17 593	9.92 010	8	18
43	9.74 436	19	9.82 435	27	0.17 565	9.92 002	9	17
44	9.74 455	19	9.82 462	27	0.17 538	9.91 993	8	16
45	9.74 474	19	9.82 489	28	0.17 511	9.91 985	9	15
46	9.74 493	19	9.82 517	27	0.17 483	9.91 976	8	14
47	9.74 512	19	9.82 544	27	0.17 456	9.91 968	9	13
48	9.74 531	18	9.82 571	28	0.17 429	9.91 959	8	12
49	9.74 549	19	9.82 599	27	0.17 401	9.91 951	9	11
50	9.74 568	19	9.82 626	27	0.17 374	9.91 942	8	10
51	9.74 587	19	9.82 653	28	0.17 347	9.91 934	9	9
52	9.74 606	19	9.82 681	27	0.17 319	9.91 925	8	8
53	9.74 625	19	9.82 708	27	0.17 292	9.91 917	9	7
54	9.74 644	18	9.82 735	27	0.17 265	9.91 908	8	6
55	9.74 662	19	9.82 762	28	0.17 238	9.91 900	9	5
56	9.74 681	19	9.82 790	27	0.17 210	9.91 891	8	4
57	9.74 700	19	9.82 817	27	0.17 183	9.91 883	9	3
58	9.74 719	18	9.82 844	27	0.17 156	9.91 874	8	2
59	9.74 737	19	9.82 871	28	0.17 129	9.91 866	9	1
60	9.74 756		9.82 899		0.17 101	9.91 857		0

| ' | L. Cos. | d. | L. Cot. | c.d. | L. Tan. | L. Sin. | d. | ' |

P. P.

"	28	27
1	0.5	0.4
2	0.9	0.9
3	1.4	1.4
4	1.9	1.8
5	2.3	2.2
6	2.8	2.7
7	3.3	3.2
8	3.7	3.6
9	4.2	4.0
10	4.7	4.5
20	9.3	9.0
30	14.0	13.5
40	18.7	18.0
50	23.3	22.5

"	20	19	18
1	0.3	0.3	0.3
2	0.7	0.6	0.6
3	1.0	1.0	0.9
4	1.3	1.3	1.2
5	1.7	1.6	1.5
6	2.0	1.9	1.8
7	2.3	2.2	2.1
8	2.7	2.5	2.4
9	3.0	2.8	2.7
10	3.3	3.2	3.0
20	6.7	6.3	6.0
30	10.0	9.5	9.0
40	13.3	12.7	12.0
50	16.7	15.8	15.0

"	9	8
1	0.2	0.1
2	0.3	0.3
3	0.4	0.4
4	0.6	0.5
5	0.8	0.7
6	0.9	0.8
7	1.0	0.9
8	1.2	1.1
9	1.4	1.2
10	1.5	1.3
20	3.0	2.7
30	4.5	4.0
40	6.0	5.3
50	7.5	6.7

	9	9	8
	28	27	27
0	1.6	1.5	1.7
1	4.7	4.5	5.1
2	7.8	7.5	8.4
3	10.9	10.5	11.8
4	14.0	13.5	15.2
5	17.1	16.5	18.6
6	20.2	19.5	21.9
7	23.3	22.5	25.3
8	26.4	25.5	—

34° (214°)   **(325°) 145°**

′	L. Sin.	d.	L. Tan.	c.d.	L. Cot.	L. Cos.	d.	′	P. P.		
0	9.74 756	19	9.82 899	27	0.17 101	9.91 857	8	60			
1	9.74 775	19	9.82 926	27	0.17 074	9.91 849	9	59	″	**28** **27** **26**	
2	9.74 794	18	9.82 953	27	0.17 047	9.91 840	8	58	1	0.5 0.4 0.4	
3	9.74 812	19	9.82 980	28	0.17 020	9.91 832	8	57	2	0.9 0.9 0.9	
4	9.74 831	19	9.83 008	27	0.16 992	9.91 823	8	56	3	1.4 1.4 1.3	
									4	1.9 1.8 1.7	
5	9.74 850	18	9.83 035	27	0.16 965	9.91 815	9	55			
6	9.74 868	19	9.83 062	27	0.16 938	9.91 806	8	54	5	2.3 2.2 2.2	
7	9.74 887	19	9.83 089	28	0.16 911	9.91 798	9	53	6	2.8 2.7 2.6	
8	9.74 906	18	9.83 117	27	0.16 883	9.91 789	8	52	7	3.3 3.2 3.0	
9	9.74 924	19	9.83 144	27	0.16 856	9.91 781	9	51	8	3.7 3.6 3.5	
									9	4.2 4.0 3.9	
10	9.74 943	18	9.83 171	27	0.16 829	9.91 772	9	50			
11	9.74 961	19	9.83 198	27	0.16 802	9.91 763	8	49	10	4.7 4.5 4.3	
12	9.74 980	19	9.83 225	27	0.16 775	9.91 755	9	48	20	9.3 9.0 8.7	
13	9.74 999	18	9.83 252	28	0.16 748	9.91 746	8	47	30	14.0 13.5 13.0	
14	9.75 017	19	9.83 280	27	0.16 720	9.91 738	9	46	40	18.7 18.0 17.3	
									50	23.3 22.5 21.7	
15	9.75 036	18	9.83 307	27	0.16 693	9.91 729	9	45			
16	9.75 054	19	9.83 334	27	0.16 666	9.91 720	8	44	″	**19** **18**	
17	9.75 073	18	9.83 361	27	0.16 639	9.91 712	9	43	1	0.3 0.3	
18	9.75 091	19	9.83 388	27	0.16 612	9.91 703	8	42	2	0.6 0.6	
19	9.75 110	18	9.83 415	27	0.16 585	9.91 695	9	41	3	1.0 0.9	
									4	1.3 1.2	
20	9.75 128	19	9.83 442	28	0.16 558	9.91 686	9	40			
21	9.75 147	18	9.83 470	27	0.16 530	9.91 677	8	39	5	1.6 1.5	
22	9.75 165	19	9.83 497	27	0.16 503	9.91 669	9	38	6	1.9 1.8	
23	9.75 184	18	9.83 524	27	0.16 476	9.91 660	9	37	7	2.2 2.1	
24	9.75 202	19	9.83 551	27	0.16 449	9.91 651	8	36	8	2.5 2.4	
									9	2.8 2.7	
25	9.75 221	18	9.83 578	27	0.16 422	9.91 643	9	35			
26	9.75 239	19	9.83 605	27	0.16 395	9.91 634	9	34	10	3.2 3.0	
27	9.75 258	18	9.83 632	27	0.16 368	9.91 625	8	33	20	6.3 6.0	
28	9.75 276	18	9.83 659	27	0.16 341	9.91 617	9	32	30	9.5 9.0	
29	9.75 294	19	9.83 686	27	0.16 314	9.91 608	9	31	40	12.7 12.0	
									50	15.8 15.0	
30	9.75 313	18	9.83 713	27	0.16 287	9.91 599	8	30			
31	9.75 331	19	9.83 740	28	0.16 260	9.91 591	9	29	″	**9** **8**	
32	9.75 350	18	9.83 768	27	0.16 232	9.91 582	9	28	1	0.2 0.1	
33	9.75 368	18	9.83 795	27	0.16 205	9.91 573	8	27	2	0.3 0.3	
34	9.75 386	19	9.83 822	27	0.16 178	9.91 565	9	26	3	0.4 0.4	
									4	0.6 0.5	
35	9.75 405	18	9.83 849	27	0.16 151	9.91 556	9	25			
36	9.75 423	18	9.83 876	27	0.16 124	9.91 547	9	24	5	0.8 0.7	
37	9.75 441	18	9.83 903	27	0.16 097	9.91 538	8	23	6	0.9 0.8	
38	9.75 459	19	9.83 930	27	0.16 070	9.91 530	9	22	7	1.0 0.9	
39	9.75 478	18	9.83 957	27	0.16 043	9.91 521	9	21	8	1.2 1.1	
									9	1.4 1.2	
40	9.75 496	18	9.83 984	27	0.16 016	9.91 512	8	20			
41	9.75 514	19	9.84 011	27	0.15 989	9.91 504	9	19	10	1.5 1.3	
42	9.75 533	18	9.84 038	27	0.15 962	9.91 495	9	18	20	3.0 2.7	
43	9.75 551	18	9.84 065	27	0.15 935	9.91 486	9	17	30	4.5 4.0	
44	9.75 569	18	9.84 092	27	0.15 908	9.91 477	8	16	40	6.0 5.3	
										50 7.5 6.7	
45	9.75 587	18	9.84 119	27	0.15 881	9.91 469	9	15			
46	9.75 605	19	9.84 146	27	0.15 854	9.91 460	9	14			
47	9.75 624	18	9.84 173	27	0.15 827	9.91 451	9	13			
48	9.75 642	18	9.84 200	27	0.15 800	9.91 442	9	12			
49	9.75 660	18	9.84 227	27	0.15 773	9.91 433	9	11		**9** **8** **8**	
50	9.75 678	18	9.84 254	26	0.15 746	9.91 425	9	10		**28** **28** **27**	
51	9.75 696	18	9.84 280	27	0.15 720	9.91 416	9	9	0		
52	9.75 714	19	9.84 307	27	0.15 693	9.91 407	9	8	1	1.6 1.8 1.7	
53	9.75 733	18	9.84 334	27	0.15 666	9.91 398	9	7	2	4.7 5.2 5.1	
54	9.75 751	18	9.84 361	27	0.15 639	9.91 389	8	6	3	7.8 8.8 8.4	
									4	10.9 12.2 11.8	
55	9.75 769	18	9.84 388	27	0.15 612	9.91 381	9	5	5	14.0 15.8 15.2	
56	9.75 787	18	9.84 415	27	0.15 585	9.91 372	9	4	6	17.1 19.2 18.6	
57	9.75 805	18	9.84 442	27	0.15 558	9.91 363	9	3	7	20.2 22.8 21.9	
58	9.75 823	18	9.84 469	27	0.15 531	9.91 354	9	2	8	23.3 26.2 25.3	
59	9.75 841	18	9.84 496	27	0.15 504	9.91 345	9	1	9	26.4 — —	
60	9.75 859		9.84 523		0.15 477	9.91 336		0			

′	L. Cos.	d.	L. Cot.	c.d.	L. Tan.	L. Sin.	d.	′	P. P.		

LOGARITHMS OF THE TRIGONOMETRIC FUNCTIONS

′	L. Sin.	d.	L. Tan.	c.d.	L. Cot.	L. Cos.	d.	′
0	9.75 859	18	9.84 523	27	0.15 477	9.91 336	8	60
1	9.75 877	18	9.84 550	26	0.15 450	9.91 328	9	59
2	9.75 895	18	9.84 576	27	0.15 424	9.91 319	9	58
3	9.75 913	18	9.84 603	27	0.15 397	9.91 310	9	57
4	9.75 931	18	9.84 630	27	0.15 370	9.91 301	9	56
5	9.75 949	18	9.84 657	27	0.15 343	9.91 292	9	55
6	9.75 967	18	9.84 684	27	0.15 316	9.91 283	9	54
7	9.75 985	18	9.84 711	27	0.15 289	9.91 274	8	53
8	9.76 003	18	9.84 738	26	0.15 262	9.91 266	9	52
9	9.76 021	18	9.84 764	27	0.15 236	9.91 257	9	51
10	9.76 039	18	9.84 791	27	0.15 209	9.91 248	9	50
11	9.76 057	18	9.84 818	27	0.15 182	9.91 239	9	49
12	9.76 075	18	9.84 845	27	0.15 155	9.91 230	9	48
13	9.76 093	18	9.84 872	27	0.15 128	9.91 221	9	47
14	9.76 111	18	9.84 899	26	0.15 101	9.91 212	9	46
15	9.76 129	17	9.84 925	27	0.15 075	9.91 203	9	45
16	9.76 146	18	9.84 952	27	0.15 048	9.91 194	9	44
17	9.76 164	18	9.84 979	27	0.15 021	9.91 185	9	43
18	9.76 182	18	9.85 006	27	0.14 994	9.91 176	9	42
19	9.76 200	18	9.85 033	26	0.14 967	9.91 167	9	41
20	9.76 218	18	9.85 059	27	0.14 941	9.91 158	9	40
21	9.76 236	17	9.85 086	27	0.14 914	9.91 149	8	39
22	9.76 253	18	9.85 113	27	0.14 887	9.91 141	9	38
23	9.76 271	18	9.85 140	26	0.14 860	9.91 132	9	37
24	9.76 289	18	9.85 166	27	0.14 834	9.91 123	9	36
25	9.76 307	17	9.85 193	27	0.14 807	9.91 114	9	35
26	9.76 324	18	9.85 220	27	0.14 780	9.91 105	9	34
27	9.76 342	18	9.85 247	26	0.14 753	9.91 096	9	33
28	9.76 360	18	9.85 273	27	0.14 727	9.91 087	9	32
29	9.76 378	17	9.85 300	27	0.14 700	9.91 078	9	31
30	9.76 395	18	9.85 327	27	0.14 673	9.91 069	9	30
31	9.76 413	18	9.85 354	26	0.14 646	9.91 060	9	29
32	9.76 431	17	9.85 380	27	0.14 620	9.91 051	9	28
33	9.76 448	18	9.85 407	27	0.14 593	9.91 042	9	27
34	9.76 466	18	9.85 434	26	0.14 566	9.91 033	10	26
35	9.76 484	17	9.85 460	27	0.14 540	9.91 023	9	25
36	9.76 501	18	9.85 487	27	0.14 513	9.91 014	9	24
37	9.76 519	18	9.85 514	26	0.14 486	9.91 005	9	23
38	9.76 537	17	9.85 540	27	0.14 460	9.90 996	9	22
39	9.76 554	18	9.85 567	27	0.14 433	9.90 987	9	21
40	9.76 572	18	9.85 594	26	0.14 406	9.90 978	9	20
41	9.76 590	17	9.85 620	27	0.14 380	9.90 969	9	19
42	9.76 607	18	9.85 647	27	0.14 353	9.90 960	9	18
43	9.76 625	17	9.85 674	26	0.14 326	9.90 951	9	17
44	9.76 642	18	9.85 700	27	0.14 300	9.90 942	9	16
45	9.76 660	17	9.85 727	27	0.14 273	9.90 933	9	15
46	9.76 677	18	9.85 754	26	0.14 246	9.90 924	9	14
47	9.76 695	17	9.85 780	27	0.14 220	9.90 915	9	13
48	9.76 712	18	9.85 807	27	0.14 193	9.90 906	10	12
49	9.76 730	17	9.85 834	26	0.14 166	9.90 896	9	11
50	9.76 747	18	9.85 860	27	0.14 140	9.90 887	9	10
51	9.76 765	17	9.85 887	26	0.14 113	9.90 878	9	9
52	9.76 782	18	9.85 913	27	0.14 087	9.90 869	9	8
53	9.76 800	17	9.85 940	27	0.14 060	9.90 860	9	7
54	9.76 817	18	9.85 967	26	0.14 033	9.90 851	9	6
55	9.76 835	17	9.85 993	27	0.14 007	9.90 842	10	5
56	9.76 852	18	9.86 020	26	0.13 980	9.90 832	9	4
57	9.76 870	17	9.86 046	27	0.13 954	9.90 823	9	3
58	9.76 887	17	9.86 073	27	0.13 927	9.90 814	9	2
59	9.76 904	18	9.86 100	26	0.13 900	9.90 805	9	1
60	9.76 922		9.86 126		0.13 874	9.90 796		0
′	L. Cos.	d.	L. Cot.	c.d.	L. Tan.	L. Sin.	d.	′

P. P.

″	27	26	18
1	0.4	0.4	0.3
2	0.9	0.9	0.6
3	1.4	1.3	0.9
4	1.8	1.7	1.2
5	2.2	2.2	1.5
6	2.7	2.6	1.8
7	3.2	3.0	2.1
8	3.6	3.5	2.4
9	4.0	3.9	2.7
10	4.5	4.3	3.0
20	9.0	8.7	6.0
30	13.5	13.0	9.0
40	18.0	17.3	12.0
50	22.5	21.7	15.0

″	17	10	9	8
1	0.3	0.2	0.2	0.1
2	0.6	0.3	0.3	0.3
3	0.8	0.5	0.4	0.4
4	1.1	0.7	0.6	0.5
5	1.4	0.8	0.8	0.7
6	1.7	1.0	0.9	0.8
7	2.0	1.2	1.0	0.9
8	2.3	1.3	1.2	1.1
9	2.6	1.5	1.4	1.2
10	2.8	1.7	1.5	1.3
20	5.7	3.3	3.0	2.7
30	8.5	5.0	4.5	4.0
40	11.3	6.7	6.0	5.3
50	14.2	8.3	7.5	6.7

	10/27	10/26
0	1.4	1.3
1	4.1	3.9
2	6.8	6.5
3	9.4	9.1
4	12.2	11.7
5	14.8	14.3
6	17.6	16.9
7	20.2	19.5
8	22.9	22.1
9	25.6	24.7
10		

	9/27	9/26
0	1.5	1.4
1	4.5	4.3
2	7.5	7.2
3	10.5	10.1
4	13.5	13.0
5	16.5	15.9
6	19.5	18.8
7	22.5	21.7
8	25.5	24.6
9		

LOGARITHMS OF THE TRIGONOMETRIC FUNCTIONS

'	L. Sin.	d.	L. Tan.	c.d.	L. Cot.	L. Cos.	d.	'
0	9.76 922	17	9.86 126	27	0.13 874	9.90 796	9	60
1	9.76 939	18	9.86 153	26	0.13 847	9.90 787	10	59
2	9.76 957	17	9.86 179	27	0.13 821	9.90 777	9	58
3	9.76 974	17	9.86 206	26	0.13 794	9.90 768	9	57
4	9.76 991	18	9.86 232	27	0.13 768	9.90 759	9	56
5	9.77 009	17	9.86 259	26	0.13 741	9.90 750	9	55
6	9.77 026	17	9.86 285	27	0.13 715	9.90 741	10	54
7	9.77 043	18	9.86 312	26	0.13 688	9.90 731	9	53
8	9.77 061	17	9.86 338	27	0.13 662	9.90 722	9	52
9	9.77 078	17	9.86 365	27	0.13 635	9.90 713	9	51
10	9.77 095	17	9.86 392	26	0.13 608	9.90 704	10	50
11	9.77 112	18	9.86 418	27	0.13 582	9.90 694	9	49
12	9.77 130	17	9.86 445	26	0.13 555	9.90 685	9	48
13	9.77 147	17	9.86 471	27	0.13 529	9.90 676	9	47
14	9.77 164	17	9.86 498	26	0.13 502	9.90 667	10	46
15	9.77 181	18	9.86 524	27	0.13 476	9.90 657	9	45
16	9.77 199	17	9.86 551	26	0.13 449	9.90 648	9	44
17	9.77 216	17	9.86 577	26	0.13 423	9.90 639	9	43
18	9.77 233	17	9.86 603	27	0.13 397	9.90 630	10	42
19	9.77 250	18	9.86 630	26	0.13 370	9.90 620	9	41
20	9.77 268	17	9.86 656	27	0.13 344	9.90 611	9	40
21	9.77 285	17	9.86 683	26	0.13 317	9.90 602	10	39
22	9.77 302	17	9.86 709	27	0.13 291	9.90 592	9	38
23	9.77 319	17	9.86 736	26	0.13 264	9.90 583	9	37
24	9.77 336	17	9.86 762	27	0.13 238	9.90 574	9	36
25	9.77 353	17	9.86 789	26	0.13 211	9.90 565	10	35
26	9.77 370	17	9.86 815	27	0.13 185	9.90 555	9	34
27	9.77 387	13	9.86 842	26	0.13 158	9.90 546	9	33
28	9.77 405	17	9.86 868	26	0.13 132	9.90 537	10	32
29	9.77 422	17	9.86 894	27	0.13 106	9.90 527	9	31
30	9.77 439	17	9.86 921	26	0.13 079	9.90 518	9	30
31	9.77 456	17	9.86 947	27	0.13 053	9.90 509	10	29
32	9.77 473	17	9.86 974	26	0.13 026	9.90 499	9	28
33	9.77 490	17	9.87 000	27	0.13 000	9.90 490	10	27
34	9.77 507	17	9.87 027	26	0.12 973	9.90 480	9	26
35	9.77 524	17	9.87 053	26	0.12 947	9.90 471	9	25
36	9.77 541	17	9.87 079	27	0.12 921	9.90 462	10	24
37	9.77 558	17	9.87 106	26	0.12 894	9.90 452	9	23
38	9.77 575	17	9.87 132	26	0.12 868	9.90 443	9	22
39	9.77 592	17	9.87 158	27	0.12 842	9.90 434	10	21
40	9.77 609	17	9.87 185	26	0.12 815	9.90 424	9	20
41	9.77 626	17	9.87 211	27	0.12 789	9.90 415	10	19
42	9.77 643	17	9.87 238	26	0.12 762	9.90 405	9	18
43	9.77 660	17	9.87 264	26	0.12 736	9.90 396	10	17
44	9.77 677	17	9.87 290	27	0.12 710	9.90 386	9	16
45	9.77 694	17	9.87 317	26	0.12 683	9.90 377	9	15
46	9.77 711	17	9.87 343	26	0.12 657	9.90 368	10	14
47	9.77 728	16	9.87 369	27	0.12 631	9.90 358	9	13
48	9.77 744	17	9.87 396	26	0.12 604	9.90 349	10	12
49	9.77 761	17	9.87 422	26	0.12 578	9.90 339	9	11
50	9.77 778	17	9.87 448	27	0.12 552	9.90 330	10	10
51	9.77 795	17	9.87 475	26	0.12 525	9.90 320	9	9
52	9.77 812	17	9.87 501	26	0.12 499	9.90 311	10	8
53	9.77 829	17	9.87 527	27	0.12 473	9.90 301	9	7
54	9.77 846	16	9.87 554	26	0.12 446	9.90 292	10	6
55	9.77 862	17	9.87 580	26	0.12 420	9.90 282	9	5
56	9.77 879	17	9.87 606	27	0.12 394	9.90 273	10	4
57	9.77 896	17	9.87 633	26	0.12 367	9.90 263	9	3
58	9.77 913	17	9.87 659	26	0.12 341	9.90 254	10	2
59	9.77 930	16	9.87 685	26	0.12 315	9.90 244	9	1
60	9.77 946		9.87 711		0.12 289	9.90 235		0
	L. Cos.	d.	L. Cot.	c.d.	L. Tan.	L. Sin.	d.	'

P. P.

" | 27 | 26
1 | 0.4 | 0.4
2 | 0.9 | 0.9
3 | 1.4 | 1.3
4 | 1.8 | 1.7
5 | 2.2 | 2.2
6 | 2.7 | 2.6
7 | 3.2 | 3.0
8 | 3.6 | 3.5
9 | 4.0 | 3.9
10 | 4.5 | 4.3
20 | 9.0 | 8.7
30 | 13.5 | 13.0
40 | 18.0 | 17.3
50 | 22.5 | 21.7

" | 18 | 17 | 16
1 | 0.3 | 0.3 | 0.3
2 | 0.6 | 0.6 | 0.5
3 | 0.9 | 0.8 | 0.8
4 | 1.2 | 1.1 | 1.1
5 | 1.5 | 1.4 | 1.3
6 | 1.8 | 1.7 | 1.6
7 | 2.1 | 2.0 | 1.9
8 | 2.4 | 2.3 | 2.1
9 | 2.7 | 2.6 | 2.4
10 | 3.0 | 2.8 | 2.7
20 | 6.0 | 5.7 | 5.3
30 | 9.0 | 8.5 | 8.0
40 | 12.0 | 11.3 | 10.7
50 | 15.0 | 14.2 | 13.3

" | 10 | 9
1 | 0.2 | 0.2
2 | 0.3 | 0.3
3 | 0.5 | 0.4
4 | 0.7 | 0.6
5 | 0.8 | 0.8
6 | 1.0 | 0.9
7 | 1.2 | 1.0
8 | 1.3 | 1.2
9 | 1.5 | 1.4
10 | 1.7 | 1.5
20 | 3.3 | 3.0
30 | 5.0 | 4.5
40 | 6.7 | 6.0
50 | 8.3 | 7.5

9 | 9
27 | 26
0
1 | 1.5 | 1.4
2 | 4.5 | 4.3
3 | 7.5 | 7.2
4 | 10.5 | 10.1
5 | 13.5 | 13.0
6 | 16.5 | 15.9
7 | 19.5 | 18.8
8 | 22.5 | 21.7
9 | 25.5 | 24.6

LOGARITHMS OF THE TRIGONOMETRIC FUNCTIONS

37° (217°) (322°) **142°**

′	L. Sin.	d.	L. Tan.	c.d.	L. Cot.	L. Cos.	d.	′	P. P.		
0	9.77 946	17	9.87 711	27	0.12 289	9.90 235	10	60			
1	9.77 963	17	9.87 738	26	0.12 262	9.90 225	9	59	″	27	26
2	9.77 980	17	9.87 764	26	0.12 236	9.90 216	9	58	1	0.4	0.4
3	9.77 997	16	9.87 790	27	0.12 210	9.90 206	10	57	2	0.9	0.9
4	9.78 013	17	9.87 817	26	0.12 183	9.90 197	9	56	3	1.4	1.3
							10		4	1.8	1.7
5	9.78 030	17	9.87 843	26	0.12 157	9.90 187	9	55			
6	9.78 047	16	9.87 869	26	0.12 131	9.90 178	10	54	5	2.2	2.2
7	9.78 063	17	9.87 895	27	0.12 105	9.90 168	10	53	6	2.7	2.6
8	9.78 080	17	9.87 922	26	0.12 078	9.90 159	10	52	7	3.2	3.0
9	9.78 097	16	9.87 948	26	0.12 052	9.90 149	10	51	8	3.6	3.5
									9	4.0	3.9
10	9.78 113	17	9.87 974	26	0.12 026	9.90 139	9	50			
11	9.78 130	17	9.88 000	27	0.12 000	9.90 130	10	49	10	4.5	4.3
12	9.78 147	17	9.88 027	26	0.11 973	9.90 120	9	48	20	9.0	8.7
13	9.78 163	17	9.88 053	26	0.11 947	9.90 111	10	47	30	13.5	13.0
14	9.78 180	17	9.88 079	26	0.11 921	9.90 101	10	46	40	18.0	17.3
									50	22.5	21.7
15	9.78 197	16	9.88 105	26	0.11 895	9.90 091	9	45			
16	9.78 213	17	9.88 131	27	0.11 869	9.90 082	10	44	″	17	16
17	9.78 230	16	9.88 158	26	0.11 842	9.90 072	9	43	1	0.3	0.3
18	9.78 246	17	9.88 184	26	0.11 816	9.90 063	10	42	2	0.6	0.5
19	9.78 263	17	9.88 210	26	0.11 790	9.90 053	10	41	3	0.8	0.8
									4	1.1	1.1
20	9.78 280	16	9.88 236	26	0.11 764	9.90 043	9	40			
21	9.78 296	17	9.88 262	27	0.11 738	9.90 034	10	39	5	1.4	1.3
22	9.78 313	16	9.88 289	26	0.11 711	9.90 024	10	38	6	1.7	1.6
23	9.78 329	17	9.88 315	26	0.11 685	9.90 014	9	37	7	2.0	1.9
24	9.78 346	16	9.88 341	26	0.11 659	9.90 005	10	36	8	2.3	2.1
									9	2.6	2.4
25	9.78 362	17	9.88 367	26	0.11 633	9.89 995	10	35			
26	9.78 379	16	9.88 393	27	0.11 607	9.89 985	9	34	10	2.8	2.7
27	9.78 395	17	9.88 420	26	0.11 580	9.89 976	10	33	20	5.7	5.3
28	9.78 412	16	9.88 446	26	0.11 554	9.89 966	10	32	30	8.5	8.0
29	9.78 428	17	9.88 472	26	0.11 528	9.89 956	9	31	40	11.3	10.7
									50	14.2	13.3
30	9.78 445	16	9.88 498	26	0.11 502	9.89 947	10	30			
31	9.78 461	17	9.88 524	26	0.11 476	9.89 937	10	29	″	10	9
32	9.78 478	16	9.88 550	27	0.11 450	9.89 927	9	28	1	0.2	0.2
33	9.78 494	16	9.88 577	26	0.11 423	9.89 918	10	27	2	0.3	0.3
34	9.78 510	17	9.88 603	26	0.11 397	9.89 908	10	26	3	0.5	0.4
									4	0.7	0.6
35	9.78 527	16	9.88 629	26	0.11 371	9.89 898	10	25	5	0.8	0.8
36	9.78 543	17	9.88 655	26	0.11 345	9.89 888	9	24	6	1.0	0.9
37	9.78 560	16	9.88 681	26	0.11 319	9.89 879	10	23	7	1.2	1.0
38	9.78 576	16	9.88 707	26	0.11 293	9.89 869	10	22	8	1.3	1.2
39	9.78 592	17	9.88 733	26	0.11 267	9.89 859	10	21	9	1.5	1.4
40	9.78 609	16	9.88 759	27	0.11 241	9.89 849	9	20	10	1.7	1.5
41	9.78 625	17	9.88 786	26	0.11 214	9.89 840	10	19	20	3.3	3.0
42	9.78 642	16	9.88 812	26	0.11 188	9.89 830	10	18	30	5.0	4.5
43	9.78 658	16	9.88 838	26	0.11 162	9.89 820	10	17	40	6.7	6.0
44	9.78 674	17	9.88 864	26	0.11 136	9.89 810	9	16	50	8.3	7.5
45	9.78 691	16	9.88 890	26	0.11 110	9.89 801	10	15			
46	9.78 707	16	9.88 916	26	0.11 084	9.89 791	10	14			
47	9.78 723	16	9.88 942	26	0.11 058	9.89 781	10	13			
48	9.78 739	17	9.88 968	26	0.11 032	9.89 771	10	12		10	10
49	9.78 756	16	9.88 994	26	0.11 006	9.89 761	9	11		—	—
										27	26
50	9.78 772	16	9.89 020	26	0.10 980	9.89 752	10	10			
51	9.78 788	17	9.89 046	27	0.10 954	9.89 742	10	9	0	1.4	1.3
52	9.78 805	16	9.89 073	26	0.10 927	9.89 732	10	8	1	4.1	3.9
53	9.78 821	16	9.89 099	26	0.10 901	9.89 722	10	7	2	6.8	6.5
54	9.78 837	16	9.89 125	26	0.10 875	9.89 712	10	6	3	9.4	9.1
									4	12.2	11.7
55	9.78 853	16	9.89 151	26	0.10 849	9.89 702	9	5	5	14.8	14.3
56	9.78 869	17	9.89 177	26	0.10 823	9.89 693	10	4	6	17.6	16.9
57	9.78 886	16	9.89 203	26	0.10 797	9.89 683	10	3	7	20.2	19.5
58	9.78 902	16	9.89 229	26	0.10 771	9.89 673	10	2	8	22.9	22.1
59	9.78 918	16	9.89 255	26	0.10 745	9.89 663	10	1	9	25.6	24.7
									10		
60	9.78 934		9.89 281		0.10 719	9.89 653		0			
′	L. Cos.	d.	L. Cot.	c.d.	L. Tan.	L. Sin.	d.	′	P. P.		

LOGARITHMS OF THE TRIGONOMETRIC FUNCTIONS

38° (218°)   **(321°) 141°**

′	L. Sin.	d.	L. Tan.	c.d.	L. Cot.	L. Cos.	d.	′	P.P.		
0	9.78 934	16	9.89 281	26	0.10 719	9.89 653	10	60	″	**26**	**25**
1	9.78 950	17	9.89 307	26	0.10 693	9.89 643	10	59	1	0.4	0.4
2	9.78 967	16	9.89 333	26	0.10 667	9.89 633	9	58	2	0.9	0.8
3	9.78 983	16	9.89 359	26	0.10 641	9.89 624	10	57	3	1.3	1.2
4	9.78 999	16	9.89 385	26	0.10 615	9.89 614	10	56	4	1.7	1.7
5	9.79 015	16	9.89 411	26	0.10 589	9.89 604	10	55	5	2.2	2.1
6	9.79 031	16	9.89 437	26	0.10 563	9.89 594	10	54	6	2.6	2.5
7	9.79 047	16	9.89 463	26	0.10 537	9.89 584	10	53	7	3.0	2.9
8	9.79 063	16	9.89 489	26	0.10 511	9.89 574	10	52	8	3.5	3.3
9	9.79 079	16	9.89 515	26	0.10 485	9.89 564	10	51	9	3.9	3.8
10	9.79 095	16	9.89 541	26	0.10 459	9.89 554	10	50	10	4.3	4.2
11	9.79 111	17	9.89 567	26	0.10 433	9.89 544	10	49	20	8.7	8.3
12	9.79 128	16	9.89 593	26	0.10 407	9.89 534	10	48	30	13.0	12.5
13	9.79 144	16	9.89 619	26	0.10 381	9.89 524	10	47	40	17.3	16.7
14	9.79 160	16	9.89 645	26	0.10 355	9.89 514	10	46	50	21.7	20.8
15	9.79 176	16	9.89 671	26	0.10 329	9.89 504	9	45	″	**17**	**16** **15**
16	9.79 192	16	9.89 697	26	0.10 303	9.89 495	10	44	1	0.3	0.3 0.2
17	9.79 208	16	9.89 723	26	0.10 277	9.89 485	10	43	2	0.6	0.5 0.5
18	9.79 224	16	9.89 749	26	0.10 251	9.89 475	10	42	3	0.8	0.8 0.8
19	9.79 240	16	9.89 775	26	0.10 225	9.89 465	10	41	4	1.1	1.1 1.0
20	9.79 256	16	9.89 801	26	0.10 199	9.89 455	10	40	5	1.4	1.3 1.2
21	9.79 272	16	9.89 827	26	0.10 173	9.89 445	10	39	6	1.7	1.6 1.5
22	9.79 288	16	9.89 853	26	0.10 147	9.89 435	10	38	7	2.0	1.9 1.8
23	9.79 304	15	9.89 879	26	0.10 121	9.89 425	10	37	8	2.3	2.1 2.0
24	9.79 319	16	9.89 905	26	0.10 095	9.89 415	10	36	9	2.6	2.4 2.2
25	9.79 335	16	9.89 931	26	0.10 069	9.89 405	10	35	10	2.8	2.7 2.5
26	9.79 351	16	9.89 957	26	0.10 043	9.89 395	10	34	20	5.7	5.3 5.0
27	9.79 367	16	9.89 983	26	0.10 017	9.89 385	10	33	30	8.5	8.0 7.5
28	9.79 383	16	9.90 009	26	0.09 991	9.89 375	11	32	40	11.3	10.7 10.0
29	9.79 399	16	9.90 035	26	0.09 965	9.89 364	10	31	50	14.2	13.3 12.5
30	9.79 415	16	9.90 061	25	0.09 939	9.89 354	10	30	″	**11**	**10** **9**
31	9.79 431	16	9.90 086	26	0.09 914	9.89 344	10	29	1	0.2	0.2 0.2
32	9.79 447	16	9.90 112	26	0.09 888	9.89 334	10	28	2	0.4	0.3 0.3
33	9.79 463	15	9.90 138	26	0.09 862	9.89 324	10	27	3	0.6	0.5 0.4
34	9.79 478	16	9.90 164	26	0.09 836	9.89 314	10	26	4	0.7	0.7 0.6
35	9.79 494	16	9.90 190	26	0.09 810	9.89 304	10	25	5	0.9	0.8 0.8
36	9.79 510	16	9.90 216	26	0.09 784	9.89 294	10	24	6	1.1	1.0 0.9
37	9.79 526	16	9.90 242	26	0.09 758	9.89 284	10	23	7	1.3	1.2 1.0
38	9.79 542	16	9.90 268	26	0.09 732	9.89 274	10	22	8	1.5	1.3 1.2
39	9.79 558	15	9.90 294	26	0.09 706	9.89 264	10	21	9	1.6	1.5 1.4
40	9.79 573	16	9.90 320	26	0.09 680	9.89 254	10	20	10	1.8	1.7 1.5
41	9.79 589	16	9.90 346	25	0.09 654	9.89 244	11	19	20	3.7	3.3 3.0
42	9.79 605	16	9.90 371	26	0.09 629	9.89 233	10	18	30	5.5	5.0 4.5
43	9.79 621	15	9.90 397	26	0.09 603	9.89 223	10	17	40	7.3	6.7 6.0
44	9.79 636	16	9.90 423	26	0.09 577	9.89 213	10	16	50	9.2	8.3 7.5
45	9.79 652	16	9.90 449	26	0.09 551	9.89 203	10	15			
46	9.79 668	16	9.90 475	26	0.09 525	9.89 193	10	14			
47	9.79 684	15	9.90 501	26	0.09 499	9.89 183	10	13			
48	9.79 699	16	9.90 527	26	0.09 473	9.89 173	11	12		**10**	**10** **9**
49	9.79 715	16	9.90 553	25	0.09 447	9.89 162	10	11		26	25 26
50	9.79 731	15	9.90 578	26	0.09 422	9.89 152	10	10	0	1.3	1.2 1.4
51	9.79 746	16	9.90 604	26	0.09 396	9.89 142	10	9	1	3.9	3.8 4.3
52	9.79 762	16	9.90 630	26	0.09 370	9.89 132	10	8	2	6.5	6.2 7.2
53	9.79 778	15	9.90 656	26	0.09 344	9.89 122	10	7	3	9.1	8.8 10.1
54	9.79 793	16	9.90 682	26	0.09 318	9.89 112	11	6	4	11.7	11.2 13.0
55	9.79 809	16	9.90 708	26	0.09 292	9.89 101	10	5	5	14.3	13.8 15.9
56	9.79 825	15	9.90 734	25	0.09 266	9.89 091	10	4	6	16.9	16.2 18.8
57	9.79 840	16	9.90 759	26	0.09 241	9.89 081	10	3	7	19.5	18.8 21.7
58	9.79 856	16	9.90 785	26	0.09 215	9.89 071	11	2	8	22.1	21.2 24.6
59	9.79 872	15	9.90 811	26	0.09 189	9.89 060	10	1	9	24.7	23.8
60	9.79 887		9.90 837		0.09 163	9.89 050		0	10		

′	L. Cos.	d.	L. Cot.	c.d.	L. Tan.	L. Sin.	d.	′	P. P.		

128° (308°)   **(231°) 51°**

LOGARITHMS OF THE TRIGONOMETRIC FUNCTIONS

39° (219°)   (320°) **140°**

′	L. Sin.	d.	L. Tan.	c.d.	L. Cot.	L. Cos.	d.	′	P. P.		
0	9.79 887	16	9.90 837	26	0.09 163	9.89 050	10	60			
1	9.79 903	15	9.90 863	26	0.09 137	9.89 040	10	59	″	**26**	**25**
2	9.79 918	16	9.90 889	25	0.09 111	9.89 030	10	58	1	0.4	0.4
3	9.79 934	16	9.90 914	26	0.09 086	9.89 020	11	57	2	0.9	0.8
4	9.79 950	15	9.90 940	26	0.09 060	9.89 009	10	56	3	1.3	1.2
									4	1.7	1.7
5	9.79 965	16	9.90 966	26	0.09 034	9.88 999	10	55			
6	9.79 981	15	9.90 992	26	0.09 008	9.88 989	11	54	5	2.2	2.1
7	9.79 996	16	9.91 018	25	0.08 982	9.88 978	10	53	6	2.6	2.5
8	9.80 012	15	9.91 043	26	0.08 957	9.88 968	10	52	7	3.0	2.9
9	9.80 027	16	9.91 069	26	0.08 931	9.88 958	10	51	8	3.5	3.3
									9	3.9	3.8
10	9.80 043	15	9.91 095	26	0.08 905	9.88 948	11	50			
11	9.80 058	16	9.91 121	26	0.08 879	9.88 937	10	49	10	4.3	4.2
12	9.80 074	15	9.91 147	25	0.08 853	9.88 927	10	48	20	8.7	8.3
13	9.80 089	16	9.91 172	26	0.08 828	9.88 917	11	47	30	13.0	12.5
14	9.80 105	15	9.91 198	26	0.08 802	9.88 906	10	46	40	17.3	16.7
									50	21.7	20.8
15	9.80 120	16	9.91 224	26	0.08 776	9.88 896	10	45			
16	9.80 136	15	9.91 250	26	0.08 750	9.88 886	10	44	″	**16**	**15**
17	9.80 151	15	9.91 276	25	0.08 724	9.88 875	11	43	1	0.3	0.2
18	9.80 166	16	9.91 301	26	0.08 699	9.88 865	10	42	2	0.5	0.5
19	9.80 182	15	9.91 327	26	0.08 673	9.88 855	11	41	3	0.8	0.8
									4	1.1	1.0
20	9.80 197	16	9.91 353	26	0.08 647	9.88 844	10	40			
21	9.80 213	15	9.91 379	25	0.08 621	9.88 834	10	39	5	1.3	1.2
22	9.80 228	16	9.91 404	26	0.08 596	9.88 824	11	38	6	1.6	1.5
23	9.80 244	15	9.91 430	26	0.08 570	9.88 813	10	37	7	1.9	1.8
24	9.80 259	15	9.91 456	26	0.08 544	9.88 803	10	36	8	2.1	2.0
									9	2.4	2.2
25	9.80 274	16	9.91 482	25	0.08 518	9.88 793	11	35			
26	9.80 290	15	9.91 507	26	0.08 493	9.88 782	10	34	10	2.7	2.5
27	9.80 305	15	9.91 533	26	0.08 467	9.88 772	11	33	20	5.3	5.0
28	9.80 320	16	9.91 559	26	0.08 441	9.88 761	10	32	30	8.0	7.5
29	9.80 336	15	9.91 585	25	0.08 415	9.88 751	10	31	40	10.7	10.0
									50	13.3	12.5
30	9.80 351	15	9.91 610	26	0.08 390	9.88 741	11	30			
31	9.80 366	16	9.91 636	26	0.08 364	9.88 730	10	29	″	**11**	**10**
32	9.80 382	15	9.91 662	26	0.08 338	9.88 720	11	28	1	0.2	0.2
33	9.80 397	15	9.91 688	25	0.08 312	9.88 709	10	27	2	0.4	0.3
34	9.80 412	16	9.91 713	26	0.08 287	9.88 699	11	26	3	0.6	0.5
									4	0.7	0.7
35	9.80 428	15	9.91 739	26	0.08 261	9.88 688	10	25			
36	9.80 443	15	9.91 765	26	0.08 235	9.88 678	10	24	5	0.9	0.8
37	9.80 458	15	9.91 791	25	0.08 209	9.88 668	11	23	6	1.1	1.0
38	9.80 473	16	9.91 816	26	0.08 184	9.88 657	10	22	7	1.3	1.2
39	9.80 489	15	9.91 842	26	0.08 158	9.88 647	11	21	8	1.5	1.3
									9	1.6	1.5
40	9.80 504	15	9.91 868	25	0.08 132	9.88 636	10	20			
41	9.80 519	15	9.91 893	26	0.08 107	9.88 626	11	19	10	1.8	1.7
42	9.80 534	16	9.91 919	26	0.08 081	9.88 615	10	18	20	3.7	3.3
43	9.80 550	15	9.91 945	26	0.08 055	9.88 605	11	17	30	5.5	5.0
44	9.80 565	15	9.91 971	25	0.08 029	9.88 594	10	16	40	7.3	6.7
									50	9.2	8.3
45	9.80 580	15	9.91 996	26	0.08 004	9.88 584	11	15			
46	9.80 595	15	9.92 022	26	0.07 978	9.88 573	11	14			
47	9.80 610	15	9.92 048	25	0.07 952	9.88 563	11	13		**11**	**11**
48	9.80 625	16	9.92 073	26	0.07 927	9.88 552	10	12			
49	9.80 641	15	9.92 099	26	0.07 901	9.88 542	11	11		**26**	**25**
50	9.80 656	15	9.92 125	25	0.07 875	9.88 531	10	10	0	1.2	1.1
51	9.80 671	15	9.92 150	26	0.07 850	9.88 521	11	9	1	3.5	3.4
52	9.80 686	15	9.92 176	26	0.07 824	9.88 510	11	8	2	5.9	5.7
53	9.80 701	15	9.92 202	25	0.07 798	9.88 499	10	7	3	8.3	7.9
54	9.80 716	15	9.92 227	26	0.07 773	9.88 489	11	6	4	10.6	10.2
									5	13.0	12.5
55	9.80 731	15	9.92 253	26	0.07 747	9.88 478	10	5	6	15.4	14.8
56	9.80 746	16	9.92 279	25	0.07 721	9.88 468	11	4	7	17.7	17.1
57	9.80 762	15	9.92 304	26	0.07 696	9.88 457	10	3	8	20.1	19.3
58	9.80 777	15	9.92 330	26	0.07 670	9.88 447	11	2	9	22.5	21.6
59	9.80 792	15	9.92 356	25	0.07 644	9.88 436	11	1	10	24.8	23.9
									11		
60	9.80 807		9.92 381		0.07 619	9.88 425		0			

′	L. Cos.	d.	L. Cot.	c.d.	L. Tan.	L. Sin.	d.	′	P. P.		

129° (309°)   (230°) **50°**

40° (220°)   (319°) **139°**

′	L. Sin.	d.	L. Tan.	c.d.	L. Cot.	L. Cos.	d.	′
0	9.80 807	15	9.92 381	26	0.07 619	9.88 425	10	60
1	9.80 822	15	9.92 407	26	0.07 593	9.88 415	11	59
2	9.80 837	15	9.92 433	25	0.07 567	9.88 404	10	58
3	9.80 852	15	9.92 458	26	0.07 542	9.88 394	11	57
4	9.80 867	15	9.92 484	26	0.07 516	9.88 383	11	56
5	9.80 882	15	9.92 510	25	0.07 490	9.88 372	10	55
6	9.80 897	15	9.92 535	26	0.07 465	9.88 362	11	54
7	9.80 912	15	9.92 561	26	0.07 439	9.88 351	11	53
8	9.80 927	15	9.92 587	25	0.07 413	9.88 340	10	52
9	9.80 942	15	9.92 612	26	0.07 388	9.88 330	11	51
10	9.80 957	15	9.92 638	25	0.07 362	9.88 319	11	50
11	9.80 972	15	9.92 663	26	0.07 337	9.88 308	10	49
12	9.80 987	15	9.92 689	26	0.07 311	9.88 298	11	48
13	9.81 002	15	9.92 715	25	0.07 285	9.88 287	11	47
14	9.81 017	15	9.92 740	26	0.07 260	9.88 276	10	46
15	9.81 032	15	9.92 766	26	0.07 234	9.88 266	11	45
16	9.81 047	14	9.92 792	25	0.07 208	9.88 255	11	44
17	9.81 061	15	9.92 817	26	0.07 183	9.88 244	10	43
18	9.81 076	15	9.92 843	25	0.07 157	9.88 234	11	42
19	9.81 091	15	9.92 868	26	0.07 132	9.88 223	11	41
20	9.81 106	15	9.92 894	26	0.07 106	9.88 212	11	40
21	9.81 121	15	9.92 920	25	0.07 080	9.88 201	10	39
22	9.81 136	15	9.92 945	26	0.07 055	9.88 191	11	38
23	9.81 151	15	9.92 971	25	0.07 029	9.88 180	11	37
24	9.81 166	14	9.92 996	26	0.07 004	9.88 169	11	36
25	9.81 180	15	9.93 022	26	0.06 978	9.88 158	10	35
26	9.81 195	15	9.93 048	25	0.06 952	9.88 148	11	34
27	9.81 210	15	9.93 073	26	0.06 927	9.88 137	11	33
28	9.81 225	15	9.93 099	25	0.06 901	9.88 126	11	32
29	9.81 240	14	9.93 124	26	0.06 876	9.88 115	10	31
30	9.81 254	15	9.93 150	25	0.06 850	9.88 105	11	30
31	9.81 269	15	9.93 175	26	0.06 825	9.88 094	11	29
32	9.81 284	15	9.93 201	26	0.06 799	9.88 083	11	28
33	9.81 299	15	9.93 227	25	0.06 773	9.88 072	11	27
34	9.81 314	14	9.93 252	26	0.06 748	9.88 061	10	26
35	9.81 328	15	9.93 278	25	0.06 722	9.88 051	11	25
36	9.81 343	15	9.93 303	26	0.06 697	9.88 040	11	24
37	9.81 358	14	9.93 329	25	0.06 671	9.88 029	11	23
38	9.81 372	15	9.93 354	26	0.06 646	9.88 018	11	22
39	9.81 387	15	9.93 380	26	0.06 620	9.88 007	11	21
40	9.81 402	15	9.93 406	25	0.06 594	9.87 996	11	20
41	9.81 417	14	9.93 431	26	0.06 569	9.87 985	10	19
42	9.81 431	15	9.93 457	25	0.06 543	9.87 975	11	18
43	9.81 446	15	9.93 482	26	0.06 518	9.87 964	11	17
44	9.81 461	14	9.93 508	25	0.06 492	9.87 953	11	16
45	9.81 475	15	9.93 533	26	0.06 467	9.87 942	11	15
46	9.81 490	15	9.93 559	25	0.06 441	9.87 931	11	14
47	9.81 505	14	9.93 584	26	0.06 416	9.87 920	11	13
48	9.81 519	15	9.93 610	26	0.06 390	9.87 909	11	12
49	9.81 534	15	9.93 636	25	0.06 364	9.87 898	11	11
50	9.81 549	14	9.93 661	26	0.06 339	9.87 887	10	10
51	9.81 563	15	9.93 687	25	0.06 313	9.87 877	11	9
52	9.81 578	14	9.93 712	26	0.06 288	9.87 866	11	8
53	9.81 592	15	9.93 738	25	0.06 262	9.87 855	11	7
54	9.81 607	15	9.93 763	26	0.06 237	9.87 844	11	6
55	9.81 622	14	9.93 789	25	0.06 211	9.87 833	11	5
56	9.81 636	15	9.93 814	26	0.06 186	9.87 822	11	4
57	9.81 651	14	9.93 840	25	0.06 160	9.87 811	11	3
58	9.81 665	15	9.93 865	26	0.06 135	9.87 800	11	2
59	9.81 680	14	9.93 891	25	0.06 109	9.87 789	11	1
60	9.81 694		9.93 916		0.06 084	9.87 778		0

P. P.

″	26	25
1	0.4	0.4
2	0.9	0.8
3	1.3	1.2
4	1.7	1.7
5	2.2	2.1
6	2.6	2.5
7	3.0	2.9
8	3.5	3.3
9	3.9	3.8
10	4.3	4.2
20	8.7	8.3
30	13.0	12.5
40	17.3	16.7
50	21.7	20.8

″	15	14
1	0.2	0.2
2	0.5	0.5
3	0.8	0.7
4	1.0	0.9
5	1.2	1.2
6	1.5	1.4
7	1.8	1.6
8	2.0	1.9
9	2.2	2.1
10	2.5	2.3
20	5.0	4.7
30	7.5	7.0
40	10.0	9.3
50	12.5	11.7

″	11	10
1	0.2	0.2
2	0.4	0.3
3	0.6	0.5
4	0.7	0.7
5	0.9	0.8
6	1.1	1.0
7	1.3	1.2
8	1.5	1.3
9	1.6	1.5
10	1.8	1.7
20	3.7	3.3
30	5.5	5.0
40	7.3	6.7
50	9.2	8.3

	11	10	10
	26	26	25
0	1.2	1.3	1.2
1	3.5	3.9	3.8
2	5.9	6.5	6.2
3	8.3	9.1	8.8
4	10.6	11.7	11.2
5	13.0	14.3	13.8
6	15.4	16.9	16.2
7	17.7	19.5	18.8
8	20.1	22.1	21.2
9	22.5	24.7	23.8
10	24.8	—	—
11			

′	L. Cos.	d.	L. Cot.	c.d.	L. Tan.	L. Sin.	d.	′	P. P.

130° (310°)   (229°) **49°**

41° (221°)   (318°) **138°**

′	L. Sin.	d.	L. Tan.	c.d.	L. Cot.	L. Cos.	d.	′
0	9.81 694	15	9.93 916	26	0.06 084	9.87 778	11	60
1	9.81 709	14	9.93 942	25	0.06 058	9.87 767	11	59
2	9.81 723	15	9.93 967	26	0.06 033	9.87 756	11	58
3	9.81 738	14	9.93 993	25	0.06 007	9.87 745	11	57
4	9.81 752	15	9.94 018	26	0.05 982	9.87 734	11	56
5	9.81 767	14	9.94 044	25	0.05 956	9.87 723	11	55
6	9.81 781	15	9.94 069	26	0.05 931	9.87 712	11	54
7	9.81 796	14	9.94 095	25	0.05 905	9.87 701	11	53
8	9.81 810	15	9.94 120	26	0.05 880	9.87 690	11	52
9	9.81 825	14	9.94 146	25	0.05 854	9.87 679	11	51
10	9.81 839	15	9.94 171	26	0.05 829	9.87 668	11	50
11	9.81 854	14	9.94 197	25	0.05 803	9.87 657	11	49
12	9.81 868	14	9.94 222	26	0.05 778	9.87 646	11	48
13	9.81 882	15	9.94 248	25	0.05 752	9.87 635	11	47
14	9.81 897	14	9.94 273	26	0.05 727	9.87 624	11	46
15	9.81 911	15	9.94 299	25	0.05 701	9.87 613	12	45
16	9.81 926	14	9.94 324	26	0.05 676	9.87 601	11	44
17	9.81 940	15	9.94 350	25	0.05 650	9.87 590	11	43
18	9.81 955	14	9.94 375	26	0.05 625	9.87 579	11	42
19	9.81 969	14	9.94 401	25	0.05 599	9.87 568	11	41
20	9.81 983	15	9.94 426	26	0.05 574	9.87 557	11	40
21	9.81 998	14	9.94 452	25	0.05 548	9.87 546	11	39
22	9.82 012	14	9.94 477	26	0.05 523	9.87 535	11	38
23	9.82 026	15	9.94 503	25	0.05 497	9.87 524	11	37
24	9.82 041	14	9.94 528	26	0.05 472	9.87 513	12	36
25	9.82 055	14	9.94 554	25	0.05 446	9.87 501	11	35
26	9.82 069	15	9.94 579	25	0.05 421	9.87 490	11	34
27	9.82 084	14	9.94 604	26	0.05 396	9.87 479	11	33
28	9.82 098	14	9.94 630	25	0.05 370	9.87 468	11	32
29	9.82 112	14	9.94 655	26	0.05 345	9.87 457	11	31
30	9.82 126	15	9.94 681	25	0.05 319	9.87 446	12	30
31	9.82 141	14	9.94 706	26	0.05 294	9.87 434	11	29
32	9.82 155	14	9.94 732	25	0.05 268	9.87 423	11	28
33	9.82 169	15	9.94 757	26	0.05 243	9.87 412	11	27
34	9.82 184	14	9.94 783	25	0.05 217	9.87 401	11	26
35	9.82 198	14	9.94 808	26	0.05 192	9.87 390	12	25
36	9.82 212	14	9.94 834	25	0.05 166	9.87 378	11	24
37	9.82 226	14	9.94 859	25	0.05 141	9.87 367	11	23
38	9.82 240	15	9.94 884	26	0.05 116	9.87 356	11	22
39	9.82 255	14	9.94 910	25	0.05 090	9.87 345	11	21
40	9.82 269	14	9.94 935	26	0.05 065	9.87 334	12	20
41	9.82 283	14	9.94 961	25	0.05 039	9.87 322	11	19
42	9.82 297	14	9.94 986	26	0.05 014	9.87 311	11	18
43	9.82 311	15	9.95 012	25	0.04 988	9.87 300	12	17
44	9.82 326	14	9.95 037	25	0.04 963	9.87 288	11	16
45	9.82 340	14	9.95 062	26	0.04 938	9.87 277	11	15
46	9.82 354	14	9.95 088	25	0.04 912	9.87 266	11	14
47	9.82 368	14	9.95 113	26	0.04 887	9.87 255	12	13
48	9.82 382	14	9.95 139	25	0.04 861	9.87 243	11	12
49	9.82 396	14	9.95 164	26	0.04 836	9.87 232	11	11
50	9.82 410	14	9.95 190	25	0.04 810	9.87 221	12	10
51	9.82 424	15	9.95 215	25	0.04 785	9.87 209	11	9
52	9.82 439	14	9.95 240	26	0.04 760	9.87 198	11	8
53	9.82 453	14	9.95 266	25	0.04 734	9.87 187	12	7
54	9.82 467	14	9.95 291	26	0.04 709	9.87 175	11	6
55	9.82 481	14	9.95 317	25	0.04 683	9.87 164	11	5
56	9.82 495	14	9.95 342	26	0.04 658	9.87 153	12	4
57	9.82 509	14	9.95 368	25	0.04 632	9.87 141	11	3
58	9.82 523	14	9.95 393	25	0.04 607	9.87 130	11	2
59	9.82 537	14	9.95 418	26	0.04 582	9.87 119	12	1
60	9.82 551		9.95 444		0.04 556	9.87 107		0

P. P.

″	26	25
1	0.4	0.4
2	0.9	0.8
3	1.3	1.2
4	1.7	1.7
5	2.2	2.1
6	2.6	2.5
7	3.0	2.9
8	3.5	3.3
9	3.9	3.8
10	4.3	4.2
20	8.7	8.3
30	13.0	12.5
40	17.3	16.7
50	21.7	20.8

″	15	14
1	0.2	0.2
2	0.5	0.5
3	0.8	0.7
4	1.0	0.9
5	1.2	1.2
6	1.5	1.4
7	1.8	1.6
8	2.0	1.9
9	2.2	2.1
10	2.5	2.3
20	5.0	4.7
30	7.5	7.0
40	10.0	9.3
50	12.5	11.7

″	12	11
1	0.2	0.2
2	0.4	0.4
3	0.6	0.6
4	0.8	0.7
5	1.0	0.9
6	1.2	1.1
7	1.4	1.3
8	1.6	1.5
9	1.8	1.6
10	2.0	1.8
20	4.0	3.7
30	6.0	5.5
40	8.0	7.3
50	10.0	9.2

	12	12	11
	26	25	25
0	1.1	1.1	1.1
1	3.2	3.1	3.4
2	5.4	5.2	5.7
3	7.6	7.3	7.9
4	9.8	9.4	10.2
5	11.9	11.5	12.5
6	14.1	13.5	14.8
7	16.2	15.6	17.1
8	18.4	17.7	19.3
9	20.6	19.8	21.6
10	22.8	21.9	23.9
11	24.9	23.9	—
12			

′	L. Cos.	d.	L. Cot.	c.d.	L. Tan.	L. Sin.	d.	′	P. P.

131° (311°)   (228°) **48°**

LOGARITHMS OF THE TRIGONOMETRIC FUNCTIONS

42° (222°) (317°) **137°**

′	L. Sin.	d.	L. Tan.	c.d.	L. Cot.	L. Cos.	d.	′	P. P.
0	9.82 551	14	9.95 444	25	0.04 556	9.87 107	11	60	
1	9.82 565	14	9.95 469	26	0.04 531	9.87 096	11	59	
2	9.82 579	14	9.95 495	25	0.04 505	9.87 085	12	58	
3	9.82 593	14	9.95 520	25	0.04 480	9.87 073	11	57	
4	9.82 607	14	9.95 545	26	0.04 455	9.87 062	12	56	
5	9.82 621	14	9.95 571	25	0.04 429	9.87 050	11	55	
6	9.82 635	14	9.95 596	26	0.04 404	9.87 039	11	54	
7	9.82 649	14	9.95 622	25	0.04 378	9.87 028	12	53	
8	9.82 663	14	9.95 647	25	0.04 353	9.87 016	11	52	
9	9.82 677	14	9.95 672	26	0.04 328	9.87 005	12	51	
10	9.82 691	14	9.95 698	25	0.04 302	9.86 993	11	50	
11	9.82 705	14	9.95 723	25	0.04 277	9.86 982	12	49	
12	9.82 719	14	9.95 748	26	0.04 252	9.86 970	11	48	
13	9.82 733	14	9.95 774	25	0.04 226	9.86 959	12	47	
14	9.82 747	14	9.95 799	26	0.04 201	9.86 947	11	46	
15	9.82 761	14	9.95 825	25	0.04 175	9.86 936	12	45	
16	9.82 775	13	9.95 850	25	0.04 150	9.86 924	11	44	
17	9.82 788	14	9.95 875	26	0.04 125	9.86 913	11	43	
18	9.82 802	14	9.95 901	25	0.04 099	9.86 902	12	42	
19	9.82 816	14	9.95 926	26	0.04 074	9.86 890	11	41	
20	9.82 830	14	9.95 952	25	0.04 048	9.86 879	12	40	
21	9.82 844	14	9.95 977	25	0.04 023	9.86 867	12	39	
22	9.82 858	14	9.96 002	26	0.03 998	9.86 855	11	38	
23	9.82 872	13	9.96 028	25	0.03 972	9.86 844	12	37	
24	9.82 885	14	9.96 053	25	0.03 947	9.86 832	11	36	
25	9.82 899	14	9.96 078	26	0.03 922	9.86 821	12	35	
26	9.82 913	14	9.96 104	25	0.03 896	9.86 809	11	34	
27	9.82 927	14	9.96 129	26	0.03 871	9.86 798	12	33	
28	9.82 941	14	9.96 155	25	0.03 845	9.86 786	11	32	
29	9.82 955	13	9.96 180	25	0.03 820	9.86 775	12	31	
30	9.82 968	14	9.96 205	26	0.03 795	9.86 763	11	30	
31	9.82 982	14	9.96 231	25	0.03 769	9.86 752	12	29	
32	9.82 996	14	9.96 256	25	0.03 744	9.86 740	12	28	
33	9.83 010	13	9.96 281	26	0.03 719	9.86 728	11	27	
34	9.83 023	14	9.96 307	25	0.03 693	9.86 717	12	26	
35	9.83 037	14	9.96 332	25	0.03 668	9.86 705	11	25	
36	9.83 051	14	9.96 357	26	0.03 643	9.86 694	12	24	
37	9.83 065	13	9.96 383	25	0.03 617	9.86 682	12	23	
38	9.83 078	14	9.96 408	25	0.03 592	9.86 670	11	22	
39	9.83 092	14	9.96 433	26	0.03 567	9.86 659	12	21	
40	9.83 106	14	9.96 459	25	0.03 541	9.86 647	12	20	
41	9.83 120	13	9.96 484	26	0.03 516	9.86 635	11	19	
42	9.83 133	14	9.96 510	25	0.03 490	9.86 624	12	18	
43	9.83 147	14	9.96 535	25	0.03 465	9.86 612	12	17	
44	9.83 161	13	9.96 560	26	0.03 440	9.86 600	11	16	
45	9.83 174	14	9.96 586	25	0.03 414	9.86 589	12	15	
46	9.83 188	14	9.96 611	25	0.03 389	9.86 577	12	14	
47	9.83 202	13	9.96 636	26	0.03 364	9.86 565	11	13	
48	9.83 215	14	9.96 662	25	0.03 338	9.86 554	12	12	
49	9.83 229	13	9.96 687	25	0.03 313	9.86 542	12	11	
50	9.83 242	14	9.96 712	26	0.03 288	9.86 530	12	10	
51	9.83 256	14	9.96 738	25	0.03 262	9.86 518	11	9	
52	9.83 270	13	9.96 763	25	0.03 237	9.86 507	12	8	
53	9.83 283	14	9.96 788	26	0.03 212	9.86 495	12	7	
54	9.83 297	13	9.96 814	25	0.03 186	9.86 483	11	6	
55	9.83 310	14	9.96 839	25	0.03 161	9.86 472	12	5	
56	9.83 324	14	9.96 864	26	0.03 136	9.86 460	12	4	
57	9.83 338	13	9.96 890	25	0.03 110	9.86 448	12	3	
58	9.83 351	14	9.96 915	25	0.03 085	9.86 436	11	2	
59	9.83 365	13	9.96 940	26	0.03 060	9.86 425	12	1	
60	9.83 378		9.96 966		0.03 034	9.86 413		0	

| ′ | L. Cos. | d. | L. Cot. | c.d. | L. Tan. | L. Sin. | d. | ′ | P. P. |

132° (312°) (227°) **47°**

P. P.

	26	25
1	0.4	0.4
2	0.9	0.8
3	1.3	1.2
4	1.7	1.7
5	2.2	2.1
6	2.6	2.5
7	3.0	2.9
8	3.5	3.3
9	3.9	3.8
10	4.3	4.2
20	8.7	8.3
30	13.0	12.5
40	17.3	16.7
50	21.7	20.8

	14	13
1	0.2	0.2
2	0.5	0.4
3	0.7	0.6
4	0.9	0.9
5	1.2	1.1
6	1.4	1.3
7	1.6	1.5
8	1.9	1.7
9	2.1	2.0
10	2.3	2.2
20	4.7	4.3
30	7.0	6.5
40	9.3	8.7
50	11.7	10.8

	12	11
1	0.2	0.2
2	0.4	0.4
3	0.6	0.6
4	0.8	0.7
5	1.0	0.9
6	1.2	1.1
7	1.4	1.3
8	1.6	1.5
9	1.8	1.8
10	2.0	1.8
20	4.0	3.7
30	6.0	5.5
40	8.0	7.3
50	10.0	9.2

	12	11	11
	26	26	25
0	1.1	1.2	1.1
1	3.2	3.5	3.4
2	5.4	5.9	5.7
3	7.6	8.3	7.9
4	9.8	10.6	10.2
5	11.9	13.0	12.5
6	14.1	15.4	14.8
7	16.2	17.7	17.1
8	18.4	20.1	19.3
9	20.6	22.5	21.6
10	22.8	24.8	23.9
11	24.9	—	—
12			

LOGARITHMS OF THE TRIGONOMETRIC FUNCTIONS

43° (223°) (316°) **136°**

′	L. Sin.	d.	L. Tan.	c.d.	L. Cot.	L. Cos.	d.	′	P. P.		
0	9.83 378	14	9.96 966	25	0.03 034	9.86 413	12	**60**			
1	9.83 392	13	9.96 991	25	0.03 009	9.86 401	12	59		**26**	**25**
2	9.83 405	14	9.97 016	26	0.02 984	9.86 389	12	58	1	0.4	0.4
3	9.83 419	13	9.97 042	25	0.02 958	9.86 377	11	57	2	0.9	0.8
4	9.83 432	14	9.97 067	25	0.02 933	9.86 366	12	56	3	1.3	1.2
									4	1.7	1.7
5	9.83 446	13	9.97 092	26	0.02 908	9.86 354	12	**55**			
6	9.83 459	14	9.97 118	25	0.02 882	9.86 342	12	54	5	2.2	2.1
7	9.83 473	13	9.97 143	25	0.02 857	9.86 330	12	53	6	2.6	2.5
8	9.83 486	14	9.97 168	25	0.02 832	9.86 318	12	52	7	3.0	2.9
9	9.83 500	13	9.97 193	26	0.02 807	9.86 306	11	51	8	3.5	3.3
									9	3.9	3.8
10	9.83 513	14	9.97 219	25	0.02 781	9.86 295	12	**50**			
11	9.83 527	13	9.97 244	25	0.02 756	9.86 283	12	49	10	4.3	4.2
12	9.83 540	14	9.97 269	26	0.02 731	9.86 271	12	48	20	8.7	8.3
13	9.83 554	13	9.97 295	25	0.02 705	9.86 259	12	47	30	13.0	12.5
14	9.83 567	14	9.97 320	25	0.02 680	9.86 247	12	46	40	17.3	16.7
									50	21.7	20.8
15	9.83 581	13	9.97 345	26	0.02 655	9.86 235	12	**45**			
16	9.83 594	14	9.97 371	25	0.02 629	9.86 223	12	44	″	**14**	**13**
17	9.83 608	13	9.97 396	25	0.02 604	9.86 211	11	43	1	0.2	0.2
18	9.83 621	13	9.97 421	26	0.02 579	9.86 200	12	42	2	0.5	0.4
19	9.83 634	14	9.97 447	25	0.02 553	9.86 188	12	41	3	0.7	0.6
									4	0.9	0.9
20	9.83 648	13	9.97 472	25	0.02 528	9.86 176	12	**40**			
21	9.83 661	13	9.97 497	26	0.02 503	9.86 164	12	39	5	1.2	1.1
22	9.83 674	13	9.97 523	25	0.02 477	9.86 152	12	38	6	1.4	1.3
23	9.83 688	13	9.97 548	25	0.02 452	9.86 140	12	37	7	1.6	1.5
24	9.83 701	14	9.97 573	25	0.02 427	9.86 128	12	36	8	1.9	1.7
									9	2.1	2.0
25	9.83 715	13	9.97 598	26	0.02 402	9.86 116	12	**35**			
26	9.83 728	13	9.97 624	25	0.02 376	9.86 104	12	34	10	2.3	2.2
27	9.83 741	14	9.97 649	25	0.02 351	9.86 092	12	33	20	4.7	4.3
28	9.83 755	13	9.97 674	26	0.02 326	9.86 080	12	32	30	7.0	6.5
29	9.83 768	13	9.97 700	25	0.02 300	9.86 068	12	31	40	9.3	8.7
									50	11.7	10.8
30	9.83 781	14	9.97 725	25	0.02 275	9.86 056	12	**30**			
31	9.83 795	13	9.97 750	26	0.02 250	9.86 044	12	29	″	**12**	**11**
32	9.83 808	13	9.97 776	25	0.02 224	9.86 032	12	28	1	0.2	0.2
33	9.83 821	13	9.97 801	25	0.02 199	9.86 020	12	27	2	0.4	0.4
34	9.83 834	14	9.97 826	25	0.02 174	9.86 008	12	26	3	0.6	0.6
									4	0.8	0.7
35	9.83 848	13	9.97 851	26	0.02 149	9.85 996	12	**25**			
36	9.83 861	13	9.97 877	25	0.02 123	9.85 984	12	24	5	1.0	0.9
37	9.83 874	13	9.97 902	25	0.02 098	9.85 972	12	23	6	1.2	1.1
38	9.83 887	14	9.97 927	26	0.02 073	9.85 960	12	22	7	1.4	1.3
39	9.83 901	13	9.97 953	25	0.02 047	9.85 948	12	21	8	1.6	1.5
									9	1.8	1.6
40	9.83 914	13	9.97 978	25	0.02 022	9.85 936	12	**20**			
41	9.83 927	13	9.98 003	26	0.01 997	9.85 924	12	19	10	2.0	1.8
42	9.83 940	14	9.98 029	25	0.01 971	9.85 912	12	18	20	4.0	3.7
43	9.83 954	13	9.98 054	25	0.01 946	9.85 900	12	17	30	6.0	5.5
44	9.83 967	13	9.98 079	25	0.01 921	9.85 888	12	16	40	8.0	7.3
									50	10.0	9.2
45	9.83 980	13	9.98 104	26	0.01 896	9.85 876	12	**15**			
46	9.83 993	13	9.98 130	25	0.01 870	9.85 864	13	14		**13**	**13**	**12**
47	9.84 006	14	9.98 155	25	0.01 845	9.85 851	13	13				
48	9.84 020	13	9.98 180	26	0.01 820	9.85 839	12	12		**26**	**25**	**25**
49	9.84 033	13	9.98 206	25	0.01 794	9.85 827	12	11	0	1.0	0.9	1.1
50	9.84 046	13	9.98 231	25	0.01 769	9.85 815	12	**10**	1	3.0	2.9	3.1
51	9.84 059	13	9.98 256	25	0.01 744	9.85 803	12	9	2	5.0	4.8	5.2
52	9.84 072	13	9.98 281	26	0.01 719	9.85 791	12	8	3	7.0	6.7	7.3
53	9.84 085	13	9.98 307	25	0.01 693	9.85 779	13	7	4	9.0	8.7	9.4
54	9.84 098	14	9.98 332	25	0.01 668	9.85 766	12	6	5	11.0	10.6	11.5
									6	13.0	12.5	13.5
55	9.84 112	13	9.98 357	26	0.01 643	9.85 754	12	**5**	7	15.0	14.4	15.6
56	9.84 125	13	9.98 383	25	0.01 617	9.85 742	12	4	8	17.0	16.3	17.7
57	9.84 138	13	9.98 408	25	0.01 592	9.85 730	12	3	9	19.0	18.3	19.8
58	9.84 151	13	9.98 433	25	0.01 567	9.85 718	12	2	10	21.0	20.2	21.9
59	9.84 164	13	9.98 458	26	0.01 542	9.85 706	13	1	11	23.0	22.1	23.9
									12	25.0	24.1	—
									13			
60	9.84 177		9.98 484		0.01 516	9.85 693		**0**			
′	L. Cos.	d.	L. Cot.	c.d.	L. Tan.	L. Sin.	d.	′	P. P.		

133° (313°) (226°) **46°**

LOGARITHMS OF THE TRIGONOMETRIC FUNCTIONS

44° (224°)   **(315°) 135°**

′	L. Sin.	d.	L. Tan.	c.d.	L. Cot.	L. Cos.	d.	′
0	9.84 177	13	9.98 484	25	0.01 516	9.85 693	12	60
1	9.84 190	13	9.98 509	25	0.01 491	9.85 681	12	59
2	9.84 203	13	9.98 534	26	0.01 466	9.85 669	12	58
3	9.84 216	13	9.98 560	25	0.01 440	9.85 657	12	57
4	9.84 229	13	9.98 585	25	0.01 415	9.85 645	13	56
5	9.84 242	13	9.98 610	25	0.01 390	9.85 632	12	55
6	9.84 255	14	9.98 635	26	0.01 365	9.85 620	12	54
7	9.84 269	13	9.98 661	25	0.01 339	9.85 608	12	53
8	9.84 282	13	9.98 686	25	0.01 314	9.85 596	13	52
9	9.84 295	13	9.98 711	26	0.01 289	9.85 583	12	51
10	9.84 308	13	9.98 737	25	0.01 263	9.85 571	12	50
11	9.84 321	13	9.98 762	25	0.01 238	9.85 559	12	49
12	9.84 334	13	9.98 787	25	0.01 213	9.85 547	13	48
13	9.84 347	13	9.98 812	26	0.01 188	9.85 534	12	47
14	9.84 360	13	9.98 838	25	0.01 162	9.85 522	12	46
15	9.84 373	12	9.98 863	25	0.01 137	9.85 510	13	45
16	9.84 385	13	9.98 888	25	0.01 112	9.85 497	12	44
17	9.84 398	13	9.98 913	26	0.01 087	9.85 485	12	43
18	9.84 411	13	9.98 939	25	0.01 061	9.85 473	13	42
19	9.84 424	13	9.98 964	25	0.01 036	9.85 460	12	41
20	9.84 437	13	9.98 989	26	0.01 011	9.85 448	12	40
21	9.84 450	13	9.99 015	25	0.00 985	9.85 436	13	39
22	9.84 463	13	9.99 040	25	0.00 960	9.85 423	12	38
23	9.84 476	13	9.99 065	25	0.00 935	9.85 411	12	37
24	9.84 489	13	9.99 090	26	0.00 910	9.85 399	13	36
25	9.84 502	13	9.99 116	25	0.00 884	9.85 386	12	35
26	9.84 515	13	9.99 141	25	0.00 859	9.85 374	13	34
27	9.84 528	12	9.99 166	25	0.00 834	9.85 361	12	33
28	9.84 540	13	9.99 191	26	0.00 809	9.85 349	12	32
29	9.84 553	13	9.99 217	25	0.00 783	9.85 337	13	31
30	9.84 566	13	9.99 242	25	0.00 758	9.85 324	12	30
31	9.84 579	13	9.99 267	26	0.00 733	9.85 312	13	29
32	9.84 592	13	9.99 293	25	0.00 707	9.85 299	12	28
33	9.84 605	13	9.99 318	25	0.00 682	9.85 287	12	27
34	9.84 618	12	9.99 343	25	0.00 657	9.85 274	12	26
35	9.84 630	13	9.99 368	26	0.00 632	9.85 262	12	25
36	9.84 643	13	9.99 394	25	0.00 606	9.85 250	13	24
37	9.84 656	13	9.99 419	25	0.00 581	9.85 237	12	23
38	9.84 669	13	9.99 444	25	0.00 556	9.85 225	13	22
39	9.84 682	12	9.99 469	26	0.00 531	9.85 212	12	21
40	9.84 694	13	9.99 495	25	0.00 505	9.85 200	13	20
41	9.84 707	13	9.99 520	25	0.00 480	9.85 187	12	19
42	9 84 720	13	9.99 545	25	0.00 455	9.85 175	13	18
43	9.84 733	12	9.99 570	26	0.00 430	9.85 162	12	17
44	9.84 745	13	9.99 596	25	0.00 404	9.85 150	13	16
45	9.84 758	13	9.99 621	25	0.00 379	9.85 137	12	15
46	9.84 771	13	9.99 646	26	0.00 354	9.85 125	13	14
47	9.84 784	12	9.99 672	25	0.00 328	9.85 112	12	13
48	9.84 796	13	9.99 697	25	0.00 303	9.85 100	13	12
49	9.84 809	13	9.99 722	25	0.00 278	9.85 087	13	11
50	9.84 822	13	9.99 747	26	0.00 253	9.85 074	12	10
51	9.84 835	12	9.99 773	25	0.00 227	9.85 062	13	9
52	9.84 847	13	9.99 798	25	0.00 202	9.85 049	12	8
53	9.84 860	13	9.99 823	25	0.00 177	9.85 037	13	7
54	9.84 873	12	9.99 848	26	0.00 152	9.85 024	12	6
55	9.84 885	13	9.99 874	25	0.00 126	9.85 012	13	5
56	9.84 898	13	9.99 899	25	0.00 101	9.84 999	13	4
57	9.84 911	12	9.99 924	25	0.00 076	9.84 986	12	3
58	9.84 923	13	9.99 949	26	0.00 051	9.84 974	13	2
59	9.84 936	13	9.99 975	25	0.00 025	9.84 961	12	1
60	9.84 949		0.00 000		0.00 000	9.84 949		0
′	L. Cos.	d.	L. Cot.	c.d.	L. Tan.	L. Sin.	d.	′

P. P.

″	26	25
1	0.4	0.4
2	0.9	0.8
3	1.3	1.2
4	1.7	1.7
5	2.2	2.1
6	2.6	2.5
7	3.0	2.9
8	3.5	3.3
9	3.9	3.8
10	4.3	4.2
20	8.7	8.3
30	13.0	12.5
40	17.3	16.7
50	21.7	20.8

″	14	13	12
1	0.2	0.2	0.2
2	0.5	0.4	0.4
3	0.7	0.6	0.6
4	0.9	0.9	0.8
5	1.2	1.1	1.0
6	1.4	1.3	1.2
7	1.6	1.5	1.4
8	1.9	1.7	1.6
9	2.1	2.0	1.8
10	2.3	2.2	2.0
20	4.7	4.3	4.0
30	7.0	6.5	6.0
40	9.3	8.7	8.0
50	11.7	10.8	10.0

	13	13
	26	25
0	1.0	0.9
1	3.0	2.9
2	5.0	4.8
3	7.0	6.7
4	9.0	8.7
5	11.0	10.6
6	13.0	12.5
7	15.0	14.4
8	17.0	16.3
9	19.0	18.3
10	21.0	20.2
11	23.0	22.1
12	25.0	24.1
13		

	12	12
	26	25
0	1.1	1.1
1	3.2	3.1
2	5.4	5.2
3	7.6	7.3
4	9.8	9.4
5	11.9	11.5
6	14.1	13.5
7	16.2	15.6
8	18.4	17.7
9	20.6	19.8
10	22.8	21.9
11	24.9	23.9
12		

134° (314°)   **(225°) 45°**

NATURAL TRIGONOMETRIC FUNCTIONS

Values of the trigonometric functions of angles for each minute from 0–360°.

For degrees indicated at the top of the page use the column headings at the top. For degrees indicated at the bottom use the column indications at the bottom.

With degrees at the left of each block (top or bottom), use the minute column at the left and with degrees at the right of each block use the minute column at the right.

NATURAL TRIGONOMETRIC FUNCTIONS

′	Sin	Tan	Cot	Cos	′	′	Sin	Tan	Cot	Cos	′
0	.00000	.00000		1.0000	60	0	.01745	.01746	57.290	.99985	60
1	.00029	.00029	3437.7	1.0000	59	1	.01774	.01775	56.351	.99984	59
2	.00058	.00058	1718.9	1.0000	58	2	.01803	.01804	55.442	.99984	58
3	.00087	.00087	1145.9	1.0000	57	3	.01832	.01833	54.561	.99983	57
4	.00116	.00116	859.44	1.0000	56	4	.01862	.01862	53.709	.99983	56
5	.00145	.00145	687.55	1.0000	55	5	.01891	.01891	52.882	.99982	55
6	.00175	.00175	572.96	1.0000	54	6	.01920	.01920	52.081	.99982	54
7	.00204	.00204	491.11	1.0000	53	7	.01949	.01949	51.303	.99981	53
8	.00233	.00233	429.72	1.0000	52	8	.01978	.01978	50.549	.99980	52
9	.00262	.00262	381.97	1.0000	51	9	.02007	.02007	49.816	.99980	51
10	.00291	.00291	343.77	1.0000	50	10	.02036	.02036	49.104	.99979	50
11	.00320	.00320	312.52	.99999	49	11	.02065	.02066	48.412	.99979	49
12	.00349	.00349	286.48	.99999	48	12	.02094	.02095	47.740	.99978	48
13	.00378	.00378	264.44	.99999	47	13	.02123	.02124	47.085	.99977	47
14	.00407	.00407	245.55	.99999	46	14	.02152	.02153	46.449	.99977	46
15	.00436	.00436	229.18	.99999	45	15	.02181	.02182	45.829	.99976	45
16	.00465	.00465	214.86	.99999	44	16	.02211	.02211	45.226	.99976	44
17	.00495	.00495	202.22	.99999	43	17	.02240	.02240	44.639	.99975	43
18	.00524	.00524	190.98	.99999	42	18	.02269	.02269	44.066	.99974	42
19	.00553	.00553	180.93	.99998	41	19	.02298	.02298	43.508	.99974	41
20	.00582	.00582	171.89	.99998	40	20	.02327	.02328	42.964	.99973	40
21	.00611	.00611	163.70	.99998	39	21	.02356	.02357	42.433	.99972	39
22	.00640	.00640	156.26	.99998	38	22	.02385	.02386	41.916	.99972	38
23	.00669	.00669	149.47	.99998	37	23	.02414	.02415	41.411	.99971	37
24	.00698	.00698	143.24	.99998	36	24	.02443	.02444	40.917	.99970	36
25	.00727	.00727	137.51	.99997	35	25	.02472	.02473	40.436	.99969	35
26	.00756	.00756	132.22	.99997	34	26	.02501	.02502	39.965	.99969	34
27	.00785	.00785	127.32	.99997	33	27	.02530	.02531	39.506	.99968	33
28	.00814	.00815	122.77	.99997	32	28	.02560	.02560	39.057	.99967	32
29	.00844	.00844	118.54	.99996	31	29	.02589	.02589	38.618	.99966	31
30	.00873	.00873	114.59	.99996	30	30	.02618	.02619	38.188	.99966	30
31	.00902	.00902	110.89	.99996	29	31	.02647	.02648	37.769	.99965	29
32	.00931	.00931	107.43	.99996	28	32	.02676	.02677	37.358	.99964	28
33	.00960	.00960	104.17	.99995	27	33	.02705	.02706	36.956	.99963	27
34	.00989	.00989	101.11	.99995	26	34	.02734	.02735	36.563	.99963	26
35	.01018	.01018	98.218	.99995	25	35	.02763	.02764	36.178	.99962	25
36	.01047	.01047	95.489	.99995	24	36	.02792	.02793	35.801	.99961	24
37	.01076	.01076	92.908	.99994	23	37	.02821	.02822	35.431	.99960	23
38	.01105	.01105	90.463	.99994	22	38	.02850	.02851	35.070	.99959	22
39	.01134	.01135	88.144	.99994	21	39	.02879	.02881	34.715	.99959	21
40	.01164	.01164	85.940	.99993	20	40	.02908	.02910	34.368	.99958	20
41	.01193	.01193	83.844	.99993	19	41	.02938	.02939	34.027	.99957	19
42	.01222	.01222	81.847	.99993	18	42	.02967	.02968	33.694	.99956	18
43	.01251	.01251	79.943	.99992	17	43	.02996	.02997	33.366	.99955	17
44	.01280	.01280	78.126	.99992	16	44	.03025	.03026	33.045	.99954	16
45	.01309	.01309	76.390	.99991	15	45	.03054	.03055	32.730	.99953	15
46	.01338	.01338	74.729	.99991	14	46	.03083	.03084	32.421	.99952	14
47	.01367	.01367	73.139	.99991	13	47	.03112	.03114	32.118	.99952	13
48	.01396	.01396	71.615	.99990	12	48	.03141	.03143	31.821	.99951	12
49	.01425	.01425	70.153	.99990	11	49	.03170	.03172	31.528	.99950	11
50	.01454	.01455	68.750	.99989	10	50	.03199	.03201	31.242	.99949	10
51	.01483	.01484	67.402	.99989	9	51	.03228	.03230	30.960	.99948	9
52	.01513	.01513	66.105	.99989	8	52	.03257	.03259	30.683	.99947	8
53	.01542	.01542	64.858	.99988	7	53	.03286	.03288	30.412	.99946	7
54	.01571	.01571	63.657	.99988	6	54	.03316	.03317	30.145	.99945	6
55	.01600	.01600	62.499	.99987	5	55	.03345	.03346	29.882	.99944	5
56	.01629	.01629	61.383	.99987	4	56	.03374	.03376	29.624	.99943	4
57	.01658	.01658	60.306	.99986	3	57	.03403	.03405	29.371	.99942	3
58	.01687	.01687	59.266	.99986	2	58	.03432	.03434	29.122	.99941	2
59	.01716	.01716	58.261	.99985	1	59	.03461	.03463	28.877	.99940	1
60	.01745	.01746	57.290	.99985	0	60	.03490	.03492	28.636	.99939	0
′	Cos	Cot	Tan	Sin	′	′	Cos	Cot	Tan	Sin	′

NATURAL TRIGONOMETRIC FUNCTIONS

′	Sin	Tan	Cot	Cos	′		′	Sin	Tan	Cot	Cos	′
0	.03490	.03492	28.636	.99939	60		0	.05234	.05241	19.081	.99863	60
1	.03519	.03521	28.399	.99938	59		1	.05263	.05270	18.976	.99861	59
2	.03548	.03550	28.166	.99937	58		2	.05292	.05299	18.871	.99860	58
3	.03577	.03579	27.937	.99936	57		3	.05321	.05328	18.768	.99858	57
4	.03606	.03609	27.712	.99935	56		4	.05350	.05357	18.666	.99857	56
5	.03635	.03638	27.490	.99934	55		5	.05379	.05387	18.564	.99855	55
6	.03664	.03667	27.271	.99933	54		6	.05408	.05416	18.464	.99854	54
7	.03693	.03696	27.057	.99932	53		7	.05437	.05445	18.366	.99852	53
8	.03723	.03725	26.845	.99931	52		8	.05466	.05474	18.268	.99851	52
9	.03752	.03754	26.637	.99930	51		9	.05495	.05503	18.171	.99849	51
10	.03781	.03783	26.432	.99929	50		10	.05524	.05533	18.075	.99847	50
11	.03810	.03812	26.230	.99927	49		11	.05553	.05562	17.980	.99846	49
12	.03839	.03842	26.031	.99926	48		12	.05582	.05591	17.886	.99844	48
13	.03868	.03871	25.835	.99925	47		13	.05611	.05620	17.793	.99842	47
14	.03897	.03900	25.642	.99924	46		14	.05640	.05649	17.702	.99841	46
15	.03926	.03929	25.452	.99923	45		15	.05669	.05678	17.611	.99839	45
16	.03955	.03958	25.264	.99922	44		16	.05698	.05708	17.521	.99838	44
17	.03984	.03987	25.080	.99921	43		17	.05727	.05737	17.431	.99836	43
18	.04013	.04016	24.898	.99919	42		18	.05756	.05766	17.343	.99834	42
19	.04042	.04046	24.719	.99918	41		19	.05785	.05795	17.256	.99833	41
20	.04071	.04075	24.542	.99917	40		20	.05814	.05824	17.169	.99831	40
21	.04100	.04104	24.368	.99916	39		21	.05844	.05854	17.084	.99829	39
22	.04129	.04133	24.196	.99915	38		22	.05873	.05883	16.999	.99827	38
23	.04159	.04162	24.026	.99913	37		23	.05902	.05912	16.915	.99826	37
24	.04188	.04191	23.859	.99912	36		24	.05931	.05941	16.832	.99824	36
25	.04217	.04220	23.695	.99911	35		25	.05960	.05970	16.750	.99822	35
26	.04246	.04250	23.532	.99910	34		26	.05989	.05999	16.668	.99821	34
27	.04275	.04279	23.372	.99909	33		27	.06018	.06029	16.587	.99819	33
28	.04304	.04308	23.214	.99907	32		28	.06047	.06058	16.507	.99817	32
29	.04333	.04337	23.058	.99906	31		29	.06076	.06087	16.428	.99815	31
30	.04362	.04366	22.904	.99905	30		30	.06105	.06116	16.350	.99813	30
31	.04391	.04395	22.752	.99904	29		31	.06134	.06145	16.272	.99812	29
32	.04420	.04424	22.602	.99902	28		32	.06163	.06175	16.195	.99810	28
33	.04449	.04454	22.454	.99901	27		33	.06192	.06204	16.119	.99808	27
34	.04478	.04483	22.308	.99900	26		34	.06221	.06233	16.043	.99806	26
35	.04507	.04512	22.164	.99898	25		35	.06250	.06262	15.969	.99804	25
36	.04536	.04541	22.022	.99897	24		36	.06279	.06291	15.895	.99803	24
37	.04565	.04570	21.881	.99896	23		37	.06308	.06321	15.821	.99801	23
38	.04594	.04599	21.743	.99894	22		38	.06337	.06350	15.748	.99799	22
39	.04623	.04628	21.606	.99893	21		39	.06366	.06379	15.676	.99797	21
40	.04653	.04658	21.470	.99892	20		40	.06395	.06408	15.605	.99795	20
41	.04682	.04687	21.337	.99890	19		41	.06424	.06438	15.534	.99793	19
42	.04711	.04716	21.205	.99889	18		42	.06453	.06467	15.464	.99792	18
43	.04740	.04745	21.075	.99888	17		43	.06482	.06496	15.394	.99790	17
44	.04769	.04774	20.946	.99886	16		44	.06511	.06525	15.325	.99788	16
45	.04798	.04803	20.819	.99885	15		45	.06540	.06554	15.257	.99786	15
46	.04827	.04833	20.693	.99883	14		46	.06569	.06584	15.189	.99784	14
47	.04856	.04862	20.569	.99882	13		47	.06598	.06613	15.122	.99782	13
48	.04885	.04891	20.446	.99881	12		48	.06627	.06642	15.056	.99780	12
49	.04914	.04920	20.325	.99879	11		49	.06656	.06671	14.990	.99778	11
50	.04943	.04949	20.206	.99878	10		50	.06685	.06700	14.924	.99776	10
51	.04972	.04978	20.087	.99876	9		51	.06714	.06730	14.860	.99774	9
52	.05001	.05007	19.970	.99875	8		52	.06743	.06759	14.795	.99772	8
53	.05030	.05037	19.855	.99873	7		53	.06773	.06788	14.732	.99770	7
54	.05059	.05066	19.740	.99872	6		54	.06802	.06817	14.669	.99768	6
55	.05088	.05095	19.627	.99870	5		55	.06831	.06847	14.606	.99766	5
56	.05117	.05124	19.516	.99869	4		56	.06860	.06876	14.544	.99764	4
57	.05146	.05153	19.405	.99867	3		57	.06889	.06905	14.482	.99762	3
58	.05175	.05182	19.296	.99866	2		58	.06918	.06934	14.421	.99760	2
59	.05205	.05212	19.188	.99864	1		59	.06947	.06963	14.361	.99758	1
60	.05234	.05241	19.081	.99863	0		60	.06976	.06993	14.301	.99756	0
′	Cos	Cot	Tan	Sin	′		′	Cos	Cot	Tan	Sin	′

NATURAL TRIGONOMETRIC FUNCTIONS

′	Sin	Tan	Cot	Cos	′	′	Sin	Tan	Cot	Cos	′
0	.06976	.06993	14.301	.99756	60	0	.08716	.08749	11.430	.99619	60
1	.07005	.07022	14.241	.99754	59	1	.08745	.08778	11.392	.99617	59
2	.07034	.07051	14.182	.99752	58	2	.08774	.08807	11.354	.99614	58
3	.07063	.07080	14.124	.99750	57	3	.08803	.08837	11.316	.99612	57
4	.07092	.07110	14.065	.99748	56	4	.08831	.08866	11.279	.99609	56
5	.07121	.07139	14.008	.99746	55	5	.08860	.08895	11.242	.99607	55
6	.07150	.07168	13.951	.99744	54	6	.08889	.08925	11.205	.99604	54
7	.07179	.07197	13.894	.99742	53	7	.08918	.08954	11.168	.99602	53
8	.07208	.07227	13.838	.99740	52	8	.08947	.08983	11.132	.99599	52
9	.07237	.07256	13.782	.99738	51	9	.08976	.09013	11.095	.99596	51
10	.07266	.07285	13.727	.99736	50	10	.09005	.09042	11.059	.99594	50
11	.07295	.07314	13.672	.99734	49	11	.09034	.09071	11.024	.99591	49
12	.07324	.07344	13.617	.99731	48	12	.09063	.09101	10.988	.99588	48
13	.07353	.07373	13.563	.99729	47	13	.09092	.09130	10.953	.99586	47
14	.07382	.07402	13.510	.99727	46	14	.09121	.09159	10.918	.99583	46
15	.07411	.07431	13.457	.99725	45	15	.09150	.09189	10.883	.99580	45
16	.07440	.07461	13.404	.99723	44	16	.09179	.09218	10.848	.99578	44
17	.07469	.07490	13.352	.99721	43	17	.09208	.09247	10.814	.99575	43
18	.07498	.07519	13.300	.99719	42	18	.09237	.09277	10.780	.99572	42
19	.07527	.07548	13.248	.99716	41	19	.09266	.09306	10.746	.99570	41
20	.07556	.07578	13.197	.99714	40	20	.09295	.09335	10.712	.99567	40
21	.07585	.07607	13.146	.99712	39	21	.09324	.09365	10.678	.99564	39
22	.07614	.07636	13.096	.99710	38	22	.09353	.09394	10.645	.99562	38
23	.07643	.07665	13.046	.99708	37	23	.09382	.09423	10.612	.99558	37
24	.07672	.07695	12.996	.99705	36	24	.09411	.09453	10.579	.99556	36
25	.07701	.07724	12.947	.99703	35	25	.09440	.09482	10.546	.99553	35
26	.07730	.07753	12.898	.99701	34	26	.09469	.09511	10.514	.99551	34
27	.07759	.07782	12.850	.99699	33	27	.09498	.09541	10.481	.99548	33
28	.07788	.07812	12.801	.99696	32	28	.09527	.09570	10.449	.99545	32
29	.07817	.07841	12.754	.99694	31	29	.09556	.09600	10.417	.99542	31
30	.07846	.07870	12.706	.99692	30	30	.09585	.09629	10.385	.99540	30
31	.07875	.07899	12.659	.99689	29	31	.09614	.09658	10.354	.99537	29
32	.07904	.07929	12.612	.99687	28	32	.09642	.09688	10.322	.99534	28
33	.07933	.07958	12.566	.99685	27	33	.09671	.09717	10.291	.99531	27
34	.07962	.07987	12.520	.99683	26	34	.09700	.09746	10.260	.99528	26
35	.07991	.08017	12.474	.99680	25	35	.09729	.09776	10.229	.99526	25
36	.08020	.08046	12.429	.99678	24	36	.09758	.09805	10.199	.99523	24
37	.08049	.08075	12.384	.99676	23	37	.09787	.09834	10.168	.99520	23
38	.08078	.08104	12.339	.99673	22	38	.09816	.09864	10.138	.99517	22
39	.08107	.08134	12.295	.99671	21	39	.09845	.09893	10.108	.99514	21
40	.08136	.08163	12.251	.99668	20	40	.09874	.09923	10.078	.99511	20
41	.08165	.08192	12.207	.99666	19	41	.09903	.09952	10.048	.99508	19
42	.08194	.08221	12.163	.99664	18	42	.09932	.09981	10.019	.99506	18
43	.08223	.08251	12.120	.99661	17	43	.09961	.10011	9.9893	.99503	17
44	.08252	.08280	12.077	.99659	16	44	.09990	.10040	9.9601	.99500	16
45	.08281	.08309	12.035	.99657	15	45	.10019	.10069	9.9310	.99497	15
46	.08310	.08339	11.992	.99654	14	46	.10048	.10099	9.9021	.99494	14
47	.08339	.08368	11.950	.99652	13	47	.10077	.10128	9.8734	.99491	13
48	.08368	.08397	11.909	.99649	12	48	.10106	.10158	9.8448	.99488	12
49	.08397	.08427	11.867	.99647	11	49	.10135	.10187	9.8164	.99485	11
50	.08426	.08456	11.826	.99644	10	50	.10164	.10216	9.7882	.99482	10
51	.08455	.08485	11.785	.99642	9	51	.10192	.10246	9.7601	.99479	9
52	.08484	.08514	11.745	.99639	8	52	.10221	.10275	9.7322	.99476	8
53	.08513	.08544	11.705	.99637	7	53	.10250	.10305	9.7044	.99473	7
54	.08542	.08573	11.664	.99635	6	54	.10279	.10334	9.6768	.99470	6
55	.08571	.08602	11.625	.99632	5	55	.10308	.10363	9.6493	.99467	5
56	.08600	.08632	11.585	.99630	4	56	.10337	.10393	9.6220	.99464	4
57	.08629	.08661	11.546	.99627	3	57	.10366	.10422	9.5949	.99461	3
58	.08658	.08690	11.507	.99625	2	58	.10395	.10452	9.5679	.99458	2
59	.08687	.08720	11.468	.99622	1	59	.10424	.10481	9.5411	.99455	1
60	.08716	.08749	11.430	.99619	0	60	.10453	.10510	9.5144	.99452	0
′	Cos	Cot	Tan	Sin	′	′	Cos	Cot	Tan	Sin	′

6° (186°)   (353°) **173°**

′	Sin	Tan	Cot	Cos	′
0	.10453	.10510	9.5144	.99452	**60**
1	.10482	.10540	9.4878	.99449	59
2	.10511	.10569	9.4614	.99446	58
3	.10540	.10599	9.4352	.99443	57
4	.10569	.10628	9.4090	.99440	56
5	.10597	.10657	9.3831	.99437	**55**
6	.10626	.10687	9.3572	.99434	54
7	.10655	.10716	9.3315	.99431	53
8	.10684	.10746	9.3060	.99428	52
9	.10713	.10775	9.2806	.99424	51
10	.10742	.10805	9.2553	.99421	**50**
11	.10771	.10834	9.2302	.99418	49
12	.10800	.10863	9.2052	.99415	48
13	.10829	.10893	9.1803	.99412	47
14	.10858	.10922	9.1555	.99409	46
15	.10887	.10952	9.1309	.99406	**45**
16	.10916	.10981	9.1065	.99402	44
17	.10945	.11011	9.0821	.99399	43
18	.10973	.11040	9.0579	.99396	42
19	.11002	.11070	9.0338	.99393	41
20	.11031	.11099	9.0098	.99390	**40**
21	.11060	.11128	8.9860	.99386	39
22	.11089	.11158	8.9623	.99383	38
23	.11118	.11187	8.9387	.99380	37
24	.11147	.11217	8.9152	.99377	36
25	.11176	.11246	8.8919	.99374	**35**
26	.11205	.11276	8.8686	.99370	34
27	.11234	.11305	8.8455	.99367	33
28	.11263	.11335	8.8225	.99364	32
29	.11291	.11364	8.7996	.99360	31
30	.11320	.11394	8.7769	.99357	**30**
31	.11349	.11423	8.7542	.99351	29
32	.11378	.11452	8.7317	.99351	28
33	.11407	.11482	8.7093	.99347	27
34	.11436	.11511	8.6870	.99344	26
35	.11465	.11541	8.6648	.99341	**25**
36	.11494	.11570	8.6427	.99337	24
37	.11523	.11600	8.6208	.99334	23
38	.11552	.11629	8.5989	.99331	22
39	.11580	.11659	8.5772	.99327	21
40	.11609	.11688	8.5555	.99324	**20**
41	.11638	.11718	8.5340	.99320	19
42	.11667	.11747	8.5126	.99317	18
43	.11696	.11777	8.4913	.99314	17
44	.11725	.11806	8.4701	.99310	16
45	.11754	.11836	8.4490	.99307	**15**
46	.11783	.11865	8.4280	.99303	14
47	.11812	.11895	8.4071	.99300	13
48	.11840	.11924	8.3863	.99297	12
49	.11869	.11954	8.3656	.99293	11
50	.11898	.11983	8.3450	.99290	**10**
51	.11927	.12013	8.3245	.99286	9
52	.11956	.12042	8.3041	.99283	8
53	.11985	.12072	8.2838	.99279	7
54	.12014	.12101	8.2636	.99276	6
55	.12043	.12131	8.2434	.99272	**5**
56	.12071	.12160	8.2234	.99269	4
57	.12100	.12190	8.2035	.99265	3
58	.12129	.12219	8.1837	.99262	2
59	.12158	.12249	8.1640	.99258	1
60	.12187	.12278	8.1443	.99255	**0**
′	Cos	Cot	Tan	Sin	′

96° (276°)   (263°) **83°**

7° (187°)   (352°) **172°**

′	Sin	Tan	Cot	Cos	′
0	.12187	.12278	8.1443	.99255	**60**
1	.12216	.12308	8.1248	.99251	59
2	.12245	.12338	8.1054	.99248	58
3	.12274	.12367	8.0860	.99244	57
4	.12302	.12397	8.0667	.99240	56
5	.12331	.12426	8.0476	.99237	**55**
6	.12360	.12456	8.0285	.99233	54
7	.12389	.12485	8.0095	.99230	53
8	.12418	.12515	7.9906	.99226	52
9	.12447	.12544	7.9718	.99222	51
10	.12476	.12574	7.9530	.99219	**50**
11	.12504	.12603	7.9344	.99215	49
12	.12533	.12633	7.9158	.99211	48
13	.12562	.12662	7.8973	.99208	47
14	.12591	.12692	7.8789	.99204	46
15	.12620	.12722	7.8606	.99200	**45**
16	.12649	.12751	7.8424	.99197	44
17	.12678	.12781	7.8243	.99193	43
18	.12706	.12810	7.8062	.99189	42
19	.12735	.12840	7.7882	.99186	41
20	.12764	.12869	7.7704	.99182	**40**
21	.12793	.12899	7.7525	.99178	39
22	.12822	.12929	7.7348	.99175	38
23	.12851	.12958	7.7171	.99171	37
24	.12880	.12988	7.6996	.99167	36
25	.12908	.13017	7.6821	.99163	**35**
26	.12937	.13047	7.6647	.99160	34
27	.12966	.13076	7.6473	.99156	33
28	.12995	.13106	7.6301	.99152	32
29	.13024	.13136	7.6129	.99148	31
30	.13053	.13165	7.5958	.99144	**30**
31	.13081	.13195	7.5787	.99141	29
32	.13110	.13224	7.5618	.99137	28
33	.13139	.13254	7.5449	.99133	27
34	.13168	.13284	7.5281	.99129	26
35	.13197	.13313	7.5113	.99125	**25**
36	.13226	.13343	7.4947	.99122	24
37	.13254	.13372	7.4781	.99118	23
38	.13283	.13402	7.4615	.99114	22
39	.13312	.13432	7.4451	.99110	21
40	.13341	.13461	7.4287	.99106	**20**
41	.13370	.13491	7.4124	.99102	19
42	.13399	.13521	7.3962	.99098	18
43	.13427	.13550	7.3800	.99094	17
44	.13456	.13580	7.3639	.99091	16
45	.13485	.13609	7.3479	.99087	**15**
46	.13514	.13639	7.3319	.99083	14
47	.13543	.13669	7.3160	.99079	13
48	.13572	.13698	7.3002	.99075	12
49	.13600	.13728	7.2844	.99071	11
50	.13629	.13758	7.2687	.99067	**10**
51	.13658	.13787	7.2531	.99063	9
52	.13687	.13817	7.2375	.99059	8
53	.13716	.13846	7.2220	.99055	7
54	.13744	.13876	7.2066	.99051	6
55	.13773	.13906	7.1912	.99047	**5**
56	.13802	.13935	7.1759	.99043	4
57	.13831	.13965	7.1607	.99039	3
58	.13860	.13995	7.1455	.99035	2
59	.13889	.14024	7.1304	.99031	1
60	.13917	.14054	7.1154	.99027	**0**
′	Cos	Cot	Tan	Sin	′

97° (277°)   (262°) **82°**

NATURAL TRIGONOMETRIC FUNCTIONS

′	Sin	Tan	Cot	Cos	′	′	Sin	Tan	Cot	Cos	′
0	.13917	.14054	7.1154	.99027	60	0	.15643	.15838	6.3138	.98769	60
1	.13946	.14084	7.1004	.99023	59	1	.15672	.15868	6.3019	.98764	59
2	.13975	.14113	7.0855	.99019	58	2	.15701	.15898	6.2901	.98760	58
3	.14004	.14143	7.0706	.99015	57	3	.15730	.15928	6.2783	.98755	57
4	.14033	.14173	7.0558	.99011	56	4	.15758	.15958	6.2666	.98751	56
5	.14061	.14202	7.0410	.99006	55	5	.15787	.15988	6.2549	.98746	55
6	.14090	.14232	7.0264	.99002	54	6	.15816	.16017	6.2432	.98741	54
7	.14119	.14262	7.0117	.98998	53	7	.15845	.16047	6.2316	.98737	53
8	.14148	.14291	6.9972	.98994	52	8	.15873	.16077	6.2200	.98732	52
9	.14177	.14321	6.9827	.98990	51	9	.15902	.16107	6.2085	.98728	51
10	.14205	.14351	6.9682	.98986	50	10	.15931	.16137	6.1970	.98723	50
11	.14234	.14381	6.9538	.98982	49	11	.15959	.16167	6.1856	.98718	49
12	.14263	.14410	6.9395	.98978	48	12	.15988	.16196	6.1742	.98714	48
13	.14292	.14440	6.9252	.98973	47	13	.16017	.16226	6.1628	.98709	47
14	.14320	.14470	6.9110	.98969	46	14	.16046	.16256	6.1515	.98704	46
15	.14349	.14499	6.8969	.98965	45	15	.16074	.16286	6.1402	.98700	45
16	.14378	.14529	6.8828	.98961	44	16	.16103	.16316	6.1290	.98695	44
17	.14407	.14559	6.8687	.98957	43	17	.16132	.16346	6.1178	.98690	43
18	.14436	.14588	6.8548	.98953	42	18	.16160	.16376	6.1066	.98686	42
19	.14464	.14618	6.8408	.98948	41	19	.16189	.16405	6.0955	.98681	41
20	.14493	.14648	6.8269	.98944	40	20	.16218	.16435	6.0844	.98676	40
21	.14522	.14678	6.8131	.98940	39	21	.16246	.16465	6.0734	.98671	39
22	.14551	.14707	6.7994	.98936	38	22	.16275	.16495	6.0624	.98667	38
23	.14580	.14737	6.7856	.98931	37	23	.16304	.16525	6.0514	.98662	37
24	.14608	.14767	6.7720	.98927	36	24	.16333	.16555	6.0405	.98657	36
25	.14637	.14796	6.7584	.98923	35	25	.16361	.16585	6.0296	.98652	35
26	.14666	.14826	6.7448	.98919	34	26	.16390	.16615	6.0188	.98648	34
27	.14695	.14856	6.7313	.98914	33	27	.16419	.16645	6.0080	.98643	33
28	.14723	.14886	6.7179	.98910	32	28	.16447	.16674	5.9972	.98638	32
29	.14752	.14915	6.7045	.98906	31	29	.16476	.16704	5.9865	.98633	31
30	.14781	.14945	6.6912	.98902	30	30	.16505	.16734	5.9758	.98629	30
31	.14810	.14975	6.6779	.98897	29	31	.16533	.16764	5.9651	.98624	29
32	.14838	.15005	6.6646	.98893	28	32	.16562	.16794	5.9545	.98619	28
33	.14867	.15034	6.6514	.98889	27	33	.16591	.16824	5.9439	.98614	27
34	.14896	.15064	6.6383	.98884	26	34	.16620	.16854	5.9333	.98609	26
35	.14925	.15094	6.6252	.98880	25	35	.16648	.16884	5.9228	.98604	25
36	.14954	.15124	6.6122	.98876	24	36	.16677	.16914	5.9124	.98600	24
37	.14982	.15153	6.5992	.98871	23	37	.16706	.16944	5.9019	.98595	23
38	.15011	.15183	6.5863	.98867	22	38	.16734	.16974	5.8915	.98590	22
39	.15040	.15213	6.5734	.98863	21	39	.16763	.17004	5.8811	.98585	21
40	.15069	.15243	6.5606	.98858	20	40	.16792	.17033	5.8708	.98580	20
41	.15097	.15272	6.5478	.98854	19	41	.16820	.17063	5.8605	.98575	19
42	.15126	.15302	6.5350	.98849	18	42	.16849	.17093	5.8502	.98570	18
43	.15155	.15332	6.5223	.98845	17	43	.16878	.17123	5.8400	.98565	17
44	.15184	.15362	6.5097	.98841	16	44	.16906	.17153	5.8298	.98561	16
45	.15212	.15391	6.4971	.98836	15	45	.16935	.17183	5.8197	.98556	15
46	.15241	.15421	6.4846	.98832	14	46	.16964	.17213	5.8095	.98551	14
47	.15270	.15451	6.4721	.98827	13	47	.16992	.17243	5.7994	.98546	13
48	.15299	.15481	6.4596	.98823	12	48	.17021	.17273	5.7894	.98541	12
49	.15327	.15511	6.4472	.98818	11	49	.17050	.17303	5.7794	.98536	11
50	.15356	.15540	6.4348	.98814	10	50	.17078	.17333	5.7694	.98531	10
51	.15385	.15570	6.4225	.98809	9	51	.17107	.17363	5.7594	.98526	9
52	.15414	.15600	6.4103	.98805	8	52	.17136	.17393	5.7495	.98521	8
53	.15442	.15630	6.3980	.98800	7	53	.17164	.17423	5.7396	.98516	7
54	.15471	.15660	6.3859	.98796	6	54	.17193	.17453	5.7297	.98511	6
55	.15500	.15689	6.3737	.98791	5	55	.17222	.17483	5.7199	.98506	5
56	.15529	.15719	6.3617	.98787	4	56	.17250	.17513	5.7101	.98501	4
57	.15557	.15749	6.3496	.98782	3	57	.17279	.17543	5.7004	.98496	3
58	.15586	.15779	6.3376	.98778	2	58	.17308	.17573	5.6906	.98491	2
59	.15615	.15809	6.3257	.98773	1	59	.17336	.17603	5.6809	.98486	1
60	.15643	.15838	6.3138	.98769	0	60	.17365	.17633	5.6713	.98481	0
′	Cos	Cot	Tan	Sin	′	′	Cos	Cot	Tan	Sin	′

NATURAL TRIGONOMETRIC FUNCTIONS

′	Sin	Tan	Cot	Cos	′		′	Sin	Tan	Cot	Cos	′
0	.17365	.17633	5.6713	.98481	60		0	.19081	.19438	5.1446	.98163	60
1	.17393	.17663	5.6617	.98476	59		1	.19109	.19468	5.1366	.98157	59
2	.17422	.17693	5.6521	.98471	58		2	.19138	.19498	5.1286	.98152	58
3	.17451	.17723	5.6425	.98466	57		3	.19167	.19529	5.1207	.98146	57
4	.17479	.17753	5.6329	.98461	56		4	.19195	.19559	5.1128	.98140	56
5	.17508	.17783	5.6234	.98455	55		5	.19224	.19589	5.1049	.98135	55
6	.17537	.17813	5.6140	.98450	54		6	.19252	.19619	5.0970	.98129	54
7	.17565	.17843	5.6045	.98445	53		7	.19281	.19649	5.0892	.98124	53
8	.17594	.17873	5.5951	.98440	52		8	.19309	.19680	5.0814	.98118	52
9	.17623	.17903	5.5857	.98435	51		9	.19338	.19710	5.0736	.98112	51
10	.17651	.17933	5.5764	.98430	50		10	.19366	.19740	5.0658	.98107	50
11	.17680	.17963	5.5671	.98425	49		11	.19395	.19770	5.0581	.98101	49
12	.17708	.17993	5.5578	.98420	48		12	.19423	.19801	5.0504	.98096	48
13	.17737	.18023	5.5485	.98414	47		13	.19452	.19831	5.0427	.98090	47
14	.17766	.18053	5.5393	.98409	46		14	.19481	.19861	5.0350	.98084	46
15	.17794	.18083	5.5301	.98404	45		15	.19509	.19891	5.0273	.98079	45
16	.17823	.18113	5.5209	.98399	44		16	.19538	.19921	5.0197	.98073	44
17	.17852	.18143	5.5118	.98394	43		17	.19566	.19952	5.0121	.98067	43
18	.17880	.18173	5.5026	.98389	42		18	.19595	.19982	5.0045	.98061	42
19	.17909	.18203	5.4936	.98383	41		19	.19623	.20012	4.9969	.98056	41
20	.17937	.18233	5.4845	.98378	40		20	.19652	.20042	4.9894	.98050	40
21	.17966	.18263	5.4755	.98373	39		21	.19680	.20073	4.9819	.98044	39
22	.17995	.18293	5.4665	.98368	38		22	.19709	.20103	4.9744	.98039	38
23	.18023	.18323	5.4575	.98362	37		23	.19737	.20133	4.9669	.98033	37
24	.18052	.18353	5.4486	.98357	36		24	.19766	.20164	4.9594	.98027	36
25	.18081	.18384	5.4397	.98352	35		25	.19794	.20194	4.9520	.98021	35
26	.18109	.18414	5.4308	.98347	34		26	.19823	.20224	4.9446	.98016	34
27	.18138	.18444	5.4219	.98341	33		27	.19851	.20254	4.9372	.98010	33
28	.18166	.18474	5.4131	.98336	32		28	.19880	.20285	4.9298	.98004	32
29	.18195	.18504	5.4043	.98331	31		29	.19908	.20315	4.9225	.97998	31
30	.18224	.18534	5.3955	.98325	30		30	.19937	.20345	4.9152	.97992	30
31	.18252	.18564	5.3868	.98320	29		31	.19965	.20376	4.9078	.97987	29
32	.18281	.18594	5.3781	.98315	28		32	.19994	.20406	4.9006	.97981	28
33	.18309	.18624	5.3694	.98310	27		33	.20022	.20436	4.8933	.97975	27
34	.18338	.18654	5.3607	.98304	26		34	.20051	.20466	4.8860	.97969	26
35	.18367	.18684	5.3521	.98299	25		35	.20079	.20497	4.8788	.97963	25
36	.18395	.18714	5.3435	.98294	24		36	.20108	.20527	4.8716	.97958	24
37	.18424	.18745	5.3349	.98288	23		37	.20136	.20557	4.8644	.97952	23
38	.18452	.18775	5.3263	.98283	22		38	.20165	.20588	4.8573	.97946	22
39	.18481	.18805	5.3178	.98277	21		39	.20193	.20618	4.8501	.97940	21
40	.18509	.18835	5.3093	.98272	20		40	.20222	.20648	4.8430	.97934	20
41	.18538	.18865	5.3008	.98267	19		41	.20250	.20679	4.8359	.97928	19
42	.18567	.18895	5.2924	.98261	18		42	.20279	.20709	4.8288	.97922	18
43	.18595	.18925	5.2839	.98256	17		43	.20307	.20739	4.8218	.97916	17
44	.18624	.18955	5.2755	.98250	16		44	.20336	.20770	4.8147	.97910	16
45	.18652	.18986	5.2672	.98245	15		45	.20364	.20800	4.8077	.97905	15
46	.18681	.19016	5.2588	.98240	14		46	.20393	.20830	4.8007	.97899	14
47	.18710	.19046	5.2505	.98234	13		47	.20421	.20861	4.7937	.97893	13
48	.18738	.19076	5.2422	.98229	12		48	.20450	.20891	4.7867	.97887	12
49	.18767	.19106	5.2339	.98223	11		49	.20478	.20921	4.7798	.97881	11
50	.18795	.19136	5.2257	.98218	10		50	.20507	.20952	4.7729	.97875	10
51	.18824	.19166	5.2174	.98212	9		51	.20535	.20982	4.7659	.97869	9
52	.18852	.19197	5.2092	.98207	8		52	.20563	.21013	4.7591	.97863	8
53	.18881	.19227	5.2011	.98201	7		53	.20592	.21043	4.7522	.97857	7
54	.18910	.19257	5.1929	.98196	6		54	.20620	.21073	4.7453	.97851	6
55	.18938	.19287	5.1848	.98190	5		55	.20649	.21104	4.7385	.97845	5
56	.18967	.19317	5.1767	.98185	4		56	.20677	.21134	4.7317	.97839	4
57	.18995	.19347	5.1686	.98179	3		57	.20706	.21164	4.7249	.97833	3
58	.19024	.19378	5.1606	.98174	2		58	.20734	.21195	4.7181	.97827	2
59	.19052	.19408	5.1526	.98168	1		59	.20763	.21225	4.7114	.97821	1
60	.19081	.19438	5.1446	.98163	0		60	.20791	.21256	4.7046	.97815	0
′	Cos	Cot	Tan	Sin	′		′	Cos	Cot	Tan	Sin	′

NATURAL TRIGONOMETRIC FUNCTIONS

′	Sin	Tan	Cot	Cos	′		′	Sin	Tan	Cot	Cos	′
0	.20791	.21256	4.7046	.97815	60		0	.22495	.23087	4.3315	.97437	60
1	.20820	.21286	4.6979	.97809	59		1	.22523	.23117	4.3257	.97430	59
2	.20848	.21316	4.6912	.97803	58		2	.22552	.23148	4.3200	.97424	58
3	.20877	.21347	4.6845	.97797	57		3	.22580	.23179	4.3143	.97417	57
4	.20905	.21377	4.6779	.97791	56		4	.22608	.23209	4.3086	.97411	56
5	.20933	.21408	4.6712	.97784	55		5	.22637	.23240	4.3029	.97404	55
6	.20962	.21438	4.6646	.97778	54		6	.22665	.23271	4.2972	.97398	54
7	.20990	.21469	4.6580	.97772	53		7	.22693	.23301	4.2916	.97391	53
8	.21019	.21499	4.6514	.97766	52		8	.22722	.23332	4.2859	.97384	52
9	.21047	.21529	4.6448	.97760	51		9	.22750	.23363	4.2803	.97378	51
10	.21076	.21560	4.6382	.97754	50		10	.22778	.23393	4.2747	.97371	50
11	.21104	.21590	4.6317	.97748	49		11	.22807	.23424	4.2691	.97365	49
12	.21132	.21621	4.6252	.97742	48		12	.22835	.23455	4.2635	.97358	48
13	.21161	.21651	4.6187	.97735	47		13	.22863	.23485	4.2580	.97351	47
14	.21189	.21682	4.6122	.97729	46		14	.22892	.23516	4.2524	.97345	46
15	.21218	.21712	4.6057	.97723	45		15	.22920	.23547	4.2468	.97338	45
16	.21246	.21743	4.5993	.97717	44		16	.22948	.23578	4.2413	.97331	44
17	.21275	.21773	4.5928	.97711	43		17	.22977	.23608	4.2358	.97325	43
18	.21303	.21804	4.5864	.97705	42		18	.23005	.23639	4.2303	.97318	42
19	.21331	.21834	4.5800	.97698	41		19	.23033	.23670	4.2248	.97311	41
20	.21360	.21864	4.5736	.97692	40		20	.23062	.23700	4.2193	.97304	40
21	.21388	.21895	4.5673	.97686	39		21	.23090	.23731	4.2139	.97298	39
22	.21417	.21925	4.5609	.97680	38		22	.23118	.23762	4.2084	.97291	38
23	.21445	.21956	4.5546	.97673	37		23	.23146	.23793	4.2030	.97284	37
24	.21474	.21986	4.5483	.97667	36		24	.23175	.23823	4.1976	.97278	36
25	.21502	.22017	4.5420	.97661	35		25	.23203	.23854	4.1922	.97271	35
26	.21530	.22047	4.5357	.97655	34		26	.23231	.23885	4.1868	.97264	34
27	.21559	.22078	4.5294	.97648	33		27	.23260	.23916	4.1814	.97257	33
28	.21587	.22108	4.5232	.97642	32		28	.23288	.23946	4.1760	.97251	32
29	.21616	.22139	4.5169	.97636	31		29	.23316	.23977	4.1706	.97244	31
30	.21644	.22169	4.5107	.97630	30		30	.23345	.24008	4.1653	.97237	30
31	.21672	.22200	4.5045	.97623	29		31	.23373	.24039	4.1600	.97230	29
32	.21701	.22231	4.4983	.97617	28		32	.23401	.24069	4.1547	.97223	28
33	.21729	.22261	4.4922	.97611	27		33	.23429	.24100	4.1493	.97217	27
34	.21758	.22292	4.4860	.97604	26		34	.23458	.24131	4.1441	.97210	26
35	.21786	.22322	4.4799	.97598	25		35	.23486	.24162	4.1388	.97203	25
36	.21814	.22353	4.4737	.97592	24		36	.23514	.24193	4.1335	.97196	24
37	.21843	.22383	4.4676	.97585	23		37	.23542	.24223	4.1282	.97189	23
38	.21871	.22414	4.4615	.97579	22		38	.23571	.24254	4.1230	.97182	22
39	.21899	.22444	4.4555	.97573	21		39	.23599	.24285	4.1178	.97176	21
40	.21928	.22475	4.4494	.97566	20		40	.23627	.24316	4.1126	.97169	20
41	.21956	.22505	4.4434	.97560	19		41	.23656	.24347	4.1074	.97162	19
42	.21985	.22536	4.4373	.97553	18		42	.23684	.24377	4.1022	.97155	18
43	.22013	.22567	4.4313	.97547	17		43	.23712	.24408	4.0970	.97148	17
44	.22041	.22597	4.4253	.97541	16		44	.23740	.24439	4.0918	.97141	16
45	.22070	.22628	4.4194	.97534	15		45	.23769	.24470	4.0867	.97134	15
46	.22098	.22658	4.4134	.97528	14		46	.23797	.24501	4.0815	.97127	14
47	.22126	.22689	4.4075	.97521	13		47	.23825	.24532	4.0764	.97120	13
48	.22155	.22719	4.4015	.97515	12		48	.23853	.24562	4.0713	.97113	12
49	.22183	.22750	4.3956	.97508	11		49	.23882	.24593	4.0662	.97106	11
50	.22212	.22781	4.3897	.97502	10		50	.23910	.24624	4.0611	.97100	10
51	.22240	.22811	4.3838	.97496	9		51	.23938	.24655	4.0560	.97093	9
52	.22268	.22842	4.3779	.97489	8		52	.23966	.24686	4.0509	.97086	8
53	.22297	.22872	4.3721	.97483	7		53	.23995	.24717	4.0459	.97079	7
54	.22325	.22903	4.3662	.97476	6		54	.24023	.24747	4.0408	.97072	6
55	.22353	.22934	4.3604	.97470	5		55	.24051	.24778	4.0358	.97065	5
56	.22382	.22964	4.3546	.97463	4		56	.24079	.24809	4.0308	.97058	4
57	.22410	.22995	4.3488	.97457	3		57	.24108	.24840	4.0257	.97051	3
58	.22438	.23026	4.3430	.97450	2		58	.24136	.24871	4.0207	.97044	2
59	.22467	.23056	4.3372	.97444	1		59	.24164	.24902	4.0158	.97037	1
60	.22495	.23087	4.3315	.97437	0		60	.24192	.24933	4.0108	.97030	0
′	Cos	Cot	Tan	Sin	′		′	Cos	Cot	Tan	Sin	′

NATURAL TRIGONOMETRIC FUNCTIONS

′	Sin	Tan	Cot	Cos	′		′	Sin	Tan	Cot	Cos	′
0	.24192	.24933	4.0108	.97030	60		0	.25882	.26795	3.7321	.96593	60
1	.24220	.24964	4.0058	.97023	59		1	.25910	.26826	3.7277	.96585	59
2	.24249	.24995	4.0009	.97015	58		2	.25938	.26857	3.7234	.96578	58
3	.24277	.25026	3.9959	.97008	57		3	.25966	.26888	3.7191	.96570	57
4	.24305	.25056	3.9910	.97001	56		4	.25994	.26920	3.7148	.96562	56
5	.24333	.25087	3.9861	.96994	55		5	.26022	.26951	3.7105	.96555	55
6	.24362	.25118	3.9812	.96987	54		6	.26050	.26982	3.7062	.96547	54
7	.24390	.25149	3.9763	.96980	53		7	.26079	.27013	3.7019	.96540	53
8	.24418	.25180	3.9714	.96973	52		8	.26107	.27044	3.6976	.96532	52
9	.24446	.25211	3.9665	.96966	51		9	.26135	.27076	3.6933	.96524	51
10	.24474	.25242	3.9617	.96959	50		10	.26163	.27107	3.6891	.96517	50
11	.24503	.25273	3.9568	.96952	49		11	.26191	.27138	3.6848	.96509	49
12	.24531	.25304	3.9520	.96945	48		12	.26219	.27169	3.6806	.96502	48
13	.24559	.25335	3.9471	.96937	47		13	.26247	.27201	3.6764	.96494	47
14	.24587	.25366	3.9423	.96930	46		14	.26275	.27232	3.6722	.96486	46
15	.24615	.25397	3.9375	.96923	45		15	.26303	.27263	3.6680	.96479	45
16	.24644	.25428	3.9327	.96916	44		16	.26331	.27294	3.6638	.96471	44
17	.24672	.25459	3.9279	.96909	43		17	.26359	.27326	3.6596	.96463	43
18	.24700	.25490	3.9232	.96902	42		18	.26387	.27357	3.6554	.96456	42
19	.24728	.25521	3.9184	.96894	41		19	.26415	.27388	3.6512	.96448	41
20	.24756	.25552	3.9136	.96887	40		20	.26443	.27419	3.6470	.96440	40
21	.24784	.25583	3.9089	.96880	39		21	.26471	.27451	3.6429	.96433	39
22	.24813	.25614	3.9042	.96873	38		22	.26500	.27482	3.6387	.96425	38
23	.24841	.25645	3.8995	.96866	37		23	.26528	.27513	3.6346	.96417	37
24	.24869	.25676	3.8947	.96858	36		24	.26556	.27545	3.6305	.96410	36
25	.24897	.25707	3.8900	.96851	35		25	.26584	.27576	3.6264	.96402	35
26	.24925	.25738	3.8854	.96844	34		26	.26612	.27607	3.6222	.96394	34
27	.24954	.25769	3.8807	.96837	33		27	.26640	.27638	3.6181	.96386	33
28	.24982	.25800	3.8760	.96829	32		28	.26668	.27670	3.6140	.96379	32
29	.25010	.25831	3.8714	.96822	31		29	.26696	.27701	3.6100	.96371	31
30	.25038	.25862	3.8667	.96815	30		30	.26724	.27732	3.6059	.96363	30
31	.25066	.25893	3.8621	.96807	29		31	.26752	.27764	3.6018	.96355	29
32	.25094	.25924	3.8575	.96800	28		32	.26780	.27795	3.5978	.96347	28
33	.25122	.25955	3.8528	.96793	27		33	.26808	.27826	3.5937	.96340	27
34	.25151	.25986	3.8482	.96786	26		34	.26836	.27858	3.5897	.96332	26
35	.25179	.26017	3.8436	.96778	25		35	.26864	.27889	3.5856	.96324	25
36	.25207	.26048	3.8391	.96771	24		36	.26892	.27921	3.5816	.96316	24
37	.25235	.26079	3.8345	.96764	23		37	.26920	.27952	3.5776	.96308	23
38	.25263	.26110	3.8299	.96756	22		38	.26948	.27983	3.5736	.96301	22
39	.25291	.26141	3.8254	.96749	21		39	.26976	.28015	3.5696	.96293	21
40	.25320	.26172	3.8208	.96742	20		40	.27004	.28046	3.5656	.96285	20
41	.25348	.26203	3.8163	.96734	19		41	.27032	.28077	3.5616	.96277	19
42	.25376	.26235	3.8118	.96727	18		42	.27060	.28109	3.5576	.96269	18
43	.25404	.26266	3.8073	.96719	17		43	.27088	.28140	3.5536	.96261	17
44	.25432	.26297	3.8028	.96712	16		44	.27116	.28172	3.5497	.96253	16
45	.25460	.26328	3.7983	.96705	15		45	.27144	.28203	3.5457	.96246	15
46	.25488	.26359	3.7938	.96697	14		46	.27172	.28234	3.5418	.96238	14
47	.25516	.26390	3.7893	.96690	13		47	.27200	.28266	3.5379	.96230	13
48	.25545	.26421	3.7848	.96682	12		48	.27228	.28297	3.5339	.96222	12
49	.25573	.26452	3.7804	.96675	11		49	.27256	.28329	3.5300	.96214	11
50	.25601	.26483	3.7760	.96667	10		50	.27284	.28360	3.5261	.96206	10
51	.25629	.26515	3.7715	.96660	9		51	.27312	.28391	3.5222	.96198	9
52	.25657	.26546	3.7671	.96653	8		52	.27340	.28423	3.5183	.96190	8
53	.25685	.26577	3.7627	.96645	7		53	.27368	.28454	3.5144	.96182	7
54	.25713	.26608	3.7583	.96638	6		54	.27396	.28486	3.5105	.96174	6
55	.25741	.26639	3.7539	.96630	5		55	.27424	.28517	3.5067	.96166	5
56	.25769	.26670	3.7495	.96623	4		56	.27452	.28549	3.5028	.96158	4
57	.25798	.26701	3.7451	.96615	3		57	.27480	.28580	3.4989	.96150	3
58	.25826	.26733	3.7408	.96608	2		58	.27508	.28612	3.4951	.96142	2
59	.25854	.26764	3.7364	.96600	1		59	.27536	.28643	3.4912	.96134	1
60	.25882	.26795	3.7321	.96593	0		60	.27564	.28675	3.4874	.96126	0
′	Cos	Cot	Tan	Sin	′		′	Cos	Cot	Tan	Sin	′

NATURAL TRIGONOMETRIC FUNCTIONS

16° (196°)   (343°) 163°   17° (197°)   (342°) 162°

′	Sin	Tan	Cot	Cos	′		′	Sin	Tan	Cot	Cos	′
0	.27564	.28675	3.4874	.96126	60		0	.29237	.30573	3.2709	.95630	60
1	.27592	.28706	3.4836	.96118	59		1	.29265	.30605	3.2675	.95622	59
2	.27620	.28738	3.4798	.96110	58		2	.29293	.30637	3.2641	.95613	58
3	.27648	.28769	3.4760	.96102	57		3	.29321	.30669	3.2607	.95605	57
4	.27676	.28801	3.4722	.96094	56		4	.29348	.30700	3.2573	.95596	56
5	.27704	.28832	3.4684	.96086	55		5	.29376	.30732	3.2539	.95588	55
6	.27731	.28864	3.4646	.96078	54		6	.29404	.30764	3.2506	.95579	54
7	.27759	.28895	3.4608	.96070	53		7	.29432	.30796	3.2472	.95571	53
8	.27787	.28927	3.4570	.96062	52		8	.29460	.30828	3.2438	.95562	52
9	.27815	.28958	3.4533	.96054	51		9	.29487	.30860	3.2405	.95554	51
10	.27843	.28990	3.4495	.96046	50		10	.29515	.30891	3.2371	.95545	50
11	.27871	.29021	3.4458	.96037	49		11	.29543	.30923	3.2338	.95536	49
12	.27899	.29053	3.4420	.96029	48		12	.29571	.30955	3.2305	.95528	48
13	.27927	.29084	3.4383	.96021	47		13	.29599	.30987	3.2272	.95519	47
14	.27955	.29116	3.4346	.96013	46		14	.29626	.31019	3.2238	.95511	46
15	.27983	.29147	3.4308	.96005	45		15	.29654	.31051	3.2205	.95502	45
16	.28011	.29179	3.4271	.95997	44		16	.29682	.31083	3.2172	.95493	44
17	.28039	.29210	3.4234	.95989	43		17	.29710	.31115	3.2139	.95485	43
18	.28067	.29242	3.4197	.95981	42		18	.29737	.31147	3.2106	.95476	42
19	.28095	.29274	3.4160	.95972	41		19	.29765	.31178	3.2073	.95467	41
20	.28123	.29305	3.4124	.95964	40		20	.29793	.31210	3.2041	.95459	40
21	.28150	.29337	3.4087	.95956	39		21	.29821	.31242	3.2008	.95450	39
22	.28178	.29368	3.4050	.95948	38		22	.29849	.31274	3.1975	.95441	38
23	.28206	.29400	3.4014	.95940	37		23	.29876	.31306	3.1943	.95433	37
24	.28234	.29432	3.3977	.95931	36		24	.29904	.31338	3.1910	.95424	36
25	.28262	.29463	3.3941	.95923	35		25	.29932	.31370	3.1878	.95415	35
26	.28290	.29495	3.3904	.95915	34		26	.29960	.31402	3.1845	.95407	34
27	.28318	.29526	3.3868	.95907	33		27	.29987	.31434	3.1813	.95398	33
28	.28346	.29558	3.3832	.95898	32		28	.30015	.31466	3.1780	.95389	32
29	.28374	.29590	3.3796	.95890	31		29	.30043	.31498	3.1748	.95380	31
30	.28402	.29621	3.3759	.95882	30		30	.30071	.31530	3.1716	.95372	30
31	.28429	.29653	3.3723	.95874	29		31	.30098	.31562	3.1684	.95363	29
32	.28457	.29685	3.3687	.95865	28		32	.30126	.31594	3.1652	.95354	28
33	.28485	.29716	3.3652	.95857	27		33	.30154	.31626	3.1620	.95345	27
34	.28513	.29748	3.3616	.95849	26		34	.30182	.31658	3.1588	.95337	26
35	.28541	.29780	3.3580	.95841	25		35	.30209	.31690	3.1556	.95328	25
36	.28569	.29811	3.3544	.95832	24		36	.30237	.31722	3.1524	.95319	24
37	.28597	.29843	3.3509	.95824	23		37	.30265	.31754	3.1492	.95310	23
38	.28625	.29875	3.3473	.95816	22		38	.30292	.31786	3.1460	.95301	22
39	.28652	.29906	3.3438	.95807	21		39	.30320	.31818	3.1429	.95293	21
40	.28680	.29938	3.3402	.95799	20		40	.30348	.31850	3.1397	.95284	20
41	.28708	.29970	3.3367	.95791	19		41	.30376	.31882	3.1366	.95275	19
42	.28736	.30001	3.3332	.95782	18		42	.30403	.31914	3.1334	.95266	18
43	.28764	.30033	3.3297	.95774	17		43	.30431	.31946	3.1303	.95257	17
44	.28792	.30065	3.3261	.95766	16		44	.30459	.31978	3.1271	.95248	16
45	.28820	.30097	3.3226	.95757	15		45	.30486	.32010	3.1240	.95240	15
46	.28847	.30128	3.3191	.95749	14		46	.30514	.32042	3.1209	.95231	14
47	.28875	.30160	3.3156	.95740	13		47	.30542	.32074	3.1178	.95222	13
48	.28903	.30192	3.3122	.95732	12		48	.30570	.32106	3.1146	.95213	12
49	.28931	.30224	3.3087	.95724	11		49	.30597	.32139	3.1115	.95204	11
50	.28959	.30255	3.3052	.95715	10		50	.30625	.32171	3.1084	.95195	10
51	.28987	.30287	3.3017	.95707	9		51	.30653	.32203	3.1053	.95186	9
52	.29015	.30319	3.2983	.95698	8		52	.30680	.32235	3.1022	.95177	8
53	.29042	.30351	3.2948	.95690	7		53	.30708	.32267	3.0991	.95168	7
54	.29070	.30382	3.2914	.95681	6		54	.30736	.32299	3.0961	.95159	6
55	.29098	.30414	3.2879	.95673	5		55	.30763	.32331	3.0930	.95150	5
56	.29126	.30446	3.2845	.95664	4		56	.30791	.32363	3.0899	.95142	4
57	.29154	.30478	3.2811	.95656	3		57	.30819	.32396	3.0868	.95133	3
58	.29182	.30509½	3.2777	.95647	2		58	.30846	.32428	3.0838	.95124	2
59	.29209	.30541	3.2743	.95639	1		59	.30874	.32460	3.0807	.95115	1
60	.29237	.30573	3.2709	.95630	0		60	.30902	.32492	3.0777	.95106	0
′	Cos	Cot	Tan	Sin	′		′	Cos	Cot	Tan	Sin	′

106° (286°)   (253°) 73°   107° (287°)   (252°) 72°

NATURAL TRIGONOMETRIC FUNCTIONS

′	Sin	Tan	Cot	Cos	′		′	Sin	Tan	Cot	Cos	′
0	.30902	.32492	3.0777	.95106	60		0	.32557	.34433	2.9042	.94552	60
1	.30929	.32524	3.0746	.95097	59		1	.32584	.34465	2.9015	.94542	59
2	.30957	.32556	3.0716	.95088	58		2	.32612	.34498	2.8987	.94533	58
3	.30985	.32588	3.0686	.95079	57		3	.32639	.34530	2.8960	.94523	57
4	.31012	.32621	3.0655	.95070	56		4	.32667	.34563	2.8933	.94514	56
5	.31040	.32653	3.0625	.95061	55		5	.32694	.34596	2.8905	.94504	55
6	.31068	.32685	3.0595	.95052	54		6	.32722	.34628	2.8878	.94495	54
7	.31095	.32717	3.0565	.95043	53		7	.32749	.34661	2.8851	.94485	53
8	.31123	.32749	3.0535	.95033	52		8	.32777	.34693	2.8824	.94476	52
9	.31151	.32782	3.0505	.95024	51		9	.32804	.34726	2.8797	.94466	51
10	.31178	.32814	3.0475	.95015	50		10	.32832	.34758	2.8770	.94457	50
11	.31206	.32846	3.0445	.95006	49		11	.32859	.34791	2.8743	.94447	49
12	.31233	.32878	3.0415	.94997	48		12	.32887	.34824	2.8716	.94438	48
13	.31261	.32911	3.0385	.94988	47		13	.32914	.34856	2.8689	.94428	47
14	.31289	.32943	3.0356	.94979	46		14	.32942	.34889	2.8662	.94418	46
15	.31316	.32975	3.0326	.94970	45		15	.32969	.34922	2.8636	.94409	45
16	.31344	.33007	3.0296	.94961	44		16	.32997	.34954	2.8609	.94399	44
17	.31372	.33040	3.0267	.94952	43		17	.33024	.34987	2.8582	.94390	43
18	.31399	.33072	3.0237	.94943	42		18	.33051	.35020	2.8556	.94380	42
19	.31427	.33104	3.0208	.94933	41		19	.33079	.35052	2.8529	.94370	41
20	.31454	.33136	3.0178	.94924	40		20	.33106	.35085	2.8502	.94361	40
21	.31482	.33169	3.0149	.94915	39		21	.33134	.35118	2.8476	.94351	39
22	.31510	.33201	3.0120	.94906	38		22	.33161	.35150	2.8449	.94342	38
23	.31537	.33233	3.0090	.94897	37		23	.33189	.35183	2.8423	.94332	37
24	.31565	.33266	3.0061	.94888	36		24	.33216	.35216	2.8397	.94322	36
25	.31593	.33298	3.0032	.94878	35		25	.33244	.35248	2.8370	.94313	35
26	.31620	.33330	3.0003	.94869	34		26	.33271	.35281	2.8344	.94303	34
27	.31648	.33363	2.9974	.94860	33		27	.33298	.35314	2.8318	.94293	33
28	.31675	.33395	2.9945	.94851	32		28	.33326	.35346	2.8291	.94284	32
29	.31703	.33427	2.9916	.94842	31		29	.33353	.35379	2.8265	.94274	31
30	.31730	.33460	2.9887	.94832	30		30	.33381	.35412	2.8239	.94264	30
31	.31758	.33492	2.9858	.94823	29		31	.33408	.35445	2.8213	.94254	29
32	.31786	.33524	2.9829	.94814	28		32	.33436	.35477	2.8187	.94245	28
33	.31813	.33557	2.9800	.94805	27		33	.33463	.35510	2.8161	.94235	27
34	.31841	.33589	2.9772	.94795	26		34	.33490	.35543	2.8135	.94225	26
35	.31868	.33621	2.9743	.94786	25		35	.33518	.35576	2.8109	.94215	25
36	.31896	.33654	2.9714	.94777	24		36	.33545	.35608	2.8083	.94206	24
37	.31923	.33686	2.9686	.94768	23		37	.33573	.35641	2.8057	.94196	23
38	.31951	.33718	2.9657	.94758	22		38	.33600	.35674	2.8032	.94186	22
39	.31979	.33751	2.9629	.94749	21		39	.33627	.35707	2.8006	.94176	21
40	.32006	.33783	2.9600	.94740	20		40	.33655	.35740	2.7980	.94167	20
41	.32034	.33816	2.9572	.94730	19		41	.33682	.35772	2.7955	.94157	19
42	.32061	.33848	2.9544	.94721	18		42	.33710	.35805	2.7929	.94147	18
43	.32089	.33881	2.9515	.94712	17		43	.33737	.35838	2.7903	.94137	17
44	.32116	.33913	2.9487	.94702	16		44	.33764	.35871	2.7878	.94127	16
45	.32144	.33945	2.9459	.94693	15		45	.33792	.35904	2.7852	.94118	15
46	.32171	.33978	2.9431	.94684	14		46	.33819	.35937	2.7827	.94108	14
47	.32199	.34010	2.9403	.94674	13		47	.33846	.35969	2.7801	.94098	13
48	.32227	.34043	2.9375	.94665	12		48	.33874	.36002	2.7776	.94088	12
49	.32254	.34075	2.9347	.94656	11		49	.33901	.36035	2.7751	.94078	11
50	.32282	.34108	2.9319	.94646	10		50	.33929	.36068	2.7725	.94068	10
51	.32309	.34140	2.9291	.94637	9		51	.33956	.36101	2.7700	.94058	9
52	.32337	.34173	2.9263	.94627	8		52	.33983	.36134	2.7675	.94049	8
53	.32364	.34205	2.9235	.94618	7		53	.34011	.36167	2.7650	.94039	7
54	.32392	.34238	2.9208	.94609	6		54	.34038	.36199	2.7625	.94029	6
55	.32419	.34270	2.9180	.94599	5		55	.34065	.36232	2.7600	.94019	5
56	.32447	.34303	2.9152	.94590	4		56	.34093	.36265	2.7575	.94009	4
57	.32474	.34335	2.9125	.94580	3		57	.34120	.36298	2.7550	.93999	3
58	.32502	.34368	2.9097	.94571	2		58	.34147	.36331	2.7525	.93989	2
59	.32529	.34400	2.9070	.94561	1		59	.34175	.36364	2.7500	.93979	1
60	.32557	.34433	2.9042	.94552	0		60	.34202	.36397	2.7475	.93969	0
′	Cos	Cot	Tan	Sin	′		′	Cos	Cot	Tan	Sin	′

NATURAL TRIGONOMETRIC FUNCTIONS

′	Sin	Tan	Cot	Cos	′
0	.34202	.36397	2.7475	.93969	60
1	.34229	.36430	2.7450	.93959	59
2	.34257	.36463	2.7425	.93949	58
3	.34284	.36496	2.7400	.93939	57
4	.34311	.36529	2.7376	.93929	56
5	.34339	.36562	2.7351	.93919	55
6	.34366	.36595	2.7326	.93909	54
7	.34393	.36628	2.7302	.93899	53
8	.34421	.36661	2.7277	.93889	52
9	.34448	.36694	2.7253	.93879	51
10	.34475	.36727	2.7228	.93869	50
11	.34503	.36760	2.7204	.93859	49
12	.34530	.36793	2.7179	.93849	48
13	.34557	.36826	2.7155	.93839	47
14	.34584	.36859	2.7130	.93829	46
15	.34612	.36892	2.7106	.93819	45
16	.34639	.36925	2.7082	.93809	44
17	.34666	.36958	2.7058	.93799	43
18	.34694	.36991	2.7034	.93789	42
19	.34721	.37024	2.7009	.93779	41
20	.34748	.37057	2.6985	.93769	40
21	.34775	.37090	2.6961	.93759	39
22	.34803	.37123	2.6937	.93748	38
23	.34830	.37157	2.6913	.93738	37
24	.34857	.37190	2.6889	.93728	36
25	.34884	.37223	2.6865	.93718	35
26	.34912	.37256	2.6841	.93708	34
27	.34939	.37289	2.6818	.93698	33
28	.34966	.37322	2.6794	.93688	32
29	.34993	.37355	2.6770	.93677	31
30	.35021	.37388	2.6746	.93667	30
31	.35048	.37422	2.6723	.93657	29
32	.35075	.37455	2.6699	.93647	28
33	.35102	.37488	2.6675	.93637	27
34	.35130	.37521	2.6652	.93626	26
35	.35157	.37554	2.6628	.93616	25
36	.35184	.37588	2.6605	.93606	24
37	.35211	.37621	2.6581	.93596	23
38	.35239	.37654	2.6558	.93585	22
39	.35266	.37687	2.6534	.93575	21
40	.35293	.37720	2.6511	.93565	20
41	.35320	.37754	2.6488	.93555	19
42	.35347	.37787	2.6464	.93544	18
43	.35375	.37820	2.6441	.93534	17
44	.35402	.37853	2.6418	.93524	16
45	.35429	.37887	2.6395	.93514	15
46	.35456	.37920	2.6371	.93503	14
47	.35484	.37953	2.6348	.93493	13
48	.35511	.37986	2.6325	.93483	12
49	.35538	.38020	2.6302	.93472	11
50	.35565	.38053	2.6279	.93462	10
51	.35592	.38086	2.6256	.93452	9
52	.35619	.38120	2.6233	.93441	8
53	.35647	.38153	2.6210	.93431	7
54	.35674	.38186	2.6187	.93420	6
55	.35701	.38220	2.6165	.93410	5
56	.35728	.38253	2.6142	.93400	4
57	.35755	.38286	2.6119	.93389	3
58	.35782	.38320	2.6096	.93379	2
59	.35810	.38353	2.6074	.93368	1
60	.35837	.38386	2.6051	.93358	0
′	Cos	Cot	Tan	Sin	′

′	Sin	Tan	Cot	Cos	′
0	.35837	.38386	2.6051	.93358	60
1	.35864	.38420	2.6028	.93348	59
2	.35891	.38453	2.6006	.93337	58
3	.35918	.38487	2.5983	.93327	57
4	.35945	.38520	2.5961	.93316	56
5	.35973	.38553	2.5938	.93306	55
6	.36000	.38587	2.5916	.93295	54
7	.36027	.38620	2.5893	.93285	53
8	.36054	.38654	2.5871	.93274	52
9	.36081	.38687	2.5848	.93264	51
10	.36108	.38721	2.5826	.93253	50
11	.36135	.38754	2.5804	.93243	49
12	.36162	.38787	2.5782	.93232	48
13	.36190	.38821	2.5759	.93222	47
14	.36217	.38854	2.5737	.93211	46
15	.36244	.38888	2.5715	.93201	45
16	.36271	.38921	2.5693	.93190	44
17	.36298	.38955	2.5671	.93180	43
18	.36325	.38988	2.5649	.93169	42
19	.36352	.39022	2.5627	.93159	41
20	.36379	.39055	2.5605	.93148	40
21	.36406	.39089	2.5583	.93137	39
22	.36434	.39122	2.5561	.93127	38
23	.36461	.39156	2.5539	.93116	37
24	.36488	.39190	2.5517	.93106	36
25	.36515	.39223	2.5495	.93095	35
26	.36542	.39257	2.5473	.93084	34
27	.36569	.39290	2.5452	.93074	33
28	.36596	.39324	2.5430	.93063	32
29	.36623	.39357	2.5408	.93052	31
30	.36650	.39391	2.5386	.93042	30
31	.36677	.39425	2.5365	.93031	29
32	.36704	.39458	2.5343	.93020	28
33	.36731	.39492	2.5322	.93010	27
34	.36758	.39526	2.5300	.92999	26
35	.36785	.39559	2.5279	.92988	25
36	.36812	.39593	2.5257	.92978	24
37	.36839	.39626	2.5236	.92967	23
38	.36867	.39660	2.5214	.92956	22
39	.36894	.39694	2.5193	.92945	21
40	.36921	.39727	2.5172	.92935	20
41	.36948	.39761	2.5150	.92924	19
42	.36975	.39795	2.5129	.92913	18
43	.37002	.39829	2.5108	.92902	17
44	.37029	.39862	2.5086	.92892	16
45	.37056	.39896	2.5065	.92881	15
46	.37083	.39930	2.5044	.92870	14
47	.37110	.39963	2.5023	.92859	13
48	.37137	.39997	2.5002	.92849	12
49	.37164	.40031	2.4981	.92838	11
50	.37191	.40065	2.4960	.92827	10
51	.37218	.40098	2.4939	.92816	9
52	.37245	.40132	2.4918	.92805	8
53	.37272	.40166	2.4897	.92794	7
54	.37299	.40200	2.4876	.92784	6
55	.37326	.40234	2.4855	.92773	5
56	.37353	.40267	2.4834	.92762	4
57	.37380	.40301	2.4813	.92751	3
58	.37407	.40335	2.4792	.92740	2
59	.37434	.40369	2.4772	.92729	1
60	.37461	.40403	2.4751	.92718	0
′	Cos	Cot	Tan	Sin	′

NATURAL TRIGONOMETRIC FUNCTIONS

22° (202°)   **(337°) 157°**   **23° (203°)**   **(336°) 156°**

′	Sin	Tan	Cot	Cos	′		′	Sin	Tan	Cot	Cos	′
0	.37461	.40403	2.4751	.92718	60		0	.39073	.42447	2.3559	.92050	60
1	.37488	.40436	2.4730	.92707	59		1	.39100	.42482	2.3539	.92039	59
2	.37515	.40470	2.4709	.92697	58		2	.39127	.42516	2.3520	.92028	58
3	.37542	.40504	2.4689	.92686	57		3	.39153	.42551	2.3501	.92016	57
4	.37569	.40538	2.4668	.92675	56		4	.39180	.42585	2.3483	.92005	56
5	.37595	.40572	2.4648	.92664	55		5	.39207	.42619	2.3464	.91994	55
6	.37622	.40606	2.4627	.92653	54		6	.39234	.42654	2.3445	.91982	54
7	.37649	.40640	2.4606	.92642	53		7	.39260	.42688	2.3426	.91971	53
8	.37676	.40674	2.4586	.92631	52		8	.39287	.42722	2.3407	.91959	52
9	.37703	.40707	2.4566	.92620	51		9	.39314	.42757	2.3388	.91948	51
10	.37730	.40741	2.4545	.92609	50		10	.39341	.42791	2.3369	.91936	50
11	.37757	.40775	2.4525	.92598	49		11	.39367	.42826	2.3351	.91925	49
12	.37784	.40809	2.4504	.92587	48		12	.39394	.42860	2.3332	.91914	48
13	.37811	.40843	2.4484	.92576	47		13	.39421	.42894	2.3313	.91902	47
14	.37838	.40877	2.4464	.92565	46		14	.39448	.42929	2.3294	.91891	46
15	.37865	.40911	2.4443	.92554	45		15	.39474	.42963	2.3276	.91879	45
16	.37892	.40945	2.4423	.92543	44		16	.39501	.42998	2.3257	.91868	44
17	.37919	.40979	2.4403	.92532	43		17	.39528	.43032	2.3238	.91856	43
18	.37946	.41013	2.4383	.92521	42		18	.39555	.43067	2.3220	.91845	42
19	.37973	.41047	2.4362	.92510	41		19	.39581	.43101	2.3201	.91833	41
20	.37999	.41081	2.4342	.92499	40		20	.39608	.43136	2.3183	.91822	40
21	.38026	.41115	2.4322	.92488	39		21	.39635	.43170	2.3164	.91810	39
22	.38053	.41149	2.4302	.92477	38		22	.39661	.43205	2.3146	.91799	38
23	.38080	.41183	2.4282	.92466	37		23	.39688	.43239	2.3127	.91787	37
24	.38107	.41217	2.4262	.92455	36		24	.39715	.43274	2.3109	.91775	36
25	.38134	.41251	2.4242	.92444	35		25	.39741	.43308	2.3090	.91764	35
26	.38161	.41285	2.4222	.92432	34		26	.39768	.43343	2.3072	.91752	34
27	.38188	.41319	2.4202	.92421	33		27	.39795	.43378	2.3053	.91741	33
28	.38215	.41353	2.4182	.92410	32		28	.39822	.43412	2.3035	.91729	32
29	.38241	.41387	2.4162	.92399	31		29	.39848	.43447	2.3017	.91718	31
30	.38268	.41421	2.4142	.92388	30		30	.39875	.43481	2.2998	.91706	30
31	.38295	.41455	2.4122	.92377	29		31	.39902	.43516	2.2980	.91694	29
32	.38322	.41490	2.4102	.92366	28		32	.39928	.43550	2.2962	.91683	28
33	.38349	.41524	2.4083	.92355	27		33	.39955	.43585	2.2944	.91671	27
34	.38376	.41558	2.4063	.92343	26		34	.39982	.43620	2.2925	.91660	26
35	.38403	.41592	2.4043	.92332	25		35	.40008	.43654	2.2907	.91648	25
36	.38430	.41626	2.4023	.92321	24		36	.40035	.43689	2.2889	.91636	24
37	.38456	.41660	2.4004	.92310	23		37	.40062	.43724	2.2871	.91625	23
38	.38483	.41694	2.3984	.92299	22		38	.40088	.43758	2.2853	.91613	22
39	.38510	.41728	2.3964	.92287	21		39	.40115	.43793	2.2835	.91601	21
40	.38537	.41763	2.3945	.92276	20		40	.40141	.43828	2.2817	.91590	20
41	.38564	.41797	2.3925	.92265	19		41	.40168	.43862	2.2799	.91578	19
42	.38591	.41831	2.3906	.92254	18		42	.40195	.43897	2.2781	.91566	18
43	.38617	.41865	2.3886	.92243	17		43	.40221	.43932	2.2763	.91555	17
44	.38644	.41899	2.3867	.92231	16		44	.40248	.43966	2.2745	.91543	16
45	.38671	.41933	2.3847	.92220	15		45	.40275	.44001	2.2727	.91531	15
46	.38698	.41968	2.3828	.92209	14		46	.40301	.44036	2.2709	.91519	14
47	.38725	.42002	2.3808	.92198	13		47	.40328	.44071	2.2691	.91508	13
48	.38752	.42036	2.3789	.92186	12		48	.40355	.44105	2.2673	.91496	12
49	.38778	.42070	2.3770	.92175	11		49	.40381	.44140	2.2655	.91484	11
50	.38805	.42105	2.3750	.92164	10		50	.40408	.44175	2.2637	.91472	10
51	.38832	.42139	2.3731	.92152	9		51	.40434	.44210	2.2620	.91461	9
52	.38859	.42173	2.3712	.92141	8		52	.40461	.44244	2.2602	.91449	8
53	.38886	.42207	2.3693	.92130	7		53	.40488	.44279	2.2584	.91437	7
54	.38912	.42242	2.3673	.92119	6		54	.40514	.44314	2.2566	.91425	6
55	.38939	.42276	2.3654	.92107	5		55	.40541	.44349	2.2549	.91414	5
56	.38966	.42310	2.3635	.92096	4		56	.40567	.44384	2.2531	.91402	4
57	.38993	.42345	2.3616	.92085	3		57	.40594	.44418	2.2513	.91390	3
58	.39020	.42379	2.3597	.92073	2		58	.40621	.44453	2.2496	.91378	2
59	.39046	.42413	2.3578	.92062	1		59	.40647	.44488	2.2478	.91366	1
60	.39073	.42447	2.3559	.92050	0		60	.40674	.44523	2.2460	.91355	0
′	Cos	Cot	Tan	Sin	′		′	Cos	Cot	Tan	Sin	′

112° (292°)   **(247°) 67°**   **113° (293°)**   **(246°) 66°**

NATURAL TRIGONOMETRIC FUNCTIONS

′	Sin	Tan	Cot	Cos	′
0	.40674	.44523	2.2460	.91355	60
1	.40700	.44558	2.2443	.91343	59
2	.40727	.44593	2.2425	.91331	58
3	.40753	.44627	2.2408	.91319	57
4	.40780	.44662	2.2390	.91307	56
5	.40806	.44697	2.2373	.91295	55
6	.40833	.44732	2.2355	.91283	54
7	.40860	.44767	2.2338	.91272	53
8	.40886	.44802	2.2320	.91260	52
9	.40913	.44837	2.2303	.91248	51
10	.40939	.44872	2.2286	.91236	50
11	.40966	.44907	2.2268	.91224	49
12	.40992	.44942	2.2251	.91212	48
13	.41019	.44977	2.2234	.91200	47
14	.41045	.45012	2.2216	.91188	46
15	.41072	.45047	2.2199	.91176	45
16	.41098	.45082	2.2182	.91164	44
17	.41125	.45117	2.2165	.91152	43
18	.41151	.45152	2.2148	.91140	42
19	.41178	.45187	2.2130	.91128	41
20	.41204	.45222	2.2113	.91116	40
21	.41231	.45257	2.2096	.91104	39
22	.41257	.45292	2.2079	.91092	38
23	.41284	.45327	2.2062	.91080	37
24	.41310	.45362	2.2045	.91068	36
25	.41337	.45397	2.2028	.91056	35
26	.41363	.45432	2.2011	.91044	34
27	.41390	.45467	2.1994	.91032	33
28	.41416	.45502	2.1977	.91020	32
29	.41443	.45538	2.1960	.91008	31
30	.41469	.45573	2.1943	.90996	30
31	.41496	.45608	2.1926	.90984	29
32	.41522	.45643	2.1909	.90972	28
33	.41549	.45678	2.1892	.90960	27
34	.41575	.45713	2.1876	.90948	26
35	.41602	.45748	2.1859	.90936	25
36	.41628	.45784	2.1842	.90924	24
37	.41655	.45819	2.1825	.90911	23
38	.41681	.45854	2.1808	.90899	22
39	.41707	.45889	2.1792	.90887	21
40	.41734	.45924	2.1775	.90875	20
41	.41760	.45960	2.1758	.90863	19
42	.41787	.45995	2.1742	.90851	18
43	.41813	.46030	2.1725	.90839	17
44	.41840	.46065	2.1708	.90826	16
45	.41866	.46101	2.1692	.90814	15
46	.41892	.46136	2.1675	.90802	14
47	.41919	.46171	2.1659	.90790	13
48	.41945	.46206	2.1642	.90778	12
49	.41972	.46242	2.1625	.90766	11
50	.41998	.46277	2.1609	.90753	10
51	.42024	.46312	2.1592	.90741	9
52	.42051	.46348	2.1576	.90729	8
53	.42077	.46383	2.1560	.90717	7
54	.42104	.46418	2.1543	.90704	6
55	.42130	.46454	2.1527	.90692	5
56	.42156	.46489	2.1510	.90680	4
57	.42183	.46525	2.1494	.90668	3
58	.42209	.46560	2.1478	.90655	2
59	.42235	.46595	2.1461	.90643	1
60	.42262	.46631	2.1445	.90631	0
′	Cos	Cot	Tan	Sin	′

′	Sin	Tan	Cot	Cos	′
0	.42262	.46631	2.1445	.90631	60
1	.42288	.46666	2.1429	.90618	59
2	.42315	.46702	2.1413	.90606	58
3	.42341	.46737	2.1396	.90594	57
4	.42367	.46772	2.1380	.90582	56
5	.42394	.46808	2.1364	.90569	55
6	.42420	.46843	2.1348	.90557	54
7	.42446	.46879	2.1332	.90545	53
8	.42473	.46914	2.1315	.90532	52
9	.42499	.46950	2.1299	.90520	51
10	.42525	.46985	2.1283	.90507	50
11	.42552	.47021	2.1267	.90495	49
12	.42578	.47056	2.1251	.90483	48
13	.42604	.47092	2.1235	.90470	47
14	.42631	.47128	2.1219	.90458	46
15	.42657	.47163	2.1203	.90446	45
16	.42683	.47199	2.1187	.90433	44
17	.42709	.47234	2.1171	.90421	43
18	.42736	.47270	2.1155	.90408	42
19	.42762	.47305	2.1139	.90396	41
20	.42788	.47341	2.1123	.90383	40
21	.42815	.47377	2.1107	.90371	39
22	.42841	.47412	2.1092	.90358	38
23	.42867	.47448	2.1076	.90346	37
24	.42894	.47483	2.1060	.90334	36
25	.42920	.47519	2.1044	.90321	35
26	.42946	.47555	2.1028	.90309	34
27	.42972	.47590	2.1013	.90296	33
28	.42999	.47626	2.0997	.90284	32
29	.43025	.47662	2.0981	.90271	31
30	.43051	.47698	2.0965	.90259	30
31	.43077	.47733	2.0950	.90246	29
32	.43104	.47769	2.0934	.90233	28
33	.43130	.47805	2.0918	.90221	27
34	.43156	.47840	2.0903	.90208	26
35	.43182	.47876	2.0887	.90196	25
36	.43209	.47912	2.0872	.90183	24
37	.43235	.47948	2.0856	.90171	23
38	.43261	.47984	2.0840	.90158	22
39	.43287	.48019	2.0825	.90146	21
40	.43313	.48055	2.0809	.90133	20
41	.43340	.48091	2.0794	.90120	19
42	.43366	.48127	2.0778	.90108	18
43	.43392	.48163	2.0763	.90095	17
44	.43418	.48198	2.0748	.90082	16
45	.43445	.48234	2.0732	.90070	15
46	.43471	.48270	2.0717	.90057	14
47	.43497	.48306	2.0701	.90045	13
48	.43523	.48342	2.0686	.90032	12
49	.43549	.48378	2.0671	.90019	11
50	.43575	.48414	2.0655	.90007	10
51	.43602	.48450	2.0640	.89994	9
52	.43628	.48486	2.0625	.89981	8
53	.43654	.48521	2.0609	.89968	7
54	.43680	.48557	2.0594	.89956	6
55	.43706	.48593	2.0579	.89943	5
56	.43733	.48629	2.0564	.89930	4
57	.43759	.48665	2.0549	.89918	3
58	.43785	.48701	2.0533	.89905	2
59	.43811	.48737	2.0518	.89892	1
60	.43837	.48773	2.0503	.89879	0
′	Cos	Cot	Tan	Sin	′

NATURAL TRIGONOMETRIC FUNCTIONS

26° (206°)   (333°) **153°**   **27°** (207°)   (332°) **152°**

′	Sin	Tan	Cot	Cos	′	′	Sin	Tan	Cot	Cos	′
0	.43837	.48773	2.0503	.89879	60	0	.45399	.50953	1.9626	.89101	60
1	.43863	.48809	2.0488	.89867	59	1	.45425	.50989	1.9612	.89087	59
2	.43889	.48845	2.0473	.89854	58	2	.45451	.51026	1.9598	.89074	58
3	.43916	.48881	2.0458	.89841	57	3	.45477	.51063	1.9584	.89061	57
4	.43942	.48917	2.0443	.89828	56	4	.45503	.51099	1.9570	.89048	56
5	.43968	.48953	2.0428	.89816	55	5	.45529	.51136	1.9556	.89035	55
6	.43994	.48989	2.0413	.89803	54	6	.45554	.51173	1.9542	.89021	54
7	.44020	.49026	2.0398	.89790	53	7	.45580	.51209	1.9528	.89008	53
8	.44046	.49062	2.0383	.89777	52	8	.45606	.51246	1.9514	.88995	52
9	.44072	.49098	2.0368	.89764	51	9	.45632	.51283	1.9500	.88981	51
10	.44098	.49134	2.0353	.89752	50	10	.45658	.51319	1.9486	.88968	50
11	.44124	.49170	2.0338	.89739	49	11	.45684	.51356	1.9472	.88955	49
12	.44151	.49206	2.0323	.89726	48	12	.45710	.51393	1.9458	.88942	48
13	.44177	.49242	2.0308	.89713	47	13	.45736	.51430	1.9444	.88928	47
14	.44203	.49278	2.0293	.89700	46	14	.45762	.51467	1.9430	.88915	46
15	.44229	.49315	2.0278	.89687	45	15	.45787	.51503	1.9416	.88902	45
16	.44255	.49351	2.0263	.89674	44	16	.45813	.51540	1.9402	.88888	44
17	.44281	.49387	2.0248	.89662	43	17	.45839	.51577	1.9388	.88875	43
18	.44307	.49423	2.0233	.89649	42	18	.45865	.51614	1.9375	.88862	42
19	.44333	.49459	2.0219	.89636	41	19	.45891	.51651	1.9361	.88848	41
20	.44359	.49495	2.0204	.89623	40	20	.45917	.51688	1.9347	.88835	40
21	.44385	.49532	2.0189	.89610	39	21	.45942	.51724	1.9333	.88822	39
22	.44411	.49568	2.0174	.89597	38	22	.45968	.51761	1.9319	.88808	38
23	.44437	.49604	2.0160	.89584	37	23	.45994	.51798	1.9306	.88795	37
24	.44464	.49640	2.0145	.89571	36	24	.46020	.51835	1.9292	.88782	36
25	.44490	.49677	2.0130	.89558	35	25	.46046	.51872	1.9278	.88768	35
26	.44516	.49713	2.0115	.89545	34	26	.46072	.51909	1.9265	.88755	34
27	.44542	.49749	2.0101	.89532	33	27	.46097	.51946	1.9251	.88741	33
28	.44568	.49786	2.0086	.89519	32	28	.46123	.51983	1.9237	.88728	32
29	.44594	.49822	2.0072	.89506	31	29	.46149	.52020	1.9223	.88715	31
30	.44620	.49858	2.0057	.89493	30	30	.46175	.52057	1.9210	.88701	30
31	.44646	.49894	2.0042	.89480	29	31	.46201	.52094	1.9196	.88688	29
32	.44672	.49931	2.0028	.89467	28	32	.46226	.52131	1.9183	.88674	28
33	.44698	.49967	2.0013	.89454	27	33	.46252	.52168	1.9169	.88661	27
34	.44724	.50004	1.9999	.89441	26	34	.46278	.52205	1.9155	.88647	26
35	.44750	.50040	1.9984	.89428	25	35	.46304	.52242	1.9142	.88634	25
36	.44776	.50076	1.9970	.89415	24	36	.46330	.52279	1.9128	.88620	24
37	.44802	.50113	1.9955	.89402	23	37	.46355	.52316	1.9115	.88607	23
38	.44828	.50149	1.9941	.89389	22	38	.46381	.52353	1.9101	.88593	22
39	.44854	.50185	1.9926	.89376	21	39	.46407	.52390	1.9088	.88580	21
40	.44880	.50222	1.9912	.89363	20	40	.46433	.52427	1.9074	.88566	20
41	.44906	.50258	1.9897	.89350	19	41	.46458	.52464	1.9061	.88553	19
42	.44932	.50295	1.9883	.89337	18	42	.46484	.52501	1.9047	.88539	18
43	.44958	.50331	1.9868	.89324	17	43	.46510	.52538	1.9034	.88526	17
44	.44984	.50368	1.9854	.89311	16	44	.46536	.52575	1.9020	.88512	16
45	.45010	.50404	1.9840	.89298	15	45	.46561	.52613	1.9007	.88499	15
46	.45036	.50441	1.9825	.89285	14	46	.46587	.52650	1.8993	.88485	14
47	.45062	.50477	1.9811	.89272	13	47	.46613	.52687	1.8980	.88472	13
48	.45088	.50514	1.9797	.89259	12	48	.46639	.52724	1.8967	.88458	12
49	.45114	.50550	1.9782	.89245	11	49	.46664	.52761	1.8953	.88445	11
50	.45140	.50587	1.9768	.89232	10	50	.46690	.52798	1.8940	.88431	10
51	.45166	.50623	1.9754	.89219	9	51	.46716	.52836	1.8927	.88417	9
52	.45192	.50660	1.9740	.89206	8	52	.46742	.52873	1.8913	.88404	8
53	.45218	.50696	1.9725	.89193	7	53	.46767	.52910	1.8900	.88390	7
54	.45243	.50733	1.9711	.89180	6	54	.46793	.52947	1.8887	.88377	6
55	.45269	.50769	1.9697	.89167	5	55	.46819	.52985	1.8873	.88363	5
56	.45295	.50806	1.9683	.89153	4	56	.46844	.53022	1.8860	.88349	4
57	.45321	.50843	1.9669	.89140	3	57	.46870	.53059	1.8847	.88336	3
58	.45347	.50879	1.9654	.89127	2	58	.46896	.53096	1.8834	.88322	2
59	.45373	.50916	1.9640	.89114	1	59	.46921	.53134	1.8820	.88308	1
60	.45399	.50953	1.9626	.89101	0	60	.46947	.53171	1.8807	.88295	0
′	Cos	Cot	Tan	Sin	′	′	Cos	Cot	Tan	Sin	′

116° (296°)   (243°) **63°**   **117°** (297°)   (242°) **62°**

NATURAL TRIGONOMETRIC FUNCTIONS

28° (208°)   (331°) **151°**   **29° (209°)**   (330°) **150°**

′	Sin	Tan	Cot	Cos	′		′	Sin	Tan	Cot	Cos	′
0	.46947	.53171	1.8807	.88295	60		0	.48481	.55431	1.8040	.87462	60
1	.46973	.53208	1.8794	.88281	59		1	.48506	.55469	1.8028	.87448	59
2	.46999	.53246	1.8781	.88267	58		2	.48532	.55507	1.8016	.87434	58
3	.47024	.53283	1.8768	.88254	57		3	.48557	.55545	1.8003	.87420	57
4	.47050	.53320	1.8755	.88240	56		4	.48583	.55583	1.7991	.87406	56
5	.47076	.53358	1.8741	.88226	55		5	.48608	.55621	1.7979	.87391	55
6	.47101	.53395	1.8728	.88213	54		6	.48634	.55659	1.7966	.87377	54
7	.47127	.53432	1.8715	.88199	53		7	.48659	.55697	1.7954	.87363	53
8	.47153	.53470	1.8702	.88185	52		8	.48684	.55736	1.7942	.87349	52
9	.47178	.53507	1.8689	.88172	51		9	.48710	.55774	1.7930	.87335	51
10	.47204	.53545	1.8676	.88158	50		10	.48735	.55812	1.7917	.87321	50
11	.47229	.53582	1.8663	.88144	49		11	.48761	.55850	1.7905	.87306	49
12	.47255	.53620	1.8650	.88130	48		12	.48786	.55888	1.7893	.87292	48
13	.47281	.53657	1.8637	.88117	47		13	.48811	.55926	1.7881	.87278	47
14	.47306	.53694	1.8624	.88103	46		14	.48837	.55964	1.7868	.87264	46
15	.47332	.53732	1.8611	.88089	45		15	.48862	.56003	1.7856	.87250	45
16	.47358	.53769	1.8598	.88075	44		16	.48888	.56041	1.7844	.87235	44
17	.47383	.53807	1.8585	.88062	43		17	.48913	.56079	1.7832	.87221	43
18	.47409	.53844	1.8572	.88048	42		18	.48938	.56117	1.7820	.87207	42
19	.47434	.53882	1.8559	.88034	41		19	.48964	.56156	1.7808	.87193	41
20	.47460	.53920	1.8546	.88020	40		20	.48989	.56194	1.7796	.87178	40
21	.47486	.53957	1.8533	.88006	39		21	.49014	.56232	1.7783	.87164	39
22	.47511	.53995	1.8520	.87993	38		22	.49040	.56270	1.7771	.87150	38
23	.47537	.54032	1.8507	.87979	37		23	.49065	.56309	1.7759	.87136	37
24	.47562	.54070	1.8495	.87965	36		24	.49090	.56347	1.7747	.87121	36
25	.47588	.54107	1.8482	.87951	35		25	.49116	.56385	1.7735	.87107	35
26	.47614	.54145	1.8469	.87937	34		26	.49141	.56424	1.7723	.87093	34
27	.47639	.54183	1.8456	.87923	33		27	.49166	.56462	1.7711	.87079	33
28	.47665	.54220	1.8443	.87909	32		28	.49192	.56501	1.7699	.87064	32
29	.47690	.54258	1.8430	.87896	31		29	.49217	.56539	1.7687	.87050	31
30	.47716	.54296	1.8418	.87882	30		30	.49242	.56577	1.7675	.87036	30
31	.47741	.54333	1.8405	.87868	29		31	.49268	.56616	1.7663	.87021	29
32	.47767	.54371	1.8392	.87854	28		32	.49293	.56654	1.7651	.87007	28
33	.47793	.54409	1.8379	.87840	27		33	.49318	.56693	1.7639	.86993	27
34	.47818	.54446	1.8367	.87826	26		34	.49344	.56731	1.7627	.86978	26
35	.47844	.54484	1.8354	.87812	25		35	.49369	.56769	1.7615	.86964	25
36	.47869	.54522	1.8341	.87798	24		36	.49394	.56808	1.7603	.86949	24
37	.47895	.54560	1.8329	.87784	23		37	.49419	.56846	1.7591	.86935	23
38	.47920	.54597	1.8316	.87770	22		38	.49445	.56885	1.7579	.86921	22
39	.47946	.54635	1.8303	.87756	21		39	.49470	.56923	1.7567	.86906	21
40	.47971	.54673	1.8291	.87743	20		40	.49495	.56962	1.7556	.86892	20
41	.47997	.54711	1.8278	.87729	19		41	.49521	.57000	1.7544	.86878	19
42	.48022	.54748	1.8265	.87715	18		42	.49546	.57039	1.7532	.86863	18
43	.48048	.54786	1.8253	.87701	17		43	.49571	.57078	1.7520	.86849	17
44	.48073	.54824	1.8240	.87687	16		44	.49596	.57116	1.7508	.86834	16
45	.48099	.54862	1.8228	.87673	15		45	.49622	.57155	1.7496	.86820	15
46	.48124	.54900	1.8215	.87659	14		46	.49647	.57193	1.7485	.86805	14
47	.48150	.54938	1.8202	.87645	13		47	.49672	.57232	1.7473	.86791	13
48	.48175	.54975	1.8190	.87631	12		48	.49697	.57271	1.7461	.86777	12
49	.48201	.55013	1.8177	.87617	11		49	.49723	.57309	1.7449	.86762	11
50	.48226	.55051	1.8165	.87603	10		50	.49748	.57348	1.7437	.86748	10
51	.48252	.55089	1.8152	.87589	9		51	.49773	.57386	1.7426	.86733	9
52	.48277	.55127	1.8140	.87575	8		52	.49798	.57425	1.7414	.86719	8
53	.48303	.55165	1.8127	.87561	7		53	.49824	.57464	1.7402	.86704	7
54	.48328	.55203	1.8115	.87546	6		54	.49849	.57503	1.7391	.86690	6
55	.48354	.55241	1.8103	.87532	5		55	.49874	.57541	1.7379	.86675	5
56	.48379	.55279	1.8090	.87518	4		56	.49899	.57580	1.7367	.86661	4
57	.48405	.55317	1.8078	.87504	3		57	.49924	.57619	1.7355	.86646	3
58	.48430	.55355	1.8065	.87490	2		58	.49950	.57657	1.7344	.86632	2
59	.48456	.55393	1.8053	.87476	1		59	.49975	.57696	1.7332	.86617	1
60	.48481	.55431	1.8040	.87462	0		60	.50000	.57735	1.7321	.86603	0
′	Cos	Cot	Tan	Sin	′		′	Cos	Cot	Tan	Sin	′

118° (298°)   (241°) **61°**   **119° (299°)**   (240°) **60°**

NATURAL TRIGONOMETRIC FUNCTIONS

′	Sin	Tan	Cot	Cos	′		′	Sin	Tan	Cot	Cos	′
0	.50000	.57735	1.7321	.86603	60		0	.51504	.60086	1.6643	.85717	60
1	.50025	.57774	1.7309	.86588	59		1	.51529	.60126	1.6632	.85702	59
2	.50050	.57813	1.7297	.86573	58		2	.51554	.60165	1.6621	.85687	58
3	.50076	.57851	1.7286	.86559	57		3	.51579	.60205	1.6610	.85672	57
4	.50101	.57890	1.7274	.86544	56		4	.51604	.60245	1.6599	.85657	56
5	.50126	.57929	1.7262	.86530	55		5	.51628	.60284	1.6588	.85642	55
6	.50151	.57968	1.7251	.86515	54		6	.51653	.60324	1.6577	.85627	54
7	.50176	.58007	1.7239	.86501	53		7	.51678	.60364	1.6566	.85612	53
8	.50201	.58046	1.7228	.86486	52		8	.51703	.60403	1.6555	.85597	52
9	.50227	.58085	1.7216	.86471	51		9	.51728	.60443	1.6545	.85582	51
10	.50252	.58124	1.7205	.86457	50		10	.51753	.60483	1.6534	.85567	50
11	.50277	.58162	1.7193	.86442	49		11	.51778	.60522	1.6523	.85551	49
12	.50302	.58201	1.7182	.86427	48		12	.51803	.60562	1.6512	.85536	48
13	.50327	.58240	1.7170	.86413	47		13	.51828	.60602	1.6501	.85521	47
14	.50352	.58279	1.7159	.86398	46		14	.51852	.60642	1.6490	.85506	46
15	.50377	.58318	1.7147	.86384	45		15	.51877	.60681	1.6479	.85491	45
16	.50403	.58357	1.7136	.86369	44		16	.51902	.60721	1.6469	.85476	44
17	.50428	.58396	1.7124	.86354	43		17	.51927	.60761	1.6458	.85461	43
18	.50453	.58435	1.7113	.86340	42		18	.51952	.60801	1.6447	.85446	42
19	.50478	.58474	1.7102	.86325	41		19	.51977	.60841	1.6436	.85431	41
20	.50503	.58513	1.7090	.86310	40		20	.52002	.60881	1.6426	.85416	40
21	.50528	.58552	1.7079	.86295	39		21	.52026	.60921	1.6415	.85401	39
22	.50553	.58591	1.7067	.86281	38		22	.52051	.60960	1.6404	.85385	38
23	.50578	.58631	1.7056	.86266	37		23	.52076	.61000	1.6393	.85370	37
24	.50603	.58670	1.7045	.86251	36		24	.52101	.61040	1.6383	.85355	36
25	.50628	.58709	1.7033	.86237	35		25	.52126	.61080	1.6372	.85340	35
26	.50654	.58748	1.7022	.86222	34		26	.52151	.61120	1.6361	.85325	34
27	.50679	.58787	1.7011	.86207	33		27	.52175	.61160	1.6351	.85310	33
28	.50704	.58826	1.6999	.86192	32		28	.52200	.61200	1.6340	.85294	32
29	.50729	.58865	1.6988	.86178	31		29	.52225	.61240	1.6329	.85279	31
30	.50754	.58905	1.6977	.86163	30		30	.52250	.61280	1.6319	.85264	30
31	.50779	.58944	1.6965	.86148	29		31	.52275	.61320	1.6308	.85249	29
32	.50804	.58983	1.6954	.86133	28		32	.52299	.61360	1.6297	.85234	28
33	.50829	.59022	1.6943	.86119	27		33	.52324	.61400	1.6287	.85218	27
34	.50854	.59061	1.6932	.86104	26		34	.52349	.61440	1.6276	.85203	26
35	.50879	.59101	1.6920	.86089	25		35	.52374	.61480	1.6265	.85188	25
36	.50904	.59140	1.6909	.86074	24		36	.52399	.61520	1.6255	.85173	24
37	.50929	.59179	1.6898	.86059	23		37	.52423	.61561	1.6244	.85157	23
38	.50954	.59218	1.6887	.86045	22		38	.52448	.61601	1.6234	.85142	22
39	.50979	.59258	1.6875	.86030	21		39	.52473	.61641	1.6223	.85127	21
40	.51004	.59297	1.6864	.86015	20		40	.52498	.61681	1.6212	.85112	20
41	.51029	.59336	1.6853	.86000	19		41	.52522	.61721	1.6202	.85096	19
42	.51054	.59376	1.6842	.85985	18		42	.52547	.61761	1.6191	.85081	18
43	.51079	.59415	1.6831	.85970	17		43	.52572	.61801	1.6181	.85066	17
44	.51104	.59454	1.6820	.85956	16		44	.52597	.61842	1.6170	.85051	16
45	.51129	.59494	1.6808	.85941	15		45	.52621	.61882	1.6160	.85035	15
46	.51154	.59533	1.6797	.85926	14		46	.52646	.61922	1.6149	.85020	14
47	.51179	.59573	1.6786	.85911	13		47	.52671	.61962	1.6139	.85005	13
48	.51204	.59612	1.6775	.85896	12		48	.52696	.62003	1.6128	.84989	12
49	.51229	.59651	1.6764	.85881	11		49	.52720	.62043	1.6118	.84974	11
50	.51254	.59691	1.6753	.85866	10		50	.52745	.62083	1.6107	.84959	10
51	.51279	.59730	1.6742	.85851	9		51	.52770	.62124	1.6097	.84943	9
52	.51304	.59770	1.6731	.85836	8		52	.52794	.62164	1.6087	.84928	8
53	.51329	.59809	1.6720	.85821	7		53	.52819	.62204	1.6076	.84913	7
54	.51354	.59849	1.6709	.85806	6		54	.52844	.62245	1.6066	.84897	6
55	.51379	.59888	1.6698	.85792	5		55	.52869	.62285	1.6055	.84882	5
56	.51404	.59928	1.6687	.85777	4		56	.52893	.62325	1.6045	.84866	4
57	.51429	.59967	1.6676	.85762	3		57	.52918	.62366	1.6034	.84851	3
58	.51454	.60007	1.6665	.85747	2		58	.52943	.62406	1.6024	.84836	2
59	.51479	.60046	1.6654	.85732	1		59	.52967	.62446	1.6014	.84820	1
60	.51504	.60086	1.6643	.85717	0		60	.52992	.62487	1.6003	.84805	0
′	Cos	Cot	Tan	Sin	′		′	Cos	Cot	Tan	Sin	′

NATURAL TRIGONOMETRIC FUNCTIONS

′	Sin	Tan	Cot	Cos	′
0	.52992	.62487	1.6003	.84805	60
1	.53017	.62527	1.5993	.84789	59
2	.53041	.62568	1.5983	.84774	58
3	.53066	.62608	1.5972	.84759	57
4	.53091	.62649	1.5962	.84743	56
5	.53115	.62689	1.5952	.84728	55
6	.53140	.62730	1.5941	.84712	54
7	.53164	.62770	1.5931	.84697	53
8	.53189	.62811	1.5921	.84681	52
9	.53214	.62852	1.5911	.84666	51
10	.53238	.62892	1.5900	.84650	50
11	.53263	.62933	1.5890	.84635	49
12	.53288	.62973	1.5880	.84619	48
13	.53312	.63014	1.5869	.84604	47
14	.53337	.63055	1.5859	.84588	46
15	.53361	.63095	1.5849	.84573	45
16	.53386	.63136	1.5839	.84557	44
17	.53411	.63177	1.5829	.84542	43
18	.53435	.63217	1.5818	.84526	42
19	.53460	.63258	1.5808	.84511	41
20	.53484	.63299	1.5798	.84495	40
21	.53509	.63340	1.5788	.84480	39
22	.53534	.63380	1.5778	.84464	38
23	.53558	.63421	1.5768	.84448	37
24	.53583	.63462	1.5757	.84433	36
25	.53607	.63503	1.5747	.84417	35
26	.53632	.63544	1.5737	.84402	34
27	.53656	.63584	1.5727	.84386	33
28	.53681	.63625	1.5717	.84370	32
29	.53705	.63666	1.5707	.84355	31
30	.53730	.63707	1.5697	.84339	30
31	.53754	.63748	1.5687	.84324	29
32	.53779	.63789	1.5677	.84308	28
33	.53804	.63830	1.5667	.84292	27
34	.53828	.63871	1.5657	.84277	26
35	.53853	.63912	1.5647	.84261	25
36	.53877	.63953	1.5637	.84245	24
37	.53902	.63994	1.5627	.84230	23
38	.53926	.64035	1.5617	.84214	22
39	.53951	.64076	1.5607	.84198	21
40	.53975	.64117	1.5597	.84182	20
41	.54000	.64158	1.5587	.84167	19
42	.54024	.64199	1.5577	.84151	18
43	.54049	.64240	1.5567	.84135	17
44	.54073	.64281	1.5557	.84120	16
45	.54097	.64322	1.5547	.84104	15
46	.54122	.64363	1.5537	.84088	14
47	.54146	.64404	1.5527	.84072	13
48	.54171	.64446	1.5517	.84057	12
49	.54195	.64487	1.5507	.84041	11
50	.54220	.64528	1.5497	.84025	10
51	.54244	.64569	1.5487	.84009	9
52	.54269	.64610	1.5477	.83994	8
53	.54293	.64652	1.5468	.83978	7
54	.54317	.64693	1.5458	.83962	6
55	.54342	.64734	1.5448	.83946	5
56	.54366	.64775	1.5438	.83930	4
57	.54391	.64817	1.5428	.83915	3
58	.54415	.64858	1.5418	.83899	2
59	.54440	.64899	1.5408	.83883	1
60	.54464	.64941	1.5399	.83867	0
′	Cos	Cot	Tan	Sin	′

′	Sin	Tan	Cot	Cos	′
0	.54464	.64941	1.5399	.83867	60
1	.54488	.64982	1.5389	.83851	59
2	.54513	.65024	1.5379	.83835	58
3	.54537	.65065	1.5369	.83819	57
4	.54561	.65106	1.5359	.83804	56
5	.54586	.65148	1.5350	.83788	55
6	.54610	.65189	1.5340	.83772	54
7	.54635	.65231	1.5330	.83756	53
8	.54659	.65272	1.5320	.83740	52
9	.54683	.65314	1.5311	.83724	51
10	.54708	.65355	1.5301	.83708	50
11	.54732	.65397	1.5291	.83692	49
12	.54756	.65438	1.5282	.83676	48
13	.54781	.65480	1.5272	.83660	47
14	.54805	.65521	1.5262	.83645	46
15	.54829	.65563	1.5253	.83629	45
16	.54854	.65604	1.5243	.83613	44
17	.54878	.65646	1.5233	.83597	43
18	.54902	.65688	1.5224	.83581	42
19	.54927	.65729	1.5214	.83565	41
20	.54951	.65771	1.5204	.83549	40
21	.54975	.65813	1.5195	.83533	39
22	.54999	.65854	1.5185	.83517	38
23	.55024	.65896	1.5175	.83501	37
24	.55048	.65938	1.5166	.83485	36
25	.55072	.65980	1.5156	.83469	35
26	.55097	.66021	1.5147	.83453	34
27	.55121	.66063	1.5137	.83437	33
28	.55145	.66105	1.5127	.83421	32
29	.55169	.66147	1.5118	.83405	31
30	.55194	.66189	1.5108	.83389	30
31	.55218	.66230	1.5099	.83373	29
32	.55242	.66272	1.5089	.83356	28
33	.55266	.66314	1.5080	.83340	27
34	.55291	.66356	1.5070	.83324	26
35	.55315	.66398	1.5061	.83308	25
36	.55339	.66440	1.5051	.83292	24
37	.55363	.66482	1.5042	.83276	23
38	.55388	.66524	1.5032	.83260	22
39	.55412	.66566	1.5023	.83244	21
40	.55436	.66608	1.5013	.83228	20
41	.55460	.66650	1.5004	.83212	19
42	.55484	.66692	1.4994	.83195	18
43	.55509	.66734	1.4985	.83179	17
44	.55533	.66776	1.4975	.83163	16
45	.55557	.66818	1.4966	.83147	15
46	.55581	.66860	1.4957	.83131	14
47	.55605	.66902	1.4947	.83115	13
48	.55630	.66944	1.4938	.83098	12
49	.55654	.66986	1.4928	.83082	11
50	.55678	.67028	1.4919	.83066	10
51	.55702	.67071	1.4910	.83050	9
52	.55726	.67113	1.4900	.83034	8
53	.55750	.67155	1.4891	.83017	7
54	.55775	.67197	1.4882	.83001	6
55	.55799	.67239	1.4872	.82985	5
56	.55823	.67282	1.4863	.82969	4
57	.55847	.67324	1.4854	.82953	3
58	.55871	.67366	1.4844	.82936	2
59	.55895	.67409	1.4835	.82920	1
60	.55919	.67451	1.4826	.82904	0
′	Cos	Cot	Tan	Sin	′

NATURAL TRIGONOMETRIC FUNCTIONS

′	Sin	Tan	Cot	Cos	′	′	Sin	Tan	Cot	Cos	′
0	.55919	.67451	1.4826	.82904	60	0	.57358	.70021	1.4281	.81915	60
1	.55943	.67493	1.4816	.82887	59	1	.57381	.70064	1.4273	.81899	59
2	.55968	.67536	1.4807	.82871	58	2	.57405	.70107	1.4264	.81882	58
3	.55992	.67578	1.4798	.82855	57	3	.57429	.70151	1.4255	.81865	57
4	.56016	.67620	1.4788	.82839	56	4	.57453	.70194	1.4246	.81848	56
5	.56040	.67663	1.4779	.82822	55	5	.57477	.70238	1.4237	.81832	55
6	.56064	.67705	1.4770	.82806	54	6	.57501	.70281	1.4229	.81815	54
7	.56088	.67748	1.4761	.82790	53	7	.57524	.70325	1.4220	.81798	53
8	.56112	.67790	1.4751	.82773	52	8	.57548	.70368	1.4211	.81782	52
9	.56136	.67832	1.4742	.82757	51	9	.57572	.70412	1.4202	.81765	51
10	.56160	.67875	1.4733	.82741	50	10	.57596	.70455	1.4193	.81748	50
11	.56184	.67917	1.4724	.82724	49	11	.57619	.70499	1.4185	.81731	49
12	.56208	.67960	1.4715	.82708	48	12	.57643	.70542	1.4176	.81714	48
13	.56232	.68002	1.4705	.82692	47	13	.57667	.70586	1.4167	.81698	47
14	.56256	.68045	1.4696	.82675	46	14	.57691	.70629	1.4158	.81681	46
15	.56280	.68088	1.4687	.82659	45	15	.57715	.70673	1.4150	.81664	45
16	.56305	.68130	1.4678	.82643	44	16	.57738	.70717	1.4141	.81647	44
17	.56329	.68173	1.4669	.82626	43	17	.57762	.70760	1.4132	.81631	43
18	.56353	.68215	1.4659	.82610	42	18	.57786	.70804	1.4124	.81614	42
19	.56377	.68258	1.4650	.82593	41	19	.57810	.70848	1.4115	.81597	41
20	.56401	.68301	1.4641	.82577	40	20	.57833	.70891	1.4106	.81580	40
21	.56425	.68343	1.4632	.82561	39	21	.57857	.70935	1.4097	.81563	39
22	.56449	.68386	1.4623	.82544	38	22	.57881	.70979	1.4089	.81546	38
23	.56473	.68429	1.4614	.82528	37	23	.57904	.71023	1.4080	.81530	37
24	.56497	.68471	1.4605	.82511	36	24	.57928	.71066	1.4071	.81513	36
25	.56521	.68514	1.4596	.82495	35	25	.57952	.71110	1.4063	.81496	35
26	.56545	.68557	1.4586	.82478	34	26	.57976	.71154	1.4054	.81479	34
27	.56569	.68600	1.4577	.82462	33	27	.57999	.71198	1.4045	.81462	33
28	.56593	.68642	1.4568	.82446	32	28	.58023	.71242	1.4037	.81445	32
29	.56617	.68685	1.4559	.82429	31	29	.58047	.71285	1.4028	.81428	31
30	.56641	.68728	1.4550	.82413	30	30	.58070	.71329	1.4019	.81412	30
31	.56665	.68771	1.4541	.82396	29	31	.58094	.71373	1.4011	.81395	29
32	.56689	.68814	1.4532	.82380	28	32	.58118	.71417	1.4002	.81378	28
33	.56713	.68857	1.4523	.82363	27	33	.58141	.71461	1.3994	.81361	27
34	.56736	.68900	1.4514	.82347	26	34	.58165	.71505	1.3985	.81344	26
35	.56760	.68942	1.4505	.82330	25	35	.58189	.71549	1.3976	.81327	25
36	.56784	.68985	1.4496	.82314	24	36	.58212	.71593	1.3968	.81310	24
37	.56808	.69028	1.4487	.82297	23	37	.58236	.71637	1.3959	.81293	23
38	.56832	.69071	1.4478	.82281	22	38	.58260	.71681	1.3951	.81276	22
39	.56856	.69114	1.4469	.82264	21	39	.58283	.71725	1.3942	.81259	21
40	.56880	.69157	1.4460	.82248	20	40	.58307	.71769	1.3934	.81242	20
41	.56904	.69200	1.4451	.82231	19	41	.58330	.71813	1.3925	.81225	19
42	.56928	.69243	1.4442	.82214	18	42	.58354	.71857	1.3916	.81208	18
43	.56952	.69286	1.4433	.82198	17	43	.58378	.71901	1.3908	.81191	17
44	.56976	.69329	1.4424	.82181	16	44	.58401	.71946	1.3899	.81174	16
45	.57000	.69372	1.4415	.82165	15	45	.58425	.71990	1.3891	.81157	15
46	.57024	.69416	1.4406	.82148	14	46	.58449	.72034	1.3882	.81140	14
47	.57047	.69459	1.4397	.82132	13	47	.58472	.72078	1.3874	.81123	13
48	.57071	.69502	1.4388	.82115	12	48	.58496	.72122	1.3865	.81106	12
49	.57095	.69545	1.4379	.82098	11	49	.58519	.72167	1.3857	.81089	11
50	.57119	.69588	1.4370	.82082	10	50	.58543	.72211	1.3848	.81072	10
51	.57143	.69631	1.4361	.82065	9	51	.58567	.72255	1.3840	.81055	9
52	.57167	.69675	1.4352	.82048	8	52	.58590	.72299	1.3831	.81038	8
53	.57191	.69718	1.4344	.82032	7	53	.58614	.72344	1.3823	.81021	7
54	.57215	.69761	1.4335	.82015	6	54	.58637	.72388	1.3814	.81004	6
55	.57238	.69804	1.4326	.81999	5	55	.58661	.72432	1.3806	.80987	5
56	.57262	.69847	1.4317	.81982	4	56	.58684	.72477	1.3798	.80970	4
57	.57286	.69891	1.4308	.81965	3	57	.58708	.72521	1.3789	.80953	3
58	.57310	.69934	1.4299	.81949	2	58	.58731	.72565	1.3781	.80936	2
59	.57334	.69977	1.4290	.81932	1	59	.58755	.72610	1.3772	.80919	1
60	.57358	.70021	1.4281	.81915	0	60	.58779	.72654	1.3764	.80902	0
′	Cos	Cot	Tan	Sin	′	′	Cos	Cot	Tan	Sin	′

NATURAL TRIGONOMETRIC FUNCTIONS

′	Sin	Tan	Cot	Cos	′		′	Sin	Tan	Cot	Cos	′
0	.58779	.72654	1.3764	.80902	60		0	.60182	.75355	1.3270	.79864	60
1	.58802	.72699	1.3755	.80885	59		1	.60205	.75401	1.3262	.79846	59
2	.58826	.72743	1.3747	.80867	58		2	.60228	.75447	1.3254	.79829	58
3	.58849	.72788	1.3739	.80850	57		3	.60251	.75492	1.3246	.79811	57
4	.58873	.72832	1.3730	.80833	56		4	.60274	.75538	1.3238	.79793	56
5	.58896	.72877	1.3722	.80816	55		5	.60298	.75584	1.3230	.79776	55
6	.58920	.72921	1.3713	.80799	54		6	.60321	.75629	1.3222	.79758	54
7	.58943	.72966	1.3705	.80782	53		7	.60344	.75675	1.3214	.79741	53
8	.58967	.73010	1.3697	.80765	52		8	.60367	.75721	1.3206	.79723	52
9	.58990	.73055	1.3688	.80748	51		9	.60390	.75767	1.3198	.79706	51
10	.59014	.73100	1.3680	.80730	50		10	.60414	.75812	1.3190	.79688	50
11	.59037	.73144	1.3672	.80713	49		11	.60437	.75858	1.3182	.79671	49
12	.59061	.73189	1.3663	.80696	48		12	.60460	.75904	1.3175	.79653	48
13	.59084	.73234	1.3655	.80679	47		13	.60483	.75950	1.3167	.79635	47
14	.59108	.73278	1.3647	.80662	46		14	.60506	.75996	1.3159	.79618	46
15	.59131	.73323	1.3638	.80644	45		15	.60529	.76042	1.3151	.79600	45
16	.59154	.73368	1.3630	.80627	44		16	.60553	.76088	1.3143	.79583	44
17	.59178	.73413	1.3622	.80610	43		17	.60576	.76134	1.3135	.79565	43
18	.59201	.73457	1.3613	.80593	42		18	.60599	.76180	1.3127	.79547	42
19	.59225	.73502	1.3605	.80576	41		19	.60622	.76226	1.3119	.79530	41
20	.59248	.73547	1.3597	.80558	40		20	.60645	.76272	1.3111	.79512	40
21	.59272	.73592	1.3588	.80541	39		21	.60668	.76318	1.3103	.79494	39
22	.59295	.73637	1.3580	.80524	38		22	.60691	.76364	1.3095	.79477	38
23	.59318	.73681	1.3572	.80507	37		23	.60714	.76410	1.3087	.79459	37
24	.59342	.73726	1.3564	.80489	36		24	.60738	.76456	1.3079	.79441	36
25	.59365	.73771	1.3555	.80472	35		25	.60761	.76502	1.3072	.79424	35
26	.59389	.73816	1.3547	.80455	34		26	.60784	.76548	1.3064	.79406	34
27	.59412	.73861	1.3539	.80438	33		27	.60807	.76594	1.3056	.79388	33
28	.59436	.73906	1.3531	.80420	32		28	.60830	.76640	1.3048	.79371	32
29	.59459	.73951	1.3522	.80403	31		29	.60853	.76686	1.3040	.79353	31
30	.59482	.73996	1.3514	.80386	30		30	.60876	.76733	1.3032	.79335	30
31	.59506	.74041	1.3506	.80368	29		31	.60899	.76779	1.3024	.79318	29
32	.59529	.74086	1.3498	.80351	28		32	.60922	.76825	1.3017	.79300	28
33	.59552	.74131	1.3490	.80334	27		33	.60945	.76871	1.3009	.79282	27
34	.59576	.74176	1.3481	.80316	26		34	.60968	.76918	1.3001	.79264	26
35	.59599	.74221	1.3473	.80299	25		35	.60991	.76964	1.2993	.79247	25
36	.59622	.74267	1.3465	.80282	24		36	.61015	.77010	1.2985	.79229	24
37	.59646	.74312	1.3457	.80264	23		37	.61038	.77057	1.2977	.79211	23
38	.59669	.74357	1.3449	.80247	22		38	.61061	.77103	1.2970	.79193	22
39	.59693	.74402	1.3440	.80230	21		39	.61084	.77149	1.2962	.79176	21
40	.59716	.74447	1.3432	.80212	20		40	.61107	.77196	1.2954	.79158	20
41	.59739	.74492	1.3424	.80195	19		41	.61130	.77242	1.2946	.79140	19
42	.59763	.74538	1.3416	.80178	18		42	.61153	.77289	1.2938	.79122	18
43	.59786	.74583	1.3408	.80160	17		43	.61176	.77335	1.2931	.79105	17
44	.59809	.74628	1.3400	.80143	16		44	.61199	.77382	1.2923	.79087	16
45	.59832	.74674	1.3392	.80125	15		45	.61222	.77428	1.2915	.79069	15
46	.59856	.74719	1.3384	.80108	14		46	.61245	.77475	1.2907	.79051	14
47	.59879	.74764	1.3375	.80091	13		47	.61268	.77521	1.2900	.79033	13
48	.59902	.74810	1.3367	.80073	12		48	.61291	.77568	1.2892	.79016	12
49	.59926	.74855	1.3359	.80056	11		49	.61314	.77615	1.2884	.78998	11
50	.59949	.74900	1.3351	.80038	10		50	.61337	.77661	1.2876	.78980	10
51	.59972	.74946	1.3343	.80021	9		51	.61360	.77708	1.2869	.78962	9
52	.59995	.74991	1.3335	.80003	8		52	.61383	.77754	1.2861	.78944	8
53	.60019	.75037	1.3327	.79986	7		53	.61406	.77801	1.2853	.78926	7
54	.60042	.75082	1.3319	.79968	6		54	.61429	.77848	1.2846	.78908	6
55	.60065	.75128	1.3311	.79951	5		55	.61451	.77895	1.2838	.78891	5
56	.60089	.75173	1.3303	.79934	4		56	.61474	.77941	1.2830	.78873	4
57	.60112	.75219	1.3295	.79916	3		57	.61497	.77988	1.2822	.78855	3
58	.60135	.75264	1.3287	.79899	2		58	.61520	.78035	1.2815	.78837	2
59	.60158	.75310	1.3278	.79881	1		59	.61543	.78082	1.2807	.78819	1
60	.60182	.75355	1.3270	.79864	0		60	.61566	.78129	1.2799	.78801	0
′	Cos	Cot	Tan	Sin	′		′	Cos	Cot	Tan	Sin	′

NATURAL TRIGONOMETRIC FUNCTIONS

′	Sin	Tan	Cot	Cos	′
0	.61566	.78129	1.2799	.78801	**60**
1	.61589	.78175	1.2792	.78783	59
2	.61612	.78222	1.2784	.78765	58
3	.61635	.78269	1.2776	.78747	57
4	.61658	.78316	1.2769	.78729	56
5	.61681	.78363	1.2761	.78711	**55**
6	.61704	.78410	1.2753	.78694	54
7	.61726	.78457	1.2746	.78676	53
8	.61749	.78504	1.2738	.78658	52
9	.61772	.78551	1.2731	.78640	51
10	.61795	.78598	1.2723	.78622	**50**
11	.61818	.78645	1.2715	.78604	49
12	.61841	.78692	1.2708	.78586	48
13	.61864	.78739	1.2700	.78568	47
14	.61887	.78786	1.2693	.78550	46
15	.61909	.78834	1.2685	.78532	**45**
16	.61932	.78881	1.2677	.78514	44
17	.61955	.78928	1.2670	.78496	43
18	.61978	.78975	1.2662	.78478	42
19	.62001	.79022	1.2655	.78460	41
20	.62024	.79070	1.2647	.78442	**40**
21	.62046	.79117	1.2640	.78424	39
22	.62069	.79164	1.2632	.78405	38
23	.62092	.79212	1.2624	.78387	37
24	.62115	.79259	1.2617	.78369	36
25	.62138	.79306	1.2609	.78351	**35**
26	.62160	.79354	1.2602	.78333	34
27	.62183	.79401	1.2594	.78315	33
28	.62206	.79449	1.2587	.78297	32
29	.62229	.79496	1.2579	.78279	31
30	.62251	.79544	1.2572	.78261	**30**
31	.62274	.79591	1.2564	.78243	29
32	.62297	.79639	1.2557	.78225	28
33	.62320	.79686	1.2549	.78206	27
34	.62342	.79734	1.2542	.78188	26
35	.62365	.79781	1.2534	.78170	**25**
36	.62388	.79829	1.2527	.78152	24
37	.62411	.79877	1.2519	.78134	23
38	.62433	.79924	1.2512	.78116	22
39	.62456	.79972	1.2504	.78098	21
40	.62479	.80020	1.2497	.78079	**20**
41	.62502	.80067	1.2489	.78061	19
42	.62524	.80115	1.2482	.78043	18
43	.62547	.80163	1.2475	.78025	17
44	.62570	.80211	1.2467	.78007	16
45	.62592	.80258	1.2460	.77988	**15**
46	.62615	.80306	1.2452	.77970	14
47	.62638	.80354	1.2445	.77952	13
48	.62660	.80402	1.2437	.77934	12
49	.62683	.80450	1.2430	.77916	11
50	.62706	.80498	1.2423	.77897	**10**
51	.62728	.80546	1.2415	.77879	9
52	.62751	.80594	1.2408	.77861	8
53	.62774	.80642	1.2401	.77843	7
54	.62796	.80690	1.2393	.77824	6
55	.62819	.80738	1.2386	.77806	**5**
56	.62842	.80786	1.2378	.77788	4
57	.62864	.80834	1.2371	.77769	3
58	.62887	.80882	1.2364	.77751	2
59	.62909	.80930	1.2356	.77733	1
60	.62932	.80978	1.2349	.77715	**0**
′	Cos	Cot	Tan	Sin	′

′	Sin	Tan	Cot	Cos	′
0	.62932	.80978	1.2349	.77715	**60**
1	.62955	.81027	1.2342	.77696	59
2	.62977	.81075	1.2334	.77678	58
3	.63000	.81123	1.2327	.77660	57
4	.63022	.81171	1.2320	.77641	56
5	.63045	.81220	1.2312	.77623	**55**
6	.63068	.81268	1.2305	.77605	54
7	.63090	.81316	1.2298	.77586	53
8	.63113	.81364	1.2290	.77568	52
9	.63135	.81413	1.2283	.77550	51
10	.63158	.81461	1.2276	.77531	**50**
11	.63180	.81510	1.2268	.77513	49
12	.63203	.81558	1.2261	.77494	48
13	.63225	.81606	1.2254	.77476	47
14	.63248	.81655	1.2247	.77458	46
15	.63271	.81703	1.2239	.77439	**45**
16	.63293	.81752	1.2232	.77421	44
17	.63316	.81800	1.2225	.77402	43
18	.63338	.81849	1.2218	.77384	42
19	.63361	.81898	1.2210	.77366	41
20	.63383	.81946	1.2203	.77347	**40**
21	.63406	.81995	1.2196	.77329	39
22	.63428	.82044	1.2189	.77310	38
23	.63451	.82092	1.2181	.77292	37
24	.63473	.82141	1.2174	.77273	36
25	.63496	.82190	1.2167	.77255	**35**
26	.63518	.82238	1.2160	.77236	34
27	.63540	.82287	1.2153	.77218	33
28	.63563	.82336	1.2145	.77199	32
29	.63585	.82385	1.2138	.77181	31
30	.63608	.82434	1.2131	.77162	**30**
31	.63630	.82483	1.2124	.77144	29
32	.63653	.82531	1.2117	.77125	28
33	.63675	.82580	1.2109	.77107	27
34	.63698	.82629	1.2102	.77088	26
35	.63720	.82678	1.2095	.77070	**25**
36	.63742	.82727	1.2088	.77051	24
37	.63765	.82776	1.2081	.77033	23
38	.63787	.82825	1.2074	.77014	22
39	.63810	.82874	1.2066	.76996	21
40	.63832	.82923	1.2059	.76977	**20**
41	.63854	.82972	1.2052	.76959	19
42	.63877	.83022	1.2045	.76940	18
43	.63899	.83071	1.2038	.76921	17
44	.63922	.83120	1.2031	.76903	16
45	.63944	.83169	1.2024	.76884	**15**
46	.63966	.83218	1.2017	.76866	14
47	.63989	.83268	1.2009	.76847	13
48	.64011	.83317	1.2002	.76828	12
49	.64033	.83366	1.1995	.76810	11
50	.64056	.83415	1.1988	.76791	**10**
51	.64078	.83465	1.1981	.76772	9
52	.64100	.83514	1.1974	.76754	8
53	.64123	.83564	1.1967	.76735	7
54	.64145	.83613	1.1960	.76717	6
55	.64167	.83662	1.1953	.76698	**5**
56	.64190	.83712	1.1946	.76679	4
57	.64212	.83761	1.1939	.76661	3
58	.64234	.83811	1.1932	.76642	2
59	.64256	.83860	1.1925	.76623	1
60	.64279	.83910	1.1918	.76604	**0**
′	Cos	Cot	Tan	Sin	′

40° (220°) (319°) **139°**   **41° (221°)** (318°) **138°**

′	Sin	Tan	Cot	Cos	′
0	.64279	.83910	1.1918	.76604	60
1	.64301	.83960	1.1910	.76586	59
2	.64323	.84009	1.1903	.76567	58
3	.64346	.84059	1.1896	.76548	57
4	.64368	.84108	1.1889	.76530	56
5	.64390	.84158	1.1882	.76511	55
6	.64412	.84208	1.1875	.76492	54
7	.64435	.84258	1.1868	.76473	53
8	.64457	.84307	1.1861	.76455	52
9	.64479	.84357	1.1854	.76436	51
10	.64501	.84407	1.1847	.76417	50
11	.64524	.84457	1.1840	.76398	49
12	.64546	.84507	1.1833	.76380	48
13	.64568	.84556	1.1826	.76361	47
14	.64590	.84606	1.1819	.76342	46
15	.64612	.84656	1.1812	.76323	45
16	.64635	.84706	1.1806	.76304	44
17	.64657	.84756	1.1799	.76286	43
18	.64679	.84806	1.1792	.76267	42
19	.64701	.84856	1.1785	.76248	41
20	.64723	.84906	1.1778	.76229	40
21	.64746	.84956	1.1771	.76210	39
22	.64768	.85006	1.1764	.76192	38
23	.64790	.85057	1.1757	.76173	37
24	.64812	.85107	1.1750	.76154	36
25	.64834	.85157	1.1743	.76135	35
26	.64856	.85207	1.1736	.76116	34
27	.64878	.85257	1.1729	.76097	33
28	.64901	.85308	1.1722	.76078	32
29	.64923	.85358	1.1715	.76059	31
30	.64945	.85408	1.1708	.76041	30
31	.64967	.85458	1.1702	.76022	29
32	.64989	.85509	1.1695	.76003	28
33	.65011	.85559	1.1688	.75984	27
34	.65033	.85609	1.1681	.75965	26
35	.65055	.85660	1.1674	.75946	25
36	.65077	.85710	1.1667	.75927	24
37	.65100	.85761	1.1660	.75908	23
38	.65122	.85811	1.1653	.75889	22
39	.65144	.85862	1.1647	.75870	21
40	.65166	.85912	1.1640	.75851	20
41	.65188	.85963	1.1633	.75832	19
42	.65210	.86014	1.1626	.75813	18
43	.65232	.86064	1.1619	.75794	17
44	.65254	.86115	1.1612	.75775	16
45	.65276	.86166	1.1606	.75756	15
46	.65298	.86216	1.1599	.75738	14
47	.65320	.86267	1.1592	.75719	13
48	.65342	.86318	1.1585	.75700	12
49	.65364	.86368	1.1578	.75680	11
50	.65386	.86419	1.1571	.75661	10
51	.65408	.86470	1.1565	.75642	9
52	.65430	.86521	1.1558	.75623	8
53	.65452	.86572	1.1551	.75604	7
54	.65474	.86623	1.1544	.75585	6
55	.65496	.86674	1.1538	.75566	5
56	.65518	.86725	1.1531	.75547	4
57	.65540	.86776	1.1524	.75528	3
58	.65562	.86827	1.1517	.75509	2
59	.65584	.86878	1.1510	.75490	1
60	.65606	.86929	1.1504	.75471	0
′	Cos	Cot	Tan	Sin	′

′	Sin	Tan	Cot	Cos	′
0	.65606	.86929	1.1504	.75471	60
1	.65628	.86980	1.1497	.75452	59
2	.65650	.87031	1.1490	.75433	58
3	.65672	.87082	1.1483	.75414	57
4	.65694	.87133	1.1477	.75395	56
5	.65716	.87184	1.1470	.75375	55
6	.65738	.87236	1.1463	.75356	54
7	.65759	.87287	1.1456	.75337	53
8	.65781	.87338	1.1450	.75318	52
9	.65803	.87389	1.1443	.75299	51
10	.65825	.87441	1.1436	.75280	50
11	.65847	.87492	1.1430	.75261	49
12	.65869	.87543	1.1423	.75241	48
13	.65891	.87595	1.1416	.75222	47
14	.65913	.87646	1.1410	.75203	46
15	.65935	.87698	1.1403	.75184	45
16	.65956	.87749	1.1396	.75165	44
17	.65978	.87801	1.1389	.75146	43
18	.66000	.87852	1.1383	.75126	42
19	.66022	.87904	1.1376	.75107	41
20	.66044	.87955	1.1369	.75088	40
21	.66066	.88007	1.1363	.75069	39
22	.66088	.88059	1.1356	.75050	38
23	.66109	.88110	1.1349	.75030	37
24	.66131	.88162	1.1343	.75011	36
25	.66153	.88214	1.1336	.74992	35
26	.66175	.88265	1.1329	.74973	34
27	.66197	.88317	1.1323	.74953	33
28	.66218	.88369	1.1316	.74934	32
29	.66240	.88421	1.1310	.74915	31
30	.66262	.88473	1.1303	.74896	30
31	.66284	.88524	1.1296	.74876	29
32	.66306	.88576	1.1290	.74857	28
33	.66327	.88628	1.1283	.74838	27
34	.66349	.88680	1.1276	.74818	26
35	.66371	.88732	1.1270	.74799	25
36	.66393	.88784	1.1263	.74780	24
37	.66414	.88836	1.1257	.74760	23
38	.66436	.88888	1.1250	.74741	22
39	.66458	.88940	1.1243	.74722	21
40	.66480	.88992	1.1237	.74703	20
41	.66501	.89045	1.1230	.74683	19
42	.66523	.89097	1.1224	.74664	18
43	.66545	.89149	1.1217	.74644	17
44	.66566	.89201	1.1211	.74625	16
45	.66588	.89253	1.1204	.74606	15
46	.66610	.89306	1.1197	.74586	14
47	.66632	.89358	1.1191	.74567	13
48	.66653	.89410	1.1184	.74548	12
49	.66675	.89463	1.1178	.74528	11
50	.66697	.89515	1.1171	.74509	10
51	.66718	.89567	1.1165	.74489	9
52	.66740	.89620	1.1158	.74470	8
53	.66762	.89672	1.1152	.74451	7
54	.66783	.89725	1.1145	.74431	6
55	.66805	.89777	1.1139	.74412	5
56	.66827	.89830	1.1132	.74392	4
57	.66848	.89883	1.1126	.74373	3
58	.66870	.89935	1.1119	.74353	2
59	.66891	.89988	1.1113	.74334	1
60	.66913	.90040	1.1106	.74314	0
′	Cos	Cot	Tan	Sin	′

NATURAL TRIGONOMETRIC FUNCTIONS

′	Sin	Tan	Cot	Cos	′		′	Sin	Tan	Cot	Cos	′
0	.66913	.90040	1.1106	.74314	60		0	.68200	.93252	1.0724	.73135	60
1	.66935	.90093	1.1100	.74295	59		1	.68221	.93306	1.0717	.73116	59
2	.66956	.90146	1.1093	.74276	58		2	.68242	.93360	1.0711	.73096	58
3	.66978	.90199	1.1087	.74256	57		3	.68264	.93415	1.0705	.73076	57
4	.66999	.90251	1.1080	.74237	56		4	.68285	.93469	1.0699	.73056	56
5	.67021	.90304	1.1074	.74217	55		5	.68306	.93524	1.0692	.73036	55
6	.67043	.90357	1.1067	.74198	54		6	.68327	.93578	1.0686	.73016	54
7	.67064	.90410	1.1061	.74178	53		7	.68349	.93633	1.0680	.72996	53
8	.67086	.90463	1.1054	.74159	52		8	.68370	.93688	1.0674	.72976	52
9	.67107	.90516	1.1048	.74139	51		9	.68391	.93742	1.0668	.72957	51
10	.67129	.90569	1.1041	.74120	50		10	.68412	.93797	1.0661	.72937	50
11	.67151	.90621	1.1035	.74100	49		11	.68434	.93852	1.0655	.72917	49
12	.67172	.90674	1.1028	.74080	48		12	.68455	.93906	1.0649	.72897	48
13	.67194	.90727	1.1022	.74061	47		13	.68476	.93961	1.0643	.72877	47
14	.67215	.90781	1.1016	.74041	46		14	.68497	.94016	1.0637	.72857	46
15	.67237	.90834	1.1009	.74022	45		15	.68518	.94071	1.0630	.72837	45
16	.67258	.90887	1.1003	.74002	44		16	.68539	.94125	1.0624	.72817	44
17	.67280	.90940	1.0996	.73983	43		17	.68561	.94180	1.0618	.72797	43
18	.67301	.90993	1.0990	.73963	42		18	.68582	.94235	1.0612	.72777	42
19	.67323	.91046	1.0983	.73944	41		19	.68603	.94290	1.0606	.72757	41
20	.67344	.91099	1.0977	.73924	40		20	.68624	.94345	1.0599	.72737	40
21	.67366	.91153	1.0971	.73904	39		21	.68645	.94400	1.0593	.72717	39
22	.67387	.91206	1.0964	.73885	38		22	.68666	.94455	1.0587	.72697	38
23	.67409	.91259	1.0958	.73865	37		23	.68688	.94510	1.0581	.72677	37
24	.67430	.91313	1.0951	.73846	36		24	.68709	.94565	1.0575	.72657	36
25	.67452	.91366	1.0945	.73826	35		25	.68730	.94620	1.0569	.72637	35
26	.67473	.91419	1.0939	.73806	34		26	.68751	.94676	1.0562	.72617	34
27	.67495	.91473	1.0932	.73787	33		27	.68772	.94731	1.0556	.72597	33
28	.67516	.91526	1.0926	.73767	32		28	.68793	.94786	1.0550	.72577	32
29	.67538	.91580	1.0919	.73747	31		29	.68814	.94841	1.0544	.72557	31
30	.67559	.91633	1.0913	.73728	30		30	.68835	.94896	1.0538	.72537	30
31	.67580	.91687	1.0907	.73708	29		31	.68857	.94952	1.0532	.72517	29
32	.67602	.91740	1.0900	.73688	28		32	.68878	.95007	1.0526	.72497	28
33	.67623	.91794	1.0894	.73669	27		33	.68899	.95062	1.0519	.72477	27
34	.67645	.91847	1.0888	.73649	26		34	.68920	.95118	1.0513	.72457	26
35	.67666	.91901	1.0881	.73629	25		35	.68941	.95173	1.0507	.72437	25
36	.67688	.91955	1.0875	.73610	24		36	.68962	.95229	1.0501	.72417	24
37	.67709	.92008	1.0869	.73590	23		37	.68983	.95284	1.0495	.72397	23
38	.67730	.92062	1.0862	.73570	22		38	.69004	.95340	1.0489	.72377	22
39	.67752	.92116	1.0856	.73551	21		39	.69025	.95395	1.0483	.72357	21
40	.67773	.92170	1.0850	.73531	20		40	.69046	.95451	1.0477	.72337	20
41	.67795	.92224	1.0843	.73511	19		41	.69067	.95506	1.0470	.72317	19
42	.67816	.92277	1.0837	.73491	18		42	.69088	.95562	1.0464	.72297	18
43	.67837	.92331	1.0831	.73472	17		43	.69109	.95618	1.0458	.72277	17
44	.67859	.92385	1.0824	.73452	16		44	.69130	.95673	1.0452	.72257	16
45	.67880	.92439	1.0818	.73432	15		45	.69151	.95729	1.0446	.72236	15
46	.67901	.92493	1.0812	.73413	14		46	.69172	.95785	1.0440	.72216	14
47	.67923	.92547	1.0805	.73393	13		47	.69193	.95841	1.0434	.72196	13
48	.67944	.92601	1.0799	.73373	12		48	.69214	.95897	1.0428	.72176	12
49	.67965	.92655	1.0793	.73353	11		49	.69235	.95952	1.0422	.72156	11
50	.67987	.92709	1.0786	.73333	10		50	.69256	.96008	1.0416	.72136	10
51	.68008	.92763	1.0780	.73314	9		51	.69277	.96064	1.0410	.72116	9
52	.68029	.92817	1.0774	.73294	8		52	.69298	.96120	1.0404	.72095	8
53	.68051	.92872	1.0768	.73274	7		53	.69319	.96176	1.0398	.72075	7
54	.68072	.92926	1.0761	.73254	6		54	.69340	.96232	1.0392	.72055	6
55	.68093	.92980	1.0755	.73234	5		55	.69361	.96288	1.0385	.72035	5
56	.68115	.93034	1.0749	.73215	4		56	.69382	.96344	1.0379	.72015	4
57	.68136	.93088	1.0742	.73195	3		57	.69403	.96400	1.0373	.71995	3
58	.68157	.93143	1.0736	.73175	2		58	.69424	.96457	1.0367	.71974	2
59	.68179	.93197	1.0730	.73155	1		59	.69445	.96513	1.0361	.71954	1
60	.68200	.93252	1.0724	.73135	0		60	.69466	.96569	1.0355	.71934	0
′	Cos	Cot	Tan	Sin	′		′	Cos	Cot	Tan	Sin	′

NATURAL TRIGONOMETRIC FUNCTIONS

′	Sin	Tan	Cot	Cos	′
0	.69466	.96569	1.0355	.71934	60
1	.69487	.96625	1.0349	.71914	59
2	.69508	.96681	1.0343	.71894	58
3	.69529	.96738	1.0337	.71873	57
4	.69549	.96794	1.0331	.71853	56
5	.69570	.96850	1.0325	.71833	55
6	.69591	.96907	1.0319	.71813	54
7	.69612	.96963	1.0313	.71792	53
8	.69633	.97020	1.0307	.71772	52
9	.69654	.97076	1.0301	.71752	51
10	.69675	.97133	1.0295	.71732	50
11	.69696	.97189	1.0289	.71711	49
12	.69717	.97246	1.0283	.71691	48
13	.69737	.97302	1.0277	.71671	47
14	.69758	.97359	1.0271	.71650	46
15	.69779	.97416	1.0265	.71630	45
16	.69800	.97472	1.0259	.71610	44
17	.69821	.97529	1.0253	.71590	43
18	.69842	.97586	1.0247	.71569	42
19	.69862	.97643	1.0241	.71549	41
20	.69883	.97700	1.0235	.71529	40
21	.69904	.97756	1.0230	.71508	39
22	.69925	.97813	1.0224	.71488	38
23	.69946	.97870	1.0218	.71468	37
24	.69966	.97927	1.0212	.71447	36
25	.69987	.97984	1.0206	.71427	35
26	.70008	.98041	1.0200	.71407	34
27	.70029	.98098	1.0194	.71386	33
28	.70049	.98155	1.0188	.71366	32
29	.70070	.98213	1.0182	.71345	31
30	.70091	.98270	1.0176	.71325	30
31	.70112	.98327	1.0170	.71305	29
32	.70132	.98384	1.0164	.71284	28
33	.70153	.98441	1.0158	.71264	27
34	.70174	.98499	1.0152	.71243	26
35	.70195	.98556	1.0147	.71223	25
36	.70215	.98613	1.0141	.71203	24
37	.70236	.98671	1.0135	.71182	23
38	.70257	.98728	1.0129	.71162	22
39	.70277	.98786	1.0123	.71141	21
40	.70298	.98843	1.0117	.71121	20
41	.70319	.98901	1.0111	.71100	19
42	.70339	.98958	1.0105	.71080	18
43	.70360	.99016	1.0099	.71059	17
44	.70381	.99073	1.0094	.71039	16
45	.70401	.99131	1.0088	.71019	15
46	.70422	.99189	1.0082	.70998	14
47	.70443	.99247	1.0076	.70978	13
48	.70463	.99304	1.0070	.70957	12
49	.70484	.99362	1.0064	.70937	11
50	.70505	.99420	1.0058	.70916	10
51	.70525	.99478	1.0052	.70896	9
52	.70546	.99536	1.0047	.70875	8
53	.70567	.99594	1.0041	.70855	7
54	.70587	.99652	1.0035	.70834	6
55	.70608	.99710	1.0029	.70813	5
56	.70628	.99768	1.0023	.70793	4
57	.70649	.99826	1.0017	.70772	3
58	.70670	.99884	1.0012	.70752	2
59	.70690	.99942	1.0006	.70731	1
60	.70711	1.0000	1.0000	.70711	0
′	Cos	Cot	Tan	Sin	′

NATURAL FUNCTIONS—SECANTS AND COSECANTS

′	Sec	Csc	′	′	Sec	Csc	′	′	Sec	Csc	′
0	1.0000		60	0	1.0002	57.299	60	0	1.0006	28.654	60
1	1.0000	3437.7	59	1	1.0002	56.359	59	1	1.0006	28.417	59
2	1.0000	1718.9	58	2	1.0002	55.451	58	2	1.0006	28.184	58
3	1.0000	1145.9	57	3	1.0002	54.570	57	3	1.0006	27.955	57
4	1.0000	859.44	56	4	1.0002	53.718	56	4	1.0007	27.730	56
5	1.0000	687.55	55	5	1.0002	52.892	55	5	1.0007	27.508	55
6	1.0000	572.96	54	6	1.0002	52.090	54	6	1.0007	27.290	54
7	1.0000	491.11	53	7	1.0002	51.313	53	7	1.0007	27.075	53
8	1.0000	429.72	52	8	1.0002	50.558	52	8	1.0007	26.864	52
9	1.0000	381.97	51	9	1.0002	49.826	51	9	1.0007	26.655	51
10	1.0000	343.78	50	10	1.0002	49.114	50	10	1.0007	26.451	50
11	1.0000	312.52	49	11	1.0002	48.422	49	11	1.0007	26.249	49
12	1.0000	286.48	48	12	1.0002	47.750	48	12	1.0007	26.050	48
13	1.0000	264.44	47	13	1.0002	47.096	47	13	1.0007	25.854	47
14	1.0000	245.55	46	14	1.0002	46.460	46	14	1.0008	25.661	46
15	1.0000	229.18	45	15	1.0002	45.840	45	15	1.0008	25.471	45
16	1.0000	214.86	44	16	1.0002	45.237	44	16	1.0008	25.284	44
17	1.0000	202.22	43	17	1.0003	44.650	43	17	1.0008	25.100	43
18	1.0000	190.99	42	18	1.0003	44.077	42	18	1.0008	24.918	42
19	1.0000	180.93	41	19	1.0003	43.520	41	19	1.0008	24.739	41
20	1.0000	171.89	40	20	1.0003	42.976	40	20	1.0008	24.562	40
21	1.0000	163.70	39	21	1.0003	42.445	39	21	1.0008	24.388	39
22	1.0000	156.26	38	22	1.0003	41.928	38	22	1.0009	24.216	38
23	1.0000	149.47	37	23	1.0003	41.423	37	23	1.0009	24.047	37
24	1.0000	143.24	36	24	1.0003	40.930	36	24	1.0009	23.880	36
25	1.0000	137.51	35	25	1.0003	40.448	35	25	1.0009	23.716	35
26	1.0000	132.22	34	26	1.0003	39.978	34	26	1.0009	23.553	34
27	1.0000	127.33	33	27	1.0003	39.519	33	27	1.0009	23.393	33
28	1.0000	122.78	32	28	1.0003	39.070	32	28	1.0009	23.235	32
29	1.0000	118.54	31	29	1.0003	38.631	31	29	1.0009	23.079	31
30	1.0000	114.59	30	30	1.0003	38.202	30	30	1.0010	22.926	30
31	1.0000	110.90	29	31	1.0004	37.782	29	31	1.0010	22.774	29
32	1.0000	107.43	28	32	1.0004	37.371	28	32	1.0010	22.624	28
33	1.0000	104.18	27	33	1.0004	36.970	27	33	1.0010	22.476	27
34	1.0000	101.11	26	34	1.0004	36.576	26	34	1.0010	22.330	26
35	1.0001	98.223	25	35	1.0004	36.191	25	35	1.0010	22.187	25
36	1.0001	95.495	24	36	1.0004	35.815	24	36	1.0010	22.044	24
37	1.0001	92.914	23	37	1.0004	35.445	23	37	1.0010	21.904	23
38	1.0001	90.469	22	38	1.0004	35.084	22	38	1.0011	21.766	22
39	1.0001	88.149	21	39	1.0004	34.730	21	39	1.0011	21.629	21
40	1.0001	85.946	20	40	1.0004	34.382	20	40	1.0011	21.494	20
41	1.0001	83.849	19	41	1.0004	34.042	19	41	1.0011	21.360	19
42	1.0001	81.853	18	42	1.0004	33.708	18	42	1.0011	21.229	18
43	1.0001	79.950	17	43	1.0004	33.381	17	43	1.0011	21.098	17
44	1.0001	78.133	16	44	1.0005	33.060	16	44	1.0011	20.970	16
45	1.0001	76.397	15	45	1.0005	32.746	15	45	1.0012	20.843	15
46	1.0001	74.736	14	46	1.0005	32.437	14	46	1.0012	20.717	14
47	1.0001	73.134	13	47	1.0005	32.134	13	47	1.0012	20.593	13
48	1.0001	71.622	12	48	1.0005	31.836	12	48	1.0012	20.471	12
49	1.0001	70.160	11	49	1.0005	31.544	11	49	1.0012	20.350	11
50	1.0001	68.757	10	50	1.0005	31.258	10	50	1.0012	20.230	10
51	1.0001	67.409	9	51	1.0005	30.976	9	51	1.0012	20.112	9
52	1.0001	66.113	8	52	1.0005	30.700	8	52	1.0013	19.995	8
53	1.0001	64.866	7	53	1.0005	30.428	7	53	1.0013	19.880	7
54	1.0001	63.665	6	54	1.0006	30.161	6	54	1.0013	19.766	6
55	1.0001	62.507	5	55	1.0006	29.899	5	55	1.0013	19.653	5
56	1.0001	61.391	4	56	1.0006	29.641	4	56	1.0013	19.541	4
57	1.0001	60.314	3	57	1.0006	29.388	3	57	1.0013	19.431	3
58	1.0001	59.274	2	58	1.0006	29.139	2	58	1.0013	19.322	2
59	1.0001	58.270	1	59	1.0006	28.894	1	59	1.0014	19.214	1
60	1.0002	57.299	0	60	1.0006	28.654	0	60	1.0014	19.107	0
′	Csc	Sec	′	′	Csc	Sec	′	′	Csc	Sec	′

3° (183°) (356°) **176°**

′	Sec	Csc	′
0	1.0014	19.107	60
1	1.0014	19.002	59
2	1.0014	18.898	58
3	1.0014	18.794	57
4	1.0014	18.692	56
5	1.0014	18.591	55
6	1.0015	18.492	54
7	1.0015	18.393	53
8	1.0015	18.295	52
9	1.0015	18.198	51
10	1.0015	18.103	50
11	1.0015	18.008	49
12	1.0016	17.914	48
13	1.0016	17.822	47
14	1.0016	17.730	46
15	1.0016	17.639	45
16	1.0016	17.549	44
17	1.0016	17.460	43
18	1.0017	17.372	42
19	1.0017	17.285	41
20	1.0017	17.198	40
21	1.0017	17.113	39
22	1.0017	17.028	38
23	1.0017	16.945	37
24	1.0018	16.862	36
25	1.0018	16.779	35
26	1.0018	16.698	34
27	1.0018	16.618	33
28	1.0018	16.538	32
29	1.0019	16.459	31
30	1.0019	16.380	30
31	1.0019	16.303	29
32	1.0019	16.226	28
33	1.0019	16.150	27
34	1.0019	16.075	26
35	1.0020	16.000	25
36	1.0020	15.926	24
37	1.0020	15.853	23
38	1.0020	15.780	22
39	1.0020	15.708	21
40	1.0021	15.637	20
41	1.0021	15.566	19
42	1.0021	15.496	18
43	1.0021	15.427	17
44	1.0021	15.358	16
45	1.0021	15.290	15
46	1.0022	15.222	14
47	1.0022	15.155	13
48	1.0022	15.089	12
49	1.0022	15.023	11
50	1.0022	14.958	10
51	1.0023	14.893	9
52	1.0023	14.829	8
53	1.0023	14.766	7
54	1.0023	14.703	6
55	1.0023	14.640	5
56	1.0024	14.578	4
57	1.0024	14.517	3
58	1.0024	14.456	2
59	1.0024	14.395	1
60	1.0024	14.336	0
′	Csc	Sec	′

93° (273°) (266°) **86°**

4° (184°) (355°) **175°**

′	Sec	Csc	′
0	1.0024	14.336	60
1	1.0025	14.276	59
2	1.0025	14.217	58
3	1.0025	14.159	57
4	1.0025	14.101	56
5	1.0025	14.044	55
6	1.0026	13.987	54
7	1.0026	13.930	53
8	1.0026	13.874	52
9	1.0026	13.818	51
10	1.0027	13.763	50
11	1.0027	13.708	49
12	1.0027	13.654	48
13	1.0027	13.600	47
14	1.0027	13.547	46
15	1.0028	13.494	45
16	1.0028	13.441	44
17	1.0028	13.389	43
18	1.0028	13.337	42
19	1.0028	13.286	41
20	1.0029	13.235	40
21	1.0029	13.184	39
22	1.0029	13.134	38
23	1.0029	13.084	37
24	1.0030	13.035	36
25	1.0030	12.985	35
26	1.0030	12.937	34
27	1.0030	12.888	33
28	1.0030	12.840	32
29	1.0031	12.793	31
30	1.0031	12.745	30
31	1.0031	12.699	29
32	1.0031	12.652	28
33	1.0032	12.606	27
34	1.0032	12.560	26
35	1.0032	12.514	25
36	1.0032	12.469	24
37	1.0033	12.424	23
38	1.0033	12.379	22
39	1.0033	12.335	21
40	1.0033	12.291	20
41	1.0034	12.248	19
42	1.0034	12.204	18
43	1.0034	12.161	17
44	1.0034	12.119	16
45	1.0034	12.076	15
46	1.0035	12.034	14
47	1.0035	11.992	13
48	1.0035	11.951	12
49	1.0035	11.909	11
50	1.0036	11.868	10
51	1.0036	11.828	9
52	1.0036	11.787	8
53	1.0036	11.747	7
54	1.0037	11.707	6
55	1.0037	11.668	5
56	1.0037	11.628	4
57	1.0037	11.589	3
58	1.0038	11.551	2
59	1.0038	11.512	1
60	1.0038	11.474	0
′	Csc	Sec	′

94° (274°) (265°) **85°**

5° (185°) (354°) **174°**

′	Sec	Csc	′
0	1.0038	11.474	60
1	1.0038	11.436	59
2	1.0039	11.398	58
3	1.0039	11.360	57
4	1.0039	11.323	56
5	1.0039	11.286	55
6	1.0040	11.249	54
7	1.0040	11.213	53
8	1.0040	11.176	52
9	1.0041	11.140	51
10	1.0041	11.105	50
11	1.0041	11.069	49
12	1.0041	11.034	48
13	1.0042	10.998	47
14	1.0042	10.963	46
15	1.0042	10.929	45
16	1.0042	10.894	44
17	1.0043	10.860	43
18	1.0043	10.826	42
19	1.0043	10.792	41
20	1.0043	10.758	40
21	1.0044	10.725	39
22	1.0044	10.692	38
23	1.0044	10.659	37
24	1.0045	10.626	36
25	1.0045	10.593	35
26	1.0045	10.561	34
27	1.0045	10.529	33
28	1.0046	10.497	32
29	1.0046	10.465	31
30	1.0046	10.433	30
31	1.0047	10.402	29
32	1.0047	10.371	28
33	1.0047	10.340	27
34	1.0047	10.309	26
35	1.0048	10.278	25
36	1.0048	10.248	24
37	1.0048	10.217	23
38	1.0049	10.187	22
39	1.0049	10.157	21
40	1.0049	10.128	20
41	1.0049	10.098	19
42	1.0050	10.068	18
43	1.0050	10.039	17
44	1.0050	10.010	16
45	1.0051	9.9812	15
46	1.0051	9.9525	14
47	1.0051	9.9239	13
48	1.0051	9.8955	12
49	1.0052	9.8672	11
50	1.0052	9.8391	10
51	1.0052	9.8112	9
52	1.0053	9.7834	8
53	1.0053	9.7558	7
54	1.0053	9.7283	6
55	1.0054	9.7010	5
56	1.0054	9.6739	4
57	1.0054	9.6469	3
58	1.0054	9.6200	2
59	1.0055	9.5933	1
60	1.0055	9.5668	0
′	Csc	Sec	′

95° (275°) (264°) **84°**

6° (186°)   (353°) **173°**   **7° (187°)**   (352°) **172°**   **8° (188°)**   (351°) **171°**

′	Sec	Csc	′	′	Sec	Csc	′	′	Sec	Csc	′
0	1.0055	9.5668	60	0	1.0075	8.2055	60	0	1.0098	7.1853	60
1	1.0055	9.5404	59	1	1.0075	8.1861	59	1	1.0099	7.1705	59
2	1.0056	9.5141	58	2	1.0076	8.1668	58	2	1.0099	7.1557	58
3	1.0056	9.4880	57	3	1.0076	8.1476	57	3	1.0100	7.1410	57
4	1.0056	9.4620	56	4	1.0077	8.1285	56	4	1.0100	7.1263	56
5	1.0057	9.4362	55	5	1.0077	8.1095	55	5	1.0100	7.1117	55
6	1.0057	9.4105	54	6	1.0077	8.0905	54	6	1.0101	7.0972	54
7	1.0057	9.3850	53	7	1.0078	8.0717	53	7	1.0101	7.0827	53
8	1.0058	9.3596	52	8	1.0078	8.0529	52	8	1.0102	7.0683	52
9	1.0058	9.3343	51	9	1.0078	8.0342	51	9	1.0102	7.0539	51
10	1.0058	9.3092	50	10	1.0079	8.0156	50	10	1.0102	7.0396	50
11	1.0059	9.2842	49	11	1.0079	7.9971	49	11	1.0103	7.0254	49
12	1.0059	9.2593	48	12	1.0079	7.9787	48	12	1.0103	7.0112	48
13	1.0059	9.2346	47	13	1.0080	7.9604	47	13	1.0104	6.9971	47
14	1.0059	9.2100	46	14	1.0080	7.9422	46	14	1.0104	6.9830	46
15	1.0060	9.1855	45	15	1.0081	7.9240	45	15	1.0105	6.9690	45
16	1.0060	9.1612	44	16	1.0081	7.9059	44	16	1.0105	6.9550	44
17	1.0060	9.1370	43	17	1.0081	7.8879	43	17	1.0105	6.9411	43
18	1.0061	9.1129	42	18	1.0082	7.8700	42	18	1.0106	6.9273	42
19	1.0061	9.0890	41	19	1.0082	7.8522	41	19	1.0106	6.9135	41
20	1.0061	9.0652	40	20	1.0082	7.8344	40	20	1.0107	6.8998	40
21	1.0062	9.0415	39	21	1.0083	7.8168	39	21	1.0107	6.8861	39
22	1.0062	9.0179	38	22	1.0083	7.7992	38	22	1.0108	6.8725	38
23	1.0062	8.9944	37	23	1.0084	7.7817	37	23	1.0108	6.8589	37
24	1.0063	8.9711	36	24	1.0084	7.7642	36	24	1.0108	6.8454	36
25	1.0063	8.9479	35	25	1.0084	7.7469	35	25	1.0109	6.8320	35
26	1.0063	8.9248	34	26	1.0085	7.7296	34	26	1.0109	6.8186	34
27	1.0064	8.9019	33	27	1.0085	7.7124	33	27	1.0110	6.8052	33
28	1.0064	8.8790	32	28	1.0086	7.6953	32	28	1.0110	6.7919	32
29	1.0064	8.8563	31	29	1.0086	7.6783	31	29	1.0111	6.7787	31
30	1.0065	8.8337	30	30	1.0086	7.6613	30	30	1.0111	6.7655	30
31	1.0065	8.8112	29	31	1.0087	7.6444	29	31	1.0112	6.7523	29
32	1.0065	8.7888	28	32	1.0087	7.6276	28	32	1.0112	6.7392	28
33	1.0066	8.7665	27	33	1.0087	7.6109	27	33	1.0112	6.7262	27
34	1.0066	8.7444	26	34	1.0088	7.5942	26	34	1.0113	6.7132	26
35	1.0066	8.7223	25	35	1.0088	7.5776	25	35	1.0113	6.7003	25
36	1.0067	8.7004	24	36	1.0089	7.5611	24	36	1.0114	6.6874	24
37	1.0067	8.6786	23	37	1.0089	7.5446	23	37	1.0114	6.6745	23
38	1.0067	8.6569	22	38	1.0089	7.5282	22	38	1.0115	6.6618	22
39	1.0068	8.6353	21	39	1.0090	7.5119	21	39	1.0115	6.6490	21
40	1.0068	8.6138	20	40	1.0090	7.4957	20	40	1.0116	6.6363	20
41	1.0068	8.5924	19	41	1.0091	7.4795	19	41	1.0116	6.6237	19
42	1.0069	8.5711	18	42	1.0091	7.4635	18	42	1.0116	6.6111	18
43	1.0069	8.5500	17	43	1.0091	7.4474	17	43	1.0117	6.5986	17
44	1.0069	8.5289	16	44	1.0092	7.4315	16	44	1.0117	6.5861	16
45	1.0070	8.5079	15	45	1.0092	7.4156	15	45	1.0118	6.5736	15
46	1.0070	8.4871	14	46	1.0093	7.3998	14	46	1.0118	6.5612	14
47	1.0070	8.4663	13	47	1.0093	7.3840	13	47	1.0119	6.5489	13
48	1.0071	8.4457	12	48	1.0093	7.3684	12	48	1.0119	6.5366	12
49	1.0071	8.4251	11	49	1.0094	7.3527	11	49	1.0120	6.5243	11
50	1.0072	8.4047	10	50	1.0094	7.3372	10	50	1.0120	6.5121	10
51	1.0072	8.3843	9	51	1.0095	7.3217	9	51	1.0120	6.4999	9
52	1.0072	8.3641	8	52	1.0095	7.3063	8	52	1.0121	6.4878	8
53	1.0073	8.3439	7	53	1.0095	7.2909	7	53	1.0121	6.4757	7
54	1.0073	8.3238	6	54	1.0096	7.2757	6	54	1.0122	6.4637	6
55	1.0073	8.3039	5	55	1.0096	7.2604	5	55	1.0122	6.4517	5
56	1.0074	8.2840	4	56	1.0097	7.2453	4	56	1.0123	6.4398	4
57	1.0074	8.2642	3	57	1.0097	7.2302	3	57	1.0123	6.4279	3
58	1.0074	8.2446	2	58	1.0097	7.2152	2	58	1.0124	6.4160	2
59	1.0075	8.2250	1	59	1.0098	7.2002	1	59	1.0124	6.4042	1
60	1.0075	8.2055	0	60	1.0098	7.1853	0	60	1.0125	6.3925	0
′	Csc	Sec	′	′	Csc	Sec	′	′	Csc	Sec	′

9° (189°)   (350°) **170°**   **10° (190°)**   (349°) **169°**   **11° (191°)**   (348°) **168°**

′	Sec	Csc	′	′	Sec	Csc	′	′	Sec	Csc	′
0	1.0125	6.3925	60	0	1.0154	5.7588	60	0	1.0187	5.2408	60
1	1.0125	6.3807	59	1	1.0155	5.7493	59	1	1.0188	5.2330	59
2	1.0126	6.3691	58	2	1.0155	5.7398	58	2	1.0188	5.2252	58
3	1.0126	6.3574	57	3	1.0156	5.7304	57	3	1.0189	5.2174	57
4	1.0127	6.3458	56	4	1.0156	5.7210	56	4	1.0189	5.2097	56
5	1.0127	6.3343	55	5	1.0157	5.7117	55	5	1.0190	5.2019	55
6	1.0127	6.3228	54	6	1.0157	5.7023	54	6	1.0191	5.1942	54
7	1.0128	6.3113	53	7	1.0158	5.6930	53	7	1.0191	5.1865	53
8	1.0128	6.2999	52	8	1.0158	5.6838	52	8	1.0192	5.1789	52
9	1.0129	6.2885	51	9	1.0159	5.6745	51	9	1.0192	5.1712	51
10	1.0129	6.2772	50	10	1.0160	5.6653	50	10	1.0193	5.1636	50
11	1.0130	6.2659	49	11	1.0160	5.6562	49	11	1.0194	5.1560	49
12	1.0130	6.2546	48	12	1.0161	5.6470	48	12	1.0194	5.1484	48
13	1.0131	6.2434	47	13	1.0161	5.6379	47	13	1.0195	5.1409	47
14	1.0131	6.2323	46	14	1.0162	5.6288	46	14	1.0195	5.1333	46
15	1.0132	6.2211	45	15	1.0162	5.6198	45	15	1.0196	5.1258	45
16	1.0132	6.2100	44	16	1.0163	5.6107	44	16	1.0197	5.1183	44
17	1.0133	6.1990	43	17	1.0163	5.6017	43	17	1.0197	5.1109	43
18	1.0133	6.1880	42	18	1.0164	5.5928	42	18	1.0198	5.1034	42
19	1.0134	6.1770	41	19	1.0164	5.5838	41	19	1.0198	5.0960	41
20	1.0134	6.1661	40	20	1.0165	5.5749	40	20	1.0199	5.0886	40
21	1.0135	6.1552	39	21	1.0165	5.5660	39	21	1.0199	5.0813	39
22	1.0135	6.1443	38	22	1.0166	5.5572	38	22	1.0200	5.0739	38
23	1.0136	6.1335	37	23	1.0166	5.5484	37	23	1.0201	5.0666	37
24	1.0136	6.1227	36	24	1.0167	5.5396	36	24	1.0201	5.0593	36
25	1.0137	6.1120	35	25	1.0168	5.5308	35	25	1.0202	5.0520	35
26	1.0137	6.1013	34	26	1.0168	5.5221	34	26	1.0202	5.0447	34
27	1.0138	6.0906	33	27	1.0169	5.5134	33	27	1.0203	5.0375	33
28	1.0138	6.0800	32	28	1.0169	5.5047	32	28	1.0204	5.0302	32
29	1.0139	6.0694	31	29	1.0170	5.4960	31	29	1.0204	5.0230	31
30	1.0139	6.0589	30	30	1.0170	5.4874	30	30	1.0205	5.0159	30
31	1.0140	6.0483	29	31	1.0171	5.4788	29	31	1.0205	5.0087	29
32	1.0140	6.0379	28	32	1.0171	5.4702	28	32	1.0206	5.0016	28
33	1.0141	6.0274	27	33	1.0172	5.4617	27	33	1.0207	4.9944	27
34	1.0141	6.0170	26	34	1.0173	5.4532	26	34	1.0207	4.9873	26
35	1.0142	6.0067	25	35	1.0173	5.4447	25	35	1.0208	4.9803	25
36	1.0142	5.9963	24	36	1.0174	5.4362	24	36	1.0209	4.9732	24
37	1.0143	5.9860	23	37	1.0174	5.4278	23	37	1.0209	4.9662	23
38	1.0143	5.9758	22	38	1.0175	5.4194	22	38	1.0210	4.9591	22
39	1.0144	5.9656	21	39	1.0175	5.4110	21	39	1.0210	4.9521	21
40	1.0144	5.9554	20	40	1.0176	5.4026	20	40	1.0211	4.9452	20
41	1.0145	5.9452	19	41	1.0176	5.3943	19	41	1.0212	4.9382	19
42	1.0145	5.9351	18	42	1.0177	5.3860	18	42	1.0212	4.9313	18
43	1.0146	5.9250	17	43	1.0178	5.3777	17	43	1.0213	4.9244	17
44	1.0146	5.9150	16	44	1.0178	5.3695	16	44	1.0213	4.9175	16
45	1.0147	5.9049	15	45	1.0179	5.3612	15	45	1.0214	4.9106	15
46	1.0147	5.8950	14	46	1.0179	5.3530	14	46	1.0215	4.9037	14
47	1.0148	5.8850	13	47	1.0180	5.3449	13	47	1.0215	4.8969	13
48	1.0148	5.8751	12	48	1.0180	5.3367	12	48	1.0216	4.8901	12
49	1.0149	5.8652	11	49	1.0181	5.3286	11	49	1.0217	4.8833	11
50	1.0149	5.8554	10	50	1.0181	5.3205	10	50	1.0217	4.8765	10
51	1.0150	5.8456	9	51	1.0182	5.3124	9	51	1.0218	4.8697	9
52	1.0150	5.8358	8	52	1.0183	5.3044	8	52	1.0218	4.8630	8
53	1.0151	5.8261	7	53	1.0183	5.2963	7	53	1.0219	4.8563	7
54	1.0151	5.8164	6	54	1.0184	5.2883	6	54	1.0220	4.8496	6
55	1.0152	5.8067	5	55	1.0184	5.2804	5	55	1.0220	4.8429	5
56	1.0152	5.7970	4	56	1.0185	5.2724	4	56	1.0221	4.8362	4
57	1.0153	5.7874	3	57	1.0185	5.2645	3	57	1.0222	4.8296	3
58	1.0153	5.7778	2	58	1.0186	5.2566	2	58	1.0222	4.8229	2
59	1.0154	5.7683	1	59	1.0187	5.2487	1	59	1.0223	4.8163	1
60	1.0154	5.7588	0	60	1.0187	5.2408	0	60	1.0223	4.8097	0
′	Csc	Sec	′	′	Csc	Sec	′	′	Csc	Sec	′

NATURAL FUNCTIONS—SECANTS AND COSECANTS (Continued)

′	Sec	Csc	′		′	Sec	Csc	′		′	Sec	Csc	′
0	1.0223	4.8097	**60**		**0**	1.0263	4.4454	**60**		**0**	1.0306	4.1336	**60**
1	1.0224	4.8032	59		1	1.0264	4.4398	59		1	1.0307	4.1287	59
2	1.0225	4.7966	58		2	1.0264	4.4342	58		2	1.0308	4.1239	58
3	1.0225	4.7901	57		3	1.0265	4.4287	57		3	1.0308	4.1191	57
4	1.0226	4.7836	56		4	1.0266	4.4231	56		4	1.0309	4.1144	56
5	1.0227	4.7771	**55**		**5**	1.0266	4.4176	**55**		**5**	1.0310	4.1096	**55**
6	1.0227	4.7706	54		6	1.0267	4.4121	54		6	1.0311	4.1048	54
7	1.0228	4.7641	53		7	1.0268	4.4066	53		7	1.0311	4.1001	53
8	1.0228	4.7577	52		8	1.0269	4.4011	52		8	1.0312	4.0954	52
9	1.0229	4.7512	51		9	1.0269	4.3956	51		9	1.0313	4.0906	51
10	1.0230	4.7448	**50**		**10**	1.0270	4.3901	**50**		**10**	1.0314	4.0859	**50**
11	1.0230	4.7384	49		11	1.0271	4.3847	49		11	1.0314	4.0812	49
12	1.0231	4.7321	48		12	1.0271	4.3792	48		12	1.0315	4.0765	48
13	1.0232	4.7257	47		13	1.0272	4.3738	47		13	1.0316	4.0718	47
14	1.0232	4.7194	46		14	1.0273	4.3684	46		14	1.0317	4.0672	46
15	1.0233	4.7130	**45**		**15**	1.0273	4.3630	**45**		**15**	1.0317	4.0625	**45**
16	1.0234	4.7067	44		16	1.0274	4.3576	44		16	1.0318	4.0579	44
17	1.0234	4.7004	43		17	1.0275	4.3522	43		17	1.0319	4.0532	43
18	1.0235	4.6942	42		18	1.0276	4.3469	42		18	1.0320	4.0486	42
19	1.0236	4.6879	41		19	1.0276	4.3415	41		19	1.0321	4.0440	41
20	1.0236	4.6817	**40**		**20**	1.0277	4.3362	**40**		**20**	1.0321	4.0394	**40**
21	1.0237	4.6755	39		21	1.0278	4.3309	39		21	1.0322	4.0348	39
22	1.0238	4.6693	38		22	1.0278	4.3256	38		22	1.0323	4.0302	38
23	1.0238	4.6631	37		23	1.0279	4.3203	37		23	1.0324	4.0256	37
24	1.0239	4.6569	36		24	1.0280	4.3150	36		24	1.0324	4.0211	36
25	1.0240	4.6507	**35**		**25**	1.0281	4.3098	**35**		**25**	1.0325	4.0165	**35**
26	1.0240	4.6446	34		26	1.0281	4.3045	34		26	1.0326	4.0120	34
27	1.0241	4.6385	33		27	1.0282	4.2993	33		27	1.0327	4.0075	33
28	1.0241	4.6324	32		28	1.0283	4.2941	32		28	1.0327	4.0029	32
29	1.0242	4.6263	31		29	1.0283	4.2889	31		29	1.0328	3.9984	31
30	1.0243	4.6202	**30**		**30**	1.0284	4.2837	**30**		**30**	1.0329	3.9939	**30**
31	1.0243	4.6142	29		31	1.0285	4.2785	29		31	1.0330	3.9894	29
32	1.0244	4.6081	28		32	1.0286	4.2733	28		32	1.0331	3.9850	28
33	1.0245	4.6021	27		33	1.0286	4.2681	27		33	1.0331	3.9805	27
34	1.0245	4.5961	26		34	1.0287	4.2630	26		34	1.0332	3.9760	26
35	1.0246	4.5901	**25**		**35**	1.0288	4.2579	**25**		**35**	1.0333	3.9716	**25**
36	1.0247	4.5841	24		36	1.0288	4.2527	24		36	1.0334	3.9672	24
37	1.0247	4.5782	23		37	1.0289	4.2476	23		37	1.0334	3.9627	23
38	1.0248	4.5722	22		38	1.0290	4.2425	22		38	1.0335	3.9583	22
39	1.0249	4.5663	21		39	1.0291	4.2375	21		39	1.0336	3.9539	21
40	1.0249	4.5604	**20**		**40**	1.0291	4.2324	**20**		**40**	1.0337	3.9495	**20**
41	1.0250	4.5545	19		41	1.0292	4.2273	19		41	1.0338	3.9451	19
42	1.0251	4.5486	18		42	1.0293	4.2223	18		42	1.0338	3.9408	18
43	1.0251	4.5428	17		43	1.0294	4.2173	17		43	1.0339	3.9364	17
44	1.0252	4.5369	16		44	1.0294	4.2122	16		44	1.0340	3.9320	16
45	1.0253	4.5311	**15**		**45**	1.0295	4.2072	**15**		**45**	1.0341	3.9277	**15**
46	1.0253	4.5253	14		46	1.0296	4.2022	14		46	1.0342	3.9234	14
47	1.0254	4.5195	13		47	1.0297	4.1973	13		47	1.0342	3.9190	13
48	1.0255	4.5137	12		48	1.0297	4.1923	12		48	1.0343	3.9147	12
49	1.0256	4.5079	11		49	1.0298	4.1873	11		49	1.0344	3.9104	11
50	1.0256	4.5022	**10**		**50**	1.0299	4.1824	**10**		**50**	1.0345	3.9061	**10**
51	1.0257	4.4964	9		51	1.0299	4.1774	9		51	1.0346	3.9018	9
52	1.0258	4.4907	8		52	1.0300	4.1725	8		52	1.0346	3.8976	8
53	1.0258	4.4850	7		53	1.0301	4.1676	7		53	1.0347	3.8933	7
54	1.0259	4.4793	6		54	1.0302	4.1627	6		54	1.0348	3.8890	6
55	1.0260	4.4736	**5**		**55**	1.0302	4.1578	**5**		**55**	1.0349	3.8848	**5**
56	1.0260	4.4679	4		56	1.0303	4.1529	4		56	1.0350	3.8806	4
57	1.0261	4.4623	3		57	1.0304	4.1481	3		57	1.0350	3.8763	3
58	1.0262	4.4566	2		58	1.0305	4.1432	2		58	1.0351	3.8721	2
59	1.0262	4.4510	1		59	1.0305	4.1384	1		59	1.0352	3.8679	1
60	1.0263	4.4454	**0**		**60**	1.0306	4.1336	**0**		**60**	1.0353	3.8637	**0**
′	Csc	Sec	′		′	Csc	Sec	′		′	Csc	Sec	′

15° (195°) (344°) **164°**   **16°** (196°) (343°) **163°**   **17°** (197°) (342°) **162°**

′	Sec	Csc	′	′	Sec	Csc	′	′	Sec	Csc	′
0	1.0353	3.8637	60	0	1.0403	3.6280	60	0	1.0457	3.4203	60
1	1.0354	3.8595	59	1	1.0404	3.6243	59	1	1.0458	3.4171	59
2	1.0354	3.8553	58	2	1.0405	3.6206	58	2	1.0459	3.4138	58
3	1.0355	3.8512	57	3	1.0406	3.6169	57	3	1.0460	3.4106	57
4	1.0356	3.8470	56	4	1.0406	3.6133	56	4	1.0461	3.4073	56
5	1.0357	3.8428	55	5	1.0407	3.6097	55	5	1.0462	3.4041	55
6	1.0358	3.8387	54	6	1.0408	3.6060	54	6	1.0463	3.4009	54
7	1.0358	3.8346	53	7	1.0409	3.6024	53	7	1.0463	3.3977	53
8	1.0359	3.8304	52	8	1.0410	3.5988	52	8	1.0464	3.3945	52
9	1.0360	3.8263	51	9	1.0411	3.5951	51	9	1.0465	3.3913	51
10	1.0361	3.8222	50	10	1.0412	3.5915	50	10	1.0466	3.3881	50
11	1.0362	3.8181	49	11	1.0413	3.5879	49	11	1.0467	3.3849	49
12	1.0363	3.8140	48	12	1.0413	3.5843	48	12	1.0468	3.3817	48
13	1.0363	3.8100	47	13	1.0414	3.5808	47	13	1.0469	3.3785	47
14	1.0364	3.8059	46	14	1.0415	3.5772	46	14	1.0470	3.3754	46
15	1.0365	3.8018	45	15	1.0416	3.5736	45	15	1.0471	3.3722	45
16	1.0366	3.7978	44	16	1.0417	3.5700	44	16	1.0472	3.3691	44
17	1.0367	3.7937	43	17	1.0418	3.5665	43	17	1.0473	3.3659	43
18	1.0367	3.7897	42	18	1.0419	3.5629	42	18	1.0474	3.3628	42
19	1.0368	3.7857	41	19	1.0420	3.5594	41	19	1.0475	3.3596	41
20	1.0369	3.7817	40	20	1.0421	3.5559	40	20	1.0476	3.3565	40
21	1.0370	3.7777	39	21	1.0421	3.5523	39	21	1.0477	3.3534	39
22	1.0371	3.7737	38	22	1.0422	3.5488	38	22	1.0478	3.3502	38
23	1.0372	3.7697	37	23	1.0423	3.5453	37	23	1.0479	3.3471	37
24	1.0372	3.7657	36	24	1.0424	3.5418	36	24	1.0480	3.3440	36
25	1.0373	3.7617	35	25	1.0425	3.5383	35	25	1.0480	3.3409	35
26	1.0374	3.7577	34	26	1.0426	3.5348	34	26	1.0481	3.3378	34
27	1.0375	3.7538	33	27	1.0427	3.5313	33	27	1.0482	3.3347	33
28	1.0376	3.7498	32	28	1.0428	3.5279	32	28	1.0483	3.3317	32
29	1.0377	3.7459	31	29	1.0429	3.5244	31	29	1.0484	3.3286	31
30	1.0377	3.7420	30	30	1.0429	3.5209	30	30	1.0485	3.3255	30
31	1.0378	3.7381	29	31	1.0430	3.5175	29	31	1.0486	3.3224	29
32	1.0379	3.7341	28	32	1.0431	3.5140	28	32	1.0487	3.3194	28
33	1.0380	3.7302	27	33	1.0432	3.5106	27	33	1.0488	3.3163	27
34	1.0381	3.7263	26	34	1.0433	3.5072	26	34	1.0489	3.3133	26
35	1.0382	3.7225	25	35	1.0434	3.5037	25	35	1.0490	3.3102	25
36	1.0382	3.7186	24	36	1.0435	3.5003	24	36	1.0491	3.3072	24
37	1.0383	3.7147	23	37	1.0436	3.4969	23	37	1.0492	3.3042	23
38	1.0384	3.7108	22	38	1.0437	3.4935	22	38	1.0493	3.3012	22
39	1.0385	3.7070	21	39	1.0438	3.4901	21	39	1.0494	3.2981	21
40	1.0386	3.7032	20	40	1.0439	3.4867	20	40	1.0495	3.2951	20
41	1.0387	3.6993	19	41	1.0439	3.4833	19	41	1.0496	3.2921	19
42	1.0388	3.6955	18	42	1.0440	3.4799	18	42	1.0497	3.2891	18
43	1.0388	3.6917	17	43	1.0441	3.4766	17	43	1.0498	3.2861	17
44	1.0389	3.6879	16	44	1.0442	3.4732	16	44	1.0499	3.2831	16
45	1.0390	3.6840	15	45	1.0443	3.4699	15	45	1.0500	3.2801	15
46	1.0391	3.6803	14	46	1.0444	3.4665	14	46	1.0501	3.2772	14
47	1.0392	3.6765	13	47	1.0445	3.4632	13	47	1.0502	3.2742	13
48	1.0393	3.6727	12	48	1.0446	3.4598	12	48	1.0503	3.2712	12
49	1.0394	3.6689	11	49	1.0447	3.4565	11	49	1.0504	3.2683	11
50	1.0394	3.6652	10	50	1.0448	3.4532	10	50	1.0505	3.2653	10
51	1.0395	3.6614	9	51	1.0449	3.4499	9	51	1.0506	3.2624	9
52	1.0396	3.6576	8	52	1.0450	3.4465	8	52	1.0507	3.2594	8
53	1.0397	3.6539	7	53	1.0450	3.4432	7	53	1.0508	3.2565	7
54	1.0398	3.6502	6	54	1.0451	3.4399	6	54	1.0509	3.2535	6
55	1.0399	3.6465	5	55	1.0452	3.4367	5	55	1.0510	3.2506	5
56	1.0400	3.6427	4	56	1.0453	3.4334	4	56	1.0511	3.2477	4
57	1.0400	3.6390	3	57	1.0454	3.4301	3	57	1.0512	3.2448	3
58	1.0401	3.6353	2	58	1.0455	3.4268	2	58	1.0513	3.2419	2
59	1.0402	3.6316	1	59	1.0456	3.4236	1	59	1.0514	3.2390	1
60	1.0403	3.6280	0	60	1.0457	3.4203	0	60	1.0515	3.2361	0
′	Csc	Sec	′	′	Csc	Sec	′	′	Csc	Sec	′

18° (198°)　　　(341°) **161°**　　　**19°** (199°)　　　(340°) **160°**　　　**20°** (200°)　　　(339°) 159°

′	Sec	Csc	′	′	Sec	Csc	′	′	Sec	Csc	′
0	1.0515	3.2361	60	0	1.0576	3.0716	60	0	1.0642	2.9238	60
1	1.0516	3.2332	59	1	1.0577	3.0690	59	1	1.0643	2.9215	59
2	1.0517	3.2303	58	2	1.0578	3.0664	58	2	1.0644	2.9191	58
3	1.0518	3.2274	57	3	1.0579	3.0638	57	3	1.0645	2.9168	57
4	1.0519	3.2245	56	4	1.0580	3.0612	56	4	1.0646	2.9145	56
5	1.0520	3.2217	55	5	1.0582	3.0586	55	5	1.0647	2.9122	55
6	1.0521	3.2188	54	6	1.0583	3.0561	54	6	1.0649	2.9099	54
7	1.0522	3.2159	53	7	1.0584	3.0535	53	7	1.0650	2.9075	53
8	1.0523	3.2131	52	8	1.0585	3.0509	52	8	1.0651	2.9052	52
9	1.0524	3.2102	51	9	1.0586	3.0484	51	9	1.0652	2.9029	51
10	1.0525	3.2074	50	10	1.0587	3.0458	50	10	1.0653	2.9006	50
11	1.0526	3.2045	49	11	1.0588	3.0433	49	11	1.0654	2.8983	49
12	1.0527	3.2017	48	12	1.0589	3.0407	48	12	1.0655	2.8960	48
13	1.0528	3.1989	47	13	1.0590	3.0382	47	13	1.0657	2.8938	47
14	1.0529	3.1960	46	14	1.0591	3.0357	46	14	1.0658	2.8915	46
15	1.0530	3.1932	45	15	1.0592	3.0331	45	15	1.0659	2.8892	45
16	1.0531	3.1904	44	16	1.0593	3.0306	44	16	1.0660	2.8869	44
17	1.0532	3.1876	43	17	1.0594	3.0281	43	17	1.0661	2.8846	43
18	1.0533	3.1848	42	18	1.0595	3.0256	42	18	1.0662	2.8824	42
19	1.0534	3.1820	41	19	1.0597	3.0231	41	19	1.0663	2.8801	41
20	1.0535	3.1792	40	20	1.0598	3.0206	40	20	1.0665	2.8779	40
21	1.0536	3.1764	39	21	1.0599	3.0181	39	21	1.0666	2.8756	39
22	1.0537	3.1736	38	22	1.0600	3.0156	38	22	1.0667	2.8733	38
23	1.0538	3.1708	37	23	1.0601	3.0131	37	23	1.0668	2.8711	37
24	1.0539	3.1681	36	24	1.0602	3.0106	36	24	1.0669	2.8688	36
25	1.0540	3.1653	35	25	1.0603	3.0081	35	25	1.0670	2.8666	35
26	1.0541	3.1625	34	26	1.0604	3.0056	34	26	1.0671	2.8644	34
27	1.0542	3.1598	33	27	1.0605	3.0031	33	27	1.0673	2.8621	33
28	1.0543	3.1570	32	28	1.0606	3.0007	32	28	1.0674	2.8599	32
29	1.0544	3.1543	31	29	1.0607	2.9982	31	29	1.0675	2.8577	31
30	1.0545	3.1515	30	30	1.0608	2.9957	30	30	1.0676	2.8555	30
31	1.0546	3.1488	29	31	1.0610	2.9933	29	31	1.0677	2.8532	29
32	1.0547	3.1461	28	32	1.0611	2.9908	28	32	1.0678	2.8510	28
33	1.0548	3.1433	27	33	1.0612	2.9884	27	33	1.0680	2.8488	27
34	1.0549	3.1406	26	34	1.0613	2.9859	26	34	1.0681	2.8466	26
35	1.0550	3.1379	25	35	1.0614	2.9835	25	35	1.0682	2.8444	25
36	1.0551	3.1352	24	36	1.0615	2.9811	24	36	1.0683	2.8422	24
37	1.0552	3.1325	23	37	1.0616	2.9786	23	37	1.0684	2.8400	23
38	1.0553	3.1298	22	38	1.0617	2.9762	22	38	1.0685	2.8378	22
39	1.0554	3.1271	21	39	1.0618	2.9738	21	39	1.0687	2.8356	21
40	1.0555	3.1244	20	40	1.0619	2.9713	20	40	1.0688	2.8334	20
41	1.0556	3.1217	19	41	1.0621	2.9689	19	41	1.0689	2.8312	19
42	1.0557	3.1190	18	42	1.0622	2.9665	18	42	1.0690	2.8291	18
43	1.0558	3.1163	17	43	1.0623	2.9641	17	43	1.0691	2.8269	17
44	1.0559	3.1137	16	44	1.0624	2.9617	16	44	1.0692	2.8247	16
45	1.0560	3.1110	15	45	1.0625	2.9593	15	45	1.0694	2.8225	15
46	1.0561	3.1083	14	46	1.0626	2.9569	14	46	1.0695	2.8204	14
47	1.0563	3.1057	13	47	1.0627	2.9545	13	47	1.0696	2.8182	13
48	1.0564	3.1030	12	48	1.0628	2.9521	12	48	1.0697	2.8161	12
49	1.0565	3.1004	11	49	1.0629	2.9498	11	49	1.0698	2.8139	11
50	1.0566	3.0977	10	50	1.0631	2.9474	10	50	1.0700	2.8117	10
51	1.0567	3.0951	9	51	1.0632	2.9450	9	51	1.0701	2.8096	9
52	1.0568	3.0925	8	52	1.0633	2.9426	8	52	1.0702	2.8075	8
53	1.0569	3.0898	7	53	1.0634	2.9403	7	53	1.0703	2.8053	7
54	1.0570	3.0872	6	54	1.0635	2.9379	6	54	1.0704	2.8032	6
55	1.0571	3.0846	5	55	1.0636	2.9355	5	55	1.0705	2.8010	5
56	1.0572	3.0820	4	56	1.0637	2.9332	4	56	1.0707	2.7989	4
57	1.0573	3.0794	3	57	1.0638	2.9308	3	57	1.0708	2.7968	3
58	1.0574	3.0768	2	58	1.0640	2.9285	2	58	1.0709	2.7947	2
59	1.0575	3.0742	1	59	1.0641	2.9261	1	59	1.0710	2.7925	1
60	1.0576	3.0716	0	60	1.0642	2.9238	0	60	1.0711	2.7904	0
′	Csc	Sec	′	′	Csc	Sec	′	′	Csc	Sec	′

21° (201°)   (338°) **158°**   **22°** (202°)   (337°) **157°**   **23°** (203°)   (336°) **156°**

′	Sec	Csc	′		′	Sec	Csc	′		′	Sec	Csc	′
0	1.0711	2.7904	60		0	1.0785	2.6695	60		0	1.0864	2.5593	60
1	1.0713	2.7883	59		1	1.0787	2.6675	59		1	1.0865	2.5576	59
2	1.0714	2.7862	58		2	1.0788	2.6656	58		2	1.0866	2.5558	58
3	1.0715	2.7841	57		3	1.0789	2.6637	57		3	1.0868	2.5541	57
4	1 0716	2.7820	56		4	1.0790	2.6618	56		4	1.0869	2.5523	56
5	1.0717	2.7799	55		5	1.0792	2.6599	55		5	1.0870	2.5506	55
6	1.0719	2.7778	54		6	1.0793	2.6580	54		6	1.0872	2.5488	54
7	1.0720	2.7757	53		7	1.0794	2.6561	53		7	1.0873	2.5471	53
8	1.0721	2.7736	52		8	1.0796	2.6542	52		8	1.0874	2.5454	52
9	1.0722	2.7715	51		9	1.0797	2.6523	51		9	1.0876	2.5436	51
10	1.0723	2.7695	50		10	1.0798	2.6504	50		10	1.0877	2.5419	50
11	1.0725	2.7674	49		11	1.0799	2.6485	49		11	1.0878	2.5402	49
12	1.0726	2.7653	48		12	1.0801	2.6466	48		12	1.0880	2.5384	48
13	1.0727	2.7632	47		13	1.0802	2.6447	47		13	1.0881	2.5367	47
14	1.0728	2.7612	46		14	1.0803	2.6429	46		14	1.0883	2.5350	46
15	1.0730	2.7591	45		15	1.0804	2.6410	45		15	1.0884	2.5333	45
16	1.0731	2.7570	44		16	1.0806	2.6391	44		16	1.0885	2.5316	44
17	1.0732	2.7550	43		17	1.0807	2.6372	43		17	1.0887	2.5299	43
18	1.0733	2.7529	42		18	1.0808	2.6354	42		18	1.0888	2.5282	42
19	1.0734	2.7509	41		19	1.0810	2.6335	41		19	1.0889	2.5264	41
20	1.0736	2.7488	40		20	1.0811	2.6316	40		20	1.0891	2.5247	40
21	1.0737	2.7468	39		21	1.0812	2.6298	39		21	1.0892	2.5230	39
22	1.0738	2.7447	38		22	1.0814	2.6279	38		22	1.0893	2.5213	38
23	1.0739	2.7427	37		23	1.0815	2.6260	37		23	1.0895	2.5196	37
24	1.0740	2.7407	36		24	1.0816	2.6242	36		24	1.0896	2.5180	36
25	1.0742	2.7386	35		25	1.0817	2.6223	35		25	1.0898	2.5163	35
26	1.0743	2.7366	34		26	1.0819	2.6205	34		26	1.0899	2.5146	34
27	1.0744	2.7346	33		27	1.0820	2.6186	33		27	1.0900	2.5129	33
28	1.0745	2.7325	32		28	1.0821	2.6168	32		28	1.0902	2.5112	32
29	1.0747	2.7305	31		29	1.0823	2.6150	31		29	1.0903	2.5095	31
30	1.0748	2.7285	30		30	1.0824	2.6131	30		30	1.0904	2.5078	30
31	1.0749	2.7265	29		31	1.0825	2.6113	29		31	1.0906	2.5062	29
32	1.0750	2.7245	28		32	1.0827	2.6095	28		32	1.0907	2.5045	28
33	1.0752	2.7225	27		33	1.0828	2.6076	27		33	1.0909	2.5028	27
34	1.0753	2.7205	26		34	1.0829	2.6058	26		34	1.0910	2.5012	26
35	1.0754	2.7185	25		35	1.0830	2.6040	25		35	1.0911	2.4995	25
36	1.0755	2.7165	24		36	1.0832	2.6022	24		36	1.0913	2.4978	24
37	1.0757	2.7145	23		37	1.0833	2.6003	23		37	1.0914	2.4962	23
38	1.0758	2.7125	22		38	1.0834	2.5985	22		38	1.0915	2.4945	22
39	1.0759	2.7105	21		39	1.0836	2.5967	21		39	1.0917	2.4928	21
40	1.0760	2.7085	20		40	1.0837	2.5949	20		40	1.0918	2.4912	20
41	1.0761	2.7065	19		41	1.0838	2.5931	19		41	1.0920	2.4895	19
42	1.0763	2.7046	18		42	1.0840	2.5913	18		42	1.0921	2.4879	18
43	1.0764	2.7026	17		43	1.0841	2.5895	17		43	1.0922	2.4862	17
44	1.0765	2.7006	16		44	1.0842	2.5877	16		44	1.0924	2.4846	16
45	1.0766	2.6986	15		45	1.0844	2.5859	15		45	1.0925	2.4830	15
46	1.0768	2.6967	14		46	1.0845	2.5841	14		46	1.0927	2.4813	14
47	1.0769	2.6947	13		47	1.0846	2.5823	13		47	1.0928	2.4797	13
48	1.0770	2.6927	12		48	1.0848	2.5805	12		48	1.0929	2.4780	12
49	1.0771	2.6908	11		49	1.0849	2.5788	11		49	1.0931	2.4764	11
50	1.0773	2.6888	10		50	1.0850	2.5770	10		50	1.0932	2.4748	10
51	1.0774	2.6869	9		51	1.0852	2.5752	9		51	1.0934	2.4731	9
52	1.0775	2.6849	8		52	1.0853	2.5734	8		52	1.0935	2.4715	8
53	1.0777	2.6830	7		53	1.0354	2.5716	7		53	1.0936	2.4699	7
54	1.0778	2.6811	6		54	1.0856	2.5699	6		54	1.0938	2.4683	6
55	1.0779	2.6791	5		55	1.0857	2 5681	5		55	1.0939	2.4667	5
56	1.0780	2.6772	4		56	1.0858	2.5663	4		56	1.0941	2.4650	4
57	1.0782	2.6752	3		57	1.0860	2.5646	3		57	1.0942	2.4634	3
58	1.0783	2.6733	2		58	1.0861	2.5628	2		58	1.0944	2.4618	2
59	1.0784	2.6714	1		59	1.0862	2.5611	1		59	1.0945	2.4602	1
60	1.0785	2.6695	0		60	1.0864	2.5593	0		60	1.0946	2.4586	0
′	Csc	Sec	′		′	Csc	Sec	′		′	Csc	Sec	′

24° (204°) (335°) 155° **25° (205°) (334°) 154°** **26° (206°) (333°) 153°**

′	Sec	Csc	′	′	Sec	Csc	′	′	Sec	Csc	′
0	1.0946	2.4586	60	0	1.1034	2.3662	60	0	1.1126	2.2812	60
1	1.0948	2.4570	59	1	1.1035	2.3647	59	1	1.1128	2.2798	59
2	1.0949	2.4554	58	2	1.1037	2.3633	58	2	1.1129	2.2785	58
3	1.0951	2.4538	57	3	1.1038	2.3618	57	3	1.1131	2.2771	57
4	1.0952	2.4522	56	4	1.1040	2.3603	56	4	1.1132	2.2757	56
5	1.0953	2.4506	55	5	1.1041	2.3588	55	5	1.1134	2.2744	55
6	1.0955	2.4490	54	6	1.1043	2.3574	54	6	1.1136	2.2730	54
7	1.0956	2.4474	53	7	1.1044	2.3559	53	7	1.1137	2.2717	53
8	1.0958	2.4458	52	8	1.1046	2.3545	52	8	1.1139	2.2703	52
9	1.0959	2.4442	51	9	1.1047	2.3530	51	9	1.1140	2.2690	51
10	1.0961	2.4426	50	10	1.1049	2.3515	50	10	1.1142	2.2677	50
11	1.0962	2.4411	49	11	1.1050	2.3501	49	11	1.1143	2.2663	49
12	1.0963	2.4395	48	12	1.1052	2.3486	48	12	1.1145	2.2650	48
13	1.0965	2.4379	47	13	1.1053	2.3472	47	13	1.1147	2.2636	47
14	1.0966	2.4363	46	14	1.1055	2.3457	46	14	1.1148	2.2623	46
15	1.0968	2.4348	45	15	1.1056	2.3443	45	15	1.1150	2.2610	45
16	1.0969	2.4332	44	16	1.1058	2.3428	44	16	1.1151	2.2596	44
17	1.0971	2.4316	43	17	1.1059	2.3414	43	17	1.1153	2.2583	43
18	1.0972	2.4300	42	18	1.1061	2.3400	42	18	1.1155	2.2570	42
19	1.0974	2.4285	41	19	1.1062	2.3385	41	19	1.1156	2.2556	41
20	1.0975	2.4269	40	20	1.1064	2.3371	40	20	1.1158	2.2543	40
21	1.0976	2.4254	39	21	1.1066	2.3356	39	21	1.1159	2.2530	39
22	1.0978	2.4238	38	22	1.1067	2.3342	38	22	1.1161	2.2517	38
23	1.0979	2.4222	37	23	1.1069	2.3328	37	23	1.1163	2.2504	37
24	1.0981	2.4207	36	24	1.1070	2.3314	36	24	1.1164	2.2490	36
25	1.0982	2.4191	35	25	1.1072	2.3299	35	25	1.1166	2.2477	35
26	1.0984	2.4176	34	26	1.1073	2.3285	34	26	1.1168	2.2464	34
27	1.0985	2.4160	33	27	1.1075	2.3271	33	27	1.1169	2.2451	33
28	1.0987	2.4145	32	28	1.1076	2.3257	32	28	1.1171	2.2438	32
29	1.0988	2.4130	31	29	1.1078	2.3242	31	29	1.1172	2.2425	31
30	1.0989	2.4114	30	30	1.1079	2.3228	30	30	1.1174	2.2412	30
31	1.0991	2.4099	29	31	1.1081	2.3214	29	31	1.1176	2.2399	29
32	1.0992	2.4083	28	32	1.1082	2.3200	28	32	1.1177	2.2385	28
33	1.0994	2.4068	27	33	1.1084	2.3186	27	33	1.1179	2.2372	27
34	1.0995	2.4053	26	34	1.1085	2.3172	26	34	1.1180	2.2359	26
35	1.0997	2.4038	25	35	1.1087	2.3158	25	35	1.1182	2.2346	25
36	1.0998	2.4022	24	36	1.1089	2.3144	24	36	1.1184	2.2333	24
37	1.1000	2.4007	23	37	1.1090	2.3130	23	37	1.1185	2.2320	23
38	1.1001	2.3992	22	38	1.1092	2.3115	22	38	1.1187	2.2308	22
39	1.1003	2.3977	21	39	1.1093	2.3101	21	39	1.1189	2.2295	21
40	1.1004	2.3961	20	40	1.1095	2.3088	20	40	1.1190	2.2282	20
41	1.1006	2.3946	19	41	1.1096	2.3074	19	41	1.1192	2.2269	19
42	1.1007	2.3931	18	42	1.1098	2.3060	18	42	1.1194	2.2256	18
43	1.1009	2.3916	17	43	1.1099	2.3046	17	43	1.1195	2.2243	17
44	1.1010	2.3901	16	44	1.1101	2.3032	16	44	1.1197	2.2230	16
45	1.1011	2.3886	15	45	1.1102	2.3018	15	45	1.1198	2.2217	15
46	1.1013	2.3871	14	46	1.1104	2.3004	14	46	1.1200	2.2205	14
47	1.1014	2.3856	13	47	1.1106	2.2990	13	47	1.1202	2.2192	13
48	1.1016	2.3841	12	48	1.1107	2.2976	12	48	1.1203	2.2179	12
49	1.1017	2.3826	11	49	1.1109	2.2962	11	49	1.1205	2.2166	11
50	1.1019	2.3811	10	50	1.1110	2.2949	10	50	1.1207	2.2153	10
51	1.1020	2.3796	9	51	1.1112	2.2935	9	51	1.1208	2.2141	9
52	1.1022	2.3781	8	52	1.1113	2.2921	8	52	1.1210	2.2128	8
53	1.1023	2.3766	7	53	1.1115	2.2907	7	53	1.1212	2.2115	7
54	1.1025	2.3751	6	54	1.1117	2.2894	6	54	1.1213	2.2103	6
55	1.1026	2.3736	5	55	1.1118	2.2880	5	55	1.1215	2.2090	5
56	1.1028	2.3721	4	56	1.1120	2.2866	4	56	1.1217	2.2077	4
57	1.1029	2.3706	3	57	1.1121	2.2853	3	57	1.1218	2.2065	3
58	1.1031	2.3692	2	58	1.1123	2.2839	2	58	1.1220	2.2052	2
59	1.1032	2.3677	1	59	1.1124	2.2825	1	59	1.1222	2.2039	1
60	1.1034	2.3662	0	60	1.1126	2.2812	0	60	1.1223	2.2027	0
′	Csc	Sec	′	′	Csc	Sec	′	′	Csc	Sec	′

NATURAL FUNCTIONS—SECANTS AND COSECANTS (Continued)

′	Sec	Csc	′	′	Sec	Csc	′	′	Sec	Csc	′
0	1.1223	2.2027	**60**	**0**	1.1326	2.1301	**60**	**0**	1.1434	2.0627	**60**
1	1.1225	2.2014	59	1	1.1327	2.1289	59	1	1.1435	2.0616	59
2	1.1227	2.2002	58	2	1.1329	2.1277	58	2	1.1437	2.0605	58
3	1.1228	2.1989	57	3	1.1331	2.1266	57	3	1.1439	2.0594	57
4	1.1230	2.1977	56	4	1.1333	2.1254	56	4	1.1441	2.0583	56
5	1.1232	2.1964	**55**	**5**	1.1334	2.1242	**55**	**5**	1.1443	2.0573	**55**
6	1.1233	2.1952	54	6	1.1336	2.1231	54	6	1.1445	2.0562	54
7	1.1235	2.1939	53	7	1.1338	2.1219	53	7	1.1446	2.0551	53
8	1.1237	2.1927	52	8	1.1340	2.1208	52	8	1.1448	2.0540	52
9	1.1238	2.1914	51	9	1.1342	2.1196	51	9	1.1450	2.0530	51
10	1.1240	2.1902	**50**	**10**	1.1343	2.1185	**50**	**10**	1.1452	2.0519	**50**
11	1.1242	2.1890	49	11	1.1345	2.1173	49	11	1.1454	2.0508	49
12	1.1243	2.1877	48	12	1.1347	2.1162	48	12	1.1456	2.0498	48
13	1.1245	2.1865	47	13	1.1349	2.1150	47	13	1.1458	2.0487	47
14	1.1247	2.1852	46	14	1.1350	2.1139	46	14	1.1460	2.0476	46
15	1.1248	2.1840	**45**	**15**	1.1352	2.1127	**45**	**15**	1.1461	2.0466	**45**
16	1.1250	2.1828	44	16	1.1354	2.1116	44	16	1.1463	2.0455	44
17	1.1252	2.1815	43	17	1.1356	2.1105	43	17	1.1465	2.0445	43
18	1.1253	2.1803	42	18	1.1357	2.1093	42	18	1.1467	2.0434	42
19	1.1255	2.1791	41	19	1.1359	2.1082	41	19	1.1469	2.0423	41
20	1.1257	2.1779	**40**	**20**	1.1361	2.1070	**40**	**20**	1.1471	2.0413	**40**
21	1.1259	2.1766	39	21	1.1363	2.1059	39	21	1.1473	2.0402	39
22	1.1260	2.1754	38	22	1.1365	2.1048	38	22	1.1474	2.0392	38
23	1.1262	2.1742	37	23	1.1366	2.1036	37	23	1.1476	2.0381	37
24	1.1264	2.1730	36	24	1.1368	2.1025	36	24	1.1478	2.0371	36
25	1.1265	2.1718	**35**	**25**	1.1370	2.1014	**35**	**25**	1.1480	2.0360	**35**
26	1.1267	2.1705	34	26	1.1372	2.1002	34	26	1.1482	2.0350	34
27	1.1269	2.1693	33	27	1.1374	2.0991	33	27	1.1484	2.0339	33
28	1.1270	2.1681	32	28	1.1375	2.0980	32	28	1.1486	2.0329	32
29	1.1272	2.1669	31	29	1.1377	2.0969	31	29	1.1488	2.0318	31
30	1.1274	2.1657	**30**	**30**	1.1379	2.0957	**30**	**30**	1.1490	2.0308	**30**
31	1.1276	2.1645	29	31	1.1381	2.0946	29	31	1.1491	2.0297	29
32	1.1277	2.1633	28	32	1.1383	2.0935	28	32	1.1493	2.0287	28
33	1.1279	2.1621	27	33	1.1384	2.0924	27	33	1.1495	2.0276	27
34	1.1281	2.1609	26	34	1.1386	2.0913	26	34	1.1497	2.0266	26
35	1.1282	2.1596	**25**	**35**	1.1388	2.0901	**25**	**35**	1.1499	2.0256	**25**
36	1.1284	2.1584	24	36	1.1390	2.0890	24	36	1.1501	2.0245	24
37	1.1286	2.1572	23	37	1.1392	2.0879	23	37	1.1503	2.0235	23
38	1.1288	2.1560	22	38	1.1393	2.0868	22	38	1.1505	2.0225	22
39	1.1289	2.1549	21	39	1.1395	2.0857	21	39	1.1507	2.0214	21
40	1.1291	2.1537	**20**	**40**	1.1397	2.0846	**20**	**40**	1.1509	2.0204	**20**
41	1.1293	2.1525	19	41	1.1399	2.0835	19	41	1.1510	2.0194	19
42	1.1294	2.1513	18	42	1.1401	2.0824	18	42	1.1512	2.0183	18
43	1.1296	2.1501	17	43	1.1402	2.0813	17	43	1.1514	2.0173	17
44	1.1298	2.1489	16	44	1.1404	2.0802	16	44	1.1516	2.0163	16
45	1.1300	2.1477	**15**	**45**	1.1406	2.0791	**15**	**45**	1.1518	2.0152	**15**
46	1.1301	2.1465	14	46	1.1408	2.0779	14	46	1.1520	2.0142	14
47	1.1303	2.1453	13	47	1.1410	2.0768	13	47	1.1522	2.0132	13
48	1.1305	2.1441	12	48	1.1412	2.0757	12	48	1.1524	2.0122	12
49	1.1307	2.1430	11	49	1.1413	2.0747	11	49	1.1526	2.0112	11
50	1.1308	2.1418	**10**	**50**	1.1415	2.0736	**10**	**50**	1.1528	2.0101	**10**
51	1.1310	2.1406	9	51	1.1417	2.0725	9	51	1.1530	2.0091	9
52	1.1312	2.1394	8	52	1.1419	2.0714	8	52	1.1532	2.0081	8
53	1.1313	2.1382	7	53	1.1421	2.0703	7	53	1.1533	2.0071	7
54	1.1315	2.1371	6	54	1.1423	2.0692	6	54	1.1535	2.0061	6
55	1.1317	2.1359	**5**	**55**	1.1424	2.0681	**5**	**55**	1.1537	2.0051	**5**
56	1.1319	2.1347	4	56	1.1426	2.0670	4	56	1.1539	2.0040	4
57	1.1320	2.1336	3	57	1.1428	2.0659	3	57	1.1541	2.0030	3
58	1.1322	2.1324	2	58	1.1430	2.0648	2	58	1.1543	2.0020	2
59	1.1324	2.1312	1	59	1.1432	2.0637	1	59	1.1545	2.0010	1
60	1.1326	2.1301	**0**	**60**	1.1434	2.0627	**0**	**60**	1.1547	2.0000	**0**
′	Csc	Sec	′	′	Csc	Sec	′	′	Csc	Sec	′

30° (210°) (329°) **149°** **31·** (211°) (328°) **148°** **32°** (212°) (327°) **147°**

′	Sec	Csc	′	′	Sec	Csc	′	′	Sec	Csc	′
0	1.1547	2.0000	60	0	1.1666	1.9416	60	0	1.1792	1.8871	60
1	1.1549	1.9990	59	1	1.1668	1.9407	59	1	1.1794	1.8862	59
2	1.1551	1.9980	58	2	1.1670	1.9397	58	2	1.1796	1.8853	58
3	1.1553	1.9970	57	3	1.1672	1.9388	57	3	1.1798	1.8844	57
4	1.1555	1.9960	56	4	1.1675	1.9379	56	4	1.1800	1.8836	56
5	1.1557	1.9950	55	5	1.1677	1.9369	55	5	1.1803	1.8827	55
6	1.1559	1.9940	54	6	1.1679	1.9360	54	6	1.1805	1.8818	54
7	1.1561	1.9930	53	7	1.1681	1.9351	53	7	1.1807	1.8810	53
8	1.1563	1.9920	52	8	1.1683	1.9341	52	8	1.1809	1.8801	52
9	1.1565	1.9910	51	9	1.1685	1.9332	51	9	1.1811	1.8792	51
10	1.1566	1.9900	50	10	1.1687	1.9323	50	10	1.1813	1.8783	50
11	1.1568	1.9890	49	11	1.1689	1.9313	49	11	1.1815	1.8775	49
12	1.1570	1.9880	48	12	1.1691	1.9304	48	12	1.1818	1.8766	48
13	1.1572	1.9870	47	13	1.1693	1.9295	47	13	1.1820	1.8757	47
14	1.1574	1.9860	46	14	1.1695	1.9285	46	14	1.1822	1.8749	46
15	1.1576	1.9850	45	15	1.1697	1.9276	45	15	1.1824	1.8740	45
16	1.1578	1.9840	44	16	1.1699	1.9267	44	16	1.1826	1.8731	44
17	1.1580	1.9830	43	17	1.1701	1.9258	43	17	1.1828	1.8723	43
18	1.1582	1.9821	42	18	1.1703	1.9249	42	18	1.1831	1.8714	42
19	1.1584	1.9811	41	19	1.1705	1.9239	41	19	1.1833	1.8706	41
20	1.1586	1.9801	40	20	1.1707	1.9230	40	20	1.1835	1.8697	40
21	1.1588	1.9791	39	21	1.1710	1.9221	39	21	1.1837	1.8688	39
22	1.1590	1.9781	38	22	1.1712	1.9212	38	22	1.1839	1.8680	38
23	1.1592	1.9771	37	23	1.1714	1.9203	37	23	1.1842	1.8671	37
24	1.1594	1.9762	36	24	1.1716	1.9194	36	24	1.1844	1.8663	36
25	1.1596	1.9752	35	25	1.1718	1.9184	35	25	1.1846	1.8654	35
26	1.1598	1.9742	34	26	1.1720	1.9175	34	26	1.1848	1.8646	34
27	1.1600	1.9732	33	27	1.1722	1.9166	33	27	1.1850	1.8637	33
28	1.1602	1.9722	32	28	1.1724	1.9157	32	28	1.1852	1.8629	32
29	1.1604	1.9713	31	29	1.1726	1.9148	31	29	1.1855	1.8620	31
30	1.1606	1.9703	30	30	1.1728	1.9139	30	30	1.1857	1.8612	30
31	1.1608	1.9693	29	31	1.1730	1.9130	29	31	1.1859	1.8603	29
32	1.1610	1.9684	28	32	1.1732	1.9121	28	32	1.1861	1.8595	28
33	1.1612	1.9674	27	33	1.1735	1.9112	27	33	1.1863	1.8586	27
34	1.1614	1.9664	26	34	1.1737	1.9103	26	34	1.1866	1.8578	26
35	1.1616	1.9654	25	35	1.1739	1.9094	25	35	1.1868	1.8569	25
36	1.1618	1.9645	24	36	1.1741	1.9084	24	36	1.1870	1.8561	24
37	1.1620	1.9635	23	37	1.1743	1.9075	23	37	1.1872	1.8552	23
38	1.1622	1.9625	22	38	1.1745	1.9066	22	38	1.1875	1.8544	22
39	1.1624	1.9616	21	39	1.1747	1.9057	21	39	1.1877	1.8535	21
40	1.1626	1.9606	20	40	1.1749	1.9048	20	40	1.1879	1.8527	20
41	1.1628	1.9597	19	41	1.1751	1.9039	19	41	1.1881	1.8519	19
42	1.1630	1.9587	18	42	1.1753	1.9031	18	42	1.1883	1.8510	18
43	1.1632	1.9577	17	43	1.1756	1.9022	17	43	1.1886	1.8502	17
44	1.1634	1.9568	16	44	1.1758	1.9013	16	44	1.1888	1.8494	16
45	1.1636	1.9558	15	45	1.1760	1.9004	15	45	1.1890	1.8485	15
46	1.1638	1.9549	14	46	1.1762	1.8995	14	46	1.1892	1.8477	14
47	1.1640	1.9539	13	47	1.1764	1.8986	13	47	1.1895	1.8468	13
48	1.1642	1.9530	12	48	1.1766	1.8977	12	48	1.1897	1.8460	12
49	1.1644	1.9520	11	49	1.1768	1.8968	11	49	1.1899	1.8452	11
50	1.1646	1.9511	10	50	1.1770	1.8959	10	50	1.1901	1.8443	10
51	1.1648	1.9501	9	51	1.1773	1.8950	9	51	1.1903	1.8435	9
52	1.1650	1.9492	8	52	1.1775	1.8941	8	52	1.1906	1.8427	8
53	1.1652	1.9482	7	53	1.1777	1.8933	7	53	1.1908	1.8419	7
54	1.1654	1.9473	6	54	1.1779	1.8924	6	54	1.1910	1.8410	6
55	1.1656	1.9463	5	55	1.1781	1.8915	5	55	1.1912	1.8402	5
56	1.1658	1.9454	4	56	1.1783	1.8906	4	56	1.1915	1.8394	4
57	1.1660	1.9444	3	57	1.1785	1.8897	3	57	1.1917	1.8385	3
58	1.1662	1.9435	2	58	1.1788	1.8888	2	58	1.1919	1.8377	2
59	1.1664	1.9425	1	59	1.1790	1.8880	1	59	1.1921	1.8369	1
60	1.1666	1.9416	0	60	1.1792	1.8871	0	60	1.1924	1.8361	0
′	Csc	Sec	′	′	Csc	Sec	′	′	Csc	Sec	′

120° (300°) (239°) **59°** **121°** (301°) (238°) **58°** **122°** (302°) (237°) **57°**

33° (213°)   (326°) **146°**   **34°** (214°)   (325°) **145°**   **35° (215°)**   (324°) **144°**

′	Sec	Csc	′	′	Sec	Csc	′	′	Sec	Csc	′
0	1.1924	1.8361	60	0	1.2062	1.7883	60	0	1.2208	1.7434	60
1	1.1926	1.8353	59	1	1.2065	1.7875	59	1	1.2210	1.7427	59
2	1.1928	1.8344	58	2	1.2067	1.7868	58	2	1.2213	1.7420	58
3	1.1930	1.8336	57	3	1.2069	1.7860	57	3	1.2215	1.7413	57
4	1.1933	1.8328	56	4	1.2072	1.7852	56	4	1.2218	1.7406	56
5	1.1935	1.8320	55	5	1.2074	1.7844	55	5	1.2220	1.7398	55
6	1.1937	1.8312	54	6	1.2076	1.7837	54	6	1.2223	1.7391	54
7	1.1939	1.8303	53	7	1.2079	1.7829	53	7	1.2225	1.7384	53
8	1.1942	1.8295	52	8	1.2081	1.7821	52	8	1.2228	1.7377	52
9	1.1944	1.8287	51	9	1.2084	1.7814	51	9	1.2230	1.7370	51
10	1.1946	1.8279	50	10	1.2086	1.7806	50	10	1.2233	1.7362	50
11	1.1949	1.8271	49	11	1.2088	1.7799	49	11	1.2235	1.7355	49
12	1.1951	1.8263	48	12	1.2091	1.7791	48	12	1.2238	1.7348	48
13	1.1953	1.8255	47	13	1.2093	1.7783	47	13	1.2240	1.7341	47
14	1.1955	1.8247	46	14	1.2096	1.7776	46	14	1.2243	1.7334	46
15	1.1958	1.8238	45	15	1.2098	1.7768	45	15	1.2245	1.7327	45
16	1.1960	1.8230	44	16	1.2100	1.7761	44	16	1.2248	1.7320	44
17	1.1962	1.8222	43	17	1.2103	1.7753	43	17	1.2250	1.7312	43
18	1.1964	1.8214	42	18	1.2105	1.7745	42	18	1.2253	1.7305	42
19	1.1967	1.8206	41	19	1.2108	1.7738	41	19	1.2255	1.7298	41
20	1.1969	1.8198	40	20	1.2110	1.7730	40	20	1.2258	1.7291	40
21	1.1971	1.8190	39	21	1.2112	1.7723	39	21	1.2260	1.7284	39
22	1.1974	1.8182	38	22	1.2115	1.7715	38	22	1.2263	1.7277	38
23	1.1976	1.8174	37	23	1.2117	1.7708	37	23	1.2265	1.7270	37
24	1.1978	1.8166	36	24	1.2120	1.7700	36	24	1.2268	1.7263	36
25	1.1981	1.8158	35	25	1.2122	1.7693	35	25	1.2271	1.7256	35
26	1.1983	1.8150	34	26	1.2124	1.7685	34	26	1.2273	1.7249	34
27	1.1985	1.8142	33	27	1.2127	1.7678	33	27	1.2276	1.7242	33
28	1.1987	1.8134	32	28	1.2129	1.7670	32	28	1.2278	1.7235	32
29	1.1990	1.8126	31	29	1.2132	1.7663	31	29	1.2281	1.7228	31
30	1.1992	1.8118	30	30	1.2134	1.7655	30	30	1.2283	1.7221	30
31	1.1994	1.8110	29	31	1.2136	1.7648	29	31	1.2286	1.7213	29
32	1.1997	1.8102	28	32	1.2139	1.7640	28	32	1.2288	1.7206	28
33	1.1999	1.8094	27	33	1.2141	1.7633	27	33	1.2291	1.7199	27
34	1.2001	1.8086	26	34	1.2144	1.7625	26	34	1.2293	1.7192	26
35	1.2004	1.8078	25	35	1.2146	1.7618	25	35	1.2296	1.7185	25
36	1.2006	1.8070	24	36	1.2149	1.7610	24	36	1.2299	1.7179	24
37	1.2008	1.8062	23	37	1.2151	1.7603	23	37	1.2301	1.7172	23
38	1.2011	1.8055	22	38	1.2154	1.7596	22	38	1.2304	1.7165	22
39	1.2013	1.8047	21	39	1.2156	1.7588	21	39	1.2306	1.7158	21
40	1.2015	1.8039	20	40	1.2158	1.7581	20	40	1.2309	1.7151	20
41	1.2018	1.8031	19	41	1.2161	1.7573	19	41	1.2311	1.7144	19
42	1.2020	1.8023	18	42	1.2163	1.7566	18	42	1.2314	1.7137	18
43	1.2022	1.8015	17	43	1.2166	1.7559	17	43	1.2317	1.7130	17
44	1.2025	1.8007	16	44	1.2168	1.7551	16	44	1.2319	1.7123	16
45	1.2027	1.8000	15	45	1.2171	1.7544	15	45	1.2322	1.7116	15
46	1.2029	1.7992	14	46	1.2173	1.7537	14	46	1.2324	1.7109	14
47	1.2032	1.7984	13	47	1.2176	1.7529	13	47	1.2327	1.7102	13
48	1.2034	1.7976	12	48	1.2178	1.7522	12	48	1.2329	1.7095	12
49	1.2036	1.7968	11	49	1.2181	1.7515	11	49	1.2332	1.7088	11
50	1.2039	1.7960	10	50	1.2183	1.7507	10	50	1.2335	1.7081	10
51	1.2041	1.7953	9	51	1.2185	1.7500	9	51	1.2337	1.7075	9
52	1.2043	1.7945	8	52	1.2188	1.7493	8	52	1.2340	1.7068	8
53	1.2046	1.7937	7	53	1.2190	1.7485	7	53	1.2342	1.7061	7
54	1.2048	1.7929	6	54	1.2193	1.7478	6	54	1.2345	1.7054	6
55	1.2050	1.7922	5	55	1.2195	1.7471	5	55	1.2348	1.7047	5
56	1.2053	1.7914	4	56	1.2198	1.7463	4	56	1.2350	1.7040	4
57	1.2055	1.7906	3	57	1.2200	1.7456	3	57	1.2353	1.7033	3
58	1.2057	1.7898	2	58	1.2203	1.7449	2	58	1.2355	1.7027	2
59	1.2060	1.7891	1	59	1.2205	1.7442	1	59	1.2358	1.7020	1
60	1.2062	1.7883	0	60	1.2208	1.7434	0	60	1.2361	1.7013	0
′	Csc	Sec	′	′	Csc	Sec	′	′	Csc	Sec	′

36° (216°)　　(323°) **143°**　　　**37°** (217°)　　(322°) **142°**　　　**38°** (218°)　　(321°) **141°**

′	Sec	Csc	′	′	Sec	Csc	′	′	Sec	Csc	′
0	1.2361	1.7013	60	0	1.2521	1.6616	60	0	1.2690	1.6243	60
1	1.2363	1.7006	59	1	1.2524	1.6610	59	1	1.2693	1.6237	59
2	1.2366	1.6999	58	2	1.2527	1.6604	58	2	1.2696	1.6231	58
3	1.2369	1.6993	57	3	1.2530	1.6597	57	3	1.2699	1.6225	57
4	1.2371	1.6986	56	4	1.2532	1.6591	56	4	1.2702	1.6219	56
5	1.2374	1.6979	55	5	1.2535	1.6584	55	5	1.2705	1.6213	55
6	1.2376	1.6972	54	6	1.2538	1.6578	54	6	1.2708	1.6207	54
7	1.2379	1.6966	53	7	1.2541	1.6572	53	7	1.2710	1.6201	53
8	1.2382	1.6959	52	8	1.2543	1.6565	52	8	1.2713	1.6195	52
9	1.2384	1.6952	51	9	1.2546	1.6559	51	9	1.2716	1.6189	51
10	1.2387	1.6945	50	10	1.2549	1.6553	50	10	1.2719	1.6183	50
11	1.2390	1.6939	49	11	1.2552	1.6546	49	11	1.2722	1.6177	49
12	1.2392	1.6932	48	12	1.2554	1.6540	48	12	1.2725	1.6171	48
13	1.2395	1.6925	47	13	1.2557	1.6534	47	13	1.2728	1.6165	47
14	1.2397	1.6918	46	14	1.2560	1.6527	46	14	1.2731	1.6159	46
15	1.2400	1.6912	45	15	1.2563	1.6521	45	15	1.2734	1.6153	45
16	1.2403	1.6905	44	16	1.2566	1.6515	44	16	1.2737	1.6147	44
17	1.2405	1.6898	43	17	1.2568	1.6508	43	17	1.2740	1.6141	43
18	1.2408	1.6892	42	18	1.2571	1.6502	42	18	1.2742	1.6135	42
19	1.2411	1.6885	41	19	1.2574	1.6496	41	19	1.2745	1.6129	41
20	1.2413	1.6878	40	20	1.2577	1.6489	40	20	1.2748	1.6123	40
21	1.2416	1.6871	39	21	1.2579	1.6483	39	21	1.2751	1.6117	39
22	1.2419	1.6865	38	22	1.2582	1.6477	38	22	1.2754	1.6111	38
23	1.2421	1.6858	37	23	1.2585	1.6471	37	23	1.2757	1.6105	37
24	1.2424	1.6852	36	24	1.2588	1.6464	36	24	1.2760	1.6099	36
25	1.2427	1.6845	35	25	1.2591	1.6458	35	25	1.2763	1.6093	35
26	1.2429	1.6838	34	26	1.2593	1.6452	34	26	1.2766	1.6087	34
27	1.2432	1.6832	33	27	1.2596	1.6446	33	27	1.2769	1.6082	33
28	1.2435	1.6825	32	28	1.2599	1.6439	32	28	1.2772	1.6076	32
29	1.2437	1.6818	31	29	1.2602	1.6433	31	29	1.2775	1.6070	31
30	1.2440	1.6812	30	30	1.2605	1.6427	30	30	1.2778	1.6064	30
31	1.2443	1.6805	29	31	1.2608	1.6421	29	31	1.2781	1.6058	29
32	1.2445	1.6799	28	32	1.2610	1.6414	28	32	1.2784	1.6052	28
33	1.2448	1.6792	27	33	1.2613	1.6408	27	33	1.2787	1.6046	27
34	1.2451	1.6785	26	34	1.2616	1.6402	26	34	1.2790	1.6040	26
35	1.2453	1.6779	25	35	1.2619	1.6396	25	35	1.2793	1.6035	25
36	1.2456	1.6772	24	36	1.2622	1.6390	24	36	1.2796	1.6029	24
37	1.2459	1.6766	23	37	1.2624	1.6383	23	37	1.2799	1.6023	23
38	1.2462	1.6759	22	38	1.2627	1.6377	22	38	1.2802	1.6017	22
39	1.2464	1.6753	21	39	1.2630	1.6371	21	39	1.2804	1.6011	21
40	1.2467	1.6746	20	40	1.2633	1.6365	20	40	1.2807	1.6005	20
41	1.2470	1.6739	19	41	1.2636	1.6359	19	41	1.2810	1.6000	19
42	1.2472	1.6733	18	42	1.2639	1.6353	18	42	1.2813	1.5994	18
43	1.2475	1.6726	17	43	1.2641	1.6346	17	43	1.2816	1.5988	17
44	1.2478	1.6720	16	44	1.2644	1.6340	16	44	1.2819	1.5982	16
45	1.2480	1.6713	15	45	1.2647	1.6334	15	45	1.2822	1.5976	15
46	1.2483	1.6707	14	46	1.2650	1.6328	14	46	1.2825	1.5971	14
47	1.2486	1.6700	13	47	1.2653	1.6322	13	47	1.2828	1.5965	13
48	1.2489	1.6694	12	48	1.2656	1.6316	12	48	1.2831	1.5959	12
49	1.2491	1.6687	11	49	1.2659	1.6310	11	49	1.2834	1.5953	11
50	1.2494	1.6681	10	50	1.2661	1.6303	10	50	1.2837	1.5948	10
51	1.2497	1.6674	9	51	1.2664	1.6297	9	51	1.2840	1.5942	9
52	1.2499	1.6668	8	52	1.2667	1.6291	8	52	1.2843	1.5936	8
53	1.2502	1.6661	7	53	1.2670	1.6285	7	53	1.2846	1.5930	7
54	1.2505	1.6655	6	54	1.2673	1.6279	6	54	1.2849	1.5925	6
55	1.2508	1.6649	5	55	1.2676	1.6273	5	55	1.2852	1.5919	5
56	1.2510	1.6642	4	56	1.2679	1.6267	4	56	1.2855	1.5913	4
57	1.2513	1.6636	3	57	1.2682	1.6261	3	57	1.2859	1.5907	3
58	1.2516	1.6629	2	58	1.2684	1.6255	2	58	1.2862	1.5902	2
59	1.2519	1.6623	1	59	1.2687	1.6249	1	59	1.2865	1.5896	1
60	1.2521	1.6616	0	60	1.2690	1.6243	0	60	1.2868	1.5890	0
′	Csc	Sec	′	′	Csc	Sec	′	′	Csc	Sec	′

39° (219°) (320°) **140°** **40° (220°)** (319°) **139°** **41° (221°)** (318°) **138°**

′	Sec	Csc	′	′	Sec	Csc	′	′	Sec	Csc	′
0	1.2868	1.5890	60	0	1.3054	1.5557	60	0	1.3250	1.5243	60
1	1.2871	1.5884	59	1	1.3057	1.5552	59	1	1.3253	1.5237	59
2	1.2874	1.5879	58	2	1.3060	1.5546	58	2	1.3257	1.5232	58
3	1.2877	1.5873	57	3	1.3064	1.5541	57	3	1.3260	1.5227	57
4	1.2880	1.5867	56	4	1.3067	1.5536	56	4	1.3264	1.5222	56
5	1.2883	1.5862	55	5	1.3070	1.5530	55	5	1.3267	1.5217	55
6	1.2886	1.5856	54	6	1.3073	1.5525	54	6	1.3270	1.5212	54
7	1.2889	1.5850	53	7	1.3076	1.5520	53	7	1.3274	1.5207	53
8	1.2892	1.5845	52	8	1.3080	1.5514	52	8	1.3277	1.5202	52
9	1.2895	1.5839	51	9	1.3083	1.5509	51	9	1.3280	1.5197	51
10	1.2898	1.5833	50	10	1.3086	1.5504	50	10	1.3284	1.5192	50
11	1.2901	1.5828	49	11	1.3089	1.5498	49	11	1.3287	1.5187	49
12	1.2904	1.5822	48	12	1.3093	1.5493	48	12	1.3291	1.5182	48
13	1.2907	1.5816	47	13	1.3096	1.5488	47	13	1.3294	1.5177	47
14	1.2910	1.5811	46	14	1.3099	1.5482	46	14	1.3297	1.5172	46
15	1.2913	1.5805	45	15	1.3102	1.5477	45	15	1.3301	1.5167	45
16	1.2916	1.5800	44	16	1.3105	1.5472	44	16	1.3304	1.5162	44
17	1.2919	1.5794	43	17	1.3109	1.5466	43	17	1.3307	1.5156	43
18	1.2923	1.5788	42	18	1.3112	1.5461	42	18	1.3311	1.5151	42
19	1.2926	1.5783	41	19	1.3115	1.5456	41	19	1.3314	1.5146	41
20	1.2929	1.5777	40	20	1.3118	1.5450	40	20	1.3318	1.5141	40
21	1.2932	1.5771	39	21	1.3122	1.5445	39	21	1.3321	1.5136	39
22	1.2935	1.5766	38	22	1.3125	1.5440	38	22	1.3325	1.5131	38
23	1.2938	1.5760	37	23	1.3128	1.5435	37	23	1.3328	1.5126	37
24	1.2941	1.5755	36	24	1.3131	1.5429	36	24	1.3331	1.5121	36
25	1.2944	1.5749	35	25	1.3135	1.5424	35	25	1.3335	1.5116	35
26	1.2947	1.5744	34	26	1.3138	1.5419	34	26	1.3338	1.5111	34
27	1.2950	1.5738	33	27	1.3141	1.5413	33	27	1.3342	1.5107	33
28	1.2953	1.5732	32	28	1.3144	1.5408	32	28	1.3345	1.5102	32
29	1.2957	1.5727	31	29	1.3148	1.5403	31	29	1.3348	1.5097	31
30	1.2960	1.5721	30	30	1.3151	1.5398	30	30	1.3352	1.5092	30
31	1.2963	1.5716	29	31	1.3154	1.5392	29	31	1.3355	1.5087	29
32	1.2966	1.5710	28	32	1.3157	1.5387	28	32	1.3359	1.5082	28
33	1.2969	1.5705	27	33	1.3161	1.5382	27	33	1.3362	1.5077	27
34	1.2972	1.5699	26	34	1.3164	1.5377	26	34	1.3366	1.5072	26
35	1.2975	1.5694	25	35	1.3167	1.5372	25	35	1.3369	1.5067	25
36	1.2978	1.5688	24	36	1.3171	1.5366	24	36	1.3373	1.5062	24
37	1.2981	1.5683	23	37	1.3174	1.5361	23	37	1.3376	1.5057	23
38	1.2985	1.5677	22	38	1.3177	1.5356	22	38	1.3380	1.5052	22
39	1.2988	1.5672	21	39	1.3180	1.5351	21	39	1.3383	1.5047	21
40	1.2991	1.5666	20	40	1.3184	1.5345	20	40	1.3386	1.5042	20
41	1.2994	1.5661	19	41	1.3187	1.5340	19	41	1.3390	1.5037	19
42	1.2997	1.5655	18	42	1.3190	1.5335	18	42	1.3393	1.5032	18
43	1.3000	1.5650	17	43	1.3194	1.5330	17	43	1.3397	1.5027	17
44	1.3003	1.5644	16	44	1.3197	1.5325	16	44	1.3400	1.5023	16
45	1.3007	1.5639	15	45	1.3200	1.5320	15	45	1.3404	1.5018	15
46	1.3010	1.5633	14	46	1.3203	1.5314	14	46	1.3407	1.5013	14
47	1.3013	1.5628	13	47	1.3207	1.5309	13	47	1.3411	1.5008	13
48	1.3016	1.5622	12	48	1.3210	1.5304	12	48	1.3414	1.5003	12
49	1.3019	1.5617	11	49	1.3213	1.5299	11	49	1.3418	1.4998	11
50	1.3022	1.5611	10	50	1.3217	1.5294	10	50	1.3421	1.4993	10
51	1.3026	1.5606	9	51	1.3220	1.5289	9	51	1.3425	1.4988	9
52	1.3029	1.5601	8	52	1.3223	1.5283	8	52	1.3428	1.4984	8
53	1.3032	1.5595	7	53	1.3227	1.5278	7	53	1.3432	1.4979	7
54	1.3035	1.5590	6	54	1.3230	1.5273	6	54	1.3435	1.4974	6
55	1.3038	1.5584	5	55	1.3233	1.5268	5	55	1.3439	1.4969	5
56	1.3041	1.5579	4	56	1.3237	1.5263	4	56	1.3442	1.4964	4
57	1.3045	1.5573	3	57	1.3240	1.5258	3	57	1.3446	1.4959	3
58	1.3048	1.5568	2	58	1.3243	1.5253	2	58	1.3449	1.4954	2
59	1.3051	1.5563	1	59	1.3247	1.5248	1	59	1.3453	1.4950	1
60	1.3054	1.5557	0	60	1.3250	1.5243	0	60	1.3456	1.4945	0
′	Csc	Sec	′	′	Csc	Sec	′	′	Csc	Sec	′

129° (309°) (230°) **50°** **130° (310°)** (229°) **49°** **131° (311°)** (228°) **48°**

42° (222°) (317°) **137°**   **43°** (223°) (316°) **136°**   **44°** (224°) (315°) **135°**

′	Sec	Csc	′	′	Sec	Csc	′	′	Sec	Csc	′
0	1.3456	1.4945	60	0	1.3673	1.4663	60	0	1.3902	1.4396	60
1	1.3460	1.4940	59	1	1.3677	1.4658	59	1	1.3906	1.4391	59
2	1.3463	1.4935	58	2	1.3681	1.4654	58	2	1.3909	1.4387	58
3	1.3467	1.4930	57	3	1.3684	1.4649	57	3	1.3913	1.4383	57
4	1.3470	1.4925	56	4	1.3688	1.4645	56	4	1.3917	1.4378	56
5	1.3474	1.4921	55	5	1.3692	1.4640	55	5	1.3921	1.4374	55
6	1.3478	1.4916	54	6	1.3696	1.4635	54	6	1.3925	1.4370	54
7	1.3481	1.4911	53	7	1.3699	1.4631	53	7	1.3929	1.4365	53
8	1.3485	1.4906	52	8	1.3703	1.4626	52	8	1.3933	1.4361	52
9	1.3488	1.4901	51	9	1.3707	1.4622	51	9	1.3937	1.4357	51
10	1.3492	1.4897	50	10	1.3711	1.4617	50	10	1.3941	1.4352	50
11	1.3495	1.4892	49	11	1.3714	1.4613	49	11	1.3945	1.4348	49
12	1.3499	1.4887	48	12	1.3718	1.4608	48	12	1.3949	1.4344	48
13	1.3502	1.4882	47	13	1.3722	1.4604	47	13	1.3953	1.4340	47
14	1.3506	1.4878	46	14	1.3726	1.4599	46	14	1.3957	1.4335	46
15	1.3510	1.4873	45	15	1.3729	1.4595	45	15	1.3961	1.4331	45
16	1.3513	1.4868	44	16	1.3733	1.4590	44	16	1.3965	1.4327	44
17	1.3517	1.4863	43	17	1.3737	1.4586	43	17	1.3969	1.4322	43
18	1.3520	1.4859	42	18	1.3741	1.4581	42	18	1.3972	1.4318	42
19	1.3524	1.4854	41	19	1.3744	1.4577	41	19	1.3976	1.4314	41
20	1.3527	1.4849	40	20	1.3748	1.4572	40	20	1.3980	1.4310	40
21	1.3531	1.4844	39	21	1.3752	1.4568	39	21	1.3984	1.4305	39
22	1.3535	1.4840	38	22	1.3756	1.4563	38	22	1.3988	1.4301	38
23	1.3538	1.4835	37	23	1.3759	1.4559	37	23	1.3992	1.4297	37
24	1.3542	1.4830	36	24	1.3763	1.4554	36	24	1.3996	1.4293	36
25	1.3545	1.4825	35	25	1.3767	1.4550	35	25	1.4000	1.4288	35
26	1.3549	1.4821	34	26	1.3771	1.4545	34	26	1.4004	1.4284	34
27	1.3553	1.4816	33	27	1.3775	1.4541	33	27	1.4008	1.4280	33
28	1.3556	1.4811	32	28	1.3778	1.4536	32	28	1.4012	1.4276	32
29	1.3560	1.4807	31	29	1.3782	1.4532	31	29	1.4016	1.4271	31
30	1.3563	1.4802	30	30	1.3786	1.4527	30	30	1.4020	1.4267	30
31	1.3567	1.4797	29	31	1.3790	1.4523	29	31	1.4024	1.4263	29
32	1.3571	1.4792	28	32	1.3794	1.4518	28	32	1.4028	1.4259	28
33	1.3574	1.4788	27	33	1.3797	1.4514	27	33	1.4032	1.4255	27
34	1.3578	1.4783	26	34	1.3801	1.4510	26	34	1.4036	1.4250	26
35	1.3582	1.4778	25	35	1.3805	1.4505	25	35	1.4040	1.4246	25
36	1.3585	1.4774	24	36	1.3809	1.4501	24	36	1.4044	1.4242	24
37	1.3589	1.4769	23	37	1.3813	1.4496	23	37	1.4048	1.4238	23
38	1.3592	1.4764	22	38	1.3817	1.4492	22	38	1.4052	1.4234	22
39	1.3596	1.4760	21	39	1.3820	1.4487	21	39	1.4057	1.4229	21
40	1.3600	1.4755	20	40	1.3824	1.4483	20	40	1.4061	1.4225	20
41	1.3603	1.4750	19	41	1.3828	1.4479	19	41	1.4065	1.4221	19
42	1.3607	1.4746	18	42	1.3832	1.4474	18	42	1.4069	1.4217	18
43	1.3611	1.4741	17	43	1.3836	1.4470	17	43	1.4073	1.4213	17
44	1.3614	1.4737	16	44	1.3840	1.4465	16	44	1.4077	1.4208	16
45	1.3618	1.4732	15	45	1.3843	1.4461	15	45	1.4081	1.4204	15
46	1.3622	1.4727	14	46	1.3847	1.4457	14	46	1.4085	1.4200	14
47	1.3625	1.4723	13	47	1.3851	1.4452	13	47	1.4089	1.4196	13
48	1.3629	1.4718	12	48	1.3855	1.4448	12	48	1.4093	1.4192	12
49	1.3633	1.4713	11	49	1.3859	1.4443	11	49	1.4097	1.4188	11
50	1.3636	1.4709	10	50	1.3863	1.4439	10	50	1.4101	1.4183	10
51	1.3640	1.4704	9	51	1.3867	1.4435	9	51	1.4105	1.4179	9
52	1.3644	1.4700	8	52	1.3871	1.4430	8	52	1.4109	1.4175	8
53	1.3647	1.4695	7	53	1.3874	1.4426	7	53	1.4113	1.4171	7
54	1.3651	1.4690	6	54	1.3878	1.4422	6	54	1.4118	1.4167	6
55	1.3655	1.4686	5	55	1.3882	1.4417	5	55	1.4122	1.4163	5
56	1.3658	1.4681	4	56	1.3886	1.4413	4	56	1.4126	1.4159	4
57	1.3662	1.4677	3	57	1.3890	1.4409	3	57	1.4130	1.4154	3
58	1.3666	1.4672	2	58	1.3894	1.4404	2	58	1.4134	1.4150	2
59	1.3670	1.4667	1	59	1.3898	1.4400	1	59	1.4138	1.4146	1
60	1.3673	1.4663	0	60	1.3902	1.4396	0	60	1.4142	1.4142	0
′	Csc	Sec	′	′	Csc	Sec	′	′	Csc	Sec	′

132° (312°) (227°) **47°**   **133°** (313°) (226°) **46°**   **134°** (314°) (225°) **45°**

NATURAL TRIGONOMETRIC FUNCTIONS FOR ANGLES IN DEGREES AND DECIMALS

Deg.	Sin	Tan	Cot	Cos	Deg.	Deg.	Sin	Tan	Cot	Cos	Deg.
0.0	0.00000	0.00000	∞	1.0000	**90.0**	**6.0**	0.10453	0.10510	9.514	0.9945	**84.0**
.1	.00175	.00175	573.0	1.0000	89.9	.1	.10626	.10687	9.357	.9943	83.9
.2	.00349	.00349	286.5	1.0000	.8	.2	.10800	.10863	9.205	.9942	.8
.3	.00524	.00524	191.0	1.0000	.7	.3	.10973	.11040	9.058	.9940	.7
.4	.00698	.00698	143.24	1.0000	.6	.4	.11147	.11217	8.915	.9938	.6
.5	.00873	.00873	114.59	1.0000	.5	.5	.11320	.11394	8.777	.9936	.5
.6	.01047	.01047	95.49	0.9999	.4	.6	.11494	.11570	8.643	.9934	.4
.7	.01222	.01222	81.85	.9999	.3	.7	.11667	.11747	8.513	.9932	.3
.8	.01396	.01396	71.62	.9999	.2	.8	.11840	.11924	8.386	.9930	.2
.9	.01571	.01571	63.66	.9999	89.1	.9	.12014	.12101	8.264	.9928	83.1
1.0	0.01745	0.01746	57.29	0.9998	**89.0**	**7.0**	0.12187	0.12278	8.144	0.9925	**83.0**
.1	.01920	.01920	52.08	.9998	88.9	.1	.12360	.12456	8.028	.9923	82.9
.2	.02094	.02095	47.74	.9998	.8	.2	.12533	.12633	7.916	.9921	.8
.3	.02269	.02269	44.07	.9997	.7	.3	.12706	.12810	7.806	.9919	.7
.4	.02443	.02444	40.92	.9997	.6	.4	.12880	.12988	7.700	.9917	.6
.5	.02618	.02619	38.19	.9997	.5	.5	.13053	.13165	7.596	.9914	.5
.6	.02792	.02793	35.80	.9996	.4	.6	.13226	.13343	7.495	.9912	.4
.7	.02967	.02968	33.69	.9996	.3	.7	.13399	.13521	7.396	.9910	.3
.8	.03141	.03143	31.82	.9995	.2	.8	.13572	.13698	7.300	.9907	.2
.9	.03316	.03317	30.14	.9995	88.1	.9	.13744	.13876	7.207	.9905	82.1
2.0	0.03490	0.03492	28.64	0.9994	**88.0**	**8.0**	0.13917	0.14054	7.115	0.9903	**82.0**
.1	.03664	.03367	27.27	.9993	87.9	.1	.14090	.14232	7.026	.9900	81.9
.2	.03839	.03842	26.03	.9993	.8	.2	.14263	.14410	6.940	.9898	.8
.3	.04013	.04016	24.90	.9992	.7	.3	.14436	.14588	6.855	.9895	.7
.4	.04188	.04191	23.86	.9991	.6	.4	.14608	.14767	6.772	.9893	.6
.5	.04362	.04366	22.90	.9990	.5	.5	.14781	.14945	6.691	.9890	.5
.6	.04536	.04541	22.02	.9990	.4	.6	.14954	.15124	6.612	.9888	.4
.7	.04711	.04716	21.20	.9989	.3	.7	.15126	.15302	6.535	.9885	.3
.8	.04885	.04891	20.45	.9988	.2	.8	.15299	.15481	6.460	.9882	.2
.9	.05059	.05066	19.74	.9987	87.1	.9	.15471	.15660	6.386	.9880	81.1
3.0	0.05234	0.05241	19.081	0.9986	**87.0**	**9.0**	0.15643	0.15838	6.314	0.9877	**81.0**
.1	.05408	.05416	18.464	.9985	86.9	.1	.15816	.16017	6.243	.9874	80.9
.2	.05582	.05591	17.886	.9984	.8	.2	.15988	.16196	6.174	.9871	.8
.3	.05756	.05766	17.343	.9983	.7	.3	.16160	.16376	6.107	.9869	.7
.4	.05931	.05941	16.832	.9982	.6	.4	.16333	.16555	6.041	.9866	.6
.5	.06105	.06116	16.350	.9981	.5	.5	.16505	.16734	5.976	.9863	.5
.6	.06279	.06291	15.895	.9980	.4	.6	.16677	.16914	5.912	.9860	.4
.7	.06453	.06467	15.464	.9979	.3	.7	.16849	.17093	5.850	.9857	.3
.8	.06627	.06642	15.056	.9978	.2	.8	.17021	.17273	5.789	.9854	.2
.9	.06802	.06817	14.669	.9977	86.1	.9	.17193	.17453	5.730	.9851	80.1
4.0	0.06976	0.06993	14.301	0.9976	**86.0**	**10.0**	0.1736	0.1763	5.671	0.9848	**80.0**
.1	.07150	.07168	13.951	.9974	85.9	.1	.1754	.1781	5.614	.9845	79.9
.2	.07324	.07344	13.617	.9973	.8	.2	.1771	.1799	5.558	.9842	.8
.3	.07498	.07519	13.300	.9972	.7	.3	.1788	.1817	5.503	.9839	.7
.4	.07672	.07695	12.996	.9971	.6	.4	.1805	.1835	5.449	.9836	.6
.5	.07846	.07870	12.706	.9969	.5	.5	.1822	.1853	5.396	.9833	.5
.6	.08020	.08046	12.429	.9968	.4	.6	.1840	.1871	5.343	.9829	.4
.7	.08194	.08221	12.163	.9966	.3	.7	.1857	.1890	5.292	.9826	.3
.8	.08368	.08397	11.909	.9965	.2	.8	.1874	.1908	5.242	.9823	.2
.9	.08542	.08573	11.664	.9963	85.1	.9	.1891	.1926	5.193	.9820	79.1
5.0	0.08716	0.08749	11.430	0.9962	**85.0**	**11.0**	0.1908	0.1944	5.145	0.9816	**79.0**
.1	.08889	.08925	11.205	.9960	84.9	.1	.1925	.1962	5.097	.9813	78.9
.2	.09063	.09101	10.988	.9959	.8	.2	.1942	.1980	5.050	.9810	.8
.3	.09237	.09277	10.780	.9957	.7	.3	.1959	.1998	5.005	.9806	.7
.4	.09411	.09453	10.579	.9956	.6	.4	.1977	.2016	4.959	.9803	.6
.5	.09585	.09629	10.385	.9954	.5	.5	.1994	.2035	4.915	.9799	.5
.6	.09758	.09805	10.199	.9952	.4	.6	.2011	.2053	4.872	.9796	.4
.7	.09932	.09981	10.019	.9951	.3	.7	.2028	.2071	4.829	.9792	.3
.8	.10106	.10158	9.845	.9949	.2	.8	.2045	.2089	4.787	.9789	.2
.9	.10279	.10334	9.677	.9947	84.1	.9	.2062	.2107	4.745	.9785	78.1
6.0	0.10453	0.10510	9.514	0.9945	**84.0**	**12.0**	0.2079	0.2126	4.705	0.9781	**78.0**
Deg.	Cos	Cot	Tan	Sin	Deg.	Deg.	Cos	Cot	Tan	Sin	Deg.

130

Deg.	Sin	Tan	Cot	Cos	Deg.
12.0	0.2079	0.2126	4.705	0.9781	**78.0**
.1	.2096	.2144	4.665	.9778	77.9
.2	.2113	.2162	4.625	.9774	.8
.3	.2130	.2180	4.586	.9770	.7
.4	.2147	.2199	4.548	.9767	.6
.5	.2164	.2217	4.511	.9763	.5
.6	.2181	.2235	4.474	.9759	.4
.7	.2198	.2254	4.437	.9755	.3
.8	.2215	.2272	4.402	.9751	.2
.9	.2233	.2290	4.366	.9748	77.1
13.0	0.2250	0.2309	4.331	0.9744	**77.0**
.1	.2267	.2327	4.297	.9740	76.9
.2	.2284	.2345	4.264	.9736	.8
.3	.2300	.2364	4.230	.9732	.7
.4	.2317	.2382	4.198	.9728	.6
.5	.2334	.2401	4.165	.9724	.5
.6	.2351	.2419	4.134	.9720	.4
.7	.2368	.2438	4.102	.9715	.3
.8	.2385	.2456	4.071	.9711	.2
.9	.2402	.2475	4.041	.9707	76.1
14.0	0.2419	0.2493	4.011	0.9703	**76.0**
.1	.2436	.2512	3.981	.9699	75.9
.2	.2453	.2530	3.952	.9694	.8
.3	.2470	.2549	3.923	.9690	.7
.4	.2487	.2568	3.895	.9686	.6
.5	.2504	.2586	3.867	.9681	.5
.6	.2521	.2605	3.839	.9677	.4
.7	.2538	.2623	3.812	.9673	.3
.8	.2554	.2642	3.785	.9668	.2
.9	.2571	.2661	3.758	.9664	75.1
15.0	0.2588	0.2679	3.732	0.9659	**75.0**
.1	.2605	.2698	3.706	.9655	74.9
.2	.2622	.2717	3.681	.9650	.8
.3	.2639	.2736	3.655	.9646	.7
.4	.2656	.2754	3.630	.9641	.6
.5	.2672	.2773	3.606	.9636	.5
.6	.2689	.2792	3.582	.9632	.4
.7	.2706	.2811	3.558	.9627	.3
.8	.2723	.2830	3.534	.9622	.2
.9	.2740	.2849	3.511	.9617	74.1
16.0	0.2756	0.2867	3.487	0.9613	**74.0**
.1	.2773	.2886	3.465	.9608	73.9
.2	.2790	.2905	3.442	.9603	.8
.3	.2807	.2924	3.420	.9598	.7
.4	.2823	.2943	3.398	.9593	.6
.5	.2840	.2962	3.376	.9588	.5
.6	.2857	.2981	3.354	.9583	.4
.7	.2874	.3000	3.333	.9578	.3
.8	.2890	.3019	3.312	.9573	.2
.9	.2907	.3038	3.291	.9568	73.1
17.0	0.2924	0.3057	3.271	0.9563	**73.0**
.1	.2940	.3076	3.251	.9558	72.9
.2	.2957	.3096	3.230	.9553	.8
.3	.2974	.3115	3.211	.9548	.7
.4	.2990	.3134	3.191	.9542	.6
.5	.3007	.3153	3.172	.9537	.5
.6	.3024	.3172	3.152	.9532	.4
.7	.3040	.3191	3.133	.9527	.3
.8	.3057	.3211	3.115	.9521	.2
.9	.3074	.3230	3.096	.9516	72.1
18.0	0.3090	0.3249	3.078	0.9511	**72.0**
Deg.	Cos	Cot	Tan	Sin	Deg.

Deg.	Sin	Tan	Cot	Cos	Deg.
18.0	0.3090	0.3249	3.078	0.9511	**72.0**
.1	.3107	.3269	3.060	.9505	71.9
.2	.3123	.3288	3.042	.9500	.8
.3	.3140	.3307	3.024	.9494	.7
.4	.3156	.3327	3.006	.9489	.6
.5	.3173	.3346	2.989	.9483	.5
.6	.3190	.3365	2.971	.9478	.4
.7	.3206	.3385	2.954	.9472	.3
.8	.3223	.3404	2.937	.9466	.2
.9	.3239	.3424	2.921	.9461	71.1
19.0	0.3256	0.3443	2.904	0.9455	**71.0**
.1	.3272	.3463	2.888	.9449	70.9
.2	.3289	.3482	2.872	.9444	.8
.3	.3305	.3502	2.856	.9438	.7
.4	.3322	.3522	2.840	.9432	.6
.5	.3338	.3541	2.824	.9426	.5
.6	.3355	.3561	2.808	.9421	.4
.7	.3371	.3581	2.793	.9415	.3
.8	.3387	.3600	2.778	.9409	.2
.9	.3404	.3620	2.762	.9403	70.1
20.0	0.3420	0.3640	2.747	0.9397	**70.0**
.1	.3437	.3659	2.733	.9391	69.9
.2	.3453	.3679	2.718	.9385	.8
.3	.3469	.3699	2.703	.9379	.7
.4	.3486	.3719	2.689	.9373	.6
.5	.3502	.3739	2.675	.9367	.5
.6	.3518	.3759	2.660	.9361	.4
.7	.3535	.3779	2.646	.9354	.3
.8	.3551	.3799	2.633	.9348	.2
.9	.3567	.3819	2.619	.9342	69.1
21.0	0.3584	0.3839	2.605	0.9336	**69.0**
.1	.3600	.3859	2.592	.9330	68.9
.2	.3616	.3879	2.578	.9323	.8
.3	.3633	.3899	2.565	.9317	.7
.4	.3649	.3919	2.552	.9311	.6
.5	.3665	.3939	2.539	.9304	.5
.6	.3681	.3959	2.526	.9298	.4
.7	.3697	.3979	2.513	.9291	.3
.8	.3714	.4000	2.500	.9285	.2
.9	.3730	.4020	2.488	.9278	68.1
22.0	0.3746	0.4040	2.475	0.9272	**68.0**
.1	.3762	.4061	2.463	.9265	67.9
.2	.3778	.4081	2.450	.9259	.8
.3	.3795	.4101	2.438	.9252	.7
.4	.3811	.4122	2.426	.9245	.6
.5	.3827	.4142	2.414	.9239	.5
.6	.3843	.4163	2.402	.9232	.4
.7	.3859	.4183	2.391	.9225	.3
.8	.3875	.4204	2.379	.9219	.2
.9	.3891	.4224	2.367	.9212	67.1
23.0	0.3907	0.4245	2.356	0.9205	**67.0**
.1	.3923	.4265	2.344	.9198	66.9
.2	.3939	.4286	2.333	.9191	.8
.3	.3955	.4307	2.322	.9184	.7
.4	.3971	.4327	2.311	.9178	.6
.5	.3987	.4348	2.300	.9171	.5
.6	.4003	.4369	2.289	.9164	.4
.7	.4019	.4390	2.278	.9157	.3
.8	.4035	.4411	2.267	.9150	.2
.9	.4051	.4431	2.257	.9143	66.1
24.0	0.4067	0.4452	2.246	0.9135	**66.0**
Deg.	Cos	Cot	Tan	Sin	Deg.

Deg.	Sin	Tan	Cot	Cos	Deg.
24.0	0.4067	0.4452	2.246	0.9135	**66.0**
.1	.4083	.4473	2.236	.9128	65.9
.2	.4099	.4494	2.225	.9121	.8
.3	.4115	.4515	2.215	.9114	.7
.4	.4131	.4536	2.204	.9107	.6
.5	.4147	.4557	2.194	.9100	.5
.6	.4163	.4578	2.184	.9092	.4
.7	.4179	.4599	2.174	.9085	.3
.8	.4195	.4621	2.164	.9078	.2
.9	.4210	.4642	2.154	.9070	65.1
25.0	0.4226	0.4663	2.145	0.9063	**65.0**
.1	.4242	.4684	2.135	.9056	64.9
.2	.4258	.4706	2.125	.9048	.8
.3	.4274	.4727	2.116	.9041	.7
.4	.4289	.4748	2.106	.9033	.6
.5	.4305	.4770	2.097	.9026	.5
.6	.4321	.4791	2.087	.9018	.4
.7	.4337	.4813	2.078	.9011	.3
.8	.4352	.4834	2.069	.9003	.2
.9	.4368	.4856	2.059	.8996	64.1
26.0	0.4384	0.4877	2.050	0.8988	**64.0**
.1	.4399	.4899	2.041	.8980	63.9
.2	.4415	.4921	2.032	.8973	.8
.3	.4431	.4942	2.023	.8965	.7
.4	.4446	.4964	2.014	.8957	.6
.5	.4462	.4986	2.006	.8949	.5
.6	.4478	.5008	1.997	.8942	.4
.7	.4493	.5029	1.988	.8934	.3
.8	.4509	.5051	1.980	.8926	.2
.9	.4524	.5073	1.971	.8918	63.1
27.0	0.4540	0.5095	1.963	0.8910	**63.0**
.1	.4555	.5117	1.954	.8902	62.9
.2	.4571	.5139	1.946	.8894	.8
.3	.4586	.5161	1.937	.8886	.7
.4	.4602	.5184	1.929	.8878	.6
.5	.4617	.5206	1.921	.8870	.5
.6	.4633	.5228	1.913	.8862	.4
.7	.4648	.5250	1.905	.8854	.3
.8	.4664	.5272	1.897	.8846	.2
.9	.4679	.5295	1.889	.8838	62.1
28.0	0.4695	0.5317	1.881	0.8829	**62.0**
.1	.4710	.5340	1.873	.8821	61.9
.2	.4726	.5362	1.865	.8813	.8
.3	.4741	.5384	1.857	.8805	.7
.4	.4756	.5407	1.849	.8796	.6
.5	.4772	.5430	1.842	.8788	.5
.6	.4787	.5452	1.834	.8780	.4
.7	.4802	.5475	1.827	.8771	.3
.8	.4818	.5498	1.819	.8763	.2
.9	.4833	.5520	1.811	.8755	61.1
29.0	0.4848	0.5543	1.804	0.8746	**61.0**
.1	.4863	.5566	1.797	.8738	60.9
.2	.4879	.5589	1.789	.8729	.8
.3	.4894	.5612	1.782	.8721	.7
.4	.4909	.5635	1.775	.8712	.6
.5	.4924	.5658	1.767	.8704	.5
.6	.4939	.5681	1.760	.8695	.4
.7	.4955	.5704	1.753	.8686	.3
.8	.4970	.5727	1.746	.8678	.2
.9	.4985	.5750	1.739	.8669	60.1
30.0	0.5000	0.5774	1.732	0.8660	**60.0**
Deg.	**Cos**	**Cot**	**Tan**	**Sin**	**Deg.**

Deg.	Sin	Tan	Cot	Cos	Deg.
30.0	0.5000	0.5774	1.7321	0.8660	**60.0**
.1	.5015	.5797	1.7251	.8652	59.9
.2	.5030	.5820	1.7182	.8643	.8
.3	.5045	.5844	1.7113	.8634	.7
.4	.5060	.5867	1.7045	.8625	.6
.5	.5075	.5890	1.6977	.8616	.5
.6	.5090	.5914	1.6909	.8607	.4
.7	.5105	.5938	1.6842	.8599	.3
.8	.5120	.5961	1.6775	.8590	.2
.9	.5135	.5985	1.6709	.8581	59.1
31.0	0.5150	0.6009	1.6643	0.8572	**59.0**
.1	.5165	.6032	1.6577	.8563	58.9
.2	.5180	.6056	1.6512	.8554	.8
.3	.5195	.6080	1.6447	.8545	.7
.4	.5210	.6104	1.6383	.8536	.6
.5	.5225	.6128	1.6319	.8526	.5
.6	.5240	.6152	1.6255	.8517	.4
.7	.5255	.6176	1.6191	.8508	.3
.8	.5270	.6200	1.6128	.8499	.2
.9	.5284	.6224	1.6066	.8490	58.1
32.0	0.5299	0.6249	1.6003	0.8480	**58.0**
.1	.5314	.6273	1.5941	.8471	57.9
.2	.5329	.6297	1.5880	.8462	.8
.3	.5344	.6322	1.5818	.8453	.7
.4	.5358	.6346	1.5757	.8443	.6
.5	.5373	.6371	1.5697	.8434	.5
.6	.5388	.6395	1.5637	.8425	.4
.7	.5402	.6420	1.5577	.8415	.3
.8	.5417	.6445	1.5517	.8406	.2
.9	.5432	.6469	1.5458	.8396	57.1
33.0	0.5446	0.6494	1.5399	0.8387	**57.0**
.1	.5461	.6519	1.5340	.8377	56.9
.2	.5476	.6544	1.5282	.8368	.8
.3	.5490	.6569	1.5224	.8358	.7
.4	.5505	.6594	1.5166	.8348	.6
.5	.5519	.6619	1.5108	.8339	.5
.6	.5534	.6644	1.5051	.8329	.4
.7	.5548	.6669	1.4994	.8320	.3
.8	.5563	.6694	1.4938	.8310	.2
.9	.5577	.6720	1.4882	.8300	56.1
34.0	0.5592	0.6745	1.4826	0.8290	**56.0**
.1	.5606	.6771	1.4770	.8281	55.9
.2	.5621	.6796	1.4715	.8271	.8
.3	.5635	.6822	1.4659	.8261	.7
.4	.5650	.6847	1.4605	.8251	.6
.5	.5664	.6873	1.4550	.8241	.5
.6	.5678	.6899	1.4496	.8231	.4
.7	.5693	.6924	1.4442	.8221	.3
.8	.5707	.6950	1.4388	.8211	.2
.9	.5721	.6976	1.4335	.8202	55.1
35.0	0.5736	0.7002	1.4281	0.8192	**55.0**
.1	.5750	.7028	1.4229	.8181	54.9
.2	.5764	.7054	1.4176	.8171	.8
.3	.5779	.7080	1.4124	.8161	.7
.4	.5793	.7107	1.4071	.8151	.6
.5	.5807	.7133	1.4019	.8141	.5
.6	.5821	.7159	1.3968	.8131	.4
.7	.5835	.7186	1.3916	.8121	.3
.8	.5850	.7212	1.3865	.8111	.2
.9	.5864	.7239	1.3814	.8100	54.1
36.0	0.5878	0.7265	1.3764	0.8090	**54.0**
Deg.	**Cos**	**Cot**	**Tan**	**Sin**	**Deg.**

Deg.	Sin	Tan	Cot	Cos	Deg.	Deg.	Sin	Tan	Cot	Cos	Deg.
36.0	0.5878	0.7265	1.3764	0.8090	54.0	40.5	0.6494	0.8541	1.1708	0.7604	49.5
.1	.5892	.7292	1.3713	.8080	53.9	.6	.6508	.8571	1.1667	.7593	.4
.2	.5906	.7319	1.3663	.8070	.8	.7	.6521	.8601	1.1626	.7581	.3
.3	.5920	.7346	1.3613	.8059	.7	.8	.6534	.8632	1.1585	.7570	.2
.4	.5934	.7373	1.3564	.8049	.6	.9	.6547	.8662	1.1544	.7559	49.1
.5	.5948	.7400	1.3514	.8039	.5	41.0	0.6561	0.8693	1.1504	0.7547	49.0
.6	.5962	.7427	1.3465	.8028	.4	.1	.6574	.8724	1.1463	.7536	48.9
.7	.5976	.7454	1.3416	.8018	.3	.2	.6587	.8754	1.1423	.7524	.8
.8	.5990	.7481	1.3367	.8007	.2	.3	.6600	.8785	1.1383	.7513	.7
.9	.6004	.7508	1.3319	.7997	53.1	.4	.6613	.8816	1.1343	.7501	.6
37.0	0.6018	0.7536	1.3270	0.7986	53.0	.5	.6626	.8847	1.1303	.7490	.5
.1	.6032	.7563	1.3222	.7976	52.9	.6	.6639	.8878	1.1263	.7478	.4
.2	.6046	.7590	1.3175	.7965	.8	.7	.6652	.8910	1.1224	.7466	.3
.3	.6060	.7618	1.3127	.7955	.7	.8	.6665	.8941	1.1184	.7455	.2
.4	.6074	.7646	1.3079	.7944	.6	.9	.6678	.8972	1.1145	.7443	48.1
.5	.6088	.7673	1.3032	.7934	.5	42.0	0.6691	0.9004	1.1106	0.7431	48.0
.6	.6101	.7701	1.2985	.7923	.4	.1	.6704	.9036	1.1067	.7420	47.9
.7	.6115	.7729	1.2938	.7912	.3	.2	.6717	.9067	1.1028	.7408	.8
.8	.6129	.7757	1.2892	.7902	.2	.3	.6730	.9099	1.0990	.7396	.7
.9	.6143	.7785	1.2846	.7891	52.1	.4	.6743	.9131	1.0951	.7385	.6
38.0	0.6157	0.7813	1.2799	0.7880	52.0	.5	.6756	.9163	1.0913	.7373	.5
.1	.6170	.7841	1.2753	.7869	51.9	.6	.6769	.9195	1.0875	.7361	.4
.2	.6184	.7869	1.2708	.7859	.8	.7	.6782	.9228	1.0837	.7349	.3
.3	.6198	.7898	1.2662	.7848	.7	.8	.6794	.9260	1.0799	.7337	.2
.4	.6211	.7926	1.2617	.7837	.6	.9	.6807	.9293	1.0761	.7325	47.1
.5	.6225	.7954	1.2572	.7826	.5	43.0	0.6820	0.9325	1.0724	0.7314	47.0
.6	.6239	.7983	1.2527	.7815	.4	.1	.6833	.9358	1.0686	.7302	46.9
.7	.6252	.8012	1.2482	.7804	.3	.2	.6845	.9391	1.0649	.7290	.8
.8	.6266	.8040	1.2437	.7793	.2	.3	.6858	.9424	1.0612	.7278	.7
.9	.6280	.8069	1.2393	.7782	51.1	.4	.6871	.9457	1.0575	.7266	.6
39.0	0.6293	0.8098	1.2349	0.7771	51.0	.5	.6884	.9490	1.0538	.7254	.5
.1	.6307	.8127	1.2305	.7760	50.9	.6	.6896	.9523	1.0501	.7242	.4
.2	.6320	.8156	1.2261	.7749	.8	.7	.6909	.9556	1.0464	.7230	.3
.3	.6334	.8185	1.2218	.7738	.7	.8	.6921	.9590	1.0428	.7218	.2
.4	.6347	.8214	1.2174	.7727	.6	.9	.6934	.9623	1.0392	.7206	46.1
.5	.6361	.8243	1.2131	.7716	.5	44.0	0.6947	0.9657	1.0355	0.7193	46.0
.6	.6374	.8273	1.2088	.7705	.4	.1	.6959	.9691	1.0319	.7181	45.9
.7	.6388	.8302	1.2045	.7694	.3	.2	.6972	.9725	1.0283	.7169	.8
.8	.6401	.8332	1.2002	.7683	.2	.3	.6984	.9759	1.0247	.7157	.7
.9	.6414	.8361	1.1960	.7672	50.1	.4	.6997	.9793	1.0212	.7145	.6
40.0	0.6428	0.8391	1.1918	0.7660	50.0	.5	.7009	.9827	1.0176	.7133	.5
.1	.6441	.8421	1.1875	.7649	49.9	.6	.7022	.9861	1.0141	.7120	.4
.2	.6455	.8451	1.1833	.7638	.8	.7	.7034	.9896	1.0105	.7108	.3
.3	.6468	.8481	1.1792	.7627	.7	.8	.7046	.9930	1.0070	.7096	.2
.4	.6481	.8511	1.1750	.7615	.6	.9	.7059	.9965	1.0035	.7083	45.1
40.5	0.6494	0.8541	1.1708	0.7604	49.5	45.0	0.7071	1.0000	1.0000	0.7071	45.0
Deg.	Cos	Cot	Tan	Sin	Deg.	Deg.	Cos	Cot	Tan	Sin	Deg.

LOGARITHMS OF TRIGONOMETRIC FUNCTIONS
FOR ANGLES IN DEGREES AND DECIMALS

Deg.	L. Sin	L. Tan	L. Cot	L. Cos	Deg.
0.0	− ∞	− ∞	∞	0.00000	**90.0**
.1	7.24188	7.24188	2.75812	0.00000	89.9
.2	7.54291	7.54291	2.45709	0.00000	.8
.3	7.71900	7.71900	2.28100	9.99999	.7
.4	7.84393	7.84394	2.15606	9.99999	.6
.5	7.94084	7.94086	2.05914	9.99998	.5
.6	8.02002	8.02004	1.97996	9.99998	.4
.7	8.08696	8.08700	1.91300	9.99997	.3
.8	8.14495	8.14500	1.85500	9.99996	.2
.9	8.19610	8.19616	1.80384	9.99995	89.1
1.0	8.24186	8.24192	1.75808	9.99993	**89.0**
.1	8.28324	8.28332	1.71668	9.99992	88.9
.2	8.32103	8.32112	1.67888	9.99990	.8
.3	8.35578	8.35590	1.64410	9.99989	.7
.4	8.38796	8.38809	1.61191	9.99987	.6
.5	8.41792	8.41807	1.58193	9.99985	.5
.6	8.44594	8.44611	1.55389	9.99983	.4
.7	8.47226	8.47245	1.52755	9.99981	.3
.8	8.49708	8.49729	1.50271	9.99979	.2
.9	8.52055	8.52079	1.47921	9.99976	88.1
2.0	8.54282	8.54308	1.45692	9.99974	**88.0**
.1	8.56400	8.56429	1.43571	9.99971	87.9
.2	8.58419	8.58451	1.41549	9.99968	.8
.3	8.60349	8.60384	1.39616	9.99965	.7
.4	8.62196	8.62234	1.37766	9.99962	.6
.5	8.63968	8.64009	1.35991	9.99959	.5
.6	8.65670	8.65715	1.34285	9.99955	.4
.7	8.67308	8.67356	1.32644	9.99952	.3
.8	8.68886	8.68938	1.31062	9.99948	.2
.9	8.70409	8.70465	1.29535	9.99944	87.1
3.0	8.71880	8.71940	1.28060	9.99940	**87.0**
.1	8.73303	8.73366	1.26634	9.99936	86.9
.2	8.74680	8.74748	1.25252	9.99932	.8
.3	8.76015	8.76087	1.23913	9.99928	.7
.4	8.77310	8.77387	1.22613	9.99923	.6
.5	8.78568	8.78649	1.21351	9.99919	.5
.6	8.79789	8.79875	1.20125	9.99914	.4
.7	8.80978	8.81068	1.18932	9.99909	.3
.8	8.82134	8.82230	1.17770	9.99904	.2
.9	8.83261	8.83361	1.16639	9.99899	86.1
4.0	8.84358	8.84464	1.15536	9.99894	**86.0**
.1	8.85429	8.85540	1.14460	9.99889	85.9
.2	8.86474	8.86591	1.13409	9.99883	.8
.3	8.87494	8.87616	1.12384	9.99878	.7
.4	8.88490	8.88618	1.11382	9.99872	.6
.5	8.89464	8.89598	1.10402	9.99866	.5
.6	8.90417	8.90557	1.09443	9.99860	.4
.7	8.91349	8.91495	1.08505	9.99854	.3
.8	8.92261	8.92414	1.07586	9.99847	.2
.9	8.93154	8.93313	1.06687	9.99841	85.1
5.0	8.94030	8.94195	1.05805	9.99834	**85.0**
.1	8.94887	8.95060	1.04940	9.99828	84.9
.2	8.95728	8.95908	1.04092	9.99821	.8
.3	8.96553	8.96739	1.03261	9.99814	.7
.4	8.97363	8.97556	1.02444	9.99807	.6
.5	8.98157	8.98358	1.01642	9.99800	.5
.6	8.98937	8.99145	1.00855	9.99792	.4
.7	8.99704	8.99919	1.00081	9.99785	.3
.8	9.00456	9.00679	0.99321	9.99777	.2
.9	9.01196	9.01427	0.98573	9.99769	84.1
6.0	9.01923	9.02162	0.97838	9.99761	**84.0**

Deg.	L. Sin	L. Tan	L. Cot	L. Cos	Deg.
6.0	9.01923	9.02162	0.97838	9.99761	**84.0**
.1	9.02639	9.02885	0.97115	9.99753	83.9
.2	9.03342	9.03597	0.96403	9.99745	.8
.3	9.04034	9.04297	0.95703	9.99737	.7
.4	9.04715	9.04987	0.95013	9.99728	.6
.5	9.05386	9.05666	0.94334	9.99720	.5
.6	9.06046	9.06335	0.93665	9.99711	.4
.7	9.06696	9.06994	0.93006	9.99702	.3
.8	9.07337	9.07643	0.92357	9.99693	.2
.9	9.07968	9.08283	0.91717	9.99684	83.1
7.0	9.08589	9.08914	0.91086	9.99675	**83.0**
.1	9.09202	9.09537	0.90463	9.99666	82.9
.2	9.09807	9.10150	0.89850	9.99656	.8
.3	9.10402	9.10756	0.89244	9.99647	.7
.4	9.10990	9.11353	0.88647	9.99637	.6
.5	9.11570	9.11943	0.88057	9.99627	.5
.6	9.12142	9.12525	0.87475	9.99617	.4
.7	9.12706	9.13099	0.86901	9.99607	.3
.8	9.13263	9.13667	0.86333	9.99596	.2
.9	9.13813	9.14227	0.85773	9.99586	82.1
8.0	9.14356	9.14780	0.85220	9.99575	**82.0**
.1	9.14891	9.15327	0.84673	9.99565	81.9
.2	9.15421	9.15867	0.84133	9.99554	.8
.3	9.15944	9.16401	0.83599	9.99543	.7
.4	9.16460	9.16928	0.83072	9.99532	.6
.5	9.16970	9.17450	0.82550	9.99520	.5
.6	9.17474	9.17965	0.82035	9.99509	.4
.7	9.17973	9.18475	0.81525	9.99497	.3
.8	9.18465	9.18979	0.81021	9.99486	.2
.9	9.18952	9.19478	0.80522	9.99474	81.1
9.0	9.19433	9.19971	0.80029	9.99462	**81.0**
.1	9.19909	9.20459	0.79541	9.99450	80.9
.2	9.20380	9.20942	0.79058	9.99438	.8
.3	9.20845	9.21420	0.78580	9.99425	.7
.4	9.21306	9.21893	0.78107	9.99413	.6
.5	9.21761	9.22361	0.77639	9.99400	.5
.6	9.22211	9.22824	0.77176	9.99388	.4
.7	9.22657	9.23283	0.76717	9.99375	.3
.8	9.23098	9.23737	0.76263	9.99362	.2
.9	9.23535	9.24186	0.75814	9.99348	80.1
10.0	9.23967	9.24632	0.75368	9.99335	**80.0**
.1	9.24395	9.25073	0.74927	9.99322	79.9
.2	9.24818	9.25510	0.74490	9.99308	.8
.3	9.25237	9.25943	0.74057	9.99294	.7
.4	9.25652	9.26372	0.73628	9.99281	.6
.5	9.26063	9.26797	0.73203	9.99267	.5
.6	9.26470	9.27218	0.72782	9.99252	.4
.7	9.26873	9.27635	0.72365	9.99238	.3
.8	9.27273	9.28049	0.71951	9.99224	.2
.9	9.27668	9.28459	0.71541	9.99209	79.1
11.0	9.28060	9.28865	0.71135	9.99195	**79.0**
.1	9.28448	9.29268	0.70732	9.99180	78.9
.2	9.28833	9.29668	0.70332	9.99165	.8
.3	9.29214	9.30064	0.69936	9.99150	.7
.4	9.29591	9.30457	0.69543	9.99135	.6
.5	9.29966	9.30846	0.69154	9.99119	.5
.6	9.30336	9.31233	0.68767	9.99104	.4
.7	9.30704	9.31616	0.68384	9.99088	.3
.8	9.31068	9.31996	0.68004	9.99072	.2
.9	9.31430	9.32373	0.67627	9.99056	78.1
12.0	9.31788	9.32747	0.67253	9.99040	**78.0**
Deg.	L. Cos	L. Cot	L. Tan	L. Sin	Deg.

Left footer row:
| Deg. | L. Cos | L. Cot | L. Tan | L. Sin | Deg. |

Deg.	L. Sin	L. Tan	L. Cot	L. Cos	Deg.
12.0	9.31788	9.32747	0.67253	9.99040	78.0
.1	9.32143	9.33119	0.66881	9.99024	77.9
.2	9.32495	9.33487	0.66513	9.99008	.8
.3	9.32844	9.33853	0.66147	9.98991	.7
.4	9.33190	9.34215	0.65785	9.98975	.6
.5	9.33534	9.34576	0.65424	9.98958	.5
.6	9.33874	9.34933	0.65067	9.98941	.4
.7	9.34212	9.35288	0.64712	9.98924	.3
.8	9.34547	9.35640	0.64360	9.98907	.2
.9	9.34879	9.35989	0.64011	9.98890	77.1
13.0	9.35209	9.36336	0.63664	9.98872	77.0
.1	9.35536	9.36681	0.63319	9.98855	76.9
.2	9.35860	9.37023	0.62977	9.98837	.8
.3	9.36182	9.37363	0.62637	9.98819	.7
.4	9.36502	9.37700	0.62300	9.98801	.6
.5	9.36819	9.38035	0.61965	6.98783	.5
.6	9.37133	9.38368	0.61632	9.98765	.4
.7	9.37445	9.38699	0.61301	9.98746	.3
.8	9.37755	9.39027	0.60973	9.98728	.2
.9	9 38062	9.39353	0.60647	9.98709	76.1
14.0	9.38368	9.39677	0.60323	9.98690	76.0
.1	9.38670	9.39999	0.60001	9.98671	75.9
.2	9.38971	9.40319	0.59681	9.98652	.8
.3	9.39270	9.40636	0.59364	9.98633	.7
.4	9.39566	9 40952	0.59048	9.98614	.6
.5	9.39860	9 41266	0.58734	9.98594	.5
.6	9.40152	9.41578	0.58422	9.98574	.4
.7	9.40442	9.41887	0.58113	9.98555	.3
.8	9.40730	9.42195	0.57805	9.98535	.2
.9	9.41016	9.42501	0.57499	9.98515	75.1
15.0	9.41300	9.42805	0.57195	9.98494	75.0
.1	9.41582	9.43108	0.56892	9.98474	74.9
.2	9.41861	9.43408	0.56592	9.98453	.8
.3	9.42140	9.43707	0.56293	9.98433	.7
.4	9.42416	9 44004	0.55996	9 98412	.6
.5	9.42690	9.44299	0.55701	9.98391	.5
.6	9.42962	9.44592	0.55408	9.98370	.4
.7	9 43233	9.44884	0.55116	9 98349	.3
.8	9.43502	9.45174	0.54826	9 98327	.2
.9	9.43769	9.45463	0.54537	9.98306	74.1
16.0	9.44034	9.45750	0.54250	9.98284	74.0
.1	9.44297	9.46035	0.53965	9.98262	73.9
.2	9.44559	9.46319	0.53681	9.98240	.8
.3	9.44819	9.46601	0.53399	9 98218	.7
.4	9.45077	9.46881	0.53119	9 98196	.6
.5	9.45334	9 47160	0.52840	9.98174	.5
.6	9.45589	9.47438	0.52562	9 98151	.4
.7	9.45843	9.47714	0.52286	9 98129	.3
.8	9.46095	9.47989	0.52011	9.98106	.2
.9	9.46345	9.48262	0.51738	9 98083	73.1
17.0	9.46594	9.48534	0.51466	9.98060	73.0
.1	9.46841	9.48804	0.51196	9 98036	72.9
.2	9.47086	9.49073	0.50927	9 98013	.8
.3	9.47330	9.49341	0.50659	9 97989	.7
.4	9.47573	9.49607	0.50393	9.97966	.6
.5	9.47814	9.49872	0.50128	9 97942	.5
.6	9.48054	9.50136	0.49864	9 97918	.4
.7	9.48292	9.50398	0.49602	9.97894	.3
.8	9.48529	9.50659	0.49341	9.97870	.2
.9	9.48764	9.50919	0.49081	9.97845	72.1
18.0	9.48998	9.51178	0.48822	9.97821	72.0
Deg.	L. Cos	L. Cot	L. Tan	L. Sin	Deg.

Deg.	L. Sin	L. Tan	L. Cot	L. Cos	Deg.
18.0	9.48998	9.51178	0.48822	9.97821	72.0
.1	9.49231	9 51435	0.48565	9.97795	71.9
.2	9.49462	9 51691	0.48309	9.97771	.8
.3	9.49692	9.51946	0.48054	9 97746	.7
.4	9.49920	9.52200	0.47801	9.97721	.6
.5	9.50148	9 52452	0.47548	9.97696	.5
.6	9.50374	9.52703	0.47297	9.97670	.4
.7	9.50598	9.52953	0 47047	9.97645	.3
.8	9.50821	9.53202	0.46798	9.97619	.2
.9	9.51043	9.53450	0.46550	9.97593	71.1
19.0	9.51264	9.53697	0.46303	9.97567	71.0
.1	9.51484	9.53943	0.46057	9.97541	70.9
.2	9.51702	9.54187	0.45813	9.97515	.8
.3	9.51919	9.54431	0 45569	9.97488	.7
.4	9 52135	9.54673	0.45327	9 97461	.6
.5	9.52350	9 54915	0 45085	9.97435	.5
.6	9.52563	9.55155	0.44845	9 97408	.4
.7	9.52775	9.55395	0.44605	9.97381	.3
.8	9.52986	9.55633	0.44367	9.97353	.2
.9	9.53196	9.55870	0.44130	9.97326	70.1
20.0	9.53405	9.56107	0.43893	9.97299	70.0
.1	9.53613	9.56342	0.43658	9.97271	69.9
.2	9.53819	9.56576	0.43424	9.97243	.8
.3	9.54025	9.56810	0.43190	9.97215	.7
.4	9 54229	9.57042	0.42958	9 97187	.6
.5	9.54433	9.57274	0.42726	9.97159	.5
.6	9.54635	9.57504	0 42496	9.97130	.4
.7	9.54836	9.57734	0.42266	9.97102	.3
.8	9.55036	9.57963	0.42037	9.97073	.2
.9	9.55235	9 58191	0.41809	9.97044	69.1
21.0	9.55433	9 58418	0.41582	9.97015	69.0
.1	9.55630	9.58644	0.41356	9.96986	68.9
.2	9 55826	9.58869	0.41131	9.96957	.8
.3	9 56021	9.59094	0.40906	9.96927	.7
.4	9.56215	9.59317	0.40683	9.96898	.6
.5	9.56407	9.59540	0.40460	9.96868	.5
.6	9.56599	9.59762	0.40238	9.96838	.4
.7	9.56790	9.59983	0.40017	9.96808	.3
.8	9.56980	9 60203	0.39797	9.96778	.2
.9	9.57169	9.60422	0.39578	9.96747	68.1
22.0	9.57358	9.60641	0.39359	9.96717	68.0
.1	9.57545	9.60859	0.39141	9.96686	67.9
.2	9.57731	9.61076	0.38924	9.96655	.8
.3	9.57916	9.61292	0.38708	9.96624	.7
.4	9.58101	9.61508	0.38492	9.96593	.6
.5	9.58284	9.61722	0.38278	9.96562	.5
.6	9.58467	9.61936	0.38064	9.96530	.4
.7	9.58648	9.62150	0.37850	9.96498	.3
.8	9.58829	9.62362	0.37638	9.96467	.2
.9	9 59009	9.62574	0.37426	9.96435	67.1
23.0	9.59188	9.62785	0.37215	9.96403	67.0
.1	9.59366	9.62996	0.37004	9.96370	66.9
.2	9.59543	9.63205	0.36794	9.96338	.8
.3	9.59720	9.63414	0.36586	9.96305	.7
.4	9.59895	9.63623	0 36377	9.96273	.6
.5	9.60070	9.63830	0 36170	9.96240	.5
.6	9.60244	9.64037	0.35963	9 96207	.4
.7	9.60417	9 64243	0.35757	9.96174	.3
.8	9.60589	9 64449	0.35551	9.96140	.2
.9	9.60761	9.64654	0.35346	9.96107	66.1
24.0	9.60931	9.64858	0.35142	9.96073	66.0
Deg.	L. Cos	L. Cot	L. Tan	L. Sin	Deg.

LOGARITHMS OF FUNCTIONS FOR DEGREES AND DECIMALS
(Continued)

Deg.	L. Sin	L. Tan	L. Cot	L. Cos	Deg.
24.0	9.60931	9.64858	0.35142	9.96073	**66.0**
.1	9.61101	9 65062	0 34938	9.96039	65.9
.2	9.61270	9 65265	0.34735	9.96005	.8
.3	9.61438	9.65467	0.34533	9 95971	.7
.4	9.61606	9.65669	0.34331	9.95937	.6
.5	9 61773	9.65870	0.34130	9.95902	.5
.6	9 61939	9.66071	0.33929	9.95868	.4
.7	9.62104	9.66271	0.33729	9.95833	.3
.8	9.62268	9.66470	0.33530	9.95798	.2
.9	9.62432	9.66669	0.33331	9.95763	65.1
25.0	9.62595	9.66867	0.33133	9.95728	**65.0**
.1	9.62757	9.67065	0.32935	9.95692	64.9
.2	9.62918	9.67262	0.32738	9.95657	.8
.3	9.63079	9.67458	0.32542	9.95621	.7
.4	9.63239	9.67654	0 32346	9.95585	.6
.5	9.63398	9.67850	0.32150	9.95549	.5
.6	9.63557	9.68044	0.31956	9 55513	.4
.7	9.63715	0.68239	0.31761	9.95476	.3
.8	9.63872	9.68432	0.31568	9.95440	.2
.9	9.64028	9.68626	0.31374	9.95403	64.1
26.0	9 64184	9.68818	0.31182	9.95366	**64.0**
.1	9.64339	9.69010	0.30990	9.95329	63.9
.2	9.64494	9.69202	0 30798	9.95292	.8
.3	9.64647	9.69392	0.30607	9.95254	.7
.4	9.64800	9.69584	0.30416	9.95217	.6
.5	9.64953	9.69774	0.30226	9 95179	.5
.6	9.65104	9.69963	0.30037	9.95141	.4
.7	9.65255	9 70152	0.29848	9.95103	.3
.8	9.65406	9 70341	0 29659	9.95065	.2
.9	9.65556	0.70529	0.29471	9.95027	63.1
27.0	9.65705	9.70717	0.29283	9.94988	**63.0**
.1	9.65853	9.70904	0 29096	9.94949	62.9
.2	9.66001	9.71090	0.28910	9.94911	.8
.3	9.66148	9.71277	0 28723	9.94871	.7
.4	9.66295	9.71462	0.28538	9.94832	.6
.5	9 66441	9.71648	0 28352	9.94793	.5
.6	9.66586	0 71833	0.28167	9.94753	.4
.7	9.66731	9.72017	0.27983	9.94714	.3
.8	9 66875	9.72201	0.27799	9.94674	.2
.9	9.67018	9.72384	0.27616	9.94634	62.1
28.0	9.67161	9.72567	0.27433	9.94593	**62.0**
.1	9.67303	9.72750	0 27250	9.94553	61.9
.2	9.67445	9.72932	0 27068	9.94513	.8
.3	9.67586	9.73114	0.26886	9.94472	.7
.4	9.67726	9 73295	0.26705	9.94431	.6
.5	9.67866	9.73476	0.26524	9.94390	.5
.6	9.68006	9.73657	0.26343	9.94349	.4
.7	9.68144	9.73837	0.26163	9.94307	.3
.8	9.68283	9.74017	0.25983	9.94266	.2
.9	9.68420	9.74196	0.25804	9.94224	61.1
29.0	9.68557	9.74375	0.25625	9.94182	**61.0**
.1	9.68694	9.74554	0.25446	9.94140	60.9
.2	9 68829	9.74732	0.25268	9.94098	.8
.3	9.68965	9.74910	0.25090	9.94055	.7
.4	9.69100	9.75087	0.24913	9.94012	.6
.5	9.69234	9.75264	0.24736	9.93970	.5
.6	9.69368	9.75441	0.24559	9.93927	.4
.7	9.69501	9.75617	0.24383	9.93884	.3
.8	9.69633	9.75793	0.24207	9.93840	.2
.9	9.69765	9.75969	0.24031	9.93797	60.1
30.0	9.69879	9.76144	0.23856	9.93753	**60.0**
Deg.	**L. Cos**	**L. Cot**	**L. Tan**	**L Sin**	**Deg.**

Deg.	L. Sin	L. Tan	L. Cot	L. Cos	Deg.
30.0	9.69897	9.76144	0.23856	9.93753	**60.0**
.1	9.70028	9.76319	0.23681	9.93709	59.9
.2	9.70159	9.76493	0.23507	9.93665	.8
.3	9.70288	9.76668	0.23332	9.93621	.7
.4	9 70418	9.76841	0.23159	9.93577	.6
.5	9 70547	9.77015	0 22985	9.93532	.5
.6	9 70675	9.77188	0.22812	9.93487	.4
.7	9.70803	9.77361	0 22639	9.93442	.3
.8	9.70931	9.77533	0.22467	9.93397	.2
.9	9.71057	9.77706	0.22294	9.93352	59.1
31.0	9.71184	9.77877	0.22123	9.93307	**59.0**
.1	9.71310	9.78049	0.21951	9.93261	58.9
.2	9.71435	9.78220	0 21780	9.93215	.8
.3	9.71560	9.78391	0.21609	9.93169	.7
.4	9.71685	9.78562	0.21438	9.93123	.6
.5	9.71809	9.78732	0.21268	9.93077	.5
.6	9.71932	9.78902	0.21098	9.93030	.4
.7	9.72055	9.79072	0.20928	9.92983	.3
.8	9.72177	9.79241	0.20759	9.92936	.2
.9	9.72299	9.79410	0.20590	9 92889	58.1
32.0	9.72421	9.79579	0.20421	9 92842	**58.0**
.1	9.72542	9.79747	0.20253	9.92795	57.9
.2	9.72663	9.79916	0.20084	9.92747	.8
.3	9 72783	9.80084	0 19916	9.92699	.7
.4	9.72902	9.80251	0.19749	9 92651	.6
.5	9 73022	9.80419	0.19581	9 92603	.5
.6	9.73140	9.80586	0.19414	9.92555	.4
.7	9.73259	9 80753	0 19247	9.92506	.3
.8	9.73376	9.80919	0.19081	9.92457	.2
.9	9.73494	9.81086	0.18914	9 92408	57.1
33.0	9.73611	9.81252	0.18748	9.92359	**57.0**
.1	9.73727	9.81418	0.18582	9 92310	56.9
.2	9.73843	9.81583	0.18417	9.92260	.8
.3	9.73959	9.81748	0.18252	9.92211	.7
.4	9.74074	9.81913	0.18087	9.92161	.6
.5	9 74189	9.82078	0.17922	9.92111	.5
.6	9.74303	9.82243	0.17757	9.92060	.4
.7	9.74417	9.82407	0 17593	9.92010	.3
.8	9.74531	9.82571	0.17429	9.91959	.2
.9	9.74644	9.82735	0.17265	9 91908	56.1
34.0	9.74756	9.82899	0.17101	9 91857	**56.0**
.1	9.74868	9.83062	0.16938	9.91806	55.9
.2	9.74980	9.83225	0.16775	9.91755	.8
.3	9.75091	9.83388	0.16612	9.91703	.7
.4	9.75202	9.83551	0.16449	9.91651	.6
.5	9.75313	9 83713	0.16287	9.91599	.5
.6	9.75423	9.83876	0.16124	9.91547	.4
.7	9.75533	9.84038	0 15962	9.91495	.3
.8	9.75642	9.84200	0.15800	9.91442	.2
.9	9.75751	9.84361	0.15639	9 91389	55.1
35.0	9.75859	9.84523	0.15477	9.91336	**55.0**
.1	9.75967	9.84684	0.15316	9.91283	54.9
.2	9.76075	9.84845	0.15155	9.91230	.8
.3	9.76182	9 85006	0.14994	9.91176	.7
.4	9.76289	9.85166	0.14834	9.91123	.6
.5	9.76395	9.85327	0.14673	9.91069	.5
.6	9.76501	9.85487	0.14513	9 91014	.4
.7	9.76607	9.85647	0.14353	9.90960	.3
.8	9.76712	9.85807	0.14193	9.90906	.2
.9	9.76817	9.85967	0.14033	9.90851	54.1
36.0	9.76922	9.86126	0 13874	9.90796	**54.0**
Deg.	**L. Cos**	**L. Cot**	**L. Tan**	**L. Sin**	**Deg.**

Deg.	L. Sin	L. Tan	L. Cot	L. Cos	Deg.
36.0	9.76922	9.86126	0.13874	9.90796	**54.0**
.1	9.77026	9.86285	0.13715	9.90741	53.9
.2	9.77130	9.86445	0.13555	9.90685	.8
.3	9.77233	9.86603	0.13397	9.90630	.7
.4	9.77336	9.86762	0.13238	9.90574	.6
.5	9.77439	9.86921	0.13079	9.90518	.5
.6	9.77541	9.87079	0.12921	9.90462	.4
.7	9.77643	9.87238	0.12762	9.90405	.3
.8	9.77744	9.87396	0.12604	9.90349	.2
.9	9.77846	9.87554	0.12446	9.90292	53.1
37.0	9.77946	9.87711	0.12289	9.90235	**53.0**
.1	9.78047	9.87869	0.12131	9.90178	52.9
.2	9.78147	9.88027	0.11973	9.90120	.8
.3	9.78246	9.88184	0.11816	9.90063	.7
.4	9.78346	9.88341	0.11659	9.90005	.6
.5	9.78445	9.88498	0.11502	9.89947	.5
.6	9.78543	9.88655	0.11345	9.89888	.4
.7	9.78642	9.88812	0.11188	9.89830	.3
.8	9.78739	9.88968	0.11032	9.89771	.2
.9	9.78837	9.89125	0.10875	9.89712	52.1
38.0	9.78934	9.89281	0.10719	9.89653	**52.0**
.1	9.79031	9.89437	0.10563	9.89594	51.9
.2	9.79128	9.89593	0.10407	9.89534	.8
.3	9.79224	9.89749	0.10251	9.89475	.7
.4	9.79319	9.89905	0.10095	9.89415	.6
.5	9.79415	9.90061	0.09939	9.89354	.5
.6	9.79510	9.90216	0.09784	9.89294	.4
.7	9.79605	9.90371	0.09629	9.89233	.3
.8	9.79699	9.90527	0.09473	9.89173	.2
.9	9.79793	9.90682	0.09318	9.89112	51.1
39.0	9.79887	9.90837	0.09163	9.89050	**51.0**
.1	9.79981	9.90992	0.09008	9.88989	50.9
.2	9.80074	9.91147	0.08853	9.88927	.8
.3	9.80166	9.91301	0.08699	9.88865	.7
.4	9.80259	9.91456	0.08544	9.88803	.6
.5	9.80351	9.91610	0.08390	9.88741	.5
.6	9.80443	9.91765	0.08235	9.88678	.4
.7	9.80534	9.91919	0.08081	9.88615	.3
.8	9.80625	9.92073	0.07927	9.88552	.2
.9	9.80716	9.92227	0.07773	9.88489	50.1
40.0	9.80807	9.92381	0.07619	9.88425	**50.0**
.1	9.80897	9.92535	0.07465	9.88362	49.9
.2	9.80987	9.92689	0.07311	9.88298	.8
.3	9.81076	9.92843	0.07157	9.88234	.7
.4	9.81166	9.92996	0.07004	9.88169	.6
.5	9.81254	9.93150	0.06850	9.88105	.5
.6	9.81343	9.93303	0.06697	9.88040	.4
.7	9.81431	9.93457	0.06543	9.87975	.3
.8	9.81519	9.93610	0.06390	9.87909	.2
.9	9.81607	9.93763	0.06237	9.87844	49.1
41.0	9.81694	9.93916	0.06084	9.87778	**49.0**
Deg.	L. Cos	L. Cot	L. Tan	L. Sin	Deg.

Deg.	L. Sin	L. Tan	L. Cot	L. Cos	Deg.
41.0	9.81694	9.93916	0.06084	9.87778	**49.0**
.1	9.81781	9.94069	0.05931	9.87712	48.9
.2	9.81868	9.94222	0.05778	9.87646	.8
.3	9.81955	9.94375	0.05625	9.87579	.7
.4	9.82041	9.94528	0.05472	9.87513	.6
.5	9.82126	9.94681	0.05319	9.87446	.5
.6	9.82212	9.94834	0.05166	9.87378	.4
.7	9.82297	9.94986	0.05014	9.87311	.3
.8	9.82382	9.95139	0.04861	9.87243	.2
.9	9.82467	9.95291	0.04709	9.87175	48.1
42.0	9.82551	9.95444	0.04556	9.87107	**48.0**
.1	9.82635	9.95596	0.04404	9.87039	47.9
.2	9.82719	9.95748	0.04252	9.86970	.8
.3	9.82802	9.95901	0.04099	9.86902	.7
.4	9.82885	9.96053	0.03947	9.86832	.6
.5	9.82968	9.96205	0 03795	9.86763	.5
.6	9.83051	9.96357	0.03643	9.86694	.4
.7	9.83133	9.96510	0 03490	9.86624	.3
.8	9.83215	9.96662	0.03338	9.86554	.2
.9	9.83297	9.96814	0.03186	9.86483	47.1
43.0	9.83378	9.96966	0.03034	9.86413	**47.0**
.1	9.83459	9.97118	0.02882	9.86342	46.9
.2	9.83540	9.97269	0.02731	9.86271	.8
.3	9 83621	9.97421	0.02579	9.86200	.7
.4	9.83701	9.97573	0.02427	9.86128	.6
.5	9.83781	9.97725	0.02275	9.86056	.5
.6	9.83861	9.97877	0 02123	9.85984	.4
.7	9.83940	9.98029	0.01971	9.85912	.3
.8	9.84020	9.98180	0.01820	9.85839	.2
.9	9.84098	9.98332	0.01668	9.85766	46.1
44.0	9.84177	9.98484	0.01516	9.85693	**46.0**
.1	9.84255	9.98635	0.01365	9.85620	45.9
.2	9.84334	9.98787	0.01213	9.85547	.8
.3	9 84411	9 98939	0.01061	9.85473	.7
.4	9.84489	9.99090	0.00910	9.85399	.6
.5	9.84566	9.99242	0.00758	9.85324	.5
.6	9.84643	9.99394	0.00606	9.85250	.4
.7	9.84720	9.99545	0.00455	9.85175	.3
.8	9.84796	9.99697	0.00303	9.85100	.2
.9	9.84873	9.99848	0.00152	9.85024	45.1
45.0	9.84949	0.00000	0.00000	9.84949	**45.0**
Deg.	L. Cos	L. Cot	L. Tan	L. Sin	Deg.

NATURAL FUNCTIONS FOR ANGLES IN RADIANS

Rad.	Sin	Tan	Cot	Cos	Rad.	Sin	Tan	Cot	Cos
.00	.00000	.00000	∞	1.00000	**.50**	.47943	.54630	1.8305	.87758
.01	.01000	.01000	99.997	0.99995	.51	.48818	.55936	1.7878	.87274
.02	.02000	.02000	49.993	.99980	.52	.49688	.57256	1.7465	.86782
.03	.03000	.03001	33.323	.99955	.53	.50553	.58592	1.7067	.86281
.04	.03999	.04002	24.987	.99920	.54	.51414	.59943	1.6683	.85771
.05	.04998	.05004	19.983	.99875	.55	.52269	.61311	1.6310	.85252
.06	.05996	.06007	16.647	.99820	.56	.53119	.62695	1.5950	.84726
.07	.06994	.07011	14.262	.99755	.57	.53963	.64097	1.5601	.84190
.08	.07991	.08017	12.473	.99680	.58	.54802	.65517	1.5263	.83646
.09	.08988	.09024	11.081	.99595	.59	.55636	.66956	1.4935	.83094
.10	.09983	.10033	9.9666	.99500	**.60**	.56464	.68414	1.4617	.82534
.11	.10978	.11045	9.0542	.99396	.61	.57287	.69892	1.4308	.81965
.12	.11971	.12058	8.2933	.99281	.62	.58104	.71391	1.4007	.81388
.13	.12963	.13074	7.6489	.99156	.63	.58914	.72911	1.3715	.80803
.14	.13954	.14092	7.0961	.99022	.64	.59720	.74454	1.3431	.80210
.15	.14944	.15114	6.6166	.98877	.65	.60519	.76020	1.3154	.79608
.16	.15932	.16138	6.1966	.98723	.66	.61312	.77610	1.2885	.78999
.17	.16918	.17166	5.8256	.98558	.67	.62099	.79225	1.2622	.78382
.18	.17903	.18197	5.4954	.98384	.68	.62879	.80866	1.2366	.77757
.19	.18886	.19232	5.1997	.98200	.69	.63654	.82534	1.2116	.77125
.20	.19867	.20271	4.9332	.98007	**.70**	.64422	.84229	1.1872	.76484
.21	.20846	.21314	4.6917	.97803	.71	.65183	.85953	1.1634	.75836
.22	.21823	.22362	4.4719	.97590	.72	.65938	.87707	1.1402	.75181
.23	.22798	.23414	4.2709	.97367	.73	.66687	.89492	1.1174	.74517
.24	.23770	.24472	4.0864	.97134	.74	.67429	.91309	1.0952	.73847
.25	.24740	.25534	3.9163	.96891	.75	.68164	.93160	1.0734	.73169
.26	.25708	.26602	3.7591	.96639	.76	.68892	.95045	1.0521	.72484
.27	.26673	.27676	3.6133	.96377	.77	.69614	.96967	1.0313	.71791
.28	.27636	.28755	3.4776	.96106	.78	.70328	.98926	1.0109	.71091
.29	.28595	.29841	3.3511	.95824	.79	.71035	1.0092	.99084	.70385
.30	.29552	.30934	3.2327	.95534	**.80**	.71736	1.0296	.97121	.69671
.31	.30506	.32033	3.1218	.95233	.81	.72429	1.0505	.95197	.68950
.32	.31457	.33139	3.0176	.94924	.82	.73115	1.0717	.93309	.68222
.33	.32404	.34252	2.9195	.94604	.83	.73793	1.0934	.91455	.67488
.34	.33349	.35374	2.8270	.94275	.84	.74464	1.1156	.89635	.66746
.35	.34290	.36503	2.7395	.93937	.85	.75128	1.1383	.87848	.65998
.36	.35227	.37640	2.6567	.93590	.86	.75784	1.1616	.86091	.65244
.37	.36162	.38786	2.5782	.93233	.87	.76433	1.1853	.84365	.64483
.38	.37092	.39941	2.5037	.92866	.88	.77074	1.2097	.82668	.63715
.39	.38019	.41105	2.4328	.92491	.89	.77707	1.2346	.80998	.62941
.40	.38942	.42279	2.3652	.92106	**.90**	.78333	1.2602	.79355	.62161
.41	.39861	.43463	2.3008	.91712	.91	.78950	1.2864	.77738	.61375
.42	.40776	.44657	2.2393	.91309	.92	.79560	1.3133	.76146	.60582
.43	.41687	.45862	2.1804	.90897	.93	.80162	1.3409	.74578	.59783
.44	.42594	.47078	2.1241	.90475	.94	.80756	1.3692	.73034	.58979
.45	.43497	.48306	2.0702	.90045	.95	.81342	1.3984	.71511	.58168
.46	.44395	.49545	2.0184	.89605	.96	.81919	1.4284	.70010	.57352
.47	.45289	.50797	1.9686	.89157	.97	.82489	1.4592	.68531	.56530
.48	.46178	.52061	1.9208	.88699	.98	.83050	1.4910	.67071	.55702
.49	.47063	.53339	1.8748	.88233	.99	.83603	1.5237	.65631	.54869
.50	.47943	.54630	1.8305	.87758	**1.00**	.84147	1.5574	.64209	.54030
Rad.	Sin	Tan	Cot	Cos	Rad.	Sin	Tan	Cot	Cos

Rad.	Sin	Tan	Cot	Cos	Rad.	Sin	Tan	Cot	Cos
1.00	.84147	1.5574	.64209	.54030	**1.50**	.99749	14.101	.07091	.07074
1.01	.84683	1.5922	.62806	.53186	1.51	.99815	16.428	.06087	.06076
1.02	.85211	1.6281	.61420	.52337	1.52	.99871	19.670	.05084	.05077
1.03	.85730	1.6652	.60051	.51482	1.53	.99917	24.498	.04082	.04079
1.04	.86240	1.7036	.58699	.50622	1.54	.99953	32.461	.03081	.03079
1.05	.86742	1.7433	.57362	.49757	1.55	.99978	48.078	.02080	.02079
1.06	.87236	1.7844	.56040	.48887	1.56	.99994	92.621	.01080	.01080
1.07	.87720	1.8270	.54734	.48012	1.57	1.00000	1255.8	.00080	.00080
1.08	.88196	1.8712	.53441	.47133	1.58	.99996	-108.65	-.00920	-.00920
1.09	.88663	1.9171	.52162	.46249	1.59	.99982	-52.067	-.01921	-.01920
1.10	.89121	1.9648	.50897	.45360	**1.60**	.99957	-34.233	-.02921	-.02920
1.11	.89570	2.0143	.49644	.44466	1.61	.99923	-25.495	-.03922	-.03919
1.12	.90010	2.0660	.48404	.43568	1.62	.99879	-20.307	-.04924	-.04918
1.13	.90441	2.1198	.47175	.42666	1.63	.99825	-16.871	-.05927	-.05917
1.14	.90863	2.1759	.45959	.41759	1.64	.99761	-14.427	-.06931	-.06915
1.15	.91276	2.2345	.44753	.40849	1.65	.99687	-12.599	-.07937	-.07912
1.16	.91680	2.2958	.43558	.39934	1.66	.99602	-11.181	-.08944	-.08909
1.17	.92075	2.3600	.42373	.39015	1.67	.99508	-10.047	-.09953	-.09904
1.18	.92461	2.4273	.41199	.38092	1.68	.99404	- 9.1208	-.10964	-.10899
1.19	.92837	2.4979	.40034	.37166	1.69	.99290	- 8.3492	-.11977	-.11892
1.20	.93204	2.5722	.38878	.36236	**1.70**	.99166	- 7.6966	-.12993	-.12884
1.21	.93562	2.6503	.37731	.35302	1.71	.99033	- 7.1373	-.14011	-.13875
1.22	.93910	2.7328	.36593	.34365	1.72	.98889	- 6.6524	-.15032	-.14865
1.23	.94249	2.8198	.35463	.33424	1.73	.98735	- 6.2281	-.16056	-.15853
1.24	.94578	2.9119	.34341	.32480	1.74	.98572	- 5.8535	-.17084	-.16840
1.25	.94898	3.0096	.33227	.31532	1.75	.98399	- 5.5204	-.18115	-.17825
1.26	.95209	3.1133	.32121	.30582	1.76	.98215	- 5.2221	-.19149	-.18808
1.27	.95510	3.2236	.31021	.29628	1.77	.98022	- 4.9534	-.20188	-.19789
1.28	.95802	3.3413	.29928	.28672	1.78	.97820	- 4.7101	-.21231	-.20768
1.29	.96084	3.4672	.28842	.27712	1.79	.97607	- 4.4887	-.22278	-.21745
1.30	.96356	3.6021	.27762	.26750	**1.80**	.97385	- 4.2863	-.23330	-.22720
1.31	.96618	3.7471	.26687	.25785	1.81	.97153	- 4.1005	-.24387	-.23693
1.32	.96872	3.9033	.25619	.24818	1.82	.96911	- 3.9294	-.25449	-.24663
1.33	.97115	4.0723	.24556	.23848	1.83	.96659	- 3.7712	-.26517	-.25631
1.34	.97348	4.2556	.23498	.22875	1.84	.96398	- 3.6245	-.27590	-.26596
1.35	.97572	4.4552	.22446	.21901	1.85	.96128	- 3.4881	-.28669	-.27559
1.36	.97786	4.6734	.21398	.20924	1.86	.95847	- 3.3608	-.29755	-.28519
1.37	.97991	4.9131	.20354	.19945	1.87	.95557	- 3.2419	-.30846	-.29476
1.38	.98185	5.1774	.19315	.18964	1.88	.95258	- 3.1304	-.31945	-.30430
1.39	.98370	5.4707	.18279	.17981	1.89	.94949	- 3.0257	-.33051	-.31381
1.40	.98545	5.7979	.17248	.16997	**1.90**	.94630	- 2.9271	-.34164	-.32329
1.41	.98710	6.1654	.16220	.16010	1.91	.94302	- 2.8341	-.35284	-.33274
1.42	.98865	6.5811	.15195	.15023	1.92	.93965	- 2.7463	-.36413	-.34215
1.43	.99010	7.0555	.14173	.14033	1.93	.93618	- 2.6632	-.37549	-.35153
1.44	.99146	7.6018	.13155	.13042	1.94	.93262	- 2.5843	-.38695	-.36087
1.45	.99271	8.2381	.12139	.12050	1.95	.92896	- 2.5095	-.39849	-.37018
1.46	.99387	8.9886	.11125	.11057	1.96	.92521	- 2.4383	-.41012	-.37945
1.47	.99492	9.8874	.10114	.10063	1.97	.92137	- 2.3705	-.42185	-.38868
1.48	.99588	10.983	.09105	.09067	1.98	.91744	- 2.3058	-.43368	-.39788
1.49	.99674	12.350	.08097	.08071	1.99	.91341	- 2.2441	-.44562	-.40703
1.50	.99749	14.101	.07091	.07074	**2.00**	.90930	- 2.1850	-.45766	-.41615
Rad.	Sin	Tan	Cot	Cos	Rad.	Sin	Tan	Cot	Cos

Rad.	L. Sin	L. Tan	L. Cot	L. Cos
.00	− ∞	− ∞	∞	0.00000
.01	7.99999	8.00001	1.99999	9.99998
.02	8.30100	8.30109	1.69891	9.99991
.03	8.47706	8.47725	1.52275	9.99980
.04	8.60194	8.60229	1.39771	9.99965
.05	8.69879	8.69933	1.30067	9.99946
.06	8.77789	8.77867	1.22133	9.99922
.07	8.84474	8.84581	1.15419	9.99894
.08	8.90263	8.90402	1.09598	9.99861
.09	8.95366	8.95542	1.04458	9.99824
.10	8.99928	9.00145	0.99855	9.99782
.11	9.04052	9.04315	0.95685	9.99737
.12	9.07814	9.08127	0.91873	9.99687
.13	9.11272	9.11640	0.88360	9.99632
.14	9.14471	9.14898	0.85102	9.99573
.15	9.17446	9.17937	0.82063	9.99510
.16	9.20227	9.20785	0.79215	9.99442
.17	9.22836	9.23466	0.76534	9.99369
.18	9.25292	9.26000	0.74000	9.99293
.19	9.27614	9.28402	0.71598	9.99211
.20	9.29813	9.30688	0.69312	9.99126
.21	9.31902	9.32867	0.67133	9.99035
.22	9.33891	9.34951	0.65049	9.98940
.23	9.35789	9.36948	0.63052	9.98841
.24	9.37603	9.38866	0.61134	9.98737
.25	9.39341	9.40712	0.59288	9.98628
.26	9.41007	9.42492	0.57508	9.98515
.27	9.42607	9.44210	0.55790	9.98397
.28	9.44147	9.45872	0.54128	9.98275
.29	9.45629	9.47482	0.52518	9.98148
.30	9.47059	9.49043	0.50957	9.98016
.31	9.48438	9.50559	0.49441	9.97879
.32	9.49771	9.52034	0.47966	9.97737
.33	9.51060	9.53469	0.46531	9.97591
.34	9.52308	9.54868	0.45132	9.97440
.35	9.53516	9.56233	0.43767	9.97284
.36	9.54688	9.57565	0.42435	9.97123
.37	9.55825	9.58868	0.41132	9.96957
.38	9.56928	9.60142	0.39858	9.96786
.39	9.58000	9.61390	0.38610	9.96610
.40	9.59042	9.62613	0.37387	9.96429
.41	9.60055	9.63812	0.36188	9.96243
.42	9.61041	9.64989	0.35011	9.96051
.43	9.62000	9.66145	0.33855	9.95855
.44	9.62935	9.67282	0.32718	9.95653
.45	9.63845	9.68400	0.31600	9.95446
.46	9.64733	9.69500	0.30500	9.95233
.47	9.65599	9.70583	0.29417	9.95015
.48	9.66443	9.71651	0.28349	9.94792
.49	9.67268	9.72704	0.27296	9.94563
.50	9.68072	9.73743	0.26257	9.94329

Rad.	L. Sin	L. Tan	L. Cot	L. Cos
.50	9.68072	9.73743	0.26257	9.94329
.51	9.68858	9.74769	0.25231	9.94089
.52	9.69625	9.75782	0.24218	9.93843
.53	9.70375	9.76784	0.23216	9.93591
.54	9.71108	9.77774	0.22226	9.93334
.55	9.71824	9.78754	0.21246	9.93071
.56	9.72525	9.79723	0.20277	9.92801
.57	9.73210	9.80684	0.19316	9.92526
.58	9.73880	9.81635	0.18365	9.92245
.59	9.74536	9.82579	0.17421	9.91957
.60	9.75177	9.83514	0.16486	9.91663
.61	9.75805	9.84443	0.15557	9.91363
.62	9.76420	9.85364	0.14636	9.91056
.63	9.77022	9.86280	0.13720	9.90743
.64	9.77612	9.87189	0.12811	9.90423
.65	9.78189	9.88093	0.11907	9.90096
.66	9.78754	9.88992	0.11008	9.89762
.67	9.79308	9.89886	0.10114	9.89422
.68	9.79851	9.90777	0.09223	9.89074
.69	9.80382	9.91663	0.08337	9.88719
.70	9.80903	9.92546	0.07454	9.88357
.71	9.81414	9.93426	0.06574	9.87988
.72	9.81914	9.94303	0.05697	9.87611
.73	9.82404	9.95178	0.04822	9.87226
.74	9.82885	9.96051	0.03949	9.86833
.75	9.83355	9.96923	0.03077	9.86433
.76	9.83817	9.97793	0.02207	9.86024
.77	9.84269	9.98662	0.01338	9.85607
.78	9.84713	9.99531	0.00469	9.85182
.79	9.85147	0.00400	9.99600	9.84748
.80	9.85573	0.01268	9.98732	9.84305
.81	9.85991	0.02138	9.97862	9.83853
.82	9.86400	0.03008	9.96992	9.83393
.83	9.86802	0.03879	9.96121	9.82922
.84	9.87195	0.04752	9.95248	9.82443
.85	9.87580	0.05627	9.94373	9.81953
.86	9.87958	0.06504	9.93496	9.81454
.87	9.88328	0.07384	9.92616	9.80944
.88	9.88691	0.08266	9.91734	9.80424
.89	9.89046	0.09153	9.90847	9.79894
.90	9.89394	0.10043	9.89957	9.79352
.91	9.89735	0.10937	9.89063	9.78799
.92	9.90070	0.11835	9.88165	9.78234
.93	9.90397	0.12739	9.87261	9.77658
.94	9.90717	0.13648	9.86352	9.77070
.95	9.91031	0.14563	9.85437	9.76469
.96	9.91339	0.15484	9.84516	9.75855
.97	9.91639	0.16412	9.83588	9.75228
.98	9.91934	0.17347	9.82653	9.74587
.99	9.92222	0.18289	9.81711	9.73933
1.00	9.92504	0.19240	9.80760	9.73264

Rad.	L. Sin	L. Tan	L. Cot	L. Cos

Rad.	L. Sin	L. Tan	L. Cot	L. Cos	Rad.	L. Sin	L. Tan	L. Cot	L. Cos
1.00	9.92504	0.19240	9.80760	9.73264	**1.50**	9.99891	1.14926	8.85074	8.84965
1.01	9.92780	0.20200	9.79800	9.72580	1.51	9.99920	1.21559	8.78441	8.78361
1.02	9.93049	0.21169	9.78831	9.71881	1.52	9.99944	1.29379	8.70621	8.70565
1.03	9.93313	0.22148	9.77852	9.71165	1.53	9.99964	1.38914	8.61086	8.61050
1.04	9.93571	0.23137	9.76863	9.70434	1.54	9.99979	1.51136	8.48864	8.48843
1.05	9.93823	0.24138	9.75862	9.69686	1.55	9.99991	1.68195	8.31805	8.31796
1.06	9.94069	0.25150	9.74850	9.68920	1.56	9.99997	1.96671	8.03329	8.03327
1.07	9.94310	0.26175	9.73825	9.68135	1.57	0.00000	3.09891	6.90109	6.90109
1.08	9.94545	0.27212	9.72788	9.67332	1.58	9.99998	2.03603*	7.96397*	7.96396*
1.09	9.94774	0.28264	9.71736	9.66510	1.59	9.99992	1.71656	8.28344	8.28336
1.10	9.94998	0.29331	9.70669	9.65667	**1.60**	9.99981	1.53444	8.46556	8.46538
1.11	9.95216	0.30413	9.69587	9.64803	1.61	9.99967	1.40645	8.59355	8.59323
1.12	9.95429	0.31512	9.68488	9.63917	1.62	9.99947	1.30765	8.69235	8.69182
1.13	9.95637	0.32628	9.67372	9.63008	1.63	9.99924	1.22714	8.77286	8.77209
1.14	9.95839	0.33763	9.66237	9.62075	1.64	9.99896	1.15918	8.84082	8.83978
1.15	9.96036	0.34918	9.65082	9.61118	1.65	9.99864	1.10035	8.89965	8.89829
1.16	9.96228	0.36093	9.63907	9.60134	1.66	9.99827	1.04847	8.95154	8.94981
1.17	9.96414	0.37291	9.62709	9.59123	1.67	9.99786	1.00204	8.99796	8.99582
1.18	9.96596	0.38512	9.61488	9.58084	1.68	9.99741	0.96003	9.03997	9.03737
1.19	9.96772	0.39757	9.60243	9.57015	1.69	9.99691	0.92165	9.07835	9.07526
1.20	9.96943	0.41030	9.58970	9.55914	**1.70**	9.99636	0.88630	9.11370	9.11007
1.21	9.97110	0.42330	9.57670	9.54780	1.71	9.99578	0.85353	9.14647	9.14225
1.22	9.97271	0.43660	9.56340	9.53611	1.72	9.99515	0.82298	9.17702	9.17217
1.23	9.97428	0.45022	9.54978	9.52406	1.73	9.99447	0.79436	9.20564	9.20012
1.24	9.97579	0.46418	9.53582	9.51161	1.74	9.99375	0.76742	9.23258	9.22634
1.25	9.97726	0.47850	9.52150	9.49875	1.75	9.99299	0.74197	9.25803	9.25102
1.26	9.97868	0.49322	9.50678	9.48546	1.76	9.99218	0.71784	9.28216	9.27434
1.27	9.98005	0.50835	9.49165	9.47170	1.77	9.99133	0.69490	9.30510	9.29642
1.28	9.98137	0.52392	9.47608	9.45745	1.78	9.99043	0.67303	9.32697	9.31740
1.29	9.98265	0.53998	9.46002	9.44267	1.79	9.98948	0.65212	9.34788	9.33736
1.30	9.98388	0.55656	9.44344	9.42732	**1.80**	9.98849	0.63208	9.36792	9.35641
1.31	9.98506	0.57369	9.42631	9.41137	1.81	9.98745	0.61284	9.38716	9.37462
1.32	9.98620	0.59144	9.40856	9.39476	1.82	9.98637	0.59432	9.40568	9.39205
1.33	9.98729	0.60984	9.39016	9.37744	1.83	9.98524	0.57648	9.42352	9.40877
1.34	9.98833	0.62896	9.37104	9.35937	1.84	9.98407	0.55925	9.44075	9.42482
1.35	9.98933	0.64887	9.35113	9.34046	1.85	9.98285	0.54258	9.45742	9.44026
1.36	9.99028	0.66964	9.33036	9.32064	1.86	9.98158	0.52645	9.47355	9.45513
1.37	9.99119	0.69135	9.30865	9.29983	1.87	9.98026	0.51080	9.48920	9.46947
1.38	9.99205	0.71411	9.28589	9.27793	1.88	9.97890	0.49560	9.50440	9.48330
1.39	9.99286	0.73804	9.26196	9.25482	1.89	9.97749	0.48082	9.51918	9.49667
1.40	9.99363	0.76327	9.23673	9.23036	**1.90**	9.97603	0.46644	9.53356	9.50959
1.41	9.99436	0.78996	9.21004	9.20440	1.91	9.97452	0.45242	9.54758	9.52210
1.42	9.99504	0.81830	9.18170	9.17674	1.92	9.97296	0.43875	9.56125	9.53422
1.43	9.99568	0.84853	9.15147	9.14716	1.93	9.97136	0.42540	9.57460	9.54597
1.44	9.99627	0.88092	9.11908	9.11536	1.94	9.96970	0.41235	9.58765	9.55735
1.45	9.99682	0.91583	9.08417	9.08100	1.95	9.96800	0.39958	9.60042	9.56841
1.46	9.99733	0.95369	9.04631	9.04364	1.96	9.96624	0.38708	9.61292	9.57916
1.47	9.99779	0.99508	9.00492	9.00271	1.97	9.96443	0.37484	9.62516	9.58960
1.48	9.99821	1.04074	8.95926	8.95747	1.98	9.96258	0.36283	9.63717	9.59975
1.49	9.99858	1.09166	8.90834	8.90692	1.99	9.96067	0.35104	9.64896	9.60963
1.50	9.99891	1.14926	8.85074	8.84965	**2.00**	9.95871	0.33946	9.66054	9.61925
Rad.	L. Sin	L. Tan	L. Cot	L. Cos	Rad.	L. Sin	L. Tan	L. Cot	L. Cos

*Values of the cosine, tangent and cotangent for angles in the table, 1.58 radians and above, are negative.

HAVERSINES

hav $\theta = \frac{1}{2}$ vers $\theta = \frac{1}{2}(1 - \cos\theta) = \sin^2\frac{1}{2}\theta$
hav $(-\theta) = $ hav θ
hav $(180° - \theta) = $ hav $(180° + \theta) = 1 - $ hav θ
Characteristics of the logarithms are omitted.

θ°	0' Value	Log	10' Value	Log	20' Value	Log	30' Value	Log	40' Value	Log	50' Value	Log
0	.00000	—	.00000	$\bar{6}$.32539	.00001	$\bar{6}$.92745	.00002	.27963	.00003	.52951	.00005	.72332
1	.00008	.88168	.00010	.01557	.00014	.13155	.00017	.23385	.00021	.32536	.00026	.40814
2	.00030	.48371	.00036	.55323	.00041	.61759	.00048	.67751	.00054	.73355	.00061	.78620
3	.00069	.83584	.00076	.88279	.00085	.92733	.00093	.96970	.00102	.01009	.00112	.04869
4	.00122	.08564	.00132	.12108	.00143	.15513	.00154	.18790	.00166	.21947	.00178	.24993
5	.00190	.27936	.00203	.30782	.00216	.33538	.00230	.36209	.00244	.38800	.00259	.41315
6	.00274	.43760	.00289	.46138	.00305	.48452	.00321	.50706	.00338	.52902	.00355	.55044
7	.00373	.57135	.00391	.59176	.00409	.61170	.00428	.63120	.00447	.65026	.00467	.66891
8	.00487	.68717	.00507	.70505	.00528	.72257	.00549	.73974	.00571	.75657	.00593	.77308
9	.00616	.78929	.00639	.80519	.00662	.82081	.00686	.83615	.00710	.85122	.00735	.86603
10	.00760	.88059	.00785	.89491	.00811	.90900	.00837	.92286	.00864	.93650	.00891	.94993
11	.00919	.96315	.00947	.97617	.00975	.98899	.01004	.00163	.01033	.01409	.01063	.02636
12	.01093	.03847	.01123	.05041	.01154	.06218	.01185	.07379	.01217	.08525	.01249	.09656
13	.01281	.10772	.01314	.11873	.01348	.12961	.01382	.14035	.01416	.15096	.01450	.16144
14	.01485	.17179	.01521	.18202	.01556	.19212	.01593	.20211	.01629	.21198	.01666	.22175
15	.01704	.23140	.01742	.24094	.01780	.25037	.01818	.25971	.01858	.26894	.01897	.27807
16	.01937	.28711	.01977	.29605	.02018	.30490	.02059	.31366	.02101	.32233	.02142	.33091
17	.02185	.33940	.02227	.34782	.02271	.35614	.02314	.36439	.02358	.37256	.02402	.38065
18	.02447	.38867	.02492	.39660	.02538	.40447	.02584	.41226	.02630	.41998	.02677	.42764
19	.02724	.43522	.02772	.44273	.02820	.45018	.02868	.45757	.02917	.46489	.02966	.47215
20	.03015	.47934	.03065	.48647	.03116	.49355	.03166	.50056	.03218	.50752	.03269	.51442
21	.03321	.52127	.03373	.52805	.03426	.53479	.03479	.54147	.03533	.54810	.03587	.55467
22	.03641	.56120	.03695	.56767	.03751	.57410	.03806	.58047	.03862	.58680	.03918	.59308
23	.03975	.59931	.04032	.60550	.04089	.61164	.04147	.61773	.04205	.62379	.04264	.62979
24	.04323	.63576	.04382	.64168	.04442	.64756	.04502	.65340	.04562	.65920	.04623	.66496
25	.04685	.67067	.04746	.67635	.04808	.68199	.04871	.68759	.04934	.69316	.04997	.69859
26	.05060	.70418	.05124	.70963	.05189	.71505	.05253	.72043	.05318	.72578	.05384	.73109
27	.05450	.73637	.05516	.74162	.05582	.74683	.05649	.75201	.05717	.75715	.05785	.76227
28	.05853	.76735	.05921	.77240	.05990	.77742	.06059	.78241	.06129	.78737	.06199	.79230
29	.06269	.79720	.06340	.80207	.06411	.80691	.06482	.81172	.06554	.81651	.06626	.82126
30	.06699	.82599	.06772	.83069	.06845	.83537	.06919	.84001	.06993	.84464	.07067	.84923
31	.07142	.85380	.07217	.85834	.07292	.86286	.07368	.86735	.07444	.87182	.07521	.87626
32	.07598	.88068	.07675	.88507	.07752	.88944	.07830	.89379	.07909	.89811	.07987	.90241
33	.08066	.90668	.08146	.91094	.08226	.91517	.08306	.91938	.08386	.92356	.08467	.92773
34	.08548	.93187	.08630	.93599	.08711	.94009	.08794	.94417	.08876	.94823	.08959	.95227
35	.09042	.95628	.09126	.96028	.09210	.96426	.09294	.96822	.09379	.97215	.09464	.97607
36	.09549	.97996	.09635	.98384	.09721	.98770	.09807	.99154	.09894	.99536	.09981	.99917
37	.10068	.00295	.10156	.00672	.10244	.01047	.10332	.01420	.10421	.01791	.10510	.02161
38	.10599	.02528	.10689	.02894	.10779	.03259	.10870	.03621	.10960	.03982	.11051	.04341
39	.11143	.04699	.11234	.05055	.11326	.05409	.11419	.05762	.11511	.06113	.11604	.06462
40	.11698	.06810	.11791	.07157	.11885	.07501	.11980	.07845	.12074	.08186	.12169	.08526
41	.12265	.08865	.12360	.09202	.12456	.09538	.12552	.09872	.12649	.10205	.12746	.10536
42	.12843	.10836	.12940	.11194	.13038	.11521	.13136	.11847	.13235	.12171	.13333	.12494
43	.13432	.12815	.13532	.13135	.13631	.13454	.13731	.13771	.13832	.14087	.13932	.14402
44	.14033	.14715	.14134	.15027	.14236	.15338	.14337	.15647	.14440	.15955	.14542	.16262
45	.14645	.16568	.14748	.16872	.14851	.17175	.14955	.17477	.15058	.17778	.15163	.18077
46	.15267	.18376	.15372	.18673	.15477	.18968	.15582	.19263	.15688	.19557	.15794	.19849
47	.15900	.20140	.16007	.20430	.16113	.20719	.16220	.21006	.16328	.21293	.16436	.21578
48	.16543	.21863	.16652	.22146	.16760	.22428	.16869	.22709	.16978	.22989	.17087	.23268
49	.17197	.23545	.17307	.23822	.17417	.24098	.17528	.24372	.17638	.24646	.17749	.24918
50	.17861	.25190	.17972	.25460	.18084	.25729	.18196	.25998	.18308	.26265	.18421	.26532
51	.18534	.26797	.18647	.27061	.18761	.27325	.18874	.27587	.18988	.27848	.19102	.28109
52	.19217	.28368	.19332	.28627	.19447	.28885	.19562	.29141	.19677	.29397	.19793	.29652
53	.19909	.29905	.20026	.30158	.20142	.30410	.20259	.30662	.20376	.30912	.20492	.31161
54	.20611	.31409	.20729	.31657	.20847	.31903	.20965	.32149	.21083	.32394	.21202	.32638
55	.21321	.32881	.21440	.33123	.21560	.33365	.21680	.33605	.21800	.33845	.21920	.34084
56	.22040	.34322	.22161	.34559	.22282	.34795	.22403	.35031	.22525	.35266	.22646	.35499
57	.22768	.35733	.22890	.35965	.23012	.36196	.23135	.36427	.23258	.36657	.23381	.36886
58	.23504	.37114	.23627	.37342	.23751	.37569	.23875	.37794	.23999	.38020	.24124	.38244
59	.24248	.38468	.24373	.38691	.24498	.38913	.24623	.39134	.24749	.39355	.24874	.39575
60	.25000	.39794	.25126	.40012	.25252	.40230	.25379	.40447	.25506	.40663	.25632	.40879

HAVERSINES

Characteristics of the logarithms are omitted.

$\theta°$	0' Value	Log	10' Value	Log	20' Value	Log	30' Value	Log	40' Value	Log	50' Value	Log
60	.25000	.39794	.25126	.40012	.25252	.40230	.25379	.40447	.25506	.40663	.25632	.40879
61	.25760	.41094	.25887	.41308	.26014	.41521	.26142	.41734	.26270	.41946	.26398	.42157
62	.26526	.42368	.26655	.42578	.26784	.42787	.26913	.42996	.27042	.43203	.27171	.43411
63	.27300	.43617	.27430	.43823	.27560	.44028	.27690	.44232	.27820	.44436	.27951	.44639
64	.28081	.44842	.28212	.45044	.28343	.45245	.28474	.45446	.28606	.45645	.28737	.45845
65	.28869	.46043	.29001	.46241	.29133	.46439	.29265	.46635	.29398	.46831	.29530	.47027
66	.29663	.47222	.29796	.47416	.29929	.47610	.30063	.47802	.30196	.47995	.30330	.48187
67	.30463	.48378	.30597	.48568	.30732	.48758	.30866	.48948	.31000	.49137	.31135	.49325
68	.31270	.49512	.31405	.49699	.31540	.49886	.31675	.50072	.31810	.50257	.31946	.50442
69	.32082	.50625	.32217	.50809	.32353	.50992	.32490	.51174	.32626	.51356	.32762	.51538
70	.32899	.51718	.33036	.51898	.33173	.52078	.33310	.52257	.33447	.52435	.33584	.52613
71	.33722	.52791	.33859	.52968	.33997	.53144	.34135	.53320	.34273	.53495	.34411	.53670
72	.34549	.53844	.34688	.54017	.34826	.54190	.34965	.54363	.35103	.54535	.35242	.54707
73	.35381	.54878	.35521	.55048	.35660	.55218	.35799	.55387	.35939	.55556	.36078	.55725
74	.36218	.55893	.36358	.56060	.36498	.56227	.36635	.56393	.36778	.56559	.36919	.56725
75	.37059	.56889	.37200	.57054	.37340	.57218	.37481	.57381	.37622	.57544	.37763	.57706
76	.37904	.57868	.38045	.58030	.38186	.58191	.38328	.58351	.38469	.58511	.38611	.58671
77	.38752	.58830	.38894	.58988	.39036	.59147	.39178	.59304	.39320	.59461	.39462	.59618
78	.39604	.59774	.39747	.59929	.39889	.60085	.40032	.60240	.40174	.60395	.40317	.60549
79	.40460	.60702	.40602	.60855	.40745	.61008	.40888	.61160	.41031	.61311	.41174	.61463
80	.41318	.61613	.41461	.61764	.41604	.61914	.41748	.62063	.41891	.62212	.42035	.62361
81	.42178	.62509	.42322	.62657	.42466	.62804	.42610	.62951	.42753	.63097	.42897	.63243
82	.43041	.63389	.43185	.63534	.43330	.63678	.43474	.63823	.43618	.63966	.43762	.64110
83	.43907	.64253	.44051	.64395	.44195	.64538	.44340	.64679	.44484	.64821	.44629	.64962
84	.44774	.65102	.44918	.65242	.45063	.65382	.45208	.65521	.45353	.65660	.45497	.65799
85	.45642	.65937	.45787	.66074	.45932	.66212	.46077	.66348	.46222	.66485	.46367	.66621
86	.46512	.66757	.46657	.66892	.46802	.67027	.46948	.67161	.47093	.67295	.47238	.67429
87	.47383	.67562	.47528	.67695	.47674	.67828	.47819	.67960	.47964	.68092	.48110	.68223
88	.48255	.68354	.48400	.68485	.48546	.68615	.48691	.68745	.48837	.68874	.48982	.69004
89	.49127	.69132	.49273	.69261	.49418	.69389	.49564	.69516	.49709	.69644	.49855	.69770
90	.50000	.69897	.50145	.70023	.50291	.70149	.50436	.70274	.50582	.70399	.50727	.70524
91	.50873	.70648	.51018	.70772	.51163	.70896	.51309	.71019	.51454	.71142	.51600	.71265
92	.51745	.71387	.51890	.71509	.52036	.71630	.52181	.71751	.52326	.71872	.52472	.71992
93	.52617	.72112	.52762	.72232	.52907	.72352	.53052	.72471	.53198	.72589	.53343	.72708
94	.53488	.72825	.53633	.72943	.53778	.73060	.53923	.73177	.54068	.73294	.54213	.73410
95	.54358	.73526	.54503	.73642	.54647	.73757	.54792	.73872	.54937	.73987	.55082	.74101
96	.55226	.74215	.55371	.74328	.55516	.74442	.55660	.74555	.55805	.74667	.55949	.74779
97	.56093	.74891	.56238	.75003	.56382	.75114	.56526	.75225	.56670	.75336	.56815	.75446
98	.56959	.75556	.57103	.75666	.57247	.75775	.57390	.75884	.57534	.75993	.57678	.76101
99	.57822	.76209	.57965	.76317	.58109	.76424	.58252	.76531	.58396	.76638	.58539	.76745
100	.58682	.76851	.58826	.76957	.58969	.77062	.59112	.77167	.59255	.77272	.59398	.77377
101	.59540	.77481	.59683	.77585	.59826	.77689	.59968	.77792	.60111	.77895	.60253	.77998
102	.60396	.78101	.60538	.78203	.60680	.78305	.60822	.78406	.60964	.78507	.61106	.78608
103	.61248	.78709	.61389	.78809	.61531	.78909	.61672	.79009	.61814	.79108	.61955	.79208
104	.62096	.79306	.62237	.79405	.62378	.79503	.62519	.79601	.62660	.79699	.62800	.79796
105	.62941	.79893	.63081	.79990	.63222	.80087	.63362	.80183	.63502	.80279	.63642	.80374
106	.63782	.80470	.63922	.80565	.64061	.80660	.64201	.80754	.64340	.80848	.64479	.80942
107	.64619	.81036	.64758	.81129	.64897	.81222	.65035	.81315	.65174	.81407	.65312	.81500
108	.65451	.81592	.65589	.81683	.65727	.81775	.65865	.81866	.66003	.81956	.66141	.82047
109	.66278	.82137	.66416	.82227	.66553	.82317	.66690	.82406	.66827	.82495	.66964	.82584
110	.67101	.82673	.67238	.82761	.67374	.82849	.67510	.82937	.67647	.83025	.67783	.83112
111	.67918	.83199	.68054	.83285	.68190	.83372	.68325	.83458	.68460	.83544	.68595	.83629
112	.68730	.83715	.68865	.83800	.69000	.83885	.69134	.83969	.69268	.84054	.69403	.84138
113	.69537	.84221	.69670	.84305	.69804	.84388	.69937	.84471	.70071	.84554	.70204	.84636
114	.70337	.84718	.70470	.84800	.70602	.84882	.70735	.84963	.70867	.85044	.70999	.85125
115	.71131	.85206	.71263	.85286	.71394	.85366	.71526	.85446	.71657	.85526	.71788	.85605
116	.71919	.85684	.72049	.85763	.72180	.85841	.72310	.85920	.72440	.85998	.72570	.86076
117	.72700	.86153	.72829	.86230	.72958	.86307	.73087	.86384	.73216	.86461	.73345	.86537
118	.73474	.86613	.73602	.86689	.73730	.86764	.73858	.86840	.73986	.86915	.74113	.86990
119	.74240	.87064	.74368	.87138	.74494	.87212	.74621	.87286	.74748	.87360	.74874	.87433
120	.75000	.87506	.75126	.87579	.75251	.87652	.75377	.87724	.75502	.87796	.75627	.87868

HAVERSINES
Characteristics of the logarithms are omitted.

θ°	0' Value	Log	10' Value	Log	20' Value	Log	30' Value	Log	40' Value	Log	50' Value	Log
120	.75000	.87506	.75126	.87579	.75251	.87652	.75377	.87724	.75502	.87796	.75627	.87868
121	.75752	.87939	.75876	.88011	.76001	.88082	.76125	.88153	.76249	.88223	.76373	.88294
122	.76496	.88364	.76619	.88434	.76742	.88503	.76865	.88573	.76988	.88642	.77110	.88711
123	.77232	.88780	.77354	.88848	.77475	.88916	.77597	.88984	.77718	.89052	.77839	.89120
124	.77960	.89187	.78080	.89254	.78200	.89321	.78320	.89387	.78440	.89454	.78560	.89520
125	.78679	.89586	.78798	.89651	.78917	.89717	.79035	.89782	.79153	.89847	.79271	.89912
126	.79389	.89976	.79507	.90040	.79624	.90104	.79741	.90168	.79858	.90232	.79974	.90295
127	.80091	.90358	.80207	.90421	.80323	.90484	.80438	.90546	.80553	.90608	.80668	.90670
128	.80783	.90732	.80898	.90794	.81012	.90855	.81126	.90916	.81239	.90977	.81353	.91037
129	.81466	.91098	.81579	.91158	.81692	.91218	.81804	.91277	.81916	.91337	.82028	.91396
130	.82139	.91455	.82251	.91514	.82362	.91573	.82472	.91631	.82583	.91689	.82693	.91747
131	.82803	.91805	.82913	.91862	.83022	.91919	.83131	.91976	.83240	.92033	.83348	.92090
132	.83457	.92146	.83564	.92202	.83672	.92258	.83780	.92314	.83887	.92369	.83993	.92425
133	.84100	.92480	.84206	.92534	.84312	.92589	.84418	.92643	.84523	.92698	.84628	.92751
134	.84733	.92805	.84837	.92859	.84942	.92912	.85045	.92965	.85149	.93018	.85252	.93071
135	.85355	.93123	.85458	.93175	.85560	.93227	.85663	.93279	.85764	.93331	.85866	.93382
136	.85967	.93433	.86068	.93484	.86168	.93535	.86269	.93585	.86369	.93636	.86468	.93686
137	.86568	.93736	.86667	.93785	.86765	.93835	.86864	.93884	.86962	.93933	.87060	.93982
138	.87157	.94030	.87254	.94079	.87351	.94127	.87448	.94175	.87544	.94223	.87640	.94270
139	.87735	.94318	.87831	.94365	.87926	.94412	.88020	.94458	.88115	.94505	.88209	.94551
140	.88302	.94597	.88396	.94643	.88489	.94689	.88581	.94734	.88674	.94779	.88766	.94824
141	.88857	.94869	.88949	.94914	.89040	.94958	.89130	.95003	.89221	.95047	.89311	.95090
142	.89401	.95134	.89490	.95177	.89579	.95221	.89668	.95264	.89756	.95306	.89844	.95349
143	.89932	.95391	.90019	.95433	.90106	.95475	.90193	.95517	.90279	.95559	.90365	.95600
144	.90451	.95641	.90536	.95682	.90621	.95723	.90706	.95763	.90790	.95804	.90874	.95844
145	.90958	.95884	.91041	.95924	.91124	.95963	.91206	.96002	.91289	.96042	.91370	.96081
146	.91452	.96119	.91533	.96158	.91614	.96196	.91694	.96234	.91774	.96272	.91854	.96310
147	.91934	.96347	.92013	.96385	.92091	.96422	.92170	.96459	.92248	.96495	.92325	.96532
148	.92402	.96568	.92479	.96604	.92556	.96640	.92632	.96676	.92708	.96712	.92783	.96747
149	.92858	.96782	.92933	.96817	.93007	.96852	.93081	.96886	.93155	.96921	.93228	.96955
150	.93301	.96989	.93374	.97023	.93446	.97056	.93518	.97089	.93589	.97123	.93660	.97156
151	.93731	.97188	.93801	.97221	.93871	.97253	.93941	.97285	.94010	.97317	.94079	.97349
152	.94147	.97381	.94215	.97412	.94283	.97443	.94351	.97475	.94418	.97505	.94484	.97536
153	.94550	.97566	.94616	.97597	.94682	.97627	.94747	.97656	.94811	.97686	.94876	.97716
154	.94940	.97745	.95003	.97774	.95066	.97803	.95129	.97831	.95194	.97861	.95254	.97888
155	.95315	.97916	.95377	.97944	.95438	.97972	.95498	.97999	.95558	.98027	.95618	.98054
156	.95677	.98081	.95736	.98108	.95795	.98134	.95853	.98161	.95911	.98187	.95968	.98213
157	.96025	.98239	.96082	.98264	.96138	.98290	.96194	.98315	.96249	.98340	.96305	.98365
158	.96359	.98389	.96413	.98414	.96467	.98438	.96521	.98462	.96574	.98486	.96627	.98510
159	.96679	.98533	.96731	.98557	.96782	.98580	.96834	.98603	.96884	.98625	.96935	.98648
160	.96985	.98670	.97034	.98692	.97083	.98714	.97132	.98736	.97180	.98758	.97228	.98779
161	.97276	.98801	.97323	.98822	.97370	.98842	.97416	.98863	.97462	.98884	.97508	.98904
162	.97553	.98924	.97598	.98944	.97642	.98964	.97686	.98983	.97729	.99003	.97773	.99022
163	.97815	.99041	.97858	.99059	.97899	.99078	.97941	.99096	.97982	.99115	.98023	.99133
164	.98063	.99151	.98103	.99168	.98142	.99186	.98182	.99203	.98220	.99220	.98258	.99237
165	.98296	.99254	.98334	.99270	.98371	.99287	.98407	.99303	.98444	.99319	.98479	.99335
166	.98515	.99350	.98550	.99366	.98584	.99381	.98618	.99396	.98652	.99411	.98686	.99425
167	.98719	.99440	.98751	.99454	.98783	.99468	.98815	.99482	.98846	.99496	.98877	.99509
168	.98907	.99523	.98937	.99536	.98967	.99549	.98996	.99562	.99025	.99574	.99053	.99587
169	.99081	.99599	.99109	.99611	.99136	.99623	.99163	.99635	.99189	.99646	.99215	.99658
170	.99240	.99669	.99265	.99680	.99290	.99691	.99314	.99701	.99338	.99712	.99361	.99722
171	.99384	.99732	.99407	.99742	.99429	.99751	.99451	.99761	.99472	.99770	.99493	.99779
172	.99513	.99788	.99533	.99797	.99553	.99805	.99572	.99814	.99591	.99822	.99609	.99830
173	.99627	.99838	.99645	.99845	.99662	.99853	.99679	.99860	.99695	.99867	.99711	.99874
174	.99726	.99881	.99741	.99887	.99756	.99894	.99770	.99900	.99784	.99906	.99797	.99912
175	.99810	.99917	.99822	.99923	.99834	.99928	.99846	.99933	.99857	.99938	.99868	.99943
176	.99878	.99947	.99888	.99951	.99898	.99956	.99907	.99959	.99915	.99963	.99924	.99967
177	.99931	.99970	.99939	.99973	.99946	.99976	.99952	.99979	.99959	.99982	.99964	.99984
178	.99970	.99987	.99974	.99989	.99979	.99991	.99983	.99993	.99986	.99994	.99990	.99995
179	.99992	.99997	.99995	.99998	.99997	.99999	.99998	.99999	.99999	.00000	1.00000	.00000
180	1.00000	.00000										

*SQUARE OF THE SINE AND COSINE AND THEIR PRODUCT

Compiled by Niel F. Beardsley.

0° (180°)   (359°) **179°**   **1° (181°)**   (358°) **178°**

'	Sin²	Sin · Cos	Cos²	'		'	Sin²	Sin · Cos	Cos²	'
0	.00000	.00000	1.00000	60		0	.00030	.01745	.99970	60
1	.00000	.00029	1.00000	59		1	.00031	.01774	.99969	59
2	.00000	.00058	1.00000	58		2	.00033	.01803	.99967	58
3	.00000	.00087	1.00000	57		3	.00034	.01832	.99966	57
4	.00000	.00116	1.00000	56		4	.00035	.01861	.99965	56
5	.00000	.00145	1.00000	55		5	.00036	.01890	.99964	55
6	.00000	.00175	1.00000	54		6	.00037	.01919	.99963	54
7	.00000	.00204	1.00000	53		7	.00038	.01948	.99962	53
8	.00001	.00233	.99999	52		8	.00039	.01978	.99961	52
9	.00001	.00262	.99999	51		9	.00040	.02007	.99960	51
10	.00001	.00291	.99999	50		10	.00041	.02036	.99959	50
11	.00001	.00320	.99999	49		11	.00043	.02065	.99957	49
12	.00001	.00349	.99999	48		12	.00044	.02094	.99956	48
13	.00001	.00378	.99999	47		13	.00045	.02123	.99955	47
14	.00002	.00407	.99998	46		14	.00046	.02152	.99954	46
15	.00002	.00436	.99998	45		15	.00048	.02181	.99952	45
16	.00002	.00465	.99998	44		16	.00049	.02210	.99951	44
17	.00002	.00495	.99998	43		17	.00050	.02239	.99950	43
18	.00003	.00524	.99997	42		18	.00051	.02268	.99949	42
19	.00003	.00553	.99997	41		19	.00053	.02297	.99947	41
20	.00003	.00582	.99997	40		20	.00054	.02326	.99946	40
21	.00004	.00611	.99996	39		21	.00056	.02355	.99944	39
22	.00004	.00640	.99996	38		22	.00057	.02384	.99943	38
23	.00004	.00669	.99996	37		23	.00058	.02413	.99942	37
24	.00005	.00698	.99995	36		24	.00060	.02442	.99940	36
25	.00005	.00727	.99995	35		25	.00061	.02472	.99939	35
26	.00006	.00756	.99994	34		26	.00063	.02501	.99937	34
27	.00006	.00785	.99994	33		27	.00064	.02530	.99936	33
28	.00007	.00814	.99993	32		28	.00066	.02559	.99934	32
29	.00007	.00844	.99993	31		29	.00067	.02588	.99933	31
30	.00008	.00873	.99992	30		30	.00069	.02617	.99931	30
31	.00008	.00902	.99992	29		31	.00070	.02646	.99930	29
32	.00009	.00931	.99991	28		32	.00072	.02675	.99928	28
33	.00009	.00960	.99991	27		33	.00073	.02704	.99927	27
34	.00010	.00989	.99990	26		34	.00075	.02733	.99925	26
35	.00010	.01018	.99990	25		35	.00076	.02762	.99924	25
36	.00011	.01047	.99989	24		36	.00078	.02791	.99922	24
37	.00012	.01076	.99988	23		37	.00080	.02820	.99920	23
38	.00012	.01105	.99988	22		38	.00081	.02849	.99919	22
39	.00013	.01134	.99987	21		39	.00083	.02878	.99917	21
40	.00014	.01163	.99986	20		40	.00085	.02907	.99915	20
41	.00014	.01193	.99986	19		41	.00086	.02936	.99914	19
42	.00015	.01222	.99985	18		42	.00088	.02965	.99912	18
43	.00016	.01251	.99984	17		43	.00090	.02994	.99910	17
44	.00016	.01280	.99984	16		44	.00091	.03023	.99909	16
45	.00017	.01309	.99983	15		45	.00093	.03052	.99907	15
46	.00018	.01338	.99982	14		46	.00095	.03081	.99905	14
47	.00019	.01367	.99981	13		47	.00097	.03110	.99903	13
48	.00019	.01396	.99981	12		48	.00099	.03140	.99901	12
49	.00020	.01425	.99980	11		49	.00100	.03169	.99900	11
50	.00021	.01454	.99979	10		50	.00102	.03198	.99898	10
51	.00022	.01483	.99978	9		51	.00104	.03227	.99896	9
52	.00023	.01512	.99977	8		52	.00106	.03256	.99894	8
53	.00024	.01541	.99976	7		53	.00108	.03285	.99892	7
54	.00025	.01571	.99975	6		54	.00110	.03314	.99890	6
55	.00026	.01600	.99974	5		55	.00112	.03343	.99888	5
56	.00027	.01629	.99973	4		56	.00114	.03372	.99886	4
57	.00027	.01658	.99973	3		57	.00116	.03401	.99884	3
58	.00028	.01687	.99972	2		58	.00118	.03430	.99882	2
59	.00029	.01716	.99971	1		59	.00120	.03459	.99880	1
60	.00030	.01745	.99970	0		60	.00122	.03488	.99878	0
'	Cos²	Sin · Cos	Sin²			'	Cos²	Sin · Cos	Sin²	'

90° (270°)   (269°) **89°**   **91° (271°)**   (268°) **88°**

* For explanation see last page of table.

SQUARE OF THE SINE AND COSINE AND THEIR PRODUCT

′	Sin²	Sin · Cos	Cos²	′
0	.00122	.03488	.99878	**60**
1	.00124	.03517	.99876	59
2	.00126	.03546	.99874	58
3	.00128	.03575	.99872	57
4	.00130	.03604	.99870	56
5	.00132	.03633	.99868	**55**
6	.00134	.03662	.99866	54
7	.00136	.03691	.99864	53
8	.00139	.03720	.99861	52
9	.00141	.03749	.99859	51
10	.00143	.03778	.99857	**50**
11	.00145	.03807	.99855	49
12	.00147	.03836	.99853	48
13	.00150	.03865	.99850	47
14	.00152	.03894	.99848	46
15	.00154	.03923	.99846	**45**
16	.00156	.03952	.99844	44
17	.00159	.03981	.99841	43
18	.00161	.04010	.99839	42
19	.00163	.04039	.99837	41
20	.00166	.04068	.99834	**40**
21	.00168	.04097	.99832	39
22	.00171	.04126	.99829	38
23	.00173	.04155	.99827	37
24	.00175	.04184	.99825	36
25	.00178	.04213	.99822	**35**
26	.00180	.04242	.99820	34
27	.00183	.04271	.99817	33
28	.00185	.04300	.99815	32
29	.00188	.04329	.99812	31
30	.00190	.04358	.99810	**30**
31	.00193	.04387	.99807	29
32	.00195	.04416	.99805	28
33	.00198	.04445	.99802	27
34	.00201	.04474	.99799	26
35	.00203	.04503	.99797	**25**
36	.00206	.04532	.99794	24
37	.00208	.04561	.99792	23
38	.00211	.04590	.99789	22
39	.00214	.04619	.99786	21
40	.00216	.04647	.99784	**20**
41	.00219	.04676	.99781	19
42	.00222	.04705	.99778	18
43	.00225	.04734	.99775	17
44	.00227	.04763	.99773	16
45	.00230	.04792	.99770	**15**
46	.00233	.04821	.99767	14
47	.00236	.04850	.99764	13
48	.00239	.04879	.99761	12
49	.00241	.04908	.99759	11
50	.00244	.04937	.99756	**10**
51	.00247	.04966	.99753	9
52	.00250	.04995	.99750	8
53	.00253	.05024	.99747	7
54	.00256	.05053	.99744	6
55	.00259	.05082	.99741	**5**
56	.00262	.05111	.99738	4
57	.00265	.05140	.99735	3
58	.00268	.05169	.99732	2
59	.00271	.05197	.99729	1
60	.00274	.05226	.99726	**0**
′	Cos²	Sin · Cos	Sin²	′

′	Sin²	Sin · Cos	Cos²	′
0	.00274	.05226	.99726	**60**
1	.00277	.05255	.99723	59
2	.00280	.05284	.99720	58
3	.00283	.05313	.99717	57
4	.00286	.05342	.99714	56
5	.00289	.05371	.99711	**55**
6	.00292	.05400	.99708	54
7	.00296	.05429	.99704	53
8	.00299	.05458	.99701	52
9	.00302	.05487	.99698	51
10	.00305	.05516	.99695	**50**
11	.00308	.05545	.99692	49
12	.00312	.05573	.99688	48
13	.00315	.05602	.99685	47
14	.00318	.05631	.99682	46
15	.00321	.05660	.99679	**45**
16	.00325	.05689	.99675	44
17	.00328	.05718	.99672	43
18	.00331	.05747	.99669	42
19	.00335	.05776	.99665	41
20	.00338	.05805	.99662	**40**
21	.00341	.05834	.99659	39
22	.00345	.05862	.99655	38
23	.00348	.05891	.99652	37
24	.00352	.05920	.99648	36
25	.00355	.05949	.99645	**35**
26	.00359	.05978	.99641	34
27	.00362	.06007	.99638	33
28	.00366	.06036	.99634	32
29	.00369	.06065	.99631	31
30	.00373	.06093	.99627	**30**
31	.00376	.06122	.99624	29
32	.00380	.06151	.99620	28
33	.00383	.06180	.99617	27
34	.00387	.06209	.99613	26
35	.00391	.06238	.99609	**25**
36	.00394	.06267	.99606	24
37	.00398	.06296	.99602	23
38	.00402	.06324	.99598	22
39	.00405	.06353	.99595	21
40	.00409	.06382	.99591	**20**
41	.00413	.06411	.99587	19
42	.00416	.06440	.99584	18
43	.00420	.06469	.99580	17
44	.00424	.06497	.99576	16
45	.00428	.06526	.99572	**15**
46	.00432	.06555	.99568	14
47	.00435	.06584	.99565	13
48	.00439	.06613	.99561	12
49	.00443	.06642	.99557	11
50	.00447	.06670	.99553	**10**
51	.00451	.06699	.99549	9
52	.00455	.06728	.99545	8
53	.00459	.06757	.99541	7
54	.00463	.06786	.99537	6
55	.00467	.06815	.99533	**5**
56	.00471	.06843	.99529	4
57	.00475	.06872	.99525	3
58	.00479	.06901	.99521	2
59	.00483	.06930	.99517	1
60	.00487	.06959	.99513	**0**
′	Cos²	Sin · Cos	Sin²	′

4° (184°)   (355°) **175°**   **5° (185°)**   (354°) **(174°)**

′	Sin²	Sin · Cos	Cos²	′		′	Sin²	Sin · Cos	Cos²	′
0	.00487	.06959	.99513	60		0	.00760	.08682	.99240	60
1	.00491	.06987	.99509	59		1	.00765	.08711	.99235	59
2	.00495	.07016	.99505	58		2	.00770	.08740	.99230	58
3	.00499	.07045	.99501	57		3	.00775	.08768	.99225	57
4	.00503	.07074	.99497	56		4	.00780	.08797	.99220	56
5	.00507	.07103	.99493	55		5	.00785	.08826	.99215	55
6	.00511	.07131	.99489	54		6	.00790	.08854	.99210	54
7	.00515	.07160	.99485	53		7	.00795	.08883	.99205	53
8	.00520	.07189	.99480	52		8	.00801	.08911	.99199	52
9	.00524	.07218	.99476	51		9	.00806	.08940	.99194	51
10	.00528	.07247	.99472	50		10	.00811	.08969	.99189	50
11	.00532	.07275	.99468	49		11	.00816	.08997	.99184	49
12	.00536	.07304	.99464	48		12	.00821	.09026	.99179	48
13	.00541	.07333	.99459	47		13	.00827	.09055	.99173	47
14	.00545	.07362	.99455	46		14	.00832	.09083	.99168	46
15	.00549	.07390	.99451	45		15	.00837	.09112	.99163	45
16	.00554	.07419	.99446	44		16	.00843	.09140	.99157	44
17	.00558	.07448	.99442	43		17	.00848	.09169	.99152	43
18	.00562	.07477	.99438	42		18	.00853	.09198	.99147	42
19	.00567	.07506	.99433	41		19	.00859	.09226	.99141	41
20	.00571	.07534	.99429	40		20	.00864	.09255	.99136	40
21	.00575	.07563	.99425	39		21	.00869	.09283	.99131	39
22	.00580	.07592	.99420	38		22	.00875	.09312	.99125	38
23	.00584	.07621	.99416	37		23	.00880	.09340	.99120	37
24	.00589	.07649	.99411	36		24	.00886	.09369	.99114	36
25	.00593	.07678	.99407	35		25	.00891	.09398	.99109	35
26	.00598	.07707	.99402	34		26	.00897	.09426	.99103	34
27	.00602	.07736	.99398	33		27	.00902	.09455	.99098	33
28	.00607	.07764	.99393	32		28	.00908	.09483	.99092	32
29	.00611	.07793	.99389	31		29	.00913	.09512	.99087	31
30	.00616	.07822	.99384	30		30	.00919	.09540	.99081	30
31	.00620	.07850	.99380	29		31	.00924	.09569	.99076	29
32	.00625	.07879	.99375	28		32	.00930	.09598	.99070	28
33	.00629	.07908	.99371	27		33	.00935	.09626	.99065	27
34	.00634	.07937	.99366	26		34	.00941	.09655	.99059	26
35	.00639	.07965	.99361	25		35	.00947	.09683	.99053	25
36	.00643	.07994	.99357	24		36	.00952	.09712	.99048	24
37	.00648	.08023	.99352	23		37	.00958	.09740	.99042	23
38	.00653	.08051	.99347	22		38	.00964	.09769	.99036	22
39	.00657	.08080	.99343	21		39	.00969	.09797	.99031	21
40	.00662	.08109	.99338	20		40	.00975	.09826	.99025	20
41	.00667	.08138	.99333	19		41	.00981	.09854	.99019	19
42	.00671	.08166	.99329	18		42	.00986	.09883	.99014	18
43	.00676	.08195	.99324	17		43	.00992	.09911	.99008	17
44	.00681	.08224	.99319	16		44	.00998	.09940	.99002	16
45	.00686	.08252	.99314	15		45	.01004	.09968	.98996	15
46	.00691	.08281	.99309	14		46	.01010	.09997	.98990	14
47	.00695	.08310	.99305	13		47	.01015	.10025	.98985	13
48	.00700	.08338	.99300	12		48	.01021	.10054	.98979	12
49	.00705	.08367	.99295	11		49	.01027	.10082	.98973	11
50	.00710	.08396	.99290	10		50	.01033	.10111	.98967	10
51	.00715	.08424	.99285	9		51	.01039	.10139	.98961	9
52	.00720	.08453	.99280	8		52	.01045	.10168	.98955	8
53	.00725	.08482	.99275	7		53	.01051	.10196	.98949	7
54	.00730	.08510	.99270	6		54	.01057	.10225	.98943	6
55	.00735	.08539	.99265	5		55	.01063	.10253	.98937	5
56	.00740	.08568	.99260	4		56	.01069	.10282	.98931	4
57	.00745	.08596	.99255	3		57	.01075	.10310	.98925	3
58	.00750	.08625	.99250	2		58	.01081	.10339	.98919	2
59	.00755	.08654	.99245	1		59	.01087	.10367	.98913	1
60	.00760	.08682	.99240	0		60	.01093	.10396	.98907	0
′	Cos²	Sin · Cos	Sin²	′		′	Cos²	Sin · Cos	Sin²	′

6° (186°)   (353°) **173°**

′	Sin²	Sin · Cos	Cos²	′
0	.01093	.10396	.98907	**60**
1	.01099	.10424	.98901	59
2	.01105	.10452	.98895	58
3	.01111	.10481	.98889	57
4	.01117	.10509	.98883	56
5	.01123	.10538	.98877	**55**
6	.01129	.10566	.98871	54
7	.01135	.10595	.98865	53
8	.01142	.10623	.98858	52
9	.01148	.10652	.98852	51
10	.01154	.10680	.98846	**50**
11	.01160	.10708	.98840	49
12	.01166	.10737	.98834	48
13	.01173	.10765	.98827	47
14	.01179	.10794	.98821	46
15	.01185	.10822	.98815	**45**
16	.01192	.10850	.98808	44
17	.01198	.10879	.98802	43
18	.01204	.10907	.98796	42
19	.01211	.10936	.98789	41
20	.01217	.10964	.98783	**40**
21	.01223	.10992	.98777	39
22	.01230	.11021	.98770	38
23	.01236	.11049	.98764	37
24	.01243	.11077	.98757	36
25	.01249	.11106	.98751	**35**
26	.01255	.11134	.98745	34
27	.01262	.11163	.98738	33
28	.01268	.11191	.98732	32
29	.01275	.11219	.98725	31
30	.01281	.11248	.98719	**30**
31	.01288	.11276	.98712	29
32	.01295	.11304	.98705	28
33	.01301	.11333	.98699	27
34	.01308	.11361	.98692	26
35	.01314	.11389	.98686	**25**
36	.01321	.11418	.98679	24
37	.01328	.11446	.98672	23
38	.01334	.11474	.98666	22
39	.01341	.11502	.98659	21
40	.01348	.11531	.98652	**20**
41	.01354	.11559	.98646	19
42	.01361	.11587	.98639	18
43	.01368	.11616	.98632	17
44	.01375	.11644	.98625	16
45	.01382	.11672	.98618	**15**
46	.01388	.11701	.98612	14
47	.01395	.11729	.98605	13
48	.01402	.11757	.98598	12
49	.01409	.11785	.98591	11
50	.01416	.11814	.98584	**10**
51	.01423	.11842	.98577	9
52	.01429	.11870	.98571	8
53	.01436	.11898	.98564	7
54	.01443	.11927	.98557	6
55	.01450	.11955	98550	**5**
56	.01457	.11983	.98543	4
57	.01464	.12011	.98536	3
58	.01471	.12040	.98529	2
59	.01478	.12068	.98522	1
60	.01485	.12096	.98515	**0**
′	Cos²	Sin · Cos	Sin²	′

96° (276°)   (263°) **83°**

7° (187°)   (352°) **172°**

′	Sin²	Sin · Cos	Cos²	′
0	.01485	.12096	.98515	**60**
1	.01492	.12124	.98508	59
2	.01499	.12153	.98501	58
3	.01506	.12181	.98494	57
4	.01513	.12209	.98487	56
5	.01521	.12237	.98479	**55**
6	.01528	.12265	.98472	54
7	.01535	.12294	.98465	53
8	.01542	.12322	.98458	52
9	.01549	.12350	.98451	51
10	.01556	.12378	.98444	**50**
11	.01564	.12406	.98436	49
12	.01571	.12434	.98429	48
13	.01578	.12463	.98422	47
14	.01585	.12491	.98415	46
15	.01593	.12519	.98407	**45**
16	.01600	.12547	.98400	44
17	.01607	.12575	.98393	43
18	.01615	.12603	.98385	42
19	.01622	.12632	.98378	41
20	.01629	.12660	.98371	**40**
21	.01637	.12688	.98363	39
22	.01644	.12716	.98356	38
23	.01651	.12744	.98349	37
24	.01659	.12772	.98341	36
25	.01666	.12800	.98334	**35**
26	.01674	.12829	.98326	34
27	.01681	.12857	.98319	33
28	.01689	.12885	.98311	32
29	.01696	.12913	.98304	31
30	.01704	.12941	.98296	**30**
31	.01711	.12969	.98289	29
32	.01719	.12997	.98281	28
33	.01726	.13025	.98274	27
34	.01734	.13053	.98266	26
35	.01742	.13081	.98258	**25**
36	.01749	.13109	.98251	24
37	.01757	.13138	.98243	23
38	.01764	.13166	.98236	22
39	.01772	.13194	.98228	21
40	.01780	.13222	.98220	**20**
41	.01788	.13250	.98212	19
42	.01795	.13278	.98205	18
43	.01803	.13306	.98197	17
44	.01811	.13334	.98189	16
45	.01818	.13362	.98182	**15**
46	.01826	.13390	.98174	14
47	.01834	.13418	.98166	13
48	.01842	.13446	.98158	12
49	.01850	.13474	.98150	11
50	.01858	.13502	.98142	**10**
51	.01865	.13530	.98135	9
52	.01873	.13558	.98127	8
53	.01881	.13586	.98119	7
54	.01889	.13614	.98111	6
55	.01897	.13642	.98103	**5**
56	.01905	.13670	.98095	4
57	.01913	.13698	.98087	3
58	.01921	.13726	.98079	2
59	.01929	.13754	.98071	1
60	.01937	.13782	.98063	**0**
′	Cos²	Sin · Cos	Sin²	′

97° (277°)   (262°) **82°**

8° (188°)   (351°) **171°**   9° (189°)   (350°) **170°**

′	Sin²	Sin · Cos	Cos²	′		′	Sin²	Sin · Cos	Cos²	′
0	.01937	.13782	.98063	**60**		**0**	.02447	.15451	.97553	**60**
1	.01945	.13810	.98055	59		1	.02456	.15479	.97544	59
2	.01953	.13838	.98047	58		2	.02465	.15506	.97535	58
3	.01961	.13866	.98039	57		3	.02474	.15534	.97526	57
4	.01969	.13894	.98031	56		4	.02483	.15561	.97517	56
5	.01977	.13922	.98023	**55**		**5**	.02492	.15589	.97508	**55**
6	.01985	.13950	.98015	54		6	.02501	.15617	.97499	54
7	.01993	.13977	.98007	53		7	.02510	.15644	.97490	53
8	.02002	.14005	.97998	52		8	.02520	.15672	.97480	52
9	.02010	.14033	.97990	51		9	.02529	.15700	.97471	51
10	.02018	.14061	.97982	**50**		**10**	.02538	.15727	.97462	**50**
11	.02026	.14089	.97974	49		11	.02547	.15755	.97453	49
12	.02034	.14117	.97966	48		12	.02556	.15782	.97444	48
13	.02043	.14145	.97957	47		13	.02565	.15810	.97435	47
14	.02051	.14173	.97949	46		14	.02575	.15838	.97425	46
15	.02059	.14201	.97941	**45**		**15**	.02584	.15865	.97416	**45**
16	.02067	.14229	.97933	44		16	.02593	.15893	.97407	44
17	.02076	.14257	.97924	43		17	.02602	.15920	.97398	43
18	.02084	.14284	.97916	42		18	.02612	.15948	.97388	42
19	.02092	.14312	.97908	41		19	.02621	.15976	.97379	41
20	.02101	.14340	.97899	**40**		**20**	.02630	.16003	.97370	**40**
21	.02109	.14368	.97891	39		21	.02639	.16031	.97361	39
22	.02117	.14396	.97883	38		22	.02649	.16058	.97351	38
23	.02126	.14424	.97874	37		23	.02658	.16086	.97342	37
24	.02134	.14452	.97866	36		24	.02668	.16113	.97332	36
25	.02142	.14479	.97858	**35**		**25**	.02677	.16141	.97323	**35**
26	.02151	.14507	.97849	34		26	.02686	.16168	.97314	34
27	.02159	.14535	.97841	33		27	.02696	.16196	.97304	33
28	.02168	.14563	.97832	32		28	.02705	.16223	.97295	32
29	.02176	.14591	.97824	31		29	.02715	.16251	.97285	31
30	.02185	.14619	.97815	**30**		**30**	.02724	.16278	.97276	**30**
31	.02193	.14646	.97807	29		31	.02734	.16306	.97266	29
32	.02202	.14674	.97798	28		32	.02743	.16333	.97257	28
33	.02210	.14702	.97790	27		33	.02753	.16361	.97247	27
34	.02219	.14730	.97781	26		34	.02762	.16388	.97238	26
35	.02227	.14758	.97773	**25**		**35**	.02772	.16416	.97228	**25**
36	.02236	.14785	.97764	24		36	.02781	.16443	.97219	24
37	.02245	.14813	.97755	23		37	.02791	.16471	.97209	23
38	.02253	.14841	.97747	22		38	.02800	.16498	.97200	22
39	.02262	.14869	.97738	21		39	.02810	.16526	.97190	21
40	.02271	.14897	.97729	**20**		**40**	.02820	.16553	.97180	**20**
41	.02279	.14924	.97721	19		41	.02829	.16581	.97171	19
42	.02288	.14952	.97712	18		42	.02839	.16608	.97161	18
43	.02297	.14980	.97703	17		43	.02849	.16635	.97151	17
44	.02305	.15008	.97695	16		44	.02858	.16663	.97142	16
45	.02314	.15035	.97686	**15**		**45**	.02868	.16690	.97132	**15**
46	.02323	.15063	.97677	14		46	.02878	.16718	.97122	14
47	.02332	.15091	.97668	13		47	.02887	.16745	.97113	13
48	.02340	.15118	.97660	12		48	.02897	.16773	.97103	12
49	.02349	.15146	.97651	11		49	.02907	.16800	.97093	11
50	.02358	.15174	.97642	**10**		**50**	.02917	.16827	.97083	**10**
51	.02367	.15202	.97633	9		51	.02926	.16855	.97074	9
52	.02376	.15229	.97624	8		52	.02936	.16882	.97064	8
53	.02385	.15257	.97615	7		53	.02946	.16910	.97054	7
54	.02394	.15285	.97606	6		54	.02956	.16937	.97044	6
55	.02402	.15312	.97598	**5**		**55**	.02966	.16964	.97034	**5**
56	.02411	.15340	.97589	4		56	.02976	.16992	.97024	4
57	.02420	.15368	.97580	3		57	.02986	.17019	.97014	3
58	.02429	.15396	.97571	2		58	.02996	.17046	.97004	2
59	.02438	.15423	.97562	1		59	.03005	.17074	.96995	1
60	.02447	.15451	.97553	**0**		**60**	.03015	.17101	.96985	**0**
′	Cos²	Sin · Cos	Sin²	′		′	Cos²	Sin · Cos	Sin²	′

98° (278°)   (261°) **81°**   99° (279°)   (260°) **80°**

SQUARE OF THE SINE AND COSINE AND THEIR PRODUCT

′	Sin²	Sin · Cos	Cos²	′	′	Sin²	Sin · Cos	Cos²	′
0	.03015	.17101	.96985	**60**	**0**	.03641	.18730	.96359	**60**
1	.03025	.17128	.96975	59	1	.03652	.18757	.96348	59
2	.03035	.17156	.96965	58	2	.03663	.18784	.96337	58
3	.03045	.17183	.96955	57	3	.03674	.18811	.96326	57
4	.03055	.17210	.96945	56	4	.03685	.18838	.96315	56
5	.03065	.17238	.96935	**55**	**5**	.03695	.18865	.96305	**55**
6	.03075	.17265	.96925	54	6	.03706	.18892	.96294	54
7	.03085	.17292	.96915	53	7	.03717	.18919	.96283	53
8	.03095	.17319	.96905	52	8	.03728	.18946	.96272	52
9	.03106	.17347	.96894	51	9	.03740	.18973	.96260	51
10	.03116	.17374	.96884	**50**	**10**	.03751	.19000	.96249	**50**
11	.03126	.17401	.96874	49	11	.03762	.19027	.96238	49
12	.03136	.17429	.96864	48	12	.03773	.19054	.96227	48
13	.03146	.17456	.96854	47	13	.03784	.19080	.96216	47
14	.03156	.17483	.96844	46	14	.03795	.19107	.96205	46
15	.03166	.17510	.96834	**45**	**15**	.03806	.19134	.96194	**45**
16	.03177	.17538	.96823	44	16	.03817	.19161	.96183	44
17	.03187	.17565	.96813	43	17	.03828	.19188	.96172	43
18	.03197	.17592	.96803	42	18	.03839	.19215	.96161	42
19	.03207	.17619	.96793	41	19	.03851	.19242	.96149	41
20	.03218	.17647	.96782	**40**	**20**	.03862	.19268	.96138	**40**
21	.03228	.17674	.96772	39	21	.03873	.19295	.96127	39
22	.03238	.17701	.96762	38	22	.03884	.19322	.96116	38
23	.03248	.17728	.96752	37	23	.03896	.19349	.96104	37
24	.03259	.17755	.96741	36	24	.03907	.19376	.96093	36
25	.03269	.17783	.96731	**35**	**25**	.03918	.19403	.96082	**35**
26	.03279	.17810	.96721	34	26	.03929	.19429	.96071	34
27	.03290	.17837	.96710	33	27	.03941	.19456	.96059	33
28	.03300	.17864	.96700	32	28	.03952	.19483	.96048	32
29	.03311	.17891	.96689	31	29	.03963	.19510	.96037	31
30	.03321	.17918	.96679	**30**	**30**	.03975	.19537	.96025	**30**
31	.03331	.17946	.96669	29	31	.03986	.19563	.96014	29
32	.03342	.17973	.96658	28	32	.03998	.19590	.96002	28
33	.03352	.18000	.96648	27	33	.04009	.19617	.95991	27
34	.03363	.18027	.96637	26	34	.04020	.19644	.95980	26
35	.03373	.18054	.96627	**25**	**35**	.04032	.19670	.95968	**25**
36	.03384	.18081	.96616	24	36	.04043	.19697	.95957	24
37	.03394	.18108	.96606	23	37	.04055	.19724	.95945	23
38	.03405	.18135	.96595	22	38	.04066	.19751	.95934	22
39	.03415	.18163	.96585	21	39	.04078	.19777	.95922	21
40	.03426	.18190	.96574	**20**	**40**	.04089	.19804	.95911	**20**
41	.03437	.18217	.96563	19	41	.04101	.19831	.95899	19
42	.03447	.18244	.96553	18	42	.04112	.19857	.95888	18
43	.03458	.18271	.96542	17	43	.04124	.19884	.95876	17
44	.03468	.18298	.96532	16	44	.04135	.19911	.95865	16
45	.03479	.18325	.96521	**15**	**45**	.04147	.19937	.95853	**15**
46	.03490	.18352	.96510	14	46	.04159	.19964	.95841	14
47	.03500	.18379	.96500	13	47	.04170	.19991	.95830	13
48	.03511	.18406	.96489	12	48	.04182	.20017	.95818	12
49	.03522	.18433	.96478	11	49	.04194	.20044	.95806	11
50	.03533	.18460	.96467	**10**	**50**	.04205	.20071	.95795	**10**
51	.03543	.18487	.96457	9	51	.04217	.20097	.95783	9
52	.03554	.18514	.96446	8	52	.04229	.20124	.95771	8
53	.03565	.18541	.96435	7	53	.04240	.20151	.95760	7
54	.03576	.18568	.96424	6	54	.04252	.20177	.95748	6
55	.03587	.18595	.96413	**5**	**55**	.04264	.20204	.95736	**5**
56	.03597	.18622	.96403	4	56	.04276	.20230	.95724	4
57	.03608	.18649	.96392	3	57	.04287	.20257	.95713	3
58	.03619	.18676	.96381	2	58	.04299	.20284	.95701	2
59	.03630	.18703	.96370	1	59	.04311	.20310	.95689	1
60	.03641	.18730	.96359	**0**	**60**	.04323	.20337	.95677	**0**
′	Cos²	Sin · Cos	Sin²	′	′	Cos²	Sin · Cos	Sin²	′

SQUARE OF THE SINE AND COSINE AND THEIR PRODUCT

12° (192°)   (347°) **167°**   **13° (193°)**   (346°) **166°**

′	Sin²	Sin·Cos	Cos²	′		′	Sin²	Sin·Cos	Cos²	′
0	.04323	.20337	.95677	**60**		**0**	.05060	.21919	.94940	**60**
1	.04335	.20363	.95665	59		1	.05073	.21945	.94927	59
2	.04346	.20390	.95654	58		2	.05086	.21971	.94914	58
3	.04358	.20417	.95642	57		3	.05099	.21997	.94901	57
4	.04370	.20443	.95630	56		4	.05111	.22023	.94889	56
5	.04382	.20470	.95618	**55**		**5**	.05124	.22049	.94876	**55**
6	.04394	.20496	.95606	54		6	.05137	.22075	.94863	54
7	.04406	.20523	.95594	53		7	.05150	.22101	.94850	53
8	.04418	.20549	.95582	52		8	.05163	.22127	.94837	52
9	.04430	.20576	.95570	51		9	.05176	.22154	.94824	51
10	.04442	.20602	.95558	**50**		**10**	.05189	.22180	.94811	**50**
11	.04454	.20629	.95546	49		11	.05201	.22206	.94799	49
12	.04466	.20655	.95534	48		12	.05214	.22232	.94786	48
13	.04478	.20682	.95522	47		13	.05227	.22258	.94773	47
14	.04490	.20708	.95510	46		14	.05240	.22284	.94760	46
15	.04502	.20735	.95498	**45**		**15**	.05253	.22310	.94747	**45**
16	.04514	.20761	.95486	44		16	.05266	.22336	.94734	44
17	.04526	.20788	.95474	43		17	.05279	.22362	.94721	43
18	.04538	.20814	.95462	42		18	.05292	.22388	.94708	42
19	.04550	.20840	.95450	41		19	.05305	.22414	.94695	41
20	.04562	.20867	.95438	**40**		**20**	.05318	.22440	.94682	**40**
21	.04575	.20893	.95425	39		21	.05331	.22466	.94669	39
22	.04587	.20920	.95413	38		22	.05345	.22492	.94655	38
23	.04599	.20946	.95401	37		23	.05358	.22518	.94642	37
24	.04611	.20973	.95389	36		24	.05371	.22544	.94629	36
25	.04623	.20999	.95377	**35**		**25**	.05384	.22570	.94616	**35**
26	.04636	.21025	.95364	34		26	.05397	.22596	.94603	34
27	.04648	.21052	.95352	33		27	.05410	.22622	.94590	33
28	.04660	.21078	.95340	32		28	.05423	.22648	.94577	32
29	.04672	.21105	.95328	31		29	.05436	.22674	.94564	31
30	.04685	.21131	.95315	**30**		**30**	.05450	.22700	.94550	**30**
31	.04697	.21157	.95303	29		31	.05463	.22725	.94537	29
32	.04709	.21184	.95291	28		32	.05476	.22751	.94524	28
33	.04722	.21210	.95278	27		33	.05489	.22777	.94511	27
34	.04734	.21236	.95266	26		34	.05503	.22803	.94497	26
35	.04746	.21263	.95254	**25**		**35**	.05516	.22829	.94484	**25**
36	.04759	.21289	.95241	24		36	.05529	.22855	.94471	24
37	.04771	.21315	.95229	23		37	.05542	.22881	.94458	23
38	.04783	.21342	.95217	22		38	.05556	.22907	.94444	22
39	.04796	.21368	.95204	21		39	.05569	.22932	.94431	21
40	.04808	.21394	.95192	**20**		**40**	.05582	.22958	.94418	**20**
41	.04821	.21420	.95179	19		41	.05596	.22984	.94404	19
42	.04833	.21447	.95167	18		42	.05609	.23010	.94391	18
43	.04846	.21473	.95154	17		43	.05623	.23036	.94377	17
44	.04858	.21499	.95142	16		44	.05636	.23062	.94364	16
45	.04871	.21526	.95129	**15**		**45**	.05649	.23087	.94351	**15**
46	.04883	.21552	.95117	14		46	.05663	.23113	.94337	14
47	.04896	.21578	.95104	13		47	.05676	.23139	.94324	13
48	.04908	.21604	.95092	12		48	.05690	.23165	.94310	12
49	.04921	.21631	.95079	11		49	.05703	.23191	.94297	11
50	.04934	.21657	.95066	**10**		**50**	.05717	.23216	.94283	**10**
51	.04946	.21683	.95054	9		51	.05730	.23242	.94270	9
52	.04959	.21709	.95041	8		52	.05744	.23268	.94256	8
53	.04971	.21735	.95029	7		53	.05757	.23294	.94243	7
54	.04984	.21762	.95016	6		54	.05771	.23319	.94229	6
55	.04997	.21788	.95003	**5**		**55**	.05785	.23345	.94215	**5**
56	.05009	.21814	.94991	4		56	.05798	.23371	.94202	4
57	.05022	.21840	.94978	3		57	.05812	.23396	.94188	3
58	.05035	.21866	.94965	2		58	.05825	.23422	.94175	2
59	.05048	.21892	.94952	1		59	.05839	.23448	.94161	1
60	.05060	.21919	.94940	**0**		**60**	.05853	.23474	.94147	**0**
′	Cos²	Sin·Cos	Sin²	′		′	Cos²	Sin·Cos	Sin²	′

102° (282°)   (257°) **77°**   **103° (283°)**   (256°) **76°**

151

14° (194°)   (345°) **165°**

′	Sin²	Sin · Cos	Cos²	′
0	.05853	.23474	.94147	60
1	.05866	.23499	.94134	59
2	.05880	.23525	.94120	58
3	.05894	.23551	.94106	57
4	.05907	.23576	.94093	56
5	.05921	.23602	.94079	55
6	.05935	.23628	.94065	54
7	.05949	.23653	.94051	53
8	.05962	.23679	.94038	52
9	.05976	.23704	.94024	51
10	.05990	.23730	.94010	50
11	.06004	.23756	.93996	49
12	.06018	.23781	.93982	48
13	.06031	.23807	.93969	47
14	.06045	.23832	.93955	46
15	.06059	.23858	.93941	45
16	.06073	.23883	.93927	44
17	.06087	.23909	.93913	43
18	.06101	.23935	.93899	42
19	.06115	.23960	.93885	41
20	.06129	.23986	.93871	40
21	.06143	.24011	.93857	39
22	.06157	.24037	.93843	38
23	.06171	.24062	.93829	37
24	.06185	.24088	.93815	36
25	.06199	.24113	.93801	35
26	.06213	.24139	.93787	34
27	.06227	.24164	.93773	33
28	.06241	.24190	.93759	32
29	.06255	.24215	.93745	31
30	.06269	.24240	.93731	30
31	.06283	.24266	.93717	29
32	.06297	.24291	.93703	28
33	.06311	.24317	.93689	27
34	.06326	.24342	.93674	26
35	.06340	.24368	.93660	25
36	.06354	.24393	.93646	24
37	.06368	.24418	.93632	23
38	.06382	.24444	.93618	22
39	.06397	.24469	.93603	21
40	.06411	.24494	.93589	20
41	.06425	.24520	.93575	19
42	.06439	.24545	.93561	18
43	.06454	.24571	.93546	17
44	.06468	.24596	.93532	16
45	.06482	.24621	.93518	15
46	.06497	.24646	.93503	14
47	.06511	.24672	.93489	13
48	.06525	.24697	.93475	12
49	.06540	.24722	.93460	11
50	.06554	.24748	.93446	10
51	.06568	.24773	.93432	9
52	.06583	.24798	.93417	8
53	.06597	.24823	.93403	7
54	.06612	.24849	.93388	6
55	.06626	.24874	.93374	5
56	.06641	.24899	.93359	4
57	.06655	.24924	.93345	3
58	.06670	.24950	.93330	2
59	.06684	.24975	.93316	1
60	.06699	.25000	.93301	0
′	Cos²	Sin · Cos	Sin²	′

104° (284°)   (255°) **75°**

15° (195°)   (344°) **164°**

′	Sin²	Sin · Cos	Cos²	′
0	.06699	.25000	.93301	60
1	.06713	.25025	.93287	59
2	.06728	.25050	.93272	58
3	.06742	.25076	.93258	57
4	.06757	.25101	.93243	56
5	.06772	.25126	.93228	55
6	.06786	.25151	.93214	54
7	.06801	.25176	.93199	53
8	.06816	.25201	.93184	52
9	.06830	.25226	.93170	51
10	.06845	.25251	.93155	50
11	.06860	.25277	.93140	49
12	.06874	.25302	.93126	48
13	.06889	.25327	.93111	47
14	.06904	.25352	.93096	46
15	.06919	.25377	.93081	45
16	.06933	.25402	.93067	44
17	.06948	.25427	.93052	43
18	.06963	.25452	.93037	42
19	.06978	.25477	.93022	41
20	.06993	.25502	.93007	40
21	.07007	.25527	.92993	39
22	.07022	.25552	.92978	38
23	.07037	.25577	.92963	37
24	.07052	.25602	.92948	36
25	.07067	.25627	.92933	35
26	.07082	.25652	.92918	34
27	.07097	.25677	.92903	33
28	.07112	.25702	.92888	32
29	.07127	.25727	.92873	31
30	.07142	.25752	.92858	30
31	.07157	.25777	.92843	29
32	.07172	.25802	.92828	28
33	.07187	.25827	.92813	27
34	.07202	.25852	.92798	26
35	.07217	.25876	.92783	25
36	.07232	.25901	.92768	24
37	.07247	.25926	.92753	23
38	.07262	.25951	.92738	22
39	.07277	.25976	.92723	21
40	.07292	.26001	.92708	20
41	.07307	.26026	.92693	19
42	.07322	.26050	.92678	18
43	.07338	.26075	.92662	17
44	.07353	.26100	.92647	16
45	.07368	.26125	.92632	15
46	.07383	.26150	.92617	14
47	.07398	.26175	.92602	13
48	.07414	.26199	.92586	12
49	.07429	.26224	.92571	11
50	.07444	.26249	.92556	10
51	.07459	.26274	.92541	9
52	.07475	.26298	.92525	8
53	.07490	.26323	.92510	7
54	.07505	.26348	.92495	6
55	.07521	.26373	.92479	5
56	.07536	.26397	.92464	4
57	.07551	.26422	.92449	3
58	.07567	.26447	.92433	2
59	.07582	.26471	.92418	1
60	.07598	.26496	.92402	0
′	Cos²	Sin · Cos	Sin²	′

105° (285°)   (254°) **74°**

16° (196°)   **(343°) 163°**   **17° (197°)**   **(342°) 162°**

′	Sin²	Sin · Cos	Cos²	′		′	Sin²	Sin · Cos	Cos²	′
0	.07598	.26494	.92402	60		0	.08548	.27960	.91452	60
1	.07613	.26521	.92387	59		1	.08564	.27984	.91436	59
2	.07628	.26545	.92372	58		2	.08581	.28008	.91419	58
3	.07644	.26570	.92356	57		3	.08597	.28032	.91403	57
4	.07659	.26595	.92341	56		4	.08613	.28056	.91387	56
5	.07675	.26619	.92325	55		5	.08630	.28080	.91370	55
6	.07690	.26644	.92310	54		6	.08646	.28104	.91354	54
7	.07706	.26668	.92294	53		7	.08662	.28128	.91338	53
8	.07721	.26693	.92279	52		8	.08679	.28152	.91321	52
9	.07737	.26718	.92263	51		9	.08695	.28176	.91305	51
10	.07752	.26742	.92248	50		10	.08711	.28200	.91289	50
11	.07768	.26767	.92232	49		11	.08728	.28224	.91272	49
12	.07784	.26791	.92216	48		12	.08744	.28248	.91256	48
13	.07799	.26816	.92201	47		13	.08761	.28272	.91239	47
14	.07815	.26840	.92185	46		14	.08777	.28296	.91223	46
15	.07830	.26865	.92170	45		15	.08794	.28320	.91206	45
16	.07846	.26890	.92154	44		16	.08810	.28344	.91190	44
17	.07862	.26914	.92138	43		17	.08827	.28368	.91173	43
18	.07877	.26939	.92123	42		18	.08843	.28392	.91157	42
19	.07893	.26963	.92107	41		19	.08860	.28416	.91140	41
20	.07909	.26988	.92091	40		20	.08876	.28440	.91124	40
21	.07924	.27012	.92076	39		21	.08893	.28464	.91107	39
22	.07940	.27036	.92060	38		22	.08909	.28488	.91091	38
23	.07956	.27061	.92044	37		23	.08926	.28512	.91074	37
24	.07972	.27085	.92028	36		24	.08943	.28536	.91057	36
25	.07987	.27110	.92013	35		25	.08959	.28560	.91041	35
26	.08003	.27134	.91997	34		26	.08976	.28583	.91024	34
27	.08019	.27159	.91981	33		27	.08992	.28607	.91008	33
28	.08035	.27183	.91965	32		28	.09009	.28631	.90991	32
29	.08051	.27208	.91949	31		29	.09026	.28655	.90974	31
30	.08066	.27232	.91934	30		30	.09042	.28679	.90958	30
31	.08082	.27256	.91918	29		31	.09059	.28703	.90941	29
32	.08098	.27281	.91902	28		32	.09076	.28726	.90924	28
33	.08114	.27305	.91886	27		33	.09093	.28750	.90907	27
34	.08130	.27329	.91870	26		34	.09109	.28774	.90891	26
35	.08146	.27354	.91854	25		35	.09126	.28798	.90874	25
36	.08162	.27378	.91838	24		36	.09143	.28822	.90857	24
37	.08178	.27402	.91822	23		37	.09160	.28845	.90840	23
38	.08194	.27427	.91806	22		38	.09176	.28869	.90824	22
39	.08210	.27451	.91790	21		39	.09193	.28893	.90807	21
40	.08226	.27475	.91774	20		40	.09210	.28917	.90790	20
41	.08242	.27500	.91758	19		41	.09227	.28940	.90773	19
42	.08258	.27524	.91742	18		42	.09244	.28964	.90756	18
43	.08274	.27548	.91726	17		43	.09260	.28988	.90740	17
44	.08290	.27573	.91710	16		44	.09277	.29011	.90723	16
45	.08306	.27597	.91694	15		45	.09294	.29035	.90706	15
46	.08322	.27621	.91678	14		46	.09311	.29059	.90689	14
47	.08338	.27645	.91662	13		47	.09328	.29082	.90672	13
48	.08354	.27670	.91646	12		48	.09345	.29106	.90655	12
49	.08370	.27694	.91630	11		49	.09362	.29130	.90638	11
50	.08386	.27718	.91614	10		50	.09379	.29153	.90621	10
51	.08402	.27742	.91598	9		51	.09396	.29177	.90604	9
52	.08418	.27766	.91582	8		52	.09413	.29201	.90587	8
53	.08435	.27791	.91565	7		53	.09430	.29224	.90570	7
54	.08451	.27815	.91549	6		54	.09447	.29248	.90553	6
55	.08467	.27839	.91533	5		55	.09464	.29271	.90536	5
56	.08483	.27863	.91517	4		56	.09481	.29295	.90519	4
57	.08499	.27887	.91501	3		57	.09498	.29319	.90502	3
58	.08516	.27911	.91484	2		58	.09515	.29342	.90485	2
59	.08532	.27936	.91468	1		59	.09532	.29366	.90468	1
60	.08548	.27960	.91452	0		60	.09549	.29389	.90451	0
′	Cos²	Sin · Cos	Sin²	′		′	Cos²	Sin · Cos	Sin²	′

106° (286°)   **(253°) 73°**   **107° (287°)**   **(252°) 72°**

SQUARE OF THE SINE AND COSINE AND THEIR PRODUCT

18° (198°)   (341°) **161°**   19° (199°)   (340°) **160°**

′	Sin²	Sin · Cos	Cos²	′	′	Sin²	Sin · Cos	Cos²	′
0	.09549	.29389	.90451	**60**	**0**	.10599	.30783	.89401	**60**
1	.09566	.29413	.90434	59	1	.10617	.30806	.89383	59
2	.09583	.29436	.90417	58	2	.10635	.30829	.89365	58
3	.09601	.29460	.90399	57	3	.10653	.30852	.89347	57
4	.09618	.29483	.90382	56	4	.10671	.30875	.89329	56
5	.09635	.29507	.90365	**55**	**5**	.10689	.30898	.89311	**55**
6	.09652	.29530	.90348	54	6	.10707	.30920	.89293	54
7	.09669	.29554	.90331	53	7	.10725	.30943	.89275	53
8	.09686	.29577	.90314	52	8	.10743	.30966	.89257	52
9	.09704	.29601	.90296	51	9	.10761	.30989	.89239	51
10	.09721	.29624	.90279	**50**	**10**	.10779	.31012	.89221	**50**
11	.09738	.29648	.90262	49	11	.10797	.31035	.89203	49
12	.09755	.29671	.90245	48	12	.10815	.31057	.89185	48
13	.09773	.29694	.90227	47	13	.10833	.31080	.89167	47
14	.09790	.29718	.90210	46	14	.10851	.31103	.89149	46
15	.09807	.29741	.90193	**45**	**15**	.10870	.31126	.89130	**45**
16	.09824	.29765	.90176	44	16	.10888	.31148	.89112	44
17	.09842	.29788	.90158	43	17	.10906	.31171	.89094	43
18	.09859	.29811	.90141	42	18	.10924	.31194	.89076	42
19	.09876	.29835	.90124	41	19	.10942	.31217	.89058	41
20	.09894	.29858	.90106	**40**	**20**	.10960	.31239	.89040	**40**
21	.09911	.29881	.90089	39	21	.10978	.31262	.89022	39
22	.09929	.29905	.90071	38	22	.10997	.31285	.89003	38
23	.09946	.29928	.90054	37	23	.11015	.31308	.88985	37
24	.09963	.29951	.90037	36	24	.11033	.31330	.88967	36
25	.09981	.29974	.90019	**35**	**25**	.11051	.31353	.88949	**35**
26	.09998	.29998	.90002	34	26	.11070	.31376	.88930	34
27	.10016	.30021	.89984	33	27	.11088	.31398	.88912	33
28	.10033	.30044	.89967	32	28	.11106	.31421	.88894	32
29	.10051	.30068	.89949	31	29	.11124	.31443	.88876	31
30	.10068	.30091	.89932	**30**	**30**	.11143	.31466	.88857	**30**
31	.10086	.30114	.89914	29	31	.11161	.31489	.88839	29
32	.10103	.30137	.89897	28	32	.11179	.31511	.88821	28
33	.10121	.30160	.89879	27	33	.11198	.31534	.88802	27
34	.10138	.30184	.89862	26	34	.11216	.31556	.88784	26
35	.10156	.30207	.89844	**25**	**35**	.11234	.31579	.88766	**25**
36	.10174	.30230	.89826	24	36	.11253	.31601	.88747	24
37	.10191	.30253	.89809	23	37	.11271	.31624	.88729	23
38	.10209	.30276	.89791	22	38	.11290	.31647	.88710	22
39	.10226	.30299	.89774	21	39	.11308	.31669	.88692	21
40	.10244	.30323	.89756	**20**	**40**	.11326	.31692	.88674	**20**
41	.10262	.30346	.89738	19	41	.11345	.31714	.88655	19
42	.10279	.30369	.89721	18	42	.11363	.31737	.88637	18
43	.10297	.30392	.89703	17	43	.11382	.31759	.88618	17
44	.10315	.30415	.89685	16	44	.11400	.31781	.88600	16
45	.10332	.30438	.89668	**15**	**45**	.11419	.31804	.88581	**15**
46	.10350	.30461	.89650	14	46	.11437	.31826	.88563	14
47	.10368	.30484	.89632	13	47	.11456	.31849	.88544	13
48	.10386	.30507	.89614	12	48	.11474	.31871	.88526	12
49	.10403	.30530	.89597	11	49	.11493	.31894	.88507	11
50	.10421	.30553	.89579	**10**	**50**	.11511	.31916	.88489	**10**
51	.10439	.30576	.89561	9	51	.11530	.31938	.88470	9
52	.10457	.30599	.89543	8	52	.11549	.31961	.88451	8
53	.10474	.30622	.89526	7	53	.11567	.31983	.88433	7
54	.10492	.30645	.89508	6	54	.11586	.32005	.88414	6
55	.10510	.30668	.89490	**5**	**55**	.11604	.32028	.88396	**5**
56	.10528	.30691	.89472	4	56	.11623	.32050	.88377	4
57	.10546	.30714	.89454	3	57	.11642	.32072	.88358	3
58	.10564	.30737	.89436	2	58	.11660	.32095	.88340	2
59	.10582	.30760	.89418	1	59	.11679	.32117	.88321	1
60	.10599	.30783	.89401	**0**	**60**	.11698	.32139	.88302	**0**
′	Cos²	Sin · Cos	Sin²	′	′	Cos²	Sin · Cos	Sin²	′

108° (288°)   (251°) **71°**   109° (289°)   (250°) **70°**

154

′	Sin²	Sin·Cos	Cos²	′	′	Sin²	Sin·Cos	Cos²	′
0	.11698	.32139	.88302	60	0	.12843	.33457	.87157	60
1	.11716	.32162	.88284	59	1	.12862	.33478	.87138	59
2	.11735	.32184	.88265	58	2	.12882	.33500	.87118	58
3	.11754	.32206	.88246	57	3	.12901	.33521	.87099	57
4	.11773	.32228	.88227	56	4	.12921	.33543	.87079	56
5	.11791	.32251	.88209	55	5	.12940	.33564	.87060	55
6	.11810	.32273	.88190	54	6	.12960	.33586	.87040	54
7	.11829	.32295	.88171	53	7	.12979	.33608	.87021	53
8	.11848	.32317	.88152	52	8	.12999	.33629	.87001	52
9	.11867	.32339	.88133	51	9	.13018	.33651	.86982	51
10	.11885	.32362	.88115	50	10	.13038	.33672	.86962	50
11	.11904	.32384	.88096	49	11	.13058	.33694	.86942	49
12	.11923	.32406	.88077	48	12	.13077	.33715	.86923	48
13	.11942	.32428	.88058	47	13	.13097	.33737	.86903	47
14	.11961	.32450	.88039	46	14	.13116	.33758	.86884	46
15	.11980	.32472	.88020	45	15	.13136	.33780	.86864	45
16	.11999	.32495	.88001	44	16	.13156	.33801	.86844	44
17	.12018	.32517	.87982	43	17	.13175	.33822	.86825	43
18	.12036	.32539	.87964	42	18	.13195	.33844	.86805	42
19	.12055	.32561	.87945	41	19	.13215	.33865	.86785	41
20	.12074	.32583	.87926	40	20	.13235	.33887	.86765	40
21	.12093	.32605	.87907	39	21	.13254	.33908	.86746	39
22	.12112	.32627	.87888	38	22	.13274	.33929	.86726	38
23	.12131	.32649	.87869	37	23	.13294	.33951	.86706	37
24	.12150	.32671	.87850	36	24	.13314	.33972	.86686	36
25	.12169	.32693	.87831	35	25	.13333	.33993	.86667	35
26	.12188	.32715	.87812	34	26	.13353	.34015	.86647	34
27	.12207	.32737	.87793	33	27	.13373	.34036	.86627	33
28	.12226	.32759	.87774	32	28	.13393	.34057	.86607	32
29	.12245	.32781	.87755	31	29	.13412	.34079	.86588	31
30	.12265	.32803	.87735	30	30	.13432	.34100	.86568	30
31	.12284	.32825	.87716	29	31	.13452	.34121	.86548	29
32	.12303	.32847	.87697	28	32	.13472	.34142	.86528	28
33	.12322	.32869	.87678	27	33	.13492	.34164	.86508	27
34	.12341	.32891	.87659	26	34	.13512	.34185	.86488	26
35	.12360	.32913	.87640	25	35	.13532	.34206	.86468	25
36	.12379	.32934	.87621	24	36	.13552	.34227	.86448	24
37	.12398	.32956	.87602	23	37	.13571	.34249	.86429	23
38	.12418	.32978	.87582	22	38	.13591	.34270	.86409	22
39	.12437	.33000	.87563	21	39	.13611	.34291	.86389	21
40	.12456	.33022	.87544	20	40	.13631	.34312	.86369	20
41	.12475	.33044	.87525	19	41	.13651	.34333	.86349	19
42	.12494	.33066	.87506	18	42	.13671	.34354	.86329	18
43	.12514	.33087	.87486	17	43	.13691	.34376	.86309	17
44	.12533	.33109	.87467	16	44	.13711	.34397	.86289	16
45	.12552	.33131	.87448	15	45	.13731	.34418	.86269	15
46	.12571	.33153	.87429	14	46	.13751	.34439	.86249	14
47	.12591	.33175	.87409	13	47	.13771	.34460	.86229	13
48	.12610	.33196	.87390	12	48	.13791	.34481	.86209	12
49	.12629	.33218	.87371	11	49	.13811	.34502	.86189	11
50	.12649	.33240	.87351	10	50	.13832	.34523	.86168	10
51	.12668	.33262	.87332	9	51	.13852	.34544	.86148	9
52	.12687	.33283	.87313	8	52	.13872	.34565	.86128	8
53	.12707	.33305	.87293	7	53	.13892	.34586	.86108	7
54	.12726	.33327	.87274	6	54	.13912	.34607	.86088	6
55	.12746	.33348	.87254	5	55	.13932	.34628	.86068	5
56	.12765	.33370	.87235	4	56	.13952	.34649	.86048	4
57	.12784	.33392	.87216	3	57	.13972	.34670	.86028	3
58	.12804	.33413	.87196	2	58	.13993	.34691	.86007	2
59	.12823	.33435	.87177	1	59	.14013	.34712	.85987	1
60	.12843	.33457	.87157	0	60	.14033	.34733	.85967	0
′	Cos²	Sin·Cos	Sin²	′	′	Cos²	Sin·Cos	Sin²	′

SQUARE OF THE SINE AND COSINE AND THEIR PRODUCT

′	Sin²	Sin · Cos	Cos²	′
0	.14033	.34733	.85967	60
1	.14053	.34754	.85947	59
2	.14073	.34775	.85927	58
3	.14094	.34796	.85906	57
4	.14114	.34817	.85886	56
5	.14134	.34837	.85866	55
6	.14154	.34858	.85846	54
7	.14175	.34879	.85825	53
8	.14195	.34900	.85805	52
9	.14215	.34921	.85785	51
10	.14236	.34942	.85764	50
11	.14256	.34962	.85744	49
12	.14276	.34983	.85724	48
13	.14297	.35004	.85703	47
14	.14317	.35025	.85683	46
15	.14337	.35045	.85663	45
16	.14358	.35066	.85642	44
17	.14378	.35087	.85622	43
18	.14399	.35108	.85601	42
19	.14419	.35128	.85581	41
20	.14440	.35149	.85560	40
21	.14460	.35170	.85540	39
22	.14480	.35190	.85520	38
23	.14501	.35211	.85499	37
24	.14521	.35232	.85479	36
25	.14542	.35252	.85458	35
26	.14562	.35273	.85438	34
27	.14583	.35294	.85417	33
28	.14604	.35314	.85396	32
29	.14624	.35335	.85376	31
30	.14645	.35355	.85355	30
31	.14665	.35376	.85335	29
32	.14686	.35396	.85314	28
33	.14706	.35417	.85294	27
34	.14727	.35438	.85273	26
35	.14748	.35458	.85252	25
36	.14768	.35479	.85232	24
37	.14789	.35499	.85211	23
38	.14810	.35520	.85190	22
39	.14830	.35540	.85170	21
40	.14851	.35560	.85149	20
41	.14872	.35581	.85128	19
42	.14892	.35601	.85108	18
43	.14913	.35622	.85087	17
44	.14934	.35642	.85066	16
45	.14955	.35663	.85045	15
46	.14975	.35683	.85025	14
47	.14996	.35703	.85004	13
48	.15017	.35724	.84983	12
49	.15038	.35744	.84962	11
50	.15058	.35764	.84942	10
51	.15079	.35785	.84921	9
52	.15100	.35805	.84900	8
53	.15121	.35825	.84879	7
54	.15142	.35846	.84858	6
55	.15163	.35866	.84837	5
56	.15183	.35886	.84817	4
57	.15204	.35906	.84796	3
58	.15225	.35927	.84775	2
59	.15246	.35947	.84754	1
60	.15267	.35967	.84733	0
′	Cos²	Sin · Cos	Sin²	′

′	Sin²	Sin · Cos	Cos²	′
0	.15267	.35967	.84733	60
1	.15288	.35987	.84712	59
2	.15309	.36007	.84691	58
3	.15330	.36028	.84670	57
4	.15351	.36048	.84649	56
5	.15372	.36068	.84628	55
6	.15393	.36088	.84607	54
7	.15414	.36108	.84586	53
8	.15435	.36128	.84565	52
9	.15456	.36148	.84544	51
10	.15477	.36168	.84523	50
11	.15498	.36189	.84502	49
12	.15519	.36209	.84481	48
13	.15540	.36229	.84460	47
14	.15561	.36249	.84439	46
15	.15582	.36269	.84418	45
16	.15603	.36289	.84397	44
17	.15624	.36309	.84376	43
18	.15646	.36329	.84354	42
19	.15667	.36349	.84333	41
20	.15688	.36369	.84312	40
21	.15709	.36389	.84291	39
22	.15730	.36409	.84270	38
23	.15751	.36429	.84249	37
24	.15773	.36448	.84227	36
25	.15794	.36468	.84206	35
26	.15815	.36488	.84185	34
27	.15836	.36508	.84164	33
28	.15858	.36528	.84142	32
29	.15879	.36548	.84121	31
30	.15900	.36568	.84100	30
31	.15921	.36588	.84079	29
32	.15943	.36607	.84057	28
33	.15964	.36627	.84036	27
34	.15985	.36647	.84015	26
35	.16007	.36667	.83993	25
36	.16028	.36686	.83972	24
37	.16049	.36706	.83951	23
38	.16071	.36726	.83929	22
39	.16092	.36746	.83908	21
40	.16113	.36765	.83887	20
41	.16135	.36785	.83865	19
42	.16156	.36805	.83844	18
43	.16178	.36825	.83822	17
44	.16199	.36844	.83801	16
45	.16220	.36864	.83780	15
46	.16242	.36884	.83758	14
47	.16263	.36903	.83737	13
48	.16285	.36923	.83715	12
49	.16306	.36942	.83694	11
50	.16328	.36962	.83672	10
51	.16349	.36982	.83651	9
52	.16371	.37001	.83629	8
53	.16392	.37021	.83608	7
54	.16414	.37040	.83586	6
55	.16436	.37060	.83564	5
56	.16457	.37079	.83543	4
57	.16479	.37099	.83521	3
58	.16500	.37118	.83500	2
59	.16522	.37138	.83478	1
60	.16543	.37157	.83457	0
′	Cos²	Sin · Cos	Sin²	′

SQUARE OF THE SINE AND COSINE AND THEIR PRODUCT

′	Sin²	Sin · Cos	Cos²	′	′	Sin²	Sin · Cos	Cos²	′
0	.16543	.37157	.83457	60	0	.17861	.38302	.82139	60
1	.16565	.37177	.83435	59	1	.17883	.38321	.82117	59
2	.16587	.37196	.83413	58	2	.17905	.38340	.82095	58
3	.16608	.37216	.83392	57	3	.17928	.38358	.82072	57
4	.16630	.37235	.83370	56	4	.17950	.38377	.82050	56
5	.16652	.37254	.83348	55	5	.17972	.38396	.82028	55
6	.16673	.37274	.83327	54	6	.17995	.38414	.82005	54
7	.16695	.37293	.83305	53	7	.18017	.38433	.81983	53
8	.16717	.37313	.83283	52	8	.18039	.38451	.81961	52
9	.16738	.37332	.83262	51	9	.18062	.38470	.81938	51
10	.16760	.37351	.83240	50	10	.18084	.38489	.81916	50
11	.16782	.37371	.83218	49	11	.18106	.38507	.81894	49
12	.16804	.37390	.83196	48	12	.18129	.38526	.81871	48
13	.16825	.37409	.83175	47	13	.18151	.38544	.81849	47
14	.16847	.37429	.83153	46	14	.18174	.38563	.81826	46
15	.16869	.37448	.83131	45	15	.18196	.38581	.81804	45
16	.16891	.37467	.83109	44	16	.18219	.38600	.81781	44
17	.16913	.37486	.83087	43	17	.18241	.38618	.81759	43
18	.16934	.37506	.83066	42	18	.18263	.38637	.81737	42
19	.16956	.37525	.83044	41	19	.18286	.38655	.81714	41
20	.16978	.37544	.83022	40	20	.18308	.38674	.81692	40
21	.17000	.37563	.83000	39	21	.18331	.38692	.81669	39
22	.17022	.37582	.82978	38	22	.18353	.38710	.81647	38
23	.17044	.37602	.82956	37	23	.18376	.38729	.81624	37
24	.17066	.37621	.82934	36	24	.18399	.38747	.81601	36
25	.17087	.37640	.82913	35	25	.18421	.38766	.81579	35
26	.17109	.37659	.82891	34	26	.18444	.38784	.81556	34
27	.17131	.37678	.82869	33	27	.18466	.38802	.81534	33
28	.17153	.37697	.82847	32	28	.18489	.38821	.81511	32
29	.17175	.37716	.82825	31	29	.18511	.38839	.81489	31
30	.17197	.37735	.82803	30	30	.18534	.38857	.81466	30
31	.17219	.37755	.82781	29	31	.18557	.38876	.81443	29
32	.17241	.37774	.82759	28	32	.18579	.38894	.81421	28
33	.17263	.37793	.82737	27	33	.18602	.38912	.81398	27
34	.17285	.37812	.82715	26	34	.18624	.38930	.81376	26
35	.17307	.37831	.82693	25	35	.18647	.38949	.81353	25
36	.17329	.37850	.82671	24	36	.18670	.38967	.81330	24
37	.17351	.37869	.82649	23	37	.18692	.38985	.81308	23
38	.17373	.37888	.82627	22	38	.18715	.39003	.81285	22
39	.17395	.37907	.82605	21	39	.18738	.39022	.81262	21
40	.17417	.37926	.82583	20	40	.18761	.39040	.81239	20
41	.17439	.37945	.82561	19	41	.18783	.39058	.81217	19
42	.17461	.37964	.82539	18	42	.18806	.39076	.81194	18
43	.17483	.37982	.82517	17	43	.18829	.39094	.81171	17
44	.17505	.38001	.82495	16	44	.18852	.39112	.81148	16
45	.17528	.38020	.82472	15	45	.18874	.39130	.81126	15
46	.17550	.38039	.82450	14	46	.18897	.39149	.81103	14
47	.17572	.38058	.82428	13	47	.18920	.39167	.81080	13
48	.17594	.38077	.82406	12	48	.18943	.39185	.81057	12
49	.17616	.38096	.82384	11	49	.18965	.39203	.81035	11
50	.17638	.38115	.82362	10	50	.18988	.39221	.81012	10
51	.17661	.38133	.82339	9	51	.19011	.39239	.80989	9
52	.17683	.38152	.82317	8	52	.19034	.39257	.80966	8
53	.17705	.38171	.82295	7	53	.19057	.39275	.80943	7
54	.17727	.38190	.82273	6	54	.19080	.39293	.80920	6
55	.17749	.38209	.82251	5	55	.19102	.39311	.80898	5
56	.17772	.38227	.82228	4	56	.19125	.39329	.80875	4
57	.17794	.38246	.82206	3	57	.19148	.39347	.80852	3
58	.17816	.38265	.82184	2	58	.19171	.39365	.80829	2
59	.17838	.38284	.82162	1	59	.19194	.39383	.80806	1
60	.17861	.38302	.82139	0	60	.19217	.39401	.80783	0
′	Cos²	Sin · Cos	Sin²	′	′	Cos²	Sin · Cos	Sin²	′

SQUARE OF THE SINE AND COSINE AND THEIR PRODUCT

26° (206°)   (333°) **153°**   **27°** (207°)   (332°) **152°**

′	Sin²	Sin · Cos	Cos²	′		′	Sin²	Sin · Cos	Cos²	′
0	.19217	.39401	.80783	**60**		**0**	.20611	.40451	.79389	**60**
1	.19240	.39418	.80760	59		1	.20634	.40468	.79366	59
2	.19263	.39436	.80737	58		2	.20658	.40485	.79342	58
3	.19286	.39454	.80714	57		3	.20681	.40502	.79319	57
4	.19309	.39472	.80691	56		4	.20705	.40519	.79295	56
5	.19332	.39490	.80668	**55**		**5**	.20729	.40536	.79271	**55**
6	.19355	.39508	.80645	54		6	.20752	.40553	.79248	54
7	.19378	.39526	.80622	53		7	.20776	.40570	.79224	53
8	.19401	.39543	.80599	52		8	.20799	.40587	.79201	52
9	.19424	.39561	.80576	51		9	.20823	.40604	.79177	51
10	.19447	.39579	.80553	**50**		**10**	.20847	.40621	.79153	**50**
11	.19470	.39597	.80530	49		11	.20870	.40638	.79130	49
12	.19493	.39614	.80507	48		12	.20894	.40655	.79106	48
13	.19516	.39632	.80484	47		13	.20918	.40672	.79082	47
14	.19539	.39650	.80461	46		14	.20941	.40689	.79059	46
15	.19562	.39668	.80438	**45**		**15**	.20965	.40706	.79035	**45**
16	.19585	.39685	.80415	44		16	.20989	.40723	.79011	44
17	.19608	.39703	.80392	43		17	.21012	.40740	.78988	43
18	.19631	.39721	.80369	42		18	.21036	.40756	.78964	42
19	.19654	.39738	.80346	41		19	.21060	.40773	.78940	41
20	.19677	.39756	.80323	**40**		**20**	.21083	.40790	.78917	**40**
21	.19701	.39774	.80299	39		21	.21107	.40807	.78893	39
22	.19724	.39791	.80276	38		22	.21131	.40824	.78869	38
23	.19747	.39809	.80253	37		23	.21155	.40840	.78845	37
24	.19770	.39826	.80230	36		24	.21178	.40857	.78822	36
25	.19793	.39844	.80207	**35**		**25**	.21202	.40874	.78798	**35**
26	.19816	.39862	.80184	34		26	.21226	.40891	.78774	34
27	.19840	.39879	.80160	33		27	.21250	.40907	.78750	33
28	.19863	.39897	.80137	32		28	.21274	.40924	.78726	32
29	.19886	.39914	.80114	31		29	.21297	.40941	.78703	31
30	.19909	.39932	.80091	**30**		**30**	.21321	.40958	.78679	**30**
31	.19932	.39949	.80068	29		31	.21345	.40974	.78655	29
32	.19956	.39967	.80044	28		32	.21369	.40991	.78631	28
33	.19979	.39984	.80021	27		33	.21393	.41008	.78607	27
34	.20002	.40002	.79998	26		34	.21417	.41024	.78583	26
35	.20026	.40019	.79974	**25**		**35**	.21440	.41041	.78560	**25**
36	.20049	.40037	.79951	24		36	.21464	.41057	.78536	24
37	.20072	.40054	.79928	23		37	.21488	.41074	.78512	23
38	.20095	.40071	.79905	22		38	.21512	.41091	.78488	22
39	.20119	.40089	.79881	21		39	.21536	.41107	.78464	21
40	.20142	.40106	.79858	**20**		**40**	.21560	.41124	.78440	**20**
41	.20165	.40124	.79835	19		41	.21584	.41140	.78416	19
42	.20189	.40141	.79811	18		42	.21608	.41157	.78392	18
43	.20212	.40158	.79788	17		43	.21632	.41173	.78368	17
44	.20235	.40176	.79765	16		44	.21656	.41190	.78344	16
45	.20259	.40193	.79741	**15**		**45**	.21680	.41206	.78320	**15**
46	.20282	.40210	.79718	14		46	.21704	.41223	.78296	14
47	.20306	.40227	.79694	13		47	.21728	.41239	.78272	13
48	.20329	.40245	.79671	12		48	.21752	.41256	.78248	12
49	.20352	.40262	.79648	11		49	.21776	.41272	.78224	11
50	.20376	.40279	.79624	**10**		**50**	.21800	.41289	.78200	**10**
51	.20399	.40296	.79601	9		51	.21824	.41305	.78176	9
52	.20423	.40314	.79577	8		52	.21848	.41321	.78152	8
53	.20446	.40331	.79554	7		53	.21872	.41338	.78128	7
54	.20470	.40348	.79530	6		54	.21896	.41354	.78104	6
55	.20493	.40365	.79507	**5**		**55**	.21920	.41370	.78080	**5**
56	.20517	.40382	.79483	4		56	.21944	.41387	.78056	4
57	.20540	.40399	.79460	3		57	.21968	.41403	.78032	3
58	.20564	.40417	.79436	2		58	.21992	.41419	.78008	2
59	.20587	.40434	.79413	1		59	.22016	.41436	.77984	1
60	.20611	.40451	.79389	**0**		**60**	.22040	.41452	.77960	**0**
′	Cos²	Sin · Cos	Sin²	′		′	Cos²	Sin · Cos	Sin²	′

116° (296°)   (243°) **63°**   **117°** (297°)   (242°) **62°**

158

28° (208°)   (331°) 151°   29° (209°)   (330°) 150°

′	Sin²	Sin · Cos	Cos²	′
0	.22040	.41452	.77960	60
1	.22064	.41468	.77936	59
2	.22089	.41484	.77911	58
3	.22113	.41501	.77887	57
4	.22137	.41517	.77863	56
5	.22161	.41533	.77839	55
6	.22185	.41549	.77815	54
7	.22209	.41565	.77791	53
8	.22234	.41582	.77766	52
9	.22258	.41598	.77742	51
10	.22282	.41614	.77718	50
11	.22306	.41630	.77694	49
12	.22330	.41646	.77670	48
13	.22355	.41662	.77645	47
14	.22379	.41678	.77621	46
15	.22403	.41694	.77597	45
16	.22427	.41710	.77573	44
17	.22452	.41726	.77548	43
18	.22476	.41742	.77524	42
19	.22500	.41758	.77500	41
20	.22525	.41774	.77475	40
21	.22549	.41790	.77451	39
22	.22573	.41806	.77427	38
23	.22598	.41822	.77402	37
24	.22622	.41838	.77378	36
25	.22646	.41854	.77354	35
26	.22671	.41870	.77329	34
27	.22695	.41886	.77305	33
28	.22719	.41902	.77281	32
29	.22744	.41918	.77256	31
30	.22768	.41934	.77232	30
31	.22792	.41949	.77208	29
32	.22817	.41965	.77183	28
33	.22841	.41981	.77159	27
34	.22866	.41997	.77134	26
35	.22890	.42013	.77110	25
36	.22915	.42028	.77085	24
37	.22939	.42044	.77061	23
38	.22964	.42060	.77036	22
39	.22988	.42076	.77012	21
40	.23012	.42091	.76988	20
41	.23037	.42107	.76963	19
42	.23061	.42123	.76939	18
43	.23086	.42138	.76914	17
44	.23110	.42154	.76890	16
45	.23135	.42170	.76865	15
46	.23160	.42185	.76840	14
47	.23184	.42201	.76816	13
48	.23209	.42216	.76791	12
49	.23233	.42232	.76767	11
50	.23258	.42248	.76742	10
51	.23282	.42263	.76718	9
52	.23307	.42279	.76693	8
53	.23332	.42294	.76668	7
54	.23356	.42310	.76644	6
55	.23381	.42325	.76619	5
56	.23405	.42341	.76595	4
57	.23430	.42356	.76570	3
58	.23455	.42372	.76545	2
59	.23479	.42387	.76521	1
60	.23504	.42402	.76496	0
′	Cos²	Sin · Cos	Sin²	′

118° (298°)   (241°) 61°

′	Sin²	Sin · Cos	Cos²	′
0	.23504	.42402	.76496	60
1	.23529	.42418	.76471	59
2	.23553	.42433	.76447	58
3	.23578	.42449	.76422	57
4	.23603	.42464	.76397	56
5	.23627	.42479	.76373	55
6	.23652	.42495	.76348	54
7	.23677	.42510	.76323	53
8	.23702	.42525	.76298	52
9	.23726	.42541	.76274	51
10	.23751	.42556	.76249	50
11	.23776	.42571	.76224	49
12	.23801	.42586	.76199	48
13	.23825	.42602	.76175	47
14	.23850	.42617	.76150	46
15	.23875	.42632	.76125	45
16	.23900	.42647	.76100	44
17	.23925	.42662	.76075	43
18	.23950	.42678	.76050	42
19	.23974	.42693	.76026	41
20	.23999	.42708	.76001	40
21	.24024	.42723	.75976	39
22	.24049	.42738	.75951	38
23	.24074	.42753	.75926	37
24	.24099	.42768	.75901	36
25	.24124	.42783	.75876	35
26	.24148	.42798	.75852	34
27	.24173	.42813	.75827	33
28	.24198	.42828	.75802	32
29	.24223	.42843	.75777	31
30	.24248	.42858	.75752	30
31	.24273	.42873	.75727	29
32	.24298	.42888	.75702	28
33	.24323	.42903	.75677	27
34	.24348	.42918	.75652	26
35	.24373	.42933	.75627	25
36	.24398	.42948	.75602	24
37	.24423	.42963	.75577	23
38	.24448	.42978	.75552	22
39	.24473	.42993	.75527	21
40	.24498	.43007	.75502	20
41	.24523	.43022	.75477	19
42	.24548	.43037	.75452	18
43	.24573	.43052	.75427	17
44	.24598	.43067	.75402	16
45	.24623	.43081	.75377	15
46	.24648	.43096	.75352	14
47	.24673	.43111	.75327	13
48	.24698	.43126	.75302	12
49	.24723	.43140	.75277	11
50	.24749	.43155	.75251	10
51	.24774	.43170	.75226	9
52	.24799	.43184	.75201	8
53	.24824	.43199	.75176	7
54	.24849	.43214	.75151	6
55	.24874	.43228	.75126	5
56	.24899	.43243	.75101	4
57	.24924	.43258	.75076	3
58	.24950	.43272	.75050	2
59	.24975	.43287	.75025	1
60	.25000	.43301	.75000	0
′	Cos²	Sin · Cos	Sin²	′

119° (299°)   (240°) 60°

30° (210°)   (329°) 149°   **31° (211°)**   (328°) 148°

′	Sin²	Sin · Cos	Cos²	′	′	Sin²	Sin · Cos	Cos²	′
0	.25000	.43301	.75000	60	0	.26526	.44147	.73474	60
1	.25025	.43316	.74975	59	1	.26552	.44161	.73448	59
2	.25050	.43330	.74950	58	2	.26578	.44175	.73422	58
3	.25076	.43345	.74924	57	3	.26604	.44188	.73396	57
4	.25101	.43359	.74899	56	4	.26629	.44202	.73371	56
5	.25126	.43374	.74874	55	5	.26655	.44215	.73345	55
6	.25151	.43388	.74849	54	6	.26681	.44229	.73319	54
7	.25177	.43403	.74823	53	7	.26706	.44243	.73294	53
8	.25202	.43417	.74798	52	8	.26732	.44256	.73268	52
9	.25227	.43432	.74773	51	9	.26758	.44270	.73242	51
10	.25252	.43446	.74748	50	10	.26784	.44283	.73216	50
11	.25278	.43460	.74722	49	11	.26809	.44297	.73191	49
12	.25303	.43475	.74697	48	12	.26835	.44310	.73165	48
13	.25328	.43489	.74672	47	13	.26861	.44324	.73139	47
14	.25354	.43503	.74646	46	14	.26887	.44337	.73113	46
15	.25379	.43518	.74621	45	15	.26913	.44351	.73087	45
16	.25404	.43532	.74596	44	16	.26938	.44364	.73062	44
17	.25429	.43546	.74571	43	17	.26964	.44377	.73036	43
18	.25455	.43561	.74545	42	18	.26990	.44391	.73010	42
19	.25480	.43575	.74520	41	19	.27016	.44404	.72984	41
20	.25506	.43589	.74494	40	20	.27042	.44418	.72958	40
21	.25531	.43603	.74469	39	21	.27068	.44431	.72932	39
22	.25556	.43618	.74444	38	22	.27093	.44444	.72907	38
23	.25582	.43632	.74418	37	23	.27119	.44458	.72881	37
24	.25607	.43646	.74393	36	24	.27145	.44471	.72855	36
25	.25632	.43660	.74368	35	25	.27171	.44484	.72829	35
26	.25658	.43674	.74342	34	26	.27197	.44497	.72803	34
27	.25683	.43689	.74317	33	27	.27223	.44511	.72777	33
28	.25709	.43703	.74291	32	28	.27249	.44524	.72751	32
29	.25734	.43717	.74266	31	29	.27275	.44537	.72725	31
30	.25760	.43731	.74240	30	30	.27300	.44550	.72700	30
31	.25785	.43745	.74215	29	31	.27326	.44564	.72674	29
32	.25810	.43759	.74190	28	32	.27352	.44577	.72648	28
33	.25836	.43773	.74164	27	33	.27378	.44590	.72622	27
34	.25861	.43787	.74139	26	34	.27404	.44603	.72596	26
35	.25887	.43801	.74113	25	35	.27430	.44616	.72570	25
36	.25912	.43815	.74088	24	36	.27456	.44629	.72544	24
37	.25938	.43829	.74062	23	37	.27482	.44642	.72518	23
38	.25963	.43843	.74037	22	38	.27508	.44655	.72492	22
39	.25989	.43857	.74011	21	39	.27534	.44669	.72466	21
40	.26014	.43871	.73986	20	40	.27560	.44682	.72440	20
41	.26040	.43885	.73960	19	41	.27586	.44695	.72414	19
42	.26065	.43899	.73935	18	42	.27612	.44708	.72388	18
43	.26091	.43913	.73909	17	43	.27638	.44721	.72362	17
44	.26117	.43927	.73883	16	44	.27664	.44734	.72336	16
45	.26142	.43941	.73858	15	45	.27690	.44747	.72310	15
46	.26168	.43955	.73832	14	46	.27716	.44760	.72284	14
47	.26193	.43969	.73807	13	47	.27742	.44773	.72258	13
48	.26219	.43982	.73781	12	48	.27768	.44786	.72232	12
49	.26244	.43996	.73756	11	49	.27794	.44799	.72206	11
50	.26270	.44010	.73730	10	50	.27820	.44811	.72180	10
51	.26296	.44024	.73704	9	51	.27846	.44824	.72154	9
52	.26321	.44038	.73679	8	52	.27873	.44837	.72127	8
53	.26347	.44051	.73653	7	53	.27899	.44850	.72101	7
54	.26372	.44065	.73628	6	54	.27925	.44863	.72075	6
55	.26398	.44079	.73602	5	55	.27951	.44876	.72049	5
56	.26424	.44093	.73576	4	56	.27977	.44889	.72023	4
57	.26449	.44106	.73551	3	57	.28003	.44901	.71997	3
58	.26475	.44120	.73525	2	58	.28029	.44914	.71971	2
59	.26501	.44134	.73499	1	59	.28055	.44927	.71945	1
60	.26526	.44147	.73474	0	60	.28081	.44940	.71919	0
′	Cos²	Sin · Cos	Sin²	′	′	Cos²	Sin · Cos	Sin²	′

120° (300°)   (239°) 59°   **121° (301°)**   (238°) 58°

32° (212°)   (327°) **147°**   **33°** (213°)   (326°) **146°**

′	Sin²	Sin · Cos	Cos²	′		′	Sin²	Sin · Cos	Cos²	′
0	.28081	.44940	.71919	**60**		**0**	.29663	.45677	.70337	**60**
1	.28108	.44952	.71892	59		1	.29690	.45689	.70310	59
2	.28134	.44965	.71866	58		2	.29716	.45701	.70284	58
3	.28160	.44978	.71840	57		3	.29743	.45713	.70257	57
4	.28186	.44991	.71814	56		4	.29770	.45724	.70230	56
5	.28212	.45003	.71788	**55**		**5**	.29796	.45736	.70204	**55**
6	.28238	.45016	.71762	54		6	.29823	.45748	.70177	54
7	.28265	.45029	.71735	53		7	.29849	.45760	.70151	53
8	.28291	.45041	.71709	52		8	.29876	.45771	.70124	52
9	.28317	.45054	.71683	51		9	.29903	.45783	.70097	51
10	.28343	.45066	.71657	**50**		**10**	.29929	.45795	.70071	**50**
11	.28369	.45079	.71631	49		11	.29956	.45806	.70044	49
12	.28396	.45092	.71604	48		12	.29983	.45818	.70017	48
13	.28422	.45104	.71578	47		13	.30009	.45830	.69991	47
14	.28448	.45117	.71552	46		14	.30036	.45841	.69964	46
15	.28474	.45129	.71526	**45**		**15**	.30063	.45853	.69937	**45**
16	.28501	.45142	.71499	44		16	.30089	.45865	.69911	44
17	.28527	.45154	.71473	43		17	.30116	.45876	.69884	43
18	.28553	.45167	.71447	42		18	.30143	.45888	.69857	42
19	.28580	.45179	.71420	41		19	.30169	.45899	.69831	41
20	.28606	.45192	.71394	**40**		**20**	.30196	.45911	.69804	**40**
21	.28632	.45204	.71368	39		21	.30223	.45922	.69777	39
22	.28658	.45217	.71342	38		22	.30249	.45934	.69751	38
23	.28685	.45229	.71315	37		23	.30276	.45945	.69724	37
24	.28711	.45241	.71289	36		24	.30303	.45957	.69697	36
25	.28737	.45254	.71263	**35**		**25**	.30330	.45968	.69670	**35**
26	.28764	.45266	.71236	34		26	.30356	.45980	.69644	34
27	.28790	.45278	.71210	33		27	.30383	.45991	.69617	33
28	.28816	.45291	.71184	32		28	.30410	.46002	.69590	32
29	.28843	.45303	.71157	31		29	.30437	.46014	.69563	31
30	.28869	.45315	.71131	**30**		**30**	.30463	.46025	.69537	**30**
31	.28895	.45328	.71105	29		31	.30490	.46037	.69510	29
32	.28922	.45340	.71078	28		32	.30517	.46048	.69483	28
33	.28948	.45352	.71052	27		33	.30544	.46059	.69456	27
34	.28975	.45364	.71025	26		34	.30571	.46071	.69429	26
35	.29001	.45377	.70999	**25**		**35**	.30597	.46082	.69403	**25**
36	.29027	.45389	.70973	24		36	.30624	.46093	.69376	24
37	.29054	.45401	.70946	23		37	.30651	.46104	.69349	23
38	.29080	.45413	.70920	22		38	.30678	.46116	.69322	22
39	.29107	.45425	.70893	21		39	.30705	.46127	.69295	21
40	.29133	.45438	.70867	**20**		**40**	.30732	.46138	.69268	**20**
41	.29160	.45450	.70840	19		41	.30758	.46149	.69242	19
42	.29186	.45462	.70814	18		42	.30785	.46161	.69215	18
43	.29212	.45474	.70788	17		43	.30812	.46172	.69188	17
44	.29239	.45486	.70761	16		44	.30839	.46183	.69161	16
45	.29265	.45498	.70735	**15**		**45**	.30866	.46194	.69134	**15**
46	.29292	.45510	.70708	14		46	.30893	.46205	.69107	14
47	.29318	.45522	.70682	13		47	.30920	.46216	.69080	13
48	.29345	.45534	.70655	12		48	.30946	.46227	.69054	12
49	.29371	.45546	.70629	11		49	.30973	.46238	.69027	11
50	.29398	.45558	.70602	**10**		**50**	.31000	.46249	.69000	**10**
51	.29424	.45570	.70576	9		51	.31027	.46260	.68973	9
52	.29451	.45582	.70549	8		52	.31054	.46272	.68946	8
53	.29477	.45594	.70523	7		53	.31081	.46283	.68919	7
54	.29504	.45606	.70496	6		54	.31108	.46294	.68892	6
55	.29530	.45618	.70470	**5**		**55**	.31135	.46305	.68865	**5**
56	.29557	.45630	.70443	4		56	.31162	.46315	.68838	4
57	.29583	.45642	.70417	3		57	.31189	.46326	.68811	3
58	.29610	.45654	.70390	2		58	.31216	.46337	.68784	2
59	.29637	.45665	.70363	1		59	.31243	.46348	.68757	1
60	.29663	.45677	.70337	**0**		**60**	.31270	.46359	.68730	**0**
′	Cos²	Sin · Cos	Sin²	′		′	Cos²	Sin · Cos	Sin²	′

122° (302°)   (237°) **57°**   **123°** (303°)   (236°) **56°**

34° (214°)   (325°) **145°**   **35° (215°)**   (324°) **144°**

'	Sin²	Sin · Cos	Cos²	'		'	Sin²	Sin · Cos	Cos²	'
0	.31270	.46359	.68730	**60**		**0**	.32899	.46985	.67101	**60**
1	.31297	.46370	.68703	59		1	.32926	.46995	.67074	59
2	.31324	.46381	.68676	58		2	.32954	.47004	.67046	58
3	.31351	.46392	.68649	57		3	.32981	.47014	.67019	57
4	.31378	.46403	.68622	56		4	.33008	.47024	.66992	56
5	.31405	.46413	.68595	**55**		**5**	.33036	.47034	.66964	**55**
6	.31432	.46424	.68568	54		6	.33063	.47044	.66937	54
7	.31459	.46435	.68541	53		7	.33090	.47054	.66910	53
8	.31486	.46446	.68514	52		8	.33118	.47064	.66882	52
9	.31513	.46457	.68487	51		9	.33145	.47074	.66855	51
10	.31540	.46467	.68460	**50**		**10**	.33173	.47083	.66827	**50**
11	.31567	.46478	.68433	49		11	.33200	.47093	.66800	49
12	.31594	.46489	.68406	48		12	.33227	.47103	.66773	48
13	.31621	.46500	.68379	47		13	.33255	.47113	.66745	47
14	.31648	.46510	.68352	46		14	.33282	.47122	.66718	46
15	.31675	.46521	.68325	**45**		**15**	.33310	.47132	.66690	**45**
16	.31702	.46532	.68298	44		16	.33337	.47142	.66663	44
17	.31729	.46542	.68271	43		17	.33365	.47151	.66635	43
18	.31756	.46553	.68244	42		18	.33392	.47161	.66608	42
19	.31783	.46563	.68217	41		19	.33419	.47171	.66581	41
20	.31810	.46574	.68190	**40**		**20**	.33447	.47180	.66553	**40**
21	.31837	.46585	.68163	39		21	.33474	.47190	.66526	39
22	.31865	.46595	.68135	38		22	.33502	.47200	.66498	38
23	.31892	.46606	.68108	37		23	.33529	.47209	.66471	37
24	.31919	.46616	.68081	36		24	.33557	.47219	.66443	36
25	.31946	.46627	.68054	**35**		**25**	.33584	.47228	.66416	**35**
26	.31973	.46637	.68027	34		26	.33612	.47238	.66388	34
27	.32000	.46648	.68000	33		27	.33639	.47247	.66361	33
28	.32027	.46658	.67973	32		28	.33667	.47257	.66333	32
29	.32054	.46669	.67946	31		29	.33694	.47266	.66306	31
30	.32082	.46679	.67918	**30**		**30**	.33722	.47276	.66278	**30**
31	.32109	.46689	.67891	29		31	.33749	.47285	.66251	29
32	.32136	.46700	.67864	28		32	.33777	.47295	.66223	28
33	.32163	.46710	.67837	27		33	.33804	.47304	.66196	27
34	.32190	.46721	.67810	26		34	.33832	.47314	.66168	26
35	.32217	.46731	.67783	**25**		**35**	.33859	.47323	.66141	**25**
36	.32245	.46741	.67755	24		36	.33887	.47332	.66113	24
37	.32272	.46752	.67728	23		37	.33914	.47342	.66086	23
38	.32299	.46762	.67701	22		38	.33942	.47351	.66058	22
39	.32326	.46772	.67674	21		39	.33969	.47361	.66031	21
40	.32353	.46782	.67647	**20**		**40**	.33997	.47370	.66003	**20**
41	.32381	.46793	.67619	19		41	.34024	.47379	.65976	19
42	.32408	.46803	.67592	18		42	.34052	.47388	.65948	18
43	.32435	.46813	.67565	17		43	.34080	.47398	.65920	17
44	.32462	.46823	.67538	16		44	.34107	.47407	.65893	16
45	.32490	.46834	.67510	**15**		**45**	.34135	.47416	.65865	**15**
46	.32517	.46844	.67483	14		46	.34162	.47425	.65838	14
47	.32544	.46854	.67456	13		47	.34190	.47435	.65810	13
48	.32571	.46864	.67429	12		48	.34218	.47444	.65782	12
49	.32599	.46874	.67401	11		49	.34245	.47453	.65755	11
50	.32626	.46884	.67374	**10**		**50**	.34273	.47462	.65727	**10**
51	.32653	.46894	.67347	9		51	.34300	.47471	.65700	9
52	.32681	.46905	.67319	8		52	.34328	.47480	.65672	8
53	.32708	.46915	.67292	7		53	.34356	.47490	.65644	7
54	.32735	.46925	.67265	6		54	.34383	.47499	.65617	6
55	.32762	.46935	.67238	**5**		**55**	.34411	.47508	.65589	**5**
56	.32790	.46945	.67210	4		56	.34439	.47517	.65561	4
57	.32817	.46955	.67183	3		57	.34466	.47526	.65534	3
58	.32844	.46965	.67156	2		58	.34494	.47535	.65506	2
59	.32872	.46975	.67128	1		59	.34521	.47544	.65479	1
60	.32899	.46985	.67101	**0**		**60**	.34549	.47553	.65451	**0**
'	Cos²	Sin · Cos	Sin²	'		'	Cos²	Sin · Cos	Sin²	'

SQUARE OF THE SINE AND COSINE AND THEIR PRODUCT

′	Sin²	Sin · Cos	Cos²	′
0	.34549	.47553	.65451	**60**
1	.34577	.47562	.65423	59
2	.34604	.47571	.65396	58
3	.34632	.47580	.65368	57
4	.34660	.47589	.65340	56
5	.34688	.47598	.65312	**55**
6	.34715	.47606	.65285	54
7	.34743	.47615	.65257	53
8	.34771	.47624	.65229	52
9	.34798	.47633	.65202	51
10	.34826	.47642	.65174	**50**
11	.34854	.47651	.65146	49
12	.34882	.47660	.65118	48
13	.34909	.47668	.65091	47
14	.34937	.47677	.65063	46
15	.34965	.47686	.65035	**45**
16	.34992	.47695	.65008	44
17	.35020	.47703	.64980	43
18	.35048	.47712	.64952	42
19	.35076	.47721	.64924	41
20	.35103	.47729	.64897	**40**
21	.35131	.47738	.64869	39
22	.35159	.47747	.64841	38
23	.35187	.47755	.64813	37
24	.35215	.47764	.64785	36
25	.35242	.47773	.64758	**35**
26	.35270	.47781	.64730	34
27	.35298	.47790	.64702	33
28	.35326	.47798	.64674	32
29	.35354	.47807	.64646	31
30	.35381	.47815	.64619	**30**
31	.35409	.47824	.64591	29
32	.35437	.47832	.64563	28
33	.35465	.47841	.64535	27
34	.35493	.47849	.64507	26
35	.35521	.47858	.64479	**25**
36	.35548	.47866	.64452	24
37	.35576	.47874	.64424	23
38	.35604	.47883	.64396	22
39	.35632	.47891	.64368	21
40	.35660	.47899	.64340	**20**
41	.35688	.47908	.64312	19
42	.35716	.47916	.64284	18
43	.35743	.47924	.64257	17
44	.35771	.47933	.64229	16
45	.35799	.47941	.64201	**15**
46	.35827	.47949	.64173	14
47	.35855	.47957	.64145	13
48	.35883	.47966	.64117	12
49	.35911	.47974	.64089	11
50	.35939	.47982	.64061	**10**
51	.35967	.47990	.64033	9
52	.35995	.47998	.64005	8
53	.36023	.48007	.63977	7
54	.36050	.48015	.63950	6
55	.36078	.48023	.63922	**5**
56	.36106	.48031	.63894	4
57	.36134	.48039	.63866	3
58	.36162	.48047	.63838	2
59	.36190	.48055	.63810	1
60	.36218	.48063	.63782	**0**
′	Cos²	Sin · Cos	Sin²	′

′	Sin²	Sin · Cos	Cos²	′
0	.36218	.48063	.63782	**60**
1	.36246	.48071	.63754	59
2	.36274	.48079	.63726	58
3	.36302	.48087	.63698	57
4	.36330	.48095	.63670	56
5	.36358	.48103	.63642	**55**
6	.36386	.48111	.63614	54
7	.36414	.48119	.63586	53
8	.36442	.48127	.63558	52
9	.36470	.48135	.63530	51
10	.36498	.48142	.63502	**50**
11	.36526	.48150	.63474	49
12	.36554	.48158	.63446	48
13	.36582	.48166	.63418	47
14	.36610	.48174	.63390	46
15	.36638	.48182	.63362	**45**
16	.36666	.48189	.63334	44
17	.36694	.48197	.63306	43
18	.36722	.48205	.63278	42
19	.36750	.48212	.63250	41
20	.36778	.48220	.63222	**40**
21	.36806	.48228	.63194	39
22	.36834	.48236	.63166	38
23	.36862	.48243	.63138	37
24	.36891	.48251	.63109	36
25	.36919	.48258	.63081	**35**
26	.36947	.48266	.63053	34
27	.36975	.48274	.63025	33
28	.37003	.48281	.62997	32
29	.37031	.48289	.62969	31
30	.37059	.48296	.62941	**30**
31	.37087	.48304	.62913	29
32	.37115	.48311	.62885	28
33	.37143	.48319	.62857	27
34	.37171	.48326	.62829	26
35	.37200	.48334	.62800	**25**
36	.37228	.48341	.62772	24
37	.37256	.48349	.62744	23
38	.37284	.48356	.62716	22
39	.37312	.48363	.62688	21
40	.37340	.48371	.62660	**20**
41	.37368	.48378	.62632	19
42	.37397	.48385	.62603	18
43	.37425	.48393	.62575	17
44	.37453	.48400	.62547	16
45	.37481	.48407	.62519	**15**
46	.37509	.48415	.62491	14
47	.37537	.48422	.62463	13
48	.37566	.48429	.62434	12
49	.37594	.48436	.62406	11
50	.37622	.48444	.62378	**10**
51	.37650	.48451	.62350	9
52	.37678	.48458	.62322	8
53	.37706	.48465	.62294	7
54	.37735	.48472	.62265	6
55	.37763	.48479	.62237	**5**
56	.37791	.48487	.62209	4
57	.37819	.48494	.62181	3
58	.37847	.48501	.62153	2
59	.37876	.48508	.62124	1
60	.37904	.48515	.62096	**0**
′	Cos²	Sin · Cos	Sin²	′

SQUARE OF THE SINE AND COSINE AND THEIR PRODUCT

′	Sin²	Sin · Cos	Cos²	′	′	Sin²	Sin · Cos	Cos²	′
0	.37904	.48515	.62096	60	0	.39604	.48907	.60396	60
1	.37932	.48522	.62068	59	1	.39633	.48913	.60367	59
2	.37960	.48529	.62040	58	2	.39661	.48919	.60339	58
3	.37989	.48536	.62011	57	3	.39690	.48925	.60310	57
4	.38017	.48543	.61983	56	4	.39718	.48931	.60282	56
5	.38045	.48550	.61955	55	5	.39747	.48937	.60253	55
6	.38073	.48557	.61927	54	6	.39775	.48943	.60225	54
7	.38102	.48564	.61898	53	7	.39804	.48949	.60196	53
8	.38130	.48571	.61870	52	8	.39832	.48955	.60168	52
9	.38158	.48577	.61842	51	9	.39861	.48961	.60139	51
10	.38186	.48584	.61814	50	10	.39889	.48967	.60111	50
11	.38215	.48591	.61785	49	11	.39918	.48973	.60082	49
12	.38243	.48598	.61757	48	12	.39946	.48979	.60054	48
13	.38271	.48605	.61729	47	13	.39975	.48985	.60025	47
14	.38299	.48612	.61701	46	14	.40003	.48990	.59997	46
15	.38328	.48618	.61672	45	15	.40032	.48996	.59968	45
16	.38356	.48625	.61644	44	16	.40060	.49002	.59940	44
17	.38384	.48632	.61616	43	17	.40089	.49008	.59911	43
18	.38413	.48639	.61587	42	18	.40117	.49014	.59883	42
19	.38441	.48646	.61559	41	19	.40146	.49019	.59854	41
20	.38469	.48652	.61531	40	20	.40174	.49025	.59826	40
21	.38498	.48659	.61502	39	21	.40203	.49031	.59797	39
22	.38526	.48666	.61474	38	22	.40231	.49036	.59769	38
23	.38554	.48672	.61446	37	23	.40260	.49042	.59740	37
24	.38582	.48679	.61418	36	24	.40288	.49048	.59712	36
25	.38611	.48686	.61389	35	25	.40317	.49053	.59683	35
26	.38639	.48692	.61361	34	26	.40345	.49059	.59655	34
27	.38667	.48699	.61333	33	27	.40374	.49065	.59626	33
28	.38696	.48705	.61304	32	28	.40402	.49070	.59598	32
29	.38724	.48712	.61276	31	29	.40431	.49076	.59569	31
30	.38752	.48719	.61248	30	30	.40460	.49081	.59540	30
31	.38781	.48725	.61219	29	31	.40488	.49087	.59512	29
32	.38809	.48732	.61191	28	32	.40517	.49092	.59483	28
33	.38837	.48738	.61163	27	33	.40545	.49098	.59455	27
34	.38866	.48745	.61134	26	34	.40574	.49103	.59426	26
35	.38894	.48751	.61106	25	35	.40602	.49109	.59398	25
36	.38923	.48757	.61077	24	36	.40631	.49114	.59369	24
37	.38951	.48764	.61049	23	37	.40660	.49120	.59340	23
38	.38979	.48770	.61021	22	38	.40688	.49125	.59312	22
39	.39008	.48777	.60992	21	39	.40717	.49131	.59283	21
40	.39036	.48783	.60964	20	40	.40745	.49136	.59255	20
41	.39064	.48789	.60936	19	41	.40774	.49141	.59226	19
42	.39093	.48796	.60907	18	42	.40802	.49147	.59198	18
43	.39121	.48802	.60879	17	43	.40831	.49152	.59169	17
44	.39150	.48808	.60850	16	44	.40860	.49157	.59140	16
45	.39178	.48815	.60822	15	45	.40888	.49163	.59112	15
46	.39206	.48821	.60794	14	46	.40917	.49168	.59083	14
47	.39235	.48827	.60765	13	47	.40945	.49173	.59055	13
48	.39263	.48834	.60737	12	48	.40974	.49179	.59026	12
49	.39292	.48840	.60708	11	49	.41003	.49184	.58997	11
50	.39320	.48846	.60680	10	50	.41031	.49189	.58969	10
51	.39348	.48852	.60652	9	51	.41060	.49194	.58940	9
52	.39377	.48858	.60623	8	52	.41089	.49199	.58911	8
53	.39405	.48865	.60595	7	53	.41117	.49205	.58883	7
54	.39434	.48871	.60566	6	54	.41146	.49210	.58854	6
55	.39462	.48877	.60538	5	55	.41174	.49215	.58826	5
56	.39491	.48883	.60509	4	56	.41203	.49220	.58797	4
57	.39519	.48889	.60481	3	57	.41232	.49225	.58768	3
58	.39548	.48895	.60452	2	58	.41260	.49230	.58740	2
59	.39576	.48901	.60424	1	59	.41289	.49235	.58711	1
60	.39604	.48907	.60396	0	60	.41318	.49240	.58682	0
′	Cos²	Sin · Cos	Sin²	′	′	Cos²	Sin · Cos	Sin²	′

40° (220°)   (319°) **139°**   **41°** (221°)   (318°) **138°**

'	Sin²	Sin · Cos	Cos²	'		'	Sin²	Sin · Cos	Cos²	'
0	.41318	.49240	.58682	**60**		**0**	.43041	.49513	.56959	**60**
1	.41346	.49245	.58654	59		1	.43070	.49517	.56930	59
2	.41375	.49250	.58625	58		2	.43099	.49521	.56901	58
3	.41404	.49255	.58596	57		3	.43128	.49525	.56872	57
4	.41432	.49260	.58568	56		4	.43157	.49529	.56843	56
5	.41461	.49265	.58539	**55**		**5**	.43185	.49533	.56815	**55**
6	.41490	.49270	.58510	54		6	.43214	.49537	.56786	54
7	.41518	.49275	.58482	53		7	.43243	.49541	.56757	53
8	.41547	.49280	.58453	52		8	.43272	.49545	.56728	52
9	.41576	.49285	.58424	51		9	.43301	.49549	.56699	51
10	.41604	.49290	.58396	**50**		**10**	.43330	.49553	.56670	**50**
11	.41633	.49295	.58367	49		11	.43358	.49557	.56642	49
12	.41662	.49300	.58338	48		12	.43387	.49561	.56613	48
13	.41690	.49305	.58310	47		13	.43416	.49565	.56584	47
14	.41719	.49309	.58281	46		14	.43445	.49568	.56555	46
15	.41748	.49314	.58252	**45**		**15**	.43474	.49572	.56526	**45**
16	.41776	.49319	.58224	44		16	.43503	.49576	.56497	44
17	.41805	.49324	.58195	43		17	.43531	.49580	.56469	43
18	.41834	.49329	.58166	42		18	.43560	.49584	.56440	42
19	.41862	.49333	.58138	41		19	.43589	.49587	.56411	41
20	.41891	.49338	.58109	**40**		**20**	.43618	.49591	.56382	**40**
21	.41920	.49343	.58080	39		21	.43647	.49595	.56353	39
22	.41949	.49347	.58051	38		22	.43676	.49598	.56324	38
23	.41977	.49352	.58023	37		23	.43704	.49602	.56296	37
24	.42006	.49357	.57994	36		24	.43733	.49606	.56267	36
25	.42035	.49361	.57965	**35**		**25**	.43762	.49609	.56238	**35**
26	.42063	.49366	.57937	34		26	.43791	.49613	.56209	34
27	.42092	.49371	.57908	33		27	.43820	.49617	.56180	33
28	.42121	.49375	.57879	32		28	.43849	.49620	.56151	32
29	.42150	.49380	.57850	31		29	.43878	.49624	.56122	31
30	.42178	.49384	.57822	**30**		**30**	.43907	.49627	.56093	**30**
31	.42207	.49389	.57793	29		31	.43935	.49631	.56065	29
32	.42236	.49393	.57764	28		32	.43964	.49634	.56036	28
33	.42264	.49398	.57736	27		33	.43993	.49638	.56007	27
34	.42293	.49402	.57707	26		34	.44022	.49641	.55978	26
35	.42322	.49407	.57678	**25**		**35**	.44051	.49645	.55949	**25**
36	.42351	.49411	.57649	24		36	.44080	.49648	.55920	24
37	.42379	.49416	.57621	23		37	.44109	.49652	.55891	23
38	.42408	.49420	.57592	22		38	.44138	.49655	.55862	22
39	.42437	.49425	.57563	21		39	.44166	.49659	.55834	21
40	.42466	.49429	.57534	**20**		**40**	.44195	.49662	.55805	**20**
41	.42494	.49433	.57506	19		41	.44224	.49665	.55776	19
42	.42523	.49438	.57477	18		42	.44253	.49669	.55747	18
43	.42552	.49442	.57448	17		43	.44282	.49672	.55718	17
44	.42581	.49446	.57419	16		44	.44311	.49675	.55689	16
45	.42610	.49451	.57390	**15**		**45**	.44340	.49679	.55660	**15**
46	.42638	.49455	.57362	14		46	.44369	.49682	.55631	14
47	.42667	.49459	.57333	13		47	.44398	.49685	.55602	13
48	.42696	.49464	.57304	12		48	.44427	.49688	.55573	12
49	.42725	.49468	.57275	11		49	.44455	.49692	.55545	11
50	.42753	.49472	.57247	**10**		**50**	.44484	.49695	.55516	**10**
51	.42782	.49476	.57218	9		51	.44513	.49698	.55487	9
52	.42811	.49480	.57189	8		52	.44542	.49701	.55458	8
53	.42840	.49485	.57160	7		53	.44571	.49704	.55429	7
54	.42869	.49489	.57131	6		54	.44600	.49708	.55400	6
55	.42897	.49493	.57103	**5**		**55**	.44629	.49711	.55371	**5**
56	.42926	.49497	.57074	4		56	.44658	.49714	.55342	4
57	.42955	.49501	.57045	3		57	.44687	.49717	.55313	3
58	.42984	.49505	.57016	2		58	.44716	.49720	.55284	2
59	.43013	.49509	.56987	1		59	.44745	.49723	.55255	1
60	.43041	.49513	.56959	**0**		**60**	.44774	.49726	.55226	**0**
'	Cos²	Sin · Cos	Sin²	'		'	Cos²	Sin · Cos	Sin²	'

SQUARE OF THE SINE AND COSINE AND THEIR PRODUCT

′	Sin²	Sin·Cos	Cos²	′		′	Sin²	Sin·Cos	Cos²	′
0	.44774	.49726	.55226	**60**		**0**	.46512	.49878	.53488	**60**
1	.44803	.49729	.55197	59		1	.46541	.49880	.53459	59
2	.44831	.49732	.55169	58		2	.46570	.49882	.53430	58
3	.44860	.49735	.55140	57		3	.46599	.49884	.53401	57
4	.44889	.49738	.55111	56		4	.46628	.49886	.53372	56
5	.44918	.49741	.55082	**55**		**5**	.46657	.49888	.53343	**55**
6	.44947	.49744	.55053	54		6	.46686	.49890	.53314	54
7	.44976	.49747	.55024	53		7	.46715	.49892	.53285	53
8	.45005	.49750	.54995	52		8	.46744	.49894	.53256	52
9	.45034	.49753	.54966	51		9	.46773	.49896	.53227	51
10	.45063	.49756	.54937	**50**		**10**	.46802	.49898	.53198	**50**
11	.45092	.49759	.54908	49		11	.46831	.49900	.53169	49
12	.45121	.49761	.54879	48		12	.46860	.49901	.53140	48
13	.45150	.49764	.54850	47		13	.46890	.49903	.53110	47
14	.45179	.49767	.54821	46		14	.46919	.49905	.53081	46
15	.45208	.49770	.54792	**45**		**15**	.46948	.49907	.53052	**45**
16	.45237	.49773	.54763	44		16	.46977	.49909	.53023	44
17	.45266	.49775	.54734	43		17	.47006	.49910	.52994	43
18	.45295	.49778	.54705	42		18	.47035	.49912	.52965	42
19	.45324	.49781	.54676	41		19	.47064	.49914	.52936	41
20	.45353	.49784	.54647	**40**		**20**	.47093	.49915	.52907	**40**
21	.45381	.49786	.54619	39		21	.47122	.49917	.52878	39
22	.45410	.49789	.54590	38		22	.47151	.49919	.52849	38
23	.45439	.49792	.54561	37		23	.47180	.49920	.52820	37
24	.45468	.49794	.54532	36		24	.47209	.49922	.52791	36
25	.45497	.49797	.54503	**35**		**25**	.47238	.49924	.52762	**35**
26	.45526	.49799	.54474	34		26	.47267	.49925	.52733	34
27	.45555	.49802	.54445	33		27	.47296	.49927	.52704	33
28	.45584	.49805	.54416	32		28	.47325	.49928	.52675	32
29	.45613	.49807	.54387	31		29	.47354	.49930	.52646	31
30	.45642	.49810	.54358	**30**		**30**	.47383	.49931	.52617	**30**
31	.45671	.49812	.54329	29		31	.47412	.49933	.52588	29
32	.45700	.49815	.54300	28		32	.47441	.49934	.52559	28
33	.45729	.49817	.54271	27		33	.47470	.49936	.52530	27
34	.45758	.49820	.54242	26		34	.47499	.49937	.52501	26
35	.45787	.49822	.54213	**25**		**35**	.47528	.49939	.52472	**25**
36	.45816	.49825	.54184	24		36	.47558	.49940	.52442	24
37	.45845	.49827	.54155	23		37	.47587	.49942	.52413	23
38	.45874	.49829	.54126	22		38	.47616	.49943	.52384	22
39	.45903	.49832	.54097	21		39	.47645	.49944	.52355	21
40	.45932	.49834	.54068	**20**		**40**	.47674	.49946	.52326	**20**
41	.45961	.49837	.54039	19		41	.47703	.49947	.52297	19
42	.45990	.49839	.54010	18		42	.47732	.49949	.52268	18
43	.46019	.49841	.53981	17		43	.47761	.49950	.52239	17
44	.46048	.49844	.53952	16		44	.47790	.49951	.52210	16
45	.46077	.49846	.53923	**15**		**45**	.47819	.49952	.52181	**15**
46	.46106	.49848	.53894	14		46	.47848	.49954	.52152	14
47	.46135	.49850	.53865	13		47	.47877	.49955	.52123	13
48	.46164	.49853	.53836	12		48	.47906	.49956	.52094	12
49	.46193	.49855	.53807	11		49	.47935	.49957	.52065	11
50	.46222	.49857	.53778	**10**		**50**	.47964	.49959	.52036	**10**
51	.46251	.49859	.53749	9		51	.47993	.49960	.52007	9
52	.46280	.49861	.53720	8		52	.48022	.49961	.51978	8
53	.46309	.49864	.53691	7		53	.48052	.49962	.51948	7
54	.46338	.49866	.53662	6		54	.48081	.49963	.51919	6
55	.46367	.49868	.53633	**5**		**55**	.48110	.49964	.51890	**5**
56	.46396	.49870	.53604	4		56	.48139	.49965	.51861	4
57	.46425	.49872	.53575	3		57	.48168	.49966	.51832	3
58	.46454	.49874	.53546	2		58	.48197	.49967	.51803	2
59	.46483	.49876	.53517	1		59	.48226	.49969	.51774	1
60	.46512	.49878	.53488	**0**		**60**	.48255	.49970	.51745	**0**
′	Cos²	Sin·Cos	Sin²	′		′	Cos²	Sin·Cos	Sin²	′

44° (224°)   **(315°) 135°**

′	Sin²	Sin · Cos	Cos²	′
0	.48255	.49970	.51745	**60**
1	.48284	.49971	.51716	59
2	.48313	.49972	.51687	58
3	.48342	.49973	.51658	57
4	.48371	.49973	.51629	56
5	.48400	.49974	.51600	**55**
6	.48429	.49975	.51571	54
7	.48459	.49976	.51541	53
8	.48488	.49977	.51512	52
9	.48517	.49978	.51483	51
10	.48546	.49979	.51454	**50**
11	.48575	.49980	.51425	49
12	.48604	.49981	.51396	48
13	.48633	.49981	.51367	47
14	.48662	.49982	.51338	46
15	.48691	.49983	.51309	**45**
16	.48720	.49984	.51280	44
17	.48749	.49984	.51251	43
18	.48778	.49985	.51222	42
19	.48807	.49986	.51193	41
20	.48837	.49986	.51163	**40**
21	.48866	.49987	.51134	39
22	.48895	.49988	.51105	38
23	.48924	.49988	.51076	37
24	.48953	.49989	.51047	36
25	.48982	.49990	.51018	**35**
26	.49011	.49990	.50989	34
27	.49040	.49991	.50960	33
28	.49069	.49991	.50931	32
29	.49098	.49992	.50902	31
30	.49127	.49992	.50873	**30**
31	.49156	.49993	.50844	29
32	.49186	.49993	.50814	28
33	.49215	.49994	.50785	27
34	.49244	.49994	.50756	26
35	.49273	.49995	.50727	**25**
36	.49302	.49995	.50698	24
37	.49331	.49996	.50669	23
38	.49360	.49996	.50640	22
39	.49389	.49996	.50611	21
40	.49418	.49997	.50582	**20**
41	.49447	.49997	.50553	19
42	.49476	.49997	.50524	18
43	.49505	.49998	.50495	17
44	.49535	.49998	.50465	16
45	.49564	.49998	.50436	**15**
46	.49593	.49998	.50407	14
47	.49622	.49999	.50378	13
48	.49651	.49999	.50349	12
49	.49680	.49999	.50320	11
50	.49709	.49999	.50291	**10**
51	.49738	.49999	.50262	9
52	.49767	.49999	.50233	8
53	.49796	.50000	.50204	7
54	.49825	.50000	.50175	6
55	.49855	.50000	.50145	**5**
56	.49884	.50000	.50116	4
57	.49913	.50000	.50087	3
58	.49942	.50000	.50058	2
59	.49971	.50000	.50029	1
60	.50000	.50000	.50000	**0**
′	Cos²	Sin · Cos	Sin²	′

134° (314°)   **(225°) 45°**

EXPLANATION

If "sin² θ cos² θ" is desired, it can be obtained by using the identity $\sin^2 \theta \cos^2 \theta = \frac{1}{4} \sin^2 2\theta$. Thus $\sin^2 10° \cos^2 10° = \frac{1}{4} \sin^2 20°$

$$= \frac{0.11698}{4}$$

$$= 0.02924.$$

0.000–0.499

N	0	1	2	3	4	5	6	7	8	9
0.00	− ∞	−6† .90776	−6 .21461	−5 .80914	−5 .52146	−5 .29832	−5 .11600	−4 .96185	−4 .82831	−4 .71053
.01	−4.60517	.50986	.42285	.34281	.26870	.19971	.13517	.07454	.01738	*.96332
.02	−3.91202	.86323	.81671	.77226	.72970	.68888	.64966	.61192	.57555	.54046
.03	.50656	.47377	.44202	.41125	.38139	.35241	.32424	.29684	.27017	.24419
.04	.21888	.19418	.17009	.14656	.12357	.10109	.07911	.05761	.03655	.01593
.05	−2.99573	.97593	.95651	.93746	.91877	.90042	.88240	.86470	.84731	.83022
.06	.81341	.79688	.78062	.76462	.74887	.73337	.71810	.70306	.68825	.67365
.07	.65926	.64508	.63109	.61730	.60369	.59027	.57702	.56395	.55105	.53831
.08	.52573	.51331	.50104	.48891	.47694	.46510	.45341	.44185	.43042	.41912
.09	.40795	.39690	.38597	.37516	.36446	.35388	.34341	.33304	.32279	.31264
0.10	−2.30259	.29263	.28278	.27303	.26336	.25379	.24432	.23493	.22562	.21641
.11	.20727	.19823	.18926	.18037	.17156	.16282	.15417	.14558	.13707	.12863
.12	.12026	.11196	.10373	.09557	.08747	.07944	.07147	.06357	.05573	.04794
.13	.04022	.03256	.02495	.01741	.00992	.00248	*.99510	*.98777	*.98050	*.97328
.14	−1.96611	.95900	.95193	.94491	.93794	.93102	.92415	.91732	.91054	.90381
.15	.89712	.89048	.88387	.87732	.87080	.86433	.85790	.85151	.84516	.83885
.16	.83258	.82635	.82016	.81401	.80789	.80181	.79577	.78976	.78379	.77786
.17	.77196	.76609	.76026	.75446	.74870	.74297	.73727	.73161	.72597	.72037
.18	.71480	.70926	.70375	.69827	.69282	.68740	.68201	.67665	.67131	.66601
.19	.66073	.65548	.65026	.64507	.63990	.63476	.62964	.62455	.61949	.61445
0.20	−1.60944	.60445	.59949	.59455	.58964	.58475	.57988	.57504	.57022	.56542
.21	.56065	.55590	.55117	.54646	.54178	.53712	.53248	.52786	.52326	.51868
.22	.51413	.50959	.50508	.50058	.49611	.49165	.48722	.48281	.47841	.47403
.23	.46968	.46534	.46102	.45672	.45243	.44817	.44392	.43970	.43548	.43129
.24	.42712	.42296	.41882	.41469	.41059	.40650	.40242	.39837	.39433	.39030
.25	.38629	.38230	.37833	.37437	.37042	.36649	.36258	.35868	.35480	.35093
.26	.34707	.34323	.33941	.33560	.33181	.32803	.32426	.32051	.31677	.31304
.27	.30933	.30564	.30195	.29828	.29463	.29098	.28735	.28374	.28013	.27654
.28	.27297	.26940	.26585	.26231	.25878	.25527	.25176	.24827	.24479	.24133
.29	.23787	.23443	.23100	.22758	.22418	.22078	.21740	.21402	.21066	.20731
0.30	−1.20397	.20065	.19733	.19402	.19073	.18744	.18417	.18091	.17766	.17441
.31	.17118	.16796	.16475	.16155	.15836	.15518	.15201	.14885	.14570	.14256
.32	.13943	.13631	.13320	.13010	.12701	.12393	.12086	.11780	.11474	.11170
.33	.10866	.10564	.10262	.09961	.09661	.09362	.09064	.08767	.08471	.08176
.34	.07881	.07587	.07294	.07002	.06711	.06421	.06132	.05843	.05555	.05268
.35	−1.04982	.04697	.04412	.04129	.03846	.03564	.03282	.03002	.02722	.02443
.36	.02165	.01888	.01611	.01335	.01060	.00786	.00512	.00239	*.99967	*.99696
.37	−0.99425	.99155	.98886	.98618	.98350	.98083	.97817	.97551	.97286	.97022
.38	.96758	.96496	.96233	.95972	.95711	.95451	.95192	.94933	.94675	.94418
.39	.94161	.93905	.93649	.93395	.93140	.92887	.92634	.92382	.92130	.91879
0.40	−0.91629	.91379	.91130	.90882	.90634	.90387	.90140	.89894	.89649	.89404
.41	.89160	.88916	.88673	.88431	.88189	.87948	.87707	.87467	.87227	.86988
.42	.86750	.86512	.86275	.86038	.85802	.85567	.85332	.85097	.84863	.84630
.43	.84397	.84165	.83933	.83702	.83471	.83241	.83011	.82782	.82554	.82326
.44	.82098	.81871	.81645	.81419	.81193	.80968	.80744	.80520	.80296	.80073
.45	.79851	.79629	.79407	.79186	.78966	.78746	.78526	.78307	.78089	.77871
.46	.77653	.77436	.77219	.77003	.76787	.76572	.76357	.76143	.75929	.75715
.47	.75502	.75290	.75078	.74866	.74655	.74444	.74234	.74024	.73814	.73605
.48	.73397	.73189	.72981	.72774	.72567	.72361	.72155	.71949	.71744	.71539
.49	.71335	.71131	.70928	.70725	.70522	.70320	.70118	.69917	.69716	.69515

† Note that the characteristics are given *above* the mantissa for the first line. In the second and following lines they are given at the left.

0.500–0.999

N	0	1	2	3	4	5	6	7	8	9
0.50	−0.69315	.69115	.68916	.68717	.68518	.68320	.68122	.67924	.67727	.67531
.51	.67334	.67139	.66943	.66748	.66553	.66359	.66165	.65971	.65778	.65585
.52	.65393	.65201	.65009	.64817	.64626	.64436	.64245	.64055	.63866	.63677
.53	.63488	.63299	.63111	.62923	.62736	.62549	.62362	.62176	.61990	.61804
.54	.61619	.61434	.61249	.61065	.60881	.60697	.60514	.60331	.60148	.59966
.55	.59784	.59602	.59421	.59240	.59059	.58879	.58699	.58519	.58340	.58161
.56	.57982	.57803	.57625	.57448	.57270	.57093	.56916	.56740	.56563	.56387
.57	.56212	.56037	.55862	.55687	.55513	.55339	.55165	.54991	.54818	.54645
.58	.54473	.54300	.54128	.53957	.53785	.53614	.53444	.53273	.53103	.52933
.59	.52763	.52594	.52425	.52256	.52088	.51919	.51751	.51584	.51416	.51249
0.60	−0.51083	.50916	.50750	.50584	.50418	.50253	.50088	.49923	.49758	.49594
.61	.49430	.49266	.49102	.48939	.48776	.48613	.48451	.48289	.48127	.47965
.62	.47804	.47642	.47482	.47321	.47160	.47000	.46840	.46681	.46522	.46362
.63	.46204	.46045	.45887	.45728	.45571	.45413	.45256	.45099	.44942	.44785
.64	.44629	.44473	.44317	.44161	.44006	.43850	.43696	.43541	.43386	.43232
.65	.43078	.42925	.42771	.42618	.42465	.42312	.42159	.42007	.41855	.41703
.66	.41552	.41400	.41249	.41098	.40947	.40797	.40647	.40497	.40347	.40197
.67	.40048	.39899	.39750	.39601	.39453	.39304	.39156	.39008	.38861	.38713
.68	.38566	.38419	.38273	.38126	.37980	.37834	.37688	.37542	.37397	.37251
.69	.37106	.36962	.36817	.36673	.36528	.36384	.36241	.36097	.35954	.35810
0.70	−0.35667	.35525	.35382	.35240	.35098	.34956	.34814	.34672	.34531	.34390
.71	.34249	.34108	.33968	.33827	.33687	.33547	.33408	.33268	.33129	.32989
.72	.32850	.32712	.32573	.32435	.32296	.32158	.32021	.31883	.31745	.31608
.73	.31471	.31334	.31197	.31061	.30925	.30788	.30653	.30517	.30381	.30246
.74	.30111	.29975	.29841	.29706	.29571	.29437	.29303	.29169	.29035	.28902
.75	.28768	.28635	.28502	.28369	.28236	.28104	.27971	.27839	.27707	.27575
.76	.27444	.27312	.27181	.27050	.26919	.26788	.26657	.26527	.26397	.26266
.77	.26136	.26007	.25877	.25748	.25618	.25489	.25360	.25231	.25103	.24974
.78	.24846	.24718	.24590	.24462	.24335	.24207	.24080	.23953	.23826	.23699
.79	.23572	.23446	.23319	.23193	.23067	.22941	.22816	.22690	.22565	.22439
0.80	−0.22314	.22189	.22065	.21940	.21816	.21691	.21567	.21443	.21319	.21196
.81	.21072	.20949	.20825	.20702	.20579	.20457	.20334	.20212	.20089	.19967
.82	.19845	.19723	.19601	.19480	.19358	.19237	.19116	.18995	.18874	.18754
.83	.18633	.18513	.18392	.18272	.18152	.18032	.17913	.17793	.17674	.17554
.84	.17435	.17316	.17198	.17079	.16960	.16842	.16724	.16605	.16487	.16370
.85	−0.16252	.16134	.16017	.15900	.15782	.15665	.15548	.15432	.15315	.15199
.86	.15082	.14966	.14850	.14734	.14618	.14503	.14387	.14272	.14156	.14041
.87	.13926	.13811	.13697	.13582	.13467	.13353	.13239	.13125	.13011	.12897
.88	.12783	.12670	.12556	.12443	.12330	.12217	.12104	.11991	.11878	.11766
.89	.11653	.11541	.11429	.11317	.11205	.11093	.10981	.10870	.10759	.10647
0.90	−0.10536	.10425	.10314	.10203	.10093	.09982	.09872	.09761	.09651	.09541
.91	.09431	.09321	.09212	.09102	.08992	.08883	.08774	.08665	.08556	.08447
.92	.08338	.08230	.08121	.08013	.07904	.07796	.07688	.07580	.07472	.07365
.93	.07257	.07150	.07042	.06935	.06828	.06721	.06614	.06507	.06401	.06294
.94	.06188	.06081	.05975	.05869	.05763	.05657	.05551	.05446	.05340	.05235
.95	.05129	.05024	.04919	.04814	.04709	.04604	.04500	.04395	.04291	.04186
.96	.04082	.03978	.03874	.03770	.03666	.03563	.03459	.03356	.03252	.03149
.97	.03046	.02943	.02840	.02737	.02634	.02532	.02429	.02327	.02225	.02122
.98	.02020	.01918	.01816	.01715	.01613	.01511	.01410	.01309	.01207	.01106
.99	.01005	.00904	.00803	.00702	.00602	.00501	.00401	.00300	.00200	.00100

To find the natural logarithm of a number which is 1/10, 1/100, 1/1000, etc. of a number whose logarithm is given, subtract from the given logarithm $\log_e$ 10, 2 $\log_e$ 10, 3 $\log_e$ 10, etc.
To find the natural logarithm of a number which is 10, 100, 1000, etc. times a number whose logarithm is given, add to the given logarithm $\log_e$ 10, 2 $\log_e$ 10, 3 $\log_e$ 10, etc.

$\log_e$ 10 =	2.30258 50930	6 $\log_e$ 10 =	13.81551 05580
2 $\log_e$ 10 =	4.60517 01860	7 $\log_e$ 10 =	16.11809 56510
3 $\log_e$ 10 =	6.90775 52790	8 $\log_e$ 10 =	18.42068 07440
4 $\log_e$ 10 =	9.21034 03720	9 $\log_e$ 10 =	20.72326 58369
5 $\log_e$ 10 =	11.51292 54650	10 $\log_e$ 10 =	23.02585 09299

See preceding table for logarithms for numbers between 0.000 and 0.999.

1.00–4.99

N	0	1	2	3	4	5	6	7	8	9
1.0	0.00000	.00995	.01980	.02956	.03922	.04879	.05827	.06766	.07696	.08618
.1	.09531	.10436	.11333	.12222	.13103	.13976	.14842	.15700	.16551	.17395
.2	.18232	.19062	.19885	.20701	.21511	.22314	.23111	.23902	.24686	.25464
.3	.26236	.27003	.27763	.28518	.29267	.30010	.30748	.31481	.32208	.32930
.4	.33647	.34359	.35066	.35767	.36464	.37156	.37844	.38526	.39204	.39878
.5	.40547	.41211	.41871	.42527	.43178	.43825	.44469	.45108	.45742	.46373
.6	.47000	.47623	.48243	.48858	.49470	.50078	.50682	.51282	.51879	.52473
.7	.53063	.53649	.54232	.54812	.55389	.55962	.56531	.57098	.57661	.58222
.8	.58779	.59333	.59884	.60432	.60977	.61519	.62058	.62594	.63127	.63658
.9	.64185	.64710	.65233	.65752	.66269	.66783	.67294	.67803	.68310	.68813
2.0	0.69315	.69813	.70310	.70804	.71295	.71784	.72271	.72755	.73237	.73716
.1	.74194	.74669	.75142	.75612	.76081	.76547	.77011	.77473	.77932	.78390
.2	.78846	.79299	.79751	.80200	.80648	.81093	.81536	.81978	.82418	.82855
.3	.83291	.83725	.84157	.84587	.85015	.85442	.85866	.86289	.86710	.87129
.4	.87547	.87963	.88377	.88789	.89200	.89609	.90016	.90422	.90826	.91228
.5	.91629	.92028	.92426	.92822	.93216	.93609	.94001	.94391	.94779	.95166
.6	.95551	.95935	.96317	.96698	.97078	.97456	.97833	.98208	.98582	.98954
.7	.99325	.99695	*.00063	*.00430	*.00796	*.01160	*.01523	*.01885	*.02245	*.02604
.8	1.02962	.03318	.03674	.04028	.04380	.04732	.05082	.05431	.05779	.06126
.9	.06471	.06815	.07158	.07500	.07841	.08181	.08519	.08856	.09192	.09527
3.0	1.09861	.10194	.10526	.10856	.11186	.11514	.11841	.12168	.12493	.12817
.1	.13140	.13462	.13783	.14103	.14422	.14740	.15057	.15373	.15688	.16002
.2	.16315	.16627	.16938	.17248	.17557	.17865	.18173	.18479	.18784	.19089
.3	.19392	.19695	.19996	.20297	.20597	.20896	.21194	.21491	.21788	.22083
.4	.22378	.22671	.22964	.23256	.23547	.23837	.24127	.24415	.24703	.24990
.5	.25276	.25562	.25846	.26130	.26413	.26695	.26976	.27257	.27536	.27815
.6	.28093	.28371	.28647	.28923	.29198	.29473	.29746	.30019	.30291	.30563
.7	.30833	.31103	.31372	.31641	.31909	.32176	.32442	.32708	.32972	.33237
.8	.33500	.33763	.34025	.34286	.34547	.34807	.35067	.35325	.35584	.35841
.9	.36098	.36354	.36609	.36864	.37118	.37372	.37624	.37877	.38128	.38379
4.0	1.38629	.38879	.39128	.39377	.39624	.39872	.40118	.40364	.40610	.40854
.1	.41099	.41342	.41585	.41828	.42070	.42311	.42552	.42792	.43031	.43270
.2	.43508	.43746	.43984	.44220	.44456	.44692	.44927	.45161	.45395	.45629
.3	.45862	.46094	.46326	.46557	.46787	.47018	.47247	.47476	.47705	.47936
.4	.48160	.48387	.48614	.48840	.49065	.49290	.49515	.49739	.49962	.50185
.5	.50408	.50630	.50851	.51072	.51293	.51513	.51732	.51951	.52170	.52388
.6	.52606	.52823	.53039	.53256	.53471	.53687	.53902	.54116	.54330	.54543
.7	.54756	.54969	.55181	.55393	.55604	.55814	.56025	.56235	.56444	.56653
.8	.56862	.57070	.57277	.57485	.57691	.57898	.58104	.58309	.58515	.58719
.9	.58924	.59127	.59331	.59534	.59737	.59939	.60141	.60342	.60543	.60744

5.00–9.99

N	0	1	2	3	4	5	6	7	8	9
5.0	1.60944	.61144	.61343	.61542	.61741	.61939	.62137	.62334	.62531	.62728
.1	.62924	.63120	.63315	.63511	.63705	.63900	.64094	.64287	.64481	.64673
.2	.64866	.65058	.65250	.65441	.65632	.65823	.66013	.66203	.86393	.66582
.3	.66771	.66959	.67147	.67335	.67523	.67710	.67896	.68083	.68269	.68455
.4	.68640	.68825	.69010	.69194	.69378	.69562	.69745	.69928	.70111	.70293
.5	.70475	.70656	.70838	.71019	.71199	.71380	.71560	.71740	.71919	.72098
.6	.72277	.72455	.72633	.72811	.72988	.73166	.73342	.73519	.73695	.73871
.7	.74047	.74222	.74397	.74572	.74746	.74920	.75094	.75267	.75440	.75613
.8	.75786	.75958	.76130	.76302	.76473	.76644	.76815	.76985	.77156	.77326
.9	.77495	.77665	.77834	.78002	.78171	.78339	.78507	.78675	.78842	.79009
6.0	1.79176	.79342	.79509	.79675	.79840	.80006	.80171	.80336	.80500	.80665
.1	.80829	.80993	.81156	.81319	.81482	.81645	.81808	.81970	.82132	.82294
.2	.82455	.82616	.82777	.82938	.83098	.83258	.83418	.83578	.83737	.83896
.3	.84055	.84214	.84372	.84530	.84688	.84845	.85003	.85160	.85317	.85473
.4	.85630	.85786	.85942	.86097	.86253	.86408	.86563	.86718	.86872	.87026
.5	.87180	.87334	.87487	.87641	.87794	.87947	.88099	.88251	.88403	.88555
.6	.88707	.88858	.89010	.89166	89311	.89462	.89612	.89762	.89912	.90061
.7	.90211	.90360	.90509	.90658	.90806	.90954	.91102	.91250	.91398	.91545
.8	.91692	.91839	.91986	.92132	.92279	.92425	.92571	.92716	.92862	.93007
.9	.93152	.93297	.93442	.93586	.93730	.93874	.94018	.94162	.94305	.94448
7.0	1.94591	.94734	.94876	.95019	.95161	.95303	.95445	.95586	.95727	.95869
.1	.96009	.96150	.96291	.96431	.96571	.96711	.96851	.96991	.97130	.97269
.2	.97408	.97547	.97685	.97824	.97962	.98100	.98238	.98376	.98513	.98650
.3	.98787	.98924	.99061	.99198	.99334	.99470	.99606	.99742	.99877	*.00013
.4	2.00148	.00283	.00418	.00553	.00687	.00821	.00956	.01089	.01223	.01357
.5	.01490	.01624	.01757	.01890	.02022	.02155	.02287	.02419	.02551	.02683
.6	.02815	.02946	.03078	.03209	.03340	.03471	.03601	.03732	.03862	.03992
.7	.04122	.04252	.04381	.04511	.04640	.04769	.04898	.05027	.05156	.05284
.8	.05412	.05540	.05668	.05796	.05924	.06051	.06179	.06306	.06433	.06560
.9	.06686	.06813	.06939	.07065	.07191	.07317	.07443	.07568	.07694	.07819
8.0	2.07944	.08069	.08194	.08318	.08443	.08567	.08691	.08815	.08939	.09063
.1	.09186	.09310	.09433	.09556	.09679	.09802	.09924	.10047	.10169	.10291
.2	.10413	.10535	.10657	.10779	.10900	.11021	.11142	.11263	.11384	.11505
.3	.11626	.11746	.11866	.11986	.12106	.12226	.12346	.12465	.12585	.12704
.4	.12823	.12942	.13061	.13180	.13298	.13417	.13535	.13653	.13771	.13889
.5	.14007	.14124	.14242	.14359	.14476	.14593	.14710	.14827	.14943	.15060
.6	.15176	.15292	.15409	.15524	.15640	.15756	.15871	.15987	.16102	.16217
.7	.16332	.16447	.16562	.16677	.16791	.16905	.17020	.17134	.17248	.17361
.8	.17475	.17589	.17702	.17816	.17929	.18042	.18155	.18267	.18380	.18493
.9	.18605	.18717	.18830	.18942	.19054	.19165	.19277	.19389	.19500	.19611
9.0	2.19722	.19834	.19944	.20055	.20166	.20276	.20387	.20497	.20607	.20717
.1	.20827	.20937	.21047	.21157	.21266	.21375	.21485	.21594	.21703	.21812
.2	.21920	.22029	.22138	.22246	.22354	.22462	.22570	.22678	.22786	.22894
.3	.23001	.23109	.23216	.23324	.23431	.23538	.23645	.23751	.23858	.23965
.4	.24071	.24177	.24284	.24390	.24496	.24601	.24707	.24813	.24918	.25024
.5	.25129	.25234	.25339	.25444	.25549	.25654	.25759	.25863	.25968	.26072
.6	.26176	.26280	.26384	.26488	.26592	.26696	.26799	.26903	.27006	.27109
.7	.27213	.27316	.27419	.27521	.27624	.27727	.27829	.27932	.28034	.28136
.8	.28238	.28340	.28442	.28544	.28646	.28747	.28849	.28950	.29051	.29152
.9	.29253	.29354	.29455	.29556	.29657	.29757	.29858	.29958	.30058	.30158

Constants

$\log_e 10$ = 2.30258 50930		6 $\log_e 10$ = 13.81551 05580
2 $\log_e 10$ = 4.60517 01860		7 $\log_e 10$ = 16.11809 56510
3 $\log_e 10$ = 6.90775 52790		8 $\log_e 10$ = 18.42068 07440
4 $\log_e 10$ = 9.21034 03720		9 $\log_e 10$ = 20.72326 58369
5 $\log_e 10$ = 11.51292 54650		10 $\log_e 10$ = 23.02585 09299

10.0–49.9

N	0	1	2	3	4	5	6	7	8	9
10.	2.30259	.31254	.32239	.33214	.34181	.35138	.36085	.37024	.37955	.38876
11.	.39790	.40695	.41591	.42480	.43361	.44235	.45101	.45959	.46810	.47654
12.	.48491	.49321	.50144	.50960	.51770	.52573	.53370	.54160	.54945	.55723
13.	.56495	.57261	.58022	.58776	.59525	.60269	.61007	.61740	.62467	.63189
14.	.63906	.64617	.65324	.66026	.66723	.67415	.68102	.68785	.69463	.70136
15.	.70805	.71469	.72130	.72785	.73437	.74084	.74727	.75366	.76001	.76632
16.	.77259	.77882	.78501	.79117	.79728	.80336	.80940	.81541	.82138	.82731
17.	.83321	.83908	.84491	.85071	.85647	.86220	.86790	.87356	.87920	.88480
18.	.89037	.89591	.90142	.90690	.91235	.91777	.92316	.92852	.93386	.93916
19.	.94444	.94969	.95491	.96011	.96527	.97041	.97553	.98062	.98568	.99072
20.	2.99573	*.00072	*.00568	*.01062	*.01553	*.02042	*.02529	*.03013	*.03495	*.03975
21.	3.04452	.04927	.05400	.05871	.06339	.06805	.07269	.07731	.08191	.08649
22.	.09104	.09558	.10009	.10459	.10906	.11352	.11795	.12236	.12676	.13114
23.	.13549	.13983	.14415	.14845	.15274	.15700	.16125	.16548	.16969	.17388
24.	.17805	.18221	.18635	.19048	.19458	.19867	.20275	.20680	.21084	.21487
25.	.21888	.22287	.22684	.23080	.23475	.23868	.24259	.24649	.25037	.25424
26.	.25810	.26194	.26576	.26957	.27336	.27714	.28091	.28466	.28840	.29213
27.	.29584	.29953	.30322	.30689	.31054	.31419	.31782	.32143	.32504	.32863
28.	.33220	.33577	.33932	.34286	.34639	.34990	.35341	.35690	.36038	.36384
29.	.36730	.37074'	.37417	.37759	.38099	.38439	.38777	.39115	.39451	.39786
30.	3.40120	.40453	.40784	.41115	.41444	.41773	.42100	.42426	.42751	.43076
31.	.43399	.43721	.44042	.44362	.44681	.44999	.45316	.45632	.45947	.46261
32.	.46574	.46886	.47197	.47507	.47816	.48124	.48431	.48738	.49043	.49347
33.	.49651	.49953	.50255	.50556	.50856	.51155	.51453	.51750	.52046	.52342
34.	.52636	.52930	.53223	.53515	.53806	.54096	.54385	.54674	.54962	.55249
35.	.55535	.55820	.56105	.56388	.56671	.56953	.57235	.57515	.57795	.58074
36.	.58352	.58629	.58906	.59182	.59457	.59731	.60005	.60278	.60550	.60821
37.	.61092	.61362	.61631	.61899	.62167	.62434	.62700	.62966	.63231	.63495
38.	.63759	.64021	.64284	.64545	.64806	.65066	.65325	.65584	.65842	.66099
39.	.66356	.66612	.66868	.67122	.67377	.67630	.67883	.68135	.68387	.68638
40.	3.68888	.69138	.69387	.69635	.69883	.70130	.70377	.70623	.70868	.71113
41.	.71357	.71601	.71844	.72086	.72328	.72569	.72810	.73050	.73290	.73529
42.	.73767	.74005	.74242	.74479	.74715	.74950	.75185	.75420	.75654	.75887
43.	.76120	.76352	.76584	.76815	.77046	.77276	.77506	.77735	.77963	.78191
44.	.78419	.78646	.78872	.79098	.79324	.79549	.79773	.79997	.80221	.80444
45.	.80666	.80888	.81110	.81331	.81551	.81771	.81991	.82210	.82428	.82647
46.	.82864	.83081	.83298	.83514	.83730	.83945	.84160	.84374	.84588	.84802
47.	.85015	.85227	.85439	.85651	.85862	.86073	.86283	.86493	.86703	.86912
48.	.87120	.87328	.87536	.87743	.87950	.88156	.88362	.88568	.88773	.88978
49.	.89182	.89386	.89589	.89792	.89995	.90197	.90399	.90600	.90801	.91002

50.0-99.9

N	0	1	2	3	4	5	6	7	8	9
50.	3.91202	.91402	.91602	.91801	.91999	.92197	.92395	.92593	.92790	.92986
51.	.93183	.93378	.93574	.93769	.93964	.94158	.94352	.94546	.94739	.94932
52.	.95124	.95316	.95508	.95700	.95891	.96081	.96272	.96462	.96651	.96840
53.	.97029	.97218	.97406	.97594	.97781	.97968	.98155	.98341	.98527	.98713
54.	.98898	.99083	.99268	.99452	.99636	.99820	*.00003	*.00186	*.00369	*.00551
55.	4.00733	.00915	.01096	.01277	.01458	.01638	.01818	.01998	.02177	.02356
56.	.02535	.02714	.02892	.03069	.03247	.03424	.03601	.03777	.03954	.04130
57.	.04305	.04480	.04655	.04830	.05004	.05178	.05352	.05526	.05699	.05872
58.	.06044	.06217	.06389	.06560	.06732	.06903	.07073	.07244	.07414	.07584
59.	.07754	.07923	.08092	.08261	.08429	.08598	.08766	.08933	.09101	.09268
60.	4.09434	.09601	.09767	.09933	.10099	.10264	.10429	.10594	.10759	.10923
61.	.11087	.11251	.11415	.11578	.11741	.11904	.12066	.12228	.12390	.12552
62.	.12713	.12875	.13036	.13196	.13357	.13517	.13677	.13836	.13996	.14155
63.	.14313	.14472	.14630	.14789	.14946	.15104	.15261	.15418	.15575	.15732
64.	.15888	.16044	.16200	.16356	.16511	.16667	.16821	.16976	.17131	.17285
65.	.17439	.17592	.17746	.17899	.18052	.18205	.18358	.18510	.18662	.18814
66.	.18965	.19117	.19268	.19419	.19570	.19720	.19870	.20020	.20170	.20320
67.	.20469	.20618	.20767	.20916	.21065	.21213	.21361	.21509	.21656	.21804
68.	.21951	.22098	.22244	.22391	.22537	.22683	.22829	.22975	.23120	.23266
69.	.23411	.23555	.23700	.23844	.23989	.24133	.24276	.24420	.24563	.24707
70.	4.24850	.24992	.25135	.25277	.25419	.25561	.25703	.25845	.25986	.26127
71.	.26268	.26409	.26549	.26690	.26830	.26970	.27110	.27249	.27388	.27528
72.	.27667	.27805	.27944	.28082	.28221	.28359	.28496	.28634	.28772	.28909
73.	.29046	.29183	.29320	.29456	.29592	.29729	.29865	.30000	.30136	.30271
74.	.30407	.30542	.30676	.30811	.30946	.31080	.31214	.31348	.31482	.31615
75.	.31749	.31882	.32015	.32149	.32281	.32413	.32546	.32678	.32810	.32942
76.	.33073	.33205	.33336	.33467	.33598	.33729	.33860	.33990	.34120	.34251
77.	.34381	.34510	.34640	.34769	.34899	.35028	.35157	.35286	.35414	.35543
78.	.35671	.35800	.35927	.36055	.36182	.36310	.36437	.36564	.36691	.36818
79.	.36945	.37071	.37198	.37324	.37450	.37576	.37701	.37827	.37952	.38078
80.	4.38203	.38328	.38452	.38577	.38701	.38826	.38950	.39074	.39198	.39321
81.	.39445	.39568	.39692	.39815	.39938	.40060	.40183	.40305	.40428	.40550
82.	.40672	.40794	.40916	.41037	.41159	.41280	.41401	.41522	.41643	.41764
83.	.41884	.42004	.42125	.42245	.42365	.42485	.42604	.42724	.42843	.42963
84.	.43082	.43201	.43319	.43438	.43557	.43675	.43793	.43912	.44030	.44147
85.	.44265	.44383	.44500	.44617	.44735	.44852	.44969	.45085	.45202	.45318
86.	.45435	.45551	.45667	.45783	.45899	.46014	.46130	.46245	.46361	.46476
87.	.46591	.46706	.46820	.46935	.47050	.47164	.47278	.47392	.47506	.47620
88.	.47734	.47847	.47961	.48074	.48187	.48300	.48413	.48526	.48639	.48751
89.	.48864	.48976	.49088	.49200	.49312	.49424	.49536	.49647	.49758	.49870
90.	4.49981	.50092	.50203	.50314	.50424	.50535	.50645	.50756	.50866	.50976
91.	.51086	.51196	.51305	.51415	.51525	.51634	.51743	.51852	.51961	.52070
92.	.52179	.52287	.52396	.52504	.52613	.52721	.52829	.52937	.53045	.53152
93.	.53260	.53367	.53475	.53582	.53689	.53796	.53903	.54010	.54116	.54223
94.	.54329	.54436	.54542	.54648	.54754	.54860	.54966	.55071	.55177	.55282
95.	.55388	.55493	.55598	.55703	.55808	.55913	.56017	.56122	.56226	.56331
96.	.56435	.56539	.56643	.56747	.56851	.56954	.57058	.57161	.57265	.57368
97.	.57471	.57574	.57677	.57780	.57883	.57985	.58088	.58190	.58292	.58395
98.	.58497	.58599	.58701	.58802	.58904	.59006	.59107	.59208	.59310	.59411
99.	.59512	.59613	.59714	.59815	.59915	.60016	.60116	.60217	.60317	.60417

0–499

N	0	1	2	3	4	5	6	7	8	9
0	∞	0.00000	0.69315	1.09861	.38629	.60944	.79176	.94591	*.07944	*.19722
1	2.30259	.39790	.48491	.56495	.63906	.70805	.77259	.83321	.89037	.94444
2	.99573	*.04452	*.09104	*.13549	*.17805	*.21888	*.25810	*.29584	*.33220	*.36730
3	3.40120	.43399	.46574	.49651	.52636	.55535	.58352	.61092	.63759	.66356
4	.68888	.71357	.73767	.76120	.78419	.80666	.82864	.85015	.87120	.89182
5	.91202	.93183	.95124	.97029	.98898	*.00733	*.02535	*.04305	*.06044	*.07754
6	4.09434	.11087	.12713	.14313	.15888	.17439	.18965	.20469	.21951	.23411
7	.24850	.26268	.27667	.29046	.30407	.31749	.33073	.34381	.35671	.36945
8	.38203	.39445	.40672	.41884	.43082	.44265	.45435	.46591	.47734	.48864
9	.49981	.51086	.52179	.53260	.54329	.55388	.56435	.57471	.58497	.59512
10	4.60517	.61512	.62497	.63473	.64439	.65396	.66344	.67283	.68213	.69135
11	.70048	.70953	.71850	.72739	.73620	.74493	.75359	.76217	.77068	.77912
12	.78749	.79579	.80402	.81218	.82028	.82831	.83628	.84419	.85203	.85981
13	.86753	.87520	.88280	.89035	.89784	.90527	.91265	.91998	.92725	.93447
14	.94164	.94876	.95583	.96284	.96981	.97673	.98361	.99043	.99721	*.00395
15	5.01064	.01728	.02388	.03044	.03695	.04343	.04986	.05625	.06260	.06890
16	.07517	.08140	.08760	.09375	.09987	.10595	.11199	.11799	.12396	.12990
17	.13580	.14166	.14749	.15329	.15906	.16479	.17048	.17615	.18178	.18739
18	.19296	.19850	.20401	.20949	.21494	.22036	.22575	.23111	.23644	.24175
19	.24702	.25227	.25750	.26269	.26786	.27300	.27811	.28320	.28827	.29330
20	5.29832	.30330	.30827	.31321	.31812	.32301	.32788	.33272	.33754	.34233
21	.34711	.35186	.35659	.36129	.36598	.37064	.37528	.37990	.38450	.38907
22	.39363	.39816	.40268	.40717	.41165	.41610	.42053	.42495	.42935	.43372
23	.43808	.44242	.44674	.45104	.45532	.45959	.46383	.46806	.47227	.47646
24	.48064	.48480	.48894	.49306	.49717	.50126	.50533	.50939	.51343	.51745
25	.52146	.52545	.52943	.53339	.53733	.54126	.54518	.54908	.55296	.55683
26	.56068	.56452	.56834	.57215	.57595	.57973	.58350	.58725	.59099	.59471
27	.59842	.60212	.60580	.60947	.61313	.61677	.62040	.62402	.62762	.63121
28	.63479	.63835	.64191	.64545	.64897	.65249	.65599	.65948	.66296	.66643
29	66988	67332	.67675	.68017	.68358	.68698	.69036	.69373	.69709	.70044
30	5.70378	70711	.71043	.71373	.71703	.72031	.72359	.72685	.73010	.73334
31	.73657	73979	.74300	.74620	.74939	.75257	.75574	.75890	.76205	.76519
32	.76832	.77144	.77455	.77765	.78074	.78383	.78690	.78996	.79301	.79606
33	.79909	.80212	.80513	.80814	.81114	.81413	.81711	.82008	.82305	.82600
34	.82895	.83188	.83481	.83773	.84064	.84354	.84644	.84932	.85220	.85507
35	.85793	.86079	.86363	.86647	.86930	.87212	.87493	.87774	.88053	.88332
36	.88610	.88888	.89164	.89440	.89715	.89990	.90263	.90536	.90808	.91080
37	.91350	.91620	.91889	.92158	.92426	.92693	.92959	.93225	.93489	.93754
38	.94017	.94280	.94542	.94803	.95064	.95324	.95584	.95842	.96101	.96358
39	.96615	.96871	.97126	.97381	.97635	.97889	.98141	.98394	.98645	.98896
40	5.99146	.99396	.99645	.99894	*.00141	*.00389	*.00635	*.00881	*.01127	*.01372
41	6.01616	.01859	.02102	.02345	.02587	.02828	.03069	.03309	.03548	.03787
42	.04025	.04263	.04501	.04737	.04973	.05209	.05444	.05678	.05912	.06146
43	.06379	.06611	.06843	.07074	.07304	.07535	.07764	.07993	.08222	.08450
44	.08677	.08904	.09131	.09357	.09582	.09807	.10032	.10256	.10479	.10702
45	.10925	.11147	.11368	.11589	.11810	.12030	.12249	.12468	.12687	.12905
46	.13123	.13340	.13556	.13773	.13988	.14204	.14419	.14633	.14847	.15060
47	.15273	.15486	.15698	.15910	.16121	.16331	.16542	.16752	.16961	.17170
48	.17379	.17587	.17794	.18002	.18208	.18415	.18621	.18826	.19032	.19236
49	.19441	.19644	.19848	.20051	.20254	.20456	.20658	.20859	.21060	21261

500–999

N	0	1	2	3	4	5	6	7	8	9
50	6.21461	.21661	.21860	.22059	.22258	.22456	.22654	.22851	.23048	.23245
51	.23441	.23637	.23832	.24028	.24222	.24417	.24611	.24804	.24998	.25190
52	.25383	.25575	.25767	.25958	.26149	.26340	.26530	.26720	.26910	.27099
53	.27288	.27476	.27664	.27852	.28040	.28227	.28413	.28600	.28786	.28972
54	.29157	.29342	.29527	.29711	.29895	.30079	.30262	.30445	.30628	.30810
55	.30992	.31173	.31355	.31536	.31716	.31897	.32077	.32257	.32436	.32615
56	.32794	.32972	.33150	.33328	.33505	.33683	.33859	.34036	.34212	.34388
57	.34564	.34739	.34914	.35089	.35263	.35437	.35611	.35784	.35957	.36130
58	.36303	.36475	.36647	.36819	.36990	.37161	.37332	.37502	.37673	.37843
59	.38012	.38182	.38351	.38519	.38688	.38856	.39024	.39192	.39359	.39526
60	6.39693	.39859	.40026	.40192	.40357	.40523	.40688	.40853	.41017	.41182
61	.41346	.41510	.41673	.41836	.41999	.42162	.42325	.42487	.42649	.42811
62	.42972	.43133	.43294	.43455	.43615	.43775	.43935	.44095	.44254	.44413
63	.44572	.44731	.44889	.45047	.45205	.45362	.45520	.45677	.45834	.45990
64	.46147	.46303	.46459	.46614	.46770	.46925	.47080	.47235	.47389	.47543
65	.47697	.47851	.48004	.48158	.48311	.48464	.48616	.48768	.48920	.49072
66	.49224	.49375	.49527	.49677	.49828	.49979	.50129	.50279	.50429	.50578
67	.50728	.50877	.51026	.51175	.51323	.51471	.51619	.51767	.51915	.52062
68	.52209	.52356	.52503	.52649	.52796	.52942	.53088	.53233	.53379	.53524
69	.53669	.53814	.53959	.54103	.54247	.54391	.54535	.54679	.54822	.54965
70	6.55108	.55251	.55393	.55536	.55678	.55820	.55962	.56103	.56244	.56386
71	.56526	.56667	.56808	.56948	.57088	.57228	.57368	.57508	.57647	.57786
72	.57925	.58064	.58203	.58341	.58479	.58617	.58755	.58893	.59030	.59167
73	.59304	.59441	.59578	.59715	.59851	.59987	.60123	.60259	.60394	.60530
74	.60665	.60800	.60935	.61070	.61204	.61338	.61473	.61607	.61740	.61874
75	.62007	.62141	.62274	.62407	.62539	.62672	.62804	.62936	.63068	.63200
76	.63332	.63463	.63595	.63726	.63857	.63988	.64118	.64249	.64379	.64509
77	.64639	.64769	.64898	.65028	.65157	.65286	.65415	.65544	.65673	.65801
78	.65929	.66058	.66185	.66313	.66441	.66568	.66696	.66823	.66950	.67077
79	.67203	.67330	.67456	.67582	.67708	.67834	.67960	.68085	.68211	.68336
·80	6.68461	.68586	.68711	.68835	.68960	.69084	.69208	.69332	.69456	.69580
81	.69703	.69827	.69950	.70073	.70196	.70319	.70441	.70564	.70686	.70808
82	.70930	.71052	.71174	.71296	.71417	.71538	.71659	.71780	.71901	.72022
83	.72143	.72263	.72383	.72503	.72623	.72743	.72863	.72982	.73102	.73221
84	.73340	.73459	.73578	.73697	.73815	.73934	.74052	.74170	.74288	.74406
85	.74524	.74641	.74759	.74876	.74993	.75110	.75227	.75344	.75460	.75577
86	.75693	.75809	.75926	.76041	.76157	.76273	.76388	.76504	.76619	.76734
87	.76849	.76964	.77079	.77194	.77308	.77422	.77537	.77651	.77765	.77878
88	.77992	.78106	.78219	.78333	.78446	.78559	.78672	.78784	.78897	.79010
89	.79122	.79234	.79347	.79459	.79571	.79682	.79794	.79906	.80017	.80128
90	6.80239	.80351	.80461	.80572	.80683	.80793	.80904	.81014	.81124	.81235
91	.81344	.81454	.81564	.81674	.81783	.81892	.82002	.82111	.82220	.82329
92	.82437	.82546	.82655	.82763	.82871	.82979	.83087	.83195	.83303	.83411
93	.83518	.83626	.83733	.83841	.83948	.84055	.84162	.84268	.84375	.84482
94	.84588	.84694	.84801	.84907	.85013	.85118	.85224	.85330	.85435	.85541
95	.85646	.85751	.85857	.85961	.86066	.86171	.86276	.86380	.86485	.86589
96	.86693	.86797	.86901	.87005	.87109	.87213	.87316	.87420	.87523	.87626
97	.87730	.87833	.87936	.88038	.88141	.88244	.88346	.88449	.88551	.88653
98	.88755	.88857	.88959	.89061	.89163	.89264	.89366	.89467	.89568	.89669
99	.89770	.89871	.89972	.90073	.90174	.90274	.90375	.90475	.90575	.90675

EXPONENTIAL FUNCTIONS

x	e^x	$\text{Log}_{10}\left(e^x\right)$	e^{-x}	x	e^x	$\text{Log}_{10}\left(e^x\right)$	e^{-x}
0.00	1.0000	0.00000	1.000000	**0.50**	1.6487	0.21715	0.606531
0.01	1.0101	.00434	0.990050	0.51	1.6653	.22149	.600496
0.02	1.0202	.00869	.980199	0.52	1.6820	.22583	.594521
0.03	1.0305	.01303	.970446	0.53	1.6989	.23018	.588605
0.04	1.0408	.01737	.960789	0.54	1.7160	.23452	.582748
0.05	1.0513	0.02171	0.951229	**0.55**	1.7333	0.23886	0.576950
0.06	1.0618	.02606	.941765	0.56	1.7507	.24320	.571209
0.07	1.0725	.03040	.932394	0.57	1.7683	.24755	.565525
0.08	1.0833	.03474	.923116	0.58	1.7860	.25189	.559898
0.09	1.0942	.03909	.913931	0.59	1.8040	.25623	.554327
0.10	1.1052	0.04343	0.904837	**0.60**	1.8221	0.26058	0.548812
0.11	1.1163	.04777	.895834	0.61	1.8404	.26492	.543351
0.12	1.1275	.05212	.886920	0.62	1.8589	.26926	.537944
0.13	1.1388	.05646	.878095	0.63	1.8776	.27361	.532592
0.14	1.1503	.06080	.869358	0.64	1.8965	.27795	.527292
0.15	1.1618	0.06514	0.860708	**0.65**	1.9155	0.28229	0.522046
0.16	1.1735	.06949	.852144	0.66	1.9348	.28663	.516851
0.17	1.1853	.07383	.843665	0.67	1.9542	.29098	.511709
0.18	1.1972	.07817	.835270	0.68	1.9739	.29532	.506617
0.19	1.2092	.08252	.826959	0.69	1.9937	.29966	.501576
0.20	1.2214	0.08686	0.818731	**0.70**	2.0138	0.30401	0.496585
0.21	1.2337	.09120	.810584	0.71	2.0340	.30835	.491644
0.22	1.2461	.09554	.802519	0.72	2.0544	.31269	.486752
0.23	1.2586	.09989	.794534	0.73	2.0751	.31703	.481909
0.24	1.2712	.10423	.786628	0.74	2.0959	.32138	.477114
0.25	1.2840	0.10857	0.778801	**0.75**	2.1170	0.32572	0.472367
0.26	1.2969	.11292	.771052	0.76	2.1383	.33006	.467666
0.27	1.3100	.11726	.763379	0.77	2.1598	.33441	.463013
0.28	1.3231	.12160	.755784	0.78	2.1815	.33875	.458406
0.29	1.3364	.12595	.748264	0.79	2.2034	.34309	.453845
0.30	1.3499	0.13029	0.740818	**0.80**	2.2255	0.34744	0.449329
0.31	1.3634	.13463	.733447	0.81	2.2479	.35178	.444858
0.32	1.3771	.13897	.726149	0.82	2.2705	.35612	.440432
0.33	1.3910	.14332	.718924	0.83	2.2933	.36046	.436049
0.34	1.4049	.14766	.711770	0.84	2.3164	.36481	.431711
0.35	1.4191	0.15200	0.704688	**0.85**	2.3396	0.36915	0.427415
0.36	1.4333	.15635	.697676	0.86	2.3632	.37349	.423162
0.37	1.4477	.16069	.690734	0.87	2.3869	.37784	.418952
0.38	1.4623	.16503	.683861	0.88	2.4109	.38218	.414783
0.39	1.4770	.16937	.677057	0.89	2.4351	.38652	.410656
0.40	1.4918	0.17372	0.670320	**0.90**	2.4596	0.39087	0.406570
0.41	1.5068	.17806	.663650	0.91	2.4843	.39521	.402524
0.42	1.5220	.18240	.657047	0.92	2.5093	.39955	.398519
0.43	1.5373	.18675	.650509	0.93	2.5345	.40389	.394554
0.44	1.5527	.19109	.644036	0.94	2.5600	.40824	.390628
0.45	1.5683	0.19543	0.637628	**0.95**	2.5857	0.41258	0.386741
0.46	1.5841	.19978	.631284	0.96	2.6117	.41692	.382893
0.47	1.6000	.20412	.625002	0.97	2.6379	.42127	.379083
0.48	1.6161	.20846	.618783	0.98	2.6645	.42561	.375311
0.49	1.6323	.21280	.612626	0.99	2.6912	.42995	.371577
0.50	1.6487	0.21715	0.606531	**1.00**	2.7183	0.43429	0.367879

x	e^x	$\mathrm{Log}_{10}\left(e^x\right)$	e^{-x}	x	e^x	$\mathrm{Log}_{10}\left(e^x\right)$	e^{-x}
1.00	2.7183	0.43429	0.367879	**1.50**	4.4817	0.65144	0.223130
1.01	2.7456	.43864	.364219	1.51	4.5267	.65578	.220910
1.02	2.7732	.44298	.360595	1.52	4.5722	.66013	.218712
1.03	2.8011	.44732	.357007	1.53	4.6182	.66447	.216536
1.04	2.8292	.45167	.353455	1.54	4.6646	.66881	.214381
1.05	2.8577	0.45601	0.349938	**1.55**	4.7115	0.67316	0.212248
1.06	2.8864	.46035	.346456	1.56	4.7588	.67750	.210136
1.07	2.9154	.46470	.343009	1.57	4.8066	.68184	.208045
1.08	2.9447	.46904	.339596	1.58	4.8550	.68619	.205975
1.09	2.9743	.47338	.336216	1.59	4.9037	.69053	.203926
1.10	3.0042	0.47772	0.332871	**1.60**	4.9530	0.69487	0.201897
1.11	3.0344	.48207	.329559	1.61	5.0028	.69921	.199888
1.12	3.0649	.48641	.326280	1.62	5.0531	.70356	.197899
1.13	3.0957	.49075	.323033	1.63	5.1039	.70790	.195930
1.14	3.1268	.49510	.319819	1.64	5.1552	.71224	.193980
1.15	3.1582	0.49944	0.316637	**1.65**	5.2070	0.71659	0.192050
1.16	3.1899	.50378	.313486	1.66	5.2593	.72093	.190139
1.17	3.2220	.50812	.310367	1.67	5.3122	.72527	.188247
1.18	3.2544	.51247	.307279	1.68	5.3656	.72961	.186374
1.19	3.2871	.51681	.304221	1.69	5.4195	.73396	.184520
1.20	3.3201	0.52115	0.301194	**1.70**	5.4739	0.73830	0.182684
1.21	3.3535	.52550	.298197	1.71	5.5290	.74264	.180866
1.22	3.3872	.52984	.295230	1.72	5.5845	.74699	.179066
1.23	3.4212	.53418	.292293	1.73	5.6407	.75133	.177284
1.24	3.4556	.53853	.289384	1 74	5.6973	.75567	.175520
1.25	3.4903	0.54287	0.286505	**1.75**	5.7546	0.76002	0.173774
1.26	3.5254	.54721	.283654	1.76	5.8124	.76436	.172045
1.27	3.5609	.55155	.280832	1.77	5.8709	.76870	.170333
1.28	3.5966	.55590	.278037	1.78	5.9299	.77304	.168638
1.29	3.6328	.56024	.275271	1.79	5.9895	.77739	.166960
1.30	3.6693	0.56458	0.272532	**1.80**	6.0496	0.78173	0.165299
1.31	3.7062	.56893	.269820	1.81	6.1104	.78607	.163654
1.32	3.7434	.57327	.267135	1.82	6.1719	.79042	.162026
1.33	3.7810	.57761	.264477	1.83	6.2339	.79476	.160414
1.34	3.8190	.58195	.261846	1.84	6.2965	.79910	.158817
1.35	3.8574	0.58630	0.259240	**1.85**	6.3598	0.80344	0.157237
1.36	3.8962	.59064	.256661	1.86	6.4237	.80779	.155673
1.37	3.9354	.59498	.254107	1.87	6.4883	.81213	.154124
1.38	3.9749	.59933	.251579	1.88	6.5535	.81647	.152590
1.39	4.0149	.60367	.249075	1.89	6.6194	.82082	.151072
1.40	4.0552	0.60801	0.246597	**1.90**	6.6859	0.82516	0.149569
1.41	4.0960	.61236	.244143	1 91	6.7531	.82950	.148080
1.42	4.1371	.61670	.241714	1.92	6.8210	.83385	.146607
1.43	4.1787	.62104	.239309	1.93	6.8895	.83819	.145148
1.44	4.2207	.62538	.236928	1.94	6.9588	.84253	.143704
1.45	4.2631	0.62973	0.234570	**1.95**	7.0287	0.84687	0.142274
1.46	4.3060	.63407	.232236	1.96	7.0993	.85122	.140858
1.47	4.3492	.63841	.229925	1.97	7.1707	.85556	.139457
1.48	4.3929	.64276	.227638	1.98	7.2427	.85990	.138069
1.49	4.4371	.64710	.225373	1.99	7.3155	.86425	.136695
1.50	4.4817	0.65144	0.223130	**2.00**	7.3891	0.86859	0.135335

x	e^x	$\text{Log}_{10}\left(e^x\right)$	e^{-x}	x	e^x	$\text{Log}_{10}\left(e^x\right)$	e^{-x}
2.00	7.3891	0.86859	0.135335	**2.50**	12.182	1.08574	0.082085
2.01	7.4633	.87293	.133989	2.51	12.305	1.09008	.081268
2.02	7.5383	.87727	.132655	2.52	12.429	1.09442	.080460
2.03	7.6141	.88162	.131336	2.53	12.554	1.09877	.079659
2.04	7.6906	.88596	.130029	2.54	12.680	1.10311	.078866
2.05	7.7679	0.89030	0.128735	**2.55**	12.807	1.10745	0.078082
2.06	7.8460	.89465	.127454	2.56	12.936	1.11179	.077305
2.07	7.9248	.89899	.126186	2.57	13.066	1.11614	.076536
2.08	8.0045	.90333	.124930	2.58	13.197	1.12048	.075774
2.09	8.0849	.90768	.123687	2.59	13.330	1.12482	.075020
2.10	8.1662	0.91202	0.122456	**2.60**	13.464	1.12917	0.074274
2.11	8.2482	.91636	.121238	2.61	13.599	1.13351	.073535
2.12	8.3311	.92070	.120032	2.62	13.736	1.13785	.072803
2.13	8.4149	.92505	.118837	2.63	13.874	1.14219	.072078
2.14	8.4994	.92939	.117655	2.64	14.013	1.14654	.071361
2.15	8.5849	0.93373	0.116484	**2.65**	14.154	1.15088	0.070651
2.16	8.6711	.93808	.115325	2.66	14.296	1.15522	.069948
2.17	8.7583	.94242	.114178	2.67	14.440	1.15957	.069252
2.18	8.8463	.94676	.113042	2.68	14.585	1.16391	.068563
2.19	8.9352	.95110	.111917	2.69	14.732	1.16825	.067881
2.20	9.0250	0.95545	0.110803	**2.70**	14.880	1.17260	0.067206
2.21	9.1157	.95979	.109701	2.71	15.029	1.17694	.066537
2.22	9.2073	.96413	.108609	2.72	15.180	1.18128	.065875
2.23	9.2999	.96848	.107528	2.73	15.333	1.18562	.065219
2.24	9.3933	.97282	.106459	2.74	15.487	1.18997	.064570
2.25	9.4877	0.97716	0.105399	**2.75**	15.643	1.19431	0.063928
2.26	9.5831	.98151	.104350	2.76	15.800	1.19865	.063292
2.27	9.6794	.98585	.103312	2.77	15.959	1.20300	.062662
2.28	9.7767	.99019	.102284	2.78	16.119	1.20734	.062039
2.29	9.8749	.99453	.101266	2.79	16.281	1.21168	.061421
2.30	9.9742	0.99888	0.100259	**2.80**	16.445	1.21602	0.060810
2.31	10.074	1.00322	.099261	2.81	16.610	1.22037	.060205
2.32	10.176	1.00756	.098274	2.82	16.777	1.22471	.059606
2.33	10.278	1.01191	.097296	2.83	16.945	1.22905	.059013
2.34	10.381	1.01625	.096328	2.84	17.116	1.23340	.058426
2.35	10.486	1.02059	0.095369	**2.85**	17.288	1.23774	0.057844
2.36	10.591	1.02493	.094420	2.86	17.462	1.24208	.057269
2.37	10.697	1.02928	.093481	2.87	17.637	1.24643	.056699
2.38	10.805	1.03362	.092551	2.88	17.814	1.25077	.056135
2.39	10.913	1.03796	.091630	2.89	17.993	1.25511	.055576
2.40	11.023	1.04231	0.090718	**2.90**	18.174	1.25945	0.055023
2.41	11.134	1.04665	.089815	2.91	18.357	1.26380	.054476
2.42	11.246	1.05099	.088922	2.92	18.541	1.26814	.053934
2.43	11.359	1.05534	.088037	2.93	18.728	1.27248	.053397
2.44	11.473	1.05968	.087161	2.94	18.916	1.27683	.052866
2.45	11.588	1.06402	0.086294	**2.95**	19.106	1.28117	0.052340
2.46	11.705	1.06836	.085435	2.96	19.298	1.28551	.051819
2.47	11.822	1.07271	.084585	2.97	19.492	1.28985	.051303
2.48	11.941	1.07705	.083743	2.98	19.688	1.29420	.050793
2.49	12.061	1.08139	.082910	2.99	19.886	1.29854	.050287
2.50	12.182	1.08574	0.082085	**3.00**	20.086	1.30288	0.049787

x	e^x	$\text{Log}_{10}\left(e^x\right)$	e^{-x}	x	e^x	$\text{Log}_{10}\left(e^x\right)$	e^{-x}
3.00	20.086	1.30288	0.049787	**3.50**	33.115	1.52003	0.030197
3.01	20.287	1.30723	.049292	3.51	33.448	1.52437	.029897
3.02	20.491	1.31157	.048801	3.52	33.784	1.52872	.029599
3.03	20.697	1.31591	.048316	3.53	34.124	1.53306	.029305
3.04	20.905	1.32026	.047835	3.54	34.467	1.53740	.029013
3.05	21.115	1.32460	0.047359	**3.55**	34.813	1.54175	0.028725
3.06	21.328	1.32894	.046888	3.56	35.163	1.54609	.028439
3.07	21.542	1.33328	.046421	3.57	35.517	1.55043	.028156
3.08	21.758	1.33763	.045959	3.58	35.874	1.55477	.027876
3.09	21.977	1.34197	.045502	3.59	36.234	1.55912	.027598
3.10	22.198	1.34631	0.045049	**3.60**	36.598	1.56346	0.027324
3.11	22.421	1.35066	.044601	3.61	36.966	1.56780	.027052
3.12	22.646	1.35500	.044157	3.62	37.338	1.57215	.026783
3.13	22.874	1.35934	.043718	3.63	37.713	1.57649	.026516
3.14	23.104	1.36368	.043283	3.64	38.092	1.58083	.026252
3.15	23.336	1.36803	0.042852	**3.65**	38.475	1.58517	0.025991
3.16	23.571	1.37237	.042426	3.66	38.861	1.58952	.025733
3.17	23.807	1.37671	.042004	3.67	39.252	1.59386	.025476
3.18	24.047	1.38106	.041586	3.68	39.646	1.59820	.025223
3.19	24.288	1.38540	.041172	3.69	40.045	1.60255	.024972
3.20	24.533	1.38974	0.040762	**3.70**	40.447	1.60689	0.024724
3.21	24.779	1.39409	.040357	3.71	40.854	1.61123	.024478
3.22	25.028	1.39843	.039955	3.72	41.264	1.61558	.024234
3.23	25.280	1.40277	.039557	3.73	41.679	1.61992	.023993
3.24	25.534	1.40711	.039164	3.74	42.098	1.62426	.023754
3.25	25.790	1.41146	0.038774	**3.75**	42.521	1.62860	0.023518
3.26	26.050	1.41580	.038388	3.76	42.948	1.63295	.023284
3.27	26.311	1.42014	.038006	3.77	43.380	1.63729	.023052
3.28	26.576	1.42449	.037628	3.78	43.816	1.64163	.022823
3.29	26.843	1.42883	.037254	3.79	44.256	1.64598	.022596
3.30	27.113	1.43317	0.036883	**3.80**	44.701	1.65032	0.022371
3.31	27.385	1.43751	.036516	3.81	45.150	1.65466	.022148
3.32	27.660	1.44186	.036153	3.82	45.604	1.65900	.021928
3.33	27.938	1.44620	.035793	3.83	46.063	1.66335	.021710
3.34	28.219	1.45054	.035437	3.84	46.525	1.66769	.021494
3.35	28.503	1.45489	0.035084	**3.85**	46.993	1.67203	0.021280
3.36	28.789	1.45923	.034735	3.86	47.465	1.67638	.021068
3.37	29.079	1.46357	.034390	3.87	47.942	1.68072	.020858
3.38	29.371	1.46792	.034047	3.88	48.424	1.68506	.020651
3.39	29.666	1.47226	.033709	3.89	48.911	1.68941	.020445
3.40	29.964	1.47660	0.033373	**3.90**	49.402	1.69375	0.020242
3.41	30.265	1.48094	.033041	3.91	49.899	1.69809	.020041
3.42	30.569	1.48529	.032712	3.92	50.400	1.70243	.019841
3.43	30.877	1.48963	.032387	3.93	50.907	1.70678	.019644
3.44	31.187	1.49397	.032065	3.94	51.419	1.71112	.019448
3.45	31.500	1.49832	0.031746	**3.95**	51.935	1.71546	0.019255
3.46	31.817	1.50266	.031430	3.96	52.457	1.71981	.019063
3.47	32.137	1.50700	.031117	3.97	52.985	1.72415	.018873
3.48	32.460	1.51134	.030807	3.98	53.517	1.72849	.018686
3.49	32.786	1.51569	.030501	3.99	54.055	1.73283	.018500
3.50	33.115	1.52003	0.030197	**4.00**	54.598	1.73718	0.018316

x	e^x	$\log_{10}\left(e^x\right)$	e^{-x}	x	e^x	$\log_{10}\left(e^x\right)$	e^{-x}
4.00	54.598	1.73718	0.018316	**4.50**	90.017	1.95433	0.011109
4.01	55.147	1.74152	.018133	4.51	90.922	1.95867	.010998
4.02	55.701	1.74586	.017953	4.52	91.836	1.96301	.010889
4.03	56.261	1.75021	.017774	4.53	92.759	1.96735	.010781
4.04	56.826	1.75455	.017597	4.54	93.691	1.97170	.010673
4.05	57.397	1.75889	0.017422	**4.55**	94.632	1.97604	0.010567
4.06	57.974	1.76324	.017249	4.56	95.583	1.98038	.010462
4.07	58.557	1.76758	.017077	4.57	96.544	1.98473	.010358
4.08	59.145	1.77192	.016907	4.58	97.514	1.98907	.010255
4.09	59.740	1.77626	.016739	4.59	98.494	1.99341	.010153
4.10	60.340	1.78061	0.016573	**4.60**	99.484	1.99775	0.010052
4.11	60.947	1.78495	.016408	4.61	100.48	2.00210	.009952
4.12	61.559	1.78929	.016245	4.62	101.49	2.00644	.009853
4.13	62.178	1.79364	.016083	4.63	102.51	2.01078	.009755
4.14	62.803	1.79798	.015923	4.64	103.54	2.01513	.009658
4.15	63.434	1.80232	0.015764	**4.65**	104.58	2.01947	0.009562
4.16	64.072	1.80667	.015608	4.66	105.64	2.02381	.009466
4.17	64.715	1.81101	.015452	4.67	106.70	2.02816	.009372
4.18	65.366	1.81535	.015299	4.68	107.77	2.03250	.009279
4.19	66.023	1.81969	.015146	4.69	108.85	2.03684	.009187
4.20	66.686	1.82404	0.014996	**4.70**	109.95	2.04118	0.009095
4.21	67.357	1.82838	.014846	4.71	111.05	2.04553	.009005
4.22	68.033	1.83272	.014699	4.72	112.17	2.04987	.008915
4.23	68.717	1.83707	.014552	4.73	113.30	2.05421	.008826
4.24	69.408	1.84141	.014408	4.74	114.43	2.05856	.008739
4.25	70.105	1.84575	0.014264	**4.75**	115.58	2.06290	0.008652
4.26	70.810	1.85009	.014122	4.76	116.75	2.06724	.008566
4.27	71.522	1.85444	.013982	4.77	117.92	2.07158	.008480
4.28	72.240	1.85878	.013843	4.78	119.10	2.07593	.008396
4.29	72.966	1.86312	.013705	4.79	120.30	2.08027	.008312
4.30	73.700	1.86747	0.013569	**4.80**	121.51	2.08461	0.008230
4.31	74.440	1.87181	.013434	4.81	122.73	2.08896	.008148
4.32	75.189	1.87615	.013300	4.82	123.97	2.09330	.008067
4.33	75.944	1.88050	.013168	4.83	125.21	2.09764	.007987
4.34	76.708	1.88484	.013037	4.84	126.47	2.10199	.007907
4.35	77.478	1.88918	0.012907	**4.85**	127.74	2.10633	0.007828
4.36	78.257	1.89352	.012778	4.86	129.02	2.11067	.007750
4.37	79.044	1.89787	.012651	4.87	130.32	2.11501	.007673
4.38	79.838	1.90221	.012525	4.88	131.63	2.11936	.007597
4.39	80.640	1.90655	.012401	4.89	132.95	2.12370	.007521
4.40	81.451	1.91090	0.012277	**4.90**	134.29	2.12804	0.007447
4.41	82.269	1.91524	.012155	4.91	135.64	2.13239	.007372
4.42	83.096	1.91958	.012034	4.92	137.00	2.13673	.007299
4.43	83.931	1.92392	.011914	4.93	138.38	2.14107	.007227
4.44	84.775	1.92827	.011796	4.94	139.77	2.14541	.007155
4.45	85.627	1.93261	0.011679	**4.95**	141.17	2.14976	0.007083
4.46	86.488	1.93695	.011562	4.96	142.59	2.15410	.007013
4.47	87.357	1.94130	.011447	4.97	144.03	2.15844	.006943
4.48	88.235	1.94564	.011333	4.98	145.47	2.16279	.006874
4.49	89.121	1.94998	.011221	4.99	146.94	2.16713	.006806
4.50	90.017	1.95433	0.011109	**5.00**	148.41	2.17147	0.006738

EXPONENTIAL FUNCTIONS (Continued)

x	e^x	$\mathrm{Log}_{10}\left(e^x\right)$	e^{-x}	x	e^x	$\mathrm{Log}_{10}\left(e^x\right)$	e^{-x}
5.00	148.41	2.17147	0.006738	**5.50**	244.69	2.38862	0.0040868
5.01	149.90	2.17582	.006671	5.55	257.24	2.41033	.0038875
5.02	151.41	2.18016	.006605	5.60	270.43	2.43205	.0036979
5.03	152.93	2.18450	.006539	5.65	284.29	2.45376	.0035175
5.04	154.47	2.18884	.006474	5.70	298.87	2.47548	.0033460
5.05	156.02	2.19319	0.006409	**5.75**	314.19	2.49719	0.0031828
5.06	157.59	2.19753	.006346	5.80	330.30	2.51891	.0030276
5.07	159.17	2.20187	.006282	5.85	347.23	2.54062	.0028799
5.08	160.77	2.20622	.006220	5.90	365.04	2.56234	.0027394
5.09	162.39	2.21056	.006158	5.95	383.75	2.58405	.0026058
5.10	164.02	2.21490	0.006097	**6.00**	403.43	2.60577	0.0024788
5.11	165.67	2.21924	.006036	6.05	424.11	2.62748	.0023579
5.12	167.34	2.22359	.005976	6.10	445.86	2.64920	.0022429
5.13	169.02	2.22793	.005917	6.15	468.72	2.67091	.0021335
5.14	170.72	2.23227	.005858	6.20	492.75	2.69263	.0020294
5.15	172.43	2.23662	0.005799	**6.25**	518.01	2.71434	0.0019305
5.16	174.16	2.24096	.005742	6.30	544.57	2.73606	.0018363
5.17	175.91	2.24530	.005685	6.35	572.49	2.75777	.0017467
5.18	177.68	2.24965	.005628	6.40	601.85	2.77948	.0016616
5.19	179.47	2.25399	.005572	6.45	632.70	2.80120	.0015805
5.20	181.27	2.25833	0.005517	**6.50**	665.14	2.82291	0.0015034
5.21	183.09	2.26267	.005462	6.55	699.24	2.84463	.0014301
5.22	184.93	2.26702	.005407	6.60	735.10	2.86634	.0013604
5.23	186.79	2.27136	.005354	6.65	772.78	2.88806	.0012940
5.24	188.67	2.27570	.005300	6.70	812.41	2.90977	.0012309
5.25	190.57	2.28005	0.005248	**6.75**	854.06	2.93149	0.0011709
5.26	192.48	2.28439	.005195	6.80	897.85	2.95320	.0011138
5.27	194.42	2.28873	.005144	6.85	943.88	2.97492	.0010595
5.28	196.37	2.29307	.005092	6.90	992.27	2.99663	.0010078
5.29	198.34	2.29742	.005042	6.95	1043.1	3.01835	.0009586
5.30	200.34	2.30176	0.004992	**7.00**	1096.6	3.04006	0.0009119
5.31	202.35	2.30610	.004942	7.05	1152.9	3.06178	.0008674
5.32	204.38	2.31045	.004893	7.10	1212.0	3.08349	.0008251
5.33	206.44	2.31479	.004844	7.15	1274.1	3.10521	.0007849
5.34	208.51	2.31913	.004796	7.20	1339.4	3.12692	.0007466
5.35	210.61	2.32348	0.004748	**5.25**	1408.1	3.14863	0.0007102
5.36	212.72	2.32782	.004701	7.30	1480.3	3.17035	.0006755
5.37	214.86	2.33216	.004654	7.35	1556.2	3.19206	.0006426
5.38	217.02	2.33650	.004608	7.40	1636.0	3.21378	.0006113
5.39	219.20	2.34085	.004562	7.45	1719.9	3.23549	.0005814
5.40	221.41	2.34519	0.004517	**7.50**	1808.0	3.25721	0.0005531
5.41	223.63	2.34953	.004472	7.55	1900.7	3.27892	.0005261
5.42	225.88	2.35388	.004427	7.60	1998.2	3.30064	.0005005
5.43	228.15	2.35822	.004383	7.65	2100.6	3.32235	.0004760
5.44	230.44	2.36256	.004339	7.70	2208.3	3.34407	.0004528
5.45	232.76	2.36690	0.004296	**7.75**	2321.6	3.36578	0.0004307
5.46	235.10	2.37125	.004254	7.80	2440.6	3.38750	.0004097
5.47	237.46	2.37559	.004211	7.85	2565.7	3.40921	.0003898
5.48	239.85	2.37993	.004169	7.90	2697.3	3.43093	.0003707
5.49	242.26	2.38428	.004128	7.95	2835.6	3.45264	.0003527
5.50	244.69	2.38862	0.004087	**8.00**	2981.0	3.47436	0.0003355

x	e^x	$\mathrm{Log}_{10}\left(e^x\right)$	e^{-x}	x	e^x	$\mathrm{Log}_{10}\left(e^x\right)$	e^{-x}
8.00	2981.0	3.47436	0.0003355	**9.00**	8103.1	3.90865	0.0001234
8.05	3133.8	3.49607	.0003191	9.05	8518.5	3.93037	.0001174
8.10	3294.5	3.51779	.0003035	9.10	8955.3	3.95208	.0001117
8.15	3463.4	3.53950	.0002887	9.15	9414.4	3.97379	.0001062
8.20	3641.0	3.56121	.0002747	9.20	9897.1	3.99551	.0001010
8.25	3827.6	3.58293	0.0002613	**9.25**	10405	4.01722	0.0000961
8.30	4023.9	3.60464	.0002485	9.30	10938	4.03894	.0000914
8.35	4230.2	3.62636	.0002364	9.35	11499	4.06065	.0000870
8.40	4447.1	3.64807	.0002249	9.40	12088	4.08237	.0000827
8.45	4675.1	3.66979	.0002139	9.45	12708	4.10408	.0000787
8.50	4914.8	3.69150	0.0002035	**9.50**	13360	4.12580	0.0000749
8.55	5166.8	3.71322	.0001935	9.55	14045	4.14751	.0000712
8.60	5431.7	3.73493	.0001841	9.60	14765	4.16923	.0000677
8.65	5710.1	3.75665	.0001751	9.65	15522	4.19094	.0000644
8.70	6002.9	3.77836	.0001666	9.70	16318	4.21266	.0000613
8.75	6310.7	3.80008	0.0001585	**9.75**	17154	4.23437	0.0000583
8.80	6634.2	3.82179	.0001507	9.80	18034	4.25609	.0000555
8.85	6974.4	3.84351	.0001434	9.85	18958	4.27780	.0000527
8.90	7332.0	3.86522	.0001364	9.90	19930	4.29952	.0000502
8.95	7707.9	3.88694	.0001297	9.95	20952	4.32123	0.0000477
9.00	8103.1	3.90865	0.0001234	10.00	22026	4.34294	0.0000454

HYPERBOLIC FUNCTIONS

The logarithms given below show the mantissa only. The proper characteristic must be added.

x	Sinh x Value	Log₁₀	Cosh x Value	Log₁₀	Tanh x Value	Log₁₀	Coth x Value	Log₁₀
0.00	0.00000	—∞	1.00000	.00000	0.00000	—∞	∞	∞
0.01	.01000	.00001	1.00005	.00002	.01000	.99999	100.003	.00001
0.02	.02000	.30106	1.00020	.00009	.02000	.30097	50.007	.69903
0.03	.03000	.47719	1.00045	.00020	.02999	.47699	33.343	.52301
0.04	.04001	.60218	1.00080	.00035	.03998	.60183	25.013	.39817
0.05	0.05002	.69915	1.00125	.00054	0.04996	.69861	20.017	.30139
0.06	.06004	.77841	1.00180	.00078	.05993	.77763	16.687	.22237
0.07	.07006	.84545	1.00245	.00106	.06989	.84439	14.309	.15561
0.08	.08009	.90355	1.00320	.00139	.07983	.90216	12.527	.09784
0.09	.09012	.95483	1.00405	.00176	.08976	.95307	11.141	.04693
0.10	0.10017	.00072	1.00500	.00217	0.09967	.99856	10.0333	.00144
0.11	.11022	.04227	1.00606	.00262	.10956	.03965	9.1275	.96035
0.12	.12029	.08022	1.00721	.00312	.11943	.07710	8.3733	.92290
0.13	.13037	.11517	1.00846	.00366	.12927	.11151	7.7356	.88849
0.14	.14046	.14755	1.00982	.00424	.13909	.14330	7.1895	.85670
0.15	0.15056	.17772	1.01127	.00487	0.14889	.17285	6.7166	.82715
0.16	.16068	.20597	1.01283	.00554	.15865	.20044	6.3032	.79956
0.17	.17082	.23254	1.01448	.00625	.16838	.22629	5.9389	.77371
0.18	.18097	.25762	1.01624	.00700	.17808	.25062	5.6154	.74938
0.19	.19115	.28136	1.01810	.00779	.18775	.27357	5.3263	.72643
0.20	0.20134	.30392	1.02007	.00863	0.19738	.29529	5.0665	.70471
0.21	.21155	.32541	1.02213	.00951	.20697	.31590	4.8317	.68410
0.22	.22178	.34592	1.02430	.01043	.21652	.33549	4.6186	.66451
0.23	.23203	.36555	1.02657	.01139	.22603	.35416	4.4242	.64584
0.24	.24231	.38437	1.02894	.01239	.23550	.37198	4.2464	.62802
0.25	0.25261	.40245	1.03141	.01343	0.24492	.38902	4.0830	.61098
0.26	.26294	.41986	1.03399	.01452	.25430	.40534	3.9324	.59466
0.27	.27329	.43663	1.03667	.01564	.26362	.42099	3.7933	.57901
0.28	.28367	.45282	1.03946	.01681	.27291	.43601	3.6643	.56399
0.29	.29408	.46847	1.04235	.01801	.28213	.45046	3.5444	.54954
0.30	0.30452	.48362	1.04534	.01926	0.29131	.46436	3.4327	.53564
0.31	.31499	.49830	1.04844	.02054	.30044	.47775	3.3285	.52225
0.32	.32549	.51254	1.05164	.02187	.30951	.49067	3.2309	.50933
0.33	.33602	.52637	1.05495	.02323	.31852	.50314	3.1395	.49686
0.34	.34659	.53981	1.05836	.02463	.32748	.51518	3.0536	.48482
0.35	0.35719	.55290	1.06188	.02607	0.33638	.52682	2.9729	.47318
0.36	.36783	.56564	1.06550	.02755	.34521	.53809	2.8968	.46191
0.37	.37850	.57807	1.06923	.02907	.35399	.54899	2.8249	.45101
0.38	.38921	.59019	1.07307	.03063	36271	.55956	2.7570	.44044
0.39	.39996	.60202	1.07702	.03222	.37136	.56980	2.6928	.43020
0.40	0.41075	.61358	1.08107	.03385	0.37995	.57973	2.6319	.42027
0.41	.42158	.62488	1.08523	.03552	.38847	.58936	2.5742	.41064
0.42	.43246	.63594	1.08950	.03723	.39693	.59871	2.5193	.40129
0.43	.44337	.64677	1.09388	.03897	.40532	.60780	2.4672	.39220
0.44	.45434	.65738	1.09837	.04075	.41364	.61663	2.4175	.38337
0.45	0.46534	.66777	1.10297	.04256	0.42190	.62521	2.3702	.37479
0.46	.47640	.67797	1.10768	.04441	.43008	.63355	2.3251	.36645
0.47	.48750	.68797	1.11250	.04630	.43820	.64167	2.2821	.35833
0.48	.49865	.69779	1.11743	.04822	.44624	.64957	2.2409	.35043
0.49	.50984	.70744	1.12247	.05018	.45422	.65726	2.2016	.34274
0.50	0.52110	.71692	1.12763	.05217	0.46212	.66475	2.1640	.33525

HYPERBOLIC FUNCTIONS (Continued)

The logarithms given below show the mantissa only. The proper characteristic must be added.

x	Sinh x Value	Log₁₀	Cosh x Value	Log₁₀	Tanh x Value	Log₁₀	Coth x Value	Log₁₀
0.50	0.52110	.71692	1.12763	.05217	0.46212	.66475	2.1640	.33525
0.51	.53240	.72624	1.13289	.05419	.46995	.67205	2.1279	.32795
0.52	.54375	.73540	1.13827	.05625	.47770	.67916	2.0934	.32084
0.53	.55516	.74442	1.14377	.05834	.48538	.68608	2.0602	.31392
0.54	.56663	.75330	1.14938	.06046	.49299	.69284	2.0284	.30716
0.55	0.57815	.76204	1.15510	.06262	0.50052	.69942	1.9979	.30058
0.56	.58973	.77065	1.16094	.06481	.50798	.70584	1.9686	.29416
0.57	.60137	.77914	1.16690	.06703	.51536	.71211	1.9404	.28789
0.58	.61307	.78751	1.17297	.06929	.52267	.71822	1.9133	.28178
0.59	.62483	.79576	1.17916	.07157	.52990	.72419	1.8872	.27581
0.60	0.63665	.80390	1.18547	.07389	0.53705	.73001	1.8620	.26999
0.61	.64854	.81194	1.19189	.07624	.54413	.73570	1.8378	.26430
0.62	.66049	.81987	1.19844	.07861	.55113	.74125	1.8145	.25875
0.63	.67251	.82770	1.20510	.08102	.55805	.74667	1.7919	.25333
0.64	.68459	.83543	1.21189	.08346	.56490	.75197	1.7702	.24803
0.65	0.69675	.84308	1.21879	.08593	0.57167	.75715	1.7493	.24285
0.66	.70897	.85063	1.22582	.08843	.57836	.76220	1.7290	.23780
0.67	.72126	.85809	1.23297	.09095	.58498	.76714	1.7095	.23286
0.68	.73363	.86548	1.24025	.09351	.59152	.77197	1.6906	.22803
0.69	.74607	.87278	1.24765	.09609	.59798	.77669	1.6723	.22331
0.70	0.75858	.88000	1.25517	.09870	0.60437	.78130	1.6546	.21870
0.71	.77117	.88715	1.26282	.10134	.61068	.78581	1.6375	.21419
0.72	.78384	.89423	1.27059	.10401	.61691	.79022	1.6210	.20978
0.73	.79659	.90123	1.27849	.10670	.62307	.79453	1.6050	.20547
0.74	.80941	.90817	1.28652	.10942	.62915	.79875	1.5895	.20125
0.75	0.82232	.91504	1.29468	.11216	0.63515	.80288	1.5744	.19712
0.76	.83530	.92185	1.30297	.11493	.64108	.80691	1.5599	.19309
0.77	.84838	.92859	1.31139	.11773	.64693	.81086	1.5458	.18914
0.78	.86153	.93527	1.31994	.12055	.65271	.81472	1.5321	.18528
0.79	.87478	.94190	1.32862	.12340	.65841	.81850	1.5188	.18150
0.80	0.88811	.94846	1.33743	.12627	0.66404	.82219	1.5059	.17781
0.81	.90152	.95498	1.34638	.12917	.66959	.82581	1.4935	.17419
0.82	.91503	.96144	1.35547	.13209	.67507	.82935	1.4813	.17065
0.83	.92863	.96784	1.36468	.13503	.68048	.83281	1.4696	.16719
0.84	.94233	.97420	1.37404	.13800	.68581	.83620	1.4581	.16380
0.85	0.95612	.98051	1.38353	.14099	0.69107	.83952	1.4470	.16048
0.86	.97000	.98677	1.39316	.14400	.69626	.84277	1.4362	.15723
0.87	.98398	.99299	1.40293	.14704	.70137	.84595	1.4258	.15405
0.88	.99806	.99916	1.41284	.15009	.70642	.84906	1.4156	.15094
0.89	1.01224	.00528	1.42289	.15317	.71139	.85211	1.4057	.14789
0.90	1.02652	.01137	1.43309	.15627	0.71630	.85509	1.3961	.14491
0.91	1.04090	.01741	1.44342	.15939	.72113	.85801	1.3867	.14199
0.92	1.05539	.02341	1.45390	.16254	.72590	.86088	1.3776	.13912
0.93	1.06998	.02937	1.46453	.16570	.73059	.86368	1.3687	.13632
0.94	1.08468	.03530	1.47530	.16888	.73522	.86642	1.3601	.13358
0.95	1.09948	.04119	1.48623	.17208	0.73978	.86910	1.3517	.13090
0.96	1.11440	.04704	1.49729	.17531	.74428	.87173	1.3436	.12827
0.97	1.12943	.05286	1.50851	.17855	.74870	.87431	1.3356	.12569
0.98	1.14457	.05864	1.51988	.18181	.75307	.87683	1.3279	.12317
0.99	1.15983	.06439	1.53141	.18509	.75736	.87930	1.3204	.12070
1.00	1.17520	.07011	1.54308	.18839	0.76159	.88172	1.3130	.11828

The logarithms given below show the mantissa only.   The proper characteristic must be added.

x	Sinh x Value	$\log_{10}$	Cosh x Value	$\log_{10}$	Tanh x Value	$\log_{10}$	Coth x Value	$\log_{10}$
1.00	1.17520	.07011	1.54308	.18839	0.76159	.88172	1.3130	.11828
1.01	1.19069	.07580	1.55491	.19171	.76576	.88409	1.3059	.11591
1.02	1.20630	.08146	1.56689	.19504	.76987	.88642	1.2989	.11358
1.03	1.22203	.08708	1.57904	.19839	.77391	.88869	1.2921	.11131
1.04	1.23788	.09268	1.59134	.20176	.77789	.89092	1.2855	.10908
1.05	1.25386	.09825	1.60379	.20515	0.78181	.89310	1.2791	.10690
1.06	1.26996	.10379	1.61641	.20855	.78566	.89524	1.2728	.10476
1.07	1.28619	.10930	1.62919	.21197	.78946	.89733	1.2667	.10267
1.08	1.30254	.11479	1.64214	.21541	.79320	.89938	1.2607	.10062
1.09	1.31903	.12025	1.65525	.21886	.79688	.90139	1.2549	.09861
1.10	1.33565	.12569	1.66852	.22233	0.80050	.90336	1.2492	.09664
1.11	1.35240	.13111	1.68196	.22582	.80406	.90529	1.2437	.09471
1.12	1.36929	.13649	1.69557	.22931	.80757	.90718	1.2383	.09282
1.13	1.38631	.14186	1.70934	.23283	.81102	.90903	1.2330	.09097
1.14	1.40347	.14720	1.72329	.23636	.81441	.91085	1.2279	.08915
1.15	1.42078	.15253	1.73741	.23990	0.81775	.91262	1.2229	.08738
1.16	1.43822	.15783	1.75171	.24346	.82104	.91436	1.2180	.08564
1.17	1.45581	.16311	1.76618	.24703	.82427	.91607	1.2132	.08393
1.18	1.47355	.16836	1.78083	.25062	.82745	.91774	1.2085	.08226
1.19	1.49143	.17360	1.79565	.25422	.83058	.91938	1.2040	.08062
1.20	1.50946	.17882	1.81066	.25784	0.83365	.92099	1.1995	.07901
1.21	1.52764	.18402	1.82584	.26146	.83668	.92256	1.1952	.07744
1.22	1.54598	.18920	1.84121	.26510	.83965	.92410	1.1910	.07590
1.23	1.56447	.19437	1.85676	.26876	.84258	.92561	1.1868	.07439
1.24	1.58311	.19951	1.87250	.27242	.84546	.92709	1.1828	.07291
1.25	1.60192	.20464	1.88842	.27610	0.84828	.92854	1.1789	.07146
1.26	1.62088	.20975	1.90454	.27979	.85106	.92996	1.1750	.07004
1.27	1.64001	.21485	1.92084	.28349	.85380	.93135	1.1712	.06865
1.28	1.65930	.21993	1.93734	.28721	.85648	.93272	1.1676	.06728
1.29	1.67876	.22499	1.95403	.29093	.85913	.93406	1.1640	.06594
1.30	1.69838	.23004	1.97091	.29467	0.86172	.93537	1.1605	.06463
1.31	1.71818	.23507	1.98800	.29842	.86428	.93665	1.1570	.06335
1.32	1.73814	.24009	2.00528	.30217	.86678	.93791	1.1537	.06209
1.33	1.75828	.24509	2.02276	.30594	.86925	.93914	1.1504	.06086
1.34	1.77860	.25008	2.04044	.30972	.87167	.94035	1.1472	.05965
1.35	1.79909	.25505	2.05833	.31352	0.87405	.94154	1.1441	.05846
1.36	1.81977	.26002	2.07643	.31732	.87639	.94270	1.1410	.05730
1.37	1.84062	.26496	2.09473	.32113	.87869	.94384	1.1381	.05616
1.38	1.86166	.26990	2.11324	.32495	.88095	.94495	1.1351	.05505
1.39	1.88289	.27482	2.13196	.32878	.88317	.94604	1.1323	.05396
1.40	1.90430	.27974	2.15090	.33262	0.88535	.94712	1.1295	.05288
1.41	1.92591	.28464	2.17005	.33647	.88749	.94817	1.1268	.05183
1.42	1.94770	.28952	2.18942	.34033	.88960	.94919	1.1241	.05081
1.43	1.96970	.29440	2.20900	.34420	.89167	.95020	1.1215	.04980
1.44	1.99188	.29926	2.22881	.34807	.89370	.95119	1.1189	.04881
1.45	2.01427	.30412	2.24884	.35196	0.89569	.95216	1.1165	.04784
1.46	2.03686	.30896	2.26910	.35585	.89765	.95311	1.1140	.04689
1.47	2.05965	.31379	2.28958	.35976	.89958	.95404	1.1116	.04596
1.48	2.08265	.31862	2.31029	.36367	.90147	.95495	1.1093	.04505
1.49	2.10586	.32343	2.33123	.36759	.90332	.95584	1.1070	.04416
1.50	2.12928	.32823	2.35241	.37151	0.90515	.95672	1.1048	.04328

HYPERBOLIC FUNCTIONS (Continued)

The logarithms given below show the mantissa only. The proper characteristic must be added

x	Sinh x Value	Log₁₀	Cosh x Value	Log₁₀	Tanh x Value	Log₁₀	Coth x Value	Log₁₀
1.50	2.12928	.32823	2.35241	.37151	0.90515	.95672	1.1048	.04328
1.51	2.15291	.33303	2.37382	.37545	.90694	.95758	1.1026	.04242
1.52	2.17676	.33781	2.39547	.37939	.90870	.95842	1.1005	.04158
1.53	2.20082	.34258	2.41736	.38334	.91042	.95924	1.0984	.04076
1.54	2.22510	.34735	2.43949	.38730	.91212	.96005	1.0963	.03995
1.55	2.24961	.35211	2.46186	.39126	0.91379	.96084	1.0943	.03916
1.56	2.27434	.35686	2.48448	.39524	.91542	.96162	1.0924	.03838
1.57	2.29930	.36160	2.50735	.39921	.91703	.96238	1.0905	.03762
1.58	2.32449	.36633	2.53047	.40320	.91860	.96313	1.0886	.03687
1.59	2.34991	.37105	2.55384	.40719	.92015	.96386	1.0868	.03614
1.60	2.37557	.37577	2.57746	.41119	0.92167	.96457	1.0850	.03543
1.61	2.40146	.38048	2.60135	.41520	.92316	.96528	1.0832	.03472
1.62	2.42760	.38518	2.62549	.41921	.92462	.96597	1.0815	.03403
1.63	2.45397	.38987	2.64990	.42323	.92606	.96664	1.0798	.03336
1.64	2.48059	.39456	2.67457	.42725	.92747	.96730	1.0782	.03270
1.65	2.50746	.39923	2.69951	.43129	0.92886	.96795	1.0766	.03205
1.66	2.53459	.40391	2.72472	.43532	.93022	.96858	1.0750	.03142
1.67	2.56196	.40857	2.75021	.43937	.93155	.96921	1.0735	.03079
1.68	2.58959	.41323	2.77596	.44341	.93286	.96982	1.0720	.03018
1.69	2.61748	.41788	2.80200	.44747	.93415	.97042	1.0705	.02958
1.70	2.64563	.42253	2.82832	.45153	0.93541	.97100	1.0691	.02900
1.71	2.67405	.42717	2.85491	.45559	.93665	.97158	1.0676	.02842
1.72	2.70273	.43180	2.88180	.45966	.93786	.97214	1.0663	.02786
1.73	2.73168	.43643	2.90897	.46374	.93906	.97269	1.0649	.02731
1.74	2.76091	.44105	2.93643	.46782	.94023	.97323	1.0636	.02677
1.75	2.79041	.44567	2.96419	.47191	0.94138	.97376	1.0623	.02624
1.76	2.82020	.45028	2.99224	.47600	.94250	.97428	1.0610	.02572
1.77	2.85026	.45488	3.02059	.48009	.94361	.97479	1.0598	.02521
1.78	2.88061	.45948	3.04925	.48419	.94470	.97529	1.0585	.02471
1.79	2.91125	.46408	3.07821	.48830	.94576	.97578	1.0574	.02422
1.80	2.94217	.46867	3.10747	.49241	0.94681	.97626	1.0562	.02374
1.81	2.97340	.47325	3.13705	.49652	.94783	.97673	1.0550	.02327
1.82	3.00492	.47783	3.16694	.50064	.94884	.97719	1.0539	.02281
1.83	3.03674	.48241	3.19715	.50476	.94983	.97764	1.0528	.02236
1.84	3.06886	.48698	3.22768	.50889	.95080	.97809	1.0518	.02191
1.85	3.10129	.49154	3.25853	.51302	0.95175	.97852	1.0507	.02148
1.86	3.13403	.49610	3.28970	.51716	.95268	.97895	1.0497	.02105
1.87	3.16709	.50066	3.32121	.52130	.95359	.97936	1.0487	.02064
1.88	3.20046	.50521	3.35305	.52544	.95449	.97977	1.0477	.02023
1.89	3.23415	.50976	3.38522	.52959	.95537	.98017	1.0467	.01983
1.90	3.26816	.51430	3.41773	.53374	0.95624	.98057	1.0458	.01943
1.91	3.30250	.51884	3.45058	.53789	.95709	.98095	1.0448	.01905
1.92	3.33718	.52338	3.48378	.54205	.95792	.98133	1.0439	.01867
1.93	3.37218	.52791	3.51733	.54621	.95873	.98170	1.0430	.01830
1.94	3.40752	.53244	3.55123	.55038	.95953	.98206	1.0422	.01794
1.95	3.44321	.53696	3.58548	.55455	0.96032	.98242	1.0413	.01758
1.96	3.47923	.54148	3.62009	.55872	.96109	.98276	1.0405	.01724
1.97	3.51561	.54600	3.65507	.56290	.96185	.98311	1.0397	.01689
1.98	3.55234	.55051	3.69041	.56707	.96259	.98344	1.0389	.01656
1.99	3.58942	.55502	3.72611	.57126	.96331	.98377	1.0381	.01623
2.00	3.62686	.55953	3.76220	.57544	0.96403	.98409	1.0373	.01591

The logarithms given below show the mantissa only.   The proper characteristic must be added

x	Sinh x Value	Sinh x Log₁₀	Cosh x Value	Cosh x Log₁₀	Tanh x Value	Tanh x Log₁₀	Coth x Value	Coth x Log₁₀
2.00	3.62686	.55953	3.76220	.57544	0.96403	.98409	1.0373	.01591
2.01	3.66466	.56403	3.79865	.57963	.96473	.98440	1.0366	.01560
2.02	3.70283	.56853	3.83549	.58382	.96541	.98471	1.0358	.01529
2.03	3.74138	.57303	3.87271	.58802	.96609	.98502	1.0351	.01498
2.04	3.78029	.57753	3.91032	.59221	.96675	.98531	1.0344	.01469
2.05	3.81958	.58202	3.94832	.59641	0.96740	.98560	1.0337	.01440
2.06	3.85926	.58650	3.98671	.60061	.96803	.98589	1.0330	.01411
2.07	3.89932	.59099	4.02550	.60482	.96865	.98617	1.0324	.01383
2.08	3.93977	.59547	4.06470	.60903	.96926	.98644	1.0317	.01356
2.09	3.98061	.59995	4.10430	.61324	.96986	.98671	1.0311	.01329
2.10	4.02186	.60443	4.14431	.61745	0.97045	.98697	1.0304	.01303
2.11	4.06350	.60890	4.18474	.62167	.97103	.98723	1.0298	.01277
2.12	4.10555	.61337	4.22558	.62589	.97159	.98748	1.0292	.01252
2.13	4.14801	.61784	4.26685	.63011	.97215	.98773	1.0286	.01227
2.14	4.19089	.62231	4.30855	.63433	.97269	.98798	1.0281	.01202
2.15	4.23419	.62677	.4.35067	.63856	0.97323	.98821	1.0275	.01179
2.16	4.27791	.63123	4.39323	.64278	.97375	.98845	1.0270	.01155
2.17	4.32205	.63569	4.43623	.64701	.97426	.98868	1.0264	.01132
2.18	4.36663	.64015	4.47967	.65125	.97477	.98890	1.0259	.01110
2.19	4.41165	.64460	4.52356	.65548	.97526	.98912	1.0254	.01088
2.20	4.45711	.64905	4.56791	.65972	0.97574	.98934	1.0249	.01066
2.21	4.50301	.65350	4.61271	.66396	.97622	.98955	1.0244	.01045
2.22	4.54936	.65795	4.65797	.66820	.97668	.98975	1.0239	.01025
2.23	4.59617	.66240	4.70370	.67244	.97714	.98996	1.0234	.01004
2.24	4.64344	.66684	4.74989	.67668	.97759	.99016	1.0229	.00984
2.25	4.69117	.67128	4.79657	.68093	0.97803	.99035	1.0225	.00965
2.26	4.73937	.67572	4.84372	.68518	.97846	.99054	1.0220	.00946
2.27	4.78804	.68016	4.89136	.68943	.97888	.99073	1.0216	.00927
2.28	4.83720	.68459	4.93948	.69368	.97929	.99091	1.0211	.00909
2.29	4.88684	.68903	4.98810	.69794	.97970	.99109	1.0207	.00891
2.30	4.93696	.69346	5.03722	.70219	0.98010	.99127	1.0203	.00873
2.31	4.98758	.69789	5.08684	.70645	.98049	.99144	1.0199	.00856
2.32	5.03870	.70232	5.13697	.71071	.98087	.99161	1.0195	.00839
2.33	5.09032	.70675	5.18762	.71497	.98124	.99178	1.0191	.00822
2.34	5.14245	.71117	5.23878	.71923	.98161	.99194	1.0187	.00806
2.35	5.19510	.71559	5.29047	.72349	0.98197	.99210	1.0184	.00790
2.36	5.24827	.72002	5.34269	.72776	.98233	.99226	1.0180	.00774
2.37	5.30196	.72444	5.39544	.73203	.98267	.99241	1.0176	.00759
2.38	5.35618	.72885	5.44873	.73630	.98301	.99256	1.0173	.00744
2.39	5.41093	.73327	.5.50256	.74056	.98335	.99271	1.0169	.00729
2.40	5.46623	.73769	5.55695	.74484	0.98367	.99285	1.0166	.00715
2.41	5.52207	.74210	5.61189	.74911	.98400	.99299	1.0163	.00701
2.42	5.57847	.74652	5.66739	.75338	.98431	.99313	1.0159	.00687
2.43	5.63542	.75093	5.72346	.75766	.98462	.99327	1.0156	.00673
2.44	5.69294	.75534	5.78010	.76194	.98492	.99340	1.0153	.00660
2.45	5.75103	.75975	5.83732	.76621	0.98522	.99353	1.0150	.00647
2.46	5.80969	.76415	5.89512	.77049	.98551	.99366	1.0147	.00634
2.47	5.86893	.76856	5.95352	.77477	.98579	.99379	1.0144	.00621
2.48	5.92876	.77296	6.01250	.77906	.98607	.99391	1.0141	.00609
2.49	5.98918	.77737	6.07209	.78334	.98635	.99403	1.0138	.00597
2.50	6.05020	.78177	6.13229	.78762	0.98661	.99415	1.0136	.00585

HYPERBOLIC FUNCTIONS (Continued)

The logarithms given below show the mantissa only. The proper characteristic must be added.

x	Sinh x Value	Log₁₀	Cosh x Value	Log₁₀	Tanh x Value	Log₁₀	Coth x Value	Log₁₀
2.50	6.05020	.78177	6.13229	.78762	0.98661	.99415	1.0136	.00585
2.51	6.11183	.78617	6.19310	.79191	.98688	.99426	1.0133	.00574
2.52	6.17407	.79057	6.25453	.79619	.98714	.99438	1.0130	.00562
2.53	6.23692	.79497	6.31658	.80048	.98739	.99449	1.0128	.00551
2.54	6.30040	.79937	6.37927	.80477	.98764	.99460	1.0125	.00540
2.55	6.36451	.80377	6.44259	.80906	0.98788	.99470	1.0123	.00530
2.56	6.42926	.80816	6.50656	.81335	.98812	.99481	1.0120	.00519
2.57	6.49464	.81256	6.57118	.81764	.98835	.99491	1.0118	.00509
2.58	6.56068	.81695	6.63646	.82194	.98858	.99501	1.0115	.00499
2.59	6.62738	.82134	6.70240	.82623	.98881	.99511	1.0113	.00489
2.60	6.69473	.82573	6.76901	.83052	0.98903	.99521	1.0111	.00479
2.61	6.76276	.83012	6.83629	.83482	.98924	.99530	1.0109	.00470
2.62	6.83146	.83451	6.90426	.83912	.98946	.99540	1.0107	.00460
2.63	6.90085	.83890	6.97292	.84341	.98966	.99549	1.0104	.00451
2.64	6.97092	.84329	7.04228	.84771	.98987	.99558	1.0102	.00442
2.65	7.04169	.84768	7.11234	.85201	0.99007	.99566	1.0100	.00434
2.66	7.11317	.85206	7.18312	.85631	.99026	.99575	1.0098	.00425
2.67	7.18536	.85645	7.25461	.86061	.99045	.99583	1.0096	.00417
2.68	7.25827	.86083	7.32683	.86492	.99064	.99592	1.0094	.00408
2.69	7.33190	.86522	7.39978	.86922	.99083	.99600	1.0093	.00400
2.70	7.40626	.86960	7.47347	.87352	0.99101	.99608	1.0091	.00392
2.71	7.48137	.87398	7.54791	.87783	.99118	.99615	1.0089	.00385
2.72	7.55722	.87836	7.62310	.88213	.99136	.99623	1.0087	.00377
2.73	7.63383	.88274	7.69905	.88644	.99153	.99631	1.0085	.00369
2.74	7.71121	.88712	7.77578	.89074	.99170	.99638	1.0084	.00362
2.75	7.78935	.89150	7.85328	.89505	0.99186	.99645	1.0082	.00355
2.76	7.86828	.89588	7.93157	.89936	.99202	.99652	1.0080	.00348
2.77	7.94799	.90026	8.01065	.90367	.99218	.99659	1.0079	.00341
2.78	8.02849	.90463	8.09053	.90798	.99233	.99666	1.0077	.00334
2.79	8.10980	.90901	8.17122	.91229	.99248	.99672	1.0076	.00328
2.80	8.19192	.91339	8.25273	.91660	0.99263	.99679	1.0074	.00321
2.81	8.27486	.91776	8.33506	.92091	.99278	.99685	1.0073	.00315
2.82	8.35862	.92213	8.41823	.92522	.99292	.99691	1.0071	.00309
2.83	8.44322	.92651	8.50224	.92953	.99306	.99698	1.0070	.00302
2.84	8.52867	.93088	8.58710	.93385	.99320	.99704	1.0069	.00296
2.85	8.61497	.93525	8.67281	.93816	0.99333	.99709	1.0067	.00291
2.86	8.70213	.93963	8.75940	.94247	.99346	.99715	1.0066	.00285
2.87	8.79016	.94400	8.84686	.94679	.99359	.99721	1.0065	.00279
2.88	8.87907	.94837	8.93520	.95110	.99372	.99726	1.0063	.00274
2.89	8.96887	.95274	9.02444	.95542	.99384	.99732	1.0062	.00268
2.90	9.05956	.95711	9.11458	.95974	0.99396	.99737	1.0061	.00263
2.91	9.15116	.96148	9.20564	.96405	.99408	.99742	1.0060	.00258
2.92	9.24368	.96584	9.29761	.96837	.99420	.99747	1.0058	.00253
2.93	9.33712	.97021	9.39051	.97269	.99431	.99752	1.0057	.00248
2.94	9.43149	.97458	9.48436	.97701	.99443	.99757	1.0056	.00243
2.95	9.52681	.97895	9.57915	.98133	0.99454	.99762	1.0055	.00238
2.96	9.62308	.98331	9.67490	.98565	.99464	.99767	1.0054	.00233
2.97	9.72031	.98768	9.77161	.98997	.99475	.99771	1.0053	.00229
2.98	9.81851	.99205	9.86930	.99429	.99485	.99776	1.0052	.00224
2.99	9.91770	.99641	9.96798	.99861	.99496	.99780	1.0051	.00220
3.00	10.01787	.00078	10.06766	.00293	0.99505	.99785	1.0050	.00215

HYPERBOLIC FUNCTIONS (Continued)

The logarithms given below show the mantissa only.   The proper characteristic must be added.

x	Sinh x Value	Log₁₀	Cosh x Value	Log₁₀	Tanh x Value	Log₁₀	Coth x Value	Log₁₀
3.0	10.0179	.00078	10.0677	.00293	0.99505	.99785	1.0050	.00215
3.1	11.0765	.04440	11.1215	.04616	.99595	.99824	1.0041	.00176
3.2	12.2459	.08799	12.2866	.08943	.99668	.99856	1.0033	.00144
3.3	13.5379	.13155	13.5748	.13273	.99728	.99882	1.0027	.00118
3.4	14.9654	.17509	14.9987	.17605	.99777	.99903	1.0022	.00097
3.5	16.5426	.21860	16.5728	.21940	0.99818	.99921	1.0018	.00079
3.6	18.2855	.26211	18.3128	.26275	.99851	.99935	1.0015	.00065
3.7	20.2113	.30559	20.2360	.30612	.99878	.99947	1.0012	.00053
3.8	22.3394	.34907	22.3618	.34951	.99900	.99957	1.0010	.00043
3.9	24.6911	.39254	24.7113	.39290	.99918	.99964	1.0008	.00036
4.0	27.2899	.43600	27.3082	.43629	0.99933	.99971	1.0007	.00029
4.1	30.1619	.47946	30.1784	.47970	.99945	.99976	1.0005	.00024
4.2	33.3357	.52291	33.3507	.52310	.99955	.99980	1.0004	.00020
4.3	36.8431	.56636	36.8567	.56652	.99963	.99984	1.0004	.00016
4.4	40.7193	.60980	40.7316	.60993	.99970	.99987	1.0003	.00013
4.5	45.0030	.65324	45.0141	.65335	0.99975	.99989	1.0002	.00011
4.6	49.7371	.69668	49.7472	.69677	.99980	.99991	1.0002	.00009
4.7	54.9690	.74012	54.9781	.74019	.99983	.99993	1.0002	.00007
4.8	60.7511	.78355	60.7593	.78361	.99986	.99994	1.0001	.00006
4.9	67.1412	.82699	67.1486	.82704	.99989	.99995	1.0001	.00005
5.0	74.2032	.87042	74.2099	.87046	0.99991	.99996	1.0001	.00004
5.1	82.008	.91386	82.014	.91389	.99993	.99997	1.0001	.00003
5.2	90.633	.95729	90.639	.95732	.99994	.99997	1.0001	.00003
5.3	100.17	.00074	100.17	.00074	.99995	.99998	1.0000	.00002
5.4	110.70	.04415	110.71	.04419	.99996	.99998	1.0000	.00002
5.5	122.34	.08757	122.35	.08760	0.99997	.99999	1.0000	.00001
5.6	135.21	.13101	135.22	.13104	.99997	.99999	1.0000	.00001
5.7	149.43	.17444	149.44	.17447	.99998	.99999	1.0000	.00001
5.8	165.15	.21788	165.15	.21788	.99998	.99999	1.0000	.00001
5.9	182.52	.26131	182.52	.26131	.99998	.99999	1.0000	.00001
6.0	201.71	.30473	201.72	.30475	0.99999	.00000	1.0000	.00000
6.1	222.93	.34817	222.93	.34817	.99999	.00000	1.0000	.00000
6.2	246.37	.39159	246.38	.39161	.99999	.00000	1.0000	.00000
6.3	272.29	.43503	272.29	.43503	.99999	.00000	1.0000	.00000
6.4	300.92	.47845	300.92	.47845	.99999	.00000	1.0000	.00000
6.5	332.57	.52188	332.57	.52188	1.0000	.00000	1.0000	.00000
6.6	367.55	.56532	367.55	.56532	1.0000	.00000	1.0000	.00000
6.7	406.20	.60874	406.20	.60874	1.0000	.00000	1.0000	.00000
6.8	448.92	.65217	448.92	.65217	1.0000	.00000	1.0000	.00000
6.9	496.14	.69560	496.14	.69560	1.0000	.00000	1.0000	.00000
7.0	548.32	.73903	548.32	.73903	1.0000	.00000	1.0000	.00000
7.1	605.98	.78246	605.98	.78246	1.0000	.00000	1.0000	.00000
7.2	669.72	.82589	669.72	.82589	1.0000	.00000	1.0000	.00000
7.3	740.15	.86932	740.15	.86932	1.0000	.00000	1.0000	.00000
7.4	817.99	.91275	817.99	.91275	1.0000	.00000	1.0000	.00000
7.5	904.02	.95618	904.02	.95618	1.0000	.00000	1.0000	.00000
7.6	999.10	.99961	999.10	.99961	1.0000	.00000	1.0000	.00000
7.7	1104.2	.04305	1104.2	.04305	1.0000	.00000	1.0000	.00000
7.8	1220.3	.08647	1220.3	.08647	1.0000	.00000	1.0000	.00000
7.9	1348.6	.12988	1348.6	.12988	1.0000	.00000	1.0000	.00000
8.0	1490.5	.17333	1490.5	.17333	1.0000	.00000	1.0000	.00000
8.1	1647.2	.21675	1647.2	.21675	1.0000	.00000	1.0000	.00000
8.2	1820.5	.26019	1820.5	.26019	1.0000	.00000	1.0000	.00000
8.3	2011.9	.30360	2011.9	.30360	1.0000	.00000	1.0000	.00000
8.4	2223.5	.34704	2223.5	.34704	1.0000	.00000	1.0000	.00000
8.5	2457.4	.39048	2457.4	.39048	1.0000	.00000	1.0000	.00000

The logarithms given below show the mantissa only.   The proper characteristic must be added.

x	Sinh x Value	Log₁₀	Cosh x Value	Log₁₀	Tanh x Value	Log₁₀	Coth x Value	Log₁₀
8.5	2457.4	.39048	2457.4	.39048	1.0000	.00000	1.0000	.00000
8.6	2715.8	.43390	2715.8	.43390	1.0000	.00000	1.0000	.00000
8.7	3001.5	.47734	3001.5	.47734	1.0000	.00000	1.0000	.00000
8.8	3317.1	.52076	3317.1	.52076	1.0000	.00000	1.0000	.00000
8.9	3666.0	.56419	3666.0	.56419	1.0000	.00000	1.0000	.00000
9.0	4051.5	.60762	4051.5	.60762	1.0000	.00000	1.0000	.00000
9.1	4477.6	.65105	4477.6	.65105	1.0000	.00000	1.0000	.00000
9.2	4948.6	.69448	4948.6	.69448	1.0000	.00000	1.0000	.00000
9.3	5469.0	.73791	5469.0	.73791	1.0000	.00000	1.0000	.00000
9.4	6044.2	.78134	6044.2	.78134	1.0000	.00000	1.0000	.00000
9.5	6679.9	.82477	6679.9	.82477	1.0000	.00000	1.0000	.00000
9.6	7382.4	.86820	7382.4	.86820	1.0000	.00000	1.0000	.00000
9.7	8158.8	.91163	8158.8	.91163	1.0000	.00000	1.0000	.00000
9.8	9016.9	.95506	9016.9	.95506	1.0000	.00000	1.0000	.00000
9.9	9965.2	.99849	9965.2	.99849	1.0000	.00000	1.0000	.00000
10.0	11013.2	.04191	11013.2	.04191	1.0000	.0000	1.0000	.00000

FACTORIALS, EXACT VALUES AND RECIPROCALS

n	$n!$	n	$n!$	n	$\dfrac{1}{n!}$	n	$\dfrac{1}{n!}$
1	1	11	39916800	1	1.	11	$.25052 \times 10^{-7}$
2	2	12	479001600	2	0.5	12	$.20877 \times 10^{-8}$
3	6	13	6227020800	3	.16667	13	$.16059 \times 10^{-9}$
4	24	14	87178291200	4	$.41667 \times 10^{-1}$	14	$.11471 \times 10^{-10}$
5	120	15	1307674368000	5	$.83333 \times 10^{-2}$	15	$.76472 \times 10^{-12}$
6	720	16	20922789888000	6	$.13889 \times 10^{-2}$	16	$.47795 \times 10^{-13}$
7	5040	17	355687428096000	7	$.19841 \times 10^{-3}$	17	$.28115 \times 10^{-14}$
8	40320	18	6402373705728000	8	$.24802 \times 10^{-4}$	18	$.15619 \times 10^{-15}$
9	362880	19	121645100408832000	9	$.27557 \times 10^{-5}$	19	$.82206 \times 10^{-17}$
10	3628800	20	2432902008176640000	10	$.27557 \times 10^{-6}$	20	$.41103 \times 10^{-18}$

MILS—RADIANS—DEGREES

6400 mils = 360° = 2π radians
1 mil = 0.05625° = 3.375′ = 202.5″
1° = 17.777778 mils
1′ = 0.296296 mils

1000 mils = 56.25° = 0.98175 radians

1 mil = 0.00098175 radians
1 radian = 1018.6 mils

DEGREES—RADIANS

1 radian = 57° 17′ 44″.80625

	log
1 radian = 57.29577 95131 degrees	1.75812 26324
1 radian = 3437.74677 07849 minutes	3.53627 38828
1 radian = 206264.80625 seconds	5.31442 51332
1 degree = 0.01745 32925 19943 radians	8.24187 73676-10
1 minute = 0.00029 08882 08666 radians	6.46372 61172-10
1 second = 0.00000 48481 36811 radians	4.68557 48668-10

DEGREES—RADIANS

The table gives in radians the angle which is expressed in degrees and minutes at the side and top. Angles expressed to the nearest minute and second can readily be converted to radians by adding to the equivalent of the whole number of degrees the equivalents of the minutes and seconds found on the third page of this table.

°	00′	10	20	30	40	50
0	0.00000	0.00291	0.00582	0.00873	0.01164	0.01454
1	0.01745	0.02036	0.02327	0.02618	0.02909	0.03200
2	0.03491	0.03782	0.04072	0.04363	0.04654	0.04945
3	0.05236	0.05527	0.05818	0.06109	0.06400	0.06690
4	0.06981	0.07272	0.07563	0.07854	0.08145	0.08436
5	0.08727	0.09018	0.09308	0.09599	0.09890	0.10181
6	0.10472	0.10763	0.11054	0.11345	0.11636	0.11926
7	0.12217	0.12508	0.12799	0.13090	0.13381	0.13672
8	0.13963	0.14254	0.14544	0.14835	0.15126	0.15417
9	0.15708	0.15999	0.16290	0.16581	0.16872	0.17162
10	0.17453	0.17744	0.18035	0.18326	0.18617	0.18908
11	0.19199	0.19490	0.19780	0.20071	0.20362	0.20653
12	0.20944	0.21235	0.21526	0.21817	0.22108	0.22398
13	0.22689	0.22980	0.23271	0.23562	0.23853	0.24144
14	0.24435	0.24725	0.25016	0.25307	0.25598	0.25889
15	0.26180	0.26471	0.26762	0.27053	0.27343	0.27634
16	0.27925	0.28216	0.28507	0.28798	0.29089	0.29380
17	0.29671	0.29961	0.30252	0.30543	0.30834	0.31125
18	0.31416	0.31707	0.31998	0.32289	0.32579	0.32870
19	0.33161	0.33452	0.33743	0.34034	0.34325	0.34616
20	0.34907	0.35197	0.35488	0.35779	0.36070	0.36361
21	0.36652	0.36943	0.37234	0.37525	0.37815	0.38106
22	0.38397	0.38688	0.38979	0.39270	0.39561	0.39852
23	0.40143	0.40433	0.40724	0.41015	0.41306	0.41597
24	0.41888	0.42179	0.42470	0.42761	0.43051	0.43342
25	0.43633	0.43924	0.44215	0.44506	0.44797	0.45088
26	0.45379	0.45669	0.45960	0.46251	0.46542	0.46833
27	0.47124	0.47415	0.47706	0.47997	0.48287	0.48578
28	0.48869	0.49160	0.49451	0.49742	0.50033	0.50324
29	0.50615	0.50905	0.51196	0.51487	0.51778	0.52069
30	0.52360	0.52651	0.52942	0.53233	0.53523	0.53814
31	0.54105	0.54396	0.54687	0.54978	0.55269	0.55560
32	0.55851	0.56141	0.56432	0.56723	0.57014	0.57305
33	0.57596	0.57887	0.58178	0.58469	0.58759	0.59050
34	0.59341	0.59632	0.59923	0.60214	0.60505	0.60796
35	0.61087	0.61377	0.61668	0.61959	0.62250	0.62541
36	0.62832	0.63123	0.63414	0.63705	0.63995	0.64286
37	0.64577	0.64868	0.65159	0.65450	0.65741	0.66032
38	0.66323	0.66613	0.66904	0.67195	0.67486	0.67777
39	0.68068	0.68359	0.68650	0.68941	0.69231	0.69522
40	0.69813	0.70104	0.70395	0.70686	0.70977	0.71268
41	0.71558	0.71849	0.72140	0.72431	0.72722	0.73013
42	0.73304	0.73595	0.73886	0.74176	0.74467	0.74758
43	0.75049	0.75340	0.75631	0.75922	0.76213	0.76504
44	0.76794	0.77085	0.77376	0.77667	0.77958	0.78249
45	0.78540	0.78831	0.79122	0.79412	0.79703	0.79994
46	0.80285	0.80576	0.80867	0.81158	0.81449	0.81740
47	0.82030	0.82321	0.82612	0.82903	0.83194	0.83485
48	0.83776	0.84067	0.84358	0.84648	0.84939	0.85230
49	0.85521	0.85812	0.86103	0.86394	0.86685	0.86976
50	0.87266	0.87557	0.87848	0.88139	0.88430	0.88721
51	0.89012	0.89303	0.89594	0.89884	0.90175	0.90466
52	0.90757	0.91048	0.91339	0.91630	0.91921	0.92212
53	0.92502	0.92793	0.93084	0.93375	0.93666	0.93957
54	0.94248	0.94539	0.94830	0.95120	0.95411	0.95702
55	0.95993	0.96284	0.96575	0.96866	0.97157	0.97448
56	0.97738	0.98029	0.98320	0.98611	0.98902	0.99193
57	0.99484	0.99775	1.00066	1.00356	1.00647	1.00938
58	1.01229	1.01520	1.01811	1.02102	1.02393	1.02684
59	1.02974	1.03265	1.03556	1.03847	1.04138	1.04429
60	1.04720	1.05011	1.05302	1.05592	1.05883	1.06174

DEGREES—RADIANS

°	00′	10	20	30	40	50
60	1.04720	1.05011	1.05302	1.05592	1.05883	1.06174
61	1.06465	1.06756	1.07047	1.07338	1.07629	1.07920
62	1.08210	1.08501	1.08792	1.09083	1.09374	1.09665
63	1.09956	1.10247	1.10538	1.10828	1.11119	1.11410
64	1.11701	1.11992	1.12283	1.12574	1.12865	1.13156
65	1.13446	1.13737	1.14028	1.14319	1.14610	1.14901
66	1.15192	1.15483	1.15774	1.16064	1.16355	1.16646
67	1.16937	1.17228	1.17519	1.17810	1.18101	1.18392
68	1.18682	1.18973	1.19264	1.19555	1.19846	1.20137
69	1.20428	1.20719	1.21009	1.21300	1.21591	1.21882
70	1.22173	1.22464	1.22755	1.23046	1.23337	1.23627
71	1.23918	1.24209	1.24500	1.24791	1.25082	1.25373
72	1.25664	1.25955	1.26245	1.26536	1.26827	1.27118
73	1.27409	1.27700	1.27991	1.28282	1.28573	1.28863
74	1.29154	1.29445	1.29736	1.30027	1.30318	1.30609
75	1.30900	1.31191	1.31481	1.31772	1.32063	1.32354
76	1.32645	1.32936	1.33227	1.33518	1.33809	1.34099
77	1.34390	1.34681	1.34972	1.35263	1.35554	1.35845
78	1.36136	1.36427	1.36717	1.37008	1.37299	1.37590
79	1.37881	1.38172	1.38463	1.38754	1.39045	1.39335
80	1.39626	1.39917	1.40208	1.40499	1.40790	1.41081
81	1.41372	1.41663	1.41953	1.42244	1.42535	1.42826
82	1.43117	1.43408	1.43699	1.43990	1.44281	1.44571
83	1.44862	1.45153	1.45444	1.45735	1.46026	1.46317
84	1.46608	1.46899	1.47189	1.47480	1.47771	1.48062
85	1.48353	1.48644	1.48935	1.49226	1.49517	1.49807
86	1.50098	1.50389	1.50680	1.50971	1.51262	1.51553
87	1.51844	1.52135	1.52425	1.52716	1.53007	1.53298
88	1.53589	1.53880	1.54171	1.54462	1.54753	1.55043
89	1.55334	1.55625	1.55916	1.56207	1.56498	1.56789
90	1.57080	1.57371	1.57661	1.57952	1.58243	1.58534
91	1.58825	1.59116	1.59407	1.59698	1.59989	1.60279
92	1.60570	1.60861	1.61152	1.61443	1.61734	1.62025
93	1.62316	1.62607	1.62897	1.63188	1.63479	1.63770
94	1.64061	1.64352	1.64643	1.64934	1.65225	1.65515
95	1.65806	1.66097	1.66388	1.66679	1.66970	1.67261
96	1.67552	1.67842	1.68133	1.68424	1.68715	1.69006
97	1.69297	1.69588	1.69879	1.70170	1.70460	1.70751
98	1.71042	1.71333	1.71624	1.71915	1.72206	1.72497
99	1.72788	1.73078	1.73369	1.73660	1.73951	1.74242
100	1.74533	1.74824	1.75115	1.75406	1.75696	1.75987
101	1.76278	1.76569	1.76860	1.77151	1.77442	1.77733
102	1.78024	1.78314	1.78605	1.78896	1.79187	1.79478
103	1.79769	1.80060	1.80351	1.80642	1.80932	1.81223
104	1.81514	1.81805	1.82096	1.82387	1.82678	1.82969
105	1.83260	1.83550	1.83841	1.84132	1.84423	1.84714
106	1.85004	1.85296	1.85587	1.85878	1.86168	1.86459
107	1.86750	1.87041	1.87332	1.87623	1.87914	1.88205
108	1.88496	1.88786	1.89077	1.89368	1.89659	1.89950
109	1.90241	1.90532	1.90823	1.91114	1.91404	1.91695
110	1.91986	1.92277	1.92568	1.92859	1.93150	1.93441
111	1.93732	1.94022	1.94313	1.94604	1.94895	1.95186
112	1.95477	1.95768	1.96059	1.96350	1.96640	1.96931
113	1.97222	1.97513	1.97804	1.98095	1.98386	1.98677
114	1.98968	1.99258	1.99549	1.99840	2.00131	2.00422
115	2.00713	2.01004	2.01295	2.01586	2.01876	2.02167
116	2.02458	2.02749	2.03040	2.03331	2.03622	2.03913
117	2.04204	2.04494	2.04785	2.05076	2.05367	2.05658
118	2.05949	2.06240	2.06531	2.06822	2.07112	2.07403
119	2.07694	2.07985	2.08276	2.08567	2.08858	2.09149
120	2.09440	2.09730	2.10021	2.10312	2.10603	2.10894

DEGREES—RADIANS

Deg.	Radians	Deg.	Radians	Min.	Radians	Sec.	Radians
90	1.57080	**150**	2.61799	**0**	0.00000	**0**	0.00000
91	1.58825	151	2.63545	1	0.00029	1	0.00000
92	1.60570	152	2.65290	2	0.00058	2	0.00001
93	1.62316	153	2.67035	3	0.00087	3	0.00001
94	1.64061	154	2.68781	4	0.00116	4	0.00002
95	1.65806	**155**	2.70526	**5**	0.00145	**5**	0.00002
96	1.67552	156	2.72271	6	0.00175	6	0.00003
97	1.69297	157	2.74017	7	0.00204	7	0.00003
98	1.71042	158	2.75762	8	0.00233	8	0.00004
99	1.72788	159	2.77507	9	0.00262	9	0.00004
100	1.74533	**160**	2.79253	**10**	0.00291	**10**	0.00005
101	1.76278	161	2.80998	11	0.00320	11	0.00005
102	1.78024	162	2.82743	12	0.00349	12	0.00006
103	1.79769	163	2.84489	13	0.00378	13	0.00006
104	1.81514	164	2.86234	14	0.00407	14	0.00007
105	1.83260	**165**	2.87979	**15**	0.00436	**15**	0.00007
106	1.85005	166	2.89725	16	0.00465	16	0.00008
107	1.86750	167	2.91470	17	0.00495	17	0.00008
108	1.88496	168	2.93215	18	0.00524	18	0.00009
109	1.90241	169	2.94961	19	0.00553	19	0.00009
110	1.91986	**170**	2.96706	**20**	0.00582	**20**	0.00010
111	1.93732	171	2.98451	21	0.00611	21	0.00010
112	1.95477	172	3.00197	22	0.00640	22	0.00011
113	1.97222	173	3.01942	23	0.00669	23	0.00011
114	1.98968	174	3.03687	24	0.00698	24	0.00012
115	2.00713	**175**	3.05433	**25**	0.00727	**25**	0.00012
116	2.02458	176	3.07178	26	0.00756	26	0.00013
117	2.04204	177	3.08923	27	0.00785	27	0.00013
118	2.05949	178	3.10669	28	0.00814	28	0.00014
119	2.07694	179	3.12414	29	0.00844	29	0.00014
120	2.09440	**180**	3.14159	**30**	0.00873	**30**	0.00015
121	2.11185	190	3.31613	31	0.00902	31	0.00015
122	2.12930	200	3.49066	32	0.00931	32	0.00016
123	2.14676	210	3.66519	33	0.00960	33	0.00016
124	2.16421	220	3.83972	34	0.00989	34	0.00016
125	2.18166	**230**	4.01426	**35**	0.01018	**35**	0.00017
126	2.19911	240	4.18879	36	0.01047	36	0.00017
127	2.21657	250	4.36332	37	0.01076	37	0.00018
128	2.23402	260	4.53786	38	0.01105	38	0.00018
129	2.25147	270	4.71239	39	0.01134	39	0.00019
130	2.26893	**280**	4.88692	**40**	0.01164	**40**	0.00019
131	2.28638	290	5.06145	41	0.01193	41	0.00020
132	2.30383	300	5.23599	42	0.01222	42	0.00020
133	2.32129	310	5.41052	43	0.01251	43	0.00021
134	2.33874	320	5.58505	44	0.01280	44	0.00021
135	2.35619	**330**	5.75959	**45**	0.01309	**45**	0.00022
136	2.37365	340	5.93412	46	0.01338	46	0.00022
137	2.39110	350	6.10865	47	0.01367	47	0.00023
138	2.40855	360	6.28319	48	0.01396	48	0.00023
139	2.42601	370	6.45772	49	0.01425	49	0.00024
140	2.44346	**380**	6.63225	**50**	0.01454	**50**	0.00024
141	2.46091	390	6.80678	51	0.01484	51	0.00025
142	2.47837	400	6.98132	52	0.01513	52	0.00025
143	2.49582	410	7.15585	53	0.01542	53	0.00026
144	2.51327	420	7.33038	54	0.01571	54	0.00026
145	2.53073	**430**	7.50492	**55**	0.01600	**55**	0.00027
146	2.54818	440	7.67945	56	0.01629	56	0.00027
147	2.56563	450	7.85398	57	0.01658	57	0.00028
148	2.58309	460	8.02851	58	0.01687	58	0.00028
149	2.60054	470	8.20305	59	0.01716	59	0.00029
150	2.61799	**480**	8.37758	**60**	0.01745	**60**	0.00029

DEGREES, MINUTES, AND SECONDS TO RADIANS

Units in degrees, minutes *or* seconds	Degrees to Radians	Minutes to Radians	Seconds to Radians
10	0.174 5329	0.002 9089	0.000 0485
20	0.349 0659	0.005 8178	0.000 0970
30	0.523 5988	0.008 7266	0.000 1454
40	0.698 1317	0.011 6355	0.000 1939
50	0.872 6646	0.014 5444	0.000 2424
60	1.047 1976	0.017 4533	0.000 2909
70	1.221 7305	(0.020 3622)	(0.000 3394)
80	1.396 2634	(0.023 2711)	(0.000 3879)
90	1.570 7963	(0.026 1800)	(0.000 4364)
100	1.745 3293	. . . .	. . . .
200	3.490 6585	. . . .	. . . .
300	5.235 9878	. . . .	. . . .

where n = 1, 2, 3, 4, etc.   n(100) = n(1.745 3293)

RADIANS TO DEGREES, MINUTES, AND SECONDS

Radians	1.0	0.1	0.01	1.00¹	0.0001
1	57° 17′ 44.8″	5° 43′ 46.5″	0° 34′ 22.6″	0° 03′ 26.3″	0° 00′ 20.6″
2	114° 35′ 29.6″	11° 27′ 33.0″	1° 08′ 45.3″	0° 06′ 52.5″	0° 00′ 41.3″
3	171° 53′ 14.4″	17° 11′ 19.4″	1° 43′ 07.9″	0° 10′ 18.8″	0° 01′ 01.9″
4	229° 10′ 59.2″	22° 55′ 05.9″	2° 17′ 30.6″	0° 13′ 45.1″	0° 01′ 22.5″
5	286° 28′ 44.0″	28° 38′ 52.4″	2° 51′ 53.2″	0° 17′ 11.3″	0° 01′ 43.1″
6	343° 46′ 28.8″	34° 22′ 38.9″	3° 26′ 15.9″	0° 20′ 37.6″	0° 02′ 03.8″
7	401° 04′ 13.6″	40° 06′ 25.4″	4° 00′ 38.5″	0° 24′ 03.9″	0° 02′ 24.4″
8	458° 21′ 58.4″	45° 50′ 11.8″	4° 35′ 01.2″	0° 27′ 30.1″	0° 02′ 45.0″
9	515° 39′ 43.3″	51° 33′ 58.3″	5° 09′ 23.8″	0° 30′ 56.4″	0° 03′ 05.6″

DEGREES AND DECIMAL FRACTIONS TO RADIANS

The table below facilitates conversion of an angle expressed in degrees and decimal fractions into radians. To convert 25.78 into radians, find the equivalents, successively, of 20°, 5°, 0°.7, 0°.08 and add.

Deg.	Radians	Deg.	Radians	Deg.	Radians	Deg.	Radians	Deg.	Radians
10	0.174533	1	0.017453	0.1	0.001745	0.01	0.000175	0.001	0.000017
20	0.349066	2	.034907	.2	.003491	.02	.000349	.002	.000035
30	0.523599	3	.052360	.3	.005236	.03	.000524	.003	.000052
40	0.698132	4	.069813	.4	.006981	.04	.000698	.004	.000070
50	0.872665	5	.087266	.5	.008727	.05	.000873	.005	.000087
60	1.047198	6	.104720	.6	.010472	.06	.001047	.006	.000105
70	1.221730	7	.122173	.7	.012217	.07	.001222	.007	.000122
80	1.396263	8	.139626	.8	.013963	.08	.001396	.008	.000140
90	1.570796	9	.157080	.9	.015708	.09	.001571	.009	.000157

RADIANS TO DEGREES AND DECIMALS

Radians	Degrees	Radians	Degrees	Radians	Degrees	Radians	Degrees
1	57.2958	0.1	5.7296	0.01	0.5730	0.001	0.0573
2	114.5916	.2	11.4592	.02	1.1459	.002	.1146
3	171.8873	.3	17.1887	.03	1.7189	.003	.1719
4	229.1831	.4	22.9183	.04	2.2918	.004	.2292
5	286.4789	.5	28.6479	.05	2.8648	.005	.2865
6	343.7747	.6	34.3775	.06	3.4377	.006	.3438
7	401.0705	.7	40.1070	.07	4.0107	.007	.4011
8	458.3662	.8	45.8366	.08	4.5837	.008	.4584
9	515.6620	.9	51.5662	.09	5.1566	.009	.5157
10	572.9578	1.0	57.2958	.10	5.7296	.010	.5730

RADIANS—DEGREES
Multiples and Fractions of π Radians in Degrees

Radians	Radians	Degrees	Radians	Radians	Degrees	Radians	Radians	Degrees
π	3.1416	180	$\pi/2$	1.5708	90	$2\pi/3$	2.0944	120
2π	6.2832	360	$\pi/3$	1.0472	60	$3\pi/4$	2.3562	135
3π	9.4248	540	$\pi/4$	0.7854	45	$5\pi/6$	2.6180	150
4π	12.5664	720	$\pi/5$	0.6283	36	$7\pi/6$	3.6652	210
5π	15.7080	900	$\pi/6$	0.5236	30	$5\pi/4$	3.9270	225
6π	18.8496	1080	$\pi/7$	0.4488	25.714	$4\pi/3$	4.1888	240
7π	21.9911	1260	$\pi/8$	0.3927	22.5	$3\pi/2$	4.7124	270
8π	25.1327	1440	$\pi/9$	0.3491	20	$5\pi/3$	5.2360	300
9π	28.2743	1620	$\pi/10$	0.3142	18	$7\pi/4$	5.4978	315
10π	31.4159	1800	$\pi/12$	0.2618	15	$11\pi/6$	5.7596	330

CONVERSION OF ANGLES FROM ARC TO TIME

Arc	Time	Arc	Time	Arc	Time	Arc	Time
°	h　　m	°	h　　m	″	s	″	s
′	m　　s	′	m　　s				
0	0　00	20	1　20	0	0.00	8	0.53
1	0　04	30	2　00	1	0.07	9	0.60
2	0　08	40	2　40	2	0.13	10	0.67
3	0　12	50	3　20	3	0.20	20	1.33
4	0　16	60	4　00	4	0.27	30	2.00
5	0　20	70	4　40	5	0.33	40	2.67
6	0　24	80	5　20	6	0.40	50	3.33
7	0　28	90	6　00	7	0.47	60	4.00
8	0　32	100	6　40				
9	0　36	200	13　20				
10	0　40	300	20　00				

MINUTES AND SECONDS TO DECIMAL PARTS OF A DEGREE

MINUTES AND SECONDS TO DECIMAL PARTS OF A DEGREE

Min.	Degrees	Sec.	Degrees
0	0.00000	0	0.00000
1	.01667	1	.00028
2	.03333	2	.00056
3	.05	3	.00083
4	.06667	4	.00111
5	.08333	5	.00139
6	.10	6	.00167
7	.11667	7	.00194
8	.13333	8	.00222
9	.15	9	.0025
10	0.16667	10	0.00278
11	.18333	11	.00306
12	.20	12	.00333
13	.21667	13	.00361
14	.23333	14	.00389
15	.25	15	.00417
16	.26667	16	.00444
17	.28333	17	.00472
18	.30	18	.005
19	.31667	19	.00528
20	0.33333	20	0.00556
21	.35	21	.00583
22	.36667	22	.00611
23	.38333	23	.00639
24	.40	24	.00667
25	.41667	25	.00694
26	.43333	26	.00722
27	.45	27	.0075
28	.46667	28	.00778
29	.48333	29	.00806
30	0.50	30	0.00833
31	.51667	31	.00861
32	.53333	32	.00889
33	.55	33	.00917
34	.56667	34	.00944
35	.58333	35	.00972
36	.60	36	.01
37	.61667	37	.01028
38	.63333	38	.01056
39	.65	39	.01083
40	0.66667	40	0.01111
41	.68333	41	.01139
42	.70	42	.01167
43	.71667	43	.01194
44	.73333	44	.01222
45	.75	45	.0125
46	.76667	46	.01278
47	.78333	47	.01306
48	.80	48	.01333
49	.81667	49	.01361
50	0.83333	50	0.01389
51	.85	51	.01417
52	.86667	52	.01444
53	.88333	53	.01472
54	.90	54	.015
55	.91667	55	.01528
56	.93333	56	.01556
57	.95	57	.01583
58	.96667	58	.01611
59	.98333	59	.01639
60	1.00	60	0.01667

DECIMAL PARTS OF A DEGREE TO MINUTES AND SECONDS

Deg.	'	"	Deg.	'	"
0.00	0	00	0.60	36	
.01	0	36	.61	36	36
.02	1	12	.62	37	12
.03	1	48	.63	37	48
.04	2	24	.64	38	24
.05	3		.65	39	
.06	3	36	.66	39	36
.07	4	12	.67	40	12
.08	4	48	.68	40	48
.09	5	24	.69	41	24
0.10	6		0.70	42	
.11	6	36	.71	42	36
.12	7	12	.72	43	12
.13	7	48	.73	43	48
.14	8	24	.74	44	24
.15	9		.75	45	
.16	9	36	.76	45	36
.17	10	12	.77	46	12
.18	10	48	.78	46	48
.19	11	24	.79	47	24
0.20	12		0.80	48	
.21	12	36	.81	48	36
.22	13	12	.82	49	12
.23	13	48	.83	49	48
.24	14	24	.84	50	24
.25	15		.85	51	
.26	15	36	.86	51	36
.27	16	12	.87	52	12
.28	16	48	.88	52	48
.29	17	24	.89	53	24
0.30	18		0.90	54	
.31	18	36	.91	54	36
.32	19	12	.92	55	12
.33	19	48	.93	55	48
.34	20	24	.94	56	24
.35	21		.95	57	
.36	21	36	.96	57	36
.37	22	12	.97	58	12
.38	22	48	.98	58	48
.39	23	24	.99	59	24
0.40	24		1.00	60	
.41	24	36			
.42	25	12			
.43	25	48			
.44	26	24			
.45	27				
.46	27	36			
.47	28	12			
.48	28	48			
.49	29	24			
0.50	30				
.51	30	36			
.52	31	12			
.53	31	48			
.54	32	24			
.55	33				
.56	33	36			
.57	34	12			
.58	34	48			
.59	35	24			
0.60	36				

Deg.	Sec.
0.000	0.0
.001	3.6
.002	7.2
.003	10.8
.004	14.4
.005	18.
.006	21.6
.007	25.2
.008	28.8
.009	32.4
0.010	36.

NUMERICAL TABLES
Reciprocals, Circumference and Area of Circles

As a matter of convenience, the values of $1000 \times (1/n)$ are given in the table. To obtain the actual value of the reciprocal, shift the decimal point three places to the left. Circumferences and areas of circles are given for the values of n as the diameter.

n	$1000\dfrac{1}{n}$	Circumference πn	Area $\dfrac{\pi n^2}{4}$	n	$1000\dfrac{1}{n}$	Circumference πn	Area $\dfrac{\pi n^2}{4}$
0	∞	0.000000	.0000000	50	20.00000	157.0796	1963.495
1	1000.000	3.141593	.7853982	51	19.60784	160.2212	2042.821
2	500.0000	6.283185	3.141593	52	19.23077	163.3628	2123.717
3	333.3333	9.424778	7.068583	53	18.86792	166.5044	2206.183
4	250.0000	12.56637	12.56637	54	18.51852	169.6460	2290.221
5	200.0000	15.70796	19.63495	55	18.18182	172.7876	2375.829
6	166.6667	18.84956	28.27433	56	17.85714	175.9292	2463.009
7	142.8571	21.99115	38.48451	57	17.54386	179.0708	2551.759
8	125.0000	25.13274	50.26548	58	17.24138	182.2124	2642.079
9	111.1111	28.27433	63.61725	59	16.94915	185.3540	2733.971
10	100.0000	31.41593	78.53982	60	16.66667	188.4956	2827.433
11	90.90909	34.55752	95.03318	61	16.39344	191.6372	2922.467
12	83.33333	37.69911	113.0973	62	16.12903	194.7787	3019.071
13	76.92308	40.84070	132.7323	63	15.87302	197.9203	3117.245
14	71.42857	43.98230	153.9380	64	15.62500	201.0619	3216.991
15	66.66667	47.12389	176.7146	65	15.38462	204.2035	3318.307
16	62.50000	50.26548	201.0619	66	15.15152	207.3451	3421.194
17	58.82353	53.40708	226.9801	67	14.92537	210.4867	3525.652
18	55.55556	56.54867	254.4690	68	14.70588	213.6283	3631.681
19	52.63158	59.69026	283.5287	69	14.49275	216.7699	3739.281
20	50.00000	62.83185	314.1593	70	14.28571	219.9115	3848.451
21	47.61905	65.97345	346.3606	71	14.08451	223.0531	3959.192
22	45.45455	69.11504	380.1327	72	13.88889	226.1947	4071.504
23	43.47826	72.25663	415.4756	73	13.69863	229.3363	4185.387
24	41.66667	75.39822	452.3893	74	13.51351	232.4779	4300.840
25	40.00000	78.53982	490.8739	75	13.33333	235.6194	4417.865
26	38.46154	81.68141	530.9292	76	13.15789	238.7610	4536.460
27	37.03704	84.82300	572.5553	77	12.98701	241.9026	4656.626
28	35.71429	87.96459	615.7522	78	12.82051	245.0442	4778.362
29	34.48276	91.10619	660.5199	79	12.65823	248.1858	4901.670
30	33.33333	94.24778	706.8583	80	12.50000	251.3274	5026.548
31	32.25806	97.38937	754.7676	81	12.34568	254.4690	5152.997
32	31.25000	100.5310	804.2477	82	12.19512	257.6106	5281.017
33	30.30303	103.6726	855.2986	83	12.04819	260.7522	5410.608
34	29.41176	106.8142	907.9203	84	11.90476	263.8938	5541.769
35	28.57143	109.9557	962.1128	85	11.76471	267.0354	5674.502
36	27.77778	113.0973	1017.876	86	11.62791	270.1770	5808.805
37	27.02703	116.2389	1075.210	87	11.49425	273.3186	5944.679
38	26.31579	119.3805	1134.115	88	11.36364	276.4602	6082.123
39	25.64103	122.5221	1194.591	89	11.23596	279.6017	6221.139
40	25.00000	125.6637	1256.637	90	11.11111	282.7433	6361.725
41	24.39024	128.8053	1320.254	91	10.98901	285.8849	6503.882
42	23.80952	131.9469	1385.442	92	10.86957	289.0265	6647.610
43	23.25581	135.0885	1452.201	93	10.75269	292.1681	6792.909
44	22.72727	138.2301	1520.531	94	10.63830	295.3097	6939.778
45	22.22222	141.3717	1590.431	95	10.52632	298.4513	7088.218
46	21.73913	144.5133	1661.903	96	10.41667	301.5929	7238.229
47	21.27660	147.6549	1734.945	97	10.30928	304.7345	7389.811
48	20.83333	150.7964	1809.557	98	10.20408	307.8761	7542.964
49	20.40816	153.9380	1885.741	99	10.10101	311.0177	7697.687
50	20.00000	157.0796	1963.495	100	10.00000	314.1593	7853.982

RECIPROCALS, CIRCUMFERENCE AND AREA OF CIRCLES

n	$1000\dfrac{1}{n}$	Circumference πn	Area $\dfrac{\pi n^2}{4}$	n	$1000\dfrac{1}{n}$	Circumference πn	Area $\dfrac{\pi n^2}{4}$
100	10.00000	314.1593	7853.982	**150**	6.666 667	471.2389	17671.46
101	9.900 990	317.3009	8011.847	151	6.622 517	474.3805	17907.86
102	9.803 922	320.4425	8171.282	152	6.578 947	477.5221	18145.84
103	9.708 738	323.5840	8332.289	153	6.535 948	480.6637	18385.39
104	9.615 385	326.7256	8494.867	154	6.493 506	483.8053	18626.50
105	9.523 810	329.8672	8659.015	155	6.451 613	486.9469	18869.19
106	9.433 962	333.0088	8824.734	156	6.410 256	490.0885	19113.45
107	9.345 794	336.1504	8992.024	157	6.369 427	493.2300	19359.28
108	9.259 259	339.2920	9160.884	158	6.329 114	496.3716	19606.68
109	9.174 312	342.4336	9331.316	159	6.289 308	499.5132	19855.65
110	9.090 909	345.5752	9503.318	**160**	6.250 000	502.6548	20106.19
111	9.009 009	348.7168	9676.891	161	6.211 180	505.7964	20358.31
112	8.928 571	351.8584	9852.035	162	6.172 840	508.9380	20611.99
113	8.849 558	355.0000	10028.75	163	6.134 969	512.0796	20867.24
114	8.771 930	358.1416	10207.03	164	6.097 561	515.2212	21124.67
115	8.695 652	361.2832	10386.89	165	6.060 606	518.3628	21382.46
116	8.620 690	364.4247	10568.32	166	6.024 096	521.5044	21642.43
117	8.547 009	367.5663	10751.32	167	5.988 024	524.6460	21903.97
118	8.474 576	370.7079	10935.88	168	5.952 381	527.7876	22167.08
119	8.403 361	373.8495	11122.02	169	5.917 160	530.9292	22431.76
120	8.333 333	376.9911	11309.73	**170**	5.882 353	534.0708	22698.01
121	8.264 463	380.1327	11499.01	171	5.847 953	537.2123	22965.83
122	8.196 721	383.2743	11689.87	172	5.813 953	540.3539	23235.22
123	8.130 081	386.4159	11882.29	173	5.780 347	543.4955	23506.18
124	8.064 516	389.5575	12076.28	174	5.747 126	546.6371	23778.71
125	8.000 000	392.6991	12271.85	175	5.714 286	549.7787	24052.82
126	7.936 508	395.8407	12468.98	176	5.681 818	552.9203	24328.49
127	7.874 016	398.9823	12667.69	177	5.649 718	556.0619	24605.74
128	7.812 500	402.1239	12867.96	178	5.617 978	559.2035	24884.56
129	7.751 938	405.2655	13069.81	179	5.586 592	562.3451	25164.94
130	7.692 308	408.4070	13273.23	**180**	5.555 556	565.4867	25446.90
131	7.633 588	411.5486	13478.22	181	5.524 862	568.6283	25730.43
132	7.575 758	414.6902	13684.78	182	5.494 505	571.7699	26015.53
133	7.518 797	417.8318	13892.91	183	5.464 481	574.9115	26302.20
134	7.462 687	420.9734	14102.61	184	5.434 783	578.0530	26590.44
135	7.407 407	424.1150	14313.88	185	5.405 405	581.1946	26880.25
136	7.352 941	427.2566	14526.72	186	5.376 344	584.3362	27171.63
137	7.299 270	430.3982	14741.14	187	5.347 594	587.4778	27464.59
138	7.246 377	433.5398	14957.12	188	5.319 149	590.6194	27759.11
139	7.194 245	436.6814	15174.68	189	5.291 005	593.7610	28055.21
140	7.142 857	439.8230	15393.80	**190**	5.263 158	596.9026	28352.87
141	7.092 199	442.9646	15614.50	191	5.235 602	600.0442	28652.11
142	7.042 254	446.1062	15836.77	192	5.208 333	603.1858	28952.92
143	6.993 007	449.2477	16060.61	193	5.181 347	606.3274	29255.30
144	6.944 444	452.3893	16286.02	194	5.154 639	609.4690	29559.25
145	6.896 552	455.5309	16513.00	195	5.128 205	612.6106	29864.77
146	6.849 315	458.6725	16741.55	196	5.102 041	615.7522	30171.86
147	6.802 721	461.8141	16971.67	197	5.076 142	618.8938	30480.52
148	6.756 757	464.9557	17203.36	198	5.050 505	622.0353	30790.75
149	6.711 409	468.0973	17436.62	199	5.025 126	625.1769	31102.55
150	6.666 667	471.2389	17671.46	**200**	5.000 000	628.3185	31415.93

n	$1000\dfrac{1}{n}$	Circumference πn	Area $\dfrac{\pi n^2}{4}$	n	$1000\dfrac{1}{n}$	Circumference πn	Area $\dfrac{\pi n^2}{4}$
200	5.000 000	628.3185	31415.93	**250**	4.000 000	785.3982	49087.39
201	4.975 124	631.4601	31730.87	251	3.984 064	788.5398	49480.87
202	4.950 495	634.6017	32047.39	252	3.968 254	791.6813	49875.92
203	4.926 108	637.7433	32365.47	253	3.952 569	794.8229	50272.55
204	4.901 961	640.8849	32685.13	254	3.937 008	797.9645	50670.75
205	4.878 049	644.0265	33006.36	255	3.921 569	801.1061	51070.52
206	4.854 369	647.1681	33329.16	256	3.906 250	804.2477	51471.85
207	4.830 918	650.3097	33653.53	257	3.891 051	807.3893	51874.76
208	4.807 692	653.4513	33979.47	258	3.875 969	810.5309	52279.24
209	4.784 689	656.5929	34306.98	259	3.861 004	813.6725	52685.29
210	4.761 905	659.7345	34636.06	**260**	3.846 154	816.8141	53092.92
211	4.739 336	662.8760	34966.71	261	3.831 418	819.9557	53502.11
212	4.716 981	666.0176	35298.94	262	3.816 794	823.0973	53912.87
213	4.694 836	669.1592	35632.73	263	3.802 281	826.2389	54325.21
214	4.672 897	672.3008	35968.09	264	3.787 879	829.3805	54739.11
215	4.651 163	675.4424	36305.03	265	3.773 585	832.5221	55154.59
216	4.629 630	678.5840	36643.54	266	3.759 398	835.6636	55571.63
217	4.608 295	681.7256	36983.61	267	3.745 318	838.8052	55990.25
218	4.587 156	684.8672	37325.26	268	3.731 343	841.9468	56410.44
219	4.566 210	688.0088	37668.48	269	3.717 472	845.0884	56832.20
220	4.545 455	691.1504	38013.27	**270**	3.703 704	848.2300	57255.53
221	4.524 887	694.2920	38359.63	271	3.690 037	851.3716	57680.43
222	4.504 505	697.4336	38707.56	272	3.676 471	854.5132	58106.90
223	4.484 305	700.5752	39057.07	273	3.663 004	857.6548	58534.94
224	4.464 286	703.7168	39408.14	274	3.649 635	860.7964	58964.55
225	4.444 444	706.8583	39760.78	275	3.636 364	863.9380	59395.74
226	4.424 779	709.9999	40115.00	276	3.623 188	867.0796	59828.49
227	4.405 286	713.1415	40470.78	277	3.610 108	870.2212	60262.82
228	4.385 965	716.2831	40828.14	278	3.597 122	873.3628	60698.71
229	4.366 812	719.4247	41187.07	279	3.584 229	876.5044	61136.18
230	4.347 826	722.5663	41547.56	**280**	3.571 429	879.6459	61575.22
231	4.329 004	725.7079	41909.63	281	3.558 719	882.7875	62015.82
232	4.310 345	728.8495	42273.27	282	3.546 099	885.9291	62458.00
233	4.291 845	731.9911	42638.48	283	3.533 569	889.0707	62901.75
234	4.273 504	735.1327	43005.26	284	3.521 127	892.2123	63347.07
235	4.255 319	738.2743	43373.61	285	3.508 772	895.3539	63793.97
236	4.237 288	741.4159	43743.54	286	3.496 503	898.4955	64242.43
237	4.219 409	744.5575	44115.03	287	3.484 321	901.6371	64692.46
238	4.201 681	747.6991	44488.09	288	3.472 222	904.7787	65144.07
239	4.184 100	750.8406	44862.73	289	3.460 208	907.9203	65597.24
240	4.166 667	753.9822	45238.93	**290**	3.448 276	911.0619	66051.99
241	4.149 378	757.1238	45616.71	291	3.436 426	914.2035	66508.30
242	4.132 231	760.2654	45996.06	292	3.424 658	917.3451	66966.19
243	4.115 226	763.4070	46376.98	293	3.412 969	920.4866	67425.65
244	4.098 361	766.5486	46759.47	294	3.401 361	923.6282	67886.68
245	4.081 633	769.6902	47143.52	295	3.389 831	926.7698	68349.28
246	4.065 041	772.8318	47529.16	296	3.378 378	929.9114	68813.45
247	4.048 583	775.9734	47916.36	297	3.367 003	933.0530	69279.19
248	4.032 258	779.1150	48305.13	298	3.355 705	936.1946	69746.50
249	4.016 064	782.2566	48695.47	299	3.344 482	939.3362	70215.38
250	4.000 000	785.3982	· 49087.39	**300**	3.333 333	942.4778	70685.83

RECIPROCALS, CIRCUMFERENCE AND AREA OF CIRCLES

n	$1000-\dfrac{1}{n}$	Circumference πn	Area $\dfrac{\pi n^2}{4}$	n	$1000-\dfrac{1}{n}$	Circumference πn	Area $\dfrac{\pi n^2}{4}$
300	3.333 333	942.4778	70685.83	**350**	2.857 143	1099.557	96211.28
301	3.322 259	945.6194	71157.86	351	2.849 003	1102.699	96761.84
302	3.311 258	948.7610	71631.45	352	2.840 909	1105.841	97313.97
303	3.300 330	951.9026	72106.62	353	2.832 861	1108.982	97867.68
304	3.289 474	955.0442	72583.36	354	2.824 859	1112.124	98422.96
305	3.278 689	958.1858	73061.66	355	2.816 901	1115.265	98979.80
306	3.267 974	961.3274	73541.54	356	2.808 989	1118.407	99538.22
307	3.257 329	964.4689	74022.99	357	2.801 120	1121.549	100 098.2
308	3.246 753	967.6105	74506.01	358	2.793 296	1124.690	100 659.8
309	3.236 246	970.7521	74990.60	359	2.785 515	1127.832	101 222.9
310	3.225 806	973.8937	75476.76	**360**	2.777 778	1130.973	101 787.6
311	3.215 434	977.0353	75964.50	361	2.770 083	1134.115	102 353.9
312	3.205 128	980.1769	76453.80	362	2.762 431	1137.257	102 921.7
313	3.194 888	983.3185	76944.67	363	2.754 821	1140.398	103 491.1
314	3.184 713	986.4601	77437.12	364	2.747 253	1143.540	104 062.1
315	3.174 603	989.6017	77931.13	365	2.739 726	1146.681	104 634.7
316	3.164 557	992.7433	78426.72	366	2.732 240	1149.823	105 208.8
317	3.154 574	995.8849	78923.88	367	2.724 796	1152.965	105 784.5
318	3.144 654	999.0265	79422.60	368	2.717 391	1156.106	106 361.8
319	3.134 796	1002.168	79922.90	369	2.710 027	1159.248	106 940.6
320	3.125 000	1005.310	80424.77	**370**	2.702 703	1162.389	107 521.0
321	3.115 265	1008.451	80928.21	371	2.695 418	1165.531	108 103.0
322	3.105 590	1011.593	81433.22	372	2.688 172	1168.672	108 686.5
323	3.095 975	1014.734	81939.80	373	2.680 965	1171.814	109 271.7
324	3.086 420	1017.876	82447.96	374	2.673 797	1174.956	109 858.4
325	3.076 923	1021.018	82957.68	375	2.666 667	1178.097	110 446.6
326	3.067 485	1024.159	83468.98	376	2.659 574	1181.239	111 036.5
327	3.058 104	1027.301	83981.84	377	2.652 520	1184.380	111 627.9
328	3.048 780	1030.442	84496.28	378	2.645 503	1187.522	112 220.8
329	3.039 514	1033.584	85012.28	379	2.638 522	1190.664	112 815.4
330	3.030 303	1036.726	85529.86	**380**	2.631 579	1193.805	113 411.5
331	3.021 148	1039.867	86049.01	381	2.624 672	1196.947	114 009.2
332	3.012 048	1043.009	86569.73	382	2.617 801	1200.088	114 608.4
333	3.003 003	1046.150	87092.02	383	2.610 966	1203.230	115 209.3
334	2.994 012	1049.292	87615.88	384	2.604 167	1206.372	115 811.7
335	2.985 075	1052.434	88141.31	385	2.597 403	1209.513	116 415.6
336	2.976 190	1055.575	88668.31	386	2.590 674	1212.655	117 021.2
337	2.967 359	1058.717	89196.88	387	2.583 979	1215.796	117 628.3
338	2.958 580	1061.858	89727.03	388	2.577 320	1218.938	118 237.0
339	2.949 853	1065.000	90258.74	389	2.570 694	1222.080	118 847.2
340	2.941 176	1068.142	90792.03	**390**	2.564 103	1225.221	119 459.1
341	2.932 551	1071.283	91326.88	391	2.557 545	1228.363	120 072.5
342	2.923 977	1074.425	91863.31	392	2.551 020	1231.504	120 687.4
343	2.915 452	1077.566	92401.31	393	2.544 529	1234.646	121 304.0
344	2.906 977	1080.708	92940.88	394	2.538 071	1237.788	121 922.1
345	2.898 551	1083.849	93482.02	395	2.531 646	1240.929	122 541.7
346	2.890 173	1086.991	94024.73	396	2.525 253	1244.071	123 163.0
347	2.881 844	1090.133	94569.01	397	2.518 892	1247.212	123 785.8
348	2.873 563	1093.274	95114.86	398	2.512 563	1250.354	124 410.2
349	2.865 330	1096.416	95662.28	399	2.506 266	1253.495	125 036.2
350	2.857 143	1099.557	96211.28	**400**	2.500 000	1256.637	125 663.7

RECIPROCALS, CIRCUMFERENCE AND AREA OF CIRCLES

n	$1000-\dfrac{1}{n}$	Circumference πn	Area $\dfrac{\pi n^2}{4}$	n	$1000-\dfrac{1}{n}$	Circumference πn	Area $\dfrac{\pi n^2}{4}$
400	2.500 000	1256.637	125 663.7	**450**	2.222 222	1413.717	159 043.1
401	2.493 766	1259.779	126 292.8	451	2.217 295	1416.858	159 750.8
402	2.487 562	1262.920	126 923.5	452	2.212 389	1420.000	160 460.0
403	2.481 390	1266.062	127 555.7	453	2.207 506	1423.141	161 170.8
404	2.475 248	1269.203	128 189.5	454	2.202 643	1426.283	161 883.1
405	2.469 136	1272.345	128 824.9	455	2.197 802	1429.425	162 597.1
406	2.463 054	1275.487	129 461.9	456	2.192 982	1432.566	163 312.6
407	2.457 002	1278.628	130 100.4	457	2.188 184	1435.708	164 029.6
408	2.450 980	1281.770	130 740.5	458	2.183 406	1438.849	164 748.3
409	2.444 988	1284.911	131 382.2	459	2.178 649	1441.991	165 468.5
410	2.439 024	1288.053	132 025.4	**460**	2.173 913	1445.133	166 190.3
411	2.433 090	1291.195	132 670.2	461	2.169 197	1448.274	166 913.6
412	2.427 184	1294.336	133 316.6	462	2.164 502	1451.416	167 638.5
413	2.421 308	1297.478	133 964.6	463	2.159 827	1454.557	168 365.0
414	2.415 459	1300.619	134 614.1	464	2.155 172	1457.699	169 093.1
415	2.409 639	1303.761	135 265.2	465	2.150 538	1460.841	169 822.7
416	2.403 846	1306.903	135 917.9	466	2.145 923	1463.982	170 553.9
417	2.398 082	1310.044	136 572.1	467	2.141 328	1467.124	171 286.7
418	2.392 344	1313.186	137 227.9	468	2.136 752	1470.265	172 021.0
419	2.386 635	1316.327	137 885.3	469	2.132 196	1473.407	172 757.0
420	2.380 952	1319.469	138 544.2	**470**	2.127 660	1476.549	173 494.5
421	2.375 297	1322.611	139 204.8	471	2.123 142	1479.690	174 233.5
422	2.369 668	1325.752	139 866.8	472	2.118 644	1482.832	174 974.1
423	2.364 066	1328.894	140 530.5	473	2.114 165	1485.973	175 716.3
424	2.358 491	1332.035	141 195.7	474	2.109 705	1489.115	176 460.1
425	2.352 941	1335.177	141 862.5	475	2.105 263	1492.257	177 205.5
426	2.347 418	1338.318	142 530.9	476	2.100 840	1495.398	177 952.4
427	2.341 920	1341.460	143 200.9	477	2.096 436	1498.540	178 700.9
428	2.336 449	1344.602	143 872.4	478	2.092 050	1501.681	179 450.9
429	2.331 002	1347.743	144 545.5	479	2.087 683	1504.823	180 202.5
430	2.325 581	1350.885	145 220.1	**480**	2.083 333	1507.964	180 955.7
431	2.320 186	1354.026	145 896.3	481	2.079 002	1511.106	181 710.5
432	2.314 815	1357.168	146 574.1	482	2.074 689	1514.248	182 466.8
433	2.309 469	1360.310	147 253.5	483	2.070 393	1517.389	183 224.8
434	2.304 147	1363.451	147 934.5	484	2.066 116	1520.531	183 984.2
435	2.298 851	1366.593	148 617.0	485	2.061 856	1523.672	184 745.3
436	2.293 578	1369.734	149 301.0	486	2.057 613	1526.814	185 507.9
437	2.288 330	1372.876	149 986.7	487	2.053 388	1529.956	186 272.1
438	2.283 105	1376.018	150 673.9	488	2.049 180	1533.097	187 037.9
439	2.277 904	1379.159	151 362.7	489	2.044 990	1536.239	187 805.2
440	2.272 727	1382.301	152 053.1	**490**	2.040 816	1539.380	188 574.1
441	2.267 574	1385.442	152 745.0	491	2.036 660	1542.522	189 344.6
442	2.262 443	1388.584	153 438.5	492	2.032 520	1545.664	190 116.6
443	2.257 336	1391.726	154 133.6	493	2.028 398	1548.805	190 890.2
444	2.252 252	1394.867	154 830.3	494	2.024 291	1551.947	191 665.4
445	2.247 191	1398.009	155 528.5	495	2.020 202	1555.088	192 442.2
446	2.242 152	1401.150	156 228.3	496	2.016 129	1558.230	193 220.5
447	2.237 136	1404.292	156 929.6	497	2.012 072	1561.372	194 000.4
448	2.232 143	1407.434	157 632.6	498	2.008 032	1564.513	194 781.9
449	2.227 171	1410.575	158 337.1	499	2.004 008	1567.655	195 564.9
450	2.222 222	1413.717	159 043.1	**500**	2.000 000	1570.796	196 349.5

n	$1000\dfrac{1}{n}$	Circumference πn	Area $\dfrac{\pi n^2}{4}$	n	$1000\dfrac{1}{n}$	Circumference πn	Area $\dfrac{\pi n^2}{4}$
500	2.000 000	1570.796	196 349.5	**550**	1.818 182	1727.876	237 582.9
501	1.996 008	1573.938	197 135.7	551	1.814 882	1731.018	238 447.7
502	1.992 032	1577.080	197 923.5	552	1.811 594	1734.159	239 314.0
503	1.988 072	1580.221	198 712.8	553	1.808 318	1737.301	240 181.8
504	1.984 127	1583.363	199 503.7	554	1.805 054	1740.442	241 051.3
505	1.980 198	1586.504	200 296.2	555	1.801 802	1743.584	241 922.3
506	1.976 285	1589.646	201 090.2	556	1.798 561	1746.726	242 794.8
507	1.972 387	1592.787	201 885.8	557	1.795 332	1749.867	243 669.0
508	1.968 504	1595.929	202 683.0	558	1.792 115	1753.009	244 544.7
509	1.964 637	1599.071	203 481.7	559	1.788 909	1756.150	245 422.0
510	1.960 784	1602.212	204 282.1	**560**	1.785 714	1759.292	246 300.9
511	1.956 947	1605.354	205 084.0	561	1.782 531	1762.433	247 181.3
512	1.953 125	1608.495	205 887.4	562	1.779 359	1765.575	248 063.3
513	1.949 318	1611.637	206 692.4	563	1.776 199	1768.717	248 946.9
514	1.945 525	1614.779	207 499.1	564	1.773 050	1771.858	249 832.0
515	1.941 748	1617.920	208 307.2	565	1.769 912	1775.000	250 718.7
516	1.937 984	1621.062	209 117.0	566	1.766 784	1778.141	251 607.0
517	1.934 236	1624.203	209 928.3	567	1.763 668	1781.283	252 496.9
518	1.930 502	1627.345	210 741.2	568	1.760 563	1784.425	253 388.3
519	1.926 782	1630.487	211 555.6	569	1.757 469	1787.566	254 281.3
520	1.923 077	1633.628	212 371.7	**570**	1.754 386	1790.708	255 175.9
521	1.919 386	1636.770	213 189.3	571	1.751 313	1793.849	256 072.0
522	1.915 709	1639.911	214 008.4	572	1.748 252	1796.991	256 969.7
523	1.912 046	1643.053	214 829.2	573	1.745 201	1800.133	257 869.0
524	1.908 397	1646.195	215 651.5	574	1.742 160	1803.274	258 769.8
525	1.904 762	1649.336	216 475.4	575	1.739 130	1806.416	259 672.3
526	1.901 141	1652.478	217 300.8	576	1.736 111	1809.557	260 576.3
527	1.897 533	1655.619	218 127.8	577	1.733 102	1812.699	261 481.8
528	1.893 939	1658.761	218 956.4	578	1.730 104	1815.841	262 389.0
529	1.890 359	1661.903	219 786.6	579	1.727 116	1818.982	263 297.7
530	1.886 792	1665.044	220 618.3	**580**	1.724 138	1822.124	264 207.9
531	1.883 239	1668.186	221 451.7	581	1.721 170	1825.265	265 119.8
532	1.879 699	1671.327	222 286.5	582	1.718 213	1828.407	266 033.2
533	1.876 173	1674.469	223 123.0	583	1.715 266	1831.549	266 948.2
534	1.872 659	1677.610	223 961.0	584	1.712 329	1834.690	267 864.8
535	1.869 159	1680.752	224 800.6	585	1.709 402	1837.832	268 782.9
536	1.865 672	1683.894	225 641.8	586	1.706 485	1840.973	269 702.6
537	1.862 197	1687.035	226 484.5	587	1.703 578	1844.115	270 623.9
538	1.858 736	1690.177	227 328.8	588	1.700 680	1847.256	271 546.7
539	1.855 288	1693.318	228 174.7	589	1.697 793	1850.398	272 471.1
540	1.851 852	1696.460	229 022.1	**590**	1.694 915	1853.540	273 397.1
541	1.848 429	1699.602	229 871.1	591	1.692 047	1856.681	274 324.7
542	1.845 018	1702.743	230 721.7	592	1.689 189	1859.823	275 253.8
543	1.841 621	1705.885	231 573.9	593	1.686 341	1862.964	276 184.5
544	1.838 235	1709.026	232 427.6	594	1.683 502	1866.106	277 116.7
545	1.834 862	1712.168	233 282.9	595	1.680 672	1869.248	278 050.6
546	1.831 502	1715.310	234 139.8	596	1.677 852	1872.389	278 986.0
547	1.828 154	1718.451	234 998.2	597	1.675 042	1875.531	279 923.0
548	1.824 818	1721.593	235 858.2	598	1.672 241	1878.672	280 861.5
549	1.821 494	1724.734	236 719.8	599	1.669 449	1881.814	281 801.6
550	1.818 182	1727.876	237 582.9	**600**	1.666 667	1884.956	282 743.3

RECIPROCALS, CIRCUMFERENCE AND AREA OF CIRCLES

n	$1000\,\dfrac{1}{n}$	Circumference πn	Area $\dfrac{\pi n^2}{4}$	n	$1000\,\dfrac{1}{n}$	Circumference πn	Area $\dfrac{\pi n^2}{4}$
600	1.666 667	1884.956	282 743.3	**650**	1.538 462	2042.035	331 830.7
601	1.663 894	1888.097	283 686.6	651	1.536 098	2045.177	332 852.5
602	1.661 130	1891.239	284 631.4	652	1.533 742	2048.318	333 875.9
603	1.658 375	1894.380	285 577.8	653	1.531 394	2051.460	334 900.8
604	1.655 629	1897.522	286 525.8	654	1.529 052	2054.602	335 927.4
605	1.652 893	1900.664	287 475.4	655	1.526 718	2057.743	336 955.4
606	1.650 165	1903.805	288 426.5	656	1.524 390	2060.885	337 985.1
607	1.647 446	1906.947	289 379.2	657	1.522 070	2064.026	339 016.3
608	1.644 737	1910.088	290 333.4	658	1.519 757	2067.168	340 049.1
609	1.642 036	1913.230	291 289.3	659	1.517 451	2070.310	341 083.5
610	1.639 344	1916.372	292 246.7	**660**	1.515 152	2073.451	342 119.4
611	1.636 661	1919.513	293 205.6	661	1.512 859	2076.593	343 157.0
612	1.633 987	1922.655	294 166.2	662	1.510 574	2079.734	344 196.0
613	1.631 321	1925.796	295 128.3	663	1.508 296	2082.876	345 236.7
614	1.628 664	1928.938	296 092.0	664	1.506 024	2086.018	346 278.9
615	1.626 016	1932.079	297 057.2	665	1.503 759	2089.159	347 322.7
616	1.623 377	1935.221	298 024.0	666	1.501 502	2092.301	348 368.1
617	1.620 746	1938.363	298 992.4	667	1.499 250	2095.442	349 415.0
618	1.618 123	1941.504	299 962.4	668	1.497 006	2098.584	350 463.5
619	1.615 509	1944.646	300 933.9	669	1.494 768	2101.725	351 513.6
620	1.612 903	1947.787	301 907.1	**670**	1.492 537	2104.867	352 565.2
621	1.610 306	1950.929	302 881.7	671	1.490 313	2108.009	353 618.5
622	1.607 717	1954.071	303 858.0	672	1.488 095	2111.150	354 673.2
623	1.605 136	1957.212	304 835.8	673	1.485 884	2114.292	355 729.6
624	1.602 564	1960.354	305 815.2	674	1.483 680	2117.433	356 787.5
625	1.600 000	1963.495	306 796.2	675	1.481 481	2120.575	357 847.0
626	1.597 444	1966.637	307 778.7	676	1.479 290	2123.717	358 908.1
627	1.594 896	1969.779	308 762.8	677	1.477 105	2126.858	359 970.8
628	1.592 357	1972.920	309 748.5	678	1.474 926	2130.000	361 035.0
629	1.589 825	1976.062	310 735.7	679	1.472 754	2133.141	362 100.8
630	1.587 302	1979.203	311 724.5	**680**	1.470 588	2136.283	363 168.1
631	1.584 786	1982.345	312 714.9	681	1.468 429	2139.425	364 237.0
632	1.582 278	1985.487	313 706.9	682	1.466 276	2142.566	365 307.5
633	1.579 779	1988.628	314 700.4	683	1.464 129	2145.708	366 379.6
634	1.577 287	1991.770	315 695.5	684	1.461 988	2148.849	367 453.2
635	1.574 803	1994.911	316 692.2	685	1.459 854	2151.991	368 528.5
636	1.572 327	1998.053	317 690.4	686	1.457 726	2155.133	369 605.2
637	1.569 859	2001.195	318 690.2	687	1.455 604	2158.274	370 683.6
638	1.567 398	2004.336	319 691.6	688	1.453 488	2161.416	371 763.5
639	1.564 945	2007.478	320 694.6	689	1.451 379	2164.557	372 845.0
640	1.562 500	2010.619	321 699.1	**690**	1.449 275	2167.699	373 928.1
641	1.560 062	2013.761	322 705.2	691	1.447 178	2170.841	375 012.7
642	1.557 632	2016.902	323 712.8	692	1.445 087	2173.982	376 098.9
643	1.555 210	2020.044	324 722.1	693	1.443 001	2177.124	377 186.7
644	1.552 795	2023.186	325 732.9	694	1.440 922	2180.265	378 276.0
645	1.550 388	2026.327	326 745.3	695	1.438 849	2183.407	379 366.9
646	1.547 988	2029.469	327 759.2	696	1.436 782	2186.548	380 459.4
647	1.545 595	2032.610	328 774.7	697	1.434 720	2189.690	381 553.5
648	1.543 210	2035.752	329 791.8	698	1.432 665	2192.832	382 649.1
649	1.540 832	2038.894	330 810.5	699	1.430 615	2195.973	383 746.3
650	1.538 462	2042.035	331 830.7	**700**	1.428 571	2199.115	384 845.1

n	$1000\dfrac{1}{n}$	Circumference πn	Area $\dfrac{\pi n^2}{4}$	n	$1000\dfrac{1}{n}$	Circumference πn	Area $\dfrac{\pi n^2}{4}$
700	1.428 571	2199.115	384 845.1	750	1.333 333	2356.194	441 786.5
701	1.426 534	2202.256	385 945.4	751	1.331 558	2359.336	442 965.3
702	1.424 501	2205.398	387 047.4	752	1.329 787	2362.478	444 145.8
703	1.422 475	2208.540	388 150.8	753	1.328 021	2365.619	445 327.8
704	1.420 455	2211.681	389 255.9	754	1.326 260	2368.761	446 511.4
705	1.418 440	2214.823	390 362.5	755	1.324 503	2371.902	447 696.6
706	1.416 431	2217.964	391 470.7	756	1.322 751	2375.044	448 883.3
707	1.414 427	2221.106	392 580.5	757	1.321 004	2378.186	450 071.6
708	1.412 429	2224.248	393 691.8	758	1.319 261	2381.327	451 261.5
709	1.410 437	2227.389	394 804.7	759	1.317 523	2384.469	452 453.0
710	1.408 451	2230.531	395 919.2	760	1.315 789	2387.610	453 646.0
711	1.406 470	2233.672	397 035.3	761	1.314 060	2390.752	454 840.6
712	1.404 494	2236.814	398 152.9	762	1.312 336	2393.894	456 036.7
713	1.402 525	2239.956	399 272.1	763	1.310 616	2397.035	457 234.5
714	1.400 560	2243.097	400 392.8	764	1.308 901	2400.177	458 433.8
715	1.398 601	2246.239	401 515.2	765	1.307 190	2403.318	459 634.6
716	1.396 648	2249.380	402 639.1	766	1.305 483	2406.460	460 837.1
717	1.394 700	2252.522	403 764.6	767	1.303 781	2409.602	462 041.1
718	1.392 758	2255.664	404 891.6	768	1.302 083	2412.743	463 246.7
719	1.390 821	2258.805	406 020.2	769	1.300 390	2415.885	464 453.8
720	1.388 889	2261.947	407 150.4	770	1.298 701	2419.026	465 662.6
721	1.386 963	2265.088	408 282.2	771	1.297 017	2422.168	466 872.9
722	1.385 042	2268.230	409 415.5	772	1.295 337	2425.310	468 084.7
723	1.383 126	2271.371	410 550.4	773	1.293 661	2428.451	469 298.2
724	1.381 215	2274.513	411 686.9	774	1.291 990	2431.593	470 513.2
725	1.379 310	2277.655	412 824.9	775	1.290 323	2434.734	471 729.8
726	1.377 410	2280.796	413 964.5	776	1.288 660	2437.876	472 947.9
727	1.375 516	2283.938	415 105.7	777	1.287 001	2441.017	474 167.6
728	1.373 626	2287.079	416 248.5	778	1.285 347	2444.159	475 388.9
729	1.371 742	2290.221	417 392.8	779	1.283 697	2447.301	476 611.8
730	1.369 863	2293.363	418 538.7	780	1.282 051	2450.442	477 836.2
731	1.367 989	2296.504	419 686.1	781	1.280 410	2453.584	479 062.2
732	1.366 120	2299.646	420 835.2	782	1.278 772	2456.725	480 289.8
733	1.364 256	2302.787	421 985.8	783	1.277 139	2459.867	481 519.0
734	1.362 398	2305.929	423 138.0	784	1.275 510	2463.009	482 749.7
735	1.360 544	2309.071	424 291.7	785	1.273 885	2466.150	483 982.0
736	1.358 696	2312.212	425 447.0	786	1.272 265	2469.292	485 215.8
737	1.356 852	2315.354	426 603.9	787	1.270 648	2472.433	486 451.3
738	1.355 014	2318.495	427 762.4	788	1.269 036	2475.575	487 688.3
739	1.353 180	2321.637	428 922.4	789	1.267 427	2478.717	488 926.9
740	1.351 351	2324.779	430 084.0	790	1.265 823	2481.858	490 167.0
741	1.349 528	2327.920	431 247.2	791	1.264 223	2485.000	491 408.7
742	1.347 709	2331.062	432 412.0	792	1.262 626	2488.141	492 652.0
743	1.345 895	2334.203	433 578.3	793	1.261 034	2491.283	493 896.8
744	1.344 086	2337.345	434 746.2	794	1.259 446	2494.425	495 143.3
745	1.342 282	2340.487	435 915.6	795	1.257 862	2497.566	496 391.3
746	1.340 483	2343.628	437 086.6	796	1.256 281	2500.708	497 640.8
747	1.338 688	2346.770	438 259.2	797	1.254 705	2503.849	498 892.0
748	1.336 898	2349.911	439 433.4	798	1.253 133	2506.991	500 144.7
749	1.335 113	2353.053	440 609.2	799	1.251 564	2510.133	501 399.0
750	1.333 333	2356.194	441 786.5	800	1.250 000	2513.274	502 654.8

n	$1000-\dfrac{1}{n}$	Circum-ference πn	Area $\dfrac{\pi n^2}{4}$	n	$1000-\dfrac{1}{n}$	Circum-ference πn	Area $\dfrac{\pi n^2}{4}$
800	1.250 000	2513.274	502 654.8	**850**	1.176 471	2670.354	567 450.2
801	1.248 439	2516.416	503 912.2	851	1.175 088	2673.495	568 786.1
802	1.246 883	2519.557	505 171.2	852	1.173 709	2676.637	570 123.7
803	1.245 330	2522.699	506 431.8	853	1.172 333	2679.779	571 462.8
804	1.243 781	2525.840	507 693.9	854	1.170 960	2682.920	572 803.4
805	1.242 236	2528.982	508 957.6	855	1.169 591	2686.062	574 145.7
806	1.240 695	2532.124	510 222.9	856	1.168 224	2689.203	575 489.5
807	1.239 157	2535.265	511 489.8	857	1.166 861	2692.345	576 834.9
808	1.237 624	2538.407	512 758.2	858	1.165 501	2695.486	578 181.9
809	1.236 094	2541.548	514 028.2	859	1.164 144	2698.628	579 530.4
810	1.234 568	2544.690	515 299.7	**860**	1.162 791	2701.770	580 880.5
811	1.233 046	2547.832	516 572.9	861	1.161 440	2704.911	582 232.2
812	1.231 527	2550.973	517 847.6	862	1.160 093	2708.053	583 585.4
813	1.230 012	2554.115	519 123.8	863	1.158 749	2711.194	584 940.2
814	1.228 501	2557.256	520 401.7	864	1.157 407	2714.336	586 296.6
815	1.226 994	2560.398	521 681.1	865	1.156 069	2717.478	587 654.5
816	1.225 490	2563.540	522 962.1	866	1.154 734	2720.619	589 014.1
817	1.223 990	2566.681	524 244.6	867	1.153 403	2723.761	590 375.2
818	1.222 494	2569.823	525 528.8	868	1.152 074	2726.902	591 737.8
819	1.221 001	2572.964	526 814.5	869	1.150 748	2730.044	593 102.1
820	1.219 512	2576.106	528 101.7	**870**	1.149 425	2733.186	594 467.9
821	1.218 027	2579.248	529 390.6	871	1.148 106	2736.327	595 835.2
822	1.216 545	2582.389	530 681.0	872	1.146 789	2739.469	597 204.2
823	1.215 067	2585.531	531 973.0	873	1.145 475	2742.610	598 574.7
824	1.213 592	2588.672	533 266.5	874	1.144 165	2745.752	599 946.8
825	1.212 121	2591.814	534 561.6	875	1.142 857	2748.894	601 320.5
826	1.210 654	2594.956	535 858.3	876	1.141 553	2752.035	602 695.7
827	1.209 190	2598.097	537 156.6	877	1.140 251	2755.177	604 072.5
828	1.207 729	2601.239	538 456.4	878	1.138 952	2758.318	605 450.9
829	1.206 273	2604.380	539 757.8	879	1.137 656	2761.460	606 830.8
830	1.204 819	2607.522	541 060.8	**880**	1.136 364	2764.602	608 212.3
831	1.203 369	2610.663	542 365.3	881	1.135 074	2767.743	609 595.4
832	1.201 923	2613.805	543 671.5	882	1.133 787	2770.885	610 980.1
833	1.200 480	2616.947	544 979.1	883	1.132 503	2774.026	612 366.3
834	1.199 041	2620.088	546 288.4	884	1.131 222	2777.168	613 754.1
835	1.197 605	2623.230	547 599.2	885	1.129 944	2780.309	615 143.5
836	1.196 172	2626.371	548 911.6	886	1.128 668	2783.451	616 534.4
837	1.194 743	2629.513	550 225.6	887	1.127 396	2786.593	617 926.9
838	1.193 317	2632.655	551 541.1	888	1.126 126	2789.734	619 321.0
839	1.191 895	2635.796	552 858.3	889	1.124 859	2792.876	620 716.7
840	1.190 476	2638.938	554 176.9	**890**	1.123 596	2796.017	622 113.9
841	1.189 061	2642.079	555 497.2	891	1.122 334	2799.159	623 512.7
842	1.187 648	2645.221	556 819.0	892	1.121 076	2802.301	624 913.0
843	1.186 240	2648.363	558 142.4	893	1.119 821	2805.442	626 315.0
844	1.184 834	2651.504	559 467.4	894	1.118 568	2808.584	627 718.5
845	1.183 432	2654.646	560 793.9	895	1.117 318	2811.725	629 123.6
846	1.182 033	2657.787	562 122.0	896	1.116 071	2814.867	630 530.2
847	1.180 638	2660.929	563 451.7	897	1.114 827	2818.009	631 938.4
848	1.179 245	2664.071	564 783.0	898	1.113 586	2821.150	633 348.2
849	1.177 856	2667.212	566 115.8	899	1.112 347	2824.292	634 759.6
850	1.176 471	2670.354	567 450.2	**900**	1.111 111	2827.433	636 172.5

RECIPROCALS, CIRCUMFERENCE AND AREA OF CIRCLES

n	$1000\frac{1}{n}$	Circumference πn	Area $\frac{\pi n^2}{4}$	n	$1000\frac{1}{n}$	Circumference πn	Area $\frac{\pi n^2}{4}$
900	1.111 111	2827.433	636 172.5	**950**	1.052 632	2984.513	708 821.8
901	1.109 878	2830.575	637 587.0	951	1.051 525	2987.655	710 314.9
902	1.108 647	2833.717	639 003.1	952	1.050 420	2990.796	711 809.5
903	1.107 420	2836.858	640 420.7	953	1.049 318	2993.938	713 305.7
904	1.106 195	2840.000	641 839.9	954	1.048 218	2997.079	714 803.4
905	1.104 972	2843.141	643 260.7	955	1.047 120	3000.221	716 302.8
906	1.103 753	2846.283	644 683.1	956	1.046 025	3003.363	717 803.7
907	1.102 536	2849.425	646 107.0	957	1.044 932	3006.504	719 306.1
908	1.101 322	2852.566	647 532.5	958	1.043 841	3009.646	720 810.2
909	1.100 110	2855.708	648 959.6	959	1.042 753	3012.787	722 315.8
910	1.098 901	2858.849	650 388.2	**960**	1.041 667	3015.929	723 822.9
911	1.097 695	2861.991	651 818.4	961	1.040 583	3019.071	725 331.7
912	1.096 491	2865.133	653 250.2	962	1.039 501	3022.212	726 842.0
913	1.095 290	2868.274	654 683.6	963	1.038 422	3025.354	728 353.9
914	1.094 092	2871.416	656 118.5	964	1.037 344	3028.495	729 867.4
915	1.092 896	2874.557	657 555.0	965	1.036 269	3031.637	731 382.4
916	1.091 703	2877.699	658 993.0	966	1.035 197	3034.779	732 899.0
917	1.090 513	2880.840	660 432.7	967	1.034 126	3037.920	734 417.2
918	1.089 325	2883.982	661 873.9	968	1.033 058	3041.062	735 936.9
919	1.088 139	2887.124	663 316.7	969	1.031 992	3044.203	737 458.2
920	1.086 957	2890.265	664 761.0	**970**	1.030 928	3047.345	738 981.1
921	1.085 776	2893.407	666 206.9	971	1.029 866	3050.486	740 505.6
922	1.084 599	2896.548	667 654.4	972	1.028 807	3053.628	742 031.6
923	1.083 424	2899.690	669 103.5	973	1.027 749	3056.770	743 559.2
924	1.082 251	2902.832	670 554.1	974	1.026 694	3059.911	745 088.4
925	1.081 081	2905.973	672 006.3	975	1.025 641	3063.053	746 619.1
926	1.079 914	2909.115	673 460.1	976	1.024 590	3066.194	748 151.4
927	1.078 749	2912.256	674 915.4	977	1.023 541	3069.336	749 685.3
928	1.077 586	2915.398	676 372.3	978	1.022 495	3072.478	751 220.8
929	1.076 426	2918.540	677 830.8	979	1.021 450	3075.619	752 757.8
930	1.075 269	2921.681	679 290.9	**980**	1.020 408	3078.761	754 296.4
931	1.074 114	2924.823	680 752.5	981	1.019 368	3081.902	755 836.6
932	1.072 961	2927.964	682 215.7	982	1.018 330	3085.044	757 378.3
933	1.071 811	2931.106	683 680.5	983	1.017 294	3088.186	758 921.6
934	1.070 664	2934.248	685 146.8	984	1.016 260	3091.327	760 466.5
935	1.069 519	2937.389	686 614.7	985	1.015 228	3094.469	762 012.9
936	1.068 376	2940.531	688 084.2	986	1.014 199	3097.610	763 561.0
937	1.067 236	2943.672	689 555.2	987	1.013 171	3100.752	765 110.5
938	1.066 098	2946.814	691 027.9	988	1.012 146	3103.894	766 661.7
939	1.064 963	2949.956	692 502.1	989	1.011 122	3107.035	768 214.4
940	1.063 830	2953.097	693 977.8	**990**	1.010 101	3110.177	769 768.7
941	1.062 699	2956.239	695 455.2	991	1.009 082	3113.318	771 324.6
942	1.061 571	2959.380	696 934.1	992	1.008 065	3116.460	772 882.1
943	1.060 445	2962.522	698 414.5	993	1.007 049	3119.602	774 441.1
944	1.059 322	2965.663	699 896.6	994	1.006 036	3122.743	776 001.7
945	1.058 201	2968.805	701 380.2	995	1.005 025	3125.885	777 563.8
946	1.057 082	2971.947	702 865.4	996	1.004 016	3129.026	779 127.5
947	1.055 966	2975.088	704 352.1	997	1.003 009	3132.168	780 692.8
948	1.054 852	2978.230	705 840.5	998	1.002 004	3135.309	782 259.7
949	1.053 741	2981.371	707 330.4	999	1.001 001	3138.451	783 828.2
950	1.052 632	2984.513	708 821.8	**1000**	1.000 000	3141.593	785 398.2

Squares, Cubes and Roots

Roots of numbers other than those given directly may be found by the following relations:

$$\sqrt{100n} = 10\sqrt{n}; \quad \sqrt{1000n} = 10\sqrt{10n}; \quad \sqrt{\frac{1}{10}n} = \frac{1}{10}\sqrt{10n}; \quad \sqrt{\frac{1}{100}n} = \frac{1}{10}\sqrt{n};$$

$$\sqrt{\frac{1}{1000}n} = \frac{1}{100}\sqrt{10n}; \quad \sqrt[3]{1000n} = 10\sqrt[3]{n}; \quad \sqrt[3]{10,000n} = 10\sqrt[3]{10n}; \quad \sqrt[3]{100,000n} =$$

$$10\sqrt[3]{100n}; \quad \sqrt[3]{\frac{1}{10}n} = \frac{1}{10}\sqrt[3]{100n}; \quad \sqrt[3]{\frac{1}{100}n} = \frac{1}{10}\sqrt[3]{10n}; \quad \sqrt[3]{\frac{1}{1000}n} = \frac{1}{10}\sqrt[3]{n}.$$

n	n^2	$\sqrt{n}$	$\sqrt{10n}$	n^3	$\sqrt[3]{n}$	$\sqrt[3]{10n}$	$\sqrt[3]{100n}$
1	1	1.000 000	3.162 278	1	1.000 000	2.154 435	4.641 589
2	4	1.414 214	4.472 136	8	1.259 921	2.714 418	5.848 035
3	9	1.732 051	5.477 226	27	1.442 250	3.107 233	6.694 330
4	16	2.000 000	6.324 555	64	1.587 401	3.419 952	7.368 063
5	25	2.236 068	7.071 068	125	1.709 976	3.684 031	7.937 005
6	36	2.449 490	7.745 967	216	1.817 121	3.914 868	8.434 327
7	49	2.645 751	8.366 600	343	1.912 931	4.121 285	8.879 040
8	64	2.828 427	8.944 272	512	2.000 000	4.308 869	9.283 178
9	81	3.000 000	9.486 833	729	2.080 084	4.481 405	9.654 894
10	100	3.162 278	10.00000	1 000	2.154 435	4.641 589	10.00000
11	121	3.316 625	10.48809	1 331	2.223 980	4.791 420	10.32280
12	144	3.464 102	10.95445	1 728	2.289 428	4.932 424	10.62659
13	169	3.605 551	11.40175	2 197	2.351 335	5.065 797	10.91393
14	196	3.741 657	11.83216	2 744	2.410 142	5.192 494	11.18689
15	225	3.872 983	12.24745	3 375	2.466 212	5.313 293	11.44714
16	256	4.000 000	12.64911	4 096	2.519 842	5.428 835	11.69607
17	289	4.123 106	13.03840	4 913	2.571 282	5.539 658	11.93483
18	324	4.242 641	13.41641	5 832	2.620 741	5.646 216	12.16440
19	361	4.358 899	13.78405	6 859	2.668 402	5.748 897	12.38562
20	400	4.472 136	14.14214	8 000	2.714 418	5.848 035	12.59921
21	441	4.582 576	14.49138	9 261	2.758 924	5.943 922	12.80579
22	484	4.690 416	14.83240	10 648	2.802 039	6.036 811	13.00591
23	529	4.795 832	15.16575	12 167	2.843 867	6.126 926	13.20006
24	576	4.898 979	15.49193	13 824	2.884 499	6.214 465	13.38866
25	625	5.000 000	15.81139	15 625	2.924 018	6.299 605	13.57209
26	676	5.099 020	16.12452	17 576	2.962 496	6.382 504	13.75069
27	729	5.196 152	16.43168	19 683	3.000 000	6.463 304	13.92477
28	784	5.291 503	16.73320	21 952	3.036 589	6.542 133	14.09460
29	841	5.385 165	17.02939	24 389	3.072 317	6.619 106	14.26043
30	900	5.477 226	17.32051	27 000	3.107 233	6.694 330	14.42250
31	961	5.567 764	17.60682	29 791	3.141 381	6.767 899	14.58100
32	1 024	5.656 854	17.88854	32 768	3.174 802	6.839 904	14.73613
33	1 089	5.744 563	18.16590	35 937	3.207 534	6.910 423	14.88806
34	1 156	5.830 952	18.43909	39 304	3.239 612	6.979 532	15.03695
35	1 225	5.916 080	18.70829	42 875	3.271 066	7.047 299	15.18294
36	1 296	6.000 000	18.97367	46 656	3.301 927	7.113 787	15.32619
37	1 369	6.082 763	19.23538	50 653	3.332 222	7.179 054	15.46680
38	1 444	6.164 414	19.49359	54 872	3.361 975	7.243 156	15.60491
39	1 521	6.244 998	19.74842	59 319	3.391 211	7.306 144	15.74061
40	1 600	6.324 555	20.00000	64 000	3.419 952	7.368 063	15.87401
41	1 681	6.403 124	20.24846	68 921	3.448 217	7.428 959	16.00521
42	1 764	6.480 741	20.49390	74 088	3.476 027	7.488 872	16.13429
43	1 849	6.557 439	20.73644	79 507	3.503 398	7.547 842	16.26133
44	1 936	6.633 250	20.97618	85 184	3.530 348	7.605 905	16.38643
45	2 025	6.708 204	21.21320	91 125	3.556 893	7.663 094	16.50964
46	2 116	6.782 330	21.44761	97 336	3.583 048	7.719 443	16.63103
47	2 209	6.855 655	21.67948	103 823	3.608 826	7.774 980	16.75069
48	2 304	6.928 203	21.90890	110 592	3.634 241	7.829 735	16.86865
49	2 401	7.000 000	22.13594	117 649	3.659 306	7.883 735	16.98499
50	2 500	7.071 068	22.36068	125 000	3.684 031	7.937 005	17.09976

n	n^2	$\sqrt{n}$	$\sqrt{10n}$	n^3	$\sqrt[3]{n}$	$\sqrt[3]{10n}$	$\sqrt[3]{100n}$
50	2 500	7.071 068	22.36068	125 000	3.684 031	7.937 005	17.09976
51	2 601	7.141 428	22.58318	132 651	3.708 430	7.989 570	17.21301
52	2 704	7.211 103	22.80351	140 608	3.732 511	8.041 452	17.32478
53	2 809	7.280 110	23.02173	148 877	3.756 286	8.092 672	17.43513
54	2 916	7.348 469	23.23790	157 464	3.779 763	8.143 253	17.54411
55	3 025	7.416 198	23.45208	166 375	3.802 952	8.193 213	17.65174
56	3 136	7.483 315	23.66432	175 616	3.825 862	8.242 571	17.75808
57	3 249	7.549 834	23.87467	185 193	3.848 501	8.291 344	17.86316
58	3 364	7.615 773	24.08319	195 112	3.870 877	8.339 551	17.96702
59	3 481	7.681 146	24.28992	205 379	3.892 996	8.387 207	18.06969
60	3 600	7.745 967	24.49490	216 000	3.914 868	8.434 327	18.17121
61	3 721	7.810 250	24.69818	226 981	3.936 497	8.480 926	18.27160
62	3 844	7.874 008	24.89980	238 328	3.957 892	8.527 019	18.37091
63	3 969	7.937 254	25.09980	250 047	3.979 057	8.572 619	18.46915
64	4 096	8.000 000	25.29822	262 144	4.000 000	8.617 739	18.56636
65	4 225	8.062 258	25.49510	274 625	4.020 726	8.662 391	18.66256
66	4 356	8.124 038	25.69047	287 496	4.041 240	8.706 588	18.75777
67	4 489	8.185 353	25.88436	300 763	4.061 548	8.750 340	18.85204
68	4 624	8.246 211	26.07681	314 432	4.081 655	8.793 659	18.94536
69	4 761	8.306 624	26.26785	328 509	4.101 566	8.836 556	19.03778
70	4 900	8.366 600	26.45751	343 000	4.121 285	8.879 040	19.12931
71	5 041	8.426 150	26.64583	357 911	4.140 818	8.921 121	19.21997
72	5 184	8.485 281	26.83282	373 248	4.160 168	8.962 809	19.30979
73	5 329	8.544 004	27.01851	389 017	4.179 339	9.004 113	19.39877
74	5 476	8.602 325	27.20294	405 224	4.198 336	9.045 042	19.48695
75	5 625	8.660 254	27.38613	421 875	4.217 163	9.085 603	19.57434
76	5 776	8.717 798	27.56810	438 976	4.235 824	9.125 805	19.66095
77	5 929	8.774 964	27.74887	456 533	4.254 321	9.165 656	19.74681
78	6 084	8.831 761	27.92848	474 552	4.272 659	9.205 164	19.83192
79	6 241	8.888 194	28.10694	493 039	4.290 840	9.244 335	19.91632
80	6 400	8.944 272	28.28427	512 000	4.308 869	9.283 178	20.00000
81	6 561	9.000 000	28.46050	531 441	4.326 749	9.321 698	20.08299
82	6 724	9.055 385	28.63564	551 368	4.344 481	9.359 902	20.16530
83	6 889	9.110 434	28.80972	571 787	4.362 071	9.397 796	20.24694
84	7 056	9.165 151	28.98275	592 704	4.379 519	9.435 388	20.32793
85	7 225	9.219 544	29.15476	614 125	4.396 830	9.472 682	20.40828
86	7 396	9.273 618	29.32576	636 056	4.414 005	9.509 685	20.48800
87	7 569	9.327 379	29.49576	658 503	4.431 048	9.546 403	20.56710
88	7 744	9.380 832	29.66479	681 472	4.447 960	9.582 840	20.64560
89	7 921	9.433 981	29.83287	704 969	4.464 745	9.619 002	20.72351
90	8 100	9.486 833	30.00000	729 000	4.481 405	9.654 894	20.80084
91	8 281	9.539 392	30.16621	753 571	4.497 941	9.690 521	20.87759
92	8 464	9.591 663	30.33150	778 688	4.514 357	9.725 888	20.95379
93	8 649	9.643 651	30.49590	804 357	4.530 655	9.761 000	21.02944
94	8 836	9.695 360	30.65942	830 584	4.546 836	9.795 861	21.10454
95	9 025	9.746 794	30.82207	857 375	4.562 903	9.830 476	21.17912
96	9 216	9.797 959	30.98387	884 736	4.578 857	9.864 848	21.25317
97	9 409	9.848 858	31.14482	912 673	4.594 701	9.898 983	21.32671
98	9 604	9.899 495	31.30495	941 192	4.610 436	9.932 884	21.39975
99	9 801	9.949 874	31.46427	970 299	4.626 065	9.966 555	21.47229
100	10 000	10.00000	31.62278	1 000 000	4.641 589	10.00000	21.54435

SQUARES, CUBES AND ROOTS

n	n^2	$\sqrt{n}$	$\sqrt{10n}$	n^3	$\sqrt[3]{n}$	$\sqrt[3]{10n}$	$\sqrt[3]{100n}$
100	10 000	10.00000	31.62278	1 000 000	4.641 589	10.00000	21.54435
101	10 201	10.04988	31.78050	1 030 301	4.657 010	10.03322	21.61592
102	10 404	10.09950	31.93744	1 061 208	4.672 329	10.06623	21.68703
103	10 609	10.14889	32.09361	1 092 727	4.687 548	10.09902	21.75767
104	10 816	10.19804	32.24903	1 124 864	4.702 669	10.13159	21.82786
105	11 025	10.24695	32.40370	1 157 625	4.717 694	10.16396	21.89760
106	11 236	10.29563	32.55764	1 191 016	4.732 623	10.19613	21.96689
107	11 449	10.34408	32.71085	1 225 043	4.747 459	10.22809	22.03575
108	11 664	10.39230	32.86335	1 259 712	4.762 203	10.25986	22.10419
109	11 881	10.44031	33.01515	1 295 029	4.776 856	10.29142	22.17220
110	12 100	10.48809	33.16625	1 331 000	4.791 420	10.32280	22.23980
111	12 321	10.53565	33.31666	1 367 631	4.805 896	10.35399	22.30699
112	12 544	10.58301	33.46640	1 404 928	4.820 285	10.38499	22.37378
113	12 769	10.63015	33.61547	1 442 897	4.834 588	10.41580	22.44017
114	12 996	10.67708	33.76389	1 481 544	4.848 808	10.44644	22.50617
115	13 225	10.72381	33.91165	1 520 875	4.862 944	10.47690	22.57179
116	13 456	10.77033	34.05877	1 560 896	4.876 999	10.50718	22.63702
117	13 689	10.81665	34.20526	1 601 613	4.890 973	10.53728	22.70189
118	13 924	10.86278	34.35113	1 643 032	4.904 868	10.56722	22.76638
119	14 161	10.90871	34.49638	1 685 159	4.918 685	10.59699	22.83051
120	14 400	10.95445	34.64102	1 728 000	4.932 424	10.62659	22.89428
121	14 641	11.00000	34.78505	1 771 561	4.946 087	10.65602	22.95770
122	14 884	11.04536	34.92850	1 815 848	4.959 676	10.68530	23.02078
123	15 129	11.09054	35.07136	1 860 867	4.973 190	10.71441	23.08350
124	15 376	11.13553	35.21363	1 906 624	4.986 631	10.74337	23.14589
125	15 625	11.18034	35.35534	1 953 125	5.000 000	10.77217	23.20794
126	15 876	11.22497	35.49648	2 000 376	5.013 298	10.80082	23.26967
127	16 129	11.26943	35.63706	2 048 383	5.026 526	10.82932	23.33107
128	16 384	11.31371	35.77709	2 097 152	5.039 684	10.85767	23.39214
129	16 641	11.35782	35.91657	2 146 689	5.052 774	10.88587	23.45290
130	16 900	11.40175	36.05551	2 197 000	5.065 797	10.91393	23.51335
131	17 161	11.44552	36.19392	2 248 091	5.078 753	10.94184	23.57348
132	17 424	11.48913	36.33180	2 299 968	5.091 643	10.96961	23.63332
133	17 689	11.53256	36.46917	2 352 637	5.104 469	10.99724	23.69285
134	17 956	11.57584	36.60601	2 406 104	5.117 230	11.02474	23.75208
135	18 225	11.61895	36.74235	2 460 375	5.129 928	11.05209	23.81102
136	18 496	11.66190	36.87818	2 515 456	5.142 563	11.07932	23.86966
137	18 769	11.70470	37.01351	2 571 353	5.155 137	11.10641	23.92803
138	19 044	11.74734	37.14835	2 628 072	5.167 649	11.13336	23.98610
139	19 321	11.78983	37.28270	2 685 619	5.180 101	11.16019	24.04390
140	19 600	11.83216	37.41657	2 744 000	5.192 494	11.18689	24.10142
141	19 881	11.87434	37.54997	2 803 221	5.204 828	11.21346	24.15867
142	20 164	11.91638	37.68289	2 863 288	5.217 103	11.23991	24.21565
143	20 449	11.95826	37.81534	2 924 207	5.229 322	11.26623	24.27236
144	20 736	12.00000	37.94733	2 985 984	5.241 483	11.29243	24.32881
145	21 025	12.04159	38.07887	3 048 625	5.253 588	11.31851	24.38499
146	21 316	12.08305	38.20995	3 112 136	5.265 637	11.34447	24.44092
147	21 609	12.12436	38.34058	3 176 523	5.277 632	11.37031	24.49660
148	21 904	12.16553	38.47077	3 241 792	5.289 572	11.39604	24.55202
149	22 201	12.20656	38.60052	3 307 949	5.301 459	11.42165	24.60719
150	22 500	12.24745	38.72983	3 375 000	5.313 293	11.44714	24.66212

n	n^2	$\sqrt{n}$	$\sqrt{10n}$	n^3	$\sqrt[3]{n}$	$\sqrt[3]{10n}$	$\sqrt[3]{100n}$
150	22 500	12.24745	38.72983	3 375 000	5.313 293	11.44714	24.66212
151	22 801	12.28821	38.85872	3 442 951	5.325 074	11.47252	24.71680
152	23 104	12.32883	38.98718	3 511 808	5.336 803	11.49779	24.77125
153	23 409	12.36932	39.11521	3 581 577	5.348 481	11.52295	24.82545
154	23 716	12.40967	39.24283	3 652 264	5.360 108	11.54800	24.87942
155	24 025	12.44990	39.37004	3 723 875	5.371 685	11.57295	24.93315
156	24 336	12.49000	39.49684	3 796 416	5.383 213	11.59778	24.98666
157	24 649	12.52996	39.62323	3 869 893	5.394 691	11.62251	25.03994
158	24 964	12.56981	39.74921	3 944 312	5.406 120	11.64713	25.09299
159	25 281	12.60952	39.87480	4 019 679	5.417 502	11.67165	25.14581
160	25 600	12.64911	40.00000	4 096 000	5.428 835	11.69607	25.19842
161	25 921	12.68858	40.12481	4 173 281	5.440 122	11.72039	25.25081
162	26 244	12.72792	40.24922	4 251 528	5.451 362	11.74460	25.30298
163	26 569	12.76715	40.37326	4 330 747	5.462 556	11.76872	25.35494
164	26 896	12.80625	40.49691	4 410 944	5.473 704	11.79274	25.40668
165	27 225	12.84523	40.62019	4 492 125	5.484 807	11.81666	25.45822
166	27 556	12.88410	40.74310	4 574 296	5.495 865	11.84048	25.50954
167	27 889	12.92285	40.86563	4 657 463	5.506 878	11.86421	25.56067
168	28 224	12.96148	40.98780	4 741 632	5.517 848	11.88784	25.61158
169	28 561	13.00000	41.10961	4 826 809	5.528 775	11.91138	25.66230
170	28 900	13.03840	41.23106	4 913 000	5.539 658	11.93483	25.71282
171	29 241	13.07670	41.35215	5 000 211	5.550 499	11.95819	25.76313
172	29 584	13.11488	41.47288	5 088 448	5.561 298	11.98145	25.81326
173	29 929	13.15295	41.59327	5 177 717	5.572 055	12.00463	25.86319
174	30 276	13.19091	41.71331	5 268 024	5.582 770	12.02771	25.91292
175	30 625	13.22876	41.83300	5 359 375	5.593 445	12.05071	25.96247
176	30 976	13.26650	41.95235	5 451 776	5.604 079	12.07362	26.01183
177	31 329	13.30413	42.07137	5 545 233	5.614 672	12.09645	26.06100
178	31 684	13.34166	42.19005	5 639 752	5.625 226	12.11918	26.10999
179	32 041	13.37909	42.30839	5 735 339	5.635 741	12.14184	26.15879
180	32 400	13.41641	42.42641	5 832 000	5.646 216	12.16440	26.20741
181	32 761	13.45362	42.54409	5 929 741	5.656 653	12.18689	26.25586
182	33 124	13.49074	42.66146	6 028 568	5.667 051	12.20929	26.30412
183	33 489	13.52775	42.77850	6 128 487	5.677 411	12.23161	26.35221
184	33 856	13.56466	42.89522	6 229 504	5.687 734	12.25385	26.40012
185	34 225	13.60147	43.01163	6 331 625	5.698 019	12.27601	26.44786
186	34 596	13.63818	43.12772	6 434 856	5.708 267	12.29809	26.49543
187	34 969	13.67479	43.24350	6 539 203	5.718 479	12.32009	26.54283
188	35 344	13.71131	43.35897	6 644 672	5.728 654	12.34201	26.59006
189	35 721	13.74773	43.47413	6 751 269	5.738 794	12.36386	26.63712
190	36 100	13.78405	43.58899	6 859 000	5.748 897	12.38562	26.68402
191	36 481	13.82027	43.70355	6 967 871	5.758 965	12.40731	26.73075
192	36 864	13.85641	43.81780	7 077 888	5.768 998	12.42893	26.77732
193	37 249	13.89244	43.93177	7 189 057	5.778 997	12.45047	26.82373
194	37 636	13.92839	44.04543	7 301 384	5.788 960	12.47194	26.86997
195	38 025	13.96424	44.15880	7 414 875	5.798 890	12.49333	26.91606
196	38 416	14.00000	44.27189	7 529 536	5.808 786	12.51465	26.96199
197	38 809	14.03567	44.38468	7 645 373	5.818 648	12.53590	27.00777
198	39 204	14.07125	44.49719	7 762 392	5.828 477	12.55707	27.05339
199	39 601	14.10674	44.60942	7 880 599	5.838 272	12.57818	27.09886
200	40 000	14.14214	44.72136	8 000 000	5.848 035	12.59921	27.14418

n	n^2	$\sqrt{n}$	$\sqrt{10n}$	n^3	$\sqrt[3]{n}$	$\sqrt[3]{10n}$	$\sqrt[3]{100n}$
200	40 000	14.14214	44.72136	8 000 000	5.848 035	12.59921	27.14418
201	40 401	14.17745	44.83302	8 120 601	5.857 766	12.62017	27.18934
202	40 804	14.21267	44.94441	8 242 408	5.867 464	12.64107	27.23436
203	41 209	14.24781	45.05552	8 365 427	5.877 131	12.66189	27.27922
204	41 616	14.28286	45.16636	8 489 664	5.886 765	12.68265	27.32394
205	42 025	14.31782	45.27693	8 615 125	5.896 369	12.70334	27.36852
206	42 436	14.35270	45.38722	8 741 816	5.905 941	12.72396	27.41295
207	42 849	14.38749	45.49725	8 869 743	5.915 482	12.74452	27.45723
208	43 264	14.42221	45.60702	8 998 912	5.924 992	12.76501	27.50138
209	43 681	14.45683	45.71652	9 129 329	5.934 472	12.78543	27.54538
210	44 100	14.49138	45.82576	9 261 000	5.943 922	12.80579	27.58924
211	44 521	14.52584	45.93474	9 393 931	5.953 342	12.82609	27.63296
212	44 944	14.56022	46.04346	9 528 128	5.962 732	12.84632	27.67655
213	45 369	14.59452	46.15192	9 663 597	5.972 093	12.86648	27.72000
214	45 796	14.62874	46.26013	9 800 344	5.981 424	12.88659	27.76331
215	46 225	14.66288	46.36809	9 938 375	5.990 726	12.90663	27.80649
216	46 656	14.69694	46.47580	10 077 696	6.000 000	12.92661	27.84953
217	47 089	14.73092	46.58326	10 218 313	6.009 245	12.94653	27.89244
218	47 524	14.76482	46.69047	10 360 232	6.018 462	12.96638	27.93522
219	47 961	14.79865	46.79744	10 503 459	6.027 650	12.98618	27.97787
220	48 400	14.83240	46.90416	10 648 000	6.036 811	13.00591	28.02039
221	48 841	14.86607	47.01064	10 793 861	6.045 944	13.02559	28.06278
222	49 284	14.89966	47.11688	10 941 048	6.055 049	13.04521	28.10505
223	49 729	14.93318	47.22288	11 089 567	6.064 127	13.06477	28.14718
224	50 176	14.96663	47.32864	11 239 424	6.073 178	13.08427	28.18919
225	50 625	15.00000	47.43416	11 390 625	6.082 202	13.10371	28.23108
226	51 076	15.03330	47.53946	11 543 176	6.091 199	13.12309	28.27284
227	51 529	15.06652	47.64452	11 697 083	6.100 170	13.14242	28.31448
228	51 984	15.09967	47.74935	11 852 352	6.109 115	13.16169	28.35600
229	52 441	15.13275	47.85394	12 008 989	6.118 033	13.18090	28.39739
230	52 900	15.16575	47.95832	12 167 000	6.126 926	13.20006	28.43867
231	53 361	15.19868	48.06246	12 326 391	6.135 792	13.21916	28.47983
232	53 824	15.23155	48.16638	12 487 168	6.144 634	13.23821	28.52086
233	54 289	15.26434	48.27007	12 649 337	6.153 449	13.25721	28.56178
234	54 756	15.29706	48.37355	12 812 904	6.162 240	13.27614	28.60259
235	55 225	15.32971	48.47680	12 977 875	6.171 006	13.29503	28.64327
236	55 696	15.36229	48.57983	13 144 256	6.179 747	13.31386	28.68384
237	56 169	15.39480	48.68265	13 312 053	6.188 463	13.33264	28.72430
238	56 644	15.42725	48.78524	13 481 272	6.197 154	13.35136	28.76464
239	57 121	15.45962	48.88763	13 651 919	6.205 822	13.37004	28.80487
240	57 600	15.49193	48.98979	13 824 000	6.214 465	13.38866	28.84499
241	58 081	15.52417	49.09175	13 997 521	6.223 084	13.40723	28.88500
242	58 564	15.55635	49.19350	14 172 488	6.231 680	13.42575	28.92489
243	59 049	15.58846	49.29503	14 348 907	6.240 251	13.44421	28.96468
244	59 536	15.62050	49.39636	14 526 784	6.248 800	13.46263	29.00436
245	60 025	15.65248	49.49747	14 706 125	6.257 325	13.48100	29.04393
246	60 516	15.68439	49.59839	14 886 936	6.265 827	13.49931	29.08339
247	61 009	15.71623	49.69909	15 069 223	6.274 305	13.51758	29.12275
248	61 504	15.74802	49.79960	15 252 992	6.282 761	13.53580	29.16199
249	62 001	15.77973	49.89990	15 438 249	6.291 195	13.55397	29.20114
250	62 500	15.81139	50.00000	15 625 000	6.299 605	13.57209	29.24018

n	n^2	$\sqrt{n}$	$\sqrt{10n}$	n^3	$\sqrt[3]{n}$	$\sqrt[3]{10n}$	$\sqrt[3]{100n}$
250	62 500	15.81139	50.00000	15 625 000	6.299 605	13.57209	29.24018
251	63 001	15.84298	50.09990	15 813 251	6.307 994	13.59016	29.27911
252	63 504	15.87451	50.19960	16 003 008	6.316 360	13.60818	29.31794
253	64 009	15.90597	50.29911	16 194 277	6.324 704	13.62616	29.35667
254	64 516	15.93738	50.39841	16 387 064	6.333 026	13.64409	29.39530
255	65 025	15.96872	50.49752	16 581 375	6.341 326	13.66197	29.43383
256	65 536	16.00000	50.59644	16 777 216	6.349 604	13.67981	29.47225
257	66 049	16.03122	50.69517	16 974 593	6.357 861	13.69760	29.51058
258	66 564	16.06238	50.79370	17 173 512	6.366 097	13.71534	29.54880
259	67 081	16.09348	50.89204	17 373 979	6.374 311	13.73304	29.58693
260	67 600	16.12452	50.99020	17 576 000	6.382 504	13.75069	29.62496
261	68 121	16.15549	51.08816	17 779 581	6.390 677	13.76830	29.66289
262	68 644	16.18641	51.18594	17 984 728	6.398 828	13.78586	29.70073
263	69 169	16.21727	51.28353	18 191 447	6.406 959	13.80337	29.73847
264	69 696	16.24808	51.38093	18 399 744	6.415 069	13.82085	29.77611
265	70 225	16.27882	51.47815	18 609 625	6.423 158	13.83828	29.81366
266	70 756	16.30951	51.57519	18 821 096	6.431 228	13.85566	29.85111
267	71 289	16.34013	51.67204	19 034 163	6.439 277	13.87300	29.88847
268	71 824	16.37071	51.76872	19 248 832	6.447 306	13.89030	29.92574
269	72 361	16.40122	51.86521	19 465 109	6.455 315	13.90755	29.96292
270	72 900	16.43168	51.96152	19 683 000	6.463 304	13.92477	30.00000
271	73 441	16.46208	52.05766	19 902 511	6.471 274	13.94194	30.03699
272	73 984	16.49242	52.15362	20 123 648	6.479 224	13.95906	30.07389
273	74 529	16.52271	52.24940	20 346 417	6.487 154	13.97615	30.11070
274	75 076	16.55295	52.34501	20 570 824	6.495 065	13.99319	30.14742
275	75 625	16.58312	52.44044	20 796 875	6.502 957	14.01020	30.18405
276	76 176	16.61325	52.53570	21 024 576	6.510 830	14.02716	30.22060
277	76 729	16.64332	52.63079	21 253 933	6.518 684	14.04408	30.25705
278	77 284	16.67333	52.72571	21 484 952	6.526 519	14.06096	30.29342
279	77 841	16.70329	52.82045	21 717 639	6.534 335	14.07780	30.32970
280	78 400	16.73320	52.91503	21 952 000	6.542 133	14.09460	30.36589
281	78 961	16.76305	53.00943	22 188 041	6.549 912	14.11136	30.40200
282	79 524	16.79286	53.10367	22 425 768	6.557 672	14.12808	30.43802
283	80 089	16.82260	53.19774	22 665 187	6.565 414	14.14476	30.47395
284	80 656	16.85230	53.29165	22 906 304	6.573 138	14.16140	30.50981
285	81 225	16.88194	53.38539	23 149 125	6.580 844	14.17800	30.54557
286	81 796	16.91153	53.47897	23 393 656	6.588 532	14.19456	30.58126
287	82 369	16.94107	53.57238	23 639 903	6.596 202	14.21109	30.61686
288	82 944	16.97056	53.66563	23 887 872	6.603 854	14.22757	30.65238
289	83 521	17.00000	53.75872	24 137 569	6.611 489	14.24402	30.68781
290	84 100	17.02939	53.85165	24 389 000	6.619 106	14.26043	30.72317
291	84 681	17.05872	53.94442	24 642 171	6.626 705	14.27680	30.75844
292	85 264	17.08801	54.03702	24 897 088	6.634 287	14.29314	30.79363
293	85 849	17.11724	54.12947	25 153 757	6.641 852	14.30944	30.82875
294	86 436	17.14643	54.22177	25 412 184	6.649 400	14.32570	30.86378
295	87 025	17.17556	54.31390	25 672 375	6.656 930	14.34192	30.89873
296	87 616	17.20465	54.40588	25 934 336	6.664 444	14.35811	30.93361
297	88 209	17.23369	54.49771	26 198 073	6.671 940	14.37426	30.96840
298	88 804	17.26268	54.58938	26 463 592	6.679 420	14.39037	31.00312
299	89 401	17.29162	54.68089	26 730 899	6.686 883	14.40645	31.03776
300	90 000	17.32051	54.77226	27 000 000	6.694 330	14.42250	31.07233

n	n^2	$\sqrt{n}$	$\sqrt{10n}$	n^3	$\sqrt[3]{n}$	$\sqrt[3]{10n}$	$\sqrt[3]{100n}$
300	90 000	17.32051	54.77226	27 000 000	6.694 330	14.42250	31.07233
301	90 601	17.34935	54.86347	27 270 901	6.701 759	14.43850	31.10681
302	91 204	17.37815	54.95453	27 543 608	6.709 173	14.45447	31.14122
303	91 809	17.40690	55.04544	27 818 127	6.716 570	14.47041	31.17556
304	92 416	17.43560	55.13620	28 094 464	6.723 951	14.48631	31.20982
305	93 025	17.46425	55.22681	28 372 625	6.731 315	14.50218	31.24400
306	93 636	17.49286	55.31727	28 652 616	6.738 664	14.51801	31.27811
307	94 249	17.52142	55.40758	28 934 443	6.745 997	14.53381	31.31214
308	94 864	17.54993	55.49775	29 218 112	6.753 313	14.54957	31.34610
309	95 481	17.57840	55.58777	29 503 629	6.760 614	14.56530	31.37999
310	96 100	17.60682	55.67764	29 791 000	6.767 899	14.58100	31.41381
311	96 721	17.63519	55.76737	30 080 231	6.775 169	14.59666	31.44755
312	97 344	17.66352	55.85696	30 371 328	6.782 423	14.61229	31.48122
313	97 969	17.69181	55.94640	30 664 297	6.789 661	14.62788	31.51482
314	98 596	17.72005	56.03570	30 959 144	6.796 884	14.64344	31.54834
315	99 225	17.74824	56.12486	31 255 875	6.804 092	14.65897	31.58180
316	99 856	17.77639	56.21388	31 554 496	6.811 285	14.67447	31.61518
317	100 489	17.80449	56.30275	31 855 013	6.818 462	14.68993	31.64850
318	101 124	17.83255	56.39149	32 157 432	6.825 624	14.70536	31.68174
319	101 761	17.86057	56.48008	32 461 759	6.832 771	14.72076	31.71492
320	102 400	17.88854	56.56854	32 768 000	6.839 904	14.73613	31.74802
321	103 041	17.91647	56.65686	33 076 161	6.847 021	14.75146	31.78106
322	103 684	17.94436	56.74504	33 386 248	6.854 124	14.76676	31.81403
323	104 329	17.97220	56.83309	33 698 267	6.861 212	14.78203	31.84693
324	104 976	18.00000	56.92100	34 012 224	6.868 285	14.79727	31.87976
325	105 625	18.02776	57.00877	34 328 125	6.875 344	14.81248	31.91252
326	106 276	18.05547	57.09641	34 645 976	6.882 389	14.82766	31.94522
327	106 929	18.08314	57.18391	34 965 783	6.889 419	14.84280	31.97785
328	107 584	18.11077	57.27128	35 287 552	6.896 434	14.85792	32.01041
329	108 241	18.13836	57.35852	35 611 289	6.903 436	14.87300	32.04291
330	108 900	18.16590	57.44563	35 937 000	6.910 423	14.88806	32.07534
331	109 561	18.19341	57.53260	36 264 691	6.917 396	14.90308	32.10771
332	110 224	18.22087	57.61944	36 594 368	6.924 356	14.91807	32.14001
333	110 889	18.24829	57.70615	36 926 037	6.931 301	14.93303	32.17225
334	111 556	18.27567	57.79273	37 259 704	6.938 232	14.94797	32.20442
335	112 225	18.30301	57.87918	37 595 375	6.945 150	14.96287	32.23653
336	112 896	18.33030	57.96551	37 933 056	6.952 053	14.97774	32.26857
337	113 569	18.35756	58.05170	38 272 753	6.958 943	14.99259	32.30055
338	114 244	18.38478	58.13777	38 614 472	6.965 820	15.00740	32.33247
339	114 921	18.41195	58.22371	38 958 219	6.972 683	15.02219	32.36433
340	115 600	18.43909	58.30952	39 304 000	6.979 532	15.03695	32.39612
341	116 281	18.46619	58.39521	39 651 821	6.986 368	15.05167	32.42785
342	116 964	18.49324	58.48077	40 001 688	6.993 191	15.06637	32.45952
343	117 649	18.52026	58.56620	40 353 607	7.000 000	15.08104	32.49112
344	118 336	18.54724	58.65151	40 707 584	7.006 796	15.09568	32.52267
345	119 025	18.57418	58.73670	41 063 625	7.013 579	15.11030	32.55415
346	119 716	18.60108	58.82176	41 421 736	7.020 349	15.12488	32.58557
347	120 409	18.62794	58.90671	41 781 923	7.027 106	15.13944	32.61694
348	121 104	18.65476	58.99152	42 144 192	7.033 850	15.15397	32.64824
349	121 801	18.68154	59.07622	42 508 549	7.040 581	15.16847	32.67948
350	122 500	18.70829	59.16080	42 875 000	7.047 299	15.18294	32.71066

n	n^2	$\sqrt{n}$	$\sqrt{10n}$	n^3	$\sqrt[3]{n}$	$\sqrt[3]{10n}$	$\sqrt[3]{100n}$
350	122 500	18.70829	59.16080	42 875 000	7.047 299	15.18294	32.71066
351	123 201	18.73499	59.24525	43 243 551	7.054 004	15.19739	32.74179
352	123 904	18.76166	59.32959	43 614 208	7.060 697	15.21181	32.77285
353	124 609	18.78829	59.41380	43 986 977	7.067 377	15.22620	32.80386
354	125 316	18.81489	59.49790	44 361 864	7.074 044	15.24057	32.83480
355	126 025	18.84144	59.58188	44 738 875	7.080 699	15.25490	32.86569
356	126 736	18.86796	59.66574	45 118 016	7.087 341	15.26921	32.89652
357	127 449	18.89444	59.74948	45 499 293	7.093 971	15.28350	32.92730
358	128 164	18.92089	59.83310	45 882 712	7.100 588	15.29775	32.95801
359	128 881	18.94730	59.91661	46 268 279	7.107 194	15.31198	32.98867
360	129 600	18.97367	60.00000	46 656 000	7.113 787	15.32619	33.01927
361	130 321	19.00000	60.08328	47 045 881	7.120 367	15.34037	33.04982
362	131 044	19.02630	60.16644	47 437 928	7.126 936	15.35452	33.08031
363	131 769	19.05256	60.24948	47 832 147	7.133 492	15.36864	33.11074
364	132 496	19.07878	60.33241	48 228 544	7.140 037	15.38274	33.14112
365	133 225	19.10497	60.41523	48 627 125	7.146 569	15.39682	33.17144
366	133 956	19.13113	60.49793	49 027 896	7.153 090	15.41087	33.20170
367	134 689	19.15724	60.58052	49 430 863	7.159 599	15.42489	33.23191
368	135 424	19.18333	60.66300	49 836 032	7.166 096	15.43889	33.26207
369	136 161	19.20937	60.74537	50 243 409	7.172 581	15.45286	33.29217
370	136 900	19.23538	60.82763	50 653 000	7.179 054	15.46680	33.32222
371	137 641	19.26136	60.90977	51 064 811	7.185 516	15.48073	33.35221
372	138 384	19.28730	60.99180	51 478 848	7.191 966	15.49462	33.38215
373	139 129	19.31321	61.07373	51 895 117	7.198 405	15.50849	33.41204
374	139 876	19.33908	61.15554	52 313 624	7.204 832	15.52234	33.44187
375	140 625	19.36492	61.23724	52 734 375	7.211 248	15.53616	33.47165
376	141 376	19.39072	61.31884	53 157 376	7.217 652	15.54996	33.50137
377	142 129	19.41649	61.40033	53 582 633	7.224 045	15.56373	33.53105
378	142 884	19.44222	61.48170	54 010 152	7.230 427	15.57748	33.56067
379	143 641	19.46792	61.56298	54 439 939	7.236 797	15.59121	33.59024
380	144 400	19.49359	61.64414	54 872 000	7.243 156	15.60491	33.61975
381	145 161	19.51922	61.72520	55 306 341	7.249 505	15.61858	33.64922
382	145 924	19.54482	61.80615	55 742 968	7.255 842	15.63224	33.67863
383	146 689	19.57039	61.88699	56 181 887	7.262 167	15.64587	33.70800
384	147 456	19.59592	61.96773	56 623 104	7.268 482	15.65947	33.73731
385	148 225	19.62142	62.04837	57 066 625	7.274 786	15.67305	33.76657
386	148 996	19.64688	62.12890	57 512 456	7.281 079	15.68661	33.79578
387	149 769	19.67232	62.20932	57 960 603	7.287 362	15.70014	33.82494
388	150 544	19.69772	62.28965	58 411 072	7.293 633	15.71366	33.85405
389	151 321	19.72308	62.36986	58 863 869	7.299 894	15.72714	33.88310
390	152 100	19.74842	62.44998	59 319 000	7.306 144	15.74061	33.91211
391	152 881	19.77372	62.52999	59 776 471	7.312 383	15.75405	33.94107
392	153 664	19.79899	62.60990	60 236 288	7.318 611	15.76747	33.96999
393	154 449	19.82423	62.68971	60 698 457	7.324 829	15.78087	33.99885
394	155 236	19.84943	62.76942	61 162 984	7.331 037	15.79424	34.02766
395	156 025	19.87461	62.84903	61 629 875	7.337 234	15.80759	34.05642
396	156 816	19.89975	62.92853	62 099 136	7.343 420	15.82092	34.08514
397	157 609	19.92486	63.00794	62 570 773	7.349 597	15.83423	34.11381
398	158 404	19.94994	63.08724	63 044 792	7.355 762	15.84751	34.14242
399	159 201	19.97498	63.16645	63 521 199	7.361 918	15.86077	34.17100
400	160 000	20.00000	63.24555	64 000 000	7.368 063	15.87401	34.19952

n	n^2	$\sqrt{n}$	$\sqrt{10n}$	n^3	$\sqrt[3]{n}$	$\sqrt[3]{10n}$	$\sqrt[3]{100n}$
400	160 000	20.00000	63.24555	64 000 000	7.368 063	15.87401	34.19952
401	160 801	20.02498	63.32456	64 481 201	7.374 198	15.88723	34.22799
402	161 604	20.04994	63.40347	64 964 808	7.380 323	15.90042	34.25642
403	162 409	20.07486	63.48228	65 450 827	7.386 437	15.91360	34.28480
404	163 216	20.09975	63.56099	65 939 264	7.392 542	15.92675	34.31314
405	164 025	20.12461	63.63961	66 430 125	7.398 636	15.93988	34.34143
406	164 836	20.14944	63.71813	66 923 416	7.404 721	15.95299	34.36967
407	165 649	20.17424	63.79655	67 419 143	7.410 795	15.96607	34.39786
408	166 464	20.19901	63.87488	67 917 312	7.416 860	15.97914	34.42601
409	167 281	20.22375	63.95311	68 417 929	7.422 914	15.99218	34.45412
410	168 100	20.24846	64.03124	68 921 000	7.428 959	16.00521	34.48217
411	168 921	20.27313	64.10928	69 426 531	7.434 994	16.01821	34.51018
412	169 744	20.29778	64.18723	69 934 528	7.441 019	16.03119	34.53815
413	170 569	20.32240	64.26508	70 444 997	7.447 034	16.04415	34.56607
414	171 396	20.34699	64.34283	70 957 944	7.453 040	16.05709	34.59395
415	172 225	20.37155	64.42049	71 473 375	7.459 036	16.07001	34.62178
416	173 056	20.39608	64.49806	71 991 296	7.465 022	16.08290	34.64956
417	173 889	20.42058	64.57554	72 511 713	7.470 999	16.09578	34.67731
418	174 724	20.44505	64.65292	73 034 632	7.476 966	16.10864	34.70500
419	175 561	20.46949	64.73021	73 560 059	7.482 924	16.12147	34.73266
420	176 400	20.49390	64.80741	74 088 000	7.488 872	16.13429	34.76027
421	177 241	20.51828	64.88451	74 618 461	7.494 811	16.14708	34.78783
422	178 084	20.54264	64.96153	75 151 448	7.500 741	16.15986	34.81535
423	178 929	20.56696	65.03845	75 686 967	7.506 661	16.17261	34.84283
424	179 776	20.59126	65.11528	76 225 024	7.512 572	16.18534	34.87027
425	180 625	20.61553	65.19202	76 765 625	7.518 473	16.19806	34.89766
426	181 476	20.63977	65.26868	77 308 776	7.524 365	16.21075	34.92501
427	182 329	20.66398	65.34524	77 854 483	7.530 248	16.22343	34.95232
428	183 184	20.68816	65.42171	78 402 752	7.536 122	16.23608	34.97958
429	184 041	20.71232	65.49809	78 953 589	7.541 987	16.24872	35.00680
430	184 900	20.73644	65.57439	79 507 000	7.547 842	16.26133	35.03398
431	185 761	20.76054	65.65059	80 062 991	7.553 689	16.27393	35.06112
432	186 624	20.78461	65.72671	80 621 568	7.559 526	16.28651	35.08821
433	187 489	20.80865	65.80274	81 182 737	7.565 355	16.29906	35.11527
434	188 356	20.83267	65.87868	81 746 504	7.571 174	16.31160	35.14228
435	189 225	20.85665	65.95453	82 312 875	7.576 985	16.32412	35.16925
436	190 096	20.88061	66.03030	82 881 856	7.582 787	16.33662	35.19618
437	190 969	20.90454	66.10598	83 453 453	7.588 579	16.34910	35.22307
438	191 844	20.92845	66.18157	84 027 672	7.594 363	16.36156	35.24991
439	192 721	20.95233	66.25708	84 604 519	7.600 139	16.37400	35.27672
440	193 600	20.97618	66.33250	85 184 000	7.605 905	16.38643	35.30348
441	194 481	21.00000	66.40783	85 766 121	7.611 663	16.39883	35.33021
442	195 364	21.02380	66.48308	86 350 888	7.617 412	16.41122	35.35689
443	196 249	21.04757	66.55825	86 938 307	7.623 152	16.42358	35.38354
444	197 136	21.07131	66.63332	87 528 384	7.628 884	16.43593	35.41014
445	198 025	21.09502	66.70832	88 121 125	7.634 607	16.44826	35.43671
446	198 916	21.11871	66.78323	88 716 536	7.640 321	16.46057	35.46323
447	199 809	21.14237	66.85806	89 314 623	7.646 027	16.47287	35.48971
448	200 704	21.16601	66.93280	89 915 392	7.651 725	16.48514	35.51616
449	201 601	21.18962	67.00746	90 518 849	7.657 414	16.49740	35.54257
450	202 500	21.21320	67.08204	91 125 000	7.663 094	16.50964	35.56893

n	n^2	$\sqrt{n}$	$\sqrt{10n}$	n^3	$\sqrt[3]{n}$	$\sqrt[3]{10n}$	$\sqrt[3]{100n}$
450	202 500	21.21320	67.08204	91 125 000	7.663 094	16.50964	35.56893
451	203 401	21.23676	67.15653	91 733 851	7.668 766	16.52186	35.59526
452	204 304	21.26029	67.23095	92 345 408	7.674 430	16.53406	35.62155
453	205 209	21.28380	67.30527	92 959 677	7.680 086	16.54624	35.64780
454	206 116	21.30728	67.37952	93 576 664	7.685 733	16.55841	35.67401
455	207 025	21.33073	67.45369	94 196 375	7.691 372	16.57056	35.70018
456	207 936	21.35416	67.52777	94 818 816	7.697 002	16.58269	35.72632
457	208 849	21.37756	67.60178	95 443 993	7.702 625	16.59480	35.75242
458	209 764	21.40093	67.67570	96 071 912	7.708 239	16.60690	35.77848
459	210 681	21.42429	67.74954	96 702 579	7.713 845	16.61897	35.80450
460	211 600	21.44761	67.82330	97 336 000	7.719 443	16.63103	35.83048
461	212 521	21.47091	67.89698	97 972 181	7.725 032	16.64308	35.85642
462	213 444	21.49419	67.97058	98 611 128	7.730 614	16.65510	35.88233
463	214 369	21.51743	68.04410	99 252 847	7.736 188	16.66711	35.90820
464	215 296	21.54066	68.11755	99 897 344	7.741 753	16.67910	35.93404
465	216 225	21.56386	68.19091	100 544 625	7.747 311	16.69108	35.95983
466	217 156	21.58703	68.26419	101 194 696	7.752 861	16.70303	35.98559
467	218 089	21.61018	68.33740	101 847 563	7.758 402	16.71497	36.01131
468	219 024	21.63331	68.41053	102 503 232	7.763 936	16.72689	36.03700
469	219 961	21.65641	68.48357	103 161 709	7.769 462	16.73880	36.06265
470	220 900	21.67948	68.55655	103 823 000	7.774 980	16.75069	36.08826
471	221 841	21.70253	68.62944	104 487 111	7.780 490	16.76256	36.11384
472	222 784	21.72556	68.70226	105 154 048	7.785 993	16.77441	36.13938
473	223 729	21.74856	68.77500	105 823 817	7.791 488	16.78625	36.16488
474	224 676	21.77154	68.84766	106 496 424	7.796 975	16.79807	36.19035
475	225 625	21.79449	68.92024	107 171 875	7.802 454	16.80988	36.21578
476	226 576	21.81742	68.99275	107 850 176	7.807 925	16.82167	36.24118
477	227 529	21.84033	69.06519	108 531 333	7.813 389	16.83344	36.26654
478	228 484	21.86321	69.13754	109 215 352	7.818 846	16.84519	36.29187
479	229 441	21.88607	69.20983	109 902 239	7.824 294	16.85693	36.31716
480	230 400	21.90890	69.28203	110 592 000	7.829 735	16.86865	36.34241
481	231 361	21.93171	69.35416	111 284 641	7.835 169	16.88036	36.36763
482	232 324	21.95450	69.42622	111 980 168	7.840 595	16.89205	36.39282
483	233 289	21.97726	69.49820	112 678 587	7.846 013	16.90372	36.41797
484	234 256	22.00000	69.57011	113 379 904	7.851 424	16.91538	36.44308
485	235 225	22.02272	69.64194	114 084 125	7.856 828	16.92702	36.46817
486	236 196	22.04541	69.71370	114 791 256	7.862 224	16.93865	36.49321
487	237 169	22.06808	69.78539	115 501 303	7.867 613	16.95026	36.51822
488	238 144	22.09072	69.85700	116 214 272	7.872 994	16.96185	36.54320
489	239 121	22.11334	69.92853	116 930 169	7.878 368	16.97343	36.56815
490	240 100	22.13594	70.00000	117 649 000	7.883 735	16.98499	36.59306
491	241 081	22.15852	70.07139	118 370 771	7.889 095	16.99654	36.61793
492	242 064	22.18107	70.14271	119 095 488	7.894 447	17.00807	36.64278
493	243 049	22.20360	70.21396	119 823 157	7.899 792	17.01959	36.66758
494	244 036	22.22611	70.28513	120 553 784	7.905 129	17.03108	36.69236
495	245 025	22.24860	70.35624	121 287 375	7.910 460	17.04257	36.71710
496	246 016	22.27106	70.42727	122 023 936	7.915 783	17.05404	36.74181
497	247 009	22.29350	70.49823	122 763 473	7.921 099	17.06549	36.76649
498	248 004	22.31591	70.56912	123 505 992	7.926 408	17.07693	36.79113
499	249 001	22.33831	70.63993	124 251 499	7.931 710	17.08835	36.81574
500	250 000	22.36068	70.71068	125 000 000	7.937 005	17.09976	36.84031

n	n^2	$\sqrt{n}$	$\sqrt{10n}$	n^3	$\sqrt[3]{n}$	$\sqrt[3]{10n}$	$\sqrt[3]{100n}$
500	250 000	22.36068	70.71068	125 000 000	7.937 005	17.09976	36.84031
501	251 001	22.38303	70.78135	125 751 501	7.942 293	17.11115	36.86486
502	252 004	22.40536	70.85196	126 506 008	7.947 574	17.12253	36.88937
503	253 009	22.42766	70.92249	127 263 527	7.952 848	17.13389	36.91385
504	254 016	22.44994	70.99296	128 024 064	7.958 114	17.14524	36.93830
505	255 025	22.47221	71.06335	128 787 625	7.963 374	17.15657	36.96271
506	256 036	22.49444	71.13368	129 554 216	7.968 627	17.16789	36.98709
507	257 049	22.51666	71.20393	130 323 843	7.973 873	17.17919	37.01144
508	258 064	22.53886	71.27412	131 096 512	7.979 112	17.19048	37.03576
509	259 081	22.56103	71.34424	131 872 229	7.984 344	17.20175	37.06004
510	260 100	22.58318	71.41428	132 651 000	7.989 570	17.21301	37.08430
511	261 121	22.60531	71.48426	133 432 831	7.994 788	17.22425	37.10852
512	262 144	22.62742	71.55418	134 217 728	8.000 000	17.23548	37.13271
513	263 169	22.64950	71.62402	135 005 697	8.005 205	17.24669	37.15687
514	264 196	22.67157	71.69379	135 796 744	8.010 403	17.25789	37.18100
515	265 225	22.69361	71.76350	136 590 875	8.015 595	17.26908	37.20509
516	266 256	22.71563	71.83314	137 388 096	8.020 779	17.28025	37.22916
517	267 289	22.73763	71.90271	138 188 413	8.025 957	17.29140	37.25319
518	268 324	22.75961	71.97222	138 991 832	8.031 129	17.30254	37.27720
519	269 361	22.78157	72.04165	139 798 359	8.036 293	17.31367	37.30117
520	270 400	22.80351	72.11103	140 608 000	8.041 452	17.32478	37.32511
521	271 441	22.82542	72.18033	141 420 761	8.046 603	17.33588	37.34902
522	272 484	22.84732	72.24957	142 236 648	8.051 748	17.34696	37.37290
523	273 529	22.86919	72.31874	143 055 667	8.056 886	17.35804	37.39675
524	274 576	22.89105	72.38784	143 877 824	8.062 018	17.36909	37.42057
525	275 625	22.91288	72.45688	144 703 125	8.067 143	17.38013	37.44436
526	276 676	22.93469	72.52586	145 531 576	8.072 262	17.39116	37.46812
527	277 729	22.95648	72.59477	146 363 183	8.077 374	17.40218	37.49185
528	278 784	22.97825	72.66361	147 197 952	8.082 480	17.41318	37.51555
529	279 841	23.00000	72.73239	148 035 889	8.087 579	17.42416	37.53922
530	280 900	23.02173	72.80110	148 877 000	8.092 672	17.43513	37.56286
531	281 961	23.04344	72.86975	149 721 291	8.097 759	17.44609	37.58647
532	283 024	23.06513	72.93833	150 568 768	8.102 839	17.45704	37.61005
533	284 089	23.08679	73.00685	151 419 437	8.107 913	17.46797	37.63360
534	285 156	23.10844	73.07530	152 273 304	8.112 980	17.47889	37.65712
535	286 225	23.13007	73.14369	153 130 375	8.118 041	17.48979	37.68061
536	287 296	23.15167	73.21202	153 990 656	8.123 096	17.50068	37.70407
537	288 369	23.17326	73.28028	154 854 153	8.128 145	17.51156	37.72751
538	289 444	23.19483	73.34848	155 720 872	8.133 187	17.52242	37.75091
539	290 521	23.21637	73.41662	156 590 819	8.138 223	17.53327	37.77429
540	291 600	23.23790	73.48469	157 464 000	8.143 253	17.54411	37.79763
541	292 681	23.25941	73.55270	158 340 421	8.148 276	17.55493	37.82095
542	293 764	23.28089	73.62065	159 220 088	8.153 294	17.56574	37.84424
543	294 849	23.30236	73.68853	160 103 007	8.158 305	17.57654	37.86750
544	295 936	23.32381	73.75636	160 989 184	8.163 310	17.58732	37.89073
545	297 025	23.34524	73.82412	161 878 625	8.168 309	17.59809	37.91393
546	298 116	23.36664	73.89181	162 771 336	8.173 302	17.60885	37.93711
547	299 209	23.38803	73.95945	163 667 323	8.178 289	17.61959	37.96025
548	300 304	23.40940	74.02702	164 566 592	8.183 269	17.63032	37.98337
549	301 401	23.43075	74.09453	165 469 149	8.188 244	17.64104	38.00646
550	302 500	23.45208	74.16198	166 375 000	8.193 213	17.65174	38.02952

n	n^2	$\sqrt{n}$	$\sqrt{10n}$	n^3	$\sqrt[3]{n}$	$\sqrt[3]{10n}$	$\sqrt[3]{100n}$
550	302 500	23.45208	74.16198	166 375 000	8.193 213	17.65174	38.02952
551	303 601	23.47339	74.22937	167 284 151	8.198 175	17.66243	38.05256
552	304 704	23.49468	74.29670	168 196 608	8.203 132	17.67311	38.07557
553	305 809	23.51595	74.36397	169 112 377	8.208 082	17.68378	38.09854
554	306 916	23.53720	74.43118	170 031 464	8.213 027	17.69443	38.12149
555	308 025	23.55844	74.49832	170 953 875	8.217 966	17.70507	38.14442
556	309 136	23.57965	74.56541	171 879 616	8.222 899	17.71570	38.16731
557	310 249	23.60085	74.63243	172 808 693	8.227 825	17.72631	38.19018
558	311 364	23.62202	74.69940	173 741 112	8.232 746	17.73691	38.21302
559	312 481	23.64318	74.76630	174 676 879	8.237 661	17.74750	38.23584
560	313 600	23.66432	74.83315	175 616 000	8.242 571	17.75808	38.25862
561	314 721	23.68544	74.89993	176 558 481	8.247 474	17.76864	38.28138
562	315 844	23.70654	74.96666	177 504 328	8.252 372	17.77920	38.30412
563	316 969	23.72762	75.03333	178 453 547	8.257 263	17.78973	38.32682
564	318 096	23.74868	75.09993	179 406 144	8.262 149	17.80026	38.34950
565	319 225	23.76973	75.16648	180 362 125	8.267 029	17.81077	38.37215
566	320 356	23.79075	75.23297	181 321 496	8.271 904	17.82128	38.39478
567	321 489	23.81176	75.29940	182 284 263	8.276 773	17.83177	38.41737
568	322 624	23.83275	75.36577	183 250 432	8.281 635	17.84224	38.43995
569	323 761	23.85372	75.43209	184 220 009	8.286 493	17.85271	38.46249
570	324 900	23.87467	75.49834	185 193 000	8.291 344	17.86316	38.48501
571	326 041	23.89561	75.56454	186 169 411	8.296 190	17.87360	38.50750
572	327 184	23.91652	75.63068	187 149 248	8.301 031	17.88403	38.52997
573	328 329	23.93742	75.69676	188 132 517	8.305 865	17.89444	38.55241
574	329 476	23.95830	75.76279	189 119 224	8.310 694	17.90485	38.57482
575	330 625	23.97916	75.82875	190 109 375	8.315 517	17.91524	38.59721
576	331 776	24.00000	75.89466	191 102 976	8.320 335	17.92562	38.61958
577	332 929	24.02082	75.96052	192 100 033	8.325 148	17.93599	38.64191
578	334 084	24.04163	76.02631	193 100 552	8.329 954	17.94634	38.66422
579	335 241	24.06242	76.09205	194 104 539	8.334 755	17.95669	38.68651
580	336 400	24.08319	76.15773	195 112 000	8.339 551	17.96702	38.70877
581	337 561	24.10394	76.22336	196 122 941	8.344 341	17.97734	38.73100
582	338 724	24.12468	76.28892	197 137 368	8.349 126	17.98765	38.75321
583	339 889	24.14539	76.35444	198 155 287	8.353 905	17.99794	38.77539
584	341 056	24.16609	76.41989	199 176 704	8.358 678	18.00823	38.79755
585	342 225	24.18677	76.48529	200 201 625	8.363 447	18.01850	38.81968
586	343 396	24.20744	76.55064	201 230 056	8.368 209	18.02876	38.84179
587	344 569	24.22808	76.61593	202 262 003	8.372 967	18.03901	38.86387
588	345 744	24.24871	76.68116	203 297 472	8.377 719	18.04925	38.88593
589	346 921	24.26932	76.74634	204 336 469	8.382 465	18.05947	38.90796
590	348 100	24.28992	76.81146	205 379 000	8.387 207	18.06969	38.92996
591	349 281	24.31049	76.87652	206 425 071	8.391 942	18.07989	38.95195
592	350 464	24.33105	76.94154	207 474 688	8.396 673	18.09008	38.97390
593	351 649	24.35159	77.00649	208 527 857	8.401 398	18.10026	38.99584
594	352 836	24.37212	77.07140	209 584 584	8.406 118	18.11043	39.01774
595	354 025	24.39262	77.13624	210 644 875	8.410 833	18.12059	39.03963
596	355 216	24.41311	77.20104	211 708 736	8.415 542	18.13074	39.06149
597	356 409	24.43358	77.26578	212 776 173	8.420 246	18.14087	39.08332
598	357 604	24.45404	77.33046	213 847 192	8.424 945	18.15099	39.10513
599	358 801	24.47448	77.39509	214 921 799	8.429 638	18.16111	39.12692
600	360 000	24.49490	77.45967	216 000 000	8.434 327	18.17121	39.14868

n	n^2	$\sqrt{n}$	$\sqrt{10n}$	n^3	$\sqrt[3]{n}$	$\sqrt[3]{10n}$	$\sqrt[3]{100n}$
600	360 000	24.49490	77.45967	216 000 000	8.434 327	18.17121	39.14868
601	361 201	24.51530	77.52419	217 081 801	8.439 010	18.18130	39.17041
602	362 404	24.53569	77.58866	218 167 208	8.443 688	18.19137	39.19213
603	363 609	24.55606	77.65307	219 256 227	8.448 361	18.20144	39.21382
604	364 816	24.57641	77.71744	220 348 864	8.453 028	18.21150	39.23548
605	366 025	24.59675	77.78175	221 445 125	8.457 691	18.22154	39.25712
606	367 236	24.61707	77.84600	222 545 016	8.462 348	18.23158	39.27874
607	368 449	24.63737	77.91020	223 648 543	8.467 000	18.24160	39.30033
608	369 664	24.65766	77.97435	224 755 712	8.471 647	18.25161	39.32190
609	370 881	24.67793	78.03845	225 866 529	8.476 289	18.26161	39.34345
610	372 100	24.69818	78.10250	226 981 000	8.480 926	18.27160	39.36497
611	373 321	24.71841	78.16649	228 099 131	8.485 558	18.28158	39.38647
612	374 544	24.73863	78.23043	229 220 928	8.490 185	18.29155	39.40795
613	375 769	24.75884	78.29432	230 346 397	8.494 807	18.30151	39.42940
614	376 996	24.77902	78.35815	231 475 544	8.499 423	18.31145	39.45083
615	378 225	24.79919	78.42194	232 608 375	8.504 035	18.32139	39.47223
616	379 456	24.81935	78.48567	233 744 896	8.508 642	18.33131	39.49362
617	380 689	24.83948	78.54935	234 885 113	8.513 243	18.34123	39.51498
618	381 924	24.85961	78.61298	236 029 032	8.517 840	18.35113	39.53631
619	383 161	24.87971	78.67655	237 176 659	8.522 432	18.36102	39.55763
620	384 400	24.89980	78.74008	238 328 000	8.527 019	18.37091	39.57892
621	385 641	24.91987	78.80355	239 483 061	8.531 601	18.38078	39.60018
622	386 884	24.93993	78.86698	240 641 848	8.536 178	18.39064	39.62143
623	388 129	24.95997	78.93035	241 804 367	8.540 750	18.40049	39.64265
624	389 376	24.97999	78.99367	242 970 624	8.545 317	18.41033	39.66385
625	390 625	25.00000	79.05694	244 140 625	8.549 880	18.42016	39.68503
626	391 876	25.01999	79.12016	245 314 376	8.554 437	18.42998	39.70618
627	393 129	25.03997	79.18333	246 491 883	8.558 990	18.43978	39.72731
628	394 384	25.05993	79.24645	247 673 152	8.563 538	18.44958	39.74842
629	395 641	25.07987	79.30952	248 858 189	8.568 081	18.45937	39.76951
630	396 900	25.09980	79.37254	250 047 000	8.572 619	18.46915	39.79057
631	398 161	25.11971	79.43551	251 239 591	8.577 152	18.47891	39.81161
632	399 424	25.13961	79.49843	252 435 968	8.581 681	18.48867	39.83263
633	400 689	25.15949	79.56130	253 636 137	8.586 205	18.49842	39.85363
634	401 956	25.17936	79.62412	254 840 104	8.590 724	18.50815	39.87461
635	403 225	25.19921	79.68689	256 047 875	8.595 238	18.51788	39.89556
636	404 496	25.21904	79.74961	257 259 456	8.599 748	18.52759	39.91649
637	405 769	25.23886	79.81228	258 474 853	8.604 252	18.53730	39.93740
638	407 044	25.25866	79.87490	259 694 072	8.608 753	18.54700	39.95829
639	408 321	25.27845	79.93748	260 917 119	8.613 248	18.55668	39.97916
640	409 600	25.29822	80.00000	262 144 000	8.617 739	18.56636	40.00000
641	410 881	25.31798	80.06248	263 374 721	8.622 225	18.57602	40.02082
642	412 164	25.33772	80.12490	264 609 288	8.626 706	18.58568	40.04162
643	413 449	25.35744	80.18728	265 847 707	8.631 183	18.59532	40.06240
644	414 736	25.37716	80.24961	267 089 984	8.635 655	18.60495	40.08316
645	416 025	25.39685	80.31189	268 336 125	8.640 123	18.61458	40.10390
646	417 316	25.41653	80.37413	269 586 136	8.644 585	18.62419	40.12461
647	418 609	25.43619	80.43631	270 840 023	8.649 044	18.63380	40.14530
648	419 904	25.45584	80.49845	272 097 792	8.653 497	18.64340	40.16598
649	421 201	25.47548	80.56054	273 359 449	8.657 947	18.65298	40.18663
650	422 500	25.49510	80.62258	274 625 000	8.662 391	18.66256	40.20726

n	n^2	$\sqrt{n}$	$\sqrt{10n}$	n^3	$\sqrt[3]{n}$	$\sqrt[3]{10n}$	$\sqrt[3]{100n}$
650	422 500	25.49510	80.62258	274 625 000	8.662 391	18.66256	40.20726
651	423 801	25.51470	80.68457	275 894 451	8.666 831	18.67212	40.22787
652	425 104	25.53429	80.74652	277 167 808	8.671 266	18.68168	40.24845
653	426 409	25.55386	80.80842	278 445 077	8.675 697	18.69122	40.26902
654	427 716	25.57342	80.87027	279 726 264	8.680 124	18.70076	40.28957
655	429 025	25.59297	80.93207	281 011 375	8.684 546	18.71029	40.31009
656	430 336	25.61250	80.99383	282 300 416	8.688 963	18.71980	40.33059
657	431 649	25.63201	81.05554	283 593 393	8.693 376	18.72931	40.35108
658	432 964	25.65151	81.11720	284 890 312	8.697 784	18.73881	40.37154
659	434 281	25.67100	81.17881	286 191 179	8.702 188	18.74830	40.39198
660	435 600	25.69047	81.24038	287 496 000	8.706 588	18.75777	40.41240
661	436 921	25.70992	81.30191	288 804 781	8.710 983	18.76724	40.43280
662	438 244	25.72936	81.36338	290 117 528	8.715 373	18.77670	40.45318
663	439 569	25.74879	81.42481	291 434 247	8.719 760	18.78615	40.47354
664	440 896	25.76820	81.48620	292 754 944	8.724 141	18.79559	40.49388
665	442 225	25.78759	81.54753	294 079 625	8.728 519	18.80502	40.51420
666	443 556	25.80698	81.60882	295 408 296	8.732 892	18.81444	40.53449
667	444 889	25.82634	81.67007	296 740 963	8.737 260	18.82386	40.55477
668	446 224	25.84570	81.73127	298 077 632	8.741 625	18.83326	40.57503
669	447 561	25.86503	81.79242	299 418 309	8.745 985	18.84265	40.59526
670	448 900	25.88436	81.85353	300 763 000	8.750 340	18.85204	40.61548
671	450 241	25.90367	81.91459	302 111 711	8.754 691	18.86141	40.63568
672	451 584	25.92296	81.97561	303 464 448	8.759 038	18.87078	40.65585
673	452 929	25.94224	82.03658	304 821 217	8.763 381	18.88013	40.67601
674	454 276	25.96151	82.09750	306 182 024	8.767 719	18.88948	40.69615
675	455 625	25.98076	82.15838	307 546 875	8.772 053	18.89882	40.71626
676	456 976	26.00000	82.21922	308 915 776	8.776 383	18.90814	40.73636
677	458 329	26.01922	82.28001	310 288 733	8.780 708	18.91746	40.75644
678	459 684	26.03843	82.34076	311 665 752	8.785 030	18.92677	40.77650
679	461 041	26.05763	82.40146	313 046 839	8.789 347	18.93607	40.79653
680	462 400	26.07681	82.46211	314 432 000	8.793 659	18.94536	40.81655
681	463 761	26.09598	82.52272	315 821 241	8.797 968	18.95465	40.83655
682	465 124	26.11513	82.58329	317 214 568	8.802 272	18.96392	40.85653
683	466 489	26.13427	82.64381	318 611 987	8.806 572	18.97318	40.87649
684	467 856	26.15339	82.70429	320 013 504	8.810 868	18.98244	40.89643
685	469 225	26.17250	32.76473	321 419 125	8.815 160	18.99169	40.91635
686	470 596	26.19160	82.82512	322 828 856	8.819 447	19.00092	40.93625
687	471 969	26.21068	82.88546	324 242 703	8.823 731	19.01015	40.95613
688	473 344	26.22975	82.94577	325 660 672	8.828 010	19.01937	40.97599
689	474 721	26.24881	83.00602	327 082 769	8.832 285	19.02858	40.99584
690	476 100	26.26785	83.06624	328 509 000	8.836 556	19.03778	41.01566
691	477 481	26.28688	83.12641	329 939 371	8.840 823	19.04698	41.03546
692	478 864	26.30589	83.18654	331 373 888	8.845 085	19.05616	41.05525
693	480 249	26.32489	83.24662	332 812 557	8.849 344	19.06533	41.07502
694	481 636	26.34388	83.30666	334 255 384	8.853 599	19.07450	41.09476
695	483 025	26.36285	83.36666	335 702 375	8.857 849	19.08366	41.11449
696	484 416	26.38181	83.42661	337 153 536	8.862 095	19.09281	41.13420
697	485 809	26.40076	83.48653	338 608 873	8.866 338	19.10195	41.15389
698	487 204	26.41969	83.54639	340 068 392	8.870 576	19.11108	41.17357
699	488 601	26.43861	83.60622	341 532 099	8.874 810	19.12020	41.19322
700	490 000	26.45751	83.66600	343 000 000	8.879 040	19.12931	41.21285

n	n^2	$\sqrt{n}$	$\sqrt{10n}$	n^3	$\sqrt[3]{n}$	$\sqrt[3]{10n}$	$\sqrt[3]{100n}$
700	490 000	26.45751	83.66600	343 000 000	8.879 040	19.12931	41.21285
701	491 401	26.47640	83.72574	344 472 101	8.883 266	19.13842	41.23247
702	492 804	26.49528	83.78544	345 948 408	8.887 488	19.14751	41.25207
703	494 209	26.51415	83.84510	347 428 927	8.891 706	19.15660	41.27164
704	495 616	26.53300	83.90471	348 913 664	8.895 920	19.16568	41.29120
705	497 025	26.55184	83.96428	350 402 625	8.900 130	19.17475	41.31075
706	498 436	26.57066	84.02381	351 895 816	8.904 337	19.18381	41.33027
707	499 849	26.58947	84.08329	353 393 243	8.908 539	19.19286	41.34977
708	501 264	26.60827	84.14274	354 894 912	8.912 737	19.20191	41.36926
709	502 681	26.62705	84.20214	356 400 829	8.916 931	19.21095	41.38873
710	504 100	26.64583	84.26150	357 911 000	8.921 121	19.21997	41.40818
711	505 521	26.66458	84.32082	359 425 431	8.925 308	19.22899	41.42761
712	506 944	26.68333	84.38009	360 944 128	8.929 490	19.23800	41.44702
713	508 369	26.70206	84.43933	362 467 097	8.933 669	19.24701	41.46642
714	509 796	26.72078	84.49852	363 994 344	8.937 843	19.25600	41.48579
715	511 225	26.73948	84.55767	365 525 875	8.942 014	19.26499	41.50515
716	512 656	26.75818	84.61678	367 061 696	8.946 181	19.27396	41.52449
717	514 089	26.77686	84.67585	368 601 813	8.950 344	19.28293	41.54382
718	515 524	26.79552	84.73488	370 146 232	8.954 503	19.29189	41.56312
719	516 961	26.81418	84.79387	371 694 959	8.958 658	19.30084	41.58241
720	518 400	26.83282	84.85281	373 248 000	8.962 809	19.30979	41.60168
721	519 841	26.85144	84.91172	374 805 361	8.966 957	19.31872	41.62093
722	521 284	26.87006	84.97058	376 367 048	8.971 101	19.32765	41.64016
723	522 729	26.88866	85.02941	377 933 067	8.975 241	19.33657	41.65938
724	524 176	26.90725	85.08819	379 503 424	8.979 377	19.34548	41.67857
725	525 625	26.92582	85.14693	381 078 125	8.983 509	19.35438	41.69775
726	527 076	26.94439	85.20563	382 657 176	8.987 637	19.36328	41.71692
727	528 529	26.96294	85.26429	384 240 583	8.991 762	19.37216	41.73606
728	529 984	26.98148	85.32292	385 828 352	8.995 883	19.38104	41.75519
729	531 441	27.00000	85.38150	387 420 489	9.000 000	19.38991	41.77430
730	532 900	27.01851	85.44004	389 017 000	9.004 113	19.39877	41.79339
731	534 361	27.03701	85.49854	390 617 891	9.008 223	19.40763	41.81247
732	535 824	27.05550	85.55700	392 223 168	9.012 329	19.41647	41.83152
733	537 289	27.07397	85.61542	393 832 837	9.016 431	19.42531	41.85056
734	538 756	27.09243	85.67380	395 446 904	9.020 529	19.43414	41.86959
735	540 225	27.11088	85.73214	397 065 375	9.024 624	19.44296	41.88859
736	541 696	27.12932	85.79044	398 688 256	9.028 715	19.45178	41.90758
737	543 169	27.14774	85.84870	400 315 553	9.032 802	19.46058	41.92655
738	544 644	27.16616	85.90692	401 947 272	9.036 886	19.46938	41.94551
739	546 121	27.18455	85.96511	403 583 419	9.040 966	19.47817	41.96444
740	547 600	27.20294	86.02325	405 224 000	9.045 042	19.48695	41.98336
741	549 081	27.22132	86.08136	406 869 021	9.049 114	19.49573	42.00227
742	550 564	27.23968	86.13942	408 518 488	9.053 183	19.50449	42.02115
743	552 049	27.25803	86.19745	410 172 407	9.057 248	19.51325	42.04002
744	553 536	27.27636	86.25543	411 830 784	9.061 310	19.52200	42.05887
745	555 025	27.29469	86.31338	413 493 625	9.065 368	19.53074	42.07771
746	556 516	27.31300	86.37129	415 160 936	9.069 422	19.53948	42.09653
747	558 009	27.33130	86.42916	416 832 723	9.073 473	19.54820	42.11533
748	559 504	27.34959	86.48699	418 508 992	9.077 520	19.55692	42.13411
749	561 001	27.36786	86.54479	420 189 749	9.081 563	19.56563	42.15288
750	562 500	27.38613	86.60254	421 875 000	9.085 603	19.57434	42.17163

n	n^2	$\sqrt{n}$	$\sqrt{10n}$	n^3	$\sqrt[3]{n}$	$\sqrt[3]{10n}$	$\sqrt[3]{100n}$
750	562 500	27.38613	86.60254	421 875 000	9.085 603	19.57434	42.17163
751	564 001	27.40438	86.66026	423 564 751	9.089 639	19.58303	42.19037
752	565 504	27.42262	86.71793	425 259 008	9.093 672	19.59172	42.20909
753	567 009	27.44085	86.77557	426 957 777	9.097 701	19.60040	42.22779
754	568 516	27.45906	86.83317	428 661 064	9.101 727	19.60908	42.24647
755	570 025	27.47726	86.89074	430 368 875	9.105 748	19.61774	42.26514
756	571 536	27.49545	86.94826	432 081 216	9.109 767	19.62640	42.28379
757	573 049	27.51363	87.00575	433 798 093	9.113 782	19.63505	42.30243
758	574 564	27.53180	87.06320	435 519 512	9.117 793	19.64369	42.32105
759	576 081	27.54995	87.12061	437 245 479	9.121 801	19.65232	42.33965
760	577 600	27.56810	87.17798	438 976 000	9.125 805	19.66095	42.35824
761	579 121	27.58623	87.23531	440 711 081	9.129 806	19.66957	42.37681
762	580 644	27.60435	87.29261	442 450 728	9.133 803	19.67818	42.39536
763	582 169	27.62245	87.34987	444 194 947	9.137 797	19.68679	42.41390
764	583 696	27.64055	87.40709	445 943 744	9.141 787	19.69538	42.43242
765	585 225	27.65863	87.46428	447 697 125	9.145 774	19.70397	42.45092
766	586 756	27.67671	87.52143	449 455 096	9.149 758	19.71256	42.46941
767	588 289	27.69476	87.57854	451 217 663	9.153 738	19.72113	42.48789
768	589 824	27.71281	87.63561	452 984 832	9.157 714	19.72970	42.50634
769	591 361	27.73085	87.69265	454 756 609	9.161 687	19.73826	42.52478
770	592 900	27.74887	87.74964	456 533 000	9.165 656	19.74681	42.54321
771	594 441	27.76689	87.80661	458 314 011	9.169 623	19.75535	42.56162
772	595 984	27.78489	87.86353	460 099 648	9.173 585	19.76389	42.58001
773	597 529	27.80288	87.92042	461 889 917	9.177 544	19.77242	42.59839
774	599 076	27.82086	87.97727	463 684 824	9.181 500	19.78094	42.61675
775	600 625	27.83882	88.03408	465 484 375	9.185 453	19.78946	42.63509
776	602 176	27.85678	88.09086	467 288 576	9.189 402	19.79797	42.65342
777	603 729	27.87472	88.14760	469 097 433	9.193 347	19.80647	42.67174
778	605 284	27.89265	88.20431	470 910 952	9.197 290	19.81496	42.69004
779	606 841	27.91057	88.26098	472 729 139	9.201 229	19.82345	42.70832
780	608 400	27.92848	88.31761	474 552 000	9.205 164	19.83192	42.72659
781	609 961	27.94638	88.37420	476 379 541	9.209 096	19.84040	42.74484
782	611 524	27.96426	88.43076	478 211 768	9.213 025	19.84886	42.76307
783	613 089	27.98214	88.48729	480 048 687	9.216 950	19.85732	42.78129
784	614 656	28.00000	88.54377	481 890 304	9.220 873	19.86577	42.79950
785	616 225	28.01785	88.60023	483 736 625	9.224 791	19.87421	42.81769
786	617 796	28.03569	88.65664	485 587 656	9.228 707	19.88265	42.83586
787	619 369	28.05352	88.71302	487 443 403	9.232 619	19.89107	42.85402
788	620 944	28.07134	88.76936	489 303 872	9.236 528	19.89950	42.87216
789	622 521	28.08914	88.82567	491 169 069	9.240 433	19.90791	42.89029
790	624 100	28.10694	88.88194	493 039 000	9.244 335	19.91632	42.90840
791	625 681	28.12472	88.93818	494 913 671	9.248 234	19.92472	42.92650
792	627 264	28.14249	88.99438	496 793 088	9.252 130	19.93311	42.94458
793	628 849	28.16026	89.05055	498 677 257	9.256 022	19.94150	42.96265
794	630 436	28.17801	89.10668	500 566 184	9.259 911	19.94987	42.98070
795	632 025	28.19574	89.16277	502 459 875	9.263 797	19.95825	42.99874
796	633 616	28.21347	89.21883	504 358 336	9.267 680	19.96661	43.01676
797	635 209	28.23119	89.27486	506 261 573	9.271 559	19.97497	43.03477
798	636 804	28.24889	89.33085	508 169 592	9.275 435	19.98332	43.05276
799	638 401	28.26659	89.38680	510 082 399	9.279 308	19.99166	43.07073
800	640 000	28.28427	89.44272	512 000 000	9.283 178	20.00000	43.08869

n	n^2	$\sqrt{n}$	$\sqrt{10n}$	n^3	$\sqrt[3]{n}$	$\sqrt[3]{10n}$	$\sqrt[3]{100n}$
800	640 000	28.28427	89.44272	512 000 000	9.283 178	20.00000	43.08869
801	641 601	28.30194	89.49860	513 922 401	9.287 044	20.00833	43.10664
802	643 204	28.31960	89.55445	515 849 608	9.290 907	20.01665	43.12457
803	644 809	28.33725	89.61027	517 781 627	9.294 767	20.02497	43.14249
804	646 416	28.35489	89.66605	519 718 464	9.298 624	20.03328	43.16039
805	648 025	28.37252	89.72179	521 660 125	9.302 477	20.04158	43.17828
806	649 636	28.39014	89.77750	523 606 616	9.306 328	20.04988	43.19615
807	651 249	28.40775	89.83318	525 557 943	9.310 175	20.05816	43.21400
808	652 864	28.42534	89.88882	527 514 112	9.314 019	20.06645	43.23185
809	654 481	28.44293	89.94443	529 475 129	9.317 860	20.07472	43.24967
810	656 100	28.46050	90.00000	531 441 000	9.321 698	20.08299	43.26749
811	657 721	28.47806	90.05554	533 411 731	9.325 532	20.09125	43.28529
812	659 344	28.49561	90.11104	535 387 328	9.329 363	20.09950	43.30307
813	660 969	28.51315	90.16651	537 367 797	9.333 192	20.10775	43.32084
814	662 596	28.53069	90.22195	539 353 144	9.337 017	20.11599	43.33859
815	664 225	28.54820	90.27735	541 343 375	9.340 839	20.12423	43.35633
816	665 856	28.56571	90.33272	543 338 496	9.344 657	20.13245	43.37406
817	667 489	28.58321	90.38805	545 338 513	9.348 473	20.14067	43.39177
818	669 124	28.60070	90.44335	547 343 432	9.352 286	20.14889	43.40947
819	670 761	28.61818	90.49862	549 353 259	9.356 095	20.15710	43.42715
820	672 400	28.63564	90.55385	551 368 000	9.359 902	20.16530	43.44481
821	674 041	28.65310	90.60905	553 387 661	9.363 705	20.17349	43.46247
822	675 684	28.67054	90.66422	555 412 248	9.367 505	20.18168	43.48011
823	677 329	28.68798	90.71935	557 441 767	9.371 302	20.18986	43.49773
824	678 976	28.70540	90.77445	559 476 224	9.375 096	20.19803	43.51534
825	680 625	28.72281	90.82951	561 515 625	9.378 887	20.20620	43.53294
826	682 276	28.74022	90.88454	563 559 976	9.382 675	20.21436	43.55052
827	683 929	28.75761	90.93954	565 609 283	9.386 460	20.22252	43.56809
828	685 584	28.77499	90.99451	567 663 552	9.390 242	20.23066	43.58564
829	687 241	28.79236	91.04944	569 722 789	9.394 021	20.23880	43.60318
830	688 900	28.80972	91.10434	571 787 000	9.397 796	20.24694	43.62071
831	690 561	28.82707	91.15920	573 856 191	9.401 569	20.25507	43.63822
832	692 224	28.84441	91.21403	575 930 368	9.405 339	20.26319	43.65572
833	693 889	28.86174	91.26883	578 009 537	9.409 105	20.27130	43.67320
834	695 556	28.87906	91.32360	580 093 704	9.412 869	20.27941	43.69067
835	697 225	28.89637	91.37833	582 182 875	9.416 630	20.28751	43.70812
836	698 896	28.91366	91.43304	584 277 056	9.420 387	20.29561	43.72556
837	700 569	28.93095	91.48770	586 376 253	9.424 142	20.30370	43.74299
838	702 244	28.94823	91.54234	588 480 472	9.427 894	20.31178	43.76041
839	703 921	28.96550	91.59694	590 589 719	9.431 642	20.31986	43.77781
840	705 600	28.98275	91.65151	592 704 000	9.435 388	20.32793	43.79519
841	707 281	29.00000	91.70605	594 823 321	9.439 131	20.33599	43.81256
842	708 964	29.01724	91.76056	596 947 688	9.442 870	20.34405	43.82992
843	710 649	29.03446	91.81503	599 077 107	9.446 607	20.35210	43.84727
844	712 336	29.05168	91.86947	601 211 584	9.450 341	20.36014	43.86460
845	714 025	29.06888	91.92388	603 351 125	9.454 072	20.36818	43.88191
846	715 716	29.08608	91.97826	605 495 736	9.457 800	20.37621	43.89922
847	717 409	29.10326	92.03260	607 645 423	9.461 525	20.38424	43.91651
848	719 104	29.12044	92.08692	609 800 192	9.465 247	20.39226	43.93378
849	720 801	29.13760	92.14120	611 960 049	9.468 966	20.40027	43.95105
850	722 500	29.15476	92.19544	614 125 000	9.472 682	20.40828	43.96830

n	n^2	$\sqrt{n}$	$\sqrt{10n}$	n^3	$\sqrt[3]{n}$	$\sqrt[3]{10n}$	$\sqrt[3]{100n}$
850	722 500	29.15476	92.19544	614 125 000	9.472 682	20.40828	43.96830
851	724 201	29.17190	92.24966	616 295 051	9.476 396	20.41628	43.98553
852	725 904	29.18904	92.30385	618 470 208	9.480 106	20.42427	44.00275
853	727 609	29.20616	92.35800	620 650 477	9.483 814	20.43226	44.01996
854	729 316	29.22328	92.41212	622 835 864	9.487 518	20.44024	44.03716
855	731 025	29.24038	92.46621	625 026 375	9.491 220	20.44821	44.05434
856	732 736	29.25748	92.52027	627 222 016	9.494 919	20.45618	44.07151
857	734 449	29.27456	92.57429	629 422 793	9.498 615	20.46415	44.08866
858	736 164	29.29164	92.62829	631 628 712	9.502 308	20.47210	44.10581
859	737 881	29.30870	92.68225	633 839 779	9.505 998	20.48005	44.12293
860	739 600	29.32576	92.73618	636 056 000	9.509 685	20.48800	44.14005
861	741 321	29.34280	92.79009	638 277 381	9.513 370	20.49593	44.15715
862	743 044	29.35984	92.84396	640 503 928	9.517 052	20.50387	44.17424
863	744 769	29.37686	92.89779	642 735 647	9.520 730	20.51179	44.19132
864	746 496	29.39388	92.95160	644 972 544	9.524 406	20.51971	44.20838
865	748 225	29.41088	93.00538	647 214 625	9.528 079	20.52762	44.22543
866	749 956	29.42788	93.05912	649 461 896	9.531 750	20.53553	44.24246
867	751 689	29.44486	93.11283	651 714 363	9.535 417	20.54343	44.25949
868	753 424	29.46184	93.16652	653 972 032	9.539 082	20.55133	44.27650
869	755 161	29.47881	93.22017	656 234 909	9.542 744	20.55922	44.29349
870	756 900	29.49576	93.27379	658 503 000	9.546 403	20.56710	44.31048
871	758 641	29.51271	93.32738	660 776 311	9.550 059	20.57498	44.32745
872	760 384	29.52965	93.38094	663 054 848	9.553 712	20.58285	44.34440
873	762 129	29.54657	93.43447	665 338 617	9.557 363	20.59071	44.36135
874	763 876	29.56349	93.48797	667 627 624	9.561 011	20.59857	44.37828
875	765 625	29.58040	93.54143	669 921 875	9.564 656	20.60643	44.39520
876	767 376	29.59730	93.59487	672 221 376	9.568 298	20.61427	44.41211
877	769 129	29.61419	93.64828	674 526 133	9.571 938	20.62211	44.42900
878	770 884	29.63106	93.70165	676 836 152	9.575 574	20.62995	44.44588
879	772 641	29.64793	93.75500	679 151 439	9.579 208	20.63778	44.46275
880	774 400	29.66479	93.80832	681 472 000	9.582 840	20.64560	44.47960
881	776 161	29.68164	93.86160	683 797 841	9.586 468	20.65342	44.49644
882	777 924	29.69848	93.91486	686 128 968	9.590 094	20.66123	44.51327
883	779 689	29.71532	93.96808	688 465 387	9.593 717	20.66904	44.53009
884	781 456	29.73214	94.02127	690 807 104	9.597 337	20.67684	44.54689
885	783 225	29.74895	94.07444	693 154 125	9.600 955	20.68463	44.56368
886	784 996	29.76575	94.12757	695 506 456	9.604 570	20.69242	44.58046
887	786 769	29.78255	94.18068	697 864 103	9.608 182	20.70020	44.59723
888	788 544	29.79933	94.23375	700 227 072	9.611 791	20.70798	44.61398
889	790 321	29.81610	94.28680	702 595 369	9.615 398	20.71575	44.63072
890	792 100	29.83287	94.33981	704 969 000	9.619 002	20.72351	44.64745
891	793 881	29.84962	94.39280	707 347 971	9.622 603	20.73127	44.66417
892	795 664	29.86637	94.44575	709 732 288	9.626 202	20.73902	44.68087
893	797 449	29.88311	94.49868	712 121 957	9.629 797	20.74677	44.69756
894	799 236	29.89983	94.55157	714 516 984	9.633 391	20.75451	44.71424
895	801 025	29.91655	94.60444	716 917 375	9.636 981	20.76225	44.73090
896	802 816	29.93326	94.65728	719 323 136	9.640 569	20.76998	44.74756
897	804 609	29.94996	94.71008	721 734 273	9.644 154	20.77770	44.76420
898	806 404	29.96665	94.76286	724 150 792	9.647 737	20.78542	44.78083
899	808 201	29.98333	94.81561	726 572 699	9.651 317	20.79313	44.79744
900	810 000	30.00000	94.86833	729 000 000	9.654 894	20.80084	44.81405

n	n^2	$\sqrt{n}$	$\sqrt{10n}$	n^3	$\sqrt[3]{n}$	$\sqrt[3]{10n}$	$\sqrt[3]{100n}$
900	810 000	30.00000	94.86833	729 000 000	9.654 894	20.80084	44.81405
901	811 801	30.01666	94.92102	731 432 701	9.658 468	20.80854	44.83064
902	813 604	30.03331	94.97368	733 870 808	9.662 040	20.81623	44.84722
903	815 409	30.04996	95.02631	736 314 327	9.665 610	20.82392	44.86379
904	817 216	30.06659	95.07891	738 763 264	9.669 176	20.83161	44.88034
905	819 025	30.08322	95.13149	741 217 625	9.672 740	20.83929	44.89688
906	820 836	30.09983	95.18403	743 677 416	9.676 302	20.84696	44.91341
907	822 649	30.11644	95.23655	746 142 643	9.679 860	20.85463	44.92993
908	824 464	30.13304	95.28903	748 613 312	9.683 417	20.86229	44.94644
909	826 281	30.14963	95.34149	751 089 429	9.686 970	20.86994	44.96293
910	828 100	30.16621	95.39392	753 571 000	9.690 521	20.87759	44.97941
911	829 921	30.18278	95.44632	756 058 031	9.694 069	20.88524	44.99588
912	831 744	30.19934	95.49869	758 550 528	9.697 615	20.89288	45.01234
913	833 569	30.21589	95.55103	761 048 497	9.701 158	20.90051	45.02879
914	835 396	30.23243	95.60335	763 551 944	9.704 699	20.90814	45.04522
915	837 225	30.24897	95.65563	766 060 875	9.708 237	20.91576	45.06164
916	839 056	30.26549	95.70789	768 575 296	9.711 772	20.92338	45.07805
917	840 889	30.28201	95.76012	771 095 213	9.715 305	20.93099	45.09445
918	842 724	30.29851	95.81232	773 620 632	9.718 835	20.93860	45.11084
919	844 561	30.31501	95.86449	776 151 559	9.722 363	20.94620	45.12721
920	846 400	30.33150	95.91663	778 688 000	9.725 888	20.95379	45.14357
921	848 241	30.34798	95.96874	781 229 961	9.729 411	20.96138	45.15992
922	850 084	30.36445	96.02083	783 777 448	9.732 931	20.96896	45.17626
923	851 929	30.38092	96.07289	786 330 467	9.736 448	20.97654	45.19259
924	853 776	30.39737	96.12492	788 889 024	9.739 963	20.98411	45.20891
925	855 625	30.41381	96.17692	791 453 125	9.743 476	20.99168	45.22521
926	857 476	30.43025	96.22889	794 022 776	9.746 986	20.99924	45.24150
927	859 329	30.44667	96.28084	796 597 983	9.750 493	21.00680	45.25778
928	861 184	30.46309	96.33276	799 178 752	9.753 998	21.01435	45.27405
929	863 041	30.47950	96.38465	801 765 089	9.757 500	21.02190	45.29030
930	864 900	30.49590	96.43651	804 357 000	9.761 000	21.02944	45.30655
931	866 761	30.51229	96.48834	806 954 491	9.764 497	21.03697	45.32278
932	868 624	30.52868	96.54015	809 557 568	9.767 992	21.04450	45.33900
933	870 489	30.54505	96.59193	812 166 237	9.771 485	21.05203	45.35521
934	872 356	30.56141	96.64368	814 780 504	9.774 974	21.05954	45.37141
935	874 225	30.57777	96.69540	817 400 375	9.778 462	21.06706	45.38760
936	876 096	30.59412	96.74709	820 025 856	9.781 946	21.07456	45.40377
937	877 969	30.61046	96.79876	822 656 953	9.785 429	21.08207	45.41994
938	879 844	30.62679	96.85040	825 293 672	9.788 909	21.08956	45.43609
939	881 721	30.64311	96.90201	827 936 019	9.792 386	21.09706	45.45223
940	883 600	30.65942	96.95360	830 584 000	9.795 861	21.10454	45.46836
941	885 481	30.67572	97.00515	833 237 621	9.799 334	21.11202	45.48448
942	887 364	30.69202	97.05668	835 896 888	9.802 804	21.11950	45.50058
943	889 249	30.70831	97.10819	838 561 807	9.806 271	21.12697	45.51668
944	891 136	30.72458	97.15966	841 232 384	9.809 736	21.13444	45.53276
945	893 025	30.74085	97.21111	843 908 625	9.813 199	21.14190	45.54883
946	894 916	30.75711	97.26253	846 590 536	9.816 659	21.14935	45.56490
947	896 809	30.77337	97.31393	849 278 123	9.820 117	21.15680	45.58095
948	898 704	30.78961	97.36529	851 971 392	9.823 572	21.16424	45.59698
949	900 601	30.80584	97.41663	854 670 349	9.827 025	21.17168	45.61301
950	902 500	30.82207	97.46794	857 375 000	9.830 476	21.17912	45.62903

n	n^2	$\sqrt{n}$	$\sqrt{10n}$	n^3	$\sqrt[3]{n}$	$\sqrt[3]{10n}$	$\sqrt[3]{100n}$
950	902 500	30.82207	97.46794	857 375 000	9.830 476	21.17912	45.62903
951	904 401	30.83829	97.51923	860 085 351	9.833 924	21.18655	45.64503
952	906 304	30.85450	97.57049	862 801 408	9.837 369	21.19397	45.66102
953	908 209	30.87070	97.62172	865 523 177	9.840 813	21.20139	45.67701
954	910 116	30.88689	97.67292	868 250 664	9.844 254	21.20880	45.69298
955	912 025	30.90307	97.72410	870 983 875	9.847 692	21.21621	45.70894
956	913 936	30.91925	97.77525	873 722 816	9.851 128	21.22361	45.72489
957	915 849	30.93542	97.82638	876 467 493	9.854 562	21.23101	45.74082
958	917 764	30.95158	97.87747	879 217 912	9.857 993	21.23840	45.75675
959	919 681	30.96773	97.92855	881 974 079	9.861 422	21.24579	45.77267
960	921 600	30.98387	97.97959	884 736 000	9.864 848	21.25317	45.78857
961	923 521	31.00000	98.03061	887 503 681	9.868 272	21.26055	45.80446
962	925 444	31.01612	98.08160	890 277 128	9.871 694	21.26792	45.82035
963	927 369	31.03224	98.13256	893 056 347	9.875 113	21.27529	45.83622
964	929 296	31.04835	98.18350	895 841 344	9.878 530	21.28265	45.85208
965	931 225	31.06445	98.23441	898 632 125	9.881 945	21.29001	45.86793
966	933 156	31.08054	98.28530	901 428 696	9.885 357	21.29736	45.88376
967	935 089	31.09662	98.33616	904 231 063	9.888 767	21.30470	45.89959
968	937 024	31.11270	98.38699	907 039 232	9.892 175	21.31204	45.91541
969	938 961	31.12876	98.43780	909 853 209	9.895 580	21.31938	45.93121
970	940 900	31.14482	98.48858	912 673 000	9.898 983	21.32671	45.94701
971	942 841	31.16087	98.53933	915 498 611	9.902 384	21.33404	45.96279
972	944 784	31.17691	98.59006	918 330 048	9.905 782	21.34136	45.97857
973	946 729	31.19295	98.64076	921 167 317	9.909 178	21.34868	45.99433
974	948 676	31.20897	98.69144	924 010 424	9.912 571	21.35599	46.01008
975	950 625	31.22499	98.74209	926 859 375	9.915 962	21.36329	46.02582
976	952 576	31.24100	98.79271	929 714 176	9.919 351	21.37059	46.04155
977	954 529	31.25700	98.84331	932 574 833	9.922 738	21.37789	46.05727
978	956 484	31.27299	98.89388	935 441 352	9.926 122	21.38518	46.07298
979	958 441	31.28898	98.94443	938 313 739	9.929 504	21.39247	46.08868
980	960 400	31.30495	98.99495	941 192 000	9.932 884	21.39975	46.10436
981	962 361	31.32092	99.04544	944 076 141	9.936 261	21.40703	46.12004
982	964 324	31.33688	99.09591	946 966 168	9.939 636	21.41430	46.13571
983	966 289	31.35283	99.14636	949 862 087	9.943 009	21.42156	46.15136
984	968 256	31.36877	99.19677	952 763 904	9.946 380	21.42883	46.16700
985	970 225	31.38471	99.24717	955 671 625	9.949 748	21.43608	46.18264
986	972 196	31.40064	99.29753	958 585 256	9.953 114	21.44333	46.19826
987	974 169	31.41656	99.34787	961 504 803	9.956 478	21.45058	46.21387
988	976 144	31.43247	99.39819	964 430 272	9.959 839	21.45782	46.22948
989	978 121	31.44837	99.44848	967 361 669	9.963 198	21.46506	46.24507
990	980 100	31.46427	99.49874	970 299 000	9.966 555	21.47229	46.26065
991	982 081	31.48015	99.54898	973 242 271	9.969 910	21.47952	46.27622
992	984 064	31.49603	99.59920	976 191 488	9.973 262	21.48674	46.29178
993	986 049	31.51190	99.64939	979 146 657	9.976 612	21.49396	46.30733
994	988 036	31.52777	99.69955	982 107 784	9.979 960	21.50117	46.32287
995	990 025	31.54362	99.74969	985 074 875	9.983 305	21.50838	46.33840
996	992 016	31.55947	99.79980	988 047 936	9.986 649	21.51558	46.35392
997	994 009	31.57531	99.84989	991 026 973	9.989 990	21.52278	46.36943
998	996 004	31.59114	99.89995	994 011 992	9.993 329	21.52997	46.38492
999	998 001	31.60696	99.94999	997 002 999	9.996 666	21.53716	46.40041
1000	1 000 000	31.62278	100.00000	1 000 000 000	10.000 000	21.54435	46.41589

POWERS OF NUMBERS

n	n^4	n^5	n^6	n^7	n^8	n^9
1	1	1	1	1	1	1
2	16	32	64	128	256	512
3	81	243	729	2187	6561	19683
4	256	1024	4096	16384	65536	262144
5	625	3125	15625	78125	390625	1953125
6	1296	7776	46656	279936	1679616	10077696
7	2401	16807	117649	823543	5764801	40353607
8	4096	32768	262144	2097152	16777216	134217728
9	6561	59049	531441	4782969	43046721	387420489
					$\times 10^8$	$\times 10^9$
10	10000	100000	1000000	10000000	1.000000	1.000000
11	14641	161051	1771561	19487171	2.143589	2.357948
12	20736	248832	2985984	35831808	4.299817	5.159780
13	28561	371293	4826809	62748517	8.157307	10.604499
14	38416	537824	7529536	105413504	14.757891	20.661047
15	50625	759375	11390625	170859375	25.628906	38.443359
16	65536	1048576	16777216	268435456	42.949673	68.719477
17	83521	1419857	24137569	410338673	69.757574	118.587876
18	104976	1889568	34012224	612220032	110.199606	198.359291
19	130321	2476099	47045881	893871739	169.835630	322.687697
			$\times 10^9$	$\times 10^9$	$\times 10^{10}$	$\times 10^{11}$
20	160000	3200000	64000000	1.280000	2.560000	5.120000
21	194481	4084101	85766121	1.801089	3.782286	7.942800
22	234256	5153632	113379904	2.494358	5.487587	12.072692
23	279841	6436343	148035889	3.404825	7.831099	18.011527
24	331776	7962624	191102976	4.586471	11.007531	26.418075
25	390625	9765625	244140625	6.103516	15.258789	38.146973
26	456976	11881376	308915776	8.031810	20.882706	54.295037
27	531441	14348907	387420489	10.460353	28.242954	76.255975
28	614656	17210368	481890304	13.492929	37.780200	105.784559
29	707281	20511149	594823321	17.249876	50.024641	145.071460
			$\times 10^8$	$\times 10^{10}$	$\times 10^{11}$	$\times 10^{13}$
30	810000	24300000	7.290000	2.187000	6.561000	1.968300
31	923521	28629151	8.875037	2.751261	8.528910	2.643962
32	1048576	33554432	10.737418	3.435974	10.995116	3.518437
33	1185921	39135393	12.914680	4.261844	14.064086	4.641148
34	1336336	45435424	15.448044	5.252335	17.857939	6.071699
35	1500625	52521875	18.382656	6.433930	22.518754	7.881564
36	1679616	60466176	21.767823	7.836416	28.211099	10.155996
37	1874161	69343957	25.657264	9.493188	35.124795	12.996174
38	2085136	79235168	30.109364	11.441558	43.477921	16.521610
39	2313441	90224199	35.187438	13.723101	53.520093	20.872836
			$\times 10^9$	$\times 10^{10}$	$\times 10^{12}$	$\times 10^{14}$
40	2560000	102400000	4.096000	16.384000	6.553600	2.621440
41	2825761	115856201	4.750104	19.475427	7.984925	3.273819
42	3111696	130691232	5.489032	23.053933	9.682652	4.066714
43	3418801	147008443	6.321363	27.181861	11.688200	5.025926
44	3748096	164916224	7.256314	31.927781	14.048224	6.181218
45	4100625	184528125	8.303766	37.366945	16.815125	7.566806
46	4477456	205962976	9.474297	43.581766	20.047612	9.221902
47	4879681	229345007	10.779215	50.662312	23.811287	11.191305
48	5308416	254803968	12.230590	58.706834	28.179280	13.526055
49	5764801	282475249	13.841287	67.822307	33.232931	16.284136
50	6250000	312500000	15.625000	78.125000	39.062500	19.531250

n	n^4	n^5	n^6	n^7	n^8	n^9
			$\times 10^9$	$\times 10^{11}$	$\times 10^{13}$	$\times 10^{14}$
50	6250000	312500000	15.625000	7.812500	3.906250	19.531250
51	6765201	345025251	17.596288	8.974107	4.576794	23.341652
52	7311616	380204032	19.770610	10.280717	5.345973	27.799059
53	7890481	418195493	22.164361	11.747111	6.225969	32.997636
54	8503056	459165024	24.794911	13.389252	7.230196	39.043059
55	9150625	503284375	27.680641	15.224352	8.373394	46.053666
56	9834496	550731776	30.840979	17.270948	9.671731	54.161695
57	10556001	601692057	34.296447	19.548975	11.142916	63.514619
58	11316496	656356768	38.068693	22.079842	12.806308	74.276588
59	12117361	714924299	42.180534	24.886515	14.683044	86.629958
		$\times 10^8$	$\times 10^{10}$	$\times 10^{11}$	$\times 10^{13}$	$\times 10^{16}$
60	12960000	7.776000	4.665600	27.993600	16.796160	1.007770
61	13845841	8.445963	5.152037	31.427428	19.170731	1.169415
62	14776336	9.161328	5.680024	35.216146	21.834011	1.353709
63	15752961	9.924365	6.252350	39.389806	24.815578	1.563381
64	16777216	10.737418	6.871948	43.980465	28.147498	1.801440
65	17850625	11.602906	7.541889	49.022279	31.864481	2.071191
66	18974736	12.523326	8.265395	54.551607	36.004061	2.376268
67	20151121	13.501251	9.045838	60.607116	40.606768	2.720653
68	21381376	14.539336	9.886748	67.229888	45.716324	3.108710
69	22667121	15.640313	10.791816	74.463533	51.379837	3.545209
		$\times 10^8$	$\times 10^{10}$	$\times 10^{12}$	$\times 10^{14}$	$\times 10^{16}$
70	24010000	16.807000	11.764900	8.235430	5.764801	4.035361
71	25411681	18.042294	12.810028	9.095120	6.457535	4.584850
72	26873856	19.349176	13.931407	10.030613	7.222041	5.199870
73	28398241	20.730716	15.133423	11.047399	8.064601	5.887159
74	29986576	22.190066	16.420649	12.151280	8.991947	6.654041
75	31640625	23.730469	17.797852	13.348389	10.011292	7.508469
76	33362176	25.355254	19.269993	14.645195	11.130348	8.459064
77	35153041	27.067842	20.842238	16.048523	12.357363	9.515169
78	37015056	28.871744	22.519960	17.565569	13.701144	10.686892
79	38950081	30.770564	24.308746	19.203909	15.171088	11.985160
		$\times 10^8$	$\times 10^{10}$	$\times 10^{12}$	$\times 10^{14}$	$\times 10^{16}$
80	40960000	32.768000	26.214400	20.971520	16.777216	13.421773
81	43046721	34.867844	28.242954	22.876792	18.530202	15.009464
82	45212176	37.073984	30.400667	24.928547	20.441409	16.761955
83	47458321	39.390406	32.694037	27.136051	22.522922	18.694026
84	49787136	41.821194	35.129803	29.509035	24.787589	20.821575
85	52200625	44.370531	37.714952	32.057709	27.249053	23.161695
86	54700816	47.042702	40.456724	34.792782	29.921793	25.732742
87	57289761	49.842092	43.362620	37.725479	32.821167	28.554415
88	59969536	52.773192	46.440409	40.867560	35.963452	31.647838
89	62742241	55.840594	49.698129	44.231335	39.365888	35.035640
		$\times 10^9$	$\times 10^{11}$	$\times 10^{13}$	$\times 10^{15}$	$\times 10^{17}$
90	65610000	5.904900	5.314410	4.782969	4.304672	3.874205
91	68574961	6.240321	5.678693	5.167610	4.702525	4.279298
92	71639296	6.590815	6.063550	5.578466	5.132189	4.721614
93	74805201	6.956884	6.469902	6.017009	5.595818	5.204111
94	78074896	7.339040	6.898698	6.484776	6.095689	5.729948
95	81450625	7.737809	7.350919	6.983373	6.634204	6.302494
96	84934656	8.153727	7.827578	7.514475	7.213896	6.925340
97	88529281	8.587340	8.329720	8.079828	7.837434	7.602311
98	92236816	9.039208	8.858424	8.681255	8.507630	8.337478
99	96059601	9.509900	9.414801	9.320653	9.227447	9.135172
100	100000000	10.000000	10.000000	10.000000	10.000000	10.000000

POWERS OF TWO

n	2^n			n	2^n				
1	2			41	21990	23255	552		
2	4			42	43980	46511	104		
3	8			43	87960	93022	208		
4	16			44	17592	18604	4416		
5	32			45	35184	37208	8832		
6	64			46	70368	74417	7664		
7	128			47	14073	74883	55328		
8	256			48	28147	49767	10656		
9	512			49	56294	99534	21312		
10	1024			50	11258	99906	84262	4	
11	2048			51	22517	99813	68524	8	
12	4096			52	45035	99627	37049	6	
13	8192			53	90071	99254	74099	2	
14	16384			54	18014	39850	94819	84	
15	32768			55	36028	79701	89639	68	
16	65536			56	72057	59403	79279	36	
17	13107	2		57	14411	51880	75855	872	
18	26214	4		58	28823	03761	51711	744	
19	52428	8		59	57646	07523	03423	488	
20	10485	76		60	11529	21504	60684	6976	
21	20971	52		61	23058	43009	21369	3952	
22	41943	04		62	46116	86018	42738	7904	
23	83886	08		63	92233	72036	85477	5808	
24	16777	216		64	18446	74407	37095	51616	
25	33554	432		65	36893	48814	74191	03232	
26	67108	864		66	73786	97629	48382	06464	
27	13421	7728		67	14757	39525	89676	41292	8
28	26843	5456		68	29514	79051	79352	82585	6
29	53687	0912		69	59029	58103	58705	65171	2
30	10737	41824		70	11805	91620	71741	13034	24
31	21474	83648		71	23611	83241	43482	26068	48
32	42949	67296		72	47223	66482	86964	52136	96
33	85899	34592		73	94447	32965	73929	04273	92
34	17179	86918	4	74	18889	46593	14785	80854	784
35	34359	73836	8	75	37778	93186	29571	61709	568
36	68719	47673	6	76	75557	86372	59143	23419	136
37	13743	89534	72	77	15111	57274	51828	64683	8272
38	27487	79069	44	78	30223	14549	03657	29367	6544
39	54975	58138	88	79	60446	29098	07314	58735	3088
40	10995	11627	776	80	12089	25819	61462	91747	06176

n	2^n						
81	24178	51639	22925	83494	12352		
82	48357	03278	45851	66988	24704		
83	96714	06556	91703	33976	49408		
84	19342	81311	38340	66795	29881	6	
85	38685	62622	76681	33590	59763	2	
86	77371	25245	53362	67181	19526	4	
87	15474	25049	10672	53436	23905	28	
88	30948	50098	21345	06872	47810	56	
89	61807	00196	42690	13744	95621	12	
90	12379	40039	28538	02748	99124	224	
91	24758	80078	57076	05497	98248	448	
92	49517	60157	14152	10995	96496	896	
93	99035	20314	28304	21991	92993	792	
94	19807	04062	85660	84398	38598	7584	
95	39614	08125	71321	68796	77197	5168	
96	79228	16251	42643	37593	54395	0336	
97	15845	63250	28528	67518	70879	00672	
98	31691	26500	57057	35037	41758	01344	
99	63382	53001	14114	70074	83516	02688	
100	12676	50600	22822	94014	96703	20537	6
101	25353	01200	45645	88029	93406	41075	2

FACTORIALS AND THEIR LOGARITHMS

n	$n!$	log $n!$	n	$n!$	log $n!$
			50	3.0414×10^{64}	64.48307
1	1.0000	0.00000	51	1.5511×10^{66}	66.19065
2	2.0000	0.30103	52	8.0658×10^{67}	67.90665
3	6.0000	0.77815	53	4.2749×10^{69}	69.63092
4	2.4000×10	1.38021	54	2.3084×10^{71}	71.36332
5	1.2000×10^{2}	2.07918	**55**	1.2696×10^{73}	73.10368
6	7.2000×10^{2}	2.85733	56	7.1100×10^{74}	74.85187
7	5.0400×10^{3}	3.70243	57	4.0527×10^{76}	76.60774
8	4.0320×10^{4}	4.60552	58	2.3506×10^{78}	78.37117
9	3.6288×10^{5}	5.55976	59	1.3868×10^{80}	80.14202
10	3.6288×10^{6}	6.55976	**60**	8.3210×10^{81}	81.92017
11	3.9917×10^{7}	7.60116	61	5.0758×10^{83}	83.70550
12	4.7900×10^{8}	8.68034	62	3.1470×10^{85}	85.49790
13	6.2270×10^{9}	9.79428	63	1.9826×10^{87}	87.29724
14	8.7178×10^{10}	10.94041	64	1.2689×10^{89}	89.10342
15	1.3077×10^{12}	12.11650	**65**	8.2477×10^{90}	90.91633
16	2.0923×10^{13}	13.32062	66	5.4435×10^{92}	92.73587
17	3.5569×10^{14}	14.55107	67	3.6471×10^{94}	94.56195
18	6.4024×10^{15}	15.80634	68	2.4800×10^{96}	96.39446
19	1.2165×10^{17}	17.08509	69	1.7112×10^{98}	98.23331
20	2.4329×10^{18}	18.38612	**70**	1.1979×10^{100}	100.07841
21	5.1091×10^{19}	19.70834	71	8.5048×10^{101}	101.92966
22	1.1240×10^{21}	21.05077	72	6.1234×10^{103}	103.78700
23	2.5852×10^{22}	22.41249	73	4.4701×10^{105}	105.65032
24	6.2045×10^{23}	23.79271	74	3.3079×10^{107}	107.51955
25	1.5511×10^{25}	25.19065	**75**	2.4809×10^{109}	109.39461
26	4.0329×10^{26}	26.60562	76	1.8855×10^{111}	111.27543
27	1.0889×10^{28}	28.03698	77	1.4518×10^{113}	113.16192
28	3.0489×10^{29}	29.48414	78	1.1324×10^{115}	115.05401
29	8.8418×10^{30}	30.94654	79	8.9462×10^{116}	116.95164
30	2.6525×10^{32}	32.42366	**80**	7.1569×10^{118}	118.85473
31	8.2228×10^{33}	33.91502	81	5.7971×10^{120}	120.76321
32	2.6313×10^{35}	35.42017	82	4.7536×10^{122}	122.67703
33	8.6833×10^{36}	36.93869	83	3.9455×10^{124}	124.59610
34	2.9523×10^{38}	38.47016	84	3.3142×10^{126}	126.52038
35	1.0333×10^{40}	40.01423	**85**	2.8171×10^{128}	128.44980
36	3.7199×10^{41}	41.57054	86	2.4227×10^{130}	130.38430
37	1.3764×10^{43}	43.13874	87	2.1078×10^{132}	132.32382
38	5.2302×10^{44}	44.71852	88	1.8548×10^{134}	134.26830
39	2.0398×10^{46}	46.30959	89	1.6508×10^{136}	136.21769
40	8.1592×10^{47}	47.91165	**90**	1.4857×10^{138}	138.17194
41	3.3453×10^{49}	49.52443	91	1.3520×10^{140}	140.13098
42	1.4050×10^{51}	51.14768	92	1.2438×10^{142}	142.09477
43	6.0415×10^{52}	52.78115	93	1.1568×10^{144}	144.06325
44	2.6583×10^{54}	54.42460	94	1.0874×10^{146}	146.03638
45	1.1962×10^{56}	56.07781	**95**	1.0330×10^{148}	148.01410
46	5.5026×10^{57}	57.74057	96	9.9168×10^{149}	149.99637
47	2.5862×10^{59}	59.41267	97	9.6193×10^{151}	151.98314
48	1.2414×10^{61}	61.09391	98	9.4269×10^{153}	153.97437
49	6.0828×10^{62}	62.78410	99	9.3326×10^{155}	155.97000
50	3.0414×10^{64}	64.48307	**100**	9.3326×10^{157}	157.97000

FACTORS FOR COMPUTING PROBABLE ERRORS

n	$\dfrac{1}{\sqrt{n}}$	$\dfrac{1}{\sqrt{n\,(n-1)}}$	$\dfrac{.6745}{\sqrt{n-1}}$	$\dfrac{.6745}{\sqrt{n\,(n-1)}}$	$\dfrac{.8453}{n\sqrt{n-1}}$	$\dfrac{.8453}{\sqrt{n\,(n-1)}}$
2	.707107	.707107	.6745	.4769	.4227	.5978
3	.577350	.408248	.4769	.2754	.1993	.3451
4	.500000	.288675	.3894	.1947	.1220	.2440
5	.447214	.223607	.3372	.1508	.0845	.1890
6	.408248	.182574	.3016	.1231	.0630	.1543
7	.377964	.154303	.2754	.1041	.0493	.1304
8	.353553	.133631	.2549	.0901	.0399	.1130
9	.333333	.117851	.2385	.0795	.0332	.0996
10	.316228	.105409	.2248	.0711	.0282	.0891
11	.301511	.095346	.2133	.0643	.0243	.0806
12	.288675	.087039	.2034	.0587	.0212	.0736
13	.277350	.080064	.1947	.0540	.0188	.0677
14	.267261	.074125	.1871	.0500	.0167	.0627
15	.258199	.069007	.1803	.0465	.0151	.0583
16	.250000	.064550	.1742	.0435	.0136	.0546
17	.242536	.060634	.1686	.0409	.0124	.0513
18	.235702	.057166	.1636	.0386	.0114	.0483
19	.229416	.054074	.1590	.0365	.0105	.0457
20	.223607	.051299	.1547	.0346	.0097	.0434
21	.218218	.048795	.1508	.0329	.0090	.0412
22	.213201	.046524	.1472	.0314	.0084	.0393
23	.208514	.044455	.1438	.0300	.0078	.0376
24	.204124	.042563	.1406	.0287	.0073	.0360
25	.200000	.040825	.1377	.0275	.0069	.0345
26	.196116	.039223	.1349	.0265	.0065	.0332
27	.192450	.037743	.1323	.0255	.0061	.0319
28	.188982	.036370	.1298	.0245	.0058	.0307
29	.185695	.035093	.1275	.0237	.0055	.0297
30	.182574	.033903	.1252	.0229	.0052	.0287
31	.179605	.032791	.1231	.0221	.0050	.0277
32	.176777	.031750	.1211	.0214	.0047	.0268
33	.174078	.030773	.1192	.0208	.0045	.0260
34	.171499	.029854	.1174	.0201	.0043	.0252
35	.169031	.028989	.1157	.0196	.0041	.0245
36	.166667	.028172	.1140	.0190	.0040	.0238
37	.164399	.027400	.1124	.0185	.0038	.0232
38	.162221	.026669	.1109	.0180	.0037	.0225
39	.160128	.025976	.1094	.0175	.0035	.0220
40	.158114	.025318	.1080	.0171	.0034	.0214
41	.156174	.024693	.1066	.0167	.0033	.0209
42	.154303	.024098	.1053	.0163	.0031	.0204
43	.152499	.023531	.1041	.0159	.0030	.0199
44	.150756	.022990	.1029	.0155	.0029	.0194
45	.149071	.022473	.1017	.0152	.0028	.0190
46	.147442	.021979	.1005	.0148	.0027	.0186
47	.145865	.021507	.0994	.0145	.0027	.0182
48	.144338	.021054	.0984	.0142	.0026	.0178
49	.142857	.020620	.0974	.0139	.0025	.0174
50	.141421	.020203	.0964	.0136	.0024	.0171

n	$\dfrac{1}{\sqrt{n}}$	$\dfrac{1}{\sqrt{n\,(n-1)}}$	$\dfrac{.6745}{\sqrt{n-1}}$	$\dfrac{.6745}{\sqrt{n(n-1)}}$	$\dfrac{.8453}{n\sqrt{n-1}}$	$\dfrac{.8453}{\sqrt{n(n-1)}}$
50	.141421	.020203	.0964	.0136	.0024	.0171
51	.140028	.019803	.0954	.0134	.0023	.0167
52	.138675	.019418	.0945	.0131	.0023	.0164
53	.137361	.019048	.0935	.0129	.0022	.0161
54	.136083	.018692	.0927	.0126	.0022	.0158
55	.134840	.018349	.0918	.0124	.0021	.0155
56	.133631	.018019	.0910	.0122	.0020	.0152
57	.132453	.017700	.0901	.0119	.0020	.0150
58	.131306	.017392	.0893	.0117	.0019	.0147
59	.130189	.017095	.0886	.0115	.0019	.0145
60	.129099	.016807	.0878	.0113	.0018	.0142
61	.128037	.016529	.0871	.0112	.0018	.0140
62	.127000	.016261	.0864	.0110	.0018	.0138
63	.125988	.016001	.0857	.0108	.0017	.0135
64	.125000	.015749	.0850	.0106	.0017	.0133
65	.124035	.015504	.0843	.0105	.0016	.0131
66	.123091	.015268	.0837	.0103	.0016	.0129
67	.122169	.015038	.0830	.0101	.0016	.0127
68	.121268	.014815	.0824	.0100	.0015	.0125
69	.120386	.014599	.0818	.0099	.0015	.0123
70	.119523	.014389	.0812	.0097	.0015	.0122
71	.118678	.014185	.0806	.0096	.0014	.0120
72	.117851	.013986	.0801	.0094	.0014	.0118
73	.117041	.013793	.0795	.0093	.0014	.0117
74	.116248	.013606	.0789	.0092	.0013	.0115
75	.115470	.013423	.0784	.0091	.0013	.0113
76	.114708	.013245	.0779	.0089	.0013	.0112
77	.113961	.013072	.0773	.0088	.0013	.0111
78	.113228	.012904	.0769	.0087	.0012	.0109
79	.112509	.012739	.0764	.0086	.0012	.0108
80	.111803	.012579	.0759	.0085	.0012	.0106
31	.111111	.012423	.0754	.0084	.0012	.0105
82	.110432	.012270	.0749	.0083	.0012	.0104
83	.109764	.012121	.0745	.0082	.0011	.0103
84	.109109	.011976	.0740	.0081	.0011	.0101
85	.108465	.011835	.0736	.0080	.0011	.0100
86	.107833	.011696	.0732	.0079	.0011	.0099
87	.107211	.011561	.0727	.0078	.0011	.0098
88	.106600	.011429	.0723	.0077	.0010	.0097
89	.106000	.011300	.0719	.0076	.0010	.0096
90	.105409	.011173	.0715	.0075	.0010	.0094
91	.104828	.011050	.0711	.0075	.0010	.0093
92	.104257	.010929	.0707	.0074	.0010	.0092
93	.103695	.010811	.0703	.0073	.0010	.0091
94	.103142	.010695	.0699	.0072	.0009	.0090
95	.102598	.010582	.0696	.0071	.0009	.0089
96	.102062	.010471	.0692	.0071	.0009	.0089
97	.101535	.010363	.0688	.0070	.0009	.0088
98	.101015	.010257	.0685	.0069	.0009	.0087
99	.100504	.010152	.0681	.0069	.0009	.0086
100	.100000	.010050	.0678	.0068	.0008	.0085

PROBABILITY OF OCCURRENCE OF DEVIATIONS

Valid for thirty or more samples.

Probability of occurrence, expressed as per cent, and odds against a deviation as great or greater than that designated is given for various ratios of the deviation to the probable error and to the standard deviation.

(From Pearl, Medical Biometry and Statistics, W. B. Saunders Company, publishers, by permission.)

Ratio, dev. to P.E.	Probable occurrence %	Odds against, to 1	Ratio dev. to std. dev.	Probable occurrence %	Odds against, to 1
1.0	50.00	1.00	0.67449	50.00	1.00
1.1	45.81	1.18	0.7	48.39	1.07
1.2	41.83	1.39	0.8	42.37	1.36
1.3	38.06	1.63	0.9	36.81	1.72
1.4	34.50	1.90	1.0	31.73	2.15
1.5	31.17	2.21	1.1	27.13	2.69
1.6	28.05	2.57	1.2	23.01	3.35
1.7	25.15	2.98	1.3	19.36	4.17
1.8	22.47	3.45	1.4	16.15	5.19
1.9	20.00	4.00	1.5	13.36	6.48
2.0	17.73	4.64	1.6	10.96	8.12
2.1	15.67	5.38	1.7	8.91	10.22
2.2	13.78	6.25	1.8	7.19	12.92
2.3	12.08	7.28	1.9	5.74	16.41
2.4	10.55	8.48	2.0	4.55	20.98
2.5	9.18	9.90	2.1	3.57	26.99
2.6	7.95	11.58	2.2	2.78	34.96
2.7	6.86	13.58	2.3	2.14	45.62
2.8	5.89	15.96	2.4	1.64	59.99
2.9	5.05	18.82	2.5	1.24	79.52
3.0	4.30	22.24	2.6	.932	106.3
3.1	3.65	26.37	2.7	.693	143.2
3.2	3.09	31.36	2.8	.511	194.7
3.3	2.60	37.42	2.9	.373	267.0
3.4	2.18	44.80	3.0	.270	369.4
3.5	1.82	53.82	3.1	.194	515.7
3.6	1.52	64.89	3.2	.137	726.7
3.7	1.26	78.53	3.3	.0967	1033.
3.8	1.04	95.38	3.4	.0674	1483.
3.9	.853	116.3	3.5	.0465	2149.
4.0	.698	142.3	3.6	.0318	3142.
4.1	.569	174.9	3.7	.0216	4637.
4.2	.461	215.8	3.8	.0145	6915.
4.3	.373	267.2	3.9	.00962	10394.
4.4	.300	332.4	4.0	.00634	15772.
4.5	.240	415.0	5.0	5.73×10^{-5}	1.744×10^{6}
4.6	.192	520.4	6.0	2.0×10^{-7}	5.0×10^{8}
4.7	.152	655.3	7.0	2.6×10^{-10}	3.9×10^{11}
4.8	.121	828.3			
4.9	.0950	1052.			
5.0	.0745	1341.			
6.0	.0052	19300.			
7.0	.00023	4.27×10^{5}			
8.0	6.8×10^{-6}	1.47×10^{7}			
9.0	1.3×10^{-7}	7.30×10^{8}			
10.0	1.5×10^{-9}	6.5×10^{10}			

AREAS, ORDINATES AND DERIVATIVES OF THE NORMAL CURVE OF ERROR

The following table gives values of the area under the curve from the ordinate at $t = 0$ to the ordinate for the values of t given in the column at the left. Values of the ordinate and of the second, third and fourth derivatives are also given. See added information on next page.

t	Area	Ordinate	Second derivative	Third derivative	Fourth derivative	t	Area	Ordinate	Second derivative	Third derivative	Fourth derivative
.00	.0000	.3989	—.3989	.0000	1.1968	**.50**	.1915	.3521	—.2641	.4841	5501
.01	.0040	.3989	—.3989	.0120	1.1965	.51	.1950	.3503	—.2592	.4895	.5279
.02	.0080	.3989	—.3987	.0239	1.1956	.52	.1985	.3485	—.2543	.4947	.5056
.03	.0120	.3988	—.3984	.0359	1.1941	.53	.2019	.3467	—.2493	.4996	.4831
.04	.0160	.3986	—.3980	.0478	1.1920	.54	.2054	.3448	—.2443	.5043	.4605
.05	.0199	.3984	—.3975	.0597	1.1894	**.55**	.2088	.3429	—.2392	.5088	.4378
.06	.0239	.3982	—.3968	.0716	1.1861	.56	.2123	.3411	—.2341	.5131	.4150
.07	.0279	.3980	—.3960	.0834	1.1822	.57	.2157	.3391	—.2289	.5171	.3921
.08	.0319	.3977	—.3951	.0952	1.1778	.58	.2190	.3372	—.2238	.5209	.3691
.09	.0359	.3973	—.3941	.1070	1.1727	.59	.2224	.3352	—.2185	.5245	.3461
.10	.0398	.3970	—.3930	.1187	1.1671	**.60**	.2258	.3332	—.2133	.5278	.3231
.11	.0438	.3965	—.3917	.1303	1.1609	.61	.2291	.3312	—.2080	.5309	.3000
.12	.0478	.3961	—.3904	.1419	1.1541	.62	.2324	.3292	—.2027	.5338	.2770
.13	.0517	.3956	—.3889	.1534	1.1468	.63	.2357	.3271	—.1973	.5365	.2539
.14	.0557	.3951	—.3873	.1648	1.1389	.64	.2389	.3251	—.1919	.5389	.2309
.15	.0596	.3945	—.3856	.1762	1.1304	**.65**	.2422	.3230	—.1865	.5411	.2078
.16	.0636	.3939	—.3838	.1874	1.1214	.66	.2454	.3209	—.1811	.5431	.1849
.17	.0675	.3932	—.3819	.1986	1.1118	.67	.2486	.3187	—.1757	.5448	.1620
.18	.0714	.3925	—.3798	.2097	1.1017	.68	.2518	.3166	—.1702	.5463	.1391
.19	.0754	.3918	—.3777	.2206	1.0911	.69	.2549	.3144	—.1647	.5476	.1164
.20	.0793	.3910	—.3754	.2315	1.0799	**.70**	.2580	.3123	—.1593	.5486	.0937
.21	.0832	.3902	—.3730	.2422	1.0682	.71	.2612	.3101	—.1538	.5495	.0712
.22	.0871	.3894	—.3706	.2529	1.0560	.72	.2642	.3079	—.1483	.5501	.0487
.23	.0910	.3885	—.3680	.2634	1.0434	.73	.2673	.3056	—.1428	.5504	.0265
.24	.0948	.3876	—.3653	.2737	1.0302	.74	.2704	.3034	—.1373	.5506	.0043
.25	.0987	.3867	—.3625	.2840	1.0165	**.75**	.2734	.3011	—.1318	.5505	—.0176
.26	.1026	.3857	—.3596	.2941	1.0024	.76	.2764	.2989	—.1262	.5502	—.0394
.27	.1064	.3847	—.3566	.3040	0.9878	.77	.2794	.2966	—.1207	.5497	—.0611
.28	.1103	.3836	—.3535	.3138	0.9727	.78	.2823	.2943	—.1153	.5490	—.0825
.29	.1141	.3825	—.3504	.3235	0.9572	.79	.2852	.2920	—.1098	.5481	—.1037
.30	.1179	.3814	—.3471	.3330	0.9413	**.80**	.2881	.2897	—.1043	.5469	—.1247
.31	.1217	.3802	—.3437	.3423	0.9250	.81	.2910	.2874	—.0988	.5456	—.1455
.32	.1255	.3790	—.3402	.3515	0.9082	.82	.2939	.2850	—.0934	.5440	—.1660
.33	.1293	.3778	—.3367	.3605	0.8910	.83	.2967	.2827	—.0880	.5423	—.1862
.34	.1331	.3765	—.3330	.3693	0.8735	.84	.2996	.2803	—.0825	.5403	—.2063
.35	.1368	.3752	—.3293	.3779	0.8556	**.85**	.3023	.2780	—.0771	.5381	—.2260
.36	.1406	.3739	—.3255	.3864	0.8373	.86	.3051	.2756	—.0718	.5358	—.2455
.37	.1443	.3726	—.3216	.3947	0.8186	.87	.3079	.2732	—.0664	.5332	—.2646
.38	.1480	.3712	—.3176	.4028	0.7996	.88	.3106	.2709	—.0611	.5305	—.2835
.39	.1517	.3697	—.3135	.4107	0.7803	.89	.3133	.2685	—.0558	.5276	—.3021
.40	.1554	.3683	—.3094	.4184	0.7607	**.90**	.3159	.2661	—.0506	.5245	—.3203
.41	.1591	.3668	—.3051	.4259	0.7408	.91	.3186	.2637	—.0453	.5212	—.3383
.42	.1628	.3653	—.3008	.4332	0.7206	.92	.3212	.2613	—.0401	.5177	—.3559
.43	.1664	.3637	—.2965	.4403	0.7001	.93	.3238	.2589	—.0350	.5140	—.3731
.44	.1700	.3621	—.2920	.4472	0.6793	.94	.3264	.2565	—.0299	.5102	—.3901
.45	.1736	.3605	—.2875	.4539	0.6583	**.95**	.3289	.2541	—.0248	.5062	—.4066
.46	.1772	.3589	—.2830	.4603	0.6371	.96	.3315	.2516	—.0197	.5021	—.4228
.47	.1808	.3572	—.2783	.4666	0.6156	.97	.3340	.2492	—.0147	.4978	—.4387
.48	.1844	.3555	—.2736	.4727	0.5940	.98	.3365	.2468	—.0098	.4933	—.4541
.49	.1879	.3538	—.2689	.4785	0.5721	.99	.3389	.2444	—.0049	.4887	—.4692
.50	.1915	.3521	—.2641	.4841	0.5501	**1.00**	.3413	.2420	.0000	.4839	—.4839

$$\phi(t) = \frac{1}{\sqrt{2\pi}} e^{-\frac{t^2}{2}}; \quad \phi^{(2)}(t) = (t^2 - 1)\phi(t); \quad \phi^{(3)}(t) = (3t - t^3)\phi(t); \quad \phi^{(4)}(t) = (t^4 - 6t^2 + 3)\phi(t),$$

where $\phi^{(2)}$, $\phi^{(3)}$, $\phi^{(4)}$, represent second, third, and fourth derivatives.

t	Area	Ordinate	Second derivative	Third derivative	Fourth derivative	t	Area	Ordinate	Second derivative	Third derivative	Fourth derivative
1.00	.3413	.2420	.0000	.4839	−.4839	**1.50**	.4332	.1295	.1619	.1457	−.7043
1.01	.3438	.2396	.0048	.4790	−.4983	1.51	.4345	.1276	.1633	.1387	−.6994
1.02	.3461	.2371	.0096	.4740	−.5122	1.52	.4357	.1257	.1647	.1317	−.6942
1.03	.3485	.2347	.0143	.4688	−.5257	1.53	.4370	.1238	.1660	.1248	−.6888
1.04	.3508	.2323	.0190	.4635	−.5389	1.54	.4382	.1219	.1672	.1180	−.6831
1.05	.3531	.2299	.0236	.4580	−.5516	**1.55**	.4394	.1200	.1683	.1111	−.6772
1.06	.3554	.2275	.0281	.4524	−.5639	1.56	.4406	.1182	.1694	.1044	−.6710
1.07	.3577	.2251	.0326	.4467	−.5758	1.57	.4418	.1163	.1704	.0977	−.6646
1.08	.3599	.2227	.0371	.4409	−.5873	1.58	.4430	.1145	.1714	.0911	−.6580
1.09	.3621	.2203	.0414	.4350	−.5984	1.59	.4441	.1127	.1722	.0846	−.6511
1.10	.3643	.2179	.0458	.4290	−.6091	**1.60**	.4452	.1109	.1730	.0781	−.6441
1.11	.3665	.2155	.0500	.4228	−.6193	1.61	.4463	.1092	.1738	.0717	−.6368
1.12	.3686	.2131	.0542	.4166	−.6292	1.62	.4474	.1074	.1745	.0654	−.6293
1.13	.3708	.2107	.0583	.4102	−.6386	1.63	.4485	.1057	.1751	.0591	−.6216
1.14	.3729	.2083	.0624	.4038	−.6476	1.64	.4495	.1040	.1757	.0529	−.6138
1.15	.3749	.2059	.0664	.3973	−.6561	**1.65**	.4505	.1023	.1762	.0468	−.6057
1.16	.3770	.2036	.0704	.3907	−.6643	1.66	.4515	.1006	.1766	.0408	−.5975
1.17	.3790	.2012	.0742	.3840	−.6720	1.67	.4525	.0989	.1770	.0349	−.5891
1.18	.3810	.1989	.0780	.3772	−.6792	1.68	.4535	.0973	.1773	.0290	−.5806
1.19	.3830	.1965	.0818	.3704	−.6861	1.69	.4545	.0957	.1776	.0233	−.5720
1.20	.3849	.1942	.0854	.3635	−.6926	**1.70**	.4554	.0941	.1778	.0176	−.5632
1.21	.3869	.1919	.0890	.3566	−.6986	1.71	.4564	.0925	.1779	.0120	−.5542
1.22	.3888	.1895	.0926	.3496	−.7042	1.72	.4573	.0909	.1780	.0065	−.5452
1.23	.3907	.1872	.0960	.3425	−.7094	1.73	.4582	.0893	.1780	.0011	−.5360
1.24	.3925	.1849	.0994	.3354	−.7141	1.74	.4591	.0878	.1780	−.0042	−.5267
1.25	.3944	.1827	.1027	.3282	−.7185	**1.75**	.4599	.0863	.1780	−.0094	−.5173
1.26	.3962	.1804	.1060	.3210	−.7224	1.76	.4608	.0848	.1778	−.0146	−.5079
1.27	.3980	.1781	.1092	.3138	−.7259	1.77	.4616	.0833	.1777	−.0196	−.4983
1.28	.3997	.1759	.1123	.3065	−.7291	1.78	.4625	.0818	.1774	−.0245	−.4887
1.29	.4015	.1736	.1153	.2992	−.7318	1.79	.4633	.0804	.1772	−.0294	−.4789
1.30	.4032	.1714	.1182	.2918	−.7341	**1.80**	.4641	.0790	.1769	−.0341	−.4692
1.31	.4049	.1692	.1211	.2845	−.7361	1.81	.4649	.0775	.1765	−.0388	−.4593
1.32	.4066	.1669	.1239	.2771	−.7376	1.82	.4656	.0761	.1761	−.0433	−.4494
1.33	.4082	.1647	.1267	.2697	−.7388	1.83	.4664	.0748	.1756	−.0477	−.4395
1.34	.4099	.1626	.1293	.2624	−.7395	1.84	.4671	.0734	.1751	−.0521	−.4295
1.35	.4115	.1604	.1319	.2550	−.7399	**1.85**	.4678	.0721	.1746	−.0563	−.4195
1.36	.4131	.1582	.1344	.2476	−.7400	1.86	.4686	.0707	.1740	−.0605	−.4095
1.37	.4147	.1561	.1369	.2402	−.7396	1.87	.4693	.0694	.1734	−.0645	−.3995
1.38	.4162	.1540	.1392	.2328	−.7389	1.88	.4700	.0681	.1727	−.0685	−.3894
1.39	.4177	.1518	.1415	.2254	−.7378	1.89	.4706	.0669	.1720	−.0723	−.3793
1.40	.4192	.1497	.1437	.2180	−.7364	**1.90**	.4713	.0656	.1713	−.0761	−.3693
1.41	.4207	.1476	.1459	.2107	−.7347	1.91	.4719	.0644	.1705	−.0797	−.3592
1.42	.4222	.1456	.1480	.2033	−.7326	1.92	.4726	.0632	.1697	−.0832	−.3492
1.43	.4236	.1435	.1500	.1960	−.7301	1.93	.4732	.0620	.1688	−.0867	−.3392
1.44	.4251	.1415	.1519	.1887	−.7274	1.94	.4738	.0608	.1679	−.0900	−.3292
1.45	.4265	.1394	.1537	.1815	−.7243	**1.95**	.4744	.0596	.1670	−.0933	−.3192
1.46	.4279	.1374	.1555	.1742	−.7209	1.96	.4750	.0584	.1661	−.0964	−.3093
1.47	.4292	.1354	.1572	.1670	−.7172	1.97	.4756	.0573	.1651	−.0994	−.2994
1.48	.4306	.1334	.1588	.1599	−.7132	1.98	.4762	.0562	.1641	−.1024	−.2895
1.49	.4319	.1315	.1604	.1528	−.7089	1.99	.4767	.0551	.1630	−.1052	−.2797
1.50	.4332	.1295	.1619	.1457	−.7043	**2.00**	.4773	.0540	.1620	−.1080	−.2700

NORMAL CURVE OF ERROR

t	Area	Ordinate	Second derivative	Third derivative	Fourth derivative	t	Area	Ordinate	Second derivative	Third derivative	Fourth derivative
2.00	.4773	.0540	.1620	−.1080	−.2700	**2.50**	.4938	.0175	.0920	−.1424	.0800
2.01	.4778	.0529	.1609	−.1106	−.2603	2.51	.4940	.0171	.0906	−.1416	.0836
2.02	.4783	.0519	.1598	−.1132	−.2506	2.52	.4941	.0167	.0892	−.1408	.0871
2.03	.4788	.0508	.1586	−.1157	−.2411	2.53	.4943	.0163	.0878	−.1399	.0905
2.04	.4793	.0498	.1575	−.1180	−.2316	2.54	.4945	.0159	.0864	−.1389	.0937
2.05	.4798	.0488	.1563	−.1203	−.2222	**2.55**	.4946	.0155	.0850	−.1380	.0968
2.06	.4803	.0478	.1550	−.1225	−.2129	2.56	.4948	.0151	.0836	−.1370	.0998
2.07	.4808	.0468	.1538	−.1245	−.2036	2.57	.4949	.0147	.0823	−.1360	.1027
2.08	.4812	.0459	.1526	−.1265	−.1945	2.58	.4951	.0143	.0809	−.1350	.1054
2.09	.4817	.0449	.1513	−.1284	−.1854	2.59	.4952	.0139	.0796	−.1339	.1080
2.10	.4821	.0440	.1500	−.1302	−.1765	**2.60**	.4953	.0136	.0782	−.1328	.1105
2.11	.4826	.0431	.1487	−.1320	−.1676	2.61	.4955	.0132	.0769	−.1317	.1129
2.12	.4830	.0422	.1474	−.1336	−.1588	2.62	.4956	.0129	.0756	−.1305	.1152
2.13	.4834	.0413	.1460	−.1351	−.1502	2.63	.4957	.0126	.0743	−.1294	.1173
2.14	.4838	.0404	.1446	−.1366	−.1416	2.64	.4959	.0122	.0730	−.1282	.1194
2.15	.4842	.0396	.1433	−.1380	−.1332	**2.65**	.4960	.0119	.0717	−.1270	.1213
2.16	.4846	.0387	.1419	−.1393	−.1249	2.66	.4961	.0116	.0705	−.1258	.1231
2.17	.4850	.0379	.1405	−.1405	−.1167	2.67	.4962	.0113	.0692	−.1245	.1248
2.18	.4854	.0371	.1391	−.1416	−.1086	2.68	.4963	.0110	.0680	−.1233	.1264
2.19	.4857	.0363	.1377	−.1426	−.1006	2.69	.4964	.0107	.0668	−.1220	.1279
2.20	.4861	.0355	.1362	−.1436	−.0927	**2.70**	.4965	.0104	.0656	−.1207	.1293
2.21	.4865	.0347	.1348	−.1445	−.0850	2.71	.4966	.0101	.0644	−.1194	.1306
2.22	.4868	.0339	.1333	−.1453	−.0774	2.72	.4967	.0099	.0632	−.1181	.1317
2.23	.4871	.0332	.1319	−.1460	−.0700	2.73	.4968	.0096	.0620	−.1168	.1328
2.24	.4875	.0325	.1304	−.1467	−.0626	2.74	.4969	.0094	.0608	−.1154	.1338
2.25	.4878	.0317	.1289	−.1473	−.0554	**2.75**	.4970	.0091	.0597	−.1141	.1347
2.26	.4881	.0310	.1275	−.1478	−.0484	2.76	.4971	.0089	.0585	−.1127	.1356
2.27	.4884	.0303	.1260	−.1483	−.0414	2.77	.4972	.0086	.0574	−.1114	.1363
2.28	.4887	.0297	.1245	−.1486	−.0346	2.78	.4973	.0084	.0563	−.1100	.1369
2.29	.4890	.0290	.1230	−.1490	−.0279	2.79	.4974	.0081	.0552	−.1087	.1375
2.30	.4893	.0283	.1215	−.1492	−.0214	**2.80**	.4974	.0079	.0541	−.1073	.1379
2.31	.4896	.0277	.1200	−.1494	−.0150	2.81	.4975	.0077	.0531	−.1059	.1383
2.32	.4898	.0271	.1185	−.1495	−.0088	2.82	.4976	.0075	.0520	−.1045	.1386
2.33	.4901	.0264	.1170	−.1496	−.0027	2.83	.4977	.0073	.0510	−.1031	.1389
2.34	.4904	.0258	.1155	−.1496	.0033	2.84	.4977	.0071	.0500	−.1017	.1390
2.35	.4906	.0252	.1141	−.1495	.0092	**2.85**	.4978	.0069	.0490	−.1003	.1391
2.36	.4909	.0246	.1126	−.1494	.0149	2.86	.4979	.0067	.0480	−.0990	.1391
2.37	.4911	.0241	.1111	−.1492	.0204	2.87	.4980	.0065	.0470	−.0976	.1391
2.38	.4913	.0235	.1096	−.1490	.0258	2.88	.4980	.0063	.0460	−.0962	.1389
2.39	.4916	.0229	.1081	−.1487	.0311	2.89	.4981	.0061	.0451	−.0948	.1388
2 40	.4918	.0224	.1066	−.1483	.0362	**2.90**	.4981	.0060	.0441	−.0934	.1385
2.41	.4920	.0219	.1051	−.1480	.0412	2.91	.4982	.0058	.0432	−.0920	.1382
2.42	.4922	.0213	.1036	−.1475	.0461	2.92	.4983	.0056	.0423	−.0906	.1378
2.43	.4925	.0208	.1022	−.1470	.0508	2.93	.4983	.0055	.0414	−.0893	.1374
2.44	.4927	.0203	.1007	−.1465	.0554	2.94	.4984	.0053	.0405	−.0879	.1369
2.45	.4929	.0198	.0992	−.1459	.0598	**2.95**	.4984	.0051	.0396	−.0865	.1364
2.46	.4931	.0194	.0978	−.1453	.0641	2.96	.4985	.0050	.0388	−.0852	.1358
2.47	.4932	.0189	.0963	−.1446	.0683	2.97	.4985	.0049	.0379	−.0838	.1352
2.48	.4934	.0184	.0949	−.1439	.0723	2.98	.4986	.0047	.0371	−.0825	.1345
2.49	.4936	.0180	.0935	−.1432	.0762	2.99	.4986	.0046	.0363	−.0811	.1337
2.50	.4938	.0175	.0920	−.1424	.0800	**3.00**	.4987	.0044	.0355	−.0798	.1330

t	Area	Ordi-nate	Second deriva-tive	Third deriva-tive	Fourth deriva-tive	t	Area	Ordi-nate	Second deriva-tive	Third deriva-tive	Fourth deriva-tive
3.00	.4987	.0044	.0355	−.0798	.1330	**3.50**	.4998	.0009	.0098	−.0283	.0694
3.01	.4987	.0043	.0347	−.0785	.1321	3.51	.4998	.0008	.0095	−.0276	.0681
3.02	.4987	.0042	.0339	−.0771	.1313	3.52	.4998	.0008	.0093	−.0269	.0669
3.03	.4988	.0041	.0331	−.0758	.1304	3.53	.4998	.0008	.0090	−.0262	.0656
3.04	.4988	.0039	.0324	−.0745	.1294	3.54	.4998	.0008	.0087	−.0256	.0643
3.05	.4989	.0038	.0316	−.0732	.1285	**3.55**	.4998	.0007	.0085	−.0249	.0631
3.06	.4989	.0037	.0309	−.0720	.1275	3.56	.4998	.0007	.0082	−.0243	.0618
3.07	.4989	.0036	.0302	−.0707	.1264	3.57	.4998	.0007	.0080	−.0237	.0606
3.08	.4990	.0035	.0295	−.0694	.1254	3.58	.4998	.0007	.0078	−.0231	.0594
3.09	.4990	.0034	.0288	−.0682	.1243	3.59	.4998	.0006	.0075	−.0225	.0582
3.10	.4990	.0033	.0281	−.0669	.1231	**3.60**	.4998	.0006	.0073	−.0219	.0570
3.11	.4991	.0032	.0275	−.0657	.1220	3.61	.4999	.0006	.0071	−.0214	.0559
3.12	.4991	.0031	.0268	−.0645	.1208	3.62	.4999	.0006	.0069	−.0208	.0547
3.13	.4991	.0030	.0262	−.0633	.1196	3.63	.4999	.0006	.0067	−.0203	.0536
3.14	.4992	.0029	.0256	−.0621	.1184	3.64	.4999	.0005	.0065	−.0198	.0524
3.15	.4992	.0028	.0249	−.0609	.1171	**3.65**	.4999	.0005	.0063	−.0192	.0513
3.16	.4992	.0027	.0243	−.0598	.1159	3.66	.4999	.0005	.0061	−.0187	.0502
3.17	.4992	.0026	.0237	−.0586	.1146	3.67	.4999	.0005	.0059	−.0182	.0492
3.18	.4993	.0025	.0232	−.0575	.1133	3 68	.4999	.0005	.0057	−.0177	.0481
3.19	.4993	.0025	.0226	−.0564	.1120	3.69	.4999	.0004	.0056	−.0173	.0470
3.20	.4993	.0024	.0220	−.0552	.1107	**3.70**	.4999	.0004	.0054	−.0168	.0460
3.21	.4993	.0023	.0215	−.0541	.1093	3.71	.4999	.0004	.0052	−.0164	.0450
3.22	.4994	.0022	.0210	−.0531	.1080	3.72	.4999	.0004	.0051	−.0159	.0440
3.23	.4994	.0022	.0204	−.0520	.1066	3.73	.4999	.0004	.0049	−.0155	.0430
3.24	.4994	.0021	.0199	−.0509	.1053	3.74	.4999	.0004	.0048	−.0150	.0420
3.25	.4994	.0020	.0194	−.0499	.1039	**3.75**	.4999	.0004	.0046	−.0146	.0410
3.26	.4994	.0020	.0189	−.0488	.1025	3.76	.4999	.0003	.0045	−.0142	.0401
3.27	.4995	.0019	.0184	−.0478	.1011	3.77	.4999	.0003	.0043	−.0138	.0392
3.28	.4995	.0018	.0180	−.0468	.0997	3.78	.4999	.0003	.0042	−.0134	.0382
3.29	.4995	.0018	.0175	−.0458	.0983	3.79	.4999	.0003	.0041	−.0131	.0373
3.30	.4995	.0017	.0170	−.0449	.0969	**3.80**	.4999	.0003	.0039	−.0127	.0365
3.31	.4995	.0017	.0166	−.0439	.0955	3.81	.4999	.0003	.0038	−.0123	.0356
3.32	.4996	.0016	.0162	−.0429	.0941	3.82	.4999	.0003	.0037	−.0120	.0347
3.33	.4996	.0016	.0157	−.0420	.0927	3.83	.4999	.0003	.0036	−.0116	.0339
3.34	.4996	.0015	.0153	−.0411	.0913	3.84	.4999	.0003	.0034	−.0113	.0331
3.35	.4996	.0015	.0149	−.0402	.0899	**3.85**	.4999	.0002	.0033	−.0110	.0323
3.36	.4996	.0014	.0145	−.0393	.0885	3.86	.4999	.0002	.0032	−.0107	.0315
3.37	.4996	.0014	.0141	−.0384	.0871	3.87	.5000	.0002	.0031	−.0104	.0307
3.38	.4996	.0013	.0138	−.0376	.0857	3.88	.5000	.0002	.0030	−.0100	.0299
3.39	.4997	.0013	.0134	−.0367	.0843	3.89	.5000	.0002	.0029	−.0098	.0292
3.40	.4997	.0012	.0130	−.0359	.0829	**3.90**	.5000	.0002	.0028	−.0095	.0284
3.41	.4997	.0012	.0127	−.0350	.0815	3.91	.5000	.0002	.0027	−.0092	.0277
3.42	.4997	.0012	.0123	−.0342	.0801	3.92	.5000	.0002	.0026	−.0089	.0270
3.43	.4997	.0011	.0120	−.0334	.0788	3.93	.5000	.0002	.0026	−.0086	.0263
3.44	.4997	.0011	.0116	−.0327	.0774	3.94	.5000	.0002	.0025	−.0084	.0256
3.45	.4997	.0010	.0113	−.0319	.0761	**3.95**	.5000	.0002	.0024	−.0081	.0250
3.46	.4997	.0010	.0110	−.0311	.0747	3.96	.5000	.0002	.0023	−.0079	.0243
3.47	.4997	.0010	.0107	−.0304	.0734	3.97	.5000	.0002	.0022	−.0076	.0237
3.48	.4998	.0009	.0104	−.0297	.0721	3.98	.5000	.0001	.0022	−.0074	.0230
3.49	.4998	.0009	.0101	−.0290	.0707	3.99	.5000	.0001	.0021	−.0072	.0224
3.50	.4998	.0009	.0098	−.0283	.0694	**4.00**	.5000	.0001	.0020	−.0070	.0218

t	Area	Ordinate	Second derivative	Third derivative	Fourth derivative	t	Area	Ordinate	Second derivative	Third derivative	Fourth derivative
4.00	.5000	.0001	.0020	−.0070	.0218	**4.50**	.5000	.0000	.0003	−.0012	.0047
4.01	.5000	.0001	.0019	−.0067	.0212	4.51	.5000	.0000	.0003	−.0012	.0045
4.02	.5000	.0001	.0019	−.0065	.0207	4.52	.5000	.0000	.0003	−.0012	.0044
4.03	.5000	.0001	.0018	−.0063	.0201	4.53	.5000	.0000	.0003	−.0011	.0042
4.04	.5000	.0001	.0018	−.0061	.0195	4.54	.5000	.0000	.0003	−.0011	.0041
4.05	.5000	.0001	.0017	−.0059	.0190	**4.55**	.5000	.0000	.0003	−.0010	.0039
4.06	.5000	.0001	.0016	−.0058	.0185	4.56	.5000	.0000	.0002	−.0010	.0038
4.07	.5000	.0001	.0016	−.0056	.0180	4.57	.5000	.0000	.0002	−.0010	.0037
4.08	.5000	.0001	.0015	−.0054	.0175	4.58	.5000	.0000	.0002	−.0009	.0035
4.09	.5000	.0001	.0015	−.0052	.0170	4.59	.5000	.0000	.0002	−.0009	.0034
4.10	.5000	.0001	.0014	−.0051	.0165	**4.60**	.5000	.0000	.0002	−.0009	.0033
4.11	.5000	.0001	.0014	−.0049	.0160	4.61	.5000	.0000	.0002	−.0008	.0032
4.12	.5000	.0001	.0013	−.0047	.0156	4.62	.5000	.0000	.0002	−.0008	.0031
4.13	.5000	.0001	.0013	−.0046	.0151	4.63	.5000	.0000	.0002	−.0008	.0030
4.14	.5000	.0001	.0012	−.0044	.0147	4.64	.5000	.0000	.0002	−.0007	.0028
4.15	.5000	.0001	.0012	−.0043	.0143	**4.65**	.5000	.0000	.0002	−.0007	.0027
4.16	.5000	.0001	.0011	−.0042	.0138	4.66	.5000	.0000	.0002	−.0007	.0026
4.17	.5000	.0001	.0011	−.0040	.0134	4.67	.5000	.0000	.0002	−.0006	.0026
4.18	.5000	.0001	.0011	−.0039	.0130	4.68	.5000	.0000	.0002	−.0006	.0025
4.19	.5000	.0001	.0010	−.0038	.0127	4.69	.5000	.0000	.0001	−.0006	.0024
4.20	.5000	.0001	.0010	−.0036	.0123	**4.70**	.5000	.0000	.0001	−.0006	.0023
4.21	.5000	.0001	.0009	−.0035	.0119	4.71	.5000	.0000	.0001	−.0006	.0022
4.22	.5000	.0001	.0009	−.0034	.0116	4.72	.5000	.0000	.0001	−.0005	.0021
4.23	.5000	.0001	.0009	−.0033	.0112	4.73	.5000	.0000	.0001	−.0005	.0020
4.24	.5000	.0001	.0009	−.0032	.0109	4.74	.5000	.0000	.0001	−.0005	.0020
4.25	.5000	.0001	.0008	−.0031	.0105	**4.75**	.5000	.0000	.0001	−.0005	.0019
4.26	.5000	.0001	.0008	−.0030	.0102	4.76	.5000	.0000	.0001	−.0005	.0018
4.27	.5000	.0000	.0008	−.0029	.0099	4.77	.5000	.0000	.0001	−.0004	.0018
4.28	.5000	.0000	.0007	−.0028	.0096	4.78	.5000	.0000	.0001	−.0004	.0017
4.29	.5000	.0000	.0007	−.0027	.0093	4.79	.5000	.0000	.0001	−.0004	.0016
4.30	.5000	.0000	.0007	−.0026	.0090	**4.80**	.5000	.0000	.0001	−.0004	.0016
4.31	.5000	.0000	.0007	−.0025	.0087	4.81	.5000	.0000	.0001	−.0004	.0015
4.32	.5000	.0000	.0006	−.0024	.0085	4.82	.5000	.0000	.0001	−.0004	.0015
4.33	.5000	.0000	.0006	−.0023	.0082	4.83	.5000	.0000	.0001	−.0003	.0014
4.34	.5000	.0000	.0006	−.0022	.0079	4.84	.5000	.0000	.0001	−.0003	.0013
4.35	.5000	.0000	.0006	−.0022	.0077	**4.85**	.5000	.0000	.0001	−.0003	.0013
4.36	.5000	.0000	.0005	−.0021	.0074	4.86	.5000	.0000	.0001	−.0003	.0012
4.37	.5000	.0000	.0005	−.0020	.0072	4.87	.5000	.0000	.0001	−.0003	.0012
4.38	.5000	.0000	.0005	−.0019	.0070	4.88	.5000	.0000	.0001	−.0003	.0012
4.39	.5000	.0000	.0005	−.0019	.0067	4.89	.5000	.0000	.0001	−.0003	.0011
4.40	.5000	.0000	.0005	−.0018	.0065	**4.90**	.5000	.0000	.0001	−.0003	.0011
4.41	.5000	.0000	.0004	−.0017	.0063	4.91	.5000	.0000	.0001	−.0002	.0010
4.42	.5000	.0000	.0004	−.0017	.0061	4.92	.5000	.0000	.0001	−.0002	.0010
4.43	.5000	.0000	.0004	−.0016	.0059	4.93	.5000	.0000	.0001	−.0002	.0009
4.44	.5000	.0000	.0004	−.0016	.0057	4.94	.5000	.0000	.0001	−.0002	.0009
4.45	.5000	.0000	.0004	−.0015	.0055	**4.95**	.5000	.0000	.0000	−.0002	.0009
4.46	.5000	.0000	.0004	−.0014	.0053	4.96	.5000	.0000	.0000	−.0002	.0008
4.47	.5000	.0000	.0004	−.0014	.0052	4.97	.5000	.0000	.0000	−.0002	.0008
4.48	.5000	.0000	.0003	−.0013	.0050	4.98	.5000	.0000	.0000	−.0002	.0008
4.49	.5000	.0000	.0003	−.0013	.0048	4.99	.5000	.0000	.0000	−.0002	.0007
4.50	.5000	.0000	.0003	−.0012	.0047						

TESTS OF SIGNIFICANCE

"*t*" test of significance between two sample means ($\bar{x}_1$ and $\bar{x}_2$).

(Use Fisher's t distribution)

Paired variates $t = \dfrac{\bar{d}}{\sqrt{\dfrac{\Sigma(d_i - \bar{d})^2}{N(N-1)}}}$ with $N - 1$ degrees of freedom

where $\bar{d} = \bar{x}_1 - \bar{x}_2$

$d_1 = x_{11} - x_{21}$

$d_2 = x_{12} - x_{22}$ etc.

$N = $ sample size

Unpaired variates $t = \dfrac{\bar{x}_1 - \bar{x}_2}{\sqrt{\dfrac{\Sigma_i(x_i - \bar{x}_1)^2 + \Sigma_i(x_{2i} - \bar{x}_2)^2}{N_1 + N_2 - 2}\left(\dfrac{1}{N_1} + \dfrac{1}{N_2}\right)}}$

with $N_1 + N_2 - 2$ degrees of freedom

where $N_1 = $ size of sample 1

$N_2 = $ size of sample 2

F TEST FOR EQUALITY OF VARIANCES

$$F = \frac{\sigma_1{}^2}{\sigma_2{}^2}$$

where $\sigma_1{}^2 = $ variance of sample with size N_1

$\sigma_2{}^2 = $ variance of sample with size N_2

with $N_1 - 1 = $ degrees of freedom for numerator

$N_2 - 1 = $ degrees of freedom for denominator

(Use Snedecor's F distribution)

t TEST OF SIGNIFICANCE

TABLE FOR t TEST OF SIGNIFICANCE BETWEEN TWO SAMPLE MEANS ($\bar{x}_1$ AND $\bar{x}_2$)

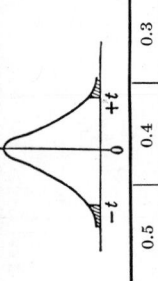

Degrees of freedom	*P = 0.9	0.8	0.7	0.6	0.5	0.4	0.3	0.2	0.1	0.05	0.02	0.01
1	0.158	0.325	0.510	0.727	1.000	1.376	1.963	3.078	6.314	12.706	31.821	63.657
2	0.142	0.289	0.445	0.617	0.816	1.061	1.386	1.886	2.920	4.303	6.965	9.925
3	0.137	0.277	0.424	0.584	0.765	0.978	1.250	1.638	2.353	3.182	4.541	5.841
4	0.134	0.271	0.414	0.569	0.741	0.941	1.190	1.533	2.132	2.776	3.747	4.604
5	0.132	0.267	0.408	0.559	0.727	0.920	1.156	1.476	2.015	2.571	3.365	4.032
6	0.131	0.265	0.404	0.553	0.718	0.906	1.134	1.440	1.943	2.447	3.143	3.707
7	0.130	0.263	0.402	0.549	0.711	0.896	1.119	1.415	1.895	2.365	2.998	3.499
8	0.130	0.262	0.399	0.546	0.706	0.889	1.108	1.397	1.860	2.306	2.896	3.355
9	0.129	0.261	0.398	0.543	0.703	0.883	1.100	1.383	1.833	2.262	2.821	3.250
10	0.129	0.260	0.397	0.542	0.700	0.879	1.093	1.372	1.812	2.228	2.764	3.169
11	0.129	0.260	0.396	0.540	0.697	0.876	1.088	1.363	1.796	2.201	2.718	3.106
12	0.128	0.259	0.395	0.539	0.695	0.873	1.083	1.356	1.782	2.179	2.681	3.055
13	0.128	0.259	0.394	0.538	0.694	0.870	1.079	1.350	1.771	2.160	2.650	3.012
14	0.128	0.258	0.393	0.537	0.692	0.868	1.076	1.345	1.761	2.145	2.624	2.977
15	0.128	0.258	0.393	0.536	0.691	0.866	1.074	1.341	1.753	2.131	2.602	2.947
16	0.128	0.258	0.392	0.535	0.690	0.865	1.071	1.337	1.746	2.120	2.583	2.921
17	0.128	0.257	0.392	0.534	0.689	0.863	1.069	1.333	1.740	2.110	2.567	2.898
18	0.127	0.257	0.392	0.534	0.688	0.862	1.067	1.330	1.734	2.101	2.552	2.878
19	0.127	0.257	0.391	0.533	0.688	0.861	1.066	1.328	1.729	2.093	2.539	2.861
20	0.127	0.257	0.391	0.533	0.687	0.860	1.064	1.325	1.725	2.086	2.528	2.845
21	0.127	0.257	0.391	0.532	0.686	0.859	1.063	1.323	1.721	2.080	2.518	2.831
22	0.127	0.256	0.390	0.532	0.686	0.858	1.061	1.321	1.717	2.074	2.508	2.819
23	0.127	0.256	0.390	0.532	0.685	0.858	1.060	1.319	1.714	2.069	2.500	2.807
24	0.127	0.256	0.390	0.531	0.685	0.857	1.059	1.318	1.711	2.064	2.492	2.797
25	0.127	0.256	0.390	0.531	0.684	0.856	1.058	1.316	1.708	2.060	2.485	2.787
26	0.127	0.256	0.390	0.531	0.684	0.856	1.058	1.315	1.706	2.056	2.479	2.779
27	0.127	0.256	0.389	0.531	0.684	0.855	1.057	1.314	1.703	2.052	2.473	2.771
28	0.127	0.256	0.389	0.530	0.683	0.855	1.056	1.313	1.701	2.048	2.467	2.763
29	0.127	0.256	0.389	0.530	0.683	0.854	1.055	1.311	1.699	2.045	2.462	2.756
30	0.127	0.256	0.389	0.530	0.683	0.854	1.055	1.310	1.697	2.042	2.457	2.750
∞	0.12566	0.25335	0.38532	0.52440	0.67449	0.84162	1.03643	1.28155	1.64485	1.95996	2.32634	2.57582

Reproduced from *Statistical Methods for Research Workers*, 6th ed., with the permission of the author, R. A. Fisher, and his publisher, Oliver and Boyd, Edinburgh.

* P is the probability of having t this large or larger in size by chance.

F TEST FOR EQUALITY OF VARIANCES

TABLE FOR F TEST FOR EQUALITY OF VARIANCES

*5% (ROMAN TYPE) AND 1% (BOLD-FACE TYPE) POINTS FOR THE DISTRIBUTION OF F

Each cell gives the 5% point (roman type) over the 1% point (bold-face type).

Degrees of freedom for lesser mean square	\ Degrees of freedom for greater mean square → 1	2	3	4	5	6	7	8	9	10	11	12	14	16	20	24	30	40	50	75	100	200	500	∞
1	161 / 4052	200 / 4999	216 / 5403	225 / 5625	230 / 5764	234 / 5859	237 / 5928	239 / 5981	241 / 6022	242 / 6056	243 / 6082	244 / 6106	245 / 6142	246 / 6169	248 / 6208	249 / 6234	250 / 6258	251 / 6286	252 / 6302	253 / 6323	253 / 6334	254 / 6352	254 / 6361	254 / 6366
2	18.51 / 98.49	19.00 / 99.01	19.16 / 99.17	19.25 / 99.25	19.30 / 99.30	19.33 / 99.33	19.36 / 99.34	19.37 / 99.36	19.38 / 99.38	19.39 / 99.40	19.40 / 99.41	19.41 / 99.42	19.42 / 99.43	19.43 / 99.44	19.44 / 99.45	19.45 / 99.46	19.46 / 99.47	19.47 / 99.48	19.47 / 99.48	19.48 / 99.49	19.49 / 99.49	19.49 / 99.49	19.50 / 99.50	19.50 / 99.50
3	10.13 / 34.12	9.55 / 30.81	9.28 / 29.46	9.12 / 28.71	9.01 / 28.24	8.94 / 27.91	8.88 / 27.67	8.84 / 27.49	8.81 / 27.34	8.78 / 27.23	8.76 / 27.13	8.74 / 27.05	8.71 / 26.92	8.69 / 26.83	8.66 / 26.69	8.64 / 26.60	8.62 / 26.50	8.60 / 26.41	8.58 / 26.30	8.57 / 26.27	8.56 / 26.23	8.54 / 26.18	8.54 / 26.14	8.53 / 26.12
4	7.71 / 21.20	6.94 / 18.00	6.59 / 16.69	6.39 / 15.98	6.26 / 15.52	6.16 / 15.21	6.09 / 14.98	6.04 / 14.80	6.00 / 14.66	5.96 / 14.54	5.93 / 14.45	5.91 / 14.37	5.87 / 14.24	5.84 / 14.15	5.80 / 14.02	5.77 / 13.93	5.74 / 13.83	5.71 / 13.74	5.70 / 13.69	5.68 / 13.61	5.66 / 13.57	5.65 / 13.52	5.64 / 13.48	5.63 / 13.46
5	6.61 / 16.26	5.79 / 13.27	5.41 / 12.06	5.19 / 11.39	5.05 / 10.97	4.95 / 10.67	4.88 / 10.45	4.82 / 10.27	4.78 / 10.15	4.74 / 10.05	4.70 / 9.96	4.68 / 9.89	4.64 / 9.77	4.60 / 9.68	4.56 / 9.55	4.53 / 9.47	4.50 / 9.38	4.46 / 9.29	4.44 / 9.24	4.42 / 9.17	4.40 / 9.13	4.38 / 9.07	4.37 / 9.04	4.36 / 9.02
6	5.99 / 13.74	5.14 / 10.92	4.76 / 9.78	4.53 / 9.15	4.39 / 8.75	4.28 / 8.47	4.21 / 8.26	4.15 / 8.10	4.10 / 7.98	4.06 / 7.87	4.03 / 7.79	4.00 / 7.72	3.96 / 7.60	3.92 / 7.52	3.87 / 7.39	3.84 / 7.31	3.81 / 7.23	3.77 / 7.14	3.75 / 7.09	3.72 / 7.02	3.71 / 6.99	3.69 / 6.94	3.68 / 6.90	3.67 / 6.88
7	5.59 / 12.25	4.74 / 9.55	4.35 / 8.45	4.12 / 7.85	3.97 / 7.46	3.87 / 7.19	3.79 / 7.00	3.73 / 6.84	3.68 / 6.71	3.63 / 6.62	3.60 / 6.54	3.57 / 6.47	3.52 / 6.35	3.49 / 6.27	3.44 / 6.15	3.41 / 6.07	3.38 / 5.98	3.34 / 5.90	3.32 / 5.85	3.29 / 5.78	3.28 / 5.75	3.25 / 5.70	3.24 / 5.67	3.23 / 5.65
8	5.32 / 11.26	4.46 / 8.65	4.07 / 7.59	3.84 / 7.01	3.69 / 6.63	3.58 / 6.37	3.50 / 6.19	3.44 / 6.03	3.39 / 5.91	3.34 / 5.82	3.31 / 5.74	3.28 / 5.67	3.23 / 5.56	3.20 / 5.48	3.15 / 5.36	3.12 / 5.28	3.08 / 5.20	3.05 / 5.11	3.03 / 5.06	3.00 / 5.00	2.98 / 4.96	2.96 / 4.91	2.94 / 4.88	2.93 / 4.86
9	5.12 / 10.56	4.26 / 8.02	3.86 / 6.99	3.63 / 6.42	3.48 / 6.06	3.37 / 5.80	3.29 / 5.62	3.23 / 5.47	3.18 / 5.35	3.13 / 5.26	3.10 / 5.18	3.07 / 5.11	3.02 / 5.00	2.98 / 4.92	2.93 / 4.80	2.90 / 4.73	2.86 / 4.64	2.82 / 4.56	2.80 / 4.51	2.77 / 4.45	2.76 / 4.41	2.73 / 4.36	2.72 / 4.33	2.71 / 4.31
10	4.96 / 10.04	4.10 / 7.56	3.71 / 6.55	3.48 / 5.99	3.33 / 5.64	3.22 / 5.39	3.14 / 5.21	3.07 / 5.06	3.02 / 4.95	2.97 / 4.85	2.94 / 4.78	2.91 / 4.71	2.86 / 4.60	2.82 / 4.52	2.77 / 4.41	2.74 / 4.33	2.70 / 4.25	2.67 / 4.17	2.64 / 4.12	2.61 / 4.05	2.59 / 4.01	2.56 / 3.96	2.55 / 3.93	2.54 / 3.91

Reprinted, by permission, from Snedecor, *Statistical Methods*, Collegiate Press, Iowa State College, Ames.
* This table gives values of F which one would expect to exceed by chance alone 5% and 1% of the time.

TABLE FOR F (Continued)

5% (ROMAN TYPE) AND 1% (BOLD-FACE TYPE) POINTS FOR THE DISTRIBUTION OF F

Each cell: top value = 5% point (Roman type); bottom value = 1% point (Bold-face type).

Degrees of freedom for lesser mean square	\\ Degrees of freedom for greater mean square →																							
	1	2	3	4	5	6	7	8	9	10	11	12	14	16	20	24	30	40	50	75	100	200	500	∞
11	4.84 / 9.65	3.98 / 7.20	3.59 / 6.22	3.36 / 5.67	3.20 / 5.32	3.09 / 5.07	3.01 / 4.88	2.95 / 4.74	2.90 / 4.63	2.86 / 4.54	2.82 / 4.46	2.79 / 4.40	2.74 / 4.29	2.70 / 4.21	2.65 / 4.10	2.61 / 4.02	2.57 / 3.94	2.53 / 3.86	2.50 / 3.80	2.47 / 3.74	2.45 / 3.70	2.42 / 3.66	2.41 / 3.62	2.40 / 3.60
12	4.75 / 9.33	3.88 / 6.93	3.49 / 5.95	3.26 / 5.41	3.11 / 5.06	3.00 / 4.82	2.92 / 4.65	2.85 / 4.50	2.80 / 4.39	2.76 / 4.30	2.72 / 4.22	2.69 / 4.16	2.64 / 4.05	2.60 / 3.98	2.54 / 3.86	2.50 / 3.78	2.46 / 3.70	2.42 / 3.61	2.40 / 3.56	2.36 / 3.49	2.35 / 3.46	2.32 / 3.41	2.31 / 3.38	2.30 / 3.36
13	4.67 / 9.07	3.80 / 6.70	3.41 / 5.74	3.18 / 5.20	3.02 / 4.86	2.92 / 4.62	2.84 / 4.44	2.77 / 4.30	2.72 / 4.19	2.67 / 4.10	2.63 / 4.02	2.60 / 3.96	2.55 / 3.85	2.51 / 3.78	2.46 / 3.67	2.42 / 3.59	2.38 / 3.51	2.34 / 3.42	2.32 / 3.37	2.28 / 3.30	2.26 / 3.27	2.24 / 3.21	2.22 / 3.18	2.21 / 3.16
14	4.60 / 8.86	3.74 / 6.51	3.34 / 5.56	3.11 / 5.03	2.96 / 4.69	2.85 / 4.46	2.77 / 4.28	2.70 / 4.14	2.65 / 4.03	2.60 / 3.94	2.56 / 3.86	2.53 / 3.80	2.48 / 3.70	2.44 / 3.62	2.39 / 3.51	2.35 / 3.43	2.31 / 3.34	2.27 / 3.26	2.24 / 3.21	2.21 / 3.14	2.19 / 3.11	2.16 / 3.06	2.14 / 3.02	2.13 / 3.00
15	4.54 / 8.68	3.68 / 6.36	3.29 / 5.42	3.06 / 4.89	2.90 / 4.56	2.79 / 4.32	2.70 / 4.14	2.64 / 4.00	2.59 / 3.89	2.55 / 3.80	2.51 / 3.73	2.48 / 3.67	2.43 / 3.56	2.39 / 3.48	2.33 / 3.36	2.29 / 3.29	2.25 / 3.20	2.21 / 3.12	2.18 / 3.07	2.15 / 3.00	2.12 / 2.97	2.10 / 2.92	2.08 / 2.89	2.07 / 2.87
16	4.49 / 8.53	3.63 / 6.23	3.24 / 5.29	3.01 / 4.77	2.85 / 4.44	2.74 / 4.20	2.66 / 4.03	2.59 / 3.89	2.54 / 3.78	2.49 / 3.69	2.45 / 3.61	2.42 / 3.55	2.37 / 3.45	2.33 / 3.37	2.28 / 3.25	2.24 / 3.18	2.20 / 3.10	2.16 / 3.01	2.13 / 2.96	2.09 / 2.89	2.07 / 2.86	2.04 / 2.80	2.02 / 2.77	2.01 / 2.75
17	4.45 / 8.40	3.59 / 6.11	3.20 / 5.18	2.96 / 4.67	2.81 / 4.34	2.70 / 4.10	2.62 / 3.93	2.55 / 3.79	2.50 / 3.68	2.45 / 3.59	2.41 / 3.52	2.38 / 3.45	2.33 / 3.35	2.29 / 3.27	2.23 / 3.16	2.19 / 3.08	2.15 / 3.00	2.11 / 2.92	2.08 / 2.86	2.04 / 2.79	2.02 / 2.76	1.99 / 2.70	1.97 / 2.67	1.96 / 2.65
18	4.41 / 8.28	3.55 / 6.01	3.16 / 5.09	2.93 / 4.58	2.77 / 4.25	2.66 / 4.01	2.58 / 3.85	2.51 / 3.71	2.46 / 3.60	2.41 / 3.51	2.37 / 3.44	2.34 / 3.37	2.29 / 3.27	2.25 / 3.19	2.19 / 3.07	2.15 / 3.00	2.11 / 2.91	2.07 / 2.83	2.04 / 2.78	2.00 / 2.71	1.98 / 2.68	1.95 / 2.62	1.93 / 2.59	1.92 / 2.57
19	4.38 / 8.18	3.52 / 5.93	3.13 / 5.01	2.90 / 4.50	2.74 / 4.17	2.63 / 3.94	2.55 / 3.77	2.48 / 3.63	2.43 / 3.52	2.38 / 3.43	2.34 / 3.36	2.31 / 3.30	2.26 / 3.19	2.21 / 3.12	2.15 / 3.00	2.11 / 2.92	2.07 / 2.84	2.02 / 2.76	2.00 / 2.70	1.96 / 2.63	1.94 / 2.60	1.91 / 2.54	1.90 / 2.51	1.88 / 2.49
20	4.35 / 8.10	3.49 / 5.85	3.10 / 4.94	2.87 / 4.43	2.71 / 4.10	2.60 / 3.87	2.52 / 3.71	2.45 / 3.56	2.40 / 3.45	2.35 / 3.37	2.31 / 3.30	2.28 / 3.23	2.23 / 3.13	2.18 / 3.05	2.12 / 2.94	2.08 / 2.86	2.04 / 2.77	1.99 / 2.69	1.96 / 2.63	1.92 / 2.56	1.90 / 2.53	1.87 / 2.47	1.85 / 2.44	1.84 / 2.42
21	4.32 / 8.02	3.47 / 5.78	3.07 / 4.87	2.84 / 4.37	2.68 / 4.04	2.57 / 3.81	2.49 / 3.65	2.42 / 3.51	2.37 / 3.40	2.32 / 3.31	2.28 / 3.24	2.25 / 3.17	2.20 / 3.07	2.15 / 2.99	2.09 / 2.88	2.05 / 2.80	2.00 / 2.72	1.96 / 2.63	1.93 / 2.58	1.89 / 2.51	1.87 / 2.47	1.84 / 2.42	1.82 / 2.38	1.81 / 2.36
22	4.30 / 7.94	3.44 / 5.72	3.05 / 4.82	2.82 / 4.31	2.66 / 3.99	2.55 / 3.76	2.47 / 3.59	2.40 / 3.45	2.35 / 3.35	2.30 / 3.26	2.26 / 3.18	2.23 / 3.12	2.18 / 3.02	2.13 / 2.94	2.09 / 2.83	2.03 / 2.75	1.98 / 2.67	1.93 / 2.58	1.91 / 2.53	1.87 / 2.46	1.84 / 2.42	1.81 / 2.37	1.80 / 2.33	1.78 / 2.31
23	4.28 / 7.88	3.42 / 5.66	3.03 / 4.76	2.80 / 4.26	2.64 / 3.94	2.53 / 3.71	2.45 / 3.54	2.38 / 3.41	2.32 / 3.30	2.28 / 3.21	2.24 / 3.14	2.20 / 3.07	2.14 / 2.97	2.10 / 2.89	2.04 / 2.78	2.00 / 2.70	1.96 / 2.62	1.91 / 2.53	1.88 / 2.48	1.84 / 2.41	1.82 / 2.37	1.79 / 2.32	1.77 / 2.28	1.76 / 2.26

In each cell the upper value is the 5% point and the lower (bold) value is the 1% point.

24	4.26 / **7.82**	3.40 / **5.61**	3.01 / **4.72**	2.78 / **4.22**	2.62 / **3.90**	2.51 / **3.67**	2.43 / **3.50**	2.36 / **3.36**	2.30 / **3.25**	2.26 / **3.17**	2.22 / **3.09**	2.18 / **3.03**	2.13 / **2.93**	2.09 / **2.85**	2.02 / **2.74**	1.98 / **2.66**	1.94 / **2.58**	1.89 / **2.49**	1.86 / **2.44**	1.82 / **2.36**	1.80 / **2.33**	1.76 / **2.27**	1.74 / **2.23**	1.73 / **2.21**
25	4.24 / **7.77**	3.38 / **5.57**	2.99 / **4.68**	2.76 / **4.18**	2.60 / **3.86**	2.49 / **3.63**	2.41 / **3.46**	2.34 / **3.32**	2.28 / **3.21**	2.24 / **3.13**	2.20 / **3.05**	2.16 / **2.99**	2.11 / **2.89**	2.06 / **2.81**	2.00 / **2.70**	1.96 / **2.62**	1.92 / **2.54**	1.87 / **2.45**	1.84 / **2.40**	1.80 / **2.32**	1.77 / **2.29**	1.74 / **2.23**	1.72 / **2.19**	1.71 / **2.17**
26	4.22 / **7.72**	3.37 / **5.53**	2.98 / **4.64**	2.74 / **4.14**	2.59 / **3.82**	2.47 / **3.59**	2.39 / **3.42**	2.32 / **3.29**	2.27 / **3.17**	2.22 / **3.09**	2.18 / **3.02**	2.15 / **2.96**	2.10 / **2.86**	2.05 / **2.77**	1.99 / **2.66**	1.95 / **2.58**	1.90 / **2.50**	1.85 / **2.41**	1.82 / **2.36**	1.78 / **2.28**	1.76 / **2.25**	1.72 / **2.19**	1.70 / **2.15**	1.69 / **2.13**
27	4.21 / **7.68**	3.35 / **5.49**	2.96 / **4.60**	2.73 / **4.11**	2.57 / **3.79**	2.46 / **3.56**	2.37 / **3.39**	2.30 / **3.26**	2.25 / **3.14**	2.20 / **3.06**	2.16 / **2.98**	2.13 / **2.93**	2.08 / **2.83**	2.03 / **2.74**	1.97 / **2.63**	1.93 / **2.55**	1.88 / **2.47**	1.84 / **2.38**	1.80 / **2.33**	1.76 / **2.25**	1.74 / **2.21**	1.71 / **2.16**	1.68 / **2.12**	1.67 / **2.10**
28	4.20 / **7.64**	3.34 / **5.45**	2.95 / **4.57**	2.71 / **4.07**	2.56 / **3.76**	2.44 / **3.53**	2.36 / **3.36**	2.29 / **3.23**	2.24 / **3.11**	2.19 / **3.03**	2.15 / **2.95**	2.12 / **2.90**	2.06 / **2.80**	2.02 / **2.71**	1.96 / **2.60**	1.91 / **2.52**	1.87 / **2.44**	1.81 / **2.35**	1.78 / **2.30**	1.75 / **2.22**	1.72 / **2.18**	1.69 / **2.13**	1.67 / **2.09**	1.65 / **2.06**
29	4.18 / **7.60**	3.33 / **5.42**	2.93 / **4.54**	2.70 / **4.04**	2.54 / **3.73**	2.43 / **3.50**	2.35 / **3.33**	2.28 / **3.20**	2.22 / **3.08**	2.18 / **3.00**	2.14 / **2.92**	2.10 / **2.87**	2.05 / **2.77**	2.00 / **2.68**	1.94 / **2.57**	1.90 / **2.49**	1.85 / **2.41**	1.80 / **2.32**	1.77 / **2.27**	1.73 / **2.19**	1.71 / **2.15**	1.68 / **2.10**	1.65 / **2.06**	1.64 / **2.03**
30	4.17 / **7.56**	3.32 / **5.39**	2.92 / **4.51**	2.69 / **4.02**	2.53 / **3.70**	2.42 / **3.47**	2.34 / **3.30**	2.27 / **3.17**	2.21 / **3.06**	2.16 / **2.98**	2.12 / **2.90**	2.09 / **2.84**	2.04 / **2.74**	1.99 / **2.66**	1.93 / **2.55**	1.89 / **2.47**	1.84 / **2.38**	1.79 / **2.29**	1.76 / **2.24**	1.72 / **2.16**	1.69 / **2.13**	1.66 / **2.07**	1.64 / **2.03**	1.62 / **2.01**
32	4.15 / **7.50**	3.30 / **5.34**	2.90 / **4.46**	2.67 / **3.97**	2.51 / **3.66**	2.40 / **3.42**	2.32 / **3.25**	2.25 / **3.12**	2.19 / **3.01**	2.14 / **2.94**	2.10 / **2.86**	2.07 / **2.80**	2.02 / **2.70**	1.97 / **2.62**	1.91 / **2.51**	1.86 / **2.42**	1.82 / **2.34**	1.76 / **2.25**	1.74 / **2.20**	1.69 / **2.12**	1.67 / **2.08**	1.64 / **2.02**	1.61 / **1.98**	1.59 / **1.96**
34	4.13 / **7.44**	3.28 / **5.29**	2.88 / **4.42**	2.65 / **3.93**	2.49 / **3.61**	2.38 / **3.38**	2.30 / **3.21**	2.23 / **3.08**	2.17 / **2.97**	2.12 / **2.89**	2.08 / **2.82**	2.05 / **2.76**	2.00 / **2.66**	1.95 / **2.58**	1.89 / **2.47**	1.84 / **2.38**	1.80 / **2.30**	1.74 / **2.21**	1.71 / **2.15**	1.67 / **2.08**	1.64 / **2.04**	1.61 / **1.98**	1.59 / **1.94**	1.57 / **1.91**
36	4.11 / **7.39**	3.26 / **5.25**	2.86 / **4.38**	2.63 / **3.89**	2.48 / **3.58**	2.36 / **3.35**	2.28 / **3.18**	2.21 / **3.04**	2.15 / **2.94**	2.10 / **2.86**	2.06 / **2.78**	2.03 / **2.72**	1.98 / **2.62**	1.93 / **2.54**	1.87 / **2.43**	1.82 / **2.35**	1.78 / **2.26**	1.72 / **2.17**	1.69 / **2.12**	1.65 / **2.04**	1.62 / **2.00**	1.59 / **1.94**	1.56 / **1.90**	1.55 / **1.87**
38	4.10 / **7.35**	3.25 / **5.21**	2.85 / **4.34**	2.62 / **3.86**	2.46 / **3.54**	2.35 / **3.32**	2.26 / **3.15**	2.19 / **3.02**	2.14 / **2.91**	2.09 / **2.82**	2.05 / **2.75**	2.02 / **2.69**	1.96 / **2.59**	1.92 / **2.51**	1.85 / **2.40**	1.80 / **2.32**	1.76 / **2.22**	1.71 / **2.14**	1.67 / **2.08**	1.63 / **2.00**	1.60 / **1.97**	1.57 / **1.90**	1.54 / **1.86**	1.53 / **1.84**
40	4.08 / **7.31**	3.23 / **5.18**	2.84 / **4.31**	2.61 / **3.83**	2.45 / **3.51**	2.34 / **3.29**	2.25 / **3.12**	2.18 / **2.99**	2.12 / **2.88**	2.07 / **2.80**	2.04 / **2.73**	2.00 / **2.66**	1.95 / **2.56**	1.90 / **2.49**	1.84 / **2.37**	1.79 / **2.29**	1.74 / **2.20**	1.69 / **2.11**	1.66 / **2.05**	1.61 / **1.97**	1.59 / **1.94**	1.55 / **1.88**	1.53 / **1.84**	1.51 / **1.81**
42	4.07 / **7.27**	3.22 / **5.15**	2.83 / **4.29**	2.59 / **3.80**	2.44 / **3.49**	2.32 / **3.26**	2.24 / **3.10**	2.17 / **2.96**	2.11 / **2.86**	2.06 / **2.77**	2.02 / **2.70**	1.99 / **2.64**	1.94 / **2.54**	1.89 / **2.46**	1.82 / **2.35**	1.78 / **2.26**	1.73 / **2.17**	1.68 / **2.08**	1.64 / **2.02**	1.60 / **1.94**	1.57 / **1.91**	1.54 / **1.85**	1.51 / **1.80**	1.49 / **1.78**
44	4.06 / **7.24**	3.21 / **5.12**	2.82 / **4.26**	2.58 / **3.78**	2.43 / **3.46**	2.31 / **3.24**	2.23 / **3.07**	2.16 / **2.94**	2.10 / **2.84**	2.05 / **2.75**	2.01 / **2.68**	1.98 / **2.62**	1.92 / **2.52**	1.88 / **2.44**	1.81 / **2.32**	1.76 / **2.22**	1.72 / **2.15**	1.66 / **2.06**	1.63 / **2.00**	1.58 / **1.92**	1.56 / **1.88**	1.52 / **1.82**	1.50 / **1.78**	1.48 / **1.75**
46	4.05 / **7.21**	3.20 / **5.10**	2.81 / **4.24**	2.57 / **3.76**	2.42 / **3.44**	2.30 / **3.22**	2.22 / **3.05**	2.14 / **2.92**	2.09 / **2.82**	2.04 / **2.73**	2.00 / **2.66**	1.97 / **2.60**	1.91 / **2.50**	1.87 / **2.42**	1.80 / **2.30**	1.75 / **2.22**	1.71 / **2.13**	1.65 / **2.04**	1.62 / **1.98**	1.57 / **1.90**	1.54 / **1.86**	1.51 / **1.80**	1.48 / **1.76**	1.46 / **1.72**
48	4.04 / **7.19**	3.19 / **5.08**	2.80 / **4.22**	2.56 / **3.74**	2.41 / **3.42**	2.30 / **3.20**	2.21 / **3.04**	2.14 / **2.90**	2.08 / **2.80**	2.03 / **2.71**	1.99 / **2.64**	1.96 / **2.58**	1.90 / **2.48**	1.86 / **2.40**	1.79 / **2.28**	1.74 / **2.20**	1.70 / **2.11**	1.64 / **2.02**	1.61 / **1.96**	1.56 / **1.88**	1.53 / **1.84**	1.50 / **1.78**	1.47 / **1.73**	1.45 / **1.70**

TABLE FOR *F* (Continued)

5% (ROMAN TYPE) AND 1% (BOLD-FACE TYPE) POINTS FOR THE DISTRIBUTION OF *F*

Degrees of freedom for greater mean square

Each cell lists the 5% point (roman) / 1% point (bold-face).

Degrees of freedom for lesser mean square	1	2	3	4	5	6	7	8	9	10	11	12	14	16	20	24	30	40	50	75	100	200	500	∞
50	4.03 / 7.17	3.18 / 5.06	2.79 / 4.20	2.56 / 3.72	2.40 / 3.41	2.29 / 3.18	2.20 / 3.02	2.13 / 2.88	2.07 / 2.78	2.02 / 2.70	1.98 / 2.62	1.95 / 2.56	1.90 / 2.46	1.85 / 2.39	1.78 / 2.26	1.74 / 2.18	1.69 / 2.10	1.63 / 2.00	1.60 / 1.94	1.55 / 1.86	1.52 / 1.82	1.48 / 1.76	1.46 / 1.71	1.44 / 1.68
55	4.02 / 7.12	3.17 / 5.01	2.78 / 4.16	2.54 / 3.68	2.38 / 3.37	2.27 / 3.15	2.18 / 2.98	2.11 / 2.85	2.05 / 2.75	2.00 / 2.66	1.97 / 2.59	1.93 / 2.53	1.88 / 2.43	1.83 / 2.35	1.76 / 2.23	1.72 / 2.15	1.67 / 2.06	1.61 / 1.96	1.58 / 1.90	1.52 / 1.82	1.50 / 1.78	1.46 / 1.71	1.43 / 1.66	1.41 / 1.64
60	4.00 / 7.08	3.15 / 4.98	2.76 / 4.13	2.52 / 3.65	2.37 / 3.34	2.25 / 3.12	2.17 / 2.95	2.10 / 2.82	2.04 / 2.72	1.99 / 2.63	1.95 / 2.56	1.92 / 2.50	1.86 / 2.40	1.81 / 2.32	1.75 / 2.20	1.70 / 2.12	1.65 / 2.03	1.59 / 1.93	1.56 / 1.87	1.50 / 1.79	1.48 / 1.74	1.44 / 1.68	1.41 / 1.63	1.39 / 1.60
65	3.99 / 7.04	3.14 / 4.95	2.75 / 4.10	2.51 / 3.62	2.36 / 3.31	2.24 / 3.09	2.15 / 2.93	2.08 / 2.79	2.02 / 2.70	1.98 / 2.61	1.94 / 2.54	1.90 / 2.47	1.85 / 2.37	1.80 / 2.30	1.73 / 2.18	1.68 / 2.09	1.63 / 2.00	1.57 / 1.90	1.54 / 1.84	1.49 / 1.76	1.46 / 1.71	1.42 / 1.64	1.39 / 1.60	1.37 / 1.56
70	3.98 / 7.01	3.13 / 4.92	2.74 / 4.08	2.50 / 3.60	2.35 / 3.29	2.23 / 3.07	2.14 / 2.91	2.07 / 2.77	2.01 / 2.67	1.97 / 2.59	1.93 / 2.51	1.89 / 2.45	1.84 / 2.35	1.79 / 2.28	1.72 / 2.15	1.67 / 2.07	1.62 / 1.98	1.56 / 1.88	1.53 / 1.82	1.47 / 1.74	1.45 / 1.69	1.40 / 1.62	1.37 / 1.56	1.35 / 1.53
80	3.96 / 6.96	3.11 / 4.88	2.72 / 4.04	2.48 / 3.56	2.33 / 3.25	2.21 / 3.04	2.12 / 2.87	2.05 / 2.74	1.99 / 2.64	1.95 / 2.55	1.91 / 2.48	1.88 / 2.41	1.82 / 2.32	1.77 / 2.24	1.70 / 2.11	1.65 / 2.03	1.60 / 1.94	1.54 / 1.84	1.51 / 1.78	1.45 / 1.70	1.42 / 1.65	1.38 / 1.57	1.35 / 1.52	1.32 / 1.49
100	3.94 / 6.90	3.09 / 4.82	2.70 / 3.98	2.46 / 3.51	2.30 / 3.20	2.19 / 2.99	2.10 / 2.82	2.03 / 2.69	1.97 / 2.59	1.92 / 2.51	1.88 / 2.43	1.85 / 2.36	1.79 / 2.26	1.75 / 2.19	1.68 / 2.06	1.63 / 1.98	1.57 / 1.89	1.51 / 1.79	1.48 / 1.73	1.42 / 1.64	1.39 / 1.59	1.34 / 1.51	1.30 / 1.46	1.28 / 1.43
125	3.92 / 6.84	3.07 / 4.78	2.68 / 3.94	2.44 / 3.47	2.29 / 3.17	2.17 / 2.95	2.08 / 2.79	2.01 / 2.65	1.95 / 2.56	1.90 / 2.47	1.86 / 2.40	1.83 / 2.33	1.77 / 2.23	1.72 / 2.15	1.65 / 2.03	1.60 / 1.94	1.55 / 1.85	1.49 / 1.75	1.45 / 1.68	1.39 / 1.59	1.36 / 1.54	1.31 / 1.46	1.27 / 1.40	1.25 / 1.37
150	3.91 / 6.81	3.06 / 4.75	2.67 / 3.91	2.43 / 3.44	2.27 / 3.13	2.16 / 2.92	2.07 / 2.76	2.00 / 2.62	1.94 / 2.53	1.89 / 2.44	1.85 / 2.37	1.82 / 2.30	1.76 / 2.20	1.71 / 2.12	1.64 / 2.00	1.59 / 1.91	1.54 / 1.83	1.47 / 1.72	1.44 / 1.66	1.37 / 1.56	1.34 / 1.51	1.29 / 1.43	1.25 / 1.37	1.22 / 1.33
200	3.89 / 6.76	3.04 / 4.71	2.65 / 3.88	2.41 / 3.41	2.26 / 3.11	2.14 / 2.90	2.05 / 2.73	1.98 / 2.60	1.92 / 2.50	1.87 / 2.41	1.83 / 2.34	1.80 / 2.28	1.74 / 2.17	1.69 / 2.09	1.62 / 1.97	1.57 / 1.88	1.52 / 1.79	1.45 / 1.69	1.42 / 1.62	1.35 / 1.53	1.32 / 1.48	1.26 / 1.39	1.22 / 1.33	1.19 / 1.28
400	3.86 / 6.70	3.02 / 4.66	2.62 / 3.83	2.39 / 3.36	2.23 / 3.06	2.12 / 2.85	2.03 / 2.69	1.96 / 2.55	1.90 / 2.46	1.85 / 2.37	1.81 / 2.29	1.78 / 2.23	1.72 / 2.12	1.67 / 2.04	1.60 / 1.92	1.54 / 1.84	1.49 / 1.74	1.42 / 1.64	1.38 / 1.57	1.32 / 1.47	1.28 / 1.42	1.22 / 1.32	1.16 / 1.24	1.13 / 1.19
1000	3.85 / 6.66	3.00 / 4.62	2.61 / 3.80	2.38 / 3.34	2.22 / 3.04	2.10 / 2.82	2.02 / 2.66	1.95 / 2.53	1.89 / 2.43	1.84 / 2.34	1.80 / 2.26	1.76 / 2.20	1.70 / 2.09	1.65 / 2.01	1.58 / 1.89	1.53 / 1.81	1.47 / 1.71	1.41 / 1.61	1.36 / 1.54	1.30 / 1.44	1.26 / 1.38	1.19 / 1.28	1.13 / 1.19	1.08 / 1.11
∞	3.84 / 6.64	2.99 / 4.60	2.60 / 3.78	2.37 / 3.32	2.21 / 3.02	2.09 / 2.80	2.01 / 2.64	1.94 / 2.51	1.88 / 2.41	1.83 / 2.32	1.79 / 2.24	1.75 / 2.18	1.69 / 2.07	1.64 / 1.99	1.57 / 1.87	1.52 / 1.79	1.46 / 1.69	1.40 / 1.59	1.35 / 1.52	1.28 / 1.41	1.24 / 1.36	1.17 / 1.25	1.11 / 1.15	1.00 / 1.00

χ^2 TABLE

Degrees of freedom	P = 0.99	0.98	0.95	0.90	0.80	0.70	0.50	0.30	0.20	0.10	0.05	0.02	0.01
1	0.000157	0.000628	0.00393	0.0158	0.0642	0.148	0.455	1.074	1.642	2.706	3.841	5.412	6.635
2	0.0201	0.0404	0.103	0.211	0.446	0.713	1.386	2.408	3.219	4.605	5.991	7.824	9.210
3	0.115	0.185	0.352	0.584	1.005	1.424	2.366	3.665	4.642	6.251	7.815	9.837	11.341
4	0.297	0.429	0.711	1.064	1.649	2.195	3.357	4.878	5.989	7.779	9.488	11.668	13.277
5	0.554	0.752	1.145	1.610	2.343	3.000	4.351	6.064	7.289	9.236	11.070	13.388	15.086
6	0.872	1.134	1.635	2.204	3.070	3.828	5.348	7.231	8.558	10.645	12.592	15.033	16.812
7	1.239	1.564	2.167	2.833	3.822	4.671	6.346	8.383	9.803	12.017	14.067	16.622	18.475
8	1.646	2.032	2.733	3.490	4.594	5.527	7.344	9.524	11.030	13.362	15.507	18.168	20.090
9	2.088	2.532	3.325	4.168	5.380	6.393	8.343	10.656	12.242	14.684	16.919	19.679	21.666
10	2.558	3.059	3.940	4.865	6.179	7.267	9.342	11.781	13.442	15.987	18.307	21.161	23.209
11	3.053	3.609	4.575	5.578	6.989	8.148	10.341	12.899	14.631	17.275	19.675	22.618	24.725
12	3.571	4.178	5.226	6.304	7.807	9.034	11.340	14.011	15.812	18.549	21.026	24.054	26.217
13	4.107	4.765	5.892	7.042	8.634	9.926	12.340	15.119	16.985	19.812	22.362	25.472	27.688
14	4.660	5.368	6.571	7.790	9.467	10.821	13.339	16.222	18.151	21.064	23.685	26.873	29.141
15	5.229	5.985	7.261	8.547	10.307	11.721	14.339	17.322	19.311	22.307	24.996	28.259	30.578
16	5.812	6.614	7.962	9.312	11.152	12.624	15.338	18.418	20.465	23.542	26.296	29.633	32.000
17	6.408	7.255	8.672	10.085	12.002	13.531	16.338	19.511	21.615	24.769	27.587	30.995	33.409
18	7.015	7.906	9.390	10.865	12.857	14.440	17.338	20.601	22.760	25.989	28.869	32.346	34.805
19	7.633	8.567	10.117	11.651	13.716	15.352	18.338	21.689	23.900	27.204	30.144	33.687	36.191
20	8.260	9.237	10.851	12.443	14.578	16.266	19.337	22.775	25.038	28.412	31.410	35.020	37.566
21	8.897	9.915	11.591	13.240	15.445	17.182	20.337	23.858	26.171	29.615	32.671	36.343	38.932
22	9.542	10.600	12.338	14.041	16.314	18.101	21.337	24.939	27.301	30.813	33.924	37.659	40.289
23	10.196	11.293	13.091	14.848	17.187	19.021	22.337	26.018	28.429	32.007	35.172	38.968	41.638
24	10.856	11.992	13.848	15.659	18.062	19.943	23.337	27.096	29.553	33.196	36.415	40.270	42.980
25	11.524	12.697	14.611	16.473	18.940	20.867	24.337	28.172	30.675	34.382	37.652	41.566	44.314
26	12.198	13.409	15.379	17.292	19.820	21.792	25.336	29.246	31.795	35.563	38.885	42.856	45.642
27	12.879	14.125	16.151	18.114	20.703	22.719	26.336	30.319	32.912	36.741	40.113	44.140	46.963
28	13.565	14.847	16.928	18.939	21.588	23.647	27.336	31.391	34.027	37.916	41.337	45.419	48.278
29	14.256	15.574	17.708	19.768	22.475	24.577	28.336	32.461	35.139	39.087	42.557	46.693	49.588
30	14.953	16.306	18.493	20.599	23.364	25.508	29.336	33.530	36.250	40.256	43.773	47.962	50.892

For degrees of freedom greater than 30, the expression $\sqrt{2\chi^2} - \sqrt{2n' - 1}$ may be used as a normal deviate with unit variance, where n' is the number of degrees of freedom.

Reproduced from *Statistical Methods for Research Workers*, 6th ed., with the permission of the author, R. A. Fisher, and his publisher, Oliver and Boyd, Edinburgh.

ELLIPTIC INTEGRALS

$$K = \int_0^{\pi/2} \frac{d\phi}{\sqrt{1 - k^2 \sin^2 \phi}}. \qquad E = \int_0^{\pi/2} \sqrt{1 - k^2 \sin^2 \phi} \cdot d\phi.$$

$\sin^{-1} k$	K	$\log K$	$\sin^{-1} k$	K	$\log K$
0°	1.5708	0.196120	**40°**	1.7868	0.252068
1	1.5709	0.196153	41	1.7992	0.255085
2	1.5713	0.196252	42	1.8122	0.258197
3	1.5719	0.196418	43	1.8256	0.261406
4	1.5727	0.196649	44	1.8396	0.264716
5	1.5738	0.196947	**45**	1.8541	0.268127
6	1.5751	0.197312	46	1.8691	0.271644
7	1.5767	0.197743	47	1.8848	0.275267
8	1.5785	0.198241	48	1.9011	0.279001
9	1.5805	0.198806	49	1.9180	0.282848
10	1.5828	0.199438	**50**	1.9356	0.286811
11	1.5854	0.200137	51	1.9539	0.290895
12	1.5882	0.200904	52	1.9729	0.295101
13	1.5913	0.201740	53	1.9927	0.299435
14	1.5946	0.202643	54	2.0133	0.303901
15	1.5981	0.203615	**55**	2.0347	0.308504
16	1.6020	0.204657	56	2.0571	0.313247
17	1.6061	0.205768	57	2.0804	0.318138
18	1.6105	0.206948	58	2.1047	0.323182
19	1.6151	0.208200	59	2.1300	0.328384
20	1.6200	0.209522	**60**	2.1565	0.333753
21	1.6252	0.210916	61	2.1842	0.339295
22	1.6307	0.212382	62	2.2132	0.345020
23	1.6365	0.213921	63	2.2435	0.350936
24	1.6426	0.215533	64	2.2754	0.357053
25	1.6490	0.217219	**65**	2.3088	0.363384
26	1.6557	0.218981	66	2.3439	0.369940
27	1.6627	0.220818	67	2.3809	0.376736
28	1.6701	0.222732	68	2.4198	0.383787
29	1.6777	0.224723	69	2.4610	0.391112
30	1.6858	0.226793	**70**	2.5046	0.398730
31	1.6941	0.228943	71	2.5507	0.406665
32	1.7028	0.231173	72	2.5998	0.414943
33	1.7119	0.233485	73	2.6521	0.423596
34	1.7214	0.235880	74	2.7081	0.432660
35	1.7312	0.238359	**75**	2.7681	0.442176
36	1.7415	0.240923	76	2.8327	0.452196
37	1.7522	0.243575	77	2.9026	0.462782
38	1.7633	0.246315	78	2.9786	0.474008
39	1.7748	0.249146	79	3.0617	0.485967
40	1.7868	0.252068	**80**	3.1534	0.498777

$\sin^{-1} k$	K	$\log K$	$\sin^{-1} k$	K	$\log K$
80°	3.1534	0.498777	**85°**	3.8317	0.583396
81	3.2553	0.512591	86	4.0528	0.607751
82	3.3699	0.527613	87	4.3387	0.637355
83	3.5004	0.544120	88	4.7427	0.676027
84	3.6519	0.562514	89	5.4349	0.735192
85	3.8317	0.583396	**90**	∞	∞

Values of K for $\sin^{-1} k = 85°$ to $89°$ by $0.1°$ and $89°$ to $90°$ by minutes

$\sin^{-1} k$	K	$\log K$	$\sin^{-1} k$		K	$\log K$
85.0°	3.832	0.58343	**89°**	**0′**	5.435	0.73520
85.1	3.852	0.58569	89	2	5.469	0.73791
85.2	3.872	0.58794	89	4	5.504	0.74068
85.3	3.893	0.59028	89	6	5.540	0.74351
85.4	3.914	0.59262	89	8	5.578	0.74648
85.5	3.936	0.59506	**89**	**10**	5.617	0.74950
85.6	3.958	0.59748	89	12	5.658	0.75266
85.7	3.981	0.59999	89	14	5.700	0.75587
85.8	4.004	0.60249	89	16	5.745	0.75929
85.9	4.028	0.60509	89	18	5.791	0.76275
86.0	4.053	0.60778	**89**	**20**	5.840	0.76641
86.1	4.078	0.61045	89	22	5.891	0.77019
86.2	4.104	0.61321	89	24	5.946	0.77422
86.3	4.130	0.61595	89	26	6.003	0.77837
86.4	4.157	0.61878	89	28	6.063	0.78269
86.5	4.185	0.62170	**89**	**30**	6.128	0.78732
86.6	4.214	0.62469	89	32	6.197	0.79218
86.7	4.244	0.62778	89	34	6.271	0.79734
86.8	4.274	0.63083	89	36	6.351	0.80284
86.9	4.306	0.63407	89	38	6.438	0.80875
87.0	4.339	0.63739	**89**	**40**	6.533	0.81511
87.1	4.372	0.64068	89	41	6.584	0.81849
87.2	4.407	0.64414	89	42	6.639	0.82210
87.3	4.444	0.64777	89	43	6.696	0.82582
87.4	4.481	0.65137	89	44	6.756	0.82969
87.5	4.520	0.65514	**89**	**45**	6.821	0.83385
87.6	4.562	0.65916	89	46	6.890	0.83822
87.7	4.603	0.66304	89	47	6.964	0.84286
87.8	4.648	0.66727	89	48	7.044	0.84782
87.9	4.694	0.67154	89	49	7.131	0.85315
88.0	4.743	0.67605	**89**	**50**	7.226	0.85890
88.1	4.794	0.68070	89	51	7.332	0.86522
88.2	4.848	0.68556	89	52	7.449	0.87210
88.3	4.905	0.69064	89	53	7.583	0.87984
88.4	4.965	0.69592	89	54	7.737	0.88857
88.5	5.030	0.70157	**89**	**55**	7.919	0.89867
88.6	5.099	0.70749	89	56	8.143	0.91078
88.7	5.173	0.71374	89	57	8.430	0.92583
88.8	5.253	0.72041	89	58	8.836	0.94626
88.9	5.340	0.72754	89	59	9.529	0.97905
89.0	5.435	0.73520	**90**	**0**	∞	∞

COMPLETE ELLIPTIC INTEGRALS

$\sin^{-1} k$	E	$\log E$	$\sin^{-1} k$	E	$\log E$
0°	1.5708	0.196120	**45°**	1.3506	0.130541
1	1.5707	0.196087	46	1.3418	0.127690
2	1.5703	0.195988	47	1.3329	0.124788
3	1.5697	0.195822	48	1.3238	0.121836
4	1.5689	0.195591	49	1.3147	0.118836
5	1.5678	0.195293	**50**	1.3055	0.115790
6	1.5665	0.194930	51	1.2963	0.112698
7	1.5649	0.194500	52	1.2870	0.109563
8	1.5632	0.194004	53	1.2776	0.106386
9	1.5611	0.193442	54	1.2681	0.103169
10	1.5589	0.192815	**55**	1.2587	0.099915
11	1.5564	0.192121	56	1.2492	0.096626
12	1.5537	0.191362	57	1.2397	0.093303
13	1.5507	0.190537	58	1.2301	0.089950
14	1.5476	0.189646	59	1.2206	0.086569
15	1.5442	0.188690	**60**	1.2111	0.083164
16	1.5405	0.187668	61	1.2015	0.079738
17	1.5367	0.186581	62	1.1920	0.076293
18	1.5326	0.185428	63	1.1826	0.072834
19	1.5283	0.184210	64	1.1732	0.069364
20	1.5238	0.182928	**65**	1.1638	0.065889
21	1.5191	0.181580	66	1.1545	0.062412
22	1.5141	0.180168	67	1.1453	0.058937
23	1.5090	0.178691	68	1.1362	0.055472
24	1.5037	0.177150	69	1.1272	0.052020
25	1.4981	0.175545	**70**	1.1184	0.048589
26	1.4924	0.173876	71	1.1096	0.045183
27	1.4864	0.172144	72	1.1011	0.041812
28	1.4803	0.170348	73	1.0927	0.038481
29	1.4740	0.168489	74	1.0844	0.035200
30	1.4675	0.166567	**75**	1.0764	0.031976
31	1.4608	0.164583	76	1.0686	0.028819
32	1.4539	0.162537	77	1.0611	0.025740
33	1.4469	0.160429	78	1.0538	0.022749
34	1.4397	0.158261	79	1.0468	0.019858
35	1.4323	0.156031	**80**	1.0401	0.017081
36	1.4248	0.153742	81	1.0338	0.014432
37	1.4171	0.151393	82	1.0278	0.011927
38	1.4092	0.148985	83	1.0223	0.009584
39	1.4013	0.146519	84	1.0172	0.007422
40	1.3931	0.143995	**85**	1.0127	0.005465
41	1.3849	0.141414	86	1.0086	0.003740
42	1.3765	0.138778	87	1.0053	0.002278
43	1.3680	0.136086	88	1.0026	0.001121
44	1.3594	0.133340	89	1.0008	0.000326
45	1.3506	0.130541	**90**	1.0000	0.000000

ELLIPTIC INTEGRALS OF THE FIRST KIND: $F(k, \phi)$

$$F(k, \phi) = \int_0^\phi \frac{d\phi}{\sqrt{1 - k^2 \sin \phi}}, \qquad \theta = \sin^{-1} k$$

ϕ \ θ	5°	10°	15°	20°	25°	30°	35°	40°	45°
1°	0.0175	0.0175	0.0175	0.0175	0.0175	0.0175	0.0175	0.0175	0.0175
2°	0.0349	0.0349	0.0349	0.0349	0.0349	0.0349	0.0349	0.0349	0.0349
3°	0.0524	0.0524	0.0524	0.0524	0.0524	0.0524	0.0524	0.0524	0.0524
4°	0.0698	0.0698	0.0698	0.0698	0.0698	0.0698	0.0698	0.0698	0.0698
5°	0.0873	0.0873	0.0873	0.0873	0.0873	0.0873	0.0873	0.0873	0.0873
6°	0.1047	0.1047	0.1047	0.1047	0.1048	0.1048	0.1048	0.1048	0.1048
7°	0.1222	0.1222	0.1222	0.1222	0.1222	0.1222	0.1223	0.1223	0.1223
8°	0.1396	0.1396	0.1397	0.1397	0.1397	0.1397	0.1398	0.1398	0.1399
9°	0.1571	0.1571	0.1571	0.1572	0.1572	0.1572	0.1573	0.1573	0.1574
10°	0.1745	0.1746	0.1746	0.1746	0.1747	0.1748	0.1748	0.1749	0.1750
11°	0.1920	0.1920	0.1921	0.1921	0.1922	0.1923	0.1924	0.1925	0.1926
12°	0.2095	0.2095	0.2095	0.2096	0.2097	0.2098	0.2099	0.2101	0.2102
13°	0.2269	0.2270	0.2270	0.2271	0.2272	0.2274	0.2275	0.2277	0.2279
14°	0.2444	0.2444	0.2445	0.2446	0.2448	0.2450	0.2451	0.2453	0.2456
15°	0.2618	0.2619	0.2620	0.2621	0.2623	0.2625	0.2628	0.2630	0.2633
16°	0.2793	0.2794	0.2795	0.2797	0.2799	0.2802	0.2804	0.2808	0.2811
17°	0.2967	0.2968	0.2970	0.2972	0.2975	0.2978	0.2981	0.2985	0.2989
18°	0.3142	0.3143	0.3145	0.3148	0.3151	0.3154	0.3159	0.3163	0.3167
19°	0.3317	0.3318	0.3320	0.3323	0.3327	0.3331	0.3336	0.3341	0.3347
20°	0.3491	0.3493	0.3495	0.3499	0.3503	0.3508	0.3514	0.3520	0.3526
21°	0.3666	0.3668	0.3671	0.3675	0.3680	0.3685	0.3692	0.3699	0.3706
22°	0.3840	0.3842	0.3846	0.3851	0.3856	0.3863	0.3871	0.3879	0.3887
23°	0.4015	0.4017	0.4021	0.4027	0.4033	0.4041	0.4049	0.4059	0.4068
24°	0.4190	0.4192	0.4197	0.4203	0.4210	0.4219	0.4229	0.4239	0.4250
25°	0.4364	0.4367	0.4372	0.4379	0.4387	0.4397	0.4408	0.4420	0.4433
26°	0.4539	0.4542	0.4548	0.4556	0.4565	0.4576	0.4588	0.4602	0.4616
27°	0.4714	0.4717	0.4724	0.4732	0.4743	0.4755	0.4769	0.4784	0.4800
28°	0.4888	0.4893	0.4899	0.4909	0.4921	0.4934	0.4950	0.4967	0.4985
29°	0.5063	0.5068	0.5075	0.5086	0.5099	0.5114	0.5132	0.5150	0.5170
30°	0.5238	0.5243	0.5251	0.5263	0.5277	0.5294	0.5313	0.5334	0.5356
31°	0.5412	0.5418	0.5427	0.5440	0.5456	0.5475	0.5496	0.5519	0.5543
32°	0.5587	0.5593	0.5603	0.5617	0.5635	0.5656	0.5679	0.5704	0.5731
33°	0.5762	0.5769	0.5780	0.5795	0.5814	0.5837	0.5862	0.5890	0.5920
34°	0.5937	0.5944	0.5956	0.5973	0.5994	0.6018	0.6046	0.6077	0.6109
35°	0.6111	0.6119	0.6133	0.6151	0.6173	0.6200	0.6231	0.6264	0.6300
36°	0.6286	0.6295	0.6309	0.6329	0.6353	0.6383	0.6416	0.6452	0.6491
37°	0.6461	0.6470	0.6486	0.6507	0.6534	0.6565	0.6602	0.6641	0.6684
38°	0.6636	0.6646	0.6662	0.6685	0.6714	0.6749	0.6788	0.6831	0.6877
39°	0.6810	0.6821	0.6839	0.6864	0.6895	0.6932	0.6975	0.7021	0.7071
40°	0.6985	0.6997	0.7016	0.7043	0.7076	0.7116	0.7162	0.7213	0.7267
41°	0.7160	0.7173	0.7193	0.7222	0.7258	0.7301	0.7350	0.7405	0.7463
42°	0.7335	0.7348	0.7370	0.7401	0.7440	0.7486	0.7539	0.7598	0.7661
43°	0.7510	0.7524	0.7548	0.7580	0.7622	0.7671	0.7728	0.7791	0.7859
44°	0.7685	0.7700	0.7725	0.7760	0.7804	0.7857	0.7918	0.7986	0.8059
45°	0.7859	0.7876	0.7903	0.7940	0.7987	0.8044	0.8109	0.8181	0.8260

ELLIPTIC INTEGRALS OF THE FIRST KIND: $F(k, \phi)$

$$F(k, \phi) = \int_0^\phi \frac{d\phi}{\sqrt{1 - k^2 \sin \phi}}, \qquad \theta = \sin^{-1} k$$

θ / ϕ	50°	55°	60°	65°	70°	75°	80°	85°	90°
1°	0.0175	0.0175	0.0175	0.0175	0.0175	0.0175	0.0175	0.0175	0.0175
2°	0.0349	0.0349	0.0349	0.0349	0.0349	0.0349	0.0349	0.0349	0.0349
3°	0.0524	0.0524	0.0524	0.0524	0.0524	0.0524	0.0524	0.0524	0.0524
4°	0.0698	0.0699	0.0699	0.0699	0.0699	0.0699	0.0699	0.0699	0.0699
5°	0.0873	0.0873	0.0873	0.0874	0.0874	0.0874	0.0874	0.0874	0.0874
6°	0.1048	0.1048	0.1049	0.1049	0.1049	0.1049	0.1049	0.1049	0.1049
7°	0.1224	0.1224	0.1224	0.1224	0.1224	0.1225	0.1225	0.1225	0.1225
8°	0.1399	0.1399	0.1400	0.1400	0.1400	0.1401	0.1401	0.1401	0.1401
9°	0.1575	0.1575	0.1576	0.1576	0.1577	0.1577	0.1577	0.1577	0.1577
10°	0.1751	0.1751	0.1752	0.1753	0.1753	0.1754	0.1754	0.1754	0.1754
11°	0.1927	0.1928	0.1929	0.1930	0.1930	0.1931	0.1931	0.1932	0.1932
12°	0.2103	0.2105	0.2106	0.2107	0.2108	0.2109	0.2109	0.2110	0.2110
13°	0.2280	0.2282	0.2284	0.2285	0.2286	0.2287	0.2288	0.2288	0.2289
14°	0.2458	0.2460	0.2462	0.2464	0.2465	0.2466	0.2467	0.2468	0.2468
15°	0.2636	0.2638	0.2641	0.2643	0.2645	0.2646	0.2647	0.2648	0.2648
16°	0.2814	0.2817	0.2820	0.2823	0.2825	0.2827	0.2828	0.2829	0.2830
17°	0.2993	0.2997	0.3000	0.3003	0.3006	0.3008	0.3010	0.3011	0.3012
18°	0.3172	0.3177	0.3181	0.3185	0.3188	0.3191	0.3193	0.3194	0.3195
19°	0.3352	0.3357	0.3362	0.3367	0.3371	0.3374	0.3377	0.3378	0.3379
20°	0.3533	0.3539	0.3545	0.3550	0.3555	0.3559	0.3561	0.3563	0.3564
21°	0.3714	0.3721	0.3728	0.3734	0.3740	0.3744	0.3747	0.3749	0.3750
22°	0.3896	0.3904	0.3912	0.3919	0.3926	0.3931	0.3935	0.3937	0.3938
23°	0.4078	0.4088	0.4097	0.4105	0.4113	0.4119	0.4123	0.4126	0.4127
24°	0.4261	0.4272	0.4283	0.4292	0.4301	0.4308	0.4313	0.4316	0.4317
25°	0.4446	0.4458	0.4470	0.4481	0.4490	0.4498	0.4504	0.4508	0.4509
26°	0.4630	0.4645	0.4658	0.4670	0.4681	0.4690	0.4697	0.4701	0.4702
27°	0.4816	0.4832	0.4847	0.4861	0.4873	0.4884	0.4891	0.4896	0.4897
28°	0.5003	0.5021	0.5038	0.5053	0.5067	0.5079	0.5087	0.5092	0.5094
29°	0.5190	0.5210	0.5229	0.5247	0.5262	0.5275	0.5285	0.5291	0.5293
30°	0.5379	0.5401	0.5422	0.5442	0.5459	0.5474	0.5484	0.5491	0.5493
31°	0.5568	0.5593	0.5617	0.5639	0.5658	0.5674	0.5686	0.5693	0.5696
32°	0.5759	0.5786	0.5812	0.5837	0.5858	0.5876	0.5889	0.5898	0.5900
33°	0.5950	0.5980	0.6010	0.6037	0.6060	0.6080	0.6095	0.6104	0.6107
34°	0.6143	0.6176	0.6208	0.6238	0.6265	0.6287	0.6303	0.6313	0.6317
35°	0.6336	0.6373	0.6408	0.6441	0.6471	0.6495	0.6513	0.6525	0.6528
36°	0.6531	0.6571	0.6610	0.6647	0.6679	0.6706	0.6726	0.6739	0.6743
37°	0.6727	0.6771	0.6814	0.6854	0.6890	0.6919	0.6941	0.6955	0.6960
38°	0.6925	0.6973	0.7019	0.7063	0.7102	0.7135	0.7159	0.7175	0.7180
39°	0.7123	0.7176	0.7227	0.7275	0.7318	0.7353	0.7380	0.7397	0.7403
40°	0.7323	0.7380	0.7436	0.7488	0.7535	0.7575	0.7604	0.7623	0.7629
41°	0.7524	0.7586	0.7647	0.7704	0.7756	0.7799	0.7831	0.7852	0.7859
42°	0.7727	0.7794	0.7860	0.7922	0.7979	0.8026	0.8062	0.8084	0.8092
43°	0.7931	0.8004	0.8075	0.8143	0.8204	0.8256	0.8295	0.8320	0.8328
44°	0.8136	0.8215	0.8293	0.8367	0.8433	0.8490	0.8533	0.8560	0.8569
45°	0.8343	0.8428	0.8512	0.8592	0.8665	0.8727	0.8774	0.8804	0.8814

ELLIPTIC INTEGRALS OF THE FIRST KIND: $F(k, \phi)$

$$F(k, \phi) = \int_0^\phi \frac{d\phi}{\sqrt{1 - k^2 \sin \phi}}, \qquad \theta = \sin^{-1} k$$

ϕ \ θ	5°	10°	15°	20°	25°	30°	35°	40°	45°
46°	0.8034	0.8052	0.8080	0.8120	0.8170	0.8230	0.8300	0.8378	0.8462
47°	0.8209	0.8227	0.8258	0.8300	0.8353	0.8418	0.8492	0.8575	0.8666
48°	0.8384	0.8403	0.8436	0.8480	0.8537	0.8606	0.8685	0.8773	0.8870
49°	0.8559	0.8579	0.8614	0.8661	0.8721	0.8794	0.8878	0.8972	0.9076
50°	0.8734	0.8756	0.8792	0.8842	0.8905	0.8982	0.9072	0.9173	0.9283
51°	0.8909	0.8932	0.8970	0.9023	0.9090	0.9172	0.9267	0.9374	0.9491
52°	0.9084	0.9108	0.9148	0.9204	0.9275	0.9361	0.9462	0.9575	0.9701
53°	0.9259	0.9284	0.9326	0.9385	0.9460	0.9551	0.9658	0.9778	0.9912
54°	0.9434	0.9460	0.9505	0.9567	0.9646	0.9742	0.9855	0.9982	1.0124
55°	0.9609	0.9637	0.9683	0.9748	0.9832	0.9933	1.0052	1.0187	1.0337
56°	0.9784	0.9813	0.9862	0.9930	1.0018	1.0125	1.0250	1.0393	1.0552
57°	0.9959	0.9989	1.0041	1.0112	1.0204	1.0317	1.0449	1.0600	1.0768
58°	1.0134	1.0166	1.0219	1.0295	1.0391	1.0509	1.0648	1.0807	1.0985
59°	1.0309	1.0342	1.0398	1.0477	1.0578	1.0702	1.0848	1.1016	1.1204
60°	1.0484	1.0519	1.0577	1.0660	1.0766	1.0896	1.1049	1.1226	1.1424
61°	1.0659	1.0695	1.0757	1.0843	1.0953	1.1089	1.1250	1.1436	1.1646
62°	1.0834	1.0872	1.0936	1.1026	1.1141	1.1284	1.1452	1.1648	1.1868
63°	1.1009	1.1049	1.1115	1.1209	1.1330	1.1478	1.1655	1.1860	1.2093
64°	1.1184	1.1225	1.1295	1.1392	1.1518	1.1674	1.1859	1.2073	1.2318
65°	1.1359	1.1402	1.1474	1.1575	1.1707	1.1869	1.2063	1.2288	1.2545
66°	1.1534	1.1579	1.1654	1.1759	1.1896	1.2065	1.2267	1.2503	1.2773
67°	1.1709	1.1756	1.1833	1.1943	1.2085	1.2262	1.2472	1.2719	1.3002
68°	1.1884	1.1932	1.2013	1.2127	1.2275	1.2458	1.2678	1.2936	1.3232
69°	1.2059	1.2109	1.2193	1.2311	1.2465	1.2655	1.2885	1.3154	1.3464
70°	1.2234	1.2286	1.2373	1.2495	1.2655	1.2853	1.3092	1.3372	1.3697
71°	1.2410	1.2463	1.2553	1.2680	1.2845	1.3051	1.3299	1.3592	1.3931
72°	1.2585	1.2640	1.2733	1.2864	1.3036	1.3249	1.3507	1.3812	1.4167
73°	1.2760	1.2817	1.2913	1.3049	1.3226	1.3448	1.3715	1.4033	1.4403
74°	1.2935	1.2994	1.3093	1.3234	1.3417	1.3647	1.3924	1.4254	1.4640
75°	1.3110	1.3171	1.3273	1.3418	1.3608	1.3846	1.4134	1.4477	1.4879
76°	1.3285	1.3348	1.3454	1.3603	1.3800	1.4045	1.4344	1.4700	1.5118
77°	1.3460	1.3525	1.3634	1.3788	1.3991	1.4245	1.4554	1.4923	1.5359
78°	1.3636	1.3702	1.3814	1.3974	1.4183	1.4445	1.4765	1.5147	1.5600
79°	1.3811	1.3879	1.3995	1.4159	1.4374	1.4645	1.4976	1.5372	1.5842
80°	1.3986	1.4056	1.4175	1.4344	1.4566	1.4846	1.5187	1.5597	1.6085
81°	1.4161	1.4234	1.4356	1.4530	1.4758	1.5046	1.5399	1.5823	1.6328
82°	1.4336	1.4411	1.4536	1.4715	1.4950	1.5247	1.5611	1.6049	1.6572
83°	1.4512	1.4588	1.4717	1.4901	1.5143	1.5448	1.5823	1.6276	1.6817
84°	1.4687	1.4765	1.4897	1.5086	1.5335	1.5649	1.6035	1.6502	1.7062
85°	1.4862	1.4942	1.5078	1.5272	1.5527	1.5850	1.6248	1.6730	1.7308
86°	1.5037	1.5120	1.5259	1.5457	1.5720	1.6052	1.6461	1.6957	1.7554
87°	1.5212	1.5297	1.5439	1.5643	1.5912	1.6253	1.6673	1.7184	1.7801
88°	1.5388	1.5474	1.5620	1.5829	1.6105	1.6454	1.6886	1.7412	1.8047
89°	1.5563	1.5651	1.5801	1.6015	1.6297	1.6656	1.7099	1.7640	1.8294
90°	1.5738	1.5828	1.5981	1.6200	1.6490	1.6858	1.7312	1.7868	1.8541

$$F(k, \phi) = \int_0^\phi \frac{d\phi}{\sqrt{1 - k^2 \sin \phi}}, \qquad \theta = \sin^{-1} k$$

θ \ φ	50°	55°	60°	[65°	70°	75°	80°	85°	90°
46°	0.8552	0.8643	0.8734	0.8821	0.8900	0.8968	0.9019	0.9052	0.9063
47°	0.8761	0.8860	0.8958	0.9053	0.9139	0.9212	0.9269	0.9304	0.9316
48°	0.8973	0.9079	0.9185	0.9287	0.9381	0.9461	0.9523	0.9561	0.9575
49°	0.9186	0.9300	0.9415	0.9525	0.9627	0.9714	0.9781	0.9824	0.9838
50°	0.9401	0.9523	0.9647	0.9766	0.9876	0.9971	1.0044	1.0091	1.0107
51°	0.9617	0.9748	0.9881	1.0010	1.0130	1.0233	1.0313	1.0364	1.0381
52°	0.9835	0.9976	1.0118	1.0258	1.0387	1.0499	1.0587	1.0642	1.0662
53°	1.0055	1.0205	1.0359	1.0509	1.0649	1.0771	1.0866	1.0927	1.0948
54°	1.0277	1.0437	1.0602	1.0764	1.0915	1.1048	1.1152	1.1219	1.1242
55°	1.0500	1.0672	1.0848	1.1022	1.1186	1.1331	1.1444	1.1517	1.1542
56°	1.0725	1.0908	1.1097	1.1285	1.1462	1.1619	1.1743	1.1823	1.1851
57°	1.0952	1.1147	1.1349	1.1551	1.1743	1.1914	1.2049	1.2136	1.2167
58°	1.1180	1.1389	1.1605	1.1822	1.2030	1.2215	1.2362	1.2458	1.2492
59°	1.1411	1.1632	1.1864	1.2097	1.2321	1.2522	1.2684	1.2789	1.2826
60°	1.1643	1.1879	1.2125	1.2376	1.2619	1.2837	1.3014	1.3129	1.3170
61°	1.1877	1.2128	1.2392	1.2660	1.2922	1.3159	1.3352	1.3480	1.3524
62°	1.2113	1.2379	1.2661	1.2949	1.3231	1.3490	1.3701	1.3841	1.3890
63°	1.2351	1.2633	1.2933	1.3242	1.3547	1.3828	1.4059	1.4214	1.4268
64°	1.2591	1.2890	1.3209	1.3541	1.3870	1.4175	1.4429	1.4599	1.4659
65°	1.2833	1.3149	1.3489	1.3844	1.4199	1.4532	1.4810	1.4998	1.5065
66°	1.3076	1.3411	1.3773	1.4153	1.4536	1.4898	1.5203	1.5411	1.5485
67°	1.3321	1.3675	1.4060	1.4467	1.4880	1.5274	1.5610	1.5840	1.5923
68°	1.3568	1.3942	1.4351	1.4786	1.5232	1.5661	1.6030	1.6287	1.6379
69°	1.3817	1.4212	1.4646	1.5111	1.5591	1.6059	1.6466	1.6752	1.6856
70°	1.4068	1.4484	1.4944	1.5441	1.5959	1.6468	1.6918	1.7237	1.7354
71°	1.4320	1.4759	1.5246	1.5777	1.6335	1.6891	1.7388	1.7745	1.7877
72°	1.4574	1.5036	1.5552	1.6118	1.6720	1.7326	1.7876	1.8277	1.8427
73°	1.4830	1.5315	1.5862	1.6465	1.7113	1.7774	1.8384	1.8837	1.9008
74°	1.5087	1.5597	1.6175	1.6818	1.7516	1.8237	1.8915	1.9427	1.9623
75°	1.5345	1.5882	1.6492	1.7176	1.7927	1.8715	1.9468	2.0050	2.0276
76°	1.5606	1.6168	1.6812	1.7540	1.8347	1.9207	2.0047	2.0711	2.0973
77°	1.5867	1.6457	1.7136	1.7909	1.8777	1.9716	2.0653	2.1414	2.1721
78°	1.6130	1.6748	1.7462	1.8284	1.9215	2.0240	2.1288	2.2164	2.2528
79°	1.6394	1.7040	1.7792	1.8664	1.9663	2.0781	2.1954	2.2969	2.3404
80°	1.6660	1.7335	1.8125	1.9048	2.0119	2.1339	2.2653	2.3836	2.4362
81°	1.6926	1.7631	1.8461	1.9438	2.0584	2.1913	2.3387	2.4775	2.5421
82°	1.7193	1.7929	1.8799	1.9831	2.1057	2.2504	2.4157	2.5795	2.6603
83°	1.7462	1.8228	1.9140	2.0229	2.1537	2.3110	2.4965	2.6911	2.7942
84°	1.7731	1.8528	1.9482	2.0630	2.2024	2.3731	2.5811	2.8136	2.9487
85°	1.8001	1.8830	1.9826	2.1035	2.2518	2.4366	2.6694	2.9487	3.1313
86°	1.8271	1.9132	2.0172	2.1442	2.3017	2.5013	2.7612	3.0978	3.3547
87°	1.8542	1.9435	2,0519	2.1852	2.3520	2.5670	2.8561	3.2620	3.6425
88°	1.8813	1.9739	2.0867	2.2263	2.4026	2.6336	2.9537	3.4412	4.0481
89°	1.9084	2.0043	2.1216	2.2675	2.4535	2.7007	3.0530	3.6328	4.7413
90°	1.9356	2.0347	2.1565	2.3088	2.5046	2.7681	3.1534	3.8317	———

ELLIPTIC INTEGRALS OF THE SECOND KIND: $E(k, \phi)$

$$E(k, \phi) = \int_0^\phi \sqrt{(1 - k^2 \sin^2 \phi)d\phi}, \quad \theta = \sin^{-1} k$$

θ \ φ	5°	10°	15°	20°	25°	30°	35°	40°	45°
1°	0.0175	0.0175	0.0175	0.0175	0.0175	0.0175	0.0175	0.0175	0.0175
2°	0.0349	0.0349	0.0349	0.0349	0.0349	0.0349	0.0349	0.0349	0.0349
3°	0.0524	0.0524	0.0524	0.0524	0.0524	0.0524	0.0524	0.0523	0.0523
4°	0.0698	0.0698	0.0698	0.0698	0.0698	0.0698	0.0698	0.0698	0.0698
5°	0.0873	0.0873	0.0873	0.0873	0.0872	0.0872	0.0872	0.0872	0.0872
6°	0.1047	0.1047	0.1047	0.1047	0.1047	0.1047	0.1047	0.1046	0.1046
7°	0.1222	0.1222	0.1222	0.1221	0.1221	0.1221	0.1221	0.1220	0.1220
8°	0.1396	0.1396	0.1396	0.1396	0.1395	0.1395	0.1395	0.1394	0.1394
9°	0.1571	0.1571	0.1570	0.1570	0.1570	0.1569	0.1569	0.1568	0.1568
10°	0.1745	0.1745	0.1745	0.1744	0.1744	0.1743	0.1742	0.1742	0.1741
11°	0.1920	0.1920	0.1919	0.1918	0.1918	0.1917	0.1916	0.1915	0.1914
12°	0.2094	0.2094	0.2093	0.2093	0.2092	0.2091	0.2089	0.2088	0.2087
13°	0.2269	0.2268	0.2268	0.2267	0.2265	0.2264	0.2263	0.2261	0.2259
14°	0.2443	0.2443	0.2442	0.2441	0.2439	0.2437	0.2436	0.2433	0.2431
15°	0.2618	0.2617	0.2616	0.2615	0.2613	0.2611	0.2608	0.2606	0.2603
16°	0.2792	0.2791	0.2790	0.2788	0.2786	0.2784	0.2781	0.2778	0.2775
17°	0.2967	0.2966	0.2964	0.2962	0.2959	0.2956	0.2953	0.2949	0.2946
18°	0.3141	0.3140	0.3138	0.3136	0.3133	0.3129	0.3125	0.3121	0.3116
19°	0.3316	0.3314	0.3312	0.3309	0.3305	0.3301	0.3296	0.3291	0.3286
20°	0.3490	0.3489	0.3486	0.3483	0.3478	0.3473	0.3468	0.3462	0.3456
21°	0.3665	0.3663	0.3660	0.3656	0.3651	0.3645	0.3639	0.3632	0.3625
22°	0.3839	0.3837	0.3834	0.3829	0.3823	0.3817	0.3809	0.3802	0.3793
23°	0.4013	0.4011	0.4007	0.4002	0.3996	0.3988	0.3980	0.3971	0.3961
24°	0.4188	0.4185	0.4181	0.4175	0.4168	0.4159	0.4150	0.4139	0.4129
25°	0.4362	0.4359	0.4354	0.4348	0.4339	0.4330	0.4319	0.4308	0.4296
26°	0.4537	0.4533	0.4528	0.4520	0.4511	0.4500	0.4488	0.4475	0.4462
27°	0.4711	0.4707	0.4701	0.4693	0.4682	0.4670	0.4657	0.4643	0.4628
28°	0.4886	0.4881	0.4874	0.4865	0.4854	0.4840	0.4825	0.4809	0.4793
29°	0.5060	0.5055	0.5048	0.5037	0.5025	0.5010	0.4993	0.4975	0.4957
30°	0.5234	0.5229	0.5221	0.5209	0.5195	0.5179	0.5161	0.5141	0.5120
31°	0.5409	0.5403	0.5394	0.5381	0.5366	0.5348	0.5327	0.5306	0.5283
32°	0.5583	0.5577	0.5567	0.5553	0.5536	0.5516	0.5494	0.5470	0.5446
33°	0.5757	0.5751	0.5740	0.5725	0.5706	0.5684	0.5660	0.5634	0.5607
34°	0.5932	0.5924	0.5912	0.5896	0.5876	0.5852	0.5826	0.5797	0.5768
35°	0.6106	0.6098	0.6085	0.6067	0.6045	0.6019	0.5991	0.5960	0.5928
36°	0.6280	0.6272	0.6258	0.6238	0.6214	0.6186	0.6155	0.6122	0.6087
37°	0.6455	0.6445	0.6430	0.6409	0.6383	0.6353	0.6319	0.6283	0.6245
38°	0.6629	0.6619	0.6602	0.6580	0.6552	0.6519	0.6483	0.6444	0.6403
39°	0.6803	0.6792	0.6775	0.6750	0.6720	0.6685	0.6646	0.6604	0.6559
40°	0.6977	0.6966	0.6947	0.6921	0.6888	0.6851	0.6808	0.6763	0.6715
41°	0.7152	0.7139	0.7119	0.7091	0.7056	0.7016	0.6970	0.6921	0.6870
42°	0.7326	0.7313	0.7291	0.7261	0.7224	0.7180	0.7132	0.7079	0.7024
43°	0.7500	0.7486	0.7463	0.7431	0.7391	0.7345	0.7293	0.7237	0.7178
44°	0.7674	0.7659	0.7634	0.7600	0.7558	0.7508	0.7453	0.7393	0.7330
45°	0.7849	0.7832	0.7806	0.7770	0.7725	0.7672	0.7613	0.7549	0.7482

ELLIPTIC INTEGRALS OF THE SECOND KIND: $E(k, \phi)$

$$E(k, \phi) = \int_0^\phi \sqrt{(1 - k^2 \sin^2 \phi)}\, d\phi, \quad \theta = \sin^{-1} k$$

θ / ϕ	50°	55°	60°	65°	70°	75°	80°	85°	90°
1°	0.0175	0.0175	0.0175	0.0175	0.0175	0.0175	0.0175	0.0175	0.0175
2°	0.0349	0.0349	0.0349	0.0349	0.0349	0.0349	0.0349	0.0349	0.0349
3°	0.0523	0.0523	0.0523	0.0523	0.0523	0.0523	0.0523	0.0523	0.0523
4°	0.0698	0.0698	0.0698	0.0698	0.0698	0.0698	0.0698	0.0698	0.0698
5°	0.0872	0.0872	0.0872	0.0872	0.0872	0.0872	0.0872	0.0872	0.0872
6°	0.1046	0.1046	0.1046	0.1046	0.1046	0.1045	0.1045	0.1045	0.1045
7°	0.1220	0.1220	0.1219	0.1219	0.1219	0.1219	0.1219	0.1219	0.1219
8°	0.1394	0.1393	0.1393	0.1393	0.1392	0.1392	0.1392	0.1392	0.1392
9°	0.1567	0.1566	0.1566	0.1566	0.1565	0.1565	0.1565	0.1564	0.1564
10°	0.1740	0.1739	0.1739	0.1738	0.1738	0.1737	0.1737	0.1737	0.1736
11°	0.1913	0.1912	0.1911	0.1910	0.1909	0.1909	0.1908	0.1908	0.1908
12°	0.2085	0.2084	0.2083	0.2082	0.2081	0.2080	0.2080	0.2079	0.2079
13°	0.2258	0.2256	0.2254	0.2253	0.2252	0.2251	0.2250	0.2250	0.2250
14°	0.2429	0.2427	0.2425	0.2424	0.2422	0.2421	0.2420	0.2419	0.2419
15°	0.2601	0.2598	0.2596	0.2594	0.2592	0.2590	0.2589	0.2588	0.2588
16°	0.2771	0.2768	0.2765	0.2763	0.2761	0.2759	0.2757	0.2757	0.2756
17°	0.2942	0.2938	0.2935	0.2932	0.2929	0.2927	0.2925	0.2924	0.2924
18°	0.3112	0.3107	0.3103	0.3099	0.3096	0.3094	0.3092	0.3091	0.3090
19°	0.3281	0.3276	0.3271	0.3267	0.3263	0.3260	0.3258	0.3256	0.3256
20°	0.3450	0.3444	0.3438	0.3433	0.3429	0.3425	0.3422	0.3421	0.3420
21°	0.3618	0.3611	0.3604	0.3598	0.3593	0.3589	0.3586	0.3584	0.3584
22°	0.3785	0.3777	0.3770	0.3763	0.3757	0.3752	0.3749	0.3747	0.3746
23°	0.3952	0.3943	0.3935	0.3927	0.3920	0.3915	0.3911	0.3908	0.3907
24°	0.4118	0.4108	0.4098	0.4090	0.4082	0.4076	0.4071	0.4068	0.4067
25°	0.4284	0.4272	0.4261	0.4251	0.4243	0.4236	0.4230	0.4227	0.4226
26°	0.4449	0.4436	0.4423	0.4412	0.4402	0.4394	0.4389	0.4385	0.4384
27°	0.4613	0.4598	0.4584	0.4572	0.4561	0.4552	0.4545	0.4541	0.4540
28°	0.4776	0.4760	0.4744	0.4730	0.4718	0.4708	0.4701	0.4696	0.4695
29°	0.4938	0.4920	0.4903	0.4887	0.4874	0.4863	0.4855	0.4850	0.4848
30°	0.5100	0.5080	0.5061	0.5044	0.5029	0.5016	0.5007	0.5002	0.5000
31°	0.5261	0.5239	0.5218	0.5199	0.5182	0.5169	0.5159	0.5152	0.5150
32°	0.5421	0.5396	0.5373	0.5352	0.5334	0.5319	0.5308	0.5301	0.5299
33°	0.5580	0.5553	0.5528	0.5505	0.5485	0.5468	0.5456	0.5449	0.5446
34°	0.5738	0.5709	0.5681	0.5656	0.5634	0.5616	0.5603	0.5595	0.5592
35°	0.5895	0.5863	0.5833	0.5806	0.5782	0.5762	0.5748	0.5739	0.5736
36°	0.6051	0.6017	0.5984	0.5954	0.5928	0.5907	0.5891	0.5881	0.5878
37°	0.6207	0.6169	0.6134	0.6101	0.6073	0.6050	0.6032	0.6022	0.6018
38°	0.6361	0.6321	0.6282	0.6247	0.6216	0.6191	0.6172	0.6160	0.6157
39°	0.6515	0.6471	0.6429	0.6391	0.6357	0.6330	0.6310	0.6297	0.6293
40°	0.6667	0.6620	0.6575	0.6533	0.6497	0.6468	0.6446	0.6432	0.6428
41°	0.6818	0.6767	0.6719	0.6674	0.6636	0.6604	0.6580	0.6566	0.6561
42°	0.6969	0.6914	0.6862	0.6814	0.6772	0.6738	0.6712	0.6697	0.6691
43°	0.7118	0.7059	0.7003	0.6952	0.6907	0.6870	0.6843	0.6826	0.6820
44°	0.7266	0.7204	0.7144	0.7088	0.7040	0.7000	0.6971	0.6953	0.6947
45°	0.7414	0.7346	0.7282	0.7223	0.7171	0.7129	0.7097	0.7078	0.7071

ELLIPTIC INTEGRALS OF THE SECOND KIND: $E(k, \phi)$

$$E(k, \phi) = \int_0^\phi \sqrt{(1 - k^2 \sin^2 \phi)}\,d\phi, \quad \theta = \sin^{-1} k$$

θ \ ϕ	5°	10°	15°	20°	25°	30°	35°	40°	45°
46°	0.8023	0.8006	0.7977	0.7939	0.7891	0.7835	0.7772	0.7704	0.7633
47°	0.8197	0.8179	0.8149	0.8108	0.8057	0.7998	0.7931	0.7858	0.7782
48°	0.8371	0.8352	0.8320	0.8277	0.8223	0.8160	0.8089	0.8012	0.7931
49°	0.8545	0.8525	0.8491	0.8446	0.8389	0.8322	0.8247	0.8165	0.8079
50°	0.8719	0.8698	0.8663	0.8614	0.8554	0.8483	0.8404	0.8317	0.8227
51°	0.8894	0.8871	0.8834	0.8783	0.8719	0.8644	0.8560	0.8469	0.8373
52°	0.9068	0.9044	0.9004	0.8951	0.8884	0.8805	0.8716	0.8620	0.8518
53°	0.9242	0.9217	0.9175	0.9119	0.9048	0.8965	0.8872	0.8770	0.8663
54°	0.9416	0.9389	0.9345	0.9287	0.9212	0.9125	0.9026	0.8919	0.8806
55°	0.9590	0.9562	0.9517	0.9454	0.9376	0.9284	0.9181	0.9068	0.8949
56°	0.9764	0.9735	0.9687	0.9622	0.9540	0.9443	0.9335	0.9216	0.9091
57°	0.9938	0.9908	0.9858	0.9789	0.9703	0.9602	0.9488	0.9363	0.9232
58°	1.0112	1.0080	1.0028	0.9956	0.9866	0.9760	0.9641	0.9510	0.9372
59°	1.0286	1.0253	1.0198	1.0123	1.0029	1.9918	0.9793	0.9656	0.9511
60°	1.0460	1.0426	1.0368	1.0290	1.0191	1.0076	0.9945	0.9801	0.9650
61°	1.0634	1.0598	1.0538	1.0456	1.0354	1.0233	1.0096	0.9946	0.9787
62°	1.0808	1.0771	1.0708	1.0623	1.0516	1.0389	1.0246	1 0090	0.9924
63°	1.0982	1.0943	1.0878	1.0789	1.0678	1.0546	1.0397	1.0233	1.0060
64°	1.1156	1.1115	1.1048	1.0955	1.0839	1.0702	1.0547	1.0376	1.0195
65°	1.1330	1.1288	1.1218	1.1121	1.1001	1.0858	1.0696	1.0518	1.0329
66°	1.1504	1.1460	1.1387	1.1287	1.1162	1.1013	1.0845	1.0660	1.0463
67°	1.1678	1.1632	1.1557	1.1453	1.1323	1.1168	1.0993	1.0801	1.0596
68°	1.1852	1.1805	1.1726	1.1618	1.1483	1.1323	1.1141	1.0941	1.0728
69°	1.2026	1.1977	1.1896	1.1784	1.1644	1.1478	1.1289	1.1081	1.0859
70°	1.2200	1.2149	1.2065	1.1949	1.1804	1.1632	1.1436	1.1221	1.0990
71°	1.2374	1.2321	1.2234	1.2114	1.1964	1.1786	1.1583	1.1359	1.1120
72°	1.2548	1.2493	1.2403	1.2280	1.2124	1.1939	1.1729	1.1498	1.1250
73°	1.2722	1.2666	1.2573	1.2445	1.2284	1.2093	1.1875	1.1636	1.1379
74°	1.2896	1.2838	1.2742	1.2609	1.2443	1.2246	1.2021	1.1773	1.1507
75°	1.3070	1.3010	1.2911	1.2774	1.2603	1.2399	1.2167	1.1910	1.1635
76°	1.3244	1.3182	1.3080	1.2939	1.2762	1.2552	1.2312	1.2047	1.1762
77°	1.3418	1.3354	1.3249	1.3104	1.2921	1.2704	1.2457	1.2183	1.1889
78°	1.3592	1.3526	1.3417	1.3268	1.3080	1.2856	1.2601	1.2319	1.2015
79°	1.3765	1.3698	1.3586	1.3432	1.3239	1.3009	1.2746	1.2454	1.2141
80°	1.3939	1.3870	1.3755	1.3597	1.3398	1.3161	1.2890	1.2590	1.2266
81°	1.4113	1.4042	1.3924	1.3761	1.3556	1.3312	1.3034	1.2725	1.2391
82°	1.4287	1.4214	1.4093	1.3925	1.3715	1.3464	1.3177	1.2859	1.2516
83°	1.4461	1.4386	1.4261	1.4090	1.3873	1.3616	1.3321	1.2994	1.2640
84°	1.4635	1.4558	1.4430	1.4254	1.4032	1.3767	1.3464	1.3128	1.2765
85°	1.4809	1.4729	1.4598	1.4418	1.4190	1.3919	1.3608	1.3262	1.2889
86°	1.4983	1.4901	1.4767	1.4582	1.4348	1.4070	1.3751	1.3396	1.3012
87°	1.5156	1.5073	1.4936	1.4746	1.4507	1.4221	1.3894	1.3530	1.3136
88°	1.5330	1.5245	1.5104	1.4910	1.4665	1.4372	1.4037	1.3664	1.3260
89°	1.5504	1.5417	1.5273	1.5074	1.4823	1.4523	1.4180	1.3798	1.3383
90°	1.5678	1.5589	1.5442	1.5238	1.4981	1.4675	1.4323	1.3931	1.3506

$$E(k, \phi) = \int_0^\phi \sqrt{(1 - k^2 \sin^2 \phi)}d\phi, \quad \theta = \sin^{-1} k$$

ϕ \ θ	50°	55°	60°	65°	70°	75°	80°	85°	90°
46°	0.7560	0.7488	0.7419	0.7356	0.7301	0.7255	0.7221	0.7200	0.7193
47°	0.7705	0.7628	0.7555	0.7488	0.7429	0.7380	0.7344	0.7321	0.7314
48°	0.7849	0.7768	0.7690	0.7618	0.7555	0.7502	0.7464	0.7440	0.7431
49°	0.7992	0.7905	0.7822	0.7746	0.7679	0.7623	0.7581	0.7556	0.7547
50°	0.8134	0.8042	0.7954	0.7872	0.7801	0.7741	0.7697	0.7670	0.7660
51°	0.8275	0.8177	0.8084	0.7997	0.7921	0.7858	0.7811	0.7781	0.7771
52°	0.8414	0.8311	0.8212	0.8120	0.8039	0.7972	0.7922	0.7891	0.7880
53°	0.8553	0.8444	0.8339	0.8241	0.8155	0.8084	0.8031	0.7998	0.7986
54°	0.8690	0.8575	0.8464	0.8361	0.8270	0.8194	0.8137	0.8102	0.8090
55°	0.8827	0.8705	0.8588	0.8479	0.8382	0.8302	0.8242	0.8204	0.8192
56°	0.8962	0.8834	0.8710	0.8595	0.8493	0.8408	0.8344	0.8304	0.8290
57°	0.9096	0.8961	0.8831	0.8709	0.8601	0.8511	0.8443	0.8401	0.8387
58°	0.9230	0.9088	0.8950	0.8822	0.8707	0.8612	0.8540	0.8496	0.8480
59°	0.9362	0.9213	0.9068	0.8932	0.8812	0.8711	0.8635	0.8588	0.8572
60°	0.9493	0.9336	0.9184	0.9042	0.8914	0.8808	0.8728	0.8677	0.8660
61°	0.9623	0.9459	0.9299	0.9149	0.9015	0.8903	0.8817	0.8764	0.8746
62°	0.9752	0.9580	0.9412	0.9254	0.9113	0.8995	0.8905	0.8849	0.8829
63°	0.9880	0.9700	0.9524	0.9358	0.9210	0.9085	0.8990	0.8930	0.8910
64°	1.0007	0.9818	0.9634	0.9460	0.9304	0.9173	0.9072	0.9009	0.8988
65°	1.0133	0.9936	0.9743	0.9561	0.9397	0.9258	0.9152	0.9086	0.9063
66°	1.0258	1.0052	0.9850	0.9659	0.9487	0.9341	0.9230	0.9159	0.9135
67°	1.0383	1.0167	0.9956	0.9756	0.9576	0.9422	0.9305	0.9230	0.9205
68°	1.0506	1.0281	1.0061	0.9852	0.9662	0.9501	0.9377	0.9299	0.9272
69°	1.0628	1.0394	1.0164	0.9946	0.9747	0.9578	0.9447	0.9364	0.9336
70°	1.0750	1.0506	1.0266	1.0038	0.9830	0.9652	0.9514	0.9427	0.9397
71°	1.0871	1.0617	1.0367	1.0129	0.9911	0.9724	0.9579	0.9487	0.9455
72°	1.0991	1.0727	1.0467	1.0218	0.9990	0.9794	0.9642	0.9544	0.9511
73°	1.1110	1.0836	1.0565	1.0306	1.0067	0.9862	0.9702	0.9599	0.9563
74°	1.1228	1.0944	1.0662	1.0392	1.0143	0.9928	0.9759	0.9650	0.9613
75°	1.1346	1.1051	1.0759	1.0477	1.0217	0.9992	0.9814	0.9699	0.9659
76°	1.1463	1.1158	1.0854	1.0561	1.0290	1.0053	0.9867	0.9745	0.9703
77°	1.1580	1.1263	1.0948	1.0643	1.0361	1.0113	0.9917	0.9789	0.9744
78°	1.1695	1.1368	1.1041	1.0724	1.0430	1.0171	0.9965	0.9829	0.9781
79°	1.1811	1.1472	1.1133	1.0805	1.0498	1.0228	1.0011	0.9867	0.9816
80°	1.1926	1.1576	1.1225	1.0884	1.0565	1.0282	1.0054	0.9902	0.9848
81°	1.2040	1.1678	1.1316	1.0962	1.0630	1.0335	1.0096	0.9935	0.9877
82°	1.2154	1.1781	1.1406	1.1040	1.0695	1.0387	1.0135	0.9965	0.9903
83°	1.2267	1.1883	1.1495	1.1116	1.0758	1.0437	1.0173	0.9992	0.9925
84°	1.2381	1.1984	1.1584	1.1192	1.0821	1.0486	1.0209	1.0017	0.9945
85°	1.2493	1.2085	1.1673	1.1267	1.0882	1.0534	1.0244	1.0039	0.9962
86°	1.2606	1.2186	1.1761	1.1342	1.0944	1.0581	1.0277	1.0060	0.9976
87°	1.2719	1.2286	1.1848	1.1417	1.1004	1.0628	1.0309	1.0078	0.9986
88°	1.2831	1.2386	1.1936	1.1491	1.1064	1.0673	1.0340	1.0095	0.9994
89°	1.2943	1.2487	1.2023	1.1565	1.1124	1.0719	1.0371	1.0111	0.9998
90°	1.3055	1.2587	1.2111	1.1638	1.1184	1.0764	1.0401	1.0127	1.0000

If n is prime the mantissa of its logarithm is given.

n	0	1	2	3	4
0		0000000	3010300	4771213	2^2
1	$2 \cdot 5$	0413927	$2^2 \cdot 3$	1139434	$2 \cdot 7$
2	$2^2 \cdot 5$	$3 \cdot 7$	$2 \cdot 11$	3617278	$2^3 \cdot 3$
3	$2 \cdot 3 \cdot 5$	4913617	2^5	$3 \cdot 11$	$2 \cdot 17$
4	$2^3 \cdot 5$	6127839	$2 \cdot 3 \cdot 7$	6334685	$2^2 \cdot 11$
5	$2 \cdot 5^2$	$3 \cdot 17$	$2^2 \cdot 13$	7242759	$2 \cdot 3^3$
6	$2^2 \cdot 3 \cdot 5$	7853298	$2 \cdot 31$	$3^2 \cdot 7$	2^6
7	$2 \cdot 5 \cdot 7$	8512583	$2^3 \cdot 3^2$	8633229	$2 \cdot 37$
8	$2^4 \cdot 5$	3^4	$2 \cdot 41$	9190781	$2^2 \cdot 3 \cdot 7$
9	$2 \cdot 3^2 \cdot 5$	$7 \cdot 13$	$2^2 \cdot 23$	$3 \cdot 31$	$2 \cdot 47$
10	$2^2 \cdot 5^2$	0043214	$2 \cdot 3 \cdot 17$	0128372	$2^3 \cdot 13$
11	$2 \cdot 5 \cdot 11$	$3 \cdot 37$	$2^4 \cdot 7$	0530784	$2 \cdot 3 \cdot 19$
12	$2^3 \cdot 3 \cdot 5$	11^2	$2 \cdot 61$	$3 \cdot 41$	$2^2 \cdot 31$
13	$2 \cdot 5 \cdot 13$	1172713	$2^2 \cdot 3 \cdot 11$	$7 \cdot 19$	$2 \cdot 67$
14	$2^2 \cdot 5 \cdot 7$	$3 \cdot 47$	$2 \cdot 71$	$11 \cdot 13$	$2^4 \cdot 3^2$
15	$2 \cdot 3 \cdot 5^2$	1789769	$2^3 \cdot 19$	$3^2 \cdot 17$	$2 \cdot 7 \cdot 11$
16	$2^5 \cdot 5$	$7 \cdot 23$	$2 \cdot 3^4$	2121876	$2^2 \cdot 41$
17	$2 \cdot 5 \cdot 17$	$3^2 \cdot 19$	$2^2 \cdot 43$	2380461	$2 \cdot 3 \cdot 29$
18	$2^2 \cdot 3^2 \cdot 5$	2576786	$2 \cdot 7 \cdot 13$	$3 \cdot 61$	$2^3 \cdot 23$
19	$2 \cdot 5 \cdot 19$	2810334	$2^6 \cdot 3$	2855573	$2 \cdot 97$
20	$2^3 \cdot 5^2$	$3 \cdot 67$	$2 \cdot 101$	$7 \cdot 29$	$2^2 \cdot 3 \cdot 17$
21	$2 \cdot 3 \cdot 5 \cdot 7$	3242825	$2 \cdot 53$	$3 \cdot 71$	$2 \cdot 107$
22	$2^2 \cdot 5 \cdot 11$	$13 \cdot 17$	$2 \cdot 3 \cdot 37$	3483049	$2^5 \cdot 7$
23	$2 \cdot 5 \cdot 23$	$3 \cdot 7 \cdot 11$	$2^3 \cdot 29$	3673559	$2 \cdot 3^2 \cdot 13$
24	$2^4 \cdot 3 \cdot 5$	3820170	$2 \cdot 11^2$	3^5	$2^2 \cdot 61$
25	$2 \cdot 5^3$	3996737	$2^2 \cdot 3^2 \cdot 7$	$11 \cdot 23$	$2 \cdot 127$
26	$2^2 \cdot 5 \cdot 13$	$3^2 \cdot 29$	$2 \cdot 131$	4199557	$2^3 \cdot 3 \cdot 11$
27	$2 \cdot 3^3 \cdot 5$	4329693	$2^4 \cdot 17$	$3 \cdot 7 \cdot 13$	$2 \cdot 137$
28	$2^3 \cdot 5 \cdot 7$	4487063	$2 \cdot 3 \cdot 47$	4517864	$2^2 \cdot 71$
29	$2 \cdot 5 \cdot 29$	$3 \cdot 97$	$2^2 \cdot 73$	4668676	$2 \cdot 3 \cdot 7^2$
30	$2^2 \cdot 3 \cdot 5^2$	$7 \cdot 43$	$2 \cdot 151$	$3 \cdot 101$	$2 \cdot 19$
31	$2 \cdot 5 \cdot 31$	4927604	$2^3 \cdot 3 \cdot 13$	4955443	$2 \cdot 157$
32	$2^6 \cdot 5$	$3 \cdot 107$	$2 \cdot 7 \cdot 23$	$17 \cdot 19$	$2^2 \cdot 3^4$
33	$2 \cdot 3 \cdot 5 \cdot 11$	5198280	$2^2 \cdot 83$	$3^2 \cdot 37$	$2 \cdot 167$
34	$2^2 \cdot 5 \cdot 17$	$11 \cdot 31$	$2 \cdot 3^2 \cdot 19$	7^3	$2^3 \cdot 43$
35	$2 \cdot 5^2 \cdot 7$	$3^3 \cdot 13$	$2^5 \cdot 11$	5477747	$2 \cdot 3 \cdot 59$
36	$2^3 \cdot 3^2 \cdot 5$	19^2	$2 \cdot 181$	$3 \cdot 11^2$	$2^2 \cdot 7 \cdot 13$
37	$2 \cdot 5 \cdot 37$	$7 \cdot 53$	$2^2 \cdot 3 \cdot 31$	5717088	$2 \cdot 11 \cdot 17$
38	$2^2 \cdot 5 \cdot 19$	$3 \cdot 127$	$2 \cdot 191$	5831988	$2^7 \cdot 3$
39	$2 \cdot 3 \cdot 5 \cdot 13$	$17 \cdot 23$	$2^3 \cdot 7^2$	$3 \cdot 131$	$2 \cdot 197$
40	$2^4 \cdot 5^2$	6031444	$2 \cdot 3 \cdot 67$	$13 \cdot 31$	$2^2 \cdot 101$
41	$2 \cdot 5 \cdot 41$	$3 \cdot 137$	$2^2 \cdot 103$	$7 \cdot 59$	$2 \cdot 3^2 \cdot 23$
42	$2^2 \cdot 3 \cdot 5 \cdot 7$	6242821	$2 \cdot 211$	$3^2 \cdot 47$	$2^3 \cdot 53$
43	$2 \cdot 5 \cdot 43$	6344773	$2^4 \cdot 3^3$	6364879	$2 \cdot 7 \cdot 31$
44	$2^3 \cdot 5 \cdot 11$	$3^2 \cdot 7^2$	$2 \cdot 13 \cdot 17$	6464037	$2^2 \cdot 3 \cdot 37$
45	$2 \cdot 3^2 \cdot 5^2$	$11 \cdot 41$	$2^2 \cdot 113$	$3 \cdot 151$	$2 \cdot 227$
46	$2^2 \cdot 5 \cdot 23$	6637009	$2 \cdot 3 \cdot 7 \cdot 11$	6655810	$2^4 \cdot 29$
47	$2 \cdot 5 \cdot 47$	$3 \cdot 157$	$2^3 \cdot 59$	$11 \cdot 43$	$2 \cdot 3 \cdot 79$
48	$2^5 \cdot 3 \cdot 5$	$13 \cdot 37$	$2 \cdot 241$	$3 \cdot 7 \cdot 23$	$2^2 \cdot 11^2$
49	$2 \cdot 5 \cdot 7^2$	6910815	$2^2 \cdot 3 \cdot 41$	$17 \cdot 29$	$2 \cdot 13 \cdot 19$
50	$2^2 \cdot 5^3$	$3 \cdot 167$	$2 \cdot 251$	7015680	$2^3 \cdot 3^2 \cdot 7$

FACTORS AND PRIMES

If *n* is not prime its prime factors are given.

n	5	6	7	8	9
0	6989700	$2 \cdot 3$	8450980	2^3	3^2
1	$3 \cdot 5$	2^4	2304489	$2 \cdot 3^2$	2787536
2	5^2	$2 \cdot 13$	3^3	$2^2 \cdot 7$	4623980
3	$5 \cdot 7$	$2^2 \cdot 3^2$	5682017	$2 \cdot 19$	$3 \cdot 13$
4	$3^2 \cdot 5$	$2 \cdot 23$	6720979	$2^4 \cdot 3$	7^2
5	$5 \cdot 11$	$2^3 \cdot 7$	$3 \cdot 19$	$2 \cdot 29$	7708520
6	$5 \cdot 13$	$2 \cdot 3 \cdot 11$	8260748	$2^2 \cdot 17$	$3 \cdot 23$
7	$3 \cdot 5^2$	$2^2 \cdot 19$	$7 \cdot 11$	$2 \cdot 3 \cdot 13$	8976271
8	$5 \cdot 17$	$2 \cdot 43$	$3 \cdot 29$	$2^3 \cdot 11$	9493900
9	$5 \cdot 19$	$2^5 \cdot 3$	9867717	$2 \cdot 7^2$	$3^2 \cdot 11$
10	$3 \cdot 5 \cdot 7$	$2 \cdot 53$	0293838	$2^2 \cdot 3^3$	0374265
11	$5 \cdot 23$	$2^2 \cdot 29$	$3^2 \cdot 13$	$2 \cdot 59$	$7 \cdot 17$
12	5^3	$2 \cdot 3^2 \cdot 7$	1038037	2^7	$3 \cdot 43$
13	$3^3 \cdot 5$	$2^3 \cdot 17$	1367206	$2 \cdot 3 \cdot 23$	1430148
14	$5 \cdot 29$	$2 \cdot 73$	$3 \cdot 7^2$	$2^2 \cdot 37$	1731863
15	$5 \cdot 31$	$2^2 \cdot 3 \cdot 13$	1958997	$2 \cdot 79$	$3 \cdot 53$
16	$3 \cdot 5 \cdot 11$	$2 \cdot 83$	2227165	$2^3 \cdot 3 \cdot 7$	13^2
17	$5^2 \cdot 7$	$2^4 \cdot 11$	$3 \cdot 59$	$2 \cdot 89$	2528530
18	$5 \cdot 37$	$2 \cdot 3 \cdot 31$	$11 \cdot 17$	$2^2 \cdot 47$	$3^3 \cdot 7$
19	$3 \cdot 5 \cdot 13$	$2^2 \cdot 7^2$	2944662	$2 \cdot 3^2 \cdot 11$	2988531
20	$5 \cdot 41$	$2 \cdot 103$	$3^2 \cdot 23$	$2^4 \cdot 13$	$11 \cdot 19$
21	$5 \cdot 43$	$2^3 \cdot 3^3$	$7 \cdot 31$	$2 \cdot 109$	$3 \cdot 73$
22	$3^2 \cdot 5^2$	$2 \cdot 113$	3560259	$2^2 \cdot 3 \cdot 19$	3598355
23	$5 \cdot 47$	$2^2 \cdot 59$	$3 \cdot 79$	$2 \cdot 7 \cdot 17$	3783979
24	$5 \cdot 7^2$	$2 \cdot 3 \cdot 41$	$13 \cdot 19$	$2^3 \cdot 31$	$3 \cdot 83$
25	$3 \cdot 5 \cdot 17$	2^8	4099331	$2 \cdot 3 \cdot 43$	$7 \cdot 37$
26	$5 \cdot 53$	$2 \cdot 7 \cdot 19$	$3 \cdot 89$	$2^2 \cdot 67$	4297523
27	$5^2 \cdot 11$	$2^2 \cdot 3 \cdot 23$	4424798	$2 \cdot 139$	$3^2 \cdot 31$
28	$3 \cdot 5 \cdot 19$	$2 \cdot 11 \cdot 13$	$7 \cdot 41$	$2^5 \cdot 3^2$	17^2
29	$5 \cdot 59$	$2^3 \cdot 37$	$3^3 \cdot 11$	$2 \cdot 149$	$13 \cdot 23$
30	$5 \cdot 61$	$2 \cdot 3^2 \cdot 17$	4871384	$2^2 \cdot 7 \cdot 11$	$3 \cdot 103$
31	$3^2 \cdot 5 \cdot 7$	$2^2 \cdot 79$	5010593	$2 \cdot 3 \cdot 53$	$11 \cdot 29$
32	$5^2 \cdot 13$	$2 \cdot 163$	$3 \cdot 109$	$2^3 \cdot 41$	$7 \cdot 47$
33	$5 \cdot 67$	$2^4 \cdot 3 \cdot 7$	5276299	$2 \cdot 13^2$	$3 \cdot 113$
34	$3 \cdot 5 \cdot 23$	$2 \cdot 173$	5403295	$2^2 \cdot 3 \cdot 29$	5428254
35	$5 \cdot 71$	$2^2 \cdot 89$	$3 \cdot 7 \cdot 17$	$2 \cdot 179$	5550944
36	$5 \cdot 73$	$2 \cdot 3 \cdot 61$	5646661	$2^4 \cdot 23$	$3^2 \cdot 41$
37	$3 \cdot 5^3$	$2^3 \cdot 47$	$13 \cdot 29$	$2 \cdot 3^3 \cdot 7$	5786392
38	$5 \cdot 7 \cdot 11$	$2 \cdot 193$	$3^2 \cdot 43$	$2^2 \cdot 97$	5899496
39	$5 \cdot 79$	$2^2 \cdot 3^2 \cdot 11$	5987905	$2 \cdot 199$	$3 \cdot 7 \cdot 19$
40	$3^4 \cdot 5$	$2 \cdot 7 \cdot 29$	$11 \cdot 37$	$2^3 \cdot 3 \cdot 17$	6117233
41	$5 \cdot 83$	$2^5 \cdot 13$	$3 \cdot 139$	$2 \cdot 11 \cdot 19$	6222140
42	$5^2 \cdot 17$	$2 \cdot 3 \cdot 71$	$7 \cdot 61$	$2^2 \cdot 107$	$3 \cdot 11 \cdot 13$
43	$3 \cdot 5 \cdot 29$	$2^2 \cdot 109$	$19 \cdot 23$	$2 \cdot 3 \cdot 73$	6424645
44	$5 \cdot 89$	$2 \cdot 223$	$3 \cdot 149$	$2^6 \cdot 7$	6522463
45	$5 \cdot 7 \cdot 13$	$2^3 \cdot 3 \cdot 19$	6599162	$2 \cdot 229$	$3^3 \cdot 17$
46	$3 \cdot 5 \cdot 31$	$2 \cdot 233$	6693169	$2^2 \cdot 3^2 \cdot 13$	$7 \cdot 67$
47	$5^2 \cdot 19$	$2^2 \cdot 7 \cdot 17$	$3^2 \cdot 53$	$2 \cdot 239$	6803355
48	$5 \cdot 97$	$2 \cdot 3^5$	6875290	$2^3 \cdot 61$	$3 \cdot 163$
49	$3^2 \cdot 5 \cdot 11$	$2^4 \cdot 31$	$7 \cdot 71$	$2 \cdot 3 \cdot 83$	6981005
50	$5 \cdot 101$	$2 \cdot 11 \cdot 23$	$3 \cdot 13^2$	$2^2 \cdot 127$	7067178

n	0	1	2	3	4
50	$2^2 \cdot 5^3$	$3 \cdot 167$	$2 \cdot 251$	**7015680**	$2^3 \cdot 3^2 \cdot 7$
51	$2 \cdot 3 \cdot 5 \cdot 17$	$7 \cdot 73$	2^9	$3^3 \cdot 19$	$2 \cdot 257$
52	$2^3 \cdot 5 \cdot 13$	**7168377**	$2 \cdot 3^2 \cdot 29$	**7185017**	$2^2 \cdot 131$
53	$2 \cdot 5 \cdot 53$	$3^2 \cdot 59$	$2^2 \cdot 7 \cdot 19$	$13 \cdot 41$	$2 \cdot 3 \cdot 89$
54	$2^2 \cdot 3^3 \cdot 5$	**7331973**	$2 \cdot 271$	$3 \cdot 181$	$2^5 \cdot 17$
55	$2 \cdot 5^2 \cdot 11$	$19 \cdot 29$	$2^3 \cdot 3 \cdot 23$	$7 \cdot 79$	$2 \cdot 277$
56	$2^4 \cdot 5 \cdot 7$	$3 \cdot 11 \cdot 17$	$2 \cdot 281$	**7505084**	$2^2 \cdot 3 \cdot 47$
57	$2 \cdot 3 \cdot 5 \cdot 19$	**7566361**	$2^2 \cdot 11 \cdot 13$	$3 \cdot 191$	$2 \cdot 7 \cdot 41$
58	$2^2 \cdot 5 \cdot 29$	$7 \cdot 83$	$2 \cdot 3 \cdot 97$	$11 \cdot 53$	$2^3 \cdot 73$
59	$2 \cdot 5 \cdot 59$	$3 \cdot 197$	$2^4 \cdot 37$	**7730547**	$2 \cdot 3^3 \cdot 11$
60	$2^3 \cdot 3 \cdot 5^2$	**7788745**	$2 \cdot 7 \cdot 43$	$3^2 \cdot 67$	$2^2 \cdot 151$
61	$2 \cdot 5 \cdot 61$	$13 \cdot 47$	$2^2 \cdot 3^2 \cdot 17$	**7874605**	$2 \cdot 307$
62	$2^2 \cdot 5 \cdot 31$	$3^3 \cdot 23$	$2 \cdot 311$	$7 \cdot 89$	$2^4 \cdot 3 \cdot 13$
63	$2 \cdot 3^2 \cdot 5 \cdot 7$	**8000294**	$2^3 \cdot 79$	$3 \cdot 211$	$2 \cdot 317$
64	$2^7 \cdot 5$	**8068580**	$2 \cdot 3 \cdot 107$	**8082110**	$2^2 \cdot 7 \cdot 23$
65	$2 \cdot 5^2 \cdot 13$	$3 \cdot 7 \cdot 31$	$2^2 \cdot 163$	**8149132**	$2 \cdot 3 \cdot 109$
66	$2^2 \cdot 3 \cdot 5 \cdot 11$	**8202015**	$2 \cdot 331$	$3 \cdot 13 \cdot 17$	$2^3 \cdot 83$
67	$2 \cdot 5 \cdot 67$	$11 \cdot 61$	$2^5 \cdot 3 \cdot 7$	**8280151**	$2 \cdot 337$
68	$2^3 \cdot 5 \cdot 17$	$3 \cdot 227$	$2 \cdot 11 \cdot 31$	**8344207**	$2^2 \cdot 3^2 \cdot 19$
69	$2 \cdot 3 \cdot 5 \cdot 23$	**8394780**	$2^2 \cdot 173$	$3^2 \cdot 7 \cdot 11$	$2 \cdot 347$
70	$2^2 \cdot 5^2 \cdot 7$	**8457180**	$2 \cdot 3^3 \cdot 13$	$19 \cdot 37$	$2^6 \cdot 11$
71	$2 \cdot 5 \cdot 71$	$3^2 \cdot 79$	$2^3 \cdot 89$	$23 \cdot 31$	$2 \cdot 3 \cdot 7 \cdot 17$
72	$2^4 \cdot 3^2 \cdot 5$	$7 \cdot 103$	$2 \cdot 19^2$	$3 \cdot 241$	$2^2 \cdot 181$
73	$2 \cdot 5 \cdot 73$	$17 \cdot 43$	$2^2 \cdot 3 \cdot 61$	**8651040**	$2 \cdot 367$
74	$2^2 \cdot 5 \cdot 37$	$3 \cdot 13 \cdot 19$	$2 \cdot 7 \cdot 53$	**8709888**	$2^3 \cdot 3 \cdot 31$
75	$2 \cdot 3 \cdot 5^3$	**8756399**	$2^4 \cdot 47$	$3 \cdot 251$	$2 \cdot 13 \cdot 29$
76	$2^3 \cdot 5 \cdot 19$	**8813847**	$2 \cdot 3 \cdot 127$	$7 \cdot 109$	$2 \cdot 191$
77	$2 \cdot 5 \cdot 7 \cdot 11$	$3 \cdot 257$	$2^2 \cdot 193$	**8881795**	$2 \cdot 3^2 \cdot 43$
78	$2^2 \cdot 3 \cdot 5 \cdot 13$	$11 \cdot 71$	$2 \cdot 17 \cdot 23$	$3^3 \cdot 29$	$2^4 \cdot 7^2$
79	$2 \cdot 5 \cdot 79$	$7 \cdot 113$	$2^3 \cdot 3^2 \cdot 11$	$13 \cdot 61$	$2 \cdot 397$
80	$2^5 \cdot 5^2$	$3^2 \cdot 89$	$2 \cdot 401$	$11 \cdot 73$	$2^2 \cdot 3 \cdot 67$
81	$2 \cdot 3^4 \cdot 5$	**9090209**	$2^2 \cdot 7 \cdot 29$	$3 \cdot 271$	$2 \cdot 11 \cdot 37$
82	$2^2 \cdot 5 \cdot 41$	**9143432**	$2 \cdot 3 \cdot 137$	**9153998**	$2 \cdot 103$
83	$2 \cdot 5 \cdot 83$	$3 \cdot 277$	$2^6 \cdot 13$	$7^2 \cdot 17$	$2 \cdot 3 \cdot 139$
84	$2^3 \cdot 3 \cdot 5 \cdot 7$	29^2	$2 \cdot 421$	$3 \cdot 281$	$2^2 \cdot 211$
85	$2 \cdot 5^2 \cdot 17$	$23 \cdot 37$	$2^2 \cdot 3 \cdot 71$	**9309490**	$2 \cdot 7 \cdot 61$
86	$2^2 \cdot 5 \cdot 43$	$3 \cdot 7 \cdot 41$	$2 \cdot 431$	**9360108**	$2 \cdot 5^3$
87	$2 \cdot 3 \cdot 5 \cdot 29$	$13 \cdot 67$	$2^3 \cdot 109$	$3^2 \cdot 97$	$2 \cdot 19 \cdot 23$
88	$2^4 \cdot 5 \cdot 11$	**9449759**	$2 \cdot 3^2 \cdot 7^2$	**9459607**	$2^2 \cdot 13 \cdot 17$
89	$2 \cdot 5 \cdot 89$	$3^4 \cdot 11$	$2^2 \cdot 223$	$19 \cdot 47$	$2 \cdot 3 \cdot 149$
90	$2^2 \cdot 3^2 \cdot 5^2$	$17 \cdot 53$	$2 \cdot 11 \cdot 41$	$3 \cdot 7 \cdot 43$	$2^3 \cdot 113$
91	$2 \cdot 5 \cdot 7 \cdot 13$	**9595184**	$2^4 \cdot 3 \cdot 19$	$11 \cdot 83$	$2 \cdot 457$
92	$2^3 \cdot 5 \cdot 23$	$3 \cdot 307$	$2 \cdot 461$	$13 \cdot 71$	$2^2 \cdot 3 \cdot 7 \cdot 11$
93	$2 \cdot 3 \cdot 5 \cdot 31$	$7^2 \cdot 19$	$2^2 \cdot 233$	$3 \cdot 311$	$2 \cdot 467$
94	$2^2 \cdot 5 \cdot 47$	**9735896**	$2 \cdot 3 \cdot 157$	$23 \cdot 41$	$2^4 \cdot 59$
95	$2 \cdot 5^2 \cdot 19$	$3 \cdot 317$	$2^3 \cdot 7 \cdot 17$	**9790929**	$2 \cdot 3^2 \cdot 53$
96	$2^6 \cdot 3 \cdot 5$	31^2	$2 \cdot 13 \cdot 37$	$3^2 \cdot 107$	$2^2 \cdot 241$
97	$2 \cdot 5 \cdot 97$	**9872192**	$2^2 \cdot 3^5$	$7 \cdot 139$	$2 \cdot 487$
98	$2^2 \cdot 5 \cdot 7^2$	$3^2 \cdot 109$	$2 \cdot 491$	**9925535**	$2^3 \cdot 3 \cdot 41$
99	$2 \cdot 3^2 \cdot 5 \cdot 11$	**9960737**	$2^5 \cdot 31$	$3 \cdot 331$	$2 \cdot 7 \cdot 71$
100	$2^3 \cdot 5^3$	$7 \cdot 11 \cdot 13$	$2 \cdot 3 \cdot 167$	$17 \cdot 59$	$2^2 \cdot 251$

n	5	6	7	8	9
50	5·101	2·11·23	3·13²	2²·127	7067178
51	5·103	2²·3·43	11·47	2·7·37	3·173
52	3·5²·7	2·263	17·31	2⁴·3·11	23²
53	5·107	2³·67	3·179	2·269	7²·11
54	5·109	2·3·7·13	7379873	2²·137	3²·61
55	3·5·37	2²·139	7458552	2·3²·31	13·43
56	5·113	2·283	3⁴·7	2³·71	7551123
57	5²·23	2⁶·3²	7611758	2·17²	3·193
58	3²·5·13	2·293	7686381	2²·3·7²	19·31
59	5·7·17	2²·149	3·199	2·13·23	7774268
60	5·11²	2·3·101	7831887	2⁵·19	3·7·29
61	3·5·41	2³·7·11	7902852	2·3·103	7916906
62	5⁴	2·313	3·11·19	2²·157	17·37
63	5·127	2²·3·53	7²·13	2·11·29	3²·71
64	3·5·43	2·17·19	8109043	2³·3⁴	11·59
65	5·131	2⁴·41	3²·73	2·7·47	8188854
66	5·7·19	2·3²·37	23·29	2²·167	3·223
67	3³·5²	2²·13²	8305887	2·3·113	7·97
68	5·137	2·7³	3·229	2⁴·43	13·53
69	5·139	2³·3·29	17·41	2·349	3·233
70	3·5·47	2·353	7·101	2²·3·59	8506462
71	5·11·13	2²·179	3·239	2·359	8567289
72	5²·29	2·3·11²	8615344	2³·7·13	3⁶
73	3·5·7²	2⁵·23	11·67	2·3²·41	8686444
74	5·149	2·373	3²·83	2²·11·17	7·107
75	5·151	2²·3³·7	8790959	2·379	3·11·23
76	3²·5·17	2·383	13·59	2⁸·3	8859263
77	5²·31	2·97	3·7·37	2·389	19·41
78	5·157	2·3·131	8959747	2²·197	3·263
79	3·5·53	2²·199	9014583	2·3·7·19	17·47
80	5·7·23	2·13·31	3·269	2³·101	9079485
81	5·163	2⁴·3·17	19·43	2·409	3²·7·13
82	3·5²·11	2·7·59	9175055	2²·3²·23	9185545
83	5·167	2²·11·19	3³·31	2·419	9237620
84	5·13²	2·3²·47	7·11²	2⁴·53	3·283
85	3²·5·19	2³·107	9329808	2·3·11·13	9339932
86	5·173	2·433	3·17²	2²·7·31	11·79
87	5³·7	2²·3·73	9429996	2·439	3·293
88	3·5·59	2·443	9479236	2³·3·37	7·127
89	5·179	2⁷·7	3·13·23	2·449	29·31
90	5·181	2·3·151	9576073	2²·227	3²·101
91	3·5·61	2²·229	7·131	2·3³·17	9633155
92	5²·37	2·463	3²·103	2⁵·29	9680157
93	5·11·17	2³·3²·13	9717396	2·7·67	3·313
94	3³·5·7	2·11·43	9763500	2²·3·79	13·73
95	5·191	2²·239	3·11·29	2·479	7·137
96	5·193	2·3·7·23	9854265	2³·11²	3·17·19
97	3·5²·13	2⁴·61	9898946	2·3·163	11·89
98	5·197	2·17·29	3·7·47	2²·13·19	23·43
99	5·199	2²·3·83	9986952	2·499	3³·37
100	3·5·67	2·503	19·53	2⁴·3²·7	0038912

n	0	1	2	3	4
100	$2^3 \cdot 5^3$	$7 \cdot 11 \cdot 13$	$2 \cdot 3 \cdot 167$	$17 \cdot 59$	$2^2 \cdot 251$
101	$2 \cdot 5 \cdot 101$	$3 \cdot 337$	$2^2 \cdot 11 \cdot 23$	**0056094**	$2 \cdot 3 \cdot 13^2$
102	$2^2 \cdot 3 \cdot 5 \cdot 17$	**0090257**	$2 \cdot 7 \cdot 73$	$3 \cdot 11 \cdot 31$	2^{10}
103	$2 \cdot 5 \cdot 103$	**0132587**	$2^3 \cdot 3 \cdot 43$	**0141003**	$2 \cdot 11 \cdot 47$
104	$2^4 \cdot 5 \cdot 13$	$3 \cdot 347$	$2 \cdot 521$	$7 \cdot 149$	$2^2 \cdot 3^2 \cdot 29$
105	$2 \cdot 3 \cdot 5^2 \cdot 7$	**0216027**	$2^2 \cdot 263$	$3^4 \cdot 13$	$2 \cdot 17 \cdot 31$
106	$2^2 \cdot 5 \cdot 53$	**0257154**	$2 \cdot 3^2 \cdot 59$	**0265333**	$2^3 \cdot 7 \cdot 19$
107	$2 \cdot 5 \cdot 107$	$3^2 \cdot 7 \cdot 17$	$2^4 \cdot 67$	$29 \cdot 37$	$2 \cdot 3 \cdot 179$
108	$2^3 \cdot 3^3 \cdot 5$	$23 \cdot 47$	$2 \cdot 541$	$3 \cdot 19^2$	$2^2 \cdot 271$
109	$2 \cdot 5 \cdot 109$	**0378248**	$2^2 \cdot 3 \cdot 7 \cdot 13$	**0386202**	$2 \cdot 547$
110	$2^2 \cdot 5^2 \cdot 11$	$3 \cdot 367$	$2 \cdot 19 \cdot 29$	**0425755**	$2^4 \cdot 3 \cdot 23$
111	$2 \cdot 3 \cdot 5 \cdot 37$	$11 \cdot 101$	$2^2 \cdot 139$	$3 \cdot 7 \cdot 53$	$2 \cdot 557$
112	$2^5 \cdot 5 \cdot 7$	$19 \cdot 59$	$2 \cdot 3 \cdot 11 \cdot 17$	**0503798**	$2^2 \cdot 281$
113	$2 \cdot 5 \cdot 113$	$3 \cdot 13 \cdot 29$	$2^2 \cdot 283$	$11 \cdot 103$	$2^3 \cdot 7$
114	$2^2 \cdot 3 \cdot 5 \cdot 19$	$7 \cdot 163$	$2 \cdot 571$	$3^2 \cdot 127$	$2^3 \cdot 11 \cdot 13$
115	$2 \cdot 5^2 \cdot 23$	**0610753**	$2^7 \cdot 3^2$	**0618293**	$2 \cdot 577$
116	$2^3 \cdot 5 \cdot 29$	$3^3 \cdot 43$	$2 \cdot 7 \cdot 83$	**0655797**	$2^2 \cdot 3 \cdot 97$
117	$2 \cdot 3^2 \cdot 5 \cdot 13$	**0685569**	$2^2 \cdot 293$	$3 \cdot 17 \cdot 23$	$2 \cdot 587$
118	$2^2 \cdot 5 \cdot 59$	**0722499**	$2 \cdot 3 \cdot 197$	$7 \cdot 13^2$	$2^5 \cdot 37$
119	$2 \cdot 5 \cdot 7 \cdot 17$	$3 \cdot 397$	$2^3 \cdot 149$	**0766404**	$2 \cdot 3 \cdot 199$
120	$2^4 \cdot 3 \cdot 5^2$	**0795430**	$2 \cdot 601$	$3 \cdot 401$	$2^2 \cdot 7 \cdot 43$
121	$2 \cdot 5 \cdot 11^2$	$7 \cdot 173$	$2^2 \cdot 3 \cdot 101$	**0838608**	$2 \cdot 607$
122	$2^2 \cdot 5 \cdot 61$	$3 \cdot 11 \cdot 37$	$2 \cdot 13 \cdot 47$	**0874265**	$2^3 \cdot 3^2 \cdot 17$
123	$2 \cdot 3 \cdot 5 \cdot 41$	**0902581**	$2^4 \cdot 7 \cdot 11$	$3^2 \cdot 137$	$2 \cdot 617$
124	$2^3 \cdot 5 \cdot 31$	$17 \cdot 73$	$2 \cdot 3^3 \cdot 23$	$11 \cdot 113$	$2^2 \cdot 311$
125	$2 \cdot 5^4$	$3^2 \cdot 139$	$2^2 \cdot 313$	$7 \cdot 179$	$2 \cdot 3 \cdot 11 \cdot 19$
126	$2^2 \cdot 3^2 \cdot 5 \cdot 7$	$13 \cdot 97$	$2 \cdot 631$	$3 \cdot 421$	$2^4 \cdot 79$
127	$2 \cdot 5 \cdot 127$	$31 \cdot 41$	$2^3 \cdot 3 \cdot 53$	$19 \cdot 67$	$2 \cdot 7^2 \cdot 13$
128	$2^8 \cdot 5$	$3 \cdot 7 \cdot 61$	$2 \cdot 641$	**1082267**	$2^2 \cdot 3 \cdot 107$
129	$2 \cdot 3 \cdot 5 \cdot 43$	**1109262**	$2^2 \cdot 17 \cdot 19$	$3 \cdot 431$	$2 \cdot 647$
130	$2^2 \cdot 5^2 \cdot 13$	**1142773**	$2 \cdot 3 \cdot 7 \cdot 31$	**1149444**	$2^3 \cdot 163$
131	$2 \cdot 5 \cdot 131$	$3 \cdot 19 \cdot 23$	$2^5 \cdot 41$	$13 \cdot 101$	$2 \cdot 3^2 \cdot 73$
132	$2^3 \cdot 3 \cdot 5 \cdot 11$	**1209028**	$2 \cdot 661$	$3^3 \cdot 7^2$	$2^2 \cdot 331$
133	$2 \cdot 5 \cdot 7 \cdot 19$	11^3	$2^2 \cdot 3^2 \cdot 37$	$31 \cdot 43$	$2 \cdot 23 \cdot 29$
134	$2^2 \cdot 5 \cdot 67$	$3^2 \cdot 149$	$2 \cdot 11 \cdot 61$	$17 \cdot 79$	$2^6 \cdot 3 \cdot 7$
135	$2 \cdot 3^3 \cdot 5^2$	$7 \cdot 193$	$2^3 \cdot 13^2$	$3 \cdot 11 \cdot 41$	$2 \cdot 677$
136	$2^4 \cdot 5 \cdot 17$	**1338581**	$2 \cdot 3 \cdot 227$	$29 \cdot 47$	$2^2 \cdot 11 \cdot 31$
137	$2 \cdot 5 \cdot 137$	$3 \cdot 457$	$2^2 \cdot 7^3$	**1376705**	$2 \cdot 3 \cdot 229$
138	$2^2 \cdot 3 \cdot 5 \cdot 23$	**1401937**	$2 \cdot 691$	$3 \cdot 461$	$2^3 \cdot 173$
139	$2 \cdot 5 \cdot 139$	$13 \cdot 107$	$2^4 \cdot 3 \cdot 29$	$7 \cdot 199$	$2 \cdot 17 \cdot 41$
140	$2^3 \cdot 5^2 \cdot 7$	$3 \cdot 467$	$2 \cdot 701$	$23 \cdot 61$	$2^2 \cdot 3^3 \cdot 13$
141	$2 \cdot 3 \cdot 5 \cdot 47$	$17 \cdot 83$	$2^2 \cdot 353$	$3^2 \cdot 157$	$2 \cdot 7 \cdot 101$
142	$2^2 \cdot 5 \cdot 71$	$7^2 \cdot 29$	$2 \cdot 3^2 \cdot 79$	**1532049**	$2^4 \cdot 89$
143	$2 \cdot 5 \cdot 11 \cdot 13$	$3^3 \cdot 53$	$2^3 \cdot 179$	**1562462**	$2 \cdot 3 \cdot 239$
144	$2^5 \cdot 3^2 \cdot 5$	$11 \cdot 131$	$2 \cdot 7 \cdot 103$	$3 \cdot 13 \cdot 37$	$2^2 \cdot 19^2$
145	$2 \cdot 5^2 \cdot 29$	**1616674**	$2^2 \cdot 3 \cdot 11^2$	**1622656**	$2 \cdot 727$
146	$2^2 \cdot 5 \cdot 73$	$3 \cdot 487$	$2 \cdot 17 \cdot 43$	$7 \cdot 11 \cdot 19$	$2^3 \cdot 3 \cdot 61$
147	$2 \cdot 3 \cdot 5 \cdot 7^2$	**1676127**	$2^6 \cdot 23$	$3 \cdot 491$	$2 \cdot 11 \cdot 67$
148	$2^3 \cdot 5 \cdot 37$	**1705551**	$2 \cdot 3 \cdot 13 \cdot 19$	**1711412**	$2^2 \cdot 7 \cdot 53$
149	$2 \cdot 5 \cdot 149$	$3 \cdot 7 \cdot 71$	$2^2 \cdot 373$	**1740598**	$2 \cdot 3^2 \cdot 83$
150	$2^2 \cdot 3 \cdot 5^3$	$19 \cdot 79$	$2 \cdot 751$	$3^2 \cdot 167$	$2^5 \cdot 47$

n	5	6	7	8	9
100	3·5·67	2·503	19·53	$2^4 \cdot 3^2 \cdot 7$	**0038912**
101	5·7·29	$2^3 \cdot 127$	$3^2 \cdot 113$	2·509	**0081742**
102	$5^2 \cdot 41$	$2 \cdot 3^3 \cdot 19$	13·79	$2^2 \cdot 257$	$3 \cdot 7^3$
103	$3^2 \cdot 5 \cdot 23$	$2^2 \cdot 7 \cdot 37$	17·61	2·3·173	**0166155**
104	5·11·19	2·523	3·349	$2^3 \cdot 131$	**0207755**
105	5·211	$2^5 \cdot 3 \cdot 11$	7·151	$2 \cdot 23^2$	3·353
106	3·5·71	2·13·41	11·97	$2^2 \cdot 3 \cdot 89$	**0289777**
107	$5^2 \cdot 43$	$2^2 \cdot 269$	3·359	$2 \cdot 7^2 \cdot 11$	13·83
108	5·7·31	2·3·181	**0362295**	$2^6 \cdot 17$	$3^2 \cdot 11^2$
109	3·5·73	$2^3 \cdot 137$	**0402066**	$2 \cdot 3^2 \cdot 61$	7·157
110	5·13·17	2·7·79	$3^3 \cdot 41$	$2^2 \cdot 277$	**0449315**
111	5·223	$2^2 \cdot 3^2 \cdot 31$	**0480532**	2·13·43	3·373
112	$3^2 \cdot 5^3$	2·563	$7^2 \cdot 23$	$2^3 \cdot 3 \cdot 47$	**0526939**
113	5·227	$2^4 \cdot 71$	3·379	2·569	17·67
114	5·229	2·3·191	31·37	$2^2 \cdot 7 \cdot 41$	3·383
115	3·5·7·11	$2^2 \cdot 17^2$	13·89	2·3·193	19·61
116	5·233	2·11·53	3·389	$2^4 \cdot 73$	7·167
117	$5^2 \cdot 47$	$2^3 \cdot 3 \cdot 7^2$	11·107	2·19·31	$3^2 \cdot 131$
118	3·5·79	2·593	**0744507**	$2^2 \cdot 3^3 \cdot 11$	29·41
119	5·239	$2^2 \cdot 13 \cdot 23$	$3^2 \cdot 7 \cdot 19$	2·599	11·109
120	5·241	$2 \cdot 3^2 \cdot 67$	17·71	$2^3 \cdot 151$	3·13·31
121	$3^5 \cdot 5$	$2^6 \cdot 19$	**0852906**	2·3·7·29	23·53
122	$5^2 \cdot 7^2$	2·613	3·409	$2^2 \cdot 307$	**0895519**
123	5·13·19	$2^2 \cdot 3 \cdot 103$	**0923697**	2·619	3·7·59
124	3·5·83	2·7·89	29·43	$2^5 \cdot 3 \cdot 13$	**0965624**
125	5·251	$2^3 \cdot 157$	3·419	2·17·37	**1000257**
126	5·11·23	2·3·211	7·181	$2^2 \cdot 317$	$3^3 \cdot 47$
127	$3 \cdot 5^2 \cdot 17$	$2^2 \cdot 11 \cdot 29$	**1061909**	$2 \cdot 3^2 \cdot 71$	**1068705**
128	5·257	2·643	$3^2 \cdot 11 \cdot 13$	$2^3 \cdot 7 \cdot 23$	**1102529**
129	5·7·37	$2^4 \cdot 3^4$	**1129400**	2·11·59	3·433
130	$3^2 \cdot 5 \cdot 29$	2·653	**1162756**	$2^2 \cdot 3 \cdot 109$	7·11·17
131	5·263	$2^2 \cdot 7 \cdot 47$	3·439	2·659	**1202448**
132	$5^2 \cdot 53$	2·3·13·17	**1228709**	$2^4 \cdot 83$	3·443
133	3·5·89	$2^3 \cdot 167$	7·191	2·3·223	13·103
134	5·269	2·673	3·449	$2^2 \cdot 337$	19·71
135	5·271	$2^2 \cdot 3 \cdot 113$	23·59	2·7·97	$3^2 \cdot 151$
136	3·5·7·13	2·683	**1357685**	$2^3 \cdot 3^2 \cdot 19$	37^2
137	$5^3 \cdot 11$	$2^5 \cdot 43$	$3^4 \cdot 17$	2·13·53	7·197
138	5·277	$2 \cdot 3^2 \cdot 7 \cdot 11$	19·73	$2^2 \cdot 347$	3·463
139	$3^2 \cdot 5 \cdot 31$	$2^2 \cdot 349$	11·127	2·3·233	**1458177**
140	5·281	2·19·37	3·7·67	$2^7 \cdot 11$	**1489110**
141	5·283	$2^3 \cdot 3 \cdot 59$	13·109	2·709	3·11·43
142	$3 \cdot 5^2 \cdot 19$	2·23·31	**1544240**	$2^2 \cdot 3 \cdot 7 \cdot 17$	**1550322**
143	5·7·41	$2^2 \cdot 359$	3·479	2·719	**1580608**
144	$5 \cdot 17^2$	2·3·241	**1604685**	$2^3 \cdot 181$	$3^2 \cdot 7 \cdot 23$
145	3·5·97	$2^4 \cdot 7 \cdot 13$	31·47	$2 \cdot 3^6$	**1640553**
146	5·293	2·733	$3^2 \cdot 163$	$2^2 \cdot 367$	13·113
147	$5^2 \cdot 59$	$2^2 \cdot 3^2 \cdot 41$	7·211	2·739	3·17·29
148	$3^3 \cdot 5 \cdot 11$	2·743	**1723110**	$2^4 \cdot 3 \cdot 31$	**1728947**
149	5·13·23	$2^3 \cdot 11 \cdot 17$	3·499	2·7·107	**1758016**
150	5·7·43	2·3·251	11·137	$2^2 \cdot 13 \cdot 29$	3·503

n	0	1	2	3	4
150	$2^2 \cdot 3 \cdot 5^3$	$19 \cdot 79$	$2 \cdot 751$	$3^2 \cdot 167$	$2^5 \cdot 47$
151	$2 \cdot 5 \cdot 151$	**1792645**	$2^3 \cdot 3^3 \cdot 7$	$17 \cdot 89$	$2 \cdot 757$
152	$2^4 \cdot 5 \cdot 19$	$3^2 \cdot 13^2$	$2 \cdot 761$	**1826999**	$2^2 \cdot 3 \cdot 127$
153	$2 \cdot 3^2 \cdot 5 \cdot 17$	**1849752**	$2^2 \cdot 383$	$3 \cdot 7 \cdot 73$	$2 \cdot 13 \cdot 59$
154	$2^2 \cdot 5 \cdot 7 \cdot 11$	$23 \cdot 67$	$2 \cdot 3 \cdot 257$	**1883659**	$2^3 \cdot 193$
155	$2 \cdot 5^2 \cdot 31$	$3 \cdot 11 \cdot 47$	$2^4 \cdot 97$	**1911715**	$2 \cdot 3 \cdot 7 \cdot 37$
156	$2^3 \cdot 3 \cdot 5 \cdot 13$	$7 \cdot 223$	$2 \cdot 11 \cdot 71$	$3 \cdot 521$	$2^2 \cdot 17 \cdot 23$
157	$2 \cdot 5 \cdot 157$	**1961762**	$2^2 \cdot 3 \cdot 131$	$11^2 \cdot 13$	$2 \cdot 787$
158	$2^2 \cdot 5 \cdot 79$	$3 \cdot 17 \cdot 31$	$2 \cdot 7 \cdot 113$	**1994809**	$2^4 \cdot 3^2 \cdot 11$
159	$2 \cdot 3 \cdot 5 \cdot 53$	$37 \cdot 43$	$2^3 \cdot 199$	$3^3 \cdot 59$	$2 \cdot 797$
160	$2^6 \cdot 5^2$	**2043913**	$2 \cdot 3^2 \cdot 89$	$7 \cdot 229$	$2^2 \cdot 401$
161	$2 \cdot 5 \cdot 7 \cdot 23$	$3^2 \cdot 179$	$2^2 \cdot 13 \cdot 31$	**2076344**	$2 \cdot 3 \cdot 269$
162	$2^2 \cdot 3^4 \cdot 5$	**2097830**	$2 \cdot 811$	$3 \cdot 541$	$2^5 \cdot 7 \cdot 29$
163	$2 \cdot 5 \cdot 163$	$7 \cdot 233$	$2^5 \cdot 3 \cdot 17$	$23 \cdot 71$	$2 \cdot 19 \cdot 43$
164	$2^3 \cdot 5 \cdot 41$	$3 \cdot 547$	$2 \cdot 821$	$31 \cdot 53$	$2^2 \cdot 3 \cdot 137$
165	$2 \cdot 3 \cdot 5^2 \cdot 11$	$13 \cdot 127$	$2^2 \cdot 7 \cdot 59$	$3 \cdot 19 \cdot 29$	$2 \cdot 827$
166	$2^2 \cdot 5 \cdot 83$	$11 \cdot 151$	$2 \cdot 3 \cdot 277$	**2208922**	$2^7 \cdot 13$
167	$2 \cdot 5 \cdot 167$	$3 \cdot 557$	$2^3 \cdot 11 \cdot 19$	$7 \cdot 239$	$2 \cdot 3^3 \cdot 31$
168	$2^4 \cdot 3 \cdot 5 \cdot 7$	41^2	$2 \cdot 29^2$	$3^2 \cdot 11 \cdot 17$	$2^4 \cdot 421$
169	$2 \cdot 5 \cdot 13^2$	$19 \cdot 89$	$2^2 \cdot 3^2 \cdot 47$	**2286570**	$2 \cdot 7 \cdot 11^2$
170	$2^2 \cdot 5^2 \cdot 17$	$3^5 \cdot 7$	$2 \cdot 23 \cdot 37$	$13 \cdot 131$	$2^3 \cdot 3 \cdot 71$
171	$2 \cdot 3^2 \cdot 5 \cdot 19$	$29 \cdot 59$	$2^4 \cdot 107$	$3 \cdot 571$	$2 \cdot 857$
172	$2^3 \cdot 5 \cdot 43$	**2357809**	$2 \cdot 3 \cdot 7 \cdot 41$	**2362853**	$2^4 \cdot 431$
173	$2 \cdot 5 \cdot 173$	$3 \cdot 577$	$2^2 \cdot 433$	**2387986**	$2 \cdot 3 \cdot 17^2$
174	$2^2 \cdot 3 \cdot 5 \cdot 29$	**2407988**	$2 \cdot 13 \cdot 67$	$3 \cdot 7 \cdot 83$	$2^4 \cdot 109$
175	$2 \cdot 5^3 \cdot 7$	$17 \cdot 103$	$2^3 \cdot 3 \cdot 73$	**2437819**	$2 \cdot 877$
176	$2^5 \cdot 5 \cdot 11$	$3 \cdot 587$	$2 \cdot 881$	$41 \cdot 43$	$2^3 \cdot 3^2 \cdot 7^2$
177	$2 \cdot 3 \cdot 5 \cdot 59$	$7 \cdot 11 \cdot 23$	$2^2 \cdot 443$	$3^2 \cdot 197$	$2 \cdot 887$
178	$2^2 \cdot 5 \cdot 89$	$13 \cdot 137$	$2 \cdot 3^4 \cdot 11$	**2511513**	$2^2 \cdot 223$
179	$2 \cdot 5 \cdot 179$	$3^2 \cdot 199$	$2^3 \cdot 7$	$11 \cdot 163$	$2 \cdot 3 \cdot 13 \cdot 23$
180	$2^3 \cdot 3^2 \cdot 5^2$	**2555137**	$2 \cdot 17 \cdot 53$	$3 \cdot 601$	$2^2 \cdot 11 \cdot 41$
181	$2 \cdot 5 \cdot 181$	**2579185**	$2^2 \cdot 3 \cdot 151$	$7^2 \cdot 37$	$2 \cdot 907$
182	$2^2 \cdot 5 \cdot 7 \cdot 13$	$3 \cdot 607$	$2 \cdot 911$	**2607867**	$2^5 \cdot 3 \cdot 19$
183	$2 \cdot 3 \cdot 5 \cdot 61$	**2626883**	$2^3 \cdot 229$	$3 \cdot 13 \cdot 47$	$2 \cdot 7 \cdot 131$
184	$2^4 \cdot 5 \cdot 23$	$7 \cdot 263$	$2 \cdot 3 \cdot 307$	$19 \cdot 97$	$2^2 \cdot 461$
185	$2 \cdot 5^2 \cdot 37$	$3 \cdot 617$	$2^2 \cdot 463$	$17 \cdot 109$	$2 \cdot 3^2 \cdot 103$
186	$2^2 \cdot 3 \cdot 5 \cdot 31$	**2697464**	$2 \cdot 7^2 \cdot 19$	$3^4 \cdot 23$	$2^3 \cdot 233$
187	$2 \cdot 5 \cdot 11 \cdot 17$	**2720738**	$2^4 \cdot 3^2 \cdot 13$	**2725378**	$2 \cdot 937$
188	$2^3 \cdot 5 \cdot 47$	$3^2 \cdot 11 \cdot 19$	$2 \cdot 941$	$7 \cdot 269$	$2^2 \cdot 3 \cdot 157$
189	$2 \cdot 3^3 \cdot 5 \cdot 7$	$31 \cdot 61$	$2^2 \cdot 11 \cdot 43$	$3 \cdot 631$	$2 \cdot 947$
190	$2^2 \cdot 5^2 \cdot 19$	**2789821**	$2 \cdot 3 \cdot 317$	$11 \cdot 173$	$2^4 \cdot 7 \cdot 17$
191	$2 \cdot 5 \cdot 191$	$3 \cdot 7^2 \cdot 13$	$2^3 \cdot 239$	**2817150**	$2 \cdot 3 \cdot 11 \cdot 29$
192	$2^7 \cdot 3 \cdot 5$	$17 \cdot 113$	$2 \cdot 31^2$	$3 \cdot 641$	$2^2 \cdot 13 \cdot 37$
193	$2 \cdot 5 \cdot 193$	**2857823**	$2^2 \cdot 3 \cdot 7 \cdot 23$	**2862319**	$2 \cdot 967$
194	$2^2 \cdot 5 \cdot 97$	$3 \cdot 647$	$2 \cdot 971$	$29 \cdot 67$	$2^3 \cdot 3^5$
195	$2 \cdot 3 \cdot 5^2 \cdot 13$	**2902573**	$2^5 \cdot 61$	$3^2 \cdot 7 \cdot 31$	$2 \cdot 977$
196	$2^3 \cdot 5 \cdot 7^2$	$37 \cdot 53$	$2 \cdot 3^2 \cdot 109$	$13 \cdot 151$	$2^2 \cdot 491$
197	$2 \cdot 5 \cdot 197$	$3^3 \cdot 73$	$2^2 \cdot 17 \cdot 29$	**2951271**	$2 \cdot 3 \cdot 7 \cdot 47$
198	$2^2 \cdot 3^2 \cdot 5 \cdot 11$	$7 \cdot 283$	$2 \cdot 991$	$3 \cdot 661$	$2^6 \cdot 31$
199	$2 \cdot 5 \cdot 199$	$11 \cdot 181$	$2^3 \cdot 3 \cdot 83$	**2995073**	$2 \cdot 997$
200	$2^4 \cdot 5^3$	$3 \cdot 23 \cdot 29$	$2 \cdot 7 \cdot 11 \cdot 13$	**3016809**	$2^2 \cdot 3 \cdot 167$

n	5	6	7	8	9
150	$5 \cdot 7 \cdot 43$	$2 \cdot 3 \cdot 251$	$11 \cdot 137$	$2^2 \cdot 13 \cdot 29$	$3 \cdot 503$
151	$3 \cdot 5 \cdot 101$	$2^2 \cdot 379$	$37 \cdot 41$	$2 \cdot 3 \cdot 11 \cdot 23$	$7^2 \cdot 31$
152	$5^2 \cdot 61$	$2 \cdot 7 \cdot 109$	$3 \cdot 509$	$2^3 \cdot 191$	$11 \cdot 139$
153	$5 \cdot 307$	$2^9 \cdot 3$	$29 \cdot 53$	$2 \cdot 769$	$3^4 \cdot 19$
154	$3 \cdot 5 \cdot 103$	$2 \cdot 773$	$7 \cdot 13 \cdot 17$	$2^2 \cdot 3^2 \cdot 43$	**1900514**
155	$5 \cdot 311$	$2^2 \cdot 389$	$3^2 \cdot 173$	$2 \cdot 19 \cdot 41$	**1928461**
156	$5 \cdot 313$	$2 \cdot 3^3 \cdot 29$	**1950690**	$2^5 \cdot 7^2$	$3 \cdot 523$
157	$3^2 \cdot 5^2 \cdot 7$	$2^3 \cdot 197$	$19 \cdot 83$	$2 \cdot 3 \cdot 263$	**1983821**
158	$5 \cdot 317$	$2 \cdot 13 \cdot 61$	$3 \cdot 23^2$	$2^2 \cdot 397$	$7 \cdot 227$
159	$5 \cdot 11 \cdot 29$	$2^2 \cdot 3 \cdot 7 \cdot 19$	**2033049**	$2 \cdot 17 \cdot 47$	$3 \cdot 13 \cdot 41$
160	$3 \cdot 5 \cdot 107$	$2 \cdot 11 \cdot 73$	**2060159**	$2^3 \cdot 3 \cdot 67$	**2065560**
161	$5 \cdot 17 \cdot 19$	$2^4 \cdot 101$	$3 \cdot 7^2 \cdot 11$	$2 \cdot 809$	**2092468**
162	$5^3 \cdot 13$	$2 \cdot 3 \cdot 271$	**2113876**	$2^2 \cdot 11 \cdot 37$	$3^2 \cdot 181$
163	$3 \cdot 5 \cdot 109$	$2^2 \cdot 409$	**2140487**	$2 \cdot 3^2 \cdot 7 \cdot 13$	$11 \cdot 149$
164	$5 \cdot 7 \cdot 47$	$2 \cdot 823$	$3^3 \cdot 61$	$2^4 \cdot 103$	$17 \cdot 97$
165	$5 \cdot 331$	$2^3 \cdot 3^2 \cdot 23$	**2193225**	$2 \cdot 829$	$3 \cdot 7 \cdot 79$
166	$3^2 \cdot 5 \cdot 37$	$2 \cdot 7^2 \cdot 17$	**2219356**	$2^2 \cdot 3 \cdot 139$	**2224563**
167	$5^2 \cdot 67$	$2^2 \cdot 419$	$3 \cdot 13 \cdot 43$	$2 \cdot 839$	$23 \cdot 73$
168	$5 \cdot 337$	$2 \cdot 3 \cdot 281$	$7 \cdot 241$	$2^3 \cdot 211$	$3 \cdot 563$
169	$3 \cdot 5 \cdot 113$	$2^5 \cdot 53$	**2296818**	$2 \cdot 3 \cdot 283$	**2301934**
170	$5 \cdot 11 \cdot 31$	$2 \cdot 853$	$3 \cdot 569$	$2^2 \cdot 7 \cdot 61$	**2327421**
171	$5 \cdot 7^3$	$2^2 \cdot 3 \cdot 11 \cdot 13$	$17 \cdot 101$	$2 \cdot 859$	$3^2 \cdot 191$
172	$3 \cdot 5^2 \cdot 23$	$2 \cdot 863$	$11 \cdot 157$	$2^6 \cdot 3^3$	$7 \cdot 13 \cdot 19$
173	$5 \cdot 347$	$2^3 \cdot 7 \cdot 31$	$3^2 \cdot 193$	$2 \cdot 11 \cdot 79$	$37 \cdot 47$
174	$5 \cdot 349$	$2 \cdot 3^2 \cdot 97$	**2422929**	$2^2 \cdot 19 \cdot 23$	$3 \cdot 11 \cdot 53$
175	$3^3 \cdot 5 \cdot 13$	$2^2 \cdot 439$	$7 \cdot 251$	$2 \cdot 3 \cdot 293$	**2452658**
176	$5 \cdot 353$	$2 \cdot 883$	$3 \cdot 19 \cdot 31$	$2^3 \cdot 13 \cdot 17$	$29 \cdot 61$
177	$5^2 \cdot 71$	$2^4 \cdot 3 \cdot 37$	**2496874**	$2 \cdot 7 \cdot 127$	$3 \cdot 593$
178	$3 \cdot 5 \cdot 7 \cdot 17$	$2 \cdot 19 \cdot 47$	**2521246**	$2^2 \cdot 3 \cdot 149$	**2526103**
179	$5 \cdot 359$	$2^2 \cdot 449$	$3 \cdot 599$	$2 \cdot 29 \cdot 31$	$7 \cdot 257$
180	$5 \cdot 19^2$	$2 \cdot 3 \cdot 7 \cdot 43$	$13 \cdot 139$	$2^4 \cdot 113$	$3^3 \cdot 67$
181	$3 \cdot 5 \cdot 11^2$	$2^3 \cdot 227$	$23 \cdot 79$	$2 \cdot 3^2 \cdot 101$	$17 \cdot 107$
182	$5^2 \cdot 73$	$2 \cdot 11 \cdot 83$	$3^2 \cdot 7 \cdot 29$	$2^2 \cdot 457$	$31 \cdot 59$
183	$5 \cdot 367$	$2^2 \cdot 3^3 \cdot 17$	$11 \cdot 167$	$2 \cdot 919$	$3 \cdot 613$
184	$3^2 \cdot 5 \cdot 41$	$2 \cdot 13 \cdot 71$	**2664669**	$2^3 \cdot 3 \cdot 7 \cdot 11$	43^2
185	$5 \cdot 7 \cdot 53$	$2^6 \cdot 29$	$3 \cdot 619$	$2 \cdot 929$	$11 \cdot 13^2$
186	$5 \cdot 373$	$2 \cdot 3 \cdot 311$	**2711443**	$2^2 \cdot 467$	$3 \cdot 7 \cdot 89$
187	$3 \cdot 5^4$	$2^2 \cdot 7 \cdot 67$	**2734643**	$2 \cdot 3 \cdot 313$	**2739268**
188	$5 \cdot 13 \cdot 29$	$2 \cdot 23 \cdot 41$	$3 \cdot 17 \cdot 37$	$2^5 \cdot 59$	**2762320**
189	$5 \cdot 379$	$2^3 \cdot 3 \cdot 79$	$7 \cdot 271$	$2 \cdot 13 \cdot 73$	$3^2 \cdot 211$
190	$3 \cdot 5 \cdot 127$	$2 \cdot 953$	**2803507**	$2^2 \cdot 3^2 \cdot 53$	$23 \cdot 83$
191	$5 \cdot 383$	$2^2 \cdot 479$	$3^3 \cdot 71$	$2 \cdot 7 \cdot 137$	$19 \cdot 101$
192	$5^2 \cdot 7 \cdot 11$	$2 \cdot 3^2 \cdot 107$	$41 \cdot 47$	$2^3 \cdot 241$	$3 \cdot 643$
193	$3^2 \cdot 5 \cdot 43$	$2^4 \cdot 11^2$	$13 \cdot 149$	$2 \cdot 3 \cdot 17 \cdot 19$	$7 \cdot 277$
194	$5 \cdot 389$	$2 \cdot 7 \cdot 139$	$3 \cdot 11 \cdot 59$	$2^2 \cdot 487$	**2898118**
195	$5 \cdot 17 \cdot 23$	$2^3 \cdot 3 \cdot 163$	$19 \cdot 103$	$2 \cdot 11 \cdot 89$	$3 \cdot 653$
196	$3 \cdot 5 \cdot 131$	$2 \cdot 983$	$7 \cdot 281$	$2^4 \cdot 3 \cdot 41$	$11 \cdot 179$
197	$5^2 \cdot 79$	$2^3 \cdot 13 \cdot 19$	$3 \cdot 659$	$2 \cdot 23 \cdot 43$	**2964458**
198	$5 \cdot 397$	$2 \cdot 3 \cdot 331$	**2981979**	$2^2 \cdot 7 \cdot 71$	$3^2 \cdot 13 \cdot 17$
199	$3 \cdot 5 \cdot 7 \cdot 19$	$2^2 \cdot 499$	**3003781**	$2 \cdot 3^3 \cdot 37$	**3008128**
200	$5 \cdot 401$	$2 \cdot 17 \cdot 59$	$3^2 \cdot 223$	$2^3 \cdot 251$	$7^2 \cdot 41$

CALCULUS

DIFFERENTIALS

$d\ ax = adx$

$d\ (u + v) = du + dv$

$d\ uv = udv + vdu$

$d\ \dfrac{u}{v} = \dfrac{vdu - udv}{v^2}$

$d\ x^n = n\ x^{n-1}dx$

$dx^y = yx^{y-1}dx + x^y \log_e x\ dy$

$d\ e^x = e^x\ dx$

$d\ e^{ax} = a\ e^{ax}dx$

$d\ a^x = a^x \log_e a\ dx$

$d\ \log_e x = x^{-1}dx$

$d\ \log_a x = x^{-1} \log_a e\ dx$

$d\ x^x = x^x\ (1 + \log_e x)\ dx$

$d\ \sin x = \cos x\ dx$

$d\ \cos x = -\sin x\ dx$

$d\ \tan x = \sec^2 x\ dx$

$d\ \cot x = -\csc^2 x\ dx$

$d\ \sec x = \tan x \sec x\ dx$

$d\ \csc x = -\cot x \cdot \csc x\ dx$

$d\ \text{vers } x = \sin x\ dx$

$d\ \sin^{-1} x = (1 - x^2)^{-\frac{1}{2}}dx$

$d\ \cos^{-1} x = -(1 - x^2)^{-\frac{1}{2}}dx$

$d\ \tan^{-1} x = (1 + x^2)^{-1}dx$

$d\ \cot^{-1} x = -(1 + x^2)^{-1}dx$

$d\ \sec^{-1} x = x^{-1}(x^2 - 1)^{-\frac{1}{2}}dx$

$d\ \csc^{-1} x = -x^{-1}(x^2 - 1)^{-\frac{1}{2}}dx$

$d\ \text{vers}^{-1} x = (2x - x^2)^{-\frac{1}{2}}\ dx$

$d\ \sinh x = \cosh x\ dx$

$d\ \cosh x = \sinh x\ dx$

$d\ \tanh x = \text{sech}^2 x\ dx$

$d\ \coth x = -\text{csch}^2 x\ dx$

$d\ \text{sech } x = -\text{sech } x \tanh x\ dx$

$d\ \text{csch } x = -\text{csch } x \coth x\ dx$

$d\ \sinh^{-1} x = (x^2 + 1)^{-\frac{1}{2}}dx$

$d\ \cosh^{-1} x = (x^2 - 1)^{-\frac{1}{2}}dx$

$d\ \tanh^{-1} x = (1 - x^2)^{-1}dx$

$d\ \coth^{-1} x = -(x^2 - 1)^{-1}dx$

$d\ \text{sech}^{-1} x = -x^{-1}(1 - x^2)^{-\frac{1}{2}}dx$

$d\ \text{csch}^{-1} x = -x^{-1}(x^2 + 1)^{-\frac{1}{2}}dx$

266

TABLE OF INTEGRALS

The following points should be observed when using this table.

1. A constant of integration is to be supplied with the answers for indefinite integrals.

2. Logarithmic expressions are to base $e = 2.71828 \cdots$, unless otherwise specified, and are to be evaluated for the absolute value of the arguments involved therein.

3. All angles are measured in radians, and inverse trigonometric functions represent principal angles.

4. If the application of a formula produces either a zero denominator or a radical involving the unit $i = \sqrt{-1}$ in the result, there is always available another form of the answer which avoids this difficulty. In many of the results, the excluded values are specified, but when such are omitted it is presumed that one can tell what these should be, especially when difficulties of the type herein mentioned are obtained.

ELEMENTARY FORMS

1. $\displaystyle\int a\,dx = ax.$

2. $\displaystyle\int a \cdot f(x)dx = a \int f(x)dx.$

3. $\displaystyle\int \phi(y)dx = \int \frac{\phi(y)}{y'}\,dy,$ where $y' = dy/dx.$

4. $\displaystyle\int (u + v)\,dx = \int u\,dx + \int v\,dx,$ where u and v are any functions of x.

5. $\displaystyle\int u\,dv = u \int dv - \int v\,du = uv - \int v\,du.$

6. $\displaystyle\int u\frac{dv}{dx}\,dx = uv - \int v\frac{du}{dx}\,dx.$

7. $\displaystyle\int x^n\,dx = \frac{x^{n+1}}{n+1},$ except $n = -1.$

8. $\displaystyle\int \frac{f'(x)\,dx}{f(x)} = \log f(x),$ $[d\,f(x) = f'(x)\,dx].$

9. $\displaystyle\int \frac{dx}{x} = \log x,$ or $\log(-x).$

10. $\displaystyle\int \frac{f'(x)\,dx}{2\sqrt{f(x)}} = \sqrt{f(x)},$ $[d\,f(x) = f'(x)\,dx].$

11. $\displaystyle\int e^x \, dx = e^x.$

12. $\displaystyle\int e^{ax} \, dx = e^{ax}/a.$

13. $\displaystyle\int b^{ax} \, dx = \frac{b^{ax}}{a \log b}.$

14. $\displaystyle\int \log x \, dx = x \log x - x.$

15. $\displaystyle\int a^x \log a \, dx = a^x.$

16. $\displaystyle\int \frac{dx}{a^2 + x^2} = \frac{1}{a} \tan^{-1}\left(\frac{x}{a}\right), \text{ or } -\frac{1}{a} \cot^{-1}\left(\frac{x}{a}\right).$

17. $\displaystyle\int \frac{dx}{a^2 - x^2} = \frac{1}{a} \tanh^{-1}\left(\frac{x}{a}\right), \text{ or } \frac{1}{2a} \log \frac{a + x}{a - x}.$

18. $\displaystyle\int \frac{dx}{x^2 - a^2} = -\frac{1}{a} \coth^{-1}\left(\frac{x}{a}\right), \text{ or } \frac{1}{2a} \log \frac{x - a}{x + a}.$

19. $\displaystyle\int \frac{dx}{\sqrt{a^2 - x^2}} = \sin^{-1}\left(\frac{x}{a}\right), \text{ or } -\cos^{-1}\left(\frac{x}{a}\right).$

20. $\displaystyle\int \frac{dx}{\sqrt{x^2 \pm a^2}} = \log\left(x + \sqrt{x^2 \pm a^2}\right).$

21. $\displaystyle\int \frac{dx}{x\sqrt{x^2 - a^2}} = \frac{1}{a} \cos^{-1}\left(\frac{a}{x}\right).$

22. $\displaystyle\int \frac{dx}{x\sqrt{a^2 \pm x^2}} = -\frac{1}{a} \log\left(\frac{a + \sqrt{a^2 \pm x^2}}{x}\right).$

23. $\displaystyle\int \frac{dx}{x\sqrt{a + bx}} = \frac{2}{\sqrt{-a}} \tan^{-1}\sqrt{\frac{a + bx}{-a}}, \text{ or}$

$$\frac{-2}{\sqrt{a}} \tanh^{-1}\sqrt{\frac{a + bx}{a}}.$$

Forms Containing $(a + bx)$

24. $\displaystyle\int (a + bx)^n \, dx = \frac{(a + bx)^{n+1}}{(n + 1)b}, \text{ except } n = -1.$

25. $\displaystyle\int x(a + bx)^n \, dx = \frac{1}{b^2(n + 2)}(a + bx)^{n+2}$

$$-\frac{a}{b^2(n + 1)}(a + bx)^{n+1}, \text{ except } n = -1 \text{ or } -2.$$

26. $\displaystyle\int x^2 (a + bx)^n \, dx = \frac{1}{b^3}\left[\frac{(a + bx)^{n+3}}{n + 3} - 2a\,\frac{(a + bx)^{n+2}}{n + 2}\right.$
$$\left. + a^2\,\frac{(a + bx)^{n+1}}{n + 1}\right].$$

27. $\displaystyle\int x^m (a + bx)^n \, dx = \frac{x^{m+1} (a + bx)^n}{m + n + 1} + \frac{an}{m + n + 1}$
$$\int x^m (a + bx)^{n-1} \, dx.$$

28. $\displaystyle\int x^m (a + bx)^n \, dx = \frac{1}{a(n + 1)}\left[-x^{m+1}(a + bx)^{n+1}\right.$
$$\left. + (m + n + 2) \int x^m (a + bx)^{n+1} \, dx\right].$$

29. $\displaystyle\int \frac{dx}{a + bx} = \frac{1}{b} \log (a + bx).$

30. $\displaystyle\int \frac{dx}{(a + bx)^2} = - \frac{1}{b\,(a + bx)}.$

31. $\displaystyle\int \frac{dx}{(a + bx)^3} = - \frac{1}{2\,b\,(a + bx)^2}.$

32. $\displaystyle\int \frac{x\,dx}{a + bx} = \frac{1}{b^2}[a + bx - a \log (a + bx)].$

33. $\displaystyle\int \frac{x\,dx}{(a + bx)^2} = \frac{1}{b^2}\left[\log (a + bx) + \frac{a}{a + bx}\right].$

34. $\displaystyle\int \frac{x\,dx}{(a + bx)^3} = \frac{1}{b^2}\left[- \frac{1}{a + bx} + \frac{a}{2(a + bx)^2}\right].$

35. $\displaystyle\int \frac{x\,dx}{(a + bx)^n} = \frac{1}{b^2}\left[\frac{-1}{(n - 2)(a + bx)^{n-2}}\right.$
$$\left. + \frac{a}{(n - 1)(a + bx)^{n-1}}\right] n \neq 1, 2.$$

36. $\displaystyle\int \frac{x^2 dx}{a + bx} = \frac{1}{b^3}\left[\frac{1}{2}(a + bx)^2 - \right.$
$$\left. 2\,a\,(a + bx) + a^2 \log (a + bx)\right].$$

37. $\displaystyle\int \frac{x^2 \, dx}{(a + bx)^2} = \frac{1}{b^3}\left[a + bx - 2\,a \log (a + bx) - \frac{a^2}{a + bx}\right].$

38. $\displaystyle\int \frac{x^2\,dx}{(a+bx)^3} = \frac{1}{b^3}\left[\log(a+bx) + \frac{2a}{a+bx} - \frac{a^2}{2(a+bx)^2}\right].$

39. $\displaystyle\int \frac{x^2\,dx}{(a+bx)^n} = \frac{1}{b^3}\left[\frac{-1}{(n-3)(a+bx)^{n-3}}\right.$

$\left.+ \frac{2a}{(n-2)(a+bx)^{n-2}} - \frac{a^2}{(n-1)(a+bx)^{n-1}}\right] n \neq 1, 2, 3.$

40. $\displaystyle\int \frac{dx}{x(a+bx)} = -\frac{1}{a}\log\frac{a+bx}{x}.$

41. $\displaystyle\int \frac{dx}{x(a+bx)^2} = \frac{1}{a(a+bx)} - \frac{1}{a^2}\log\frac{a+bx}{x}.$

42. $\displaystyle\int \frac{dx}{x^2(a+bx)} = -\frac{1}{ax} + \frac{b}{a^2}\log\frac{a+bx}{x}.$

43. $\displaystyle\int \frac{dx}{x^2(a+bx)^2} = -\frac{a+2\,bx}{a^2x\,(a+bx)} + \frac{2b}{a^3}\log\frac{a+bx}{x}.$

FORMS CONTAINING $c^2 \pm x^2$, $x^2 - c^2$

44. $\displaystyle\int \frac{dx}{c^2+x^2} = \frac{1}{c}\tan^{-1}\frac{x}{c}, \text{ or } \frac{1}{c}\sin^{-1}\frac{x}{\sqrt{c^2+x^2}}.$

45. $\displaystyle\int \frac{dx}{c^2-x^2} = \frac{1}{2c}\log\frac{c+x}{c-x}, \text{ or } \frac{1}{c}\tanh^{-1}\left(\frac{x}{c}\right).$

46. $\displaystyle\int \frac{dx}{x^2-c^2} = \frac{1}{2c}\log\frac{x-c}{x+c}, \text{ or } -\frac{1}{c}\coth^{-1}\left(\frac{x}{c}\right).$

FORMS CONTAINING $a + bx$ AND $a' + b'x$

47. $\displaystyle\int \frac{dx}{(a+bx)(a'+b'x)} = \frac{1}{ab'-a'b}\cdot\log\left(\frac{a'+b'x}{a+bx}\right).$

48. $\displaystyle\int \frac{x\,dx}{(a+bx)(a'+b'x)} = \frac{1}{ab'-a'b}\left[\frac{a}{b}\log(a+bx)\right.$

$\left.- \frac{a'}{b'}\log(a'+b'x)\right].$

49. $\displaystyle\int \frac{dx}{(a+bx)^2(a'+b'x)} = \frac{1}{ab'-a'b}\left(\frac{1}{a+bx} + \frac{b'}{ab'-a'b}\right.$

$\left.\log\frac{a'+b'x}{a+bx}\right).$

50. $\displaystyle\int \frac{x\,dx}{(a+bx)^2(a'+b'x)} = \frac{-a}{b(ab'-a'b)(a+bx)}$
$$-\frac{a'}{(ab'-a'b)^2}\log\frac{a'+b'x}{a+bx}.$$

51. $\displaystyle\int \frac{x^2\,dx}{(a+bx)^2(a'+b'x)} = \frac{a^2}{b^2(ab'-a'b)(a+bx)} +$
$$\frac{1}{(ab'-a'b)^2}\left[\frac{a'^2}{b'}\log(a'+b'x) + \frac{a(ab'-2\,a'b)}{b^2}\log(a+bx)\right].$$

52. $\displaystyle\int \frac{dx}{(a+bx)^n(a'+b'x)^m} = \frac{1}{(m-1)(ab'-a'b)}$
$$\left(\frac{-1}{(a+bx)^{n-1}(a'+b'x)^{m-1}} - (m+n-2)b\right.$$
$$\left.\int \frac{dx}{(a+bx)^n(a'+b'x)^{m-1}}\right).$$

53. $\displaystyle\int \frac{a+bx}{a'+b'x}\,dx = \frac{bx}{b'} + \frac{ab'-a'b}{b'^2}\log(a'+b'x).$

54. $\displaystyle\int \frac{(a+bx)^m\,dx}{(a'+b'x)^n} = -\frac{1}{(n-1)(ab'-a'b)}\left[\frac{(a+bx)^{m+1}}{(a'+b'x)^{n-1}}\right.$
$$\left.+ b(n-m-2)\int \frac{(a+bx)^m\,dx}{(a'+b'x)^{n-1}}\right]$$
$$= -\frac{1}{b'(n-m-1)}\left[\frac{(a+bx)^m}{(a'+b'x)^{n-1}}\right.$$
$$\left.+ m(ab'-a'b)\int \frac{(a+bx)^{m-1}\,dx}{(a'+b'x)^n}\right]$$
$$= -\frac{-1}{(n-1)b'}\left[\frac{(a+bx)^m}{(a'+b'x)^{n-1}} - mb\int \frac{(a+bx)^{m-1}\,dx}{(a'+b'x)^{n-1}}\right].$$

FORMS CONTAINING $\sqrt{a+bx}$ AND $\sqrt{a'+b'x}$ $\quad u = a+bx$
$$v = a'+b'x \quad k = ab'-a'b$$

55. $\displaystyle\int \sqrt{uv}\,dx = \frac{k+2\,bv}{4\,bb'}\sqrt{uv} - \frac{k^2}{8\,bb'}\int \frac{dx}{\sqrt{uv}}.$

56. $\displaystyle\int \frac{dx}{v\sqrt{u}} = \frac{1}{\sqrt{kb'}}\log\frac{b'\sqrt{u}-\sqrt{kb'}}{b'\sqrt{u}+\sqrt{kb'}} = \frac{2}{\sqrt{-kb'}}$
$$\tan^{-1}\frac{b'\sqrt{u}}{\sqrt{-kb'}}.$$

57. $\int \dfrac{dx}{\sqrt{uv}} = \dfrac{2}{\sqrt{bb'}} \log \left(\sqrt{bb'\, u} + b\sqrt{v}\right) = \dfrac{2}{\sqrt{-bb'}} \tan^{-1}$

$$\sqrt{\dfrac{-b'u}{bv}},$$

$$\text{or } \dfrac{2}{\sqrt{bb'}} \tanh^{-1} \sqrt{\dfrac{b'u}{bv}} = \dfrac{1}{\sqrt{-bb'}} \sin^{-1} \dfrac{2bb'\,x + a'b + ab'}{k}.$$

58. $\int \dfrac{x\,dx}{\sqrt{uv}} = \dfrac{\sqrt{uv}}{bb'} - \dfrac{ab' + a'b}{2bb'} \int \dfrac{dx}{\sqrt{uv}}.$

59. $\int \dfrac{dx}{v\sqrt{uv}} = -\dfrac{2\sqrt{u}}{k\sqrt{v}}.$

60. $\int \dfrac{\sqrt{v}\,dx}{\sqrt{u}} = \dfrac{1}{b}\sqrt{uv} - \dfrac{k}{2b} \int \dfrac{dx}{\sqrt{uv}}.$

61. $\int v^m \sqrt{u}\,dx = \dfrac{1}{(2m+3)b'} \left(2v^{m+1}\sqrt{u} + k \int \dfrac{v^m dx}{\sqrt{u}}\right).$

62. $\int \dfrac{dx}{v^m \sqrt{u}} = -\dfrac{1}{(m-1)k} \left(\dfrac{\sqrt{u}}{v^{m-1}} + \left(m - \dfrac{3}{2}\right)b \int \dfrac{dx}{v^{m-1}\sqrt{u}}\right).$

FORMS CONTAINING $(a + bx^n)$

63. $\int \dfrac{dx}{a + bx^2} = \dfrac{1}{\sqrt{ab}} \tan^{-1} \dfrac{x\sqrt{ab}}{a}.$

64. $\int \dfrac{dx}{a + bx^2} = \dfrac{1}{2\sqrt{-ab}} \log \dfrac{a + x\sqrt{-ab}}{a - x\sqrt{-ab}}, \text{ or}$

$$\dfrac{1}{\sqrt{-ab}} \tanh^{-1} \dfrac{x\sqrt{-ab}}{a}.$$

65. $\int \dfrac{x\,dx}{a + bx^2} = \dfrac{1}{2b} \log \left(x^2 + \dfrac{a}{b}\right).$

66. $\int \dfrac{x^2\,dx}{a + bx^2} = \dfrac{x}{b} - \dfrac{a}{b} \int \dfrac{dx}{a + bx^2}.$

67. $\int \dfrac{dx}{(a + bx^2)^2} = \dfrac{x}{2a(a + bx^2)} + \dfrac{1}{2a} \int \dfrac{dx}{a + bx^2}.$

68. $\int \dfrac{dx}{(a + bx^2)^{m+1}} = \dfrac{1}{2ma} \dfrac{x}{(a + bx^2)^m} + \dfrac{2m-1}{2\,ma} \int \dfrac{dx}{(a + bx^2)^m}.$

69. $\int \dfrac{x\,dx}{(a + bx^2)^{m+1}} = \dfrac{1}{2} \int \dfrac{dz}{(a + bz)^{m+1}}, \qquad [z = x^2].$

70. $\int \dfrac{x^2\,dx}{(a + bx^2)^{m+1}} = \dfrac{-x}{2\,mb(a + bx^2)^m} + \dfrac{1}{2\,mb} \int \dfrac{dx}{(a + bx^2)^m}.$

71. $\displaystyle\int \frac{dx}{x(a + bx^2)} = \frac{1}{2a} \log \frac{x^2}{a + bx^2}.$

72. $\displaystyle\int \frac{dx}{x^2(a + bx^2)} = -\frac{1}{ax} - \frac{b}{a} \int \frac{dx}{a + bx^2}.$

73. $\displaystyle\int \frac{dx}{x(a + bx^2)^{m+1}} = \frac{1}{2am(a + bx^2)^m} + \frac{1}{a} \int \frac{dx}{x(a + bx^2)^m}$

$$m \neq 0.$$

74. $\displaystyle\int \frac{dx}{x^2(a + bx^2)^{m+1}} = \frac{1}{a} \int \frac{dx}{x^2(a + bx^2)^m} - \frac{b}{a} \int \frac{dx}{(a + bx^2)^{m+1}}.$

75. $\displaystyle\int \frac{dx}{a + bx^3} = \frac{k}{3a} \left[\frac{1}{2} \log \frac{(k + x)^2}{k^2 - kx + x^2} + \sqrt{3} \tan^{-1} \right.$

$$\left. \frac{2x - k}{k \sqrt{3}} \right], \ [bk^3 = a].$$

76. $\displaystyle\int \frac{xdx}{a + bx^3} = \frac{1}{3bk} \left[\frac{1}{2} \log \frac{k^2 - kx + x^2}{(k + x)^2} + \sqrt{3} \tan^{-1} \right.$

$$\left. \frac{2x - k}{k \sqrt{3}} \right], \ [bk^3 = a].$$

77. $\displaystyle\int \frac{dx}{x(a + bx^n)} = \frac{1}{an} \log \frac{x^n}{a + bx^n}.$

78. $\displaystyle\int \frac{dx}{(a + bx^n)^{m+1}} = \frac{1}{a} \int \frac{dx}{(a + bx^n)^m} - \frac{b}{a} \int \frac{x^n dx}{(a + bx^n)^{m+1}}.$

79. $\displaystyle\int \frac{x^m dx}{(a + bx^n)^{p+1}} = \frac{1}{b} \int \frac{x^{m-n}dx}{(a + bx^n)^p} - \frac{a}{b} \int \frac{x^{m-n}dx}{(a + bx^n)^{p+1}}.$

80. $\displaystyle\int \frac{dx}{x^m(a + bx^n)^{p+1}} = \frac{1}{a} \int \frac{dx}{x^m(a + bx^n)^p} - \frac{b}{a}$

$$\int \frac{dx}{x^{m-n}(a + bx^n)^{p+1}}.$$

81. $\displaystyle\int x^m(a + bx^n)^p dx = \frac{x^{m-n+1}(a + bx^n)^{p+1}}{b(np + m + 1)} -$

$$\frac{a(m - n + 1)}{b(np + m + 1)} \int x^{m-n}(a + bx^n)^p \, dx.$$

82. $\displaystyle\int x^m(a + bx^n)^p \, dx = \frac{x^{m+1}(a + bx^n)^p}{np + m + 1} +$

$$\frac{anp}{np + m + 1} \int x^m(a + bx^n)^{p-1} \, dx.$$

83. $\int x^{m-1}(a + bx^n)^p \, dx = \dfrac{1}{b(m + np)} \left[x^{m-n}(a + bx^n)^{p+1} - \right.$
$$\left. (m - n) \, a \int x^{m-n-1}(a + bx^n)^p \, dx \right].$$

84. $\int x^{m-1}(a + bx^n)^p \, dx = \dfrac{1}{m + np} \left[x^m(a + bx^n)^p + \right.$
$$\left. npa \int x^{m-1}(a + bx^n)^{p-1} \, dx \right].$$

85. $\int x^{m-1}(a + bx^n)^p \, dx = \dfrac{1}{ma} \left[x^m(a + bx^n)^{p+1} - (m + \right.$
$$\left. np + n)b \int x^{m+n-1}(a + bx^n)^p \, dx \right].$$

86. $\int x^{m-1}(a + bx^n)^p \, dx = \dfrac{1}{an(p + 1)} \left[- x^m(a + bx^n)^{p+1} + \right.$
$$\left. (m + np + n) \int x^{m-1}(a + bx^n)^{p+1} \, dx \right].$$

Forms Containing $(a + bx + cx^2)$
$$X = a + bx + cx^2 \text{ and } q = 4 ac - b^2$$

87. $\int \dfrac{dx}{X} = \dfrac{2}{\sqrt{q}} \tan^{-1} \dfrac{2 \, cx + b}{\sqrt{q}}.$

88. $\int \dfrac{dx}{X} = \dfrac{- 2}{\sqrt{- q}} \tanh^{-1} \dfrac{2 \, cx + b}{\sqrt{- q}}.$

89. $\int \dfrac{dx}{X} = \dfrac{1}{\sqrt{- q}} \log \dfrac{2 \, cx + b - \sqrt{- q}}{2 \, cx + b + \sqrt{- q}}.$

90. $\int \dfrac{dx}{X^2} = \dfrac{2 \, cx + b}{qX} + \dfrac{2c}{q} \int \dfrac{dx}{X}.$

91. $\int \dfrac{dx}{X^3} = \dfrac{2 \, cx + b}{q} \left(\dfrac{1}{2 \, X^2} + \dfrac{3c}{qX} \right) + \dfrac{6c^2}{q^2} \int \dfrac{dx}{X}.$

92. $\int \dfrac{dx}{X^{n+1}} = \dfrac{2 \, cx + b}{nqX^n} + \dfrac{2 \, (2n - 1) \, c}{qn} \int \dfrac{dx}{X^n}.$

93. $\int \dfrac{xdx}{X} = \dfrac{1}{2c} \log X - \dfrac{b}{2c} \int \dfrac{dx}{X}.$

94. $\int \dfrac{xdx}{X^2} = - \dfrac{bx + 2a}{qX} - \dfrac{b}{q} \int \dfrac{dx}{X}.$

95. $\int \dfrac{xdx}{X^{n+1}} = - \dfrac{2 \, a + bx}{nqX^n} - \dfrac{b \, (2 \, n - 1)}{nq} \int \dfrac{dx}{X^n}.$

96. $\displaystyle\int \frac{x^2}{X}\,dx = \frac{x}{c} - \frac{b}{2\,c^2}\log X + \frac{b^2 - 2\,ac}{2\,c^2}\int \frac{dx}{X}.$

97. $\displaystyle\int \frac{x^2}{X^2}\,dx = \frac{(b^2 - 2\,ac)x + ab}{cqX} + \frac{2\,a}{q}\int \frac{dx}{X}.$

98. $\displaystyle\int \frac{x^m\,dx}{X^{n+1}} = -\frac{x^{m-1}}{(2\,n - m + 1)cX^n} - \frac{n - m + 1}{2n - m + 1}\cdot\frac{b}{c}$
$$\int \frac{x^{m-1}\,dx}{X^{n+1}} + \frac{m - 1}{2\,n - m + 1}\cdot\frac{a}{c}\int \frac{x^{m-2}\,dx}{X^{n+1}}.$$

99. $\displaystyle\int \frac{dx}{xX} = \frac{1}{2a}\log\frac{x^2}{X} - \frac{b}{2\,a}\int \frac{dx}{X}.$

100. $\displaystyle\int \frac{dx}{x^2X} = \frac{b}{2\,a^2}\log\frac{X}{x^2} - \frac{1}{ax} + \left(\frac{b^2}{2\,a^2} - \frac{c}{a}\right)\int \frac{dx}{X}.$

101. $\displaystyle\int \frac{dx}{xX^n} = \frac{1}{2a(n-1)X^{n-1}} - \frac{b}{2a}\int \frac{dx}{X^n} + \frac{1}{a}\int \frac{dx}{xX^{n-1}}.$

102. $\displaystyle\int \frac{dx}{x^mX^{n+1}} = -\frac{1}{(m-1)ax^{m-1}X^n} - \frac{n + m - 1}{m - 1}\cdot\frac{b}{a}$
$$\int \frac{dx}{x^{m-1}X^{n+1}} - \frac{2\,n + m - 1}{m - 1}\cdot\frac{c}{a}\int \frac{dx}{x^{m-2}X^{n+1}}.$$

Forms Containing $\sqrt{a + bx}$

103. $\displaystyle\int \sqrt{a + bx}\,dx = \frac{2}{3b}\sqrt{(a + bx)^3}.$

104. $\displaystyle\int x\sqrt{a + bx}\,dx = -\frac{2(2a - 3\,bx)\sqrt{(a + bx)^3}}{15\,b^2}.$

105. $\displaystyle\int x^2\sqrt{a + bx}\,dx = \frac{2(8\,a^2 - 12\,abx + 15\,b^2x^2)\sqrt{(a + bx)^3}}{105\,b^3}.$

106. $\displaystyle\int x^m\sqrt{a + bx}\,dx = \frac{2}{b(2m + 3)}\left[x^m\sqrt{(a + bx)^3}\right.$
$$\left. - ma\int x^{m-1}\sqrt{a + bx}\,dx\right].$$

107. $\displaystyle\int \frac{\sqrt{a + bx}}{x}\,dx = 2\sqrt{a + bx} + a\int \frac{dx}{x\sqrt{a + bx}}.$
(see No. 114 and No. 115).

108. $\displaystyle\int \frac{\sqrt{a + bx}}{x^2}\,dx = -\frac{\sqrt{a + bx}}{x} + \frac{b}{2}\int \frac{dx}{x\sqrt{a + bx}}.$
(see No. 114 and No. 115).

109. $\displaystyle\int \frac{\sqrt{a+bx}}{x^m} = -\frac{1}{(m-1)_a}\left[\frac{\sqrt{(a+bx)^3}}{x^{m-1}} + \frac{(2m-5)b}{2}\int \frac{\sqrt{a+bx}\,dx}{x^{m-1}}\right] m \neq 1.$

110. $\displaystyle\int \frac{dx}{\sqrt{a+bx}} = \frac{2\sqrt{a+bx}}{b}.$

111. $\displaystyle\int \frac{x\,dx}{\sqrt{a+bx}} = -\frac{2(2a-bx)}{3b^2}\sqrt{a+bx}.$

112. $\displaystyle\int \frac{x^2\,dx}{\sqrt{a+bx}} = \frac{2(8a^2-4abx+3b^2x^2)}{15b^3}\sqrt{a+bx}.$

113. $\displaystyle\int \frac{x^m\,dx}{\sqrt{a+bx}} = \frac{2x^m\sqrt{a+bx}}{(2m+1)b} - \frac{2ma}{(2m+1)b}\int \frac{x^{m-1}dx}{\sqrt{a+bx}}.$

114. $\displaystyle\int \frac{dx}{x\sqrt{a+bx}} = \frac{1}{\sqrt{a}}\log\left(\frac{\sqrt{a+bx}-\sqrt{a}}{\sqrt{a+bx}+\sqrt{a}}\right).$

115. $\displaystyle\int \frac{dx}{x\sqrt{a+bx}} = \frac{-2}{\sqrt{a}}\tanh^{-1}\sqrt{\frac{a+bx}{a}}.$

116. $\displaystyle\int \frac{dx}{x^2\sqrt{a+bx}} = -\frac{\sqrt{a+bx}}{ax} - \frac{b}{2a}\int \frac{dx}{x\sqrt{a+bx}}.$

117. $\displaystyle\int \frac{dx}{x^n\sqrt{a+bx}} = -\frac{\sqrt{a+bx}}{(n-1)ax^{n-1}} - \frac{(2n-3)b}{(2n-2)a}\int \frac{dx}{x^{n-1}\sqrt{a+bx}}.$

118. $\displaystyle\int (a+bx)^{\pm n/2}dx = \frac{2(a+bx)^{\frac{2\pm n}{2}}}{b(2\pm n)}.$

119. $\displaystyle\int x(a+bx)^{\pm n/2}dx = \frac{2}{b^2}\left[\frac{(a+bx)^{\frac{4\pm n}{2}}}{4\pm n} - \frac{a(a+bx)^{\frac{2\pm n}{2}}}{2\pm n}\right].$

120. $\displaystyle\int \frac{dx}{x(a+bx)^{m/2}} = \frac{1}{a}\int \frac{dx}{x(a+bx)^{\frac{m-2}{2}}} - \frac{b}{a}\int \frac{dx}{(a+bx)^{m/2}}.$

121. $\displaystyle\int \frac{(a+bx)^{n/2}dx}{x} = b\int (a+bx)^{\frac{n-2}{2}}dx + a\int \frac{(a+bx)^{\frac{n-2}{2}}}{x}dx.$

122. $\displaystyle\int f(x,\sqrt{a+bx})\,dx = \frac{2}{b}\int f\left(\frac{z^2-a}{b}, z\right)z\,dz$

$(z^2 = a+bx).$

Forms Containing $\sqrt{x^2 \pm a^2}$

123. $\displaystyle\int \sqrt{x^2 \pm a^2}\, dx = \frac{1}{2}[x\sqrt{x^2 \pm a^2} \pm a^2 \log(x + \sqrt{x^2 \pm a^2})].$

124. $\displaystyle\int \frac{dx}{\sqrt{x^2 \pm a^2}} = \log(x + \sqrt{x^2 \pm a^2}).$

125. $\displaystyle\int \frac{dx}{x\sqrt{x^2 - a^2}} = \frac{1}{a}\cos^{-1}\left(\frac{a}{x}\right), \text{ or } \frac{1}{a}\sec^{-1}\left(\frac{x}{a}\right).$

126. $\displaystyle\int \frac{dx}{x\sqrt{x^2 + a^2}} = -\frac{1}{a}\log\left(\frac{a + \sqrt{x^2 + a^2}}{x}\right).$

127. $\displaystyle\int \frac{\sqrt{x^2 + a^2}}{x}\, dx = \sqrt{x^2 + a^2} - a\log\left(\frac{a + \sqrt{x^2 + a^2}}{x}\right).$

128. $\displaystyle\int \frac{\sqrt{x^2 - a^2}}{x}\, dx = \sqrt{x^2 - a^2} - a\cos^{-1}\frac{a}{x}.$

129. $\displaystyle\int \frac{x\, dx}{\sqrt{x^2 \pm a^2}} = \sqrt{x^2 \pm a^2}.$

130. $\displaystyle\int x\sqrt{x^2 \pm a^2}\, dx = \frac{1}{3}\sqrt{(x^2 \pm a^2)^3}.$

131. $\displaystyle\int \sqrt{(x^2 \pm a^2)^3}\, dx = \frac{1}{4}\left[x\sqrt{(x^2 \pm a^2)^3} \pm \frac{3\,a^2x}{2}\sqrt{x^2 \pm a^2} + \frac{3\,a^4}{2}\log(x + \sqrt{x^2 \pm a^2})\right].$

132. $\displaystyle\int \frac{dx}{\sqrt{(x^2 \pm a^2)^3}} = \frac{\pm x}{a^2\sqrt{x^2 \pm a^2}}.$

133. $\displaystyle\int \frac{x\, dx}{\sqrt{(x^2 \pm a^2)^3}} = \frac{-1}{\sqrt{x^2 \pm a^2}}.$

134. $\displaystyle\int x\sqrt{(x^2 \pm a^2)^3}\, dx = \frac{1}{5}\sqrt{(x^2 \pm a^2)^5}.$

135. $\displaystyle\int x^2\sqrt{x^2 \pm a^2}\, dx = \frac{x}{4}\sqrt{(x^2 \pm a^2)^3} \mp \frac{a^2}{8}x\sqrt{x^2 \pm a^2} - \frac{a^4}{8}\log(x + \sqrt{x^2 \pm a^2}).$

136. $\displaystyle\int x^3\sqrt{x^2 + a^2}\, dx = \left(\frac{1}{5}x^2 - \frac{2}{15}a^2\right)\sqrt{(a^2 + x^2)^3}.$

137. $\int x^3 \sqrt{x^2 - a^2}\, dx = \frac{1}{5} \sqrt{(x^2 - a^2)^5} + \frac{a^2}{3} \sqrt{(x^2 - a^2)^3}.$

138. $\int \frac{x^2 dx}{\sqrt{x^2 \pm a^2}} = \frac{x}{2} \sqrt{x^2 \pm a^2} \mp \frac{a^2}{2} \log (x + \sqrt{x^2 \pm a^2}).$

139. $\int \frac{x^3 dx}{\sqrt{x^2 \pm a^2}} = \frac{1}{3} \sqrt{(a^2 \pm a^2)^3} \mp a^2 \sqrt{x^2 \pm a^2}.$

140. $\int \frac{dx}{x^2 \sqrt{x^2 \pm a^2}} = \mp \frac{\sqrt{x^2 \pm a^2}}{a^2 x}.$

141. $\int \frac{dx}{x^3 \sqrt{x^2 + a^2}} = -\frac{\sqrt{x^2 + a^2}}{2a^2 x^2} + \frac{1}{2a^3} \log \frac{a + \sqrt{x^2 + a^2}}{x}.$

142. $\int \frac{dx}{x^3 \sqrt{x^2 - a^2}} = \frac{\sqrt{x^2 - a^2}}{2a^2 x^2} + \frac{1}{2a^3} \arccos \frac{a}{x}.$

143. $\int x^2 \sqrt{(x^2 \pm a^2)^3}\, dx = \frac{x}{6} \sqrt{(x^2 \pm a^2)^5}$

$$\mp \frac{a^2 x}{24} \sqrt{(x^2 \pm a^2)^3} - \frac{a^4 x}{16} \sqrt{x^2 \pm a^2} \mp \frac{a^6}{16} \log (x + \sqrt{x^2 \pm a^2}).$$

144. $\int x^3 \sqrt{(x^2 \pm a^2)^3}\, dx = \frac{1}{7} \sqrt{(x^2 \pm a^2)^7} \mp \frac{a^2}{5} \sqrt{(x^2 \pm a^2)^5}.$

145. $\int \frac{\sqrt{x^2 \pm a^2}\, dx}{x^2} = -\frac{\sqrt{x^2 \pm a^2}}{x} + \log (x + \sqrt{x^2 \pm a^2}).$

146. $\int \frac{\sqrt{x^2 + a^2}}{x^3}\, dx = -\frac{\sqrt{x^2 + a^2}}{2x^2} - \frac{1}{2a} \log \frac{a + \sqrt{x^2 + a^2}}{x}.$

147. $\int \frac{\sqrt{x^2 - a^2}}{x^3}\, dx = -\frac{\sqrt{x^2 - a^2}}{2x^2} + \frac{1}{2a} \arccos \frac{a}{x}.$

148. $\int \frac{x^2 dx}{\sqrt{(x^2 \pm a^2)^3}} = \frac{-x}{\sqrt{x^2 \pm a^2}} + \log (x + \sqrt{x^2 \pm a^2}).$

149. $\int \frac{x^3 dx}{\sqrt{(x^2 \pm a^2)^3}} = \sqrt{x^2 \pm a^2} \pm \frac{a^2}{\sqrt{x^2 \pm a^2}}.$

150. $\int \frac{dx}{x \sqrt{(x^2 + a^2)^3}} = \frac{1}{a^2 \sqrt{x^2 + a^2}} - \frac{1}{a^3} \log \frac{a + \sqrt{x^2 + a^2}}{x}.$

151. $\int \frac{dx}{x \sqrt{(x^2 - a^2)^3}} = -\frac{1}{a^2 \sqrt{x^2 - a^2}} - \frac{1}{a^3} \arccos \frac{a}{x}.$

152. $\int \frac{dx}{x^2 \sqrt{(x^2 \pm a^2)^3}} = -\frac{1}{a^4} \left[\frac{\sqrt{x^2 \pm a^2}}{x} + \frac{x}{\sqrt{x^2 \pm a^2}} \right].$

153. $\int \dfrac{dx}{x^3 \sqrt{(x^2 + a^2)^3}} = -\dfrac{1}{2a^2x^2 \sqrt{x^2 + a^2}} - \dfrac{3}{2a^4 \sqrt{x^2 + a^2}}$
$$+ \dfrac{3}{2a^5} \log \dfrac{a + \sqrt{x^2 + a^2}}{x}.$$

154. $\int \dfrac{dx}{x^3 \sqrt{(x^2 - a^2)^3}} = \dfrac{1}{2a^2x^2 \sqrt{x^2 - a^2}} - \dfrac{3}{2a^4 \sqrt{x^2 - a^2}}$
$$- \dfrac{3}{2a^5} \text{arc cos} \dfrac{a}{x}.$$

155. $\int f(x, \sqrt{x^2 + a^2}) \, dx = a \int f(a \tan u, a \sec u) \sec^2 u \, du$
$$(x = a \tan u)$$

156. $\int f(x, \sqrt{x^2 - a^2}) \, dx = a \int f(a \sec u, a \tan u) \sec u \tan u \, du$
$$(x = a \sec u).$$

FORMS CONTAINING $\sqrt{a^2 - x^2}$

157. $\int \sqrt{a^2 - x^2} \, dx = \dfrac{1}{2} \left[x \sqrt{a^2 - x^2} + a^2 \sin^{-1}\left(\dfrac{a}{x}\right) \right].$

158. $\int \dfrac{dx}{\sqrt{a^2 - x^2}} = \sin^{-1}\left(\dfrac{x}{a}\right), \text{ or } -\cos^{-1}\left(\dfrac{x}{a}\right).$

159. $\int \dfrac{dx}{x \sqrt{a^2 - x^2}} = -\dfrac{1}{a} \log \left(\dfrac{a + \sqrt{a^2 - x^2}}{x}\right).$

160. $\int \dfrac{\sqrt{a^2 - x^2}}{x} \, dx = \sqrt{a^2 - x^2} - a \log \left(\dfrac{a + \sqrt{a^2 - x^2}}{x}\right).$

161. $\int \dfrac{x \, dx}{\sqrt{a^2 - x^2}} = -\sqrt{a^2 - x^2}.$

162. $\int x \sqrt{a^2 - x^2} \, dx = -\dfrac{1}{3} \sqrt{(a^2 - x^2)^3}.$

163. $\int \sqrt{(a^2 - x^2)^3} \, dx = \dfrac{1}{4} \left[x \sqrt{(a^2 - x^2)^3} + \dfrac{3}{2} a^2 x \right.$
$$\left. \sqrt{a^2 - x^2} + \dfrac{3}{2} a^4 \sin^{-1} \dfrac{x}{a} \right].$$

164. $\int \dfrac{dx}{\sqrt{(a^2 - x^2)^3}} = \dfrac{x}{a^2 \sqrt{a^2 - x^2}}.$

165. $\int \dfrac{x \, dx}{\sqrt{(a^2 - x^2)^3}} = \dfrac{1}{\sqrt{a^2 - x^2}}.$

166. $\int x \sqrt{(a^2 - x^2)^3} \, dx = -\dfrac{1}{5} \sqrt{(a^2 - x^2)^5}.$

167. $\int x^2 \sqrt{a^2 - x^2}\, dx = -\frac{x}{4} \sqrt{(a^2 - x^2)^3} + \frac{a^2}{8}$
$$\left(x \sqrt{a^2 - x^2} + a^2 \sin^{-1} \frac{x}{a} \right).$$

168. $\int x^3 \sqrt{a^2 - x^2}\, dx = (-\frac{1}{5}x^2 - \frac{2}{15}a^2) \sqrt{(a^2 - x^2)^3}.$

169. $\int x^2 \sqrt{(a^2 - x^2)^3}\, dx = -\frac{1}{6} x \sqrt{(a^2 - x^2)^5}$
$$+ \frac{a^2 x}{24} \sqrt{(a^2 - x^2)^3} + \frac{a^4 x}{16} \sqrt{a^2 - x^2} + \frac{a^6}{16} \text{arc} \sin \frac{x}{a}.$$

170. $\int x^3 \sqrt{(a^2 - x^2)^3}\, dx = \frac{1}{7} \sqrt{(a^2 - x^2)^7} - \frac{a^2}{5} \sqrt{(a^2 - x^2)^5}.$

171. $\int \frac{x^2\, dx}{\sqrt{a^2 - x^2}} = -\frac{x}{2} \sqrt{a^2 - x^2} + \frac{a^2}{2} \sin^{-1} \frac{x}{a}.$

172. $\int \frac{dx}{x^2 \sqrt{a^2 - x^2}} = -\frac{\sqrt{a^2 - x^2}}{a^2 x}.$

173. $\int \frac{\sqrt{a^2 - x^2}}{x^2}\, dx = -\frac{\sqrt{a^2 - x^2}}{x} - \sin^{-1} \frac{x}{a}.$

174. $\int \frac{x^2\, dx}{\sqrt{(a^2 - x^2)^3}} = \frac{x}{\sqrt{a^2 - x^2}} - \sin^{-1} \frac{x}{a}.$

175. $\int \frac{x^3\, dx}{\sqrt{a^2 - x^2}} = \frac{1}{3} \sqrt{(a^2 - x^2)^3} - a^2 \sqrt{a^2 - x^2}.$

176. $\int \frac{x^3\, dx}{\sqrt{(a^2 - x^2)^3}} = \sqrt{a^2 - x^2} + \frac{a^2}{\sqrt{a^2 - x^2}}.$

177. $\int \frac{dx}{x^3 \sqrt{a^2 - x^2}} = -\frac{\sqrt{a^2 - x^2}}{2a^2 x^2} - \frac{1}{2a^3} \log \frac{a + \sqrt{a^2 - x^2}}{x}.$

178. $\int \frac{dx}{x^2 \sqrt{(a^2 - x^2)^3}} = \frac{1}{a^4} \left[-\frac{\sqrt{a^2 - x^2}}{x} + \frac{x}{\sqrt{a^2 - x^2}} \right].$

179. $\int \frac{dx}{x^3 \sqrt{(a^2 - x^2)^3}} = -\frac{1}{2a^2 x^2 \sqrt{a^2 - x^2}} + \frac{3}{2a^4 \sqrt{a^2 - x^2}}$
$$- \frac{3}{2a^5} \log \frac{a + \sqrt{a^2 - x^2}}{x}.$$

180. $\int f(x, \sqrt{a^2 - x^2})\, dx = a \int f(a \sin u, a \cos u) \cos u\, du$
$$(x = a \sin u).$$

Forms Containing $\sqrt{a + bx + cx^2}$

$$X = a + bx + cx^2, \quad q = 4ac - b^2, \quad \text{and} \quad k = \frac{4c}{q}.$$

181. $\displaystyle\int \frac{dx}{\sqrt{X}} = \frac{1}{\sqrt{c}} \log\left(\sqrt{X} + x\sqrt{c} + \frac{b}{2\sqrt{c}}\right).$

182. $\displaystyle\int \frac{dx}{\sqrt{X}} = \frac{1}{\sqrt{c}} \sinh^{-1}\left(\frac{2cx + b}{\sqrt{4ac - b^2}}\right), \qquad \text{if } c > 0.$

183. $\displaystyle\int \frac{dx}{\sqrt{X}} = \frac{1}{\sqrt{-c}} \sin^{-1}\left(\frac{-2cx - b}{\sqrt{b^2 - 4ac}}\right), \qquad \text{if } c < 0.$

184. $\displaystyle\int \frac{dx}{X\sqrt{X}} = \frac{2(2cx + b)}{q\sqrt{X}}.$

185. $\displaystyle\int \frac{dx}{X^2\sqrt{X}} = \frac{2(2cx + b)}{3q\sqrt{X}}\left(\frac{1}{X} + 2k\right).$

186. $\displaystyle\int \frac{dx}{X^n\sqrt{X}} = \frac{2(2cx + b)\sqrt{X}}{(2n - 1)qX^n} + \frac{2k(n - 1)}{2n - 1}\int \frac{dx}{X^{n-1}\sqrt{X}}.$

187. $\displaystyle\int \sqrt{X}\, dx = \frac{(2cx + b)\sqrt{X}}{4c} + \frac{1}{2k}\int \frac{dx}{\sqrt{X}}.$

188. $\displaystyle\int X\sqrt{X}\, dx = \frac{(2cx + b)\sqrt{X}}{8c}\left(X + \frac{3}{2k}\right) + \frac{3}{8k^2}\int \frac{dx}{\sqrt{X}}.$

189. $\displaystyle\int X^2\sqrt{X}\, dx = \frac{(2cx + b)\sqrt{X}}{12c}\left(X^2 + \frac{5X}{4k} + \frac{15}{8k^2}\right) + \frac{5}{16k^3}\int \frac{dx}{\sqrt{X}}.$

190. $\displaystyle\int X^n\sqrt{X}\, dx = \frac{(2cx + b)X^n\sqrt{X}}{4(n + 1)c} + \frac{2n + 1}{2(n + 1)k}\int \frac{X^n dx}{\sqrt{X}}.$

191. $\displaystyle\int \frac{x\, dx}{\sqrt{X}} = \frac{\sqrt{X}}{c} - \frac{b}{2c}\int \frac{dx}{\sqrt{X}}.$

192. $\displaystyle\int \frac{x\, dx}{X\sqrt{X}} = -\frac{2(bx + 2a)}{q\sqrt{X}}.$

193. $\displaystyle\int \frac{x\, dx}{X^n\sqrt{X}} = -\frac{\sqrt{X}}{(2n - 1)cX^n} - \frac{b}{2c}\int \frac{dx}{X^n\sqrt{X}}.$

194. $\displaystyle \int \frac{x^2\,dx}{\sqrt{X}} = \left(\frac{x}{2\,c} - \frac{3\,b}{4\,c^2}\right)\sqrt{X} + \frac{3\,b^2 - 4\,ac}{8\,c^2}\int \frac{dx}{\sqrt{X}}.$

195. $\displaystyle \int \frac{x^2\,dx}{X\sqrt{X}} = \frac{(2\,b^2 - 4\,ac)x + 2\,ab}{cq\sqrt{X}} + \frac{1}{c}\int \frac{dx}{\sqrt{X}}.$

196. $\displaystyle \int \frac{x^2\,dx}{X^n\sqrt{X}} = \frac{(2\,b^2 - 4\,ac)x + 2\,ab}{(2n-1)\,cq\,X^{n-1}\sqrt{X}} +$

$$\frac{4\,ac + (2\,n - 3)b^2}{(2n-1)\,cq}\int \frac{dx}{X^{n-1}\sqrt{X}}.$$

197. $\displaystyle \int \frac{x^3\,dx}{\sqrt{X}} = \left(\frac{x^2}{3\,c} - \frac{5\,bx}{12\,c^2} + \frac{5\,b^2}{8\,c^3} - \frac{2\,a}{3\,c^2}\right)\sqrt{X} +$

$$\left(\frac{3}{4}\frac{ab}{c^2} - \frac{5\,b^3}{16\,c^3}\right)\int \frac{dx}{\sqrt{X}}.$$

198. $\displaystyle \int x\sqrt{X}\,dx = \frac{X\sqrt{X}}{3\,c} - \frac{b}{2\,c}\int \sqrt{X}\,dx.$

199. $\displaystyle \int x\,X\sqrt{X}\,dx = \frac{X^2\sqrt{X}}{5\,c} - \frac{b}{2\,c}\int X\sqrt{X}\,dx.$

200. $\displaystyle \int \frac{x\,X^n\,dx}{\sqrt{X}} = \frac{X^n\sqrt{X}}{(2n+1)c} - \frac{b}{2\,c}\int \frac{X^n\,dx}{\sqrt{X}}.$

201. $\displaystyle \int x^2\sqrt{X}\,dx = \left(x - \frac{5\,b}{6\,c}\right)\frac{X\sqrt{X}}{4\,c} + \frac{5\,b^2 - 4\,ac}{16\,c^2}\int \sqrt{X}\,dx.$

202. $\displaystyle \int \frac{dx}{x\sqrt{X}} = -\frac{1}{\sqrt{a}}\log\left(\frac{\sqrt{X} + \sqrt{a}}{x} + \frac{b}{2\sqrt{a}}\right),$ if $a > 0$.

203. $\displaystyle \int \frac{dx}{x\sqrt{X}} = \frac{1}{\sqrt{-a}}\sin^{-1}\left(\frac{bx + 2\,a}{x\sqrt{b^2 - 4\,ac}}\right),$ if $a < 0$.

204. $\displaystyle \int \frac{dx}{x\sqrt{X}} = -\frac{2\sqrt{X}}{bx},$ if $a = 0$.

205. $\displaystyle \int \frac{dx}{x^2\sqrt{X}} = -\frac{\sqrt{X}}{ax} - \frac{b}{2\,a}\int \frac{dx}{x\sqrt{X}}.$

206. $\displaystyle \int \frac{\sqrt{X}\,dx}{x} = \sqrt{X} + \frac{b}{2}\int \frac{dx}{\sqrt{X}} + a\int \frac{dx}{x\sqrt{X}}.$

207. $\displaystyle \int \frac{\sqrt{X}\,dx}{x^2} = -\frac{\sqrt{X}}{x} + \frac{b}{2}\int \frac{dx}{x\sqrt{X}} + c\int \frac{dx}{\sqrt{X}}.$

Forms Involving $\sqrt{2ax - x^2}$

208. $\int \sqrt{2\,ax - x^2}\, dx = \frac{1}{2}\left[(x - a)\sqrt{2\,ax - x^2} + \right.$
$$\left. a^2 \sin^{-1}(x - a)/a\right].$$

209. $\int \dfrac{dx}{\sqrt{2\,ax - x^2}} = \cos^{-1}\left(\dfrac{a - x}{a}\right).$

210. $\int x^n \sqrt{2ax - x^2}\, dx = -\dfrac{x^{n-1}(2ax - x^2)^{\frac{3}{2}}}{n + 2}$
$$+ \frac{(2n + 1)a}{n + 2}\int x^{n-1}\sqrt{2ax - x^2}\, dx \quad n \neq -2.$$

211. $\int \dfrac{\sqrt{2ax - x^2}}{x^n}\, dx = \dfrac{(2ax - x^2)^{\frac{3}{2}}}{(3 - 2n)ax^n}$
$$+ \frac{n - 3}{(2n - 3)a}\int \frac{\sqrt{2ax - x^2}}{x^{n-1}}\, dx \quad n \neq \frac{3}{2}.$$

212. $\int \dfrac{x^n dx}{\sqrt{2ax - x^2}} = \dfrac{-x^{n-1}\sqrt{2ax - x^2}}{n}$
$$+ \frac{a(2n - 1)}{n}\int \frac{x^{n-1}}{\sqrt{2ax - x^2}}\, dx \quad n \neq 0.$$

213. $\int \dfrac{dx}{x^n \sqrt{2ax - x^2}} = \dfrac{\sqrt{2ax - x^2}}{a(1 - 2n)\,x^n}$
$$+ \frac{n - 1}{(2n - 1)a}\int \frac{dx}{x^{n-1}\sqrt{2ax - x^2}} \quad n \neq \frac{1}{2}.$$

214. $\int \dfrac{dx}{(2ax - x^2)^{\frac{3}{2}}} = \dfrac{x - a}{a^2\sqrt{2ax - x^2}}.$

215. $\int \dfrac{x\, dx}{(2ax - x^2)^{\frac{3}{2}}} = \dfrac{x}{a\sqrt{2ax - x^2}}.$

216. $\int \dfrac{dx}{\sqrt{2ax + x^2}} = \log(x + a + \sqrt{2ax + x^2}).$

Miscellaneous Algebraic Forms

217. $\int \sqrt{ax^2 + c}\, dx = \dfrac{x}{2}\sqrt{ax^2 + c} + \dfrac{c}{2\sqrt{a}}\log(x\sqrt{a} + \right.$
$$\sqrt{ax^2 + c}), \quad [a > 0],$$
$$= \frac{x}{2}\sqrt{ax^2 + c} + \frac{c}{2\sqrt{-a}}\sin^{-1}\left(x\sqrt{\frac{-a}{c}}\right), \quad [a < 0].$$

218. $\int \dfrac{dx}{\sqrt{a + bx} \cdot \sqrt{a' + b'x}} = \dfrac{2}{\sqrt{-bb'}} \tan^{-1} \sqrt{\dfrac{-b'(a + bx)}{b(a' + b'x)}}.$

219. $\int \sqrt{\dfrac{1 + x}{1 - x}}\, dx = \sin^{-1} x - \sqrt{1 - x^2}.$

220. $\int \dfrac{dx}{\sqrt{a \pm 2bx + cx^2}} = \dfrac{1}{\sqrt{c}} \log (\pm b + cx +$
$$\sqrt{c}\, \sqrt{a \pm 2bx + cx^2}).$$

221. $\int \dfrac{dx}{\sqrt{a \pm 2bx - cx^2}} = \dfrac{1}{\sqrt{c}} \sin^{-1} \dfrac{cx \mp b}{\sqrt{b^2 + ac}}.$

222. $\int \dfrac{x\,dx}{\sqrt{a \pm 2bx + cx^2}} = \dfrac{1}{c} \sqrt{a \pm 2bx + cx^2} -$
$$\dfrac{b}{\sqrt{c^3}} \log (\pm b + cx + \sqrt{c}\, \sqrt{a \pm 2bx + cx^2}).$$

223. $\int \dfrac{x\,dx}{\sqrt{a \pm 2bx - cx^2}} = \dfrac{1}{c} \sqrt{a \pm 2bx - cx^2} \pm$
$$\dfrac{b}{\sqrt{c^3}} \sin^{-1} \dfrac{cx \mp b}{\sqrt{b^2 + ac}}.$$

224. $\int \sin x\, dx = - \cos x,$ or versin $x.$

225. $\int \cos x\, dx = \sin x,$ or $-$ coversin $x.$

226. $\int \tan x\, dx = - \log \cos x.$

227. $\int \cot x\, dx = \log \sin x.$

228. $\int \sec x\, dx = \log (\sec x + \tan x) = \log \tan \left(\dfrac{\pi}{4} + \dfrac{x}{2} \right).$

229. $\int \csc x\, dx = \log (\csc x - \cot x) = \log \tan \dfrac{x}{2}.$

230. $\int \sin^2 x\, dx = - \tfrac{1}{2} \cos x \sin x + \tfrac{1}{2} x = \tfrac{1}{2} x - \tfrac{1}{4} \sin 2x.$

231. $\int \sin^3 x\, dx = - \tfrac{1}{3} \cos x (\sin^2 x + 2).$

232. $\int \sin^n x\, dx = - \dfrac{\sin^{n-1} x \cos x}{n} + \dfrac{n - 1}{n} \int \sin^{n-2} x\, dx.$

INTEGRALS

233. $\int \cos^2 x \, dx = \frac{1}{2} \sin x \cos x + \frac{1}{2} x = \frac{1}{2} x + \frac{1}{4} \sin 2x.$

234. $\int \cos^3 x \, dx = \frac{1}{3} \sin x \, (\cos^2 x + 2).$

235. $\int \cos^n x \, dx = \frac{1}{n} \cos^{n-1} x \sin x + \frac{n-1}{n} \int \cos^{n-2} x \, dx.$

236. $\int \sin \frac{x}{a} \, dx = - a \cos \frac{x}{a}.$

237. $\int \cos \frac{x}{a} \, dx = a \sin \frac{x}{a}.$

238. $\int \sin (a + bx) \, dx = - \frac{1}{b} \cos (a + bx).$

239. $\int \cos (a + bx) \, dx = \frac{1}{b} \sin (a + bx).$

240. $\int \frac{dx}{\sin x} = \int \csc x \, dx = \log (\csc x - \cot x)$
$$= - \frac{1}{2} \log \frac{1 + \cos x}{1 - \cos x} = \log \tan \frac{x}{2}.$$

241. $\int \frac{dx}{\cos x} = \int \sec x \, dx = \log (\sec x + \tan x)$
$$= \frac{1}{2} \log \left(\frac{1 + \sin x}{1 - \sin x} \right) = \log \tan \left(\frac{\pi}{4} + \frac{x}{2} \right).$$

242. $\int \frac{dx}{\cos^2 x} = \int \sec^2 x \, dx = \tan x.$

243. $\int \frac{dx}{\cos^n x} = \frac{1}{n-1} \cdot \frac{\sin x}{\cos^{n-1} x} + \frac{n-2}{n-1} \int \frac{dx}{\cos^{n-2} x}.$

244. $\int \frac{dx}{1 \pm \sin x} = \mp \tan \left(\frac{\pi}{4} \mp \frac{x}{2} \right).$

245. $\int \frac{dx}{1 + \cos x} = \tan \frac{x}{2}.$

246. $\int \frac{dx}{1 - \cos x} = - \cot \frac{x}{2}.$

247. $\int \frac{dx}{a + b \sin x} = \frac{2}{\sqrt{a^2 - b^2}} \tan^{-1} \frac{a \tan \frac{1}{2} x + b}{\sqrt{a^2 - b^2}}$
$$= \frac{1}{\sqrt{b^2 - a^2}} \log \frac{a \tan \frac{1}{2} x + b - \sqrt{b^2 - a^2}}{a \tan \frac{1}{2} x + b + \sqrt{b^2 - a^2}}.$$

248. $\int \dfrac{dx}{a + b \cos x} = \dfrac{2}{\sqrt{a^2 - b^2}} \tan^{-1} \dfrac{\sqrt{a^2 - b^2} \tan \frac{1}{2} x}{a + b}$

$$= \dfrac{1}{\sqrt{b^2 - a^2}} \log \left(\dfrac{\sqrt{b^2 - a^2} \tan \frac{1}{2} x + a + b}{\sqrt{b^2 - a^2} \tan \frac{1}{2} x - a - b} \right).$$

249. $\int \dfrac{dx}{a + b \cos x + c \cos x}$

$$= \begin{cases} \dfrac{1}{\sqrt{b^2 + c^2 - a^2}} \log \dfrac{b - \sqrt{b^2 + c^2 - a^2} + (a - c) \tan \frac{x}{2}}{b + \sqrt{b^2 + c^2 - a^2} + (a - c) \tan \frac{x}{2}} \\ \qquad\qquad\qquad\qquad\qquad\qquad \text{if } a^2 < b^2 + c^2. \\[2em] \dfrac{2}{\sqrt{a^2 - b^2 - c^2}} \tan^{-1} \dfrac{b + (a - c) \tan \frac{x}{2}}{\sqrt{a^2 - b^2 - c^2}} \\ \qquad\qquad\qquad\qquad\qquad\qquad \text{if } a^2 > b^2 + c^2. \end{cases}$$

250. $\int \sqrt{1 - \cos x}\; dx = -2 \sqrt{2} \cos \dfrac{x}{2}.$

251. $\int \sqrt{1 + \cos x}\; dx = 2 \sqrt{2} \sin \dfrac{x}{2}.$

252. $\int \sin mx \sin nx\; dx = \dfrac{\sin (m - n) x}{2(m - n)} - \dfrac{\sin (m + n) x}{2(m + n)},$
$$[m^2 \neq n^2].$$

253. $\int x \sin^2 x\; dx = \dfrac{x^2}{4} - \dfrac{x \sin 2x}{4} - \dfrac{\cos 2x}{8}.$

254. $\int x^2 \sin^2 x\; dx = \dfrac{x^3}{6} - \left(\dfrac{x^2}{4} - \dfrac{1}{8} \right) \sin 2x - \dfrac{x \cos 2x}{4}.$

255. $\int x \sin^3 x\; dx = \dfrac{x \cos 3x}{12} - \dfrac{\sin 3x}{36} - \dfrac{3}{4} x \cos x + \dfrac{3}{4} \sin x.$

256. $\int \sin^4 x\; dx = \dfrac{3x}{8} - \dfrac{\sin 2x}{4} + \dfrac{\sin 4x}{32}.$

257. $\int \cos mx \cos nx\; dx = \dfrac{\sin (m - n)x}{2(m - n)} + \dfrac{\sin (m + n)x}{2(m + n)},$
$$[m^2 \neq n^2]$$

258. $\int x \cos^2 x\; dx = \dfrac{x^2}{4} + \dfrac{x \sin 2x}{4} + \dfrac{\cos 2x}{8}.$

259. $\displaystyle\int x^2 \cos^2 x \, dx = \frac{x^3}{6} + \left(\frac{x^2}{4} - \frac{1}{8}\right) \sin 2x + \frac{x \cos 2x}{4}.$

260. $\displaystyle\int x \cos^3 x \, dx = \frac{x \sin 3x}{12} + \frac{\cos 3x}{36} + \frac{3}{4} x \sin x + \frac{3}{4} \cos x.$

261. $\displaystyle\int \cos^4 x \, dx = \frac{3x}{8} + \frac{\sin 2x}{4} + \frac{\sin 4x}{32}.$

262. $\displaystyle\int \frac{\sin x \, dx}{x^m} = -\frac{\sin x}{(m-1)\, x^{m-1}} + \frac{1}{m-1} \int \frac{\cos x \, dx}{x^{m-1}}.$

263. $\displaystyle\int \frac{\cos x \, dx}{x^m} = -\frac{\cos x}{(m-1)x^{m-1}} - \frac{1}{m-1} \int \frac{\sin x \, dx}{x^{m-1}}.$

264. $\displaystyle\int \tan^3 x \, dx = \tfrac{1}{2} \tan^2 x + \log \cos x.$

265. $\displaystyle\int \tan^4 x \, dx = \tfrac{1}{3} \tan^3 x - \tan x + x.$

266. $\displaystyle\int \cot^3 x \, dx = -\tfrac{1}{2} \cot^2 x - \log \sin x.$

267. $\displaystyle\int \cot^4 x \, dx = -\tfrac{1}{3} \cot^3 x + \cot x + x.$

268. $\displaystyle\int \cot^n x \, dx = -\frac{\cot^{n-1} x}{n-1} - \int \cot^{n-2} x \, dx,$ $\qquad [n \neq 1].$

269. $\displaystyle\int \sin x \cos x \, dx = \tfrac{1}{2} \sin^2 x.$

270. $\displaystyle\int \sin mx \cos nx \, dx = -\frac{\cos(m-n)x}{2(m-n)} - \frac{\cos(m+n)x}{2(m+n)}.$

271. $\displaystyle\int \sin^2 x \cos^2 x \, dx = -\tfrac{1}{8}(\tfrac{1}{4} \sin 4x - x).$

272. $\displaystyle\int \sin x \cos^m x \, dx = -\frac{\cos^{m+1} x}{m+1}.$

273. $\displaystyle\int \sin^m x \cos x \, dx = \frac{\sin^{m+1} x}{m+1}.$

274. $\displaystyle\int \cos^m x \sin^n x \, dx = \frac{\cos^{m-1} x \, \sin^{n+1} x}{m+n} +$

$$\frac{m-1}{m+n} \int \cos^{m-2} x \sin^n x \, dx.$$

275. $\displaystyle\int \cos^m x \sin^n x \, dx = -\frac{\sin^{n-1} x \cos^{m+1} x}{m+n} +$
$$\frac{n-1}{m+n}\int \cos^m x \sin^{n-2} x \, dx.$$

276. $\displaystyle\int \frac{\cos^m x \, dx}{\sin^n x} = -\frac{\cos^{m+1} x}{(n-1)\sin^{n-1} x} -$
$$\frac{m-n+2}{n-1}\int \frac{\cos^m x \, dx}{\sin^{n-2} x}.$$

277. $\displaystyle\int \frac{\cos^m x \, dx}{\sin^n x} = \frac{\cos^{m-1} x}{(m-n)\sin^{n-1} x} + \frac{m-1}{m-n}\int \frac{\cos^{m-2} x \, dx}{\sin^n x}.$

278. $\displaystyle\int \frac{\sin^m x \, dx}{\cos^n x} = -\int \frac{\cos^m\left(\frac{\pi}{2}-x\right) d\left(\frac{\pi}{2}-x\right)}{\sin^n\left(\frac{\pi}{2}-x\right)}.$

279. $\displaystyle\int \frac{\sin x \, dx}{\cos^2 x} = \frac{1}{\cos x} = \sec x.$

280. $\displaystyle\int \frac{\sin^2 x \, dx}{\cos x} = -\sin x + \log\tan\left(\frac{\pi}{4}+\frac{x}{2}\right).$

281. $\displaystyle\int \frac{\cos x \, dx}{\sin^2 x} = \frac{-1}{\sin x} = -\operatorname{cosec} x.$

282. $\displaystyle\int \frac{dx}{\sin x \cos x} = \log\tan x.$

283. $\displaystyle\int \frac{dx}{\sin x \cos^2 x} = \frac{1}{\cos x} + \log\tan\frac{x}{2}.$

284. $\displaystyle\int \frac{dx}{\sin x \cos^n x} = \frac{1}{(n-1)\cos^{n-1} x} + \int \frac{dx}{\sin x \cos^{n-2} x},$
$$[n \neq 1].$$

285. $\displaystyle\int \frac{dx}{\sin^2 x \cos x} = -\frac{1}{\sin x} + \log\tan\left(\frac{\pi}{4}+\frac{x}{2}\right).$

286. $\displaystyle\int \frac{dx}{\sin^2 x \cos^2 x} = -2\cot 2x.$

287. $\displaystyle\int \frac{dx}{\sin^m x \cos^n x} = -\frac{1}{m-1}\cdot\frac{1}{\sin^{m-1} x \cdot \cos^{n-1} x} +$
$$\frac{m+n-2}{m-1}\int \frac{dx}{\sin^{m-2} x \cdot \cos^n x}.$$

288. $\int \dfrac{dx}{\sin^m x} = -\dfrac{1}{m-1} \cdot \dfrac{\cos x}{\sin^{m-1} x} + \dfrac{m-2}{m-1} \int \dfrac{dx}{\sin^{m-2} x}.$

289. $\int \dfrac{dx}{\sin^2 x} = -\cot x.$

---

290. $\int \tan^2 x \, dx = \tan x - x.$

291. $\int \tan^n x \, dx = \dfrac{\tan^{n-1} x}{n-1} - \int \tan^{n-2} x \, dx.$

292. $\int \cot^2 x \, dx = -\cot x - x.$

293. $\int \cot^n x \, dx = -\dfrac{\cot^{n-1} x}{n-1} - \int \cot^{n-2} x \, dx.$

294. $\int \sec^2 x \, dx = \tan x.$

295. $\int \sec^n x \, dx = \int \dfrac{dx}{\cos^n x}.$

296. $\int \csc^2 x \, dx = -\cot x.$

297. $\int \csc^n x \, dx = \int \dfrac{dx}{\sin^n x}.$

---

298. $\int x \sin x \, dx = \sin x - x \cos x.$

299. $\int x^2 \sin x \, dx = 2 x \sin x - (x^2 - 2) \cos x.$

300. $\int x^3 \sin x \, dx = (3 x^2 - 6) \sin x - (x^3 - 6 x) \cos x.$

301. $\int x^m \sin x \, dx = - x^m \cos x + m \int x^{m-1} \cos x \, dx.$

302. $\int x \cos x \, dx = \cos x + x \sin x.$

303. $\int x^2 \cos x \, dx = 2 x \cos x + (x^2 - 2) \sin x.$

304. $\int x^3 \cos x \, dx = (3 x^2 - 6) \cos x + (x^3 - 6 x) \sin x.$

305. $\displaystyle\int x^m \cos x \, dx = x^m \sin x - m \int x^{m-1} \sin x \, dx.$

306. $\displaystyle\int \frac{\sin x}{x} \, dx = x - \frac{x^3}{3 \cdot 3!} + \frac{x^5}{5 \cdot 5!} - \frac{x^7}{7 \cdot 7!} + \frac{x^9}{9 \cdot 9!} \cdots$

307. $\displaystyle\int \frac{\cos x}{x} \, dx = \log x - \frac{x^2}{2 \cdot 2!} + \frac{x^4}{4 \cdot 4!} - \frac{x^6}{6 \cdot 6!} + \frac{x^8}{8 \cdot 8!} \cdots$

---

308. $\displaystyle\int \sin^{-1} x \, dx = x \sin^{-1} x + \sqrt{1 - x^2}.$

309. $\displaystyle\int \cos^{-1} x \, dx = x \cos^{-1} x - \sqrt{1 - x^2}.$

310. $\displaystyle\int \tan^{-1} x \, dx = x \tan^{-1} x - \tfrac{1}{2} \log (1 + x^2).$

311. $\displaystyle\int \cot^{-1} x \, dx = x \cot^{-1} x + \tfrac{1}{2} \log (1 + x^2).$

312. $\displaystyle\int \sec^{-1} x \, dx = x \sec^{-1} x - \log (x + \sqrt{x^2 - 1}).$

313. $\displaystyle\int \csc^{-1} x \, dx = x \csc^{-1} x + \log (x + \sqrt{x^2 - 1}).$

314. $\displaystyle\int \mathrm{vers}^{-1} x \, dx = (x - 1) \, \mathrm{vers}^{-1} x + \sqrt{2x - x^2}.$

315. $\displaystyle\int \sin^{-1} \frac{x}{a} \, dx = x \sin^{-1} \frac{x}{a} + \sqrt{a^2 - x^2}.$

316. $\displaystyle\int \cos^{-1} \frac{x}{a} \, dx = x \cos^{-1} \frac{x}{a} - \sqrt{a^2 - x^2}.$

317. $\displaystyle\int \tan^{-1} \frac{x}{a} \, dx = x \tan^{-1} \frac{x}{a} - \frac{a}{2} \log (a^2 + x^2).$

318. $\displaystyle\int \cot^{-1} \frac{x}{a} \, dx = x \cot^{-1} \frac{x}{a} + \frac{a}{2} \log (a^2 + x^2).$

319. $\displaystyle\int (\sin^{-1} x)^2 \, dx = x \, (\sin^{-1} x)^2 - 2x + 2 \sqrt{1 - x^2} \, (\sin^{-1} x).$

320. $\displaystyle\int (\cos^{-1} x)^2 \, dx = x \, (\cos^{-1} x)^2 - 2x - 2 \sqrt{1 - x^2} \, (\cos^{-1} x).$

321. $\displaystyle\int x \cdot \sin^{-1} x \, dx = \tfrac{1}{4} \left[(2 x^2 - 1) \sin^{-1} x + x \sqrt{1 - x^2} \right].$

322. $\displaystyle \int x^n \sin^{-1} x \, dx = \frac{x^{n+1} \sin^{-1} x}{n+1} - \frac{1}{n+1} \int \frac{x^{n+1} \, dx}{\sqrt{1-x^2}}.$

323. $\displaystyle \int x^n \cos^{-1} x \, dx = \frac{x^{n+1} \cos^{-1} x}{n+1} + \frac{1}{n+1} \int \frac{x^{n+1} \, dx}{\sqrt{1-x^2}}.$

324. $\displaystyle \int x^n \tan^{-1} x \, dx = \frac{x^{n+1} \tan^{-1} x}{n+1} - \frac{1}{n+1} \int \frac{x^{n+1} \, dx}{1+x^2}.$

325. $\displaystyle \int \frac{\sin^{-1} x \, dx}{x^2} = \log\left(\frac{1-\sqrt{1-x^2}}{x}\right) - \frac{\sin^{-1} x}{x}.$

326. $\displaystyle \int \frac{\tan^{-1} x \, dx}{x^2} = \log x - \frac{1}{2}\log(1+x^2) - \frac{\tan^{-1} x}{x}.$

327. $\displaystyle \int f(\sin x) \, dx = 2\int f\left(\frac{2z}{1+z^2}\right) \cdot \frac{dz}{1+z^2}; \left(z = \tan\frac{x}{2}\right).$

328. $\displaystyle \int f(\cos x) \, dx = 2\int f\left(\frac{1-z^2}{1+z^2}\right) \frac{dz}{1+z^2}; \left(z = \tan\frac{x}{2}\right).$

329. $\displaystyle \int f(\sin x) \, dx = \int f(u) \frac{du}{\sqrt{1-u^2}}; \ (u = \sin x).$

330. $\displaystyle \int f(\cos x) \, dx = -\int f(u) \frac{du}{\sqrt{1-u^2}}; \ (u = \cos x).$

331. $\displaystyle \int f(\sin x, \cos x) \, dx = \int f(u, \sqrt{1-u^2}) \frac{du}{\sqrt{1-u^2}};$
$$(u = \sin x).$$

332. $\displaystyle \int f(\sin x, \cos x) \, dx = 2\int f\left(\frac{2z}{1+z^2}, \frac{1-z^2}{1+z^2}\right) \frac{dz}{1+z^2};$
$$\left(z = \tan\frac{x}{2}\right).$$

333. $\displaystyle \int \frac{dx}{a + b\tan x} = \frac{1}{a^2+b^2}\left[ax + b\log(a\cos x + b\sin x)\right].$

334. $\displaystyle \int \frac{dx}{a + b\cot x} = \frac{1}{a^2+b^2}\left[ax - b\log(a\sin x + b\cos x)\right].$

LOGARITHMIC FORMS

335. $\displaystyle \int \log x \, dx = x\log x - x.$

336. $\displaystyle \int x\log x \, dx = \frac{x^2}{2}\log x - \frac{x^2}{4}.$

337. $\int x^2 \log x \, dx = \dfrac{x^3}{3} \log x - \dfrac{x^3}{9}.$

338. $\int x^p \log (ax) \, dx = \dfrac{x^{p+1}}{p+1} \log (ax) - \dfrac{x^{p+1}}{(p+1)^2}$ $\quad [p \neq -1].$

339. $\int (\log x)^2 \, dx = x \, (\log x)^2 - 2x \log x + 2x.$

340. $\int (\log x)^n \, dx = x \, (\log x)^n - n \int (\log x)^{n-1} \, dx, \quad [n \neq -1].$

341. $\int \dfrac{(\log x)^n}{x} \, dx = \dfrac{1}{n+1} \, (\log x)^{n+1}.$

342. $\int \dfrac{dx}{\log x} = \log (\log x) + \log x + \dfrac{(\log x)^2}{2 \cdot 2!} + \dfrac{(\log x)^3}{3 \cdot 3!} + \cdots$

343. $\int \dfrac{dx}{x \log x} = \log (\log x).$

344. $\int \dfrac{dx}{x \, (\log x)^n} = - \dfrac{1}{(n-1) \, (\log x)^{n-1}}.$

345. $\int \dfrac{x^m \, dx}{(\log x)^n} = - \dfrac{x^{m+1}}{(n-1) \, (\log x)^{n-1}} + \dfrac{m+1}{n-1} \int \dfrac{x^m \, dx}{(\log x)^{n-1}}.$

346. $\int x^m \log x \, dx = x^{m+1} \left[\dfrac{\log x}{m+1} - \dfrac{1}{(m+1)^2} \right].$

347. $\int x^m \, (\log x)^n \, dx = \dfrac{x^{m+1} \, (\log x)^n}{m+1} - \dfrac{n}{m+1} \int x^m \, (\log x)^{n-1} \, dx, [m, n \neq -1].$

348. $\int \sin \log x \, dx = \tfrac{1}{2}x \sin \log x - \tfrac{1}{2}x \cos \log x.$

349. $\int \cos \log x \, dx = \tfrac{1}{2}x \sin \log x + \tfrac{1}{2}x \cos \log x.$

Exponential Forms

350. $\int e^x \, dx = e^x.$

351. $\int e^{-x} \, dx = -e^{-x}.$

352. $\int e^{ax} \, dx = \dfrac{e^{ax}}{a}.$

353. $\int x \, e^{ax} \, dx = \dfrac{e^{ax}}{a^2} (ax - 1).$

354. $\displaystyle\int x^m\, e^{ax}\, dx = \frac{x^m\, e^{ax}}{a} - \frac{m}{a}\int x^{m-1}\, e^{ax}\, dx.$

355. $\displaystyle\int \frac{e^{ax}\, dx}{x} = \log x + \frac{ax}{1!} + \frac{a^2 x^2}{2\cdot 2!} + \frac{a^3 x^3}{3\cdot 3!} + \cdots$

356. $\displaystyle\int \frac{e^{ax}}{x^m}\, dx = -\frac{1}{m-1}\frac{e^{ax}}{x^{m-1}} + \frac{a}{m-1}\int \frac{e^{ax}}{x^{m-1}}\, dx.$

357. $\displaystyle\int e^{ax} \log x\, dx = \frac{e^{ax} \log x}{a} - \frac{1}{a}\int \frac{e^{ax}}{x}\, dx.$

358. $\displaystyle\int e^{ax}\cdot \sin px\, dx = \frac{e^{ax}\,(a\,\sin px - p\,\cos px)}{a^2 + p^2}.$

359. $\displaystyle\int e^{ax}\cdot \cos px\, dx = \frac{e^{ax}\,(a\,\cos px + p\,\sin px)}{a^2 + p^2}.$

360. $\displaystyle\int \frac{dx}{1 + e^x} = x - \log\,(1 + e^x) = \log \frac{e^x}{1 + e^x}.$

361. $\displaystyle\int \frac{dx}{a + be^{px}} = \frac{x}{a} - \frac{1}{ap} \log\,(a + be^{px}).$

362. $\displaystyle\int \frac{dx}{ae^{mx} + be^{-mx}} = \frac{1}{m\,\sqrt{ab}}\tan^{-1}\left(e^{mx}\sqrt{\frac{a}{b}}\right).$

363. $\displaystyle\int e^{ax} \sin^n bx\, dx = \frac{1}{a^2 + n^2 b^2}\Big((a\,\sin bx - nb\,\cos bx)$

$$e^{ax} \sin^{n-1} bx + n\,(n-1)b^2 \int e^{ax} \sin^{n-2} bx\cdot dx\Big).$$

364. $\displaystyle\int e^{ax} \cos^n bx\, dx = \frac{1}{a^2 + n^2 b^2}\Big((a\,\cos bx + nb\,\sin bx)$

$$e^{ax} \cos^{n-1} bx + n\,(n-1)b^2 \int e^{ax} \cos^{n-2} bx\, dx\Big).$$

Hyperbolic Forms

365. $\displaystyle\int \sinh x\, dx = \cosh x.$

366. $\displaystyle\int \cosh x\, dx = \sinh x.$

367. $\displaystyle\int \tanh x\, dx = \log \cosh x.$

368. $\displaystyle\int \coth x\, dx = \log \sinh x.$

369. $\displaystyle\int \text{sech } x \, dx = 2 \tan^{-1}(e^x) = \tan^{-1}(\sinh x).$

370. $\displaystyle\int \text{csch } x \, dx = \log \tanh\left(\frac{x}{2}\right).$

371. $\displaystyle\int x \sinh x \, dx = x \cosh x - \sinh x.$

372. $\displaystyle\int x \cosh x \, dx = x \sinh x - \cosh x.$

373. $\displaystyle\int \text{sech } x \tanh x \, dx = - \text{sech } x.$

374. $\displaystyle\int \text{csch } x \coth x \, dx = - \text{csch } x.$

375. $\displaystyle\int \sinh^2 x \, dx = \frac{\sinh 2x}{4} - \frac{x}{2}.$

376. $\displaystyle\int \tanh^2 x \, dx = x - \tanh x.$

377. $\displaystyle\int \text{sech}^2 x \, dx = \tanh x.$

378. $\displaystyle\int \cosh^2 x \, dx = \frac{\sinh 2x}{4} + \frac{x}{2}.$

379. $\displaystyle\int \coth^2 x \, dx = x - \text{ctnh } x.$

380. $\displaystyle\int \text{csch}^2 x \, dx = - \text{ctnh } x.$

381. $\displaystyle\int \sinh mx \sinh nx \, dx = \frac{\sinh (m+n)x}{2(m+n)}$
$$- \frac{\sinh (m-n)x}{2(m-n)} \qquad m^2 \neq n^2.$$

382. $\displaystyle\int \cosh mx \cosh nx \, dx = \frac{\sinh (m+n)x}{2(m+n)}$
$$+ \frac{\sinh (m-n)x}{2(m-n)} \qquad m^2 \neq n^2.$$

383. $\displaystyle\int \sinh mx \cosh mx \, dx = \frac{\cosh (m+n)x}{2(m+n)}$
$$+ \frac{\cosh (m-n)x}{2(m-n)} \qquad m^2 \neq n^2.$$

384. $\int \text{arc sinh} \dfrac{x}{a} \, dx = x \, \text{arc sinh} \dfrac{x}{a} - \sqrt{x^2 + a^2}$.

385. $\int x \, \text{arc sinh} \dfrac{x}{a} \, dx = \left(\dfrac{x^2}{2} + \dfrac{a^2}{4} \right) \text{arc sinh} \dfrac{x}{a} - \dfrac{x}{4} \sqrt{x^2 + a^2}$.

386. $\int \text{arc cosh} \dfrac{x}{a} \, dx = x \, \text{arc cosh} \dfrac{x}{a} - \sqrt{x^2 - a^2}, \left[\text{arc cosh} \dfrac{x}{a} > 0 \right]$.

$\qquad = x \, \text{arc cosh} \dfrac{x}{a} + \sqrt{x^2 - a^2}, \left[\text{arc cosh} \dfrac{x}{a} < 0 \right]$.

387. $\int \text{arc tanh} \dfrac{x}{a} \, dx = x \, \text{arc tanh} \dfrac{x}{a} + \dfrac{a}{2} \log (a^2 - x^2)$.

388. $\int x \, \text{arc tanh} \dfrac{x}{a} \, dx = \dfrac{x^2 - a^2}{2} \text{arc tanh} \dfrac{x}{a} + \dfrac{ax}{2}$.

DEFINITE INTEGRALS

389. $\displaystyle\int_0^\infty x^{n-1} e^x \, dx = \int_0^1 \left(\log \dfrac{1}{x} \right)^{n-1} dx = \Gamma(n)$.   (Gamma function).

390. $\Gamma(n)$ is finite if $n > 0$, $\Gamma(n + 1) = n\Gamma(n)$.

391. $\Gamma(n) \cdot \Gamma(1 - n) = \dfrac{\pi}{\sin n\pi}$.

392. $\Gamma(n) = (n - 1)!$ if $n = $ integer > 0.

393. $\Gamma\left(\tfrac{1}{2}\right) = \sqrt{\pi}$.

394. $\Gamma\left(n + \dfrac{1}{2} \right) = \dfrac{1 \cdot 3 \cdot 5 \cdot 7 \, \cdots \, (2n - 1)}{2^n} \sqrt{\pi}$, where n is an integer and > 0. (see values of $\Gamma(n)$ at end of integral table)

395. $\displaystyle\int_0^1 x^{m-1}(1 - x)^{n-1} \, dx = B(m,n)$.   (Beta function).

396. $B(m,n) = B(n,m) = \dfrac{\Gamma(m)\Gamma(n)}{\Gamma(m + n)}$, where m and n are any positive real members.

397. $\displaystyle\int_0^1 x^{m-1} (1 - x)^{n-1} \, dx = \int_0^\infty \dfrac{x^{m-1} \, dx}{(1 + x)^{m+n}} = \dfrac{\Gamma(m) \, \Gamma(n)}{\Gamma(m + n)}$.

398. $\displaystyle\int_1^\infty \dfrac{dx}{x^m} = \dfrac{1}{m - 1}$, $[m > 1]$.

399. $\displaystyle\int_0^\infty \dfrac{dx}{(1 + x)x^p} = \pi \csc p\pi$, $[p < 1]$.

400. $\int_0^\infty \dfrac{dx}{(1-x)x^p} = -\pi \cot p\pi,$ $[p < 1].$

401. $\int_0^\infty \dfrac{x^{p-1}\,dx}{1+x} = \dfrac{\pi}{\sin p\pi},$ $[0 < p < 1].$

402. $\int_0^\infty \dfrac{x^{m-1}\,dx}{1+x^n} = \dfrac{\pi}{n \sin \dfrac{m\pi}{n}},$ $[0 < m < n].$

403. $\int_0^\infty \dfrac{dx}{(1+x)\sqrt{x}} = \pi.$

404. $\int_0^\infty \dfrac{a\,dx}{a^2+x^2} = \dfrac{\pi}{2},$ if $a > 0$; 0, if $a = 0$; $-\dfrac{\pi}{2},$ if $a < 0.$

405. $\int_0^{\pi/2} \sin^n x\,dx = \int_0^{\pi/2} \cos^n x\,dx$

$\qquad = \dfrac{1 \cdot 3 \cdot 5 \cdots (n-1)}{2 \cdot 4 \cdot 6 \cdots (n)} \cdot \dfrac{\pi}{2},$ [n an even integer],

$\qquad = \dfrac{2 \cdot 4 \cdot 6 \cdots (n-1)}{1 \cdot 3 \cdot 5 \cdot 7 \cdots n},$ [n an odd integer]

$\qquad = \dfrac{1}{2}\sqrt{\pi}\,\dfrac{\Gamma\left(\dfrac{n+1}{2}\right)}{\Gamma\left(\dfrac{n}{2}+1\right)},$ $[n > -1].$

406. $\int_0^\infty \dfrac{\sin mx\,dx}{x} = \dfrac{\pi}{2},$ if $m > 0$; 0, if $m = 0$; $-\dfrac{\pi}{2},$ if $m < 0.$

407. $\int_0^\infty \dfrac{\cos x\,dx}{x} = \infty.$

408. $\int_0^\infty \dfrac{\tan x\,dx}{x} = \dfrac{\pi}{2}.$

409. $\int_0^\pi \sin kx \cdot \sin mx\,dx = \int_0^\pi \cos kx \cdot \cos mx\,dx = 0,$

$\qquad\qquad\qquad\qquad [k \neq m;\ m,\ n = \text{integers}].$

410. $\int_0^\infty \dfrac{\sin x \cos mx\,dx}{x} = 0,$ if $m < -1$ or $m > 1,$

$\qquad\qquad = \dfrac{\pi}{4},$ if $m = \pm 1$; $= \dfrac{\pi}{2},$ if $m^2 < 1.$

411. $\int_0^\pi \sin^2 mx\,dx = \int_0^\pi \cos^2 mx\,dx = \dfrac{\pi}{2}.$

412. $\displaystyle\int_0^\infty \frac{\sin^2 x \, dx}{x^2} = \frac{\pi}{2}.$

413. $\displaystyle\int_0^\infty \frac{\cos mx}{1 + x^2} \, dx = \frac{\pi}{2} e^{-m},$ $\qquad\qquad$ [$m > 0$].

$\qquad\qquad\qquad\qquad\quad = \frac{\pi}{2} e^{m},$ $\qquad\qquad\qquad$ [$m < 0$].

414. $\displaystyle\int_0^\infty \cos(x^2) \, dx = \int_0^\infty \sin(x^2) \, dx = \frac{1}{2}\sqrt{\frac{\pi}{2}}.$

415. $\displaystyle\int_0^\infty \frac{\sin x \, dx}{\sqrt{x}} = \int_0^\infty \frac{\cos x \, dx}{\sqrt{x}} = \sqrt{\frac{\pi}{2}}.$

416. $\displaystyle\int_0^{\pi/2} \frac{dx}{1 + a \cos x} = \frac{\cos^{-1} a}{\sqrt{1 - a^2}},$ $\qquad\qquad$ [$a < 1$].

417. $\displaystyle\int_0^{2\pi} \frac{dx}{1 + a \cos x} = \frac{2\pi}{\sqrt{1 - a^2}},$ $\qquad\qquad$ ($a^2 < 1$).

418. $\displaystyle\int_0^\infty \frac{\cos ax - \cos bx}{x} \, dx = \log \frac{b}{a}.$

419. $\displaystyle\int_0^{\pi/2} \frac{dx}{a^2 \sin^2 x + b^2 \cos^2 x} = \frac{\pi}{2ab}.$

420. $\displaystyle\int_0^{\pi/2} \sin^{n-1} x \cos^{m-1} x \, dx = \frac{1}{2} \, \mathrm{B}\left(\frac{n}{2}, \frac{m}{2}\right),$

$\qquad\qquad\qquad\qquad\qquad$ m and n positive integers.

421. $\displaystyle\int_0^\infty e^{-ax} \, dx = \frac{1}{a}.$ $\qquad\qquad\qquad\qquad$ [$a > 0$].

422. $\displaystyle\int_0^\infty x^n e^{-ax} \, dx = \frac{\Gamma(n + 1)}{a^{n+1}},$ $\qquad\qquad$ [$n > -1, a > 0$],

$\qquad\qquad\qquad\qquad\quad = \frac{n!}{a^{n+1}},$ $\qquad\qquad$ [n pos. integ., $a > 0$].

423. $\displaystyle\int_0^\infty e^{-a^2 x^2} \, dx = \frac{1}{2a}\sqrt{\pi} = \frac{1}{2a}\Gamma\left(\frac{1}{2}\right),$ $\qquad\qquad$ [$a > 0$].

424. $\displaystyle\int_0^\infty x e^{-x^2} \, dx = \frac{1}{2}.$

425. $\displaystyle\int_0^\infty x^2 e^{-x^2} \, dx = \frac{\sqrt{\pi}}{4}.$

426. $\displaystyle\int_0^\infty x^{2n} e^{-ax^2} \, dx = \frac{1 \cdot 3 \cdot 5 \cdots (2n - 1)}{2^{n+1} a^n}\sqrt{\frac{\pi}{a}}.$

427. $\displaystyle\int_0^\infty e^{(-x^2 - a^2/x^2)}\,dx = \frac{e^{-2a}\sqrt{\pi}}{2}.$

428. $\displaystyle\int_0^\infty e^{-nx}\sqrt{x}\,dx = \frac{1}{2n}\sqrt{\frac{\pi}{n}}.$

429. $\displaystyle\int_0^\infty \frac{e^{-nx}}{\sqrt{x}}\,dx = \sqrt{\frac{\pi}{n}}.$

430. $\displaystyle\int_0^\infty e^{-ax}\cos mx\,dx = \frac{a}{a^2 + m^2},$ $\qquad\qquad [a > 0].$

431. $\displaystyle\int_0^\infty e^{-ax}\sin mx\,dx = \frac{m}{a^2 + m^2},$ $\qquad\qquad [a > 0].$

432. $\displaystyle\int_0^\infty e^{-a^2x^2}\cos bx\,dx = \frac{\sqrt{\pi}\cdot e^{-b^2/4a^2}}{2a},$ $\qquad\qquad [a > 0].$

433. $\displaystyle\int_0^1 (\log x)^n\,dx = (-1)^n \cdot n!.$

434. $\displaystyle\int_0^1 \left(\log\frac{1}{x}\right)^{\frac{1}{2}}\,dx = \frac{\sqrt{\pi}}{2}.$

435. $\displaystyle\int_0^1 \left(\log\frac{1}{x}\right)^{-\frac{1}{2}}\,dx = \sqrt{\pi}.$

436. $\displaystyle\int_0^1 \left(\log\frac{1}{x}\right)^{n}\,dx = n!.$

437. $\displaystyle\int_0^1 x\log(1 - x)\,dx = -\frac{3}{4}.$

438. $\displaystyle\int_0^1 x\log(1 + x)\,dx = \frac{1}{4}.$

439. $\displaystyle\int_0^1 \frac{\log x}{1 + x}\,dx = -\frac{\pi^2}{12}.$

440. $\displaystyle\int_0^1 \frac{\log x}{1 - x}\,dx = -\frac{\pi^2}{6}.$

441. $\displaystyle\int_0^1 \frac{\log x}{1 - x^2}\,dx = -\frac{\pi^2}{8}.$

442. $\displaystyle\int_0^1 \log\left(\frac{1 + x}{1 - x}\right)\cdot\frac{dx}{x} = \frac{\pi^2}{4}.$

443. $\displaystyle\int_0^1 \frac{\log x\,dx}{\sqrt{1 - x^2}} = -\frac{\pi}{2}\log 2.$

444. $\displaystyle\int_0^1 x^m \log\left(\frac{1}{x}\right)^n dx = \frac{\Gamma(n+1)}{(m+1)^{n+1}}$, if $m+1>0$, $n+1>0$.

445. $\displaystyle\int_0^1 \frac{(x^p - x^q)\,dx}{\log x} = \log\left(\frac{p+1}{q+1}\right)$, $\qquad [p+1>0,\ q+1>0]$.

446. $\displaystyle\int_0^1 \frac{dx}{\sqrt{\log\left(\dfrac{1}{x}\right)}} = \sqrt{\pi}$.

447. $\displaystyle\int_0^\infty \log\left(\frac{e^x+1}{e^x-1}\right) dx = \frac{\pi^2}{4}$.

448. $\displaystyle\int_0^{\pi/2} \log \sin x\, dx = \int_0^{\pi/2} \log \cos x\, dx = -\frac{\pi}{2}\log 2$.

449. $\displaystyle\int_0^{\pi/2} \log \sec x\, dx = \int_0^{\pi/2} \log \csc x\, dx = \frac{\pi}{2}\log 2$.

450. $\displaystyle\int_0^\pi x \log \sin x\, dx = -\frac{\pi^2}{2}\log 2$.

451. $\displaystyle\int_0^{\pi/2} \sin x \log \sin x\, dx = \log 2 - 1$.

452. $\displaystyle\int_0^{\pi/2} \log \tan x\, dx = 0$.

453. $\displaystyle\int_0^\pi \log(a \pm b \cos x)\, dx = \pi \log\left(\frac{a+\sqrt{a^2-b^2}}{2}\right)$, $\qquad [a \geqq b]$.

454. $\displaystyle\int_0^\infty \frac{dx}{\sinh ax} = \frac{\pi}{2a}$.

455. $\displaystyle\int_0^\infty \frac{x\,dx}{\sinh ax} = \frac{\pi}{4a^2}$.

456. $\displaystyle\int_0^\infty e^{-ax} \cosh bx\, dx = \frac{a}{a^2-b^2}$ $\qquad\qquad a>0$.

457. $\displaystyle\int_0^\infty e^{-ax} \sinh bx\, dx = \frac{b}{a^2-b^2}$ $\qquad\qquad a>0$.

458. $\displaystyle\int_{+\infty}^1 \frac{e^{-xu}}{u}\,du = \gamma + \log x - x + \frac{x^2}{2\cdot2!} - \frac{x^3}{3\cdot3!} + \frac{x^4}{4\cdot4!}$

$\qquad - \cdots$, where $\gamma = \lim_{z\to\infty}\left(1 + \frac{1}{2} + \frac{1}{3}\right.$

$\qquad \left.+ \cdots + \frac{1}{z} - \log z\right) = 0.5772157\cdots$, $0 < x < \infty$.

459. $\displaystyle\int_0^{\pi/2} \frac{dx}{\sqrt{1-k^2\sin^2 x}} = \frac{\pi}{2}\left[1 + \left(\frac{1}{2}\right)^2 k^2 + \left(\frac{1\cdot 3}{2\cdot 4}\right)^2 k^4 \right.$
$$\left. + \left(\frac{1\cdot 3\cdot 5}{2\cdot 4\cdot 6}\right)^2 k^6 + \cdots \right], \text{ if } k^2 < 1.$$

460. $\displaystyle\int_0^{\pi/2} \sqrt{1-k^2\sin^2 x}\, dx = \frac{\pi}{2}\left[1 - \left(\frac{1}{2}\right)^2 k^2 \right.$
$$\left. - \left(\frac{1\cdot 3}{2\cdot 4}\right)^2 \frac{k^4}{3} - \left(\frac{1\cdot 3\cdot 5}{2\cdot 4\cdot 6}\right)^2 \frac{k^6}{5} - \cdots \right], \text{ if } k^2 < 1.$$

461. $\displaystyle\int_0^\infty e^{-x}\log x\, dx = -\gamma = -0.5772157\cdots$

462. $\displaystyle\int_0^\infty \left(\frac{1}{1-e^{-x}} - \frac{1}{x}\right) e^{-x} dx = \gamma = 0.5772157\cdots$

[Euler's Constant].

463. $\displaystyle\int_0^\infty \frac{1}{x}\left(\frac{1}{1+x} - e^{-x}\right) dx = \gamma = 0.5772157\cdots$

GAMMA FUNCTION

Values of $\Gamma(n) = \displaystyle\int_0^\infty \epsilon^{-x} x^{n-1}\, dx;\ \Gamma(n+1) = n\Gamma(n)$

n	$\Gamma(n)$	n	$\Gamma(n)$	n	$\Gamma(n)$	n	$\Gamma(n)$
1.00	1.00000	1.25	.90640	1.50	.88623	1.75	.91906
1.01	.99433	1.26	.90440	1.51	.88659	1.76	.92137
1.02	.98884	1.27	.90250	1.52	.88704	1.77	.92376
1.03	.98355	1.28	.90072	1.53	.88757	1.78	.92623
1.04	.97844	1.29	.89904	1.54	.88818	1.79	.92877
1.05	.97350	1.30	.89747	1.55	.88887	1.80	.93138
1.06	.96874	1.31	.89600	1.56	.88964	1.81	.93408
1.07	.96415	1.32	.89464	1.57	.89049	1.82	.93685
1.08	.95973	1.33	.89338	1.58	.89142	1.83	.93969
1.09	.95546	1.34	.89222	1.59	.89243	1.84	.94261
1.10	.95135	1.35	.89115	1.60	.89352	1.85	.94561
1.11	.94739	1.36	.89018	1.61	.89468	1.86	.94869
1.12	.94359	1.37	.88931	1.62	89592	1.87	.95184
1.13	.93993	1.38	.88854	1.63	.89724	1.88	.95507
1.14	.93642	1.39	.88785	1.64	.89864	1.89	.95838
1.15	.93304	1.40	.88726	1.65	.90012	1.90	.96177
1.16	.92980	1.41	.88676	1.66	.90167	1.91	.96523
1.17	.92670	1.42	.88636	1.67	.90330	1.92	.96878
1.18	.92373	1.43	.88604	1.68	.90500	1.93	.97240
1.19	.92088	1.44	.88580	1.69	.90678	1.94	.97610
1.20	.91817	1.45	.88565	1.70	.90864	1.95	.97988
1.21	.91558	1.46	.88560	1.71	.91057	1.96	.98374
1.22	.91311	1.47	.88563	1.72	.91258	1.97	.98768
1.23	.91075	1.48	.88575	1.73	.91466	1.98	.99171
1.24	.90852	1.49	.88595	1.74	.91683	1.99	.99581
						2.00	1.00000

BESSEL FUNCTIONS $J_0(x)$ AND $J_1(x)$

x	$J_0(x)$	$J_1(x)$	x	$J_0(x)$	$J_1(x)$	x	$J_0(x)$	$J_1(x)$
0.0	1.0000	.0000	**5.0**	− .1776	− .3276	**10.0**	− .2459	.0435
0.1	.9975	.0499	5.1	− .1443	− .3371	10.1	− .2490	.0184
0.2	.9900	.0995	5.2	− .1103	− .3432	10.2	− .2496	− .0066
0.3	.9776	.1483	5.3	− .0758	− .3460	10.3	− .2477	− .0313
0.4	.9604	.1960	5.4	− .0412	− .3453	10.4	− .2434	− .0555
0.5	.9385	.2423	**5.5**	− .0068	− .3414	**10.5**	− .2366	− .0789
0.6	.9120	.2867	5.6	.0270	− .3343	10.6	− .2276	− .1012
0.7	.8812	.3290	5.7	.0599	− .3241	10.7	− .2164	− .1224
0.8	.8463	.3688	5.8	.0917	− .3110	10.8	− .2032	− .1422
0.9	.8075	.4059	5.9	.1220	− .2951	10.9	− .1881	− .1603
1.0	.7652	.4401	**6.0**	.1506	− .2767	**11.0**	− .1712	− .1768
1.1	.7196	.4709	6.1	.1773	− .2559	11.1	− .1528	− .1913
1.2	.6711	.4983	6.2	.2017	− .2329	11.2	− .1330	− .2039
1.3	.6201	.5220	6.3	.2238	− .2081	11.3	− .1121	− .2143
1.4	.5669	.5419	6.4	.2433	− .1816	11.4	− .0902	− .2225
1.5	.5118	.5579	**6.5**	.2601	− .1538	**11.5**	− .0677	− .2284
1.6	.4554	.5699	6.6	.2740	− .1250	11.6	− .0446	− .2320
1.7	.3980	.5778	6.7	.2851	− .0953	11.7	− .0213	− .2333
1.8	.3400	.5815	6.8	.2931	− .0652	11.8	.0020	− .2323
1.9	.2818	.5812	6.9	.2981	− .0349	11.9	.0250	− .2290
2.0	.2239	.5767	**7.0**	.3001	− .0047	**12.0**	.0477	− .2234
2.1	.1666	.5683	7.1	.2991	.0252	12.1	.0697	− .2157
2.2	.1104	.5560	7.2	.2951	.0543	12.2	.0908	− .2060
2.3	.0555	.5399	7.3	.2882	.0826	12.3	.1108	− .1943
2.4	.0025	.5202	7.4	.2786	.1096	12.4	.1296	− .1807
2.5	− .0484	.4971	**7.5**	.2663	.1352	**12.5**	.1469	− .1655
2.6	− .0968	.4708	7.6	.2516	.1592	12.6	.1626	− .1487
2.7	− .1424	.4416	7.7	.2346	.1813	12.7	.1766	− .1307
2.8	− .1850	.4097	7.8	.2154	.2014	12.8	.1887	− .1114
2.9	− .2243	.3754	7.9	.1944	.2192	12.9	.1988	− .0912
3.0	− .2601	.3391	**8.0**	.1717	.2346	**13.0**	.2069	− .0703
3.1	− .2921	.3009	8.1	.1475	.2476	13.1	.2129	− .0489
3.2	− .3202	.2613	8.2	.1222	.2580	13.2	.2167	− .0271
3.3	− .3443	.2207	8.3	.0960	.2657	13.3	.2183	− .0052
3.4	− .3643	.1792	8.4	.0692	.2708	13.4	.2177	.0166
3.5	− .3801	.1374	**8.5**	.0419	.2731	**13.5**	.2150	.0380
3.6	− .3918	.0955	8.6	.0146	.2728	13.6	.2101	.0590
3.7	− .3992	.0538	8.7	− .0125	.2697	13.7	.2032	.0791
3.8	− .4026	.0128	8.8	− .0392	.2641	13.8	.1943	.0984
3.9	− .4018	− .0272	8.9	− .0653	.2559	13.9	.1836	.1165
4.0	− .3971	− .0660	**9.0**	− .0903	.2453	**14.0**	.1711	.1334
4.1	− .3887	− .1033	9.1	− .1142	.2324	14.1	.1570	.1488
4.2	− .3766	− .1386	9.2	− .1367	.2174	14.2	.1414	.1626
4.3	− .3610	− .1719	9.3	− .1577	.2004	14.3	.1245	.1747
4.4	− .3423	− .2028	9.4	− .1768	.1816	14.4	.1065	.1850
4.5	− .3205	− .2311	**9.5**	− .1939	.1613	**14.5**	.0875	.1934
4.6	− .2961	− .2566	9.6	− .2090	.1395	14.6	.0679	.1999
4.7	− .2693	− .2791	9.7	− .2218	.1166	14.7	.0476	.2043
4.8	− .2404	− .2985	9.8	− .2323	.0928	14.8	.0271	.2066
4.9	− .2097	− .3147	9.9	− .2403	.0684	14.9	.0064	.2069

$J_0(x) = 0$: $x = 2.405,\ 5.520,\ 8.654,\ 11.792$.
$J_1(x) = 0$: $x = 3.832,\ 7.016,\ 10.173,\ 13.324$.

BESSEL FUNCTIONS FOR SPHERICAL COORDINATES

$$j_n(x) = \sqrt{\pi/2x}\, J_{n+\frac{1}{2}}(x), \qquad n_n(x) = \sqrt{\pi/2x}\, N_{n+\frac{1}{2}}(x)$$

x	$j_0(x)$	$n_0(x)$	$j_1(x)$	$n_1(x)$	$j_2(x)$	$n_2(x)$
0.0	1.0000	$-\infty$	0.0000	$-\infty$	0.0000	$-\infty$
0.1	0.9983	-9.9500	0.0333	-100.50	0.0007	-3005.0
0.2	0.9933	-4.9003	0.0664	-25.495	0.0027	-377.52
0.4	0.9735	-2.3027	0.1312	-6.7302	0.0105	-48.174
0.6	0.9411	-1.3756	0.1929	-3.2337	0.0234	-14.793
0.8	0.8967	-0.8709	0.2500	-1.9853	0.0408	-6.5740
1.0	0.8415	-0.5403	0.3012	-1.3818	0.0620	-3.6050
1.2	0.7767	-0.3020	0.3453	-1.0283	0.0865	-2.2689
1.4	0.7039	-0.1214	0.3814	-0.7906	0.1133	-1.5728
1.6	0.6247	$+0.0183$	0.4087	-0.6133	0.1416	-1.1682
1.8	0.5410	0.1262	0.4268	-0.4709	0.1703	-0.9111
2.0	0.4546	0.2081	0.4354	-0.3506	0.1985	-0.7340
2.2	0.3675	0.2675	0.4346	-0.2459	0.2251	-0.6028
2.4	0.2814	0.3072	0.4245	-0.1534	0.2492	-0.4990
2.6	0.1983	0.3296	0.4058	-0.0715	0.2700	-0.4121
2.8	0.1196	0.3365	0.3792	$+0.0005$	0.2867	-0.3359
3.0	$+0.0470$	0.3300	0.3457	0.0630	0.2986	-0.2670
3.2	-0.0182	0.3120	0.3063	0.1157	0.3084	-0.2035
3.4	-0.0752	0.2844	0.2623	0.1588	0.3066	-0.1442
3.6	-0.1229	0.2491	0.2150	0.1921	0.3021	-0.0890
3.8	-0.1610	0.2082	0.1658	0.2158	0.2919	-0.0378
4.0	-0.1892	0.1634	0.1161	0.2300	0.2763	$+0.0091$
4.2	-0.2075	0.1167	0.0673	0.2353	0.2556	0.0514
4.4	-0.2163	0.0699	$+0.0207$	0.2321	0.2304	0.0884
4.6	-0.2160	$+0.0244$	-0.0226	0.2213	0.2013	0.1200
4.8	-0.2075	-0.0182	-0.0615	0.2037	0.1691	0.1456
5.0	-0.1918	-0.0567	-0.0951	0.1804	0.1347	0.1650
5.2	-0.1699	-0.0901	-0.1228	0.1526	0.0991	0.1781
5.4	-0.1431	-0.1175	-0.1440	0.1213	0.0631	0.1850
5.6	-0.1127	-0.1385	-0.1586	0.0880	$+0.0278$	0.1856
5.8	-0.0801	-0.1527	-0.1665	0.0538	-0.0060	0.1805
6.0	-0.0466	-0.1600	-0.1678	$+0.0199$	-0.0373	0.1700
6.2	-0.0134	-0.1607	-0.1629	-0.0125	-0.0654	0.1547
6.4	$+0.0182$	-0.1552	-0.1523	-0.0425	-0.0896	0.1353
6.6	0.0472	-0.1440	-0.1368	-0.0690	-0.1094	0.1126
6.8	0.0727	-0.1278	-0.1172	-0.0915	-0.1243	0.0875
7.0	0.0939	-0.1077	-0.0943	-0.1092	-0.1343	0.0609
7.2	0.1102	-0.0845	-0.0692	-0.1220	-0.1391	0.0337
7.4	0.1215	-0.0593	-0.0429	-0.1294	-0.1388	$+0.0068$
7.6	0.1274	-0.0331	-0.0163	-0.1317	-0.1338	-0.0189
7.8	0.1280	-0.0069	$+0.0095$	-0.1289	-0.1244	-0.0427
8.0	0.1237	$+0.0182$	0.0336	-0.1214	-0.1111	-0.0637

Taken from Vibration and Sound with the permission of Philip Morse, author, and McGraw-Hill Book Company, Inc., publisher.

HYPERBOLIC BESSEL FUNCTIONS

$$I_m(z) = i^{-m} J_m(iz)$$

z	$I_0(z)$	$I_1(z)$	$I_2(z)$
0.0	1.0000	0.0000	0.0000
0.1	1.0025	0.0501	0.0012
0.2	1.0100	0.1005	0.0050
0.4	1.0404	0.2040	0.0203
0.6	1.0921	0.3137	0.0464
0.8	1.1665	0.4329	0.0843
1.0	1.2661	0.5652	0.1358
1.2	1.3937	0.7147	0.2026
1.4	1.5534	0.8861	0.2876
1.6	1.7500	1.0848	0.3940
1.8	1.9895	1.3172	0.5260
2.0	2.2796	1.5906	0.6890
2.2	2.6292	1.9141	0.8891
2.4	3.0492	2.2981	1.1111
2.6	3.5532	2.7554	1.4338
2.8	4.1574	3.3011	1.7994
3.0	4.8808	3.9534	2.2452
3.2	5.7472	4.7343	2.7884
3.4	6.7848	5.6701	3.4495
3.6	8.0278	6.7926	4.2538
3.8	9.5169	8.1405	5.2323
4.0	11.302	9.7594	6.4224
4.2	13.443	11.705	7.8683
4.4	16.010	14.046	9.6259
4.6	19.097	16.863	11.761
4.8	22.794	20.253	14.355
5.0	27.240	24.335	17.505
5.2	32.584	29.254	21.332
5.4	39.010	35.181	25.980
5.6	46.738	42.327	31.621
5.8	56.039	50.945	38.472
6.0	67.235	61.341	46.788
6.2	80.717	73.888	56.882
6.4	96.963	89.025	69.143
6.6	116.54	107.31	84.021
6.8	140.14	129.38	102.08
7.0	168.59	156.04	124.01
7.2	202.92	188.25	150.63
7.4	244.34	227.17	182.94
7.6	294.33	274.22	222.17
7.8	354.68	331.10	269.79
8.0	427.57	399.87	327.60

Taken from Vibration and Sound with the permission of Philip Morse, author, and McGraw-Hill Book Company, Inc., publisher.

SINE, COSINE, AND EXPONENTIAL INTEGRALS

$$Si(x) = \int_0^x \frac{\sin v}{v}\, dv; \qquad Ci(x) = \int_\infty^x \frac{\cos v}{v}\, dv;$$

$$Ei(x) = \int_{-\infty}^x \frac{e^v}{v}\, dv; \qquad -Ei(-x) = \int_x^\infty \frac{e^{-v}}{v}\, dv$$

x	$Si(x)$	$Ci(x)$	$Ei(x)$	$-Ei(-x)$
0.0	0.00000	$-\infty$	$-\infty$	$+\infty$
0.1	0.09994	-1.72787	-1.62281	1.82292
0.2	.19956	-1.04221	$-\ .82176$	1.22265
0.3	.29850	$-\ .64917$	$-\ .30267$	.90568
0.4	.39646	$-\ .37881$	$-\ .10477$	.70238
0.5	.49311	$-\ .17778$	.45422	.55977
0.6	.58813	$-\ .02227$	.76988	.45438
0.7	.68122	.10051	1.06491	.37377
0.8	.77210	.19828	1.34740	.31060
0.9	.86047	.27607	1.62281	.26018
1.0	.94608	.33740	1.89512	.21938
1.1	1.02869	.38487	2.16738	.18599
1.2	1.10805	.42046	2.44209	.15841
1.3	1.18396	.44574	2.72140	.13545
1.4	1.25623	.46201	3.00721	.11622
1.5	1.32468	.47036	3.30128	.10002
1.6	1.38918	.47173	3.60532	.08631
1.7	1.44959	.46697	3.92096	.07465
1.8	1.50582	.45681	4.24987	.06471
1.9	1.55778	.44194	4.59371	.05620
2.0	1.60541	.42298	4.95423	.04890
2.1	1.64870	.40051	5.33324	.04261
2.2	1.68762	.37507	5.73261	.03719
2.3	1.72221	.34718	6.15438	.03250
2.4	1.75249	.31729	6.60067	.02844
2.5	1.77852	.28587	7.07377	.02491
2.6	1.80039	.25337	7.57611	.02185
2.7	1.81821	.22008	8.11035	.01918
2.8	1.83210	.18649	8.67930	.01686
2.9	1.84219	.15290	9.28602	.01482
3.0	1.84865	.11963	9.93383	.01305
3.1	1.85166	.08699	10.6263	.01149
3.2	1.85140	.05526	11.3673	.01013
3.3	1.84808	.02468	12.1610	.00894
3.4	1.84191	$-\ .00452$	13.0121	.00789
3.5	1.83313	$-\ .03213$	13.9254	.00697
3.6	1.82195	$-\ .05797$	14.9063	.00616
3.7	1.80862	$-\ .08190$	15.9606	.00545
3.8	1.79339	$-\ .10378$	17.0948	.00482
3.9	1.77650	$-\ .12350$	18.3157	.00427
4.0	1.75820	$-\ .14098$	19.6309	.00378
4.1	1.73874	$-\ .15617$	21.0485	.00335
4.2	1.71837	$-\ .16901$	22.5774	.00297
4.3	1.69732	$-\ .17951$	24.2274	.00263
4.4	1.67583	$-\ .18766$	26.0090	.00234
4.5	1.65414	$-\ .19349$	27.9337	.00207
4.6	1.63246	$-\ .19705$	30.0141	.00184
4.7	1.61100	$-\ .19839$	32.2639	.00164
4.8	1.58998	$-\ .19760$	34.6979	.00145
4.9	1.56956	$-\ .19478$	37.3325	.00129
5.0	1.54993	$-\ .19002$	40.1853	.00115
5.1	1.53125	$-\ .18348$	43.2757	.00102
5.2	1.51367	$-\ .17525$	46.6249	.00091

x	$Si(x)$	$Ci(x)$	$Ei(x)$	$-Ei(-x)$
5.3	1.49731	− .16551	50.2557	.00081
5.4	1.48230	− .15439	54.1935	.00072
5.5	1.46872	− .14205	58.4655	.00064
5.6	1.45667	− .12867	63.1018	.00057
5.7	1.44620	− .11441	68.1350	.00051
5.8	1.43736	− .09944	73.6008	.00045
5.9	1.43018	− .08393	79.5382	.00040
6.0	1.42469	− .06806	85.9898	.00036
6.1	1.42087	− .05198	93.0020	.00032
6.2	1.41871	− .03587	100.626	.00029
6.3	1.41817	− .01988	108.916	.00026
6.4	1.41922	− .00418	117.935	.00023
6.5	1.42179	+ .01110	127.747	.00020
6.6	1.42582	+ .02582	138.426	.00018
6.7	1.43121	.03986	150.050	.00016
6.8	1.43787	.05308	162.707	.00014
6.9	1.44570	.06539	176.491	.00013
7.0	1.45460	.07670	191.505	.00012
7.1	1.46443	.08691	207.863	.00010
7.2	1.47509	.09596	225.688	.00009
7.3	1.48644	.10379	245.116	.00008
7.4	1.49834	.11036	266.296	.00007
7.5	1.51068	.11563	289.388	.00007
7.6	1.52331	.11960	314.572	.00006
7.7	1.53611	.12225	342.040	.00005
7.8	1.54894	.12359	372.006	.00005
7.9	1.56167	.12364	404.701	.00004
8.0	1.57419	.12243	440.380	.00004
8.1	1.58637	.12002	479.322	.00003
8.2	1.59810	.11644	521.831	.00003
8.3	1.60928	.11177	568.242	.00003
8.4	1.61981	.10607	618.919	.00002
8.5	1.62960	.09943	674.264	.00002
8.6	1.63857	.09194	734.714	.00002
8.7	1.64665	.08368	800.749	.00002
8.8	1.65379	.07476	872.895	.00002
8.9	1.65993	.06528	951.728	.00001
9.0	1.66504	.05535	1037.88	.00001
9.1	1.66908	.04507	1132.04	.00001
9.2	1.67205	.03455	1234.96	.00001
9.3	1.67393	.02391	1347.48	.00001
9.4	1.67473	.01325	1470.51	.00001
9.5	1.67446	.00268	1605.03	.00001
9.6	1.67316	− .00771	1752.14	.00001
9.7	1.67084	− .01780	1913.05	.00001
9.8	1.66757	− .02752	2089.05	.00001
9.9	1.66338	− .03676	2281.58	.00000
10.0	1.65834	− .04546	2492.23	.00000
10.5	1.62294	− .07828	3883.74	.00000
11.0	1.57831	− .08956	6071.41	.00000
11.5	1.53572	− .07857	9518.20	.00000
12.0	1.50497	− .04978	14959.5	.00000
12.5	1.49234	− .01141	23565.1	.00000
13.0	1.49936	+ .02676	37197.7	.00000
13.5	1.52291	+ .05576	58827.0	.00000
14.0	1.55621	.06940	93193.0	.00000
14.5	1.59072	.06554	147866.	.00000
15.0	1.61819	.04628	234955.	.00000

LAPLACE TRANSFORMS

The following tables of Operations and Transforms were taken from "Modern Operational Mathematics in Engineering" by permission from the author, R. V. Churchill, and the publisher, McGraw-Hill Book Company, Inc.

The operational method of solving differential equations makes use of the Laplace transformation which associates with a given function $F(t)$ and a second function $f(s)$, such that

$$f(s) = L\{F(t)\} = \int_0^\infty e^{-st}F(t)\, dt,$$

where t = a real variable, $F(t)$ = a real function of t; $F(t) = 0$, $t < 0$; $f(s)$ = a function of s; s = a complex variable; and $e = 2.71828 \ldots$

$f(s)$ is called the Laplace transform of $F(t)$

$F(t)$ can also be expressed as follows:

$$F(t) = \frac{1}{2\pi i} \int_{a - i\infty}^{a + i\infty} e^{st}f(s)\, ds,$$

where a is chosen to the right of any singularity of $f(s)$

The following tables give many useful theorems and important transform pairs.

	$F(t)$	$f(s)$
1	$F(t)$	$\int_0^\infty e^{-st}F(t)\,dt$
2	$AF(t) + BG(t)$	$Af(s) + Bg(s)$
3	$F'(t)$	$sf(s) - F(+0)$
4	$F^{(n)}(t)$	$s^n f(s) - s^{n-1}F(+0)$ $- s^{n-2}F'(+0) - \cdots$ $- F^{(n-1)}(+0)$
5	$\int_0^t F(\tau)\,d\tau$	$\dfrac{1}{s}f(s)$
6	$\int_0^t \int_0^r F(\lambda)\,d\lambda\,d\tau$	$\dfrac{1}{s^2}f(s)$
7	$\int_0^t F_1(t-\tau)F_2(\tau)\,d\tau = F_1 {}^{*}F_2$	$f_1(s)f_2(s)$
8	$tF(t)$	$-f'(s)$
9	$t^n F(t)$	$(-1)^n f^{(n)}(s)$
10	$\dfrac{1}{t}F(t)$	$\int_s^\infty f(x)\,dx$
11	$e^{at}F(t)$	$f(s-a)$
12	$F(t-b)$, where $F(t) = 0$ when $t < 0$	$e^{-bs}f(s)$
13	$\dfrac{1}{c}F\left(\dfrac{t}{c}\right)$	$f(cs)$
14	$\dfrac{1}{c}e^{\frac{bt}{c}}F\left(\dfrac{t}{c}\right)$	$f(cs-b)$
15	$F(t+a) = F(t)$	$\dfrac{\int_0^a e^{-st}F(t)\,dt}{1 - e^{-as}}$
16	$F(t+a) = -F(t)$	$\dfrac{\int_0^a e^{-st}F(t)\,dt}{1 + e^{-as}}$
17	$F_1(t)$, the half-wave rectification of $F(t)$ in No. 16	$\dfrac{f(s)}{1 - e^{-as}}$
18	$F_2(t)$, the full-wave rectification of $F(t)$ in No. 16	$f(s)\coth\dfrac{as}{2}$
19	$\displaystyle\sum_1^m \dfrac{p(a_n)}{q'(a_n)}e^{a_n t}$	$\dfrac{p(s)}{q(s)}$, $q(s) = (s-a_1)(s-a_2)$ $\cdots (s-a_m)$
20	$\displaystyle e^{at}\sum_{n=1}^r \dfrac{\phi^{(r-n)}(a)}{(r-n)!}\dfrac{t^{n-1}}{(n-1)!} + \cdots$	$\dfrac{p(s)}{q(s)} = \dfrac{\phi(s)}{(s-a)^r}$

LAPLACE TRANSFORMS

	$f(s)$	$F(t)$
1	$\dfrac{1}{s}$	1
2	$\dfrac{1}{s^2}$	t
3	$\dfrac{1}{s^n}\ (n = 1, 2, \cdots)$	$\dfrac{t^{n-1}}{(n-1)!}$
4	$\dfrac{1}{\sqrt{s}}$	$\dfrac{1}{\sqrt{\pi t}}$
5	$s^{-\frac{3}{2}}$	$2\sqrt{\dfrac{t}{\pi}}$
6	$s^{-(n+\frac{1}{2})}\ (n = 1, 2, \cdots)$	$\dfrac{2^n t^{n-\frac{1}{2}}}{1 \cdot 3 \cdot 5 \cdots (2n-1)\sqrt{\pi}}$
7	$\dfrac{\Gamma(k)}{s^k}\ (k > 0)$	t^{k-1}
8	$\dfrac{1}{s-a}$	e^{at}
9	$\dfrac{1}{(s-a)^2}$	te^{at}
10	$\dfrac{1}{(s-a)^n}\ (n = 1, 2, \cdots)$	$\dfrac{1}{(n-1)!}\,t^{n-1}e^{at}$
11	$\dfrac{\Gamma(k)}{(s-a)^k}\ (k > 0)$	$t^{k-1}e^{at}$
12*	$\dfrac{1}{(s-a)(s-b)}$	$\dfrac{1}{a-b}\,(e^{at} - e^{bt})$
13*	$\dfrac{s}{(s-a)(s-b)}$	$\dfrac{1}{a-b}\,(ae^{at} - be^{bt})$
14*	$\dfrac{1}{(s-a)(s-b)(s-c)}$	$-\dfrac{(b-c)e^{at} + (c-a)e^{bt} + (a-b)e^{ct}}{(a-b)(b-c)(c-a)}$
15	$\dfrac{1}{s^2 + a^2}$	$\dfrac{1}{a}\sin at$
16	$\dfrac{s}{s^2 + a^2}$	$\cos at$

* Here a, b, and (in 14) c represent distinct constants.

	$f(s)$	$F(t)$
17	$\dfrac{1}{s^2 - a^2}$	$\dfrac{1}{a}\sinh at$
18	$\dfrac{s}{s^2 - a^2}$	$\cosh at$
19	$\dfrac{1}{s(s^2 + a^2)}$	$\dfrac{1}{a^2}(1 - \cos at)$
20	$\dfrac{1}{s^2(s^2 + a^2)}$	$\dfrac{1}{a^3}(at - \sin at)$
21	$\dfrac{1}{(s^2 + a^2)^2}$	$\dfrac{1}{2a^3}(\sin at - at\cos at)$
22	$\dfrac{s}{(s^2 + a^2)^2}$	$\dfrac{t}{2a}\sin at$
23	$\dfrac{s^2}{(s^2 + a^2)^2}$	$\dfrac{1}{2a}(\sin at + at\cos at)$
24	$\dfrac{s^2 - a^2}{(s^2 + a^2)^2}$	$t\cos at$
25	$\dfrac{s}{(s^2 + a^2)(s^2 + b^2)}\ (a^2 \neq b^2)$	$\dfrac{\cos at - \cos bt}{b^2 - a^2}$
26	$\dfrac{1}{(s - a)^2 + b^2}$	$\dfrac{1}{b}e^{at}\sin bt$
27	$\dfrac{s - a}{(s - a)^2 + b^2}$	$e^{at}\cos bt$
28	$\dfrac{3a^2}{s^3 + a^3}$	$e^{-at} - e^{\frac{at}{2}}\left(\cos\dfrac{at\sqrt{3}}{2} - \sqrt{3}\sin\dfrac{at\sqrt{3}}{2}\right)$
29	$\dfrac{4a^3}{s^4 + 4a^4}$	$\sin at\cosh at - \cos at\sinh at$
30	$\dfrac{s}{s^4 + 4a^4}$	$\dfrac{1}{2a^2}\sin at\sinh at$
31	$\dfrac{1}{s^4 - a^4}$	$\dfrac{1}{2a^3}(\sinh at - \sin at)$
32	$\dfrac{s}{s^4 - a^4}$	$\dfrac{1}{2a^2}(\cosh at - \cos at)$
33	$\dfrac{8a^3 s^2}{(s^2 + a^2)^3}$	$(1 + a^2 t^2)\sin at - at\cos at$
34*	$\dfrac{1}{s}\left(\dfrac{s - 1}{s}\right)^n$	$L_n(t) = \dfrac{e^t}{n!}\dfrac{d^n}{dt^n}(t^n e^{-t})$
35	$\dfrac{s}{(s - a)^{\frac{3}{2}}}$	$\dfrac{1}{\sqrt{\pi t}}e^{at}(1 + 2at)$
36	$\sqrt{s - a} - \sqrt{s - b}$	$\dfrac{1}{2\sqrt{\pi t^3}}(e^{bt} - e^{at})$

* $L_n(t)$ is the Laguerre polynomial of degree n.

	$f(s)$	$F(t)$
37	$\dfrac{1}{\sqrt{s}+a}$	$\dfrac{1}{\sqrt{\pi t}} - ae^{a^2t}\,\text{erfc}\,(a\sqrt{t})$
38	$\dfrac{\sqrt{s}}{s-a^2}$	$\dfrac{1}{\sqrt{\pi t}} + ae^{a^2t}\,\text{erf}\,(a\sqrt{t})$
39	$\dfrac{\sqrt{s}}{s+a^2}$	$\dfrac{1}{\sqrt{\pi t}} - \dfrac{2a}{\sqrt{\pi}}e^{-a^2t}\displaystyle\int_0^{a\sqrt{t}} e^{\lambda^2}\,d\lambda$
40	$\dfrac{1}{\sqrt{s}\,(s-a^2)}$	$\dfrac{1}{a}e^{a^2t}\,\text{erf}\,(a\sqrt{t})$
41	$\dfrac{1}{\sqrt{s}\,(s+a^2)}$	$\dfrac{2}{a\sqrt{\pi}}e^{-a^2t}\displaystyle\int_0^{a\sqrt{t}} e^{\lambda^2}\,d\lambda$
42	$\dfrac{b^2-a^2}{(s-a^2)(b+\sqrt{s})}$	$e^{a^2t}[b - a\,\text{erf}\,(a\sqrt{t})]$ $\qquad - be^{b^2t}\,\text{erfc}\,(b\sqrt{t})$
43	$\dfrac{1}{\sqrt{s}\,(\sqrt{s}+a)}$	$e^{a^2t}\,\text{erfc}\,(a\sqrt{t})$
44	$\dfrac{1}{(s+a)\sqrt{s+b}}$	$\dfrac{1}{\sqrt{b-a}}e^{-at}\,\text{erf}\,(\sqrt{b-a}\,\sqrt{t})$
45	$\dfrac{b^2-a^2}{\sqrt{s}\,(s-a^2)(\sqrt{s}+b)}$	$e^{a^2t}\left[\dfrac{b}{a}\,\text{erf}\,(a\sqrt{t}) - 1\right]$ $\qquad + e^{b^2t}\,\text{erfc}\,(b\sqrt{t})$
46*	$\dfrac{(1-s)^n}{s^{n+\frac{1}{2}}}$	$\dfrac{n!}{(2n)!\sqrt{\pi t}}H_{2n}(\sqrt{t})$
47	$\dfrac{(1-s)^n}{s^{n+\frac{3}{2}}}$	$-\dfrac{n!}{\sqrt{\pi}\,(2n+1)!}H_{2n+1}(\sqrt{t})$
48†	$\dfrac{\sqrt{s+2a}}{\sqrt{s}} - 1$	$ae^{-at}[I_1(at) + I_0(at)]$
49	$\dfrac{1}{\sqrt{s+a}\sqrt{s+b}}$	$e^{-\frac{1}{2}(a+b)t}I_0\left(\dfrac{a-b}{2}t\right)$
50	$\dfrac{\Gamma(k)}{(s+a)^k(s+b)^k}\ (k>0)$	$\sqrt{\pi}\left(\dfrac{t}{a-b}\right)^{k-\frac{1}{2}}e^{-\frac{1}{2}(a+b)t}$ $\qquad\qquad I_{k-\frac{1}{2}}\left(\dfrac{a-b}{2}t\right)$
51	$\dfrac{1}{(s+a)^{\frac{1}{2}}(s+b)^{\frac{3}{2}}}$	$te^{-\frac{1}{2}(a+b)t}\left[I_0\left(\dfrac{a-b}{2}t\right)\right.$ $\qquad\qquad \left. + I_1\left(\dfrac{a-b}{2}t\right)\right]$
52	$\dfrac{\sqrt{s+2a}-\sqrt{s}}{\sqrt{s+2a}+\sqrt{s}}$	$\dfrac{1}{t}e^{-at}I_1(at)$

* $H_n(x)$ is the Hermite polynomial, $H_n(x) = e^{x^2}\dfrac{d^n}{dx^n}(e^{-x^2})$.

† $I_n(x) = i^{-n}J_n(ix)$, where J_n is Bessel's function of the first kind.

	$f(s)$	$F(t)$
53	$\dfrac{(a-b)^k}{(\sqrt{s+a}+\sqrt{s+b})^{2k}}$ $(k>0)$	$\dfrac{k}{t}\,e^{-\frac{1}{2}(a+b)t}I_k\left(\dfrac{a-b}{2}\,t\right)$
54	$\dfrac{(\sqrt{s+a}+\sqrt{s})^{-2\nu}}{\sqrt{s}\,\sqrt{s+a}}$ $(\nu>-1)$	$\dfrac{1}{a^\nu}\,e^{-\frac{1}{2}at}I_\nu\left(\dfrac{1}{2}\,at\right)$
55	$\dfrac{1}{\sqrt{s^2+a^2}}$	$J_0(at)$
56	$\dfrac{(\sqrt{s^2+a^2}-s)^\nu}{\sqrt{s^2+a^2}}$ $(\nu>-1)$	$a^\nu J_\nu(at)$
57	$\dfrac{1}{(s^2+a^2)^k}$ $(k>0)$	$\dfrac{\sqrt{\pi}}{\Gamma(k)}\left(\dfrac{t}{2a}\right)^{k-\frac{1}{2}}J_{k-\frac{1}{2}}(at)$
58	$(\sqrt{s^2+a^2}-s)^k$ $(k>0)$	$\dfrac{ka^k}{t}\,J_k(at)$
59	$\dfrac{(s-\sqrt{s^2-a^2})^\nu}{\sqrt{s^2-a^2}}$ $(\nu>-1)$	$a^\nu I_\nu(at)$
60	$\dfrac{1}{(s^2-a^2)^k}$ $(k>0)$	$\dfrac{\sqrt{\pi}}{\Gamma(k)}\left(\dfrac{t}{2a}\right)^{k-\frac{1}{2}}I_{k-\frac{1}{2}}(at)$
61	$\dfrac{e^{-ks}}{s}$	$S_k(t)=\begin{cases}0 \text{ when } 0<t<k\\ 1 \text{ when } t>k\end{cases}$
62	$\dfrac{e^{-ks}}{s^2}$	$\begin{cases}0 \quad\text{ when } 0<t<k\\ t-k \text{ when } t>k\end{cases}$
63	$\dfrac{e^{-ks}}{s^\mu}$ $(\mu>0)$	$\begin{cases}0 \qquad\text{ when } 0<t<k\\ \dfrac{(t-k)^{\mu-1}}{\Gamma(\mu)} \text{ when } t>k\end{cases}$
64	$\dfrac{1-e^{-ks}}{s}$	$\begin{cases}1 \text{ when } 0<t<k\\ 0 \text{ when } t>k\end{cases}$
65	$\dfrac{1}{s(1-e^{-ks})}=\dfrac{1+\coth\frac{1}{2}ks}{2s}$	$S(k,t)=n$ when $(n-1)k$ $<t<nk(n=1,2,\cdots)$
66	$\dfrac{1}{s(e^{ks}-a)}$	$\begin{cases}0 \quad\text{when } 0<t<k\\ 1+a+a^2+\cdots+a^{n-1}\\ \quad\text{when } nk<t<(n+1)k\\ \qquad\qquad(n=1,2,\cdots)\end{cases}$
67	$\dfrac{1}{s}\tanh ks$	$M(2k,t)=(-1)^{n-1}$ when $2k(n-1)<t<2kn$ $(n=1,2,\cdots)$
68	$\dfrac{1}{s(1+e^{-ks})}$	$\dfrac{1}{2}M(k,t)+\dfrac{1}{2}=\dfrac{1-(-1)^n}{2}$ when $(n-1)k<t<nk$
69	$\dfrac{1}{s^2}\tanh ks$	$H(2k,t)$

	$f(s)$	$F(t)$
70	$\dfrac{1}{s \sinh ks}$	$2S(2k,\, t+k) - 2 = 2(n-1)$ when $(2n-3)k < t < (2n-1)k$ $(t > 0)$
71	$\dfrac{1}{s \cosh ks}$	$M(2k,\, t+3k) + 1 = 1 + (-1)^n$ when $(2n-3)k < t < (2n-1)k$ $(t > 0)$
72	$\dfrac{1}{s} \coth ks$	$2S(2k,\, t) - 1 = 2n - 1$ when $2k(n-1) < t < 2kn$
73	$\dfrac{k}{s^2 + k^2} \coth \dfrac{\pi s}{2k}$	$|\sin kt|$
74	$\dfrac{1}{(s^2 + 1)(1 - e^{-\pi s})}$	$\begin{cases} \sin t \text{ when } (2n-2)\pi \\ \qquad\qquad < t < (2n-1)\pi \\ 0 \quad \text{when } (2n-1)\pi \\ \qquad\qquad\qquad < t < 2n\pi \end{cases}$
75	$\dfrac{1}{s} e^{-\frac{k}{s}}$	$J_0(2\sqrt{kt})$
76	$\dfrac{1}{\sqrt{s}} e^{-\frac{k}{s}}$	$\dfrac{1}{\sqrt{\pi t}} \cos 2\sqrt{kt}$
77	$\dfrac{1}{\sqrt{s}} e^{\frac{k}{s}}$	$\dfrac{1}{\sqrt{\pi t}} \cosh 2\sqrt{kt}$
78	$\dfrac{1}{s^{\frac{3}{2}}} e^{-\frac{k}{s}}$	$\dfrac{1}{\sqrt{\pi k}} \sin 2\sqrt{kt}$
79	$\dfrac{1}{s^{\frac{3}{2}}} e^{\frac{k}{s}}$	$\dfrac{1}{\sqrt{\pi k}} \sinh 2\sqrt{kt}$
80	$\dfrac{1}{s^{\mu}} e^{-\frac{k}{s}}\ (\mu > 0)$	$\left(\dfrac{t}{k}\right)^{\frac{\mu-1}{2}} J_{\mu-1}(2\sqrt{kt})$
81	$\dfrac{1}{s^{\mu}} e^{\frac{k}{s}}\ (\mu > 0)$	$\left(\dfrac{t}{k}\right)^{\frac{\mu-1}{2}} I_{\mu-1}(2\sqrt{kt})$
82	$e^{-k\sqrt{s}}\ (k > 0)$	$\dfrac{k}{2\sqrt{\pi t^3}} \exp\left(-\dfrac{k^2}{4t}\right)$
83	$\dfrac{1}{s} e^{-k\sqrt{s}}\ (k \geqq 0)$	$\operatorname{erfc}\left(\dfrac{k}{2\sqrt{t}}\right)$
84	$\dfrac{1}{\sqrt{s}} e^{-k\sqrt{s}}\ (k \geqq 0)$	$\dfrac{1}{\sqrt{\pi t}} \exp\left(-\dfrac{k^2}{4t}\right)$
85	$s^{-\frac{3}{2}} e^{-k\sqrt{s}}\ (k \geqq 0)$	$2\sqrt{\dfrac{t}{\pi}} \exp\left(-\dfrac{k^2}{4t}\right)$ $- k \operatorname{erfc}\left(\dfrac{k}{2\sqrt{t}}\right)$

	$f(s)$	$F(t)$
86	$\dfrac{ae^{-k\sqrt{s}}}{s(a + \sqrt{s})}\ (k \geqq 0)$	$-e^{ak}e^{a^2t}\,\text{erfc}\left(a\,\sqrt{t} + \dfrac{k}{2\,\sqrt{t}}\right)$ $+ \text{erfc}\left(\dfrac{k}{2\,\sqrt{t}}\right)$
87	$\dfrac{e^{-k\sqrt{s}}}{\sqrt{s}\,(a + \sqrt{s})}\ (k \geqq 0)$	$e^{ak}e^{a^2t}\,\text{erfc}\left(a\,\sqrt{t} + \dfrac{k}{2\,\sqrt{t}}\right)$
88	$\dfrac{e^{-k\sqrt{s(s+a)}}}{\sqrt{s(s+a)}}$	$\begin{cases} 0 & \text{when } 0 < t < k \\ e^{-\frac{1}{2}at}I_0(\frac{1}{2}a\,\sqrt{t^2 - k^2}) \\ & \text{when } t > k \end{cases}$
89	$\dfrac{e^{-k\sqrt{s^2+a^2}}}{\sqrt{s^2 + a^2}}$	$\begin{cases} 0 & \text{when } 0 < t < k \\ J_0(a\,\sqrt{t^2 - k^2}) & \text{when } t > k \end{cases}$
90	$\dfrac{e^{-k\sqrt{s^2-a^2}}}{\sqrt{s^2 - a^2}}$	$\begin{cases} 0 & \text{when } 0 < t < k \\ I_0(a\,\sqrt{t^2 - k^2}) & \text{when } t > k \end{cases}$
91	$\dfrac{e^{-k(\sqrt{s^2+a^2}-s)}}{\sqrt{s^2 + a^2}}\ (k \geqq 0)$	$J_0(a\,\sqrt{t^2 + 2kt})$
92	$e^{-ks} - e^{-k\sqrt{s^2+a^2}}$	$\begin{cases} 0 & \text{when } 0 < t < k \\ \dfrac{ak}{\sqrt{t^2 - k^2}}\, J_1(a\,\sqrt{t^2 - k^2}) \\ & \text{when } t > k \end{cases}$
93	$e^{-k\sqrt{s^2-a^2}} - e^{-ks}$	$\begin{cases} 0 & \text{when } 0 < t < k \\ \dfrac{ak}{\sqrt{t^2 - k^2}}\, I_1(a\,\sqrt{t^2 - k^2}) \\ & \text{when } t > k \end{cases}$
94	$\dfrac{a^\nu e^{-k\sqrt{s^2+a^2}}}{\sqrt{s^2 + a^2}\,(\sqrt{s^2 + a^2} + s)^\nu}$ $(\nu > -1)$	$\begin{cases} 0 & \text{when } 0 < t < k \\ \left(\dfrac{t - k}{t + k}\right)^{\frac{1}{2}\nu} J_\nu(a\,\sqrt{t^2 - k^2}) \\ & \text{when } t > k \end{cases}$
95	$\dfrac{1}{s}\log s$	$\Gamma'(1) - \log t \quad [\Gamma'(1) = -0.5772]$
96	$\dfrac{1}{s^k}\log s\ (k > 0)$	$t^{k-1}\left\{\dfrac{\Gamma'(k)}{[\Gamma(k)]^2} - \dfrac{\log t}{\Gamma(k)}\right\}$
97	$\dfrac{\log s}{s - a}\ (a > 0)$	$e^{at}[\log a - \text{Ei}(-at)]$
98	$\dfrac{\log s}{s^2 + 1}$	$\cos t\ \text{Si}(t) - \sin t\ \text{Ci}(t)$

LAPLACE TRANSFORMS

	$f(s)$	$F(t)$
99	$\dfrac{s \log s}{s^2 + 1}$	$- \sin t \, \mathrm{Si}(t) - \cos t \, \mathrm{Ci}(t)$
100	$\dfrac{1}{s} \log (1 + ks) \; (k > 0)$	$-\mathrm{Ei}\left(-\dfrac{t}{k}\right)$
101	$\log \dfrac{s - a}{s - b}$	$\dfrac{1}{t} (e^{bt} - e^{at})$
102	$\dfrac{1}{s} \log (1 + k^2 s^2)$	$-2\mathrm{Ci}\left(\dfrac{t}{k}\right)$
103	$\dfrac{1}{s} \log (s^2 + a^2) \; (a > 0)$	$2 \log a - 2\mathrm{Ci}(at)$
104	$\dfrac{1}{s^2} \log (s^2 + a^2) \; (a > 0)$	$\dfrac{2}{a} [at \log a + \sin at - at \, \mathrm{Ci}(at)]$
105	$\log \dfrac{s^2 + a^2}{s^2}$	$\dfrac{2}{t} (1 - \cos at)$
106	$\log \dfrac{s^2 - a^2}{s^2}$	$\dfrac{2}{t} (1 - \cosh at)$
107	$\arctan \dfrac{k}{s}$	$\dfrac{1}{t} \sin kt$
108	$\dfrac{1}{s} \arctan \dfrac{k}{s}$	$\mathrm{Si}(kt)$
109	$e^{k^2 s^2} \mathrm{erfc} \, (ks) \; (k > 0)$	$\dfrac{1}{k \sqrt{\pi}} \exp\left(-\dfrac{t^2}{4k^2}\right)$
110	$\dfrac{1}{s} e^{k^2 s^2} \mathrm{erfc} \, (ks) \; (k > 0)$	$\mathrm{erf}\left(\dfrac{t}{2k}\right)$
111	$e^{ks} \mathrm{erfc} \, \sqrt{ks} \; (k > 0)$	$\dfrac{\sqrt{k}}{\pi \sqrt{t(t + k)}}$
112	$\dfrac{1}{\sqrt{s}} \mathrm{erfc} \, (\sqrt{ks})$	$\begin{cases} 0 & \text{when } 0 < t < k \\ (\pi t)^{-\frac{1}{2}} & \text{when } t > k \end{cases}$
113	$\dfrac{1}{\sqrt{s}} e^{ks} \mathrm{erfc} \, (\sqrt{ks}) \; (k > 0)$	$\dfrac{1}{\sqrt{\pi(t + k)}}$
114	$\mathrm{erf}\left(\dfrac{k}{\sqrt{s}}\right)$	$\dfrac{1}{\pi t} \sin (2k \sqrt{t})$
115	$\dfrac{1}{\sqrt{s}} e^{\frac{k^2}{s}} \mathrm{erfc}\left(\dfrac{k}{\sqrt{s}}\right)$	$\dfrac{1}{\sqrt{\pi t}} e^{-2k\sqrt{t}}$
116*	$K_0(ks)$	$\begin{cases} 0 & \text{when } 0 < t < k \\ (t^2 - k^2)^{-\frac{1}{2}} & \text{when } t > k \end{cases}$
117	$K_0(k \sqrt{s})$	$\dfrac{1}{2t} \exp\left(-\dfrac{k^2}{4t}\right)$

* $K_n(x)$ is Bessel's function of the second kind for the imaginary argument.

	$f(s)$	$F(t)$
118	$\dfrac{1}{s} e^{ks} K_1(ks)$	$\dfrac{1}{k} \sqrt{t(t+2k)}$
119	$\dfrac{1}{\sqrt{s}} K_1(k \sqrt{s})$	$\dfrac{1}{k} \exp\left(-\dfrac{k^2}{4t}\right)$
120	$\dfrac{1}{\sqrt{s}} e^{\frac{k}{s}} K_0\left(\dfrac{k}{s}\right)$	$\dfrac{2}{\sqrt{\pi t}} K_0(2\sqrt{2kt})$
121	$\pi e^{-ks} I_0(ks)$	$\begin{cases} [t(2k-t)]^{-\frac{1}{2}} & \text{when } 0 < t < 2k \\ 0 & \text{when } t > 2k \end{cases}$
122*	$e^{-ks} I_1(ks)$	$\begin{cases} \dfrac{k-t}{\pi k \sqrt{t(2k-t)}} & \text{when } 0 < t < 2k \\ 0 & \text{when } t > 2k \end{cases}$

* Several additional transforms, especially those involving other Bessel functions, can be found in the tables by G. A. Campbell and R. M. Foster, "Fourier Integrals for Practical Applications," or N. W. McLachlan and P. Humbert, "Formulaire pour le calcul symbolique." In the tables by Campbell and Foster, only those entries containing the condition $0 < g$ or $k < g$, where g is our t, are Laplace transforms.

ALGEBRA

FACTORS AND EXPANSIONS

$(a \pm b)^2 = a^2 \pm 2ab + b^2.$

$(a \pm b)^3 = a^3 \pm 3a^2b + 3ab^2 \pm b^3.$

$(a \pm b)^4 = a^4 \pm 4a^3b + 6a^2b^2 \pm 4ab^3 + b^4.$

$a^2 - b^2 = (a - b)(a + b).$

$a^2 + b^2 = (a + b\sqrt{-1})(a - b\sqrt{-1}).$

$a^3 - b^3 = (a - b)(a^2 + ab + b^2).$

$a^3 + b^3 = (a + b)(a^2 - ab + b^2).$

$a^4 + b^4 = (a^2 + ab\sqrt{2} + b^2)(a^2 - ab\sqrt{2} + b^2).$

$a^n - b^n = (a - b)(a^{n-1} + a^{n-2}b + \ldots + b^{n-1}).$

$a^n - b^n = (a + b)(a^{n-1} - a^{n-2}b + \ldots - b^{n-1}),$

for even values of n.

$a^n + b^n = (a + b)(a^{n-1} - a^{n-2}b + \ldots + b^{n-1}),$

for odd values of n.

$a^4 + a^2b^2 + b^4 = (a^2 + ab + b^2)(a^2 - ab + b^2).$

$(a + b + c)^2 = a^2 + b^2 + c^2 + 2ab + 2ac + 2bc.$

$(a + b + c)^3 = a^3 + b^3 + c^3 + 3a^2(b + c) + 3b^2(a + c) + 3c^2(a + b) + 6abc.$

$(a + b + c + d + \ldots)^2 = a^2 + b^2 + c^2 + d^2 + \ldots + 2a(b + c + d + \ldots) + 2b(c + d + \ldots) + 2c(d + \ldots) + \ldots$

See also under Series.

POWERS AND ROOTS

$a^x \times a^y = a^{(x+y)}.$ $\qquad a^0 = 1 \, [\text{if } a \neq 0]$ $(ab)^x = a^x b^x.$

$\dfrac{a^x}{a^y} = a^{(x-y)}.$ $\qquad a^{-x} = \dfrac{1}{a^x}.$ $\qquad \left(\dfrac{a}{b}\right)^x = \dfrac{a^x}{b^x}.$

$(a^x)^y = a^{xy}.$ $\qquad a^{\frac{1}{x}} = \sqrt[x]{a}.$ $\qquad \sqrt[x]{ab} = \sqrt[x]{a}\,\sqrt[x]{b}.$

$\sqrt[x]{\sqrt[y]{a}} = \sqrt[xy]{a}.$ $\qquad a^{\frac{x}{y}} = \sqrt[y]{a^x}.$ $\qquad \sqrt[x]{\dfrac{a}{b}} = \dfrac{\sqrt[x]{a}}{\sqrt[x]{b}}.$

PROPORTION

If $\quad \dfrac{a}{b} = \dfrac{c}{d},\quad$ then $\qquad \dfrac{a + b}{b} = \dfrac{c + d}{d},$

$\dfrac{a - b}{b} = \dfrac{c - d}{d}, \qquad \dfrac{a - b}{a + b} = \dfrac{c - d}{c + d}.$

ALGEBRA
SUMS OF NUMBERS

The sum of the first n numbers, —

$$\Sigma(n) = 1 + 2 + 3 + 4 + 5 \ldots + n = \frac{n(n+1)}{2}$$

The sum of the squares of the first n numbers,

$$\Sigma(n^2) = 1^2 + 2^2 + 3^2 + 4^2 + 5^2 \ldots + n^2 = \frac{n(n+1)(2n+1)}{6}$$

The sum of the cubes of the first n numbers,

$$\Sigma(n^3) = 1^3 + 2^3 + 3^3 + 4^3 + 5^3 \ldots + n^3 = \frac{n^2(n+1)^2}{4}$$

ARITHMETICAL PROGRESSION

If a is the first term; l, the last term; d, the common difference; n, the number of terms and s, the sum of n terms, —

$$l = a + (n-1)d \qquad s = \frac{n}{2}(a+l)$$

$$s = \frac{n}{2}\left\{2a + (n-1)d\right\}$$

GEOMETRICAL PROGRESSION

If a is the first term; l, the last term; r, the common ratio; n, the number of terms and s, the sum of n terms, —

$$l = ar^{n-1} \qquad\qquad s = a\frac{(1-r^n)}{1-r}$$

$$s = a\frac{(r^n-1)}{r-1} \qquad\qquad s = \frac{lr-a}{r-1}$$

If n is infinity and r^2 less than unity, $\quad s = \frac{a}{1-r}$

FACTORIALS

$$\underline{|n} = n! = e^{-n}n^n\sqrt{2\pi n}, \text{ approximately.}$$

PERMUTATIONS

If M denote the number of permutations of n things taken p at a time, —

$$M = n(n-1)(n-2) \ldots (n-p+1)$$

COMBINATIONS

If M denote the number of combinations of n things taken p at a time, —

$$M = \frac{n(n-1)(n-2) \ldots (n-p+1)}{p!} = \frac{n!}{p!(n-p)!}$$

QUADRATIC EQUATIONS

Any quadratic equation may be reduced to the form, —

$$ax^2 + bx + c = 0.$$

Then $$x = \frac{-b \pm \sqrt{b^2 - 4ac}}{2a}.$$

If $b^2 - 4ac$ is positive the roots are real and unequal.

If $b^2 - 4ac$ is zero the roots are real and equal.

If $b^2 - 4ac$ is negative the roots are imaginary and unequal.

If $b^2 - 4ac$ is a perfect square the roots are rational and unequal.

CUBIC EQUATIONS

A cubic equation, $y^3 + py^2 + qy + r = 0$ may be reduced to the form, —

$$x^3 + ax + b = 0$$

by substituting for y the value, $x - \frac{p}{3}$. Here

$$a = \tfrac{1}{3}(3q - p^2) \text{ and } b = \tfrac{1}{27}(2p^3 - 9pq + 27r).$$

For solution let, —

$$A = \sqrt[3]{-\frac{b}{2} + \sqrt{\frac{b^2}{4} + \frac{a^3}{27}}}, \qquad B = \sqrt[3]{-\frac{b}{2} - \sqrt{\frac{b^2}{4} + \frac{a^3}{27}}},$$

then the values of x will be given by,

$$x = A + B, \qquad -\frac{A+B}{2} + \frac{A-B}{2}\sqrt{-3}, \qquad -\frac{A+B}{2} - \frac{A-B}{2}\sqrt{-3}.$$

If $\dfrac{b^2}{4} + \dfrac{a^3}{27} > 0$, there will be one real root and two conjugate imaginary roots.

If $\dfrac{b^2}{4} + \dfrac{a^3}{27} = 0$, there will be three real roots of which at least two are equal.

If $\dfrac{b^2}{4} + \dfrac{a^3}{27} < 0$, there will be three real and unequal roots.

In the last case a trigonometric solution is useful. Compute the value of the angle ϕ in the expression,—

$$\cos \phi = -\frac{b}{2} \div \sqrt{\left(-\frac{a^3}{27}\right)},$$

then x will have the following values:—

$$2\sqrt{-\frac{a}{3}} \cos \frac{\phi}{3}, \qquad 2\sqrt{-\frac{a}{3}} \cos\left(\frac{\phi}{3} + 120°\right),$$

$$2\sqrt{-\frac{a}{3}} \cos\left(\frac{\phi}{3} + 240°\right).$$

APPROXIMATIONS

If a and b are small quantities, the following relations are approximately true,—

$$(1 \pm a)^m = 1 \pm ma,$$
$$(1 \pm a)^m (1 \pm b)^n = 1 \pm ma \pm nb.$$

If n is nearly equal to m,

$$\sqrt{mn} = \frac{n+m}{2}, \text{ approximately.}$$

If θ is a very small angle expressed in radians,—

$$\frac{\sin\theta}{\theta} = 1 \text{ and } \frac{\tan\theta}{\theta} = 1, \text{ approximately.}$$

SERIES

The expression in parentheses following certain of the series indicates the region of convergence. If not otherwise indicated it is to be understood that the series converges for all finite values of x.

BINOMIAL

$$(x+y)^n = x^n + nx^{n-1}y + \frac{n(n-1)}{2!}x^{n-2}y^2 +$$
$$\frac{n(n-1)(n-2)}{3!}x^{(n-3)}y^3 + \ldots . \quad (y^2 < x^2)$$

$$(1 \pm x)^n = 1 \pm nx + \frac{n(n-1)x^2}{2!} \pm \frac{n(n-1)(n-2)x^3}{3!} + \ldots \text{ etc.}$$
$$(x^2 < 1)$$

$$(1 \pm x)^{-n} = 1 \mp nx + \frac{n(n+1)x^2}{2!} \mp \frac{n(n+1)(n+2)x^3}{3!} + \ldots \text{ etc.}$$
$$(x^2 < 1)$$

$$(1 \pm x)^{-1} = 1 \mp x + x^2 \mp x^3 + x^4 \mp x^5 + \ldots \qquad (x^2 < 1)$$

$$(1 \pm x)^{-2} = 1 \mp 2x + 3x^2 \mp 4x^3 + 5x^4 \mp 6x^5 + \ldots \qquad (x^2 < 1)$$

TAYLOR'S SERIES

$$f(x+h) = f(x) + hf'(x) + \frac{h^2}{2!}f''(x) + \frac{h^3}{3!}f'''(x) + \ldots$$

$$= f(h) + xf'(h) + \frac{x^2}{2!}f''(h) + \frac{x^3}{3!}f'''(h) + \ldots$$

MACLAURIN'S SERIES

$$f(x) = f(o) + xf'(o) + \frac{x^2}{2!}f''(o) + \frac{x^3}{3!}f'''(o) + \ldots$$

EXPONENTIAL

$$e = 1 + \frac{1}{1} + \frac{1}{2!} + \frac{1}{3!} + \frac{1}{4!} + \ldots$$

$$e^x = 1 + x + \frac{x^2}{2!} + \frac{x^3}{3!} + \frac{x^4}{4!} + \ldots$$

$$a^x = 1 + x \log_e a + \frac{(x \log a)^2}{2!} + \frac{(x \log a)^3}{3!} + \ldots$$

ALGEBRA

LOGARITHMIC

$$\log_e x = \frac{x-1}{x} + \frac{1}{2}\left(\frac{x-1}{x}\right)^2 + \frac{1}{3}\left(\frac{x-1}{x}\right)^3 + \ldots$$
$$(x > \tfrac{1}{2})$$

$$\log_e x = (x-1) - \tfrac{1}{2}(x-1)^2 + \tfrac{1}{3}(x-1)^3 - \ldots$$
$$(2 > x > 0)$$

$$\log_e x = 2\left[\frac{x-1}{x+1} + \frac{1}{3}\left(\frac{x-1}{x+1}\right)^3 + \frac{1}{5}\left(\frac{x-1}{x+1}\right)^5 + \ldots\right]$$
$$(x > 0)$$

$$\log_e(1+x) = x - \tfrac{1}{2}x^2 + \tfrac{1}{3}x^3 - \tfrac{1}{4}x^4 + \ldots \quad (-1 < x < 1)$$

$$\log_e(n+1) - \log_e(n-1) = 2\left[\frac{1}{n} + \frac{1}{3n^3} + \frac{1}{5n^5} + \ldots\right]$$

$$\log_e(a+x) = \log_e a + 2\left[\frac{x}{2a+x} + \frac{1}{3}\left(\frac{x}{2a+x}\right)^3 + \frac{1}{5}\left(\frac{x}{2a+x}\right)^5 + \ldots\right]$$
$$(a > 0, -a < x < +\infty)$$

TRIGONOMETRIC

$$\sin x = x - \frac{x^3}{3!} + \frac{x^5}{5!} - \frac{x^7}{7!} + \ldots$$

$$\cos x = 1 - \frac{x^2}{2!} + \frac{x^4}{4!} - \frac{x^6}{6!} + \ldots$$

$$\tan x = x + \frac{x^3}{3} + \frac{2x^5}{15} + \frac{17x^7}{315} + \frac{62x^9}{2835} + \ldots \quad \left(x^2 < \frac{\pi^2}{4}\right)$$

$$\sin^{-1}x = x + \frac{x^3}{6} + \frac{1}{2}\cdot\frac{3}{4}\cdot\frac{x^5}{5} + \frac{1}{2}\cdot\frac{3}{4}\cdot\frac{5}{6}\cdot\frac{x^7}{7} + \ldots \quad (x^2 < 1)$$

$$\tan^{-1}x = x - \tfrac{1}{3}x^3 + \tfrac{1}{5}x^5 - \tfrac{1}{7}x^7 + \ldots \quad (x^2 < 1)$$

$$= \frac{\pi}{2} - \frac{1}{x} + \frac{1}{3x^3} - \frac{1}{5x^5} + \ldots \quad (x^2 > 1)$$

$$\log_e \sin x = \log_e x - \frac{x^2}{6} - \frac{x^4}{180} - \frac{x^6}{2835} - \ldots \quad (x^2 < \pi^2)$$

$$\log_e \cos x = -\frac{x^2}{2} - \frac{x^4}{12} - \frac{x^6}{45} - \frac{17x^8}{2520} - \ldots \quad \left(x^2 < \frac{\pi^2}{4}\right)$$

$$\log_e \tan x = \log_e x + \frac{x^2}{3} + \frac{7x^4}{90} + \frac{62x^6}{2835} + \ldots \quad \left(x^2 < \frac{\pi^2}{4}\right)$$

$$e^{\sin x} = 1 + x + \frac{x^2}{2!} - \frac{3x^4}{4!} - \frac{8x^5}{5!} - \frac{3x^6}{6!} + \frac{56x^7}{7!} + \ldots$$

$$e^{\cos x} = e\left(1 - \frac{x^2}{2!} + \frac{4x^4}{4!} - \frac{31x^6}{6!} + \ldots\right)$$

$$e^{\tan x} = 1 + x + \frac{x^2}{2!} + \frac{3x^3}{3!} + \frac{9x^4}{4!} + \frac{37x^5}{5!} + \ldots \quad \left(x^2 < \frac{\pi^2}{4}\right)$$

FOURIER SERIES

If $f(x) = \dfrac{a_0}{2} + a_1 \cos \dfrac{2\pi x}{T} + a_2 \cos \dfrac{4\pi x}{T} + \cdots + a_m \cos \dfrac{2\pi m x}{T} + \cdots$

$\qquad\qquad + b_1 \sin \dfrac{2\pi x}{T} + b_2 \sin \dfrac{4\pi x}{T} + b_3 \sin \dfrac{6\pi x}{T} + \cdots$

$\qquad\qquad\qquad\qquad\qquad\qquad + b_n \sin \dfrac{2\pi n x}{T} + \cdots,$

where

$a_0 = \dfrac{2}{T}\displaystyle\int_c^{c+T} f(x)dx, \quad a_m = \dfrac{2}{T}\displaystyle\int_c^{c+T} f(x)\ \cos \dfrac{2\pi m x}{T}\ dx,\ b_n =$

$\dfrac{2}{T}\displaystyle\int_c^{c+T} f(x)\ \sin\dfrac{2\pi n x}{T}dx,$ and $f(x + T) = f(x),$ with c and T constants.

VECTOR ANALYSIS
Definitions

Any quantity which is completely determined by its magnitude is called a *scalar*. Examples of such are mass, density, temperature, etc. Any quantity which is completely determined by its magnitude and direction is called a *vector*. Examples of such are velocity, acceleration, force, etc. A vector quantity is represented by a directed line segment, the length of which represents the magnitude of the vector. A vector quantity is usually represented by a bold-faced letter such as $\mathbf{V}$. Two vectors $\mathbf{V}_1$ and $\mathbf{V}_2$ are equal to one another if they have equal magnitudes and are acting in the same directions. A negative vector, written as $-\mathbf{V}$ is one which acts in the opposite direction to $\mathbf{V}$, but is of equal magnitude to it. If we represent the magnitude of $\mathbf{V}$ by v, we write $|\mathbf{V}| = v$. A vector parallel to $\mathbf{V}$, but equal to the reciprocal of its magnitude is written as $\mathbf{V}^{-1}$ or as $\frac{1}{\mathbf{V}}$.

The unit vector $\frac{\mathbf{V}}{|\mathbf{V}|}$ $(\mathbf{V} \neq 0)$ is the one which has the same direction as $\mathbf{V}$, but has a magnitude of 1.

Vector Algebra

The vector sum of $\mathbf{V}_1$ and $\mathbf{V}_2$ is represented by $\mathbf{V}_1 + \mathbf{V}_2$. The vector sum of $\mathbf{V}_1$ and $-\mathbf{V}_2$, or the difference of the vector $\mathbf{V}_2$ from $\mathbf{V}_1$ is represented by $\mathbf{V}_1 - \mathbf{V}_2$.

If r is a scalar, then $r\mathbf{V} = \mathbf{V}r$, and represents a vector r times the magnitude of $\mathbf{V}$, in the same direction as $\mathbf{V}$ if r is positive, and in the opposite direction if r is negative. If r and s are scalars, $\mathbf{V}_1$, $\mathbf{V}_2$, $\mathbf{V}_3$, vectors, then the following rules of scalars and vectors hold:

$$\mathbf{V}_1 + \mathbf{V}_2 = \mathbf{V}_2 + \mathbf{V}_1$$
$$(r + s)\mathbf{V}_1 = r\mathbf{V}_1 + s\mathbf{V}_1; \qquad r(\mathbf{V}_1 + \mathbf{V}_2) = r\mathbf{V}_1 + r\mathbf{V}_2$$
$$\mathbf{V}_1 + (\mathbf{V}_2 + \mathbf{V}_3) = (\mathbf{V}_1 + \mathbf{V}_2) + \mathbf{V}_3 = \mathbf{V}_1 + \mathbf{V}_2 + \mathbf{V}_3$$

If $\mathbf{V}_1$ is a vector in space, and a_1, b_1, c_1, the respective magnitudes of the projections of the vector along the coordinate Ox, Oy, Oz axes, then

$\mathbf{V}_1 = a_1\mathbf{i} + b_1\mathbf{j} + c_1\mathbf{k}$, where $\mathbf{i}$, $\mathbf{j}$, $\mathbf{k}$ are respectively the unit vectors along Ox, Oy, and Oz. Its magnitude is

$$|\mathbf{V}_1| = \sqrt{a_1^2 + b_1^2 + c_1^2},$$

and its direction cosines satisfy the proportion

$$a_1 : b_1 : c_1 = \cos\alpha : \cos\beta : \cos\gamma.$$

Thus, if $\mathbf{V}_1 = a_1\mathbf{i} + b_1\mathbf{j} + c_1\mathbf{k}$ and $\mathbf{V}_2 = a_2\mathbf{i} + b_2\mathbf{j} + c_2\mathbf{k}$,
Then $\mathbf{V}_1 + \mathbf{V}_2 = (a_1 + a_2)\mathbf{i} + (b_1 + b_2)\mathbf{j} + (c_1 + c_2)\mathbf{k}$

The Scalar, Dot, or Inner Product of Two Vectors $\mathbf{V}_1$ and $\mathbf{V}_2$

This product is represented as $\mathbf{V}_1 \cdot \mathbf{V}_2$ and is defined to be equal to $|\mathbf{V}_1|\,|\mathbf{V}_2|\cos\theta$, where θ is the angle from $\mathbf{V}_1$ to $\mathbf{V}_2$, i.e.,

$$\mathbf{V}_1 \cdot \mathbf{V}_2 = |\mathbf{V}_1|\,|\mathbf{V}_2|\cos\theta$$

The following rules apply for this product:

$$\mathbf{V}_1 \cdot \mathbf{V}_2 = a_1a_2 + b_1b_2 + c_1c_2 = \mathbf{V}_2 \cdot \mathbf{V}_1$$

It should be noted that scalar multiplication is commutative.
If $\mathbf{V}_1 = \mathbf{V}_2$, then $\mathbf{V}_1 \cdot \mathbf{V}_2 = |\mathbf{V}_1|^2$

$$(\mathbf{V}_1 + \mathbf{V}_2) \cdot \mathbf{V}_3 = \mathbf{V}_1 \cdot \mathbf{V}_3 + \mathbf{V}_2 \cdot \mathbf{V}_3$$
$$\mathbf{V}_1 \cdot (\mathbf{V}_2 + \mathbf{V}_3) = \mathbf{V}_1 \cdot \mathbf{V}_2 + \mathbf{V}_1 \cdot \mathbf{V}_3$$
$$\mathbf{i} \cdot \mathbf{i} = \mathbf{j} \cdot \mathbf{j} = \mathbf{k} \cdot \mathbf{k} = 1; \quad \mathbf{i} \cdot \mathbf{j} = \mathbf{j} \cdot \mathbf{k} = \mathbf{k} \cdot \mathbf{i} = 0$$

The Vector or Cross Product of Vectors $\mathbf{V}_1$ and $\mathbf{V}_2$

This product is represented as $\mathbf{V}_1 \times \mathbf{V}_2$ and is defined to be equal to $|\mathbf{V}_1|\,|\mathbf{V}_2|(\sin\theta)\mathbf{l}$, where θ is the angle from $\mathbf{V}_1$ to $\mathbf{V}_2$ and $\mathbf{l}$ is a unit vector perpendicular to the plane of $\mathbf{V}_1$ and $\mathbf{V}_2$ and so directed that a right-handed screw driven in the direction of $\mathbf{l}$ would carry $\mathbf{V}_1$ into $\mathbf{V}_2$, i.e.,

$$\mathbf{V}_1 \times \mathbf{V}_2 = |\mathbf{V}_1|\,|\mathbf{V}_2|(\sin\theta)\mathbf{l}$$

The following rules apply for vector products:

$$\mathbf{V}_1 \times \mathbf{V}_2 = -\mathbf{V}_2 \times \mathbf{V}_1$$
$$\mathbf{V}_1 \times (\mathbf{V}_2 + \mathbf{V}_3) = \mathbf{V}_1 \times \mathbf{V}_2 + \mathbf{V}_1 \times \mathbf{V}_3$$
$$(\mathbf{V}_1 + \mathbf{V}_2) \times \mathbf{V}_3 = \mathbf{V}_1 \times \mathbf{V}_3 + \mathbf{V}_2 \times \mathbf{V}_3$$
$$\mathbf{V}_1 \times (\mathbf{V}_2 \times \mathbf{V}_3) = \mathbf{V}_2(\mathbf{V}_1 \cdot \mathbf{V}_3) - \mathbf{V}_3(\mathbf{V}_1 \cdot \mathbf{V}_2)$$
$$\mathbf{i} \times \mathbf{i} = \mathbf{j} \times \mathbf{j} = \mathbf{k} \times \mathbf{k} = 0.\mathbf{l} \text{ (zero vector)}$$
$$= 0$$
$$\mathbf{i} \times \mathbf{j} = \mathbf{k}, \quad \mathbf{j} \times \mathbf{k} = \mathbf{i}, \quad \mathbf{k} \times \mathbf{i} = \mathbf{j}$$

If $\mathbf{V}_1 = a_1\mathbf{i} + b_1\mathbf{j} + c_1\mathbf{k}$, $\quad \mathbf{V}_2 = a_2\mathbf{i} + b_2\mathbf{j} + c_2\mathbf{k}$,
$\quad \mathbf{V}_3 = a_3\mathbf{i} + b_3\mathbf{j} + c_3\mathbf{k}$,

then

$$\mathbf{V}_1 \times \mathbf{V}_2 = \begin{vmatrix} \mathbf{i} & \mathbf{j} & \mathbf{k} \\ a_1 & b_1 & c_1 \\ a_2 & b_2 & c_2 \end{vmatrix} = (b_1c_2 - b_2c_1)\mathbf{i} + (c_1a_2 - c_2a_1)\mathbf{j} + (a_1b_2 - a_2b_1)\mathbf{k}$$

It should be noted that, since $\mathbf{V}_1 \times \mathbf{V}_2 = -\mathbf{V}_2 \times \mathbf{V}_1$, the vector product is not commutative.

$$\mathbf{V}_1 \cdot (\mathbf{V}_2 \times \mathbf{V}_3) = (\mathbf{V}_1 \times \mathbf{V}_2) \cdot \mathbf{V}_3 = \mathbf{V}_2 \cdot (\mathbf{V}_3 \times \mathbf{V}_1)$$

$$= (\mathbf{V}_1 \mathbf{V}_2 \mathbf{V}_3) = \begin{vmatrix} a_1 & b_1 & c_1 \\ a_2 & b_2 & c_2 \\ a_3 & b_3 & c_3 \end{vmatrix}$$

which is equal to the volume of a parallelepiped whose three determining edges are $\mathbf{V}_1$, $\mathbf{V}_2$, $\mathbf{V}_3$.

Differentiation of Vectors

If $\mathbf{V}_1 = a_1\mathbf{i} + b_1\mathbf{j} + c_1\mathbf{k}$, and $\mathbf{V}_2 = a_2\mathbf{i} + b_2\mathbf{j} + c_2\mathbf{k}$, and if $\mathbf{V}_1$ and $\mathbf{V}_2$ are functions of the scalar t, then

$$\frac{d}{dt}(\mathbf{V}_1 + \mathbf{V}_2 + \cdots) = \frac{d\mathbf{V}_1}{dt} + \frac{d\mathbf{V}_2}{dt} + \cdots,$$

where $\dfrac{d\mathbf{V}_1}{dt} = \dfrac{da_1}{dt}\mathbf{i} + \dfrac{db_1}{dt}\mathbf{j} + \dfrac{dc_1}{dt}\mathbf{k}$, etc.

$$\frac{d}{dt}(\mathbf{V}_1 \cdot \mathbf{V}_2) = \frac{d\mathbf{V}_1}{dt} \cdot \mathbf{V}_2 + \mathbf{V}_1 \cdot \frac{d\mathbf{V}_2}{dt}$$

$$\frac{d}{dt}(\mathbf{V}_1 \times \mathbf{V}_2) = \frac{d\mathbf{V}_1}{dt} \times \mathbf{V}_2 + \mathbf{V}_1 \times \frac{d\mathbf{V}_2}{dt}$$

Differential Operators—Rectangular Coordinates

By definition

$$\nabla \equiv \text{del} \equiv \mathbf{i}\frac{\delta}{\delta x} + \mathbf{j}\frac{\delta}{\delta y} + \mathbf{k}\frac{\delta}{\delta z}$$

$$\nabla^2 \equiv \text{Laplacian} \equiv \frac{\delta^2}{\delta x^2} + \frac{\delta^2}{\delta y^2} + \frac{\delta^2}{\delta z^2}$$

If S is a scalar function, then

$$\nabla S \equiv \text{grad } S \equiv \frac{\delta S}{\delta x}\mathbf{i} + \frac{\delta S}{\delta y}\mathbf{j} + \frac{\delta S}{\delta z}\mathbf{k}$$

The *distributive* law holds for finding a gradient. Thus if S and T are scalar functions

$$\nabla(S + T) = \nabla S + \nabla T$$

The *associative* law becomes the rule for differentiating a product:

$$\nabla(ST) = S\nabla T + T\nabla S$$

If $\mathbf{V}$ is a vector function with the magnitudes of the components parallel to the three coordinate axes V_x, V_y, V_z, then

$$\nabla \cdot \mathbf{V} \equiv \text{div } \mathbf{V} \equiv \frac{\delta V_x}{\delta x} + \frac{\delta V_y}{\delta y} + \frac{\delta V_z}{\delta z}$$

The divergence obeys the distributive law. Thus, if **V** and **U** are vector functions, then

$$\nabla \cdot (\mathbf{V} + \mathbf{U}) = \nabla \cdot \mathbf{V} + \nabla \cdot \mathbf{U}$$

$$\nabla \times \mathbf{V} \equiv \operatorname{curl} \mathbf{V} \equiv \operatorname{rot} \mathbf{V} \equiv \begin{vmatrix} \mathbf{i} & \mathbf{j} & \mathbf{k} \\ \dfrac{\delta}{\delta x} & \dfrac{\delta}{\delta y} & \dfrac{\delta}{\delta z} \\ V_x & V_y & V_z \end{vmatrix}$$

The operator ∇ can be used more than once. The number of possibilities where ∇ is used twice are

$$\nabla \cdot (\nabla \theta) \equiv \operatorname{div} \operatorname{grad} \theta$$
$$\nabla \times (\nabla \theta) \equiv \operatorname{curl} \operatorname{grad} \theta$$
$$\nabla(\nabla \cdot \mathbf{V}) \equiv \operatorname{grad} \operatorname{div} \mathbf{V}$$
$$\nabla \cdot (\nabla \times \mathbf{V}) \equiv \operatorname{div} \operatorname{curl} \mathbf{V}$$
$$\nabla \times (\nabla \times \mathbf{V}) \equiv \operatorname{curl} \operatorname{curl} \mathbf{V}$$

Thus: $\operatorname{div} \operatorname{grad} S \equiv \nabla \cdot (\nabla S) \equiv \operatorname{Laplacian} S \equiv \nabla^2 S$

$$\equiv \frac{\delta^2 S}{\delta x^2} + \frac{\delta^2 S}{\delta y^2} + \frac{\delta^2 S}{\delta z^2}$$

$\operatorname{curl} \operatorname{grad} S \equiv 0;$ $\operatorname{curl} \operatorname{curl} \mathbf{V} \equiv \operatorname{grad} \operatorname{div} \mathbf{V} - \nabla \mathbf{V};$

$$\operatorname{div} \operatorname{curl} \mathbf{V} \equiv 0$$

Green's Theorem

Let **F** be a vector function and v a volume bounded by a surface s, then

$$\iiint_{(v)} \operatorname{div} \mathbf{F} = \iiint_{(v)} \nabla \cdot \mathbf{F} \, dv = \iint_{(s)} \mathbf{F} \cdot ds,$$

where the integrations are to be carried out over the volume v and the surface s.

Stokes Theorem

Let **F** be a vector function and s a surface bounded by a simple closed curve c, then

$$\int_{(c)} \mathbf{F} \cdot d\mathbf{1} = \iint_{(s)} (\nabla \times \mathbf{F}) \cdot ds = \iint_{(s)} \operatorname{curl} \mathbf{F} \cdot ds,$$

where the integrations are to be carried out over the curve c and the surface s.   It should be noted that

$$d\mathbf{1} = dx \, \mathbf{i} + dy \, \mathbf{j} + dz \, \mathbf{k}$$

The theorem implies that the line integral of **F** over the contour c equals the surface integral of $\nabla \times \mathbf{F}$ over a surface s which is bounded by c.

MISCELLANEOUS

THE SUM (Σ, = SIGMA) AND PRODUCT (Π, = PI) NOTATIONS

Σ denotes the **sum,** and Π, the **product** of all quantities of a given collection. In particular,

$$\sum_{i=m}^{m+n} x_i \text{ means } x_m + x_{m+1} + \ldots + x_{m+n}, \ (n+1 \text{ terms in all}),$$

$$\prod_{i=m}^{m+n} x_i \text{ means } x_m x_{m+1} \ldots x_{m+n}, \ (n+1 \text{ factors in all}).$$

For indicated **range,** R, (such as $m \leqq i \leqq m + n$), one may write $\sum_R x_i, \prod_R x_i$, respectively. Where the range is clear from the context one writes $\Sigma x_i, \Pi x_i$, or even $\Sigma x, \Pi x$, respectively. For c a constant and for x_i and y_i with common range (say of n elements),

$$\Sigma c x_i = c \Sigma x_i, \quad \Sigma(x_i + y_i) = \Sigma x_i + \Sigma y_i, \quad \Sigma(x_i + c) = nc + \Sigma x_i.$$

SPECIAL NUMERICAL RELATIONS

(i) For range, $i = 1, 2, \ldots, n$, with $x_i = i$.
$\Sigma x_i = n(n+1)/2$, $\Sigma(2x_i - 1) = n^2$,
$\Sigma x_i^2 = n(n+1)(2n+1)/6$.
$\Sigma x_i^3 = (\Sigma x_i)^2$, $\Sigma x_i^4 = (\Sigma x_i^2)[6(\Sigma x_i) - 1]/5$.
$\Pi(c + 1 - x_i) = c^{(n)}$, $\Pi x_i = n^{(n)} = n!$ (**"factorial n"**).
Hence $n! = n . (n-1)!$ $0!$ is defined to be 1.

Stirling's formula (used for n large),

$$\sqrt{2n\pi}(n/e)^n < n! < \sqrt{2n\pi}(n/e)^n\left(1 + \frac{1}{12n-1}\right),$$

$$(\pi = 3.14159 \ldots, e = 2.71828 \ldots).$$

$n!/(n-m)!$ gives the number of **permutations of n distinct things taken m at a time.**

(ii) For range, $i = -\left(\dfrac{n-1}{2}\right), -\left(\dfrac{n-1}{2}\right) + 1, \ldots,$

$$\left(\frac{n-1}{2}\right) - 1, \left(\frac{n-1}{2}\right), \text{ with}$$

$x_i = i$ (whether n is odd or even),

$$\sum x_i = \sum x_i^3 = 0, \quad \sum x_i^2 = \frac{n(n^2-1)}{12}, \quad \sum x_i^4 = \frac{3n^2-7}{20}\sum x_i^2.$$

(iii) The Binomial Coefficients, $\binom{n}{m}$.

$\binom{n}{m} = n!/[(n-m)!m!]$, for integers m, n, $0 \leq m \leq n$. $\binom{n}{0} = \binom{n}{n} = 1$.

$(x+c)^n = \sum_r \binom{n}{r} x^{n-r} c^r$, $(0 \leq r \leq n)$, the **binomial expansion.** $\binom{n}{m}$

gives also the number of **combinations of n distinct things taken m at a time.**

$\binom{n}{m} + \binom{n}{m+1} = \binom{n+1}{m+1}$, **recursion relation** for binomial coefficients.

$$\binom{n}{n-m} = \binom{n}{m}, \quad \sum_r (-1)^r \binom{n}{r} = 0, \quad \sum_r \binom{n}{r}^2 = \binom{2n}{n}, \quad \sum_{s=m}^{n} \binom{s}{m} = \binom{n+1}{m+1}.$$

TABLE OF BINOMIAL COEFFICIENTS

n	$\binom{n}{0}$	$\binom{n}{1}$	$\binom{n}{2}$	$\binom{n}{3}$	$\binom{n}{4}$	$\binom{n}{5}$	$\binom{n}{6}$	$\binom{n}{7}$	$\binom{n}{8}$	$\binom{n}{9}$	$\binom{n}{10}$
0	1										
1	1	1									
2	1	2	1								
3	1	3	3	1							
4	1	4	6	4	1						
5	1	5	10	10	5	1					
6	1	6	15	20	15	6	1				
7	1	7	21	35	35	21	7	1			
8	1	8	28	56	70	56	28	8	1		
9	1	9	36	84	126	126	84	36	9	1	
10	1	10	45	120	210	252	210	120	45	10	1
11	1	11	55	165	330	462	462	330	165	55	11
12	1	12	66	220	495	792	924	792	495	220	66
13	1	13	78	286	715	1287	1716	1716	1287	715	286
14	1	14	91	364	1001	2002	3003	3432	3003	2002	1001
15	1	15	105	455	1365	3003	5005	6435	6435	5005	3003
16	1	16	120	560	1820	4368	8008	11440	12870	11440	8008
17	1	17	136	680	2380	6188	12376	19448	24310	24310	19448
18	1	18	153	816	3060	8568	18564	31824	43758	48620	43758
19	1	19	171	969	3876	11628	27132	50388	75582	92378	92378
20	1	20	190	1140	4845	15504	38760	77520	125970	167960	184756

NOTE: $\binom{n}{m} = \dfrac{n(n-1)(n-2)\ldots(n-m+1)}{m(m-1)(m-2)\ldots 3.2.1}$: $\binom{n}{0} = 1$; $\binom{n}{1} = n$.

For coefficients missing from the above table, use the relation

$\binom{n}{m} = \binom{n}{n-m}$, e.g. $\binom{20}{11} = \binom{20}{9} = 167960$.

FINITE DIFFERENCES

For equi-spaced arguments x_i, and associated y_i, the successive **advancing** y-**differences** are, $\Delta^0 y_i = y_i$, $\Delta y_i = y_{i+1} - y_i$, $\Delta^2 y_i = \Delta y_{i+1} - \Delta y_i = y_{i+2} - 2y_{i+1} + y_i$, $\ldots$, $\Delta^m y_i = \Delta^{m-1} y_{i+1} - \Delta^{m-1} y_i = \sum_r (-1)^r \binom{m}{r} y_{i+m-r}$. With arbitrary origin A and class-interval length, $x_{i+1} - x_i = h$, using $u_i = (x_i - A)/h$, write $y(u_i)$ for y_i. Then if for some fixed m, for the portion of the table considered, the values of $\Delta^{m+1} y_i$ be zero (or approximately, if these be regarded as negligible) **Newton's formula** gives

$$y(u) = \sum \frac{u^{(r)}}{r!} \Delta^r y(0) = y(0) + u\Delta y(0) + \frac{u(u-1)}{1 \cdot 2}\Delta^2 y(0) + \ldots$$

$$+ \frac{u(u-1)\ldots(u-m+1)}{m!}\Delta^m y(0).$$

This formula reduces to an identity for $u = u_0, u_1, \ldots, u_n, (u_i = i)$, and may be used to interpolate for intermediate values.

Example. Given

x	-4, -2, 0, 2, 4, 6, 8, $\ldots$
y	10, 14, 30, 64, 122, 210, 334, $\ldots$

to find a value for y when $x = 10$, and when $x = 1$. Suppose for some reason A has been taken at $x = 2$. The work may be arranged as follows:

u	x	y	Δ	Δ^2	Δ^3	Δ^4
-3	-4	10				
			4			
-2	-2	14		12		
			16		6	
-1	0	30		18		0
			34		6	
0	2	64		24		0
			58		6	
1	4	122		30		0
			88		6	
2	6	210		36		—
			124		—	
3	8	334		—		—
—	—	—		—		—

$$y(u) = 64 + 58u + 30\frac{u(u-1)}{1 \cdot 2} + 6\frac{u(u-1)(u-2)}{1 \cdot 2 \cdot 3},$$

$$= 64 + 58u + 15u(u-1) + u(u-1)(u-2).$$

At $x = 10$, $u = 4$. Substituting $u = 4$, one has $y|_{x=10} = 500$.
At $x = 1$, $u = -\frac{1}{2}$. Substituting $u = -\frac{1}{2}$, one has $y|_{x=1} = 44\frac{3}{8}$.

STATISTICS

CENTRAL MEASURES

Here the range of i is from 1 to n. With each value x_i is associated a weighting factor $f_i \geq 0$ (such as the frequency, the probability, the mass, the reliability, or other multiplier).

N, the **total weight,** $= \Sigma f_i$.

$\bar{x}$, the **arithmetic mean,** $= \Sigma f_i x_i / N = \Sigma f_i x_i / \Sigma f_i$.

GM, the **geometric mean** (available when each x_i is positive), $= \sqrt[N]{\Pi x_i{}^{f_i}}$. Log $GM = \Sigma f_i \log x_i / N$.

Mo, the **mode,** $=$ value among $(x_1, \ldots, x_n)$ having maximum associated f_i (usually obtained by interpolating after the data are graduated). For unweighted items, x_i, a mode is a value about which the values of x_i cluster most densely.

RMS, the **root-mean-square,** $= \sqrt{\Sigma f_i x_i{}^2 / N}$.

Md, the **median** (see below). For unweighted items, the median is the value, equaled or exceeded by exactly half of the values x_i in the given list. In case of a central pair, the median is usually taken as the arithmetic mean of this pair.

Mm, the **mid-mean** (see below). For unweighted items, the mid-mean is the arithmetic mean of the half-list obtained upon dropping out the highest quarter and lowest quarter of the items.

Cum $f|_x$, the value of "cumulative f" at X, $= \displaystyle\sum_{x_i < X} f_i$ (interpolation being used for X if necessary).

THE M-TILES

For **ungrouped data,** X is called the rth **m-tile** (or rth **m-tile mark**) $(r = 0, 1, \ldots, m)$ if simultaneously, $\displaystyle\sum_{x_i < X} f_i / N \leq r/m$, and $\displaystyle\sum_{x_i > X} f_i / N \leq (m - r)/m$. In particular the zeroth m-tile is **min,** the minimal value among the list $(x_1, \ldots, x_n)$, and the mth m-tile is **max,** the maximal value among the list.

For **grouped data,** the rth m-tile mark, X, is such that

$$\text{Cum } f|_x = Nr/m, \quad (r = 0, 1, 2, \ldots, m).$$
$$\text{Cum } f|_{\min} = 0, \qquad \text{Cum } f|_{\max} = N.$$

In particular, certain intermediate $(0 < r < m)$ m-tile marks are named as follows:

m	$r = 1$	2	3	$\ldots$
2	Md (median)			
3	T_1 (lower tertile)	T_2 (upper tertile)		
4	Q_1 (lower quartile)	Md	Q_3 (upper quartile)	
10	D_1 (first decile)	D_2	D_3	etc.
100	PC_1 (first percentile)	PC_2	PC_3	etc.

The term "rth **m-tile**" ($r = 1, \ldots, m$) is also used to denote the class interval extending from the $(r-1)$st to rth m-tile mark as defined above.

Mm, the **mid-mean**, $= 2 \displaystyle\sum_{Q_1 \leq x_i \leq Q_3} f_i x_i / N = \sum_{Q_1 \leq x_i \leq Q_3} f_i x_i / \sum_{Q_1 \leq x_i \leq Q_3} f_i.$

When each x_i is positive, and not all are equal, one always has $0 < \min < GM < \bar{x} < RMS < \max.$

For moderately-skewed distributions, one has approximately $Mo - \bar{x} = 3(Md - \bar{x})$, or $3Md = Mo + 2\bar{x}.$

MEASURES OF DISPERSION AND SKEWNESS

Here A is an arbitrary reference value, usually a convenient integral measure near $\bar{x}$.

ν_k, kth **moment about** A, $= \Sigma f_i (x_i - A)^k / N$, $(k = 0, 1, \ldots)$.

$\nu_0 = 1$, $\nu_1 = \bar{x} - A$. ν_2 as function of A is minimum for $A = \bar{x}$.

μ_k, kth **moment about** $\bar{x}$, $= \Sigma f_i (x_i - \bar{x})^k / N$, $(k = 0, 1, \ldots)$.

$$\mu_0 = 1,$$
$$\mu_1 = 0,$$
$$\mu_2 = \nu_2 - \nu_1^2 \ (\mu_2 = \textbf{variance}),$$
$$\mu_3 = \nu_3 - 3\nu_1\nu_2 + 2\nu_1^3,$$
$$\mu_4 = \nu_4 - 4\nu_1\nu_3 + 6\nu_1^2\nu_2 - 3\nu_1^4.$$
$$\beta_1 = \mu_3^2/\mu_2^3, \ \beta_2 = \mu_4/\mu_2^2.$$

σ, **standard deviation**, $= \sqrt{\mu_2}$.

$\alpha_3/2$, **momental skewness**; $\alpha_3 = \sqrt{\beta_1} = \mu_3/\sigma^3$.

$(\alpha_4 - 3)/2$, **kurtosis**; $\alpha_4 = \beta_2$.

MD, **mean deviation** (from the mean), $= \Sigma f_i |x_i - \bar{x}| / N$

$= 2\left[\bar{x} \displaystyle\sum_{x_i < \bar{x}} f_i - \sum_{x_i < \bar{x}} f_i x_i \right] / N.$ (This latter form is convenient for computation.)

s, **quartile deviation**, $= |Q_3 - Q_1|/2$.

$P.E.$, **probable error**, $= 0.6745\sigma$.

V, **coefficient of variation**, $= 100\sigma/\bar{x} \ \%$.

Pearson's measure of skewness $= (\bar{x} - Mo)/\sigma$. (Usually approximately $\alpha_3/2$.)

Bowley's measure of skewness $= (Q_3 - 2Md + Q_1)/(2s)$.

(Bowley's measure of skewness lies between -1 and $+1$.)

THE CLASS INTERVAL

$$\Delta x_i = x_{i+1} - x_i.$$

For equi-spaced arguments, $\Delta x_i = h$, the **length** of the **class interval**, x_i is the **mid-value** or **class mark**. The interval from $x_i - (h/2)$ to $x_i + (h/2)$ is the **class interval** with these as given **initial** and **terminal end values.**

$$u_i = (x_i - A)/h.$$
$$\bar{u} = \Sigma f_i u_i / N, \quad \bar{x} = h\bar{u} + A.$$
$$(\mu_k)_x = h^k(\mu_k)_u, \quad (k = 0, 1, \ldots).$$
$$\sigma_u{}^2 = [\Sigma f_i u_i{}^2 / N] - \bar{u}^2, \quad \sigma_x = h\sigma_u.$$
$$(\beta_1)_x = (\beta_1)_u, \quad (\beta_2)_x = (\beta_2)_u.$$

Sheppard's corrections (to correct approximately for the error due to treating all elements in a given class interval of length h as though concentrated at the class mark).

For μ_0, μ_1, μ_3, no corrections.

In x-units,

corrected $(\mu_2)_x$ = uncorrected $(\mu_2)_x - h^2/12$,

corrected $(\mu_4)_x$ = uncorrected $(\mu_4)_x - h^2$ uncorrected $(\mu_2)_x/2 +$
$$7h^4/240.$$

In u-units, replace h by 1 in the formulae given above.

LEAST SQUARES

The **normal equations** for finding coefficients, $a_0, a_1, \ldots, a_m$, in fitting a curve of the form $y = a_0 + a_1 x + \ldots + a_m x^m$ to data (X_i, Y_i), $i = 1, \ldots, n$, $(n > m)$, are $m + 1$ in number as follows:

$$\Sigma Y_i = a_0 n + a_1 \Sigma X_i + a_2 \Sigma X_i{}^2 + \ldots + a_m \Sigma X_i{}^m,$$
$$\Sigma X_i Y_i = a_0 \Sigma X_i + a_1 \Sigma X_i{}^2 + a_2 \Sigma X_i{}^3 + \ldots + a_m \Sigma X_i{}^{m+1},$$
$$\cdots\cdots\cdots\cdots\cdots\cdots\cdots\cdots\cdots\cdots\cdots$$
$$\Sigma X_i{}^m Y_i = a_0 \Sigma X_i{}^m + a_1 \Sigma X_i{}^{m+1} + a_2 \Sigma X_i{}^{m+2} + \ldots + a_m \Sigma X_i{}^{2m}.$$

Deviation from fitted curve,

$$d_i = Y_i - (a_0 + a_1 X_i + \ldots + a_m X_i{}^m).$$
$$\Sigma d_i{}^2 = \Sigma Y_i{}^2 - (a_0 \Sigma Y_i + a_1 \Sigma X_i Y_i + \ldots + a_m \Sigma X_i{}^m Y_i).$$

For $z = ab^x$, use $y = \log z$, $a_0 = \log a$, $a_1 = \log b$.

For $z = at^p$, use $y = \log z$, $a_0 = \log a$, $a_1 = p$, $x = \log t$.

S_y, **standard error of estimate,** = root-mean-square of the y-deviations about a fitted curve = $\sqrt{\Sigma d_i{}^2/n}$.

SIMPLE CORRELATION

Product Moment Method

Given n equi-spaced measurements X_i, $i = 1, 2, \ldots, n$, with $h = X_{i+1} - X_i$, $x_i = X_i - \bar{X}$; and m equi-spaced measurements Y_j, $j = 1, 2, \ldots, m$, with $k = Y_{i+1} - Y_i$, $y_i = Y_j - \bar{Y}$; and a weight (frequency, probability, etc.) e_{ij} (≥ 0), associated with (X_i, Y_j). Here e_{ij} is an entry in the table.

$$f_i = \sum_j e_{ij}, \; g_j = \sum_i e_{ij}.$$

$$N = \sum_{ij} e_{ij} = \sum_i f_i = \sum_j g_j. \quad \text{(Check)}$$

$$\bar{x} = \sum_{ij} e_{ij}X_i/N = \sum_i f_iX_i/N; \; \bar{y} = \sum_{ij} e_{ij}Y_j/N = \sum_j g_jY_j/N.$$

Let A and B be arbitrary reference values, usually convenient integral measures near $\overline{X}$ and $\overline{Y}$, respectively.

$$u_i = (X_i - A)/h, \; v_j = (Y_j - B)/k;$$

$$\bar{u} = \Sigma f_i u_i/N, \; \overline{X} = h\bar{u} + A, \; \bar{v} = \Sigma g_j v_j/N, \; \overline{Y} = k\bar{v} + B.$$

$$\sigma_u{}^2 = (\mu_2)_u = (\Sigma f_i u_i{}^2/N) - \bar{u}^2, \; \sigma_x = h\sigma_u. \left.\right\} \text{Apply Sheppard's correc-}$$
$$\sigma_v{}^2 = (\mu_2)_v = (\Sigma g_j v_j{}^2/N) - \bar{v}^2, \; \sigma_y = k\sigma_v. \left.\right\} \quad \text{tions.}$$

$$U_j = \sum_i e_{ij}u_i, \; V_i = \sum_j e_{ij}v_j, \; P = \sum_i u_iV_i = \sum_j v_jU_j. \quad \text{(Check)}$$

$$p_{uv} = \sum_{ij} e_{ij}(u_i - \bar{u})(v_j - \bar{v})/N$$

$$= (P/N) - \overline{uv}.$$

$$p_{xy} = hkp_{uv}.$$

$r = p_{uv}/(\sigma_u\sigma_v) = p_{xy}/(\sigma_x\sigma_y)$ **(product-moment) coefficient of correlation.** In every case $-1 \le r \le 1$.

$Y - \overline{Y} = r\dfrac{\sigma_y}{\sigma_x}(X - \overline{X})$, or $y = r\dfrac{\sigma_y}{\sigma_x}x$, **regression line of y on x.**

$X - \overline{X} = r\dfrac{\sigma_x}{\sigma_y}(Y - \overline{Y})$, or $x = r\dfrac{\sigma_x}{\sigma_y}y$, **regression line of x on y.**

EXAMPLE OF COMPUTATION FOR PRODUCT-MOMENT COEFFICIENT OF CORRELATION

v_j \ y_j → u_i \ x_i	-3 12	-2 16	-1 20	0 24	1 28	2 32	g_j	g_jv_j	$g_jv_j{}^2$	$U_j \left(=\sum_i e_{ij}u_i\right)$	v_jU_j
2 \ 21			1	5	7	1	14	28	56	8	16
1 \ 18		1	3	7	5	2	18	18	18	4	4
0 \ 15		2	3	4	1		10	0	0	0	0
−1 \ 12		3	1	1			5	−5	5	−7	7
−2 \ 9	2	1					3	−6	12	−8	16
f_i	2	7	8	17	13	3	50	35	91		43
f_iu_i	−6	−14	−8	0	13	6	−9				
$f_iu_i{}^2$	18	28	8	0	13	12	79				
$V_i\left(=\sum_j e_{ij}v_j\right)$	−4	−4	4		19	4					
u_iV_i	12	8	−4	0	19	8	43				

$A = 24, B = 15,$
$h = 4, k = 3,$
$N = \Sigma f_i = \Sigma g_j = 50,$
$\Sigma f_i u_i = -9, \Sigma g_j v_j = 35,$
$\Sigma f_i u_i{}^2 = 79, \Sigma g_j v_j{}^2 = 91,$
$P = \Sigma u_i V_i = \Sigma v_j U_j = 43.$

$\bar{u} = -\frac{9}{50} = -.18 \qquad \bar{v} = \frac{35}{50} = .70$

$\sigma_u{}^2 = \left(\frac{79}{50}\right) - (-.18)^2 - .083 = 1.46, \qquad \sigma_u = 1.21$

$\sigma_v{}^2 = \left(\frac{91}{50}\right) - (.70)^2 - .083 = 1.247, \qquad \sigma_v = 1.117$

$p_{uv} = \left(\frac{43}{50}\right) - (-.18)(.70) = +0.986$

$r = +0.986/(1.21 \times 1.117) = +.730 \qquad\qquad \text{Ans. } r = +.730$

RANK DIFFERENCE METHOD

Given n corresponding pairs of measured items (X_i, Y_i), $(i = 1, \ldots, n)$. Let (u_i, v_i) be the corresponding rank numbers. Here $u_i = 1$ for the largest X_i, 2 for the next largest X_i, etc., and similarly $v_i = 1$ for the largest Y_i, 2 for the next largest Y_i, etc. $\rho = 1 - \dfrac{6\Sigma(u_i - v_i)^2}{n(n^2 - 1)}$, (**rank difference**) **coefficient of correlation.**

In every case $-1 \le \rho \le 1$. Check: $\Sigma(u_i - v_i) = 0$.

EXAMPLE OF COMPUTATION FOR RANK-DIFFERENCE COEFFICIENT OF CORRELATION

X_i	Y_i	u_i	v_i	$u_i - v_i$	$(u_i-v_i)^2$	
76	52	3	1	+2	4	Check: $\Sigma(u_i - v_i) = 0.$
66	34	8	9	−1	1	
63	32	10	10	0	0	$\rho = 1 - \dfrac{6 \times 62}{10(10^2 - 1)}$
74	45	4	4	0	0	
79	50	1	2	−1	1	
69	37	7	7	0	0	$= +0.63$
77	35	2	8	−6	36	
65	42	9	5	+4	16	Ans. $\rho = +.63$
71	40	6	6	0	0	
73	48	5	3	+2	4	
$N = 10$				0	62	

PROBABILITY

If among $a + b$ equi-probable and mutually exclusive events, a are regarded as favorable and b unfavorable, then for a single trial

p, probability of favorable outcome. $= \dfrac{a}{a + b}$,

q, probability of unfavorable outcome, $= 1 - p = \dfrac{b}{a + b}$.

The successive terms in the binomial expansion $(p + q)^n = \sum_r \binom{n}{r}p^{n-r}q^r$ give the respective probabilities that in n trials, the event will be favorable exactly $n - r$ times, $r = 0, \ldots, n$.

The mean number of favorable events is np, of unfavorable, nq; the standard deviation is $\sigma = \sqrt{npq}$, $\alpha_3 = (p - q)/\sigma$ (the positive direction being that of increasing unfavorability).

Normal curve (x measured in σ-units from the mean, and with area $= 1$):

$$y = \frac{1}{\sqrt{2\pi}}e^{-x^2/2} = 0.3989e^{-x^2/2}.$$

MD (mean deviation from the mean) $= \sigma\sqrt{2/\pi} = 0.7979\sigma$.

s (quartile deviation from the mean) $= 0.6745\sigma = 0.845\ MD$.

Percentage areas, under normal curve, for successive class intervals measured from the mean:

Multiples of σ: 34%, 14%, 2%.

Multiples of s: 25%, 16%, 7%, 2%.

Normal Surface (x measured in σ_x-units, y in σ_y-units, from their means),

$$z = \frac{1}{2\pi\sqrt{1 - r^2}}e^{-(x^2 - 2rxy + y^2)/[2(1-r^2)]}.$$

Goodness of Fit. For a universe of objects falling into n mutually exclusive classes with class marks, $x_i(i = 1, 2, \ldots, n)$, let p_i be the probability for the ith class. Given a sample of N items, with f_i items in the ith class ($\Sigma f_i = N$), the probability that a random sample of N items gives no better fit, expressed in terms of n and χ^2 ("Chi square"), $= \Sigma(f_i - Np_i)^2/(Np_i)$, is given by a table, portions of which are as follows:

PROBABILITY THAT A RANDOM SAMPLE GIVES NO BETTER FIT

n \ χ^2	1	2	3	4	6	8	10	15	20
3	.607	.368	.223	.135	.050	.018	.007	.001	.000
4	.801	.572	.392	.261	.112	.046	.019	.002	.000
5	.910	.736	.558	.406	.199	.092	.040	.005	.000
6	.963	.849	.700	.549	.306	.156	.075	.010	.001
7	.986	.920	.809	.677	.423	.238	.125	.020	.003
8	.995	.960	.885	.780	.540	.333	.189	.036	.006
9	.998	.981	.934	.857	.647	.433	.265	.059	.010
10	.999	.991	.964	.911	.740	.534	.350	.091	.018
11	1.000	.996	.981	.947	.815	.629	.440	.132	.029
12	1.000	.998	.991	.970	.873	.713	.530	.182	.045

n \ χ^2	8	10	12	14	16	18	20	25	30
10	.534	.350	.213	.122	.067	.035	.018	.003	.000
11	.629	.440	.285	.173	.100	.055	.029	.005	.001
12	.713	.530	.363	.233	.141	.082	.045	.009	.002
13	.785	.616	.446	.301	.191	.116	.067	.015	.003
14	.844	.694	.528	.374	.249	.158	.095	.023	.005
15	.889	.762	.606	.450	.313	.207	.130	.035	.008
16	.924	.820	.679	.526	.382	.263	.172	.050	.012
17	.949	.867	.744	.599	.453	.324	.220	.070	.018
18	.967	.904	.800	.667	.524	.389	.274	.095	.026
19	.979	.932	.847	.729	.593	.456	.333	.125	.037
20	.987	.953	.886	.784	.657	.522	.395	.161	.052

MENSURATION FORMULAE
PLANE FIGURES BOUNDED BY STRAIGHT LINES

The **area of a triangle** whose base is b and altitude h

$$= \frac{hb}{2}.$$

The area of a **triangle** with angles A, B, and C and sides opposite a, b, and c, respectively

$$= \tfrac{1}{2}ab \sin C.$$

or
$$= \sqrt{s(s-a)(s-b)(s-c)},$$

where $s = \tfrac{1}{2}(a + b + c)$.

A **rectangle** with sides a and b has an area $= ab$.

The area of a **parallelogram** with side b and the perpendicular distance to the parallel side h

$$= bh.$$

The area of a **parallelogram** with sides a and b and the included angle θ

$$= ab \sin \theta.$$

The area of a **rhombus** with diagonals c and d,

$$= \tfrac{1}{2}cd.$$

The area of a **trapezoid** whose parallel sides are a and b and altitude h

$$= \tfrac{1}{2}(a + b)h.$$

The area of any **quadrilateral** with diagonals a and b and the angle between them θ

$$= \tfrac{1}{2}ab \sin \theta.$$

The area of a **regular polygon** with n sides, each of length l,

$$= \tfrac{1}{4}nl^2 \cot \frac{180°}{n}.$$

For a regular polygon of n sides, each side of length l, the radius of the **inscribed circle**,

$$= \frac{l}{2} \cot \frac{180°}{n}.$$

The radius of the **circumscribed circle**,

$$= \frac{l}{2} \operatorname{cosec} \frac{180°}{n}.$$

AREA, RADIUS OF INSCRIBED AND CIRCUMSCRIBED CIRCLES FOR REGULAR POLYGONS

l = length of one side

Name	Number of sides	Area	Radius of inscribed circle	Radius of circumscribed circle
Triangle, equilateral......	3	$0.43301l^2$	$0.28867l$	$0.57735l$
Square.................	4	$1.00000l^2$	$0.50000l$	$0.70710l$
Pentagon.............	5	$1.72048l^2$	$0.68819l$	$0.85065l$
Hexagon...............	6	$2.59808l^2$	$0.86602l$	$1.0000l$
Heptagon.............	7	$3.63391l^2$	$1.0383l$	$1.1523l$
Octagon...............	8	$4.82843l^2$	$1.2071l$	$1.3065l$
Nonagon..............	9	$6.18182l^2$	$1.3737l$	$1.4619l$
Decagon..............	10	$7.69421l^2$	$1.5388l$	$1.6180l$
Undecagon...........	11	$9.36564l^2$	$1.7028l$	$1.7747l$
Dodecagon............	12	$11.19615l^2$	$1.8660l$	$1.9318l$

Radius of circle inscribed in any triangle, whose sides are a, b, and c, where $s = \frac{1}{2}(a + b + c)$ is given by r

$$= \frac{\sqrt{s(s-a)(s-b)(s-c)}}{s}.$$

The radius of the **circumscribed** circle is given by R

$$= \frac{abc}{4\sqrt{s(s-a)(s-b)(s-c)}}.$$

The **perimeter of a polygon inscribed in a circle** of radius r, where n is the number of sides,

$$= 2nr \sin \frac{\pi}{n}. \qquad (\pi \text{ radians } = 180°)$$

The area of the **inscribed** polygon,

$$= \tfrac{1}{2}nr^2 \sin \frac{2\pi}{n}.$$

The **perimeter of a polygon circumscribed about a circle** of radius r, number of sides n

$$= 2nr \tan \frac{\pi}{n}.$$

The area of the **circumscribed** polygon

$$= nr^2 \tan \frac{\pi}{n}.$$

PLANE FIGURES BOUNDED BY CURVED LINES

The **circumference of a circle** whose radius is r and diameter $d\,(d = 2r)$
$$= 2\pi r = \pi d. \qquad (\pi = 3.14159)$$

The **area of a circle**
$$= \pi r^2 = \tfrac{1}{4}\pi d^2 = .7854 d^2.$$

The **length of an arc** of a circle for an arc of θ degrees
$$= \frac{\pi r \theta}{180}.$$

NOTE—In this and following similar formulae r denotes the radius of the circle, (OC, Fig. 1).

For an arc of θ radians the length s
$$= r\theta.$$

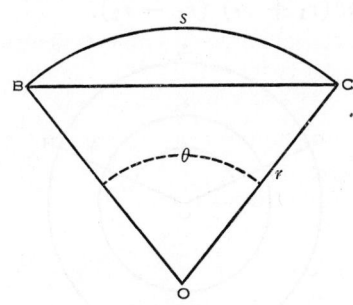

Fig. 1

The **length of a chord** subtending an angle θ
$$= 2r \sin \tfrac{1}{2}\theta.$$

The **area of a sector** where θ is the angle between the **radii in degrees**
$$= \frac{\pi r^2 \theta}{360}.$$

If s is the length of the arc, the area of the sector
$$= \frac{sr}{2}.$$

The **area of a segment** where θ is the angle between the two radii in degrees
$$= \frac{\pi r^2 \theta}{360} - \frac{r^2 \sin \theta}{2}. \qquad \left[\begin{array}{l} \theta° = 180° - [2x \sin^{-1}(x/r)] \\ x = \perp \text{ dist. center to chord} \end{array}\right]$$

337

If θ is in radians the area $= \frac{1}{2}r^2(\theta - \sin\theta)$.

The **area of the segment of a circle**

$$= \frac{\pi r^2}{2} - \left[\, x\sqrt{r^2 - x^2} + r^2 \operatorname{Sin}^{-1}\left(\frac{x}{r}\right)\,\right]$$

where r is the radius of the circle and x the perpendicular distance of the chord from the center. The principal angle must be used in this formula.

The **area of the ring** between two circles of radius r_1 and r_2, one of which encloses the other,

$$= \pi(r_1 + r_2)\,(r_1 - r_2).$$

The two circles are not necessarily concentric.

Area of the sector of an annulus. (Fig. 2.) — If angle $GOH = \theta$ and the lines GO and $JO = r_1$ and r_2 respectively, the area $GHIJ = \frac{1}{2}\theta(r_1 + r_2)\,(r_1 - r_2)$.

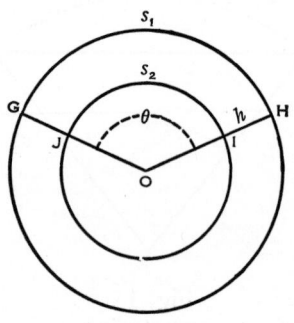

Fig. 2

If $s_1 = $ the length of the arc GH and $s_2 = $ the arc JI and $h = HI = r_1 - r_2$, the area $GHIJ = \frac{1}{2}h(s_1 + s_2)$.

The **circumference of an ellipse** whose semiaxes are a and b

$$= 2\pi\sqrt{\frac{a^2 + b^2}{2}}\ \text{(approx.)} = 4aE\ \text{exactly.}$$

See tables of elliptic integrals for E, using $K = \sqrt{\dfrac{a^2 - b^2}{a}}$

The **area of an ellipse** $= \pi ab$.

The length of the **arc of a parabola,** as arc SPQ in Fig. 3, where $x = PR$, and $y = QR$

$$\sqrt{4x^2 + y^2} + \frac{y^2}{2x}\log_e\ \frac{2x + \sqrt{4x^2 + y^2}}{y}$$

The **area of the section of the parabola** $PQRS = \frac{4}{3}xy$.

MENSURATION FORMULAE

SOLIDS BOUNDED BY PLANES

The **lateral area of a regular prism** = perimeter of a right section × the length.

The **volume of a regular prism** = area of base × the altitude.

The **lateral area of a regular pyramid,** slant height l, length of one side of base a, and a number of sides n,

$$= \tfrac{1}{2}nal.$$

The **volume of a pyramid** = $\tfrac{1}{3}$ area of base × altitude.

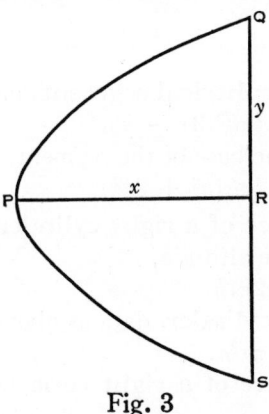

Fig. 3

SURFACE AND VOLUME OF REGULAR POLYHEDRA

Surface and volume of regular polyhedra in terms of the length of one edge l.

Name	Nature of Surface	Surface	Volume
Tetrahedron...........	4 equilateral triangles....	$1.73205l^2$	$0.11785l^3$
Hexahedron or cube....	6 squares..............	$6.00000l^2$	$1.00000l^3$
Octahedron...........	8 equilateral triangles....	$3.46410l^2$	$0.47140l^3$
Dodecahedron.........	12 pentagons...........	$20.64573l^2$	$7.66312l^3$
Icosahedron...........	20 equilateral triangles....	$8.66025l^2$	$2.18170l^3$

SOLIDS BOUNDED BY CURVED SURFACES

The **surface of a sphere** of radius r and diameter $d (= 2r)$
$$= 4\pi r^2 = \pi d^2 = 12.57 r^2.$$

The **volume of a sphere**
$$= \tfrac{4}{3}\pi r^3 = \tfrac{1}{6}\pi d^3 = 4.189 r^3.$$

The **area of a lune** on the surface of a sphere of radius r, included between two great circles whose inclination is θ radians

$$= 2r^2\theta.$$

The **area of a spherical triangle** whose angles are A, B, and C (radians) on a sphere of radius r

$$= (A + B + C - \pi)r^2.$$

The **area of a spherical polygon** of n sides where θ is the sum of its angles in radians

$$= [\theta - (n - 2)\pi]r^2.$$

The area of the curved surface of a **spherical segment** of height h, radius of sphere r

$$= 2\pi rh.$$

The **volume of a spherical segment**, data as above

$$= \tfrac{1}{3}\pi h^2(3r - h).$$

If a = radius of the base of the segment, the volume

$$= \tfrac{1}{6}\pi h(h^2 + 3a^2).$$

The **curved surface of a right cylinder** where r = the radius of the base and h, the altitude,

$$= 2\pi rh.$$

The **volume of a cylinder,** data as above,

$$= \pi r^2h.$$

The **curved surface of a right cone** whose altitude is h and radius of base r

$$= \pi r \sqrt{r^2 + h^2}.$$

The **volume of a cone,** data as above,

$$= \frac{\pi}{3}r^2h = 1.047\,r^2h.$$

The **curved surface of the frustum of a right cone,** radius of base r_1, of top r_2 and altitude h,

$$= \pi(r_1 + r_2) \sqrt{h^2 + (r_1 - r_2)^2}.$$

The **volume of the frustum of a cone,** data as above,

$$= \pi\frac{h}{3}(r_1{}^2 + r_1r_2 + r_2{}^2).$$

The **oblate spheroid** is formed by the rotation of an ellipse about its minor axis. If a and b are the major and minor semi-axes respectively, and e the eccentricity, the surface

$$= 2\pi a^2 + \pi\frac{b^2}{e}\log_\epsilon\frac{1 + e}{1 - e},$$

and volume $\qquad = \tfrac{4}{3}\pi a^2b.$

The **prolate spheroid** is formed by the rotation of an ellipse about its major axis $(2a)$, data as above.

Surface $= 2\pi b^2 + 2\pi \dfrac{ab}{e} \sin^{-1} e,$

volume $= \frac{4}{3}\pi a b^2.$

SIMPSON'S RULE FOR IRREGULAR AREAS

Divide the area into an even number $(2m)$ of panels by means of $2m + 1$ parallel lines, drawn at constant distance h apart; and denote the lengths of the intercepted segments by $y_0, y_1 \ldots ,$ y_{2m-1}, y_{2m}. The first and last of these may be zero. The area will then be

$$A = \tfrac{1}{3}h[(y_0 + y_{2m}) + 4(y_1 + y_3 + \ldots + y_{2m-1}) + 2(y_2 + y_4 + \ldots + y_{2m-2})]$$

While the formula is exact in many simple cases, ordinarily the formula provides only an approximation, for which the accuracy increases with an increase in the number of divisions. Simpson's Rule may be applied to finding volumes, if the measures $y_0, y_1, \ldots,$ y_{2m} be interpreted as the areas of parallel plane sections at constant distance h apart.

PRISMOIDAL FORMULA

As a special case where $m = 1$, and $H, (= 2h)$ is the distance between two limiting parallel planes, one has for the volume of a solid figure,

$$V = \tfrac{1}{6}H(S_0 + 4S_1 + S_2).$$

Here S_0 and S_2 are the cross-sectional areas in these limiting planes (lower and upper bases, respectively), and S_1 is the cross section of the mid-section. The formula is exact for the cone, sphere, ellipsoid, and prismoid.

TRIGONOMETRY

TRIGONOMETRIC FUNCTIONS IN A RIGHT-ANGLED TRIANGLE

If A, B, and C are the vertices (C the right angle), and a, b, and h the sides opposite respectively,

sine $A = \sin A = \dfrac{a}{h}$,

cosine $A = \cos A = \dfrac{b}{h}$,

tangent $A = \tan A = \dfrac{a}{b}$,

cotangent $A = \cot A = \operatorname{ctn} A = \dfrac{b}{a}$,

secant $A = \sec A = \dfrac{h}{b}$,

cosecant $A = \csc A = \dfrac{h}{a}$.

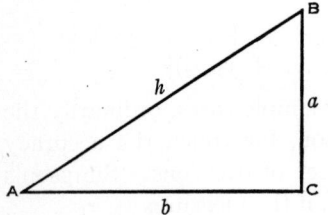

Fig. 4

exsecant $A = \operatorname{exsec} A = \sec A - 1$

versine $A = \operatorname{vers} A = 1 - \cos A$

coversine $A = \operatorname{covers} A = 1 - \sin A$

haversine $A = \operatorname{hav} A = \tfrac{1}{2}\operatorname{vers} A$

SIGNS AND LIMITS OF VALUE ASSUMED BY THE FUNCTIONS

Function	Quadrant I		Quadrant II		Quadrant III		Quadrant IV	
	Sign	Value	Sign	Value	Sign	Value	Sign	Value
sin........	+	0 to 1	+	1 to 0	—	0 to 1	—	1 to 0
cos........	+	1 to 0	—	0 to 1	—	1 to 0	+	0 to 1
tan........	+	0 to ∞	—	∞ to 0	+	0 to ∞	—	∞ to 0
cot........	+	∞ to 0	—	0 to ∞	+	∞ to 0	—	0 to ∞
sec........	+	1 to ∞	—	∞ to 1	—	1 to ∞	+	∞ to 1
cosec.......	+	∞ to 1	+	1 to ∞	—	∞ to 1	—	1 to ∞

TRIGONOMETRY

VALUE OF THE FUNCTIONS OF VARIOUS ANGLES

	0°	30°	45°	60°	90°	180°	270°
sin	0	$\frac{1}{2}$	$\frac{1}{2}\sqrt{2}$	$\frac{1}{2}\sqrt{3}$	1	0	−1
cos	1	$\frac{1}{2}\sqrt{3}$	$\frac{1}{2}\sqrt{2}$	$\frac{1}{2}$	0	−1	0
tan	0	$\frac{1}{3}\sqrt{3}$	1	$\sqrt{3}$	∞	0	∞
cot	∞	$\sqrt{3}$	1	$\frac{1}{3}\sqrt{3}$	0	∞	0
sec	1	$\frac{2\sqrt{3}}{3}$	$\sqrt{2}$	2	∞	−1	∞
cosec	∞	2	$\sqrt{2}$	$\frac{2\sqrt{3}}{3}$	1	∞	−1

EXPONENTIAL DEFINITIONS OF CIRCULAR FUNCTIONS

$$\sin x = \frac{1}{2i}(e^{ix} - e^{-ix}) \qquad \mathrm{cosec}\, x = \frac{2i}{e^{ix} - e^{-ix}}$$

$$(i^2 = -1)$$

$$\cos x = \frac{e^{ix} + e^{-ix}}{2} \qquad \sec x = \frac{2}{e^{ix} + e^{-ix}}$$

$$\tan x = \frac{e^{ix} - e^{-ix}}{ie^{ix} + ie^{-ix}} \qquad \cot x = \frac{ie^{ix} + ie^{-ix}}{e^{ix} - e^{-ix}}$$

RELATIONS OF THE FUNCTIONS

$$\sin x = \frac{1}{\mathrm{cosec}\, x}. \qquad\qquad \mathrm{cosec}\, x = \frac{1}{\sin x}.$$

$$\cos x = \frac{1}{\sec x}. \qquad\qquad \sec x = \frac{1}{\cos x}.$$

$$\tan x = \frac{1}{\cot x} = \frac{\sin x}{\cos x}. \qquad \sin^2 x + \cos^2 x = 1.$$

$$\cot x = \frac{1}{\tan x} = \frac{\cos x}{\sin x}. \qquad 1 + \tan^2 x = \sec^2 x.$$
$$1 + \cot^2 x = \mathrm{cosec}^2 x.$$

*$\sin x = \pm\sqrt{1 - \cos^2 x}.$ $\qquad \cos x = \pm\sqrt{1 - \sin^2 x}.$

$\tan x = \pm\sqrt{\sec^2 x - 1}.$ $\qquad \sec x = \pm\sqrt{\tan^2 x + 1}.$

$\cot x = \pm\sqrt{\mathrm{cosec}^2 x - 1}.$ $\qquad \mathrm{cosec}\, x = \pm\sqrt{\cot^2 x + 1}.$

$\sin x = \cos(90° - x) = \sin(180° - x).$

$\cos x = \sin(90° - x) = -\cos(180° - x).$

$\tan x = \cot(90° - x) = -\tan(180° - x).$

$\cot x = \tan(90° - x) = -\cot(180° - x).$

$$\mathrm{cosec}\, x = \cot\frac{x}{2} - \cot x.$$

* The sign in front of radical depends on quadrant in which x falls.

343

FUNCTIONS OF SUMS OF ANGLES

$\sin (x \pm y) = \sin x \cos y \pm \cos x \sin y.$

$\cos (x \pm y) = \cos x \cos y \mp \sin x \sin y.$

$\tan (x \pm y) = \dfrac{\tan x \pm \tan y}{1 \mp \tan x \tan y}.$

FUNCTIONS OF MULTIPLE ANGLES

$\sin 2x = 2 \sin x \cos x.$

$\cos 2x = \cos^2 x - \sin^2 x = 2 \cos^2 x - 1 = 1 - 2 \sin^2 x.$

$\sin 3x = 3 \sin x - 4 \sin^3 x.$

$\cos 3x = 4 \cos^3 x - 3 \cos x.$

$\sin 4x = 8 \cos^3 x \sin x - 4 \cos x \sin x.$

$\cos 4x = 8 \cos^4 x - 8 \cos^2 x + 1.$

$\sin 5x = 5 \sin x - 20 \sin^3 x + 16 \sin^5 x.$

$\cos 5x = 16 \cos^5 x - 20 \cos^3 x + 5 \cos x.$

$\sin 6x = 32 \cos^5 x \sin x - 32 \cos^3 x \sin x + 6 \cos x \sin x.$

$\cos 6x = 32 \cos^6 x - 48 \cos^4 x + 18 \cos^2 x - 1.$

$\tan 2x = \dfrac{2 \tan x}{1 - \tan^2 x}.$

$\cot 2x = \dfrac{\cot^2 x - 1}{2 \cot x}.$

$\tan 3x = \dfrac{3 \tan x - \tan^3 x}{1 - 3 \tan^2 x}.$

*$\sin \tfrac{1}{2}x = \pm \sqrt{\dfrac{1 - \cos x}{2}}$

$\cos \tfrac{1}{2}x = \pm \sqrt{\dfrac{1 + \cos x}{2}}.$

$\tan \tfrac{1}{2}x = \pm \sqrt{\dfrac{1 - \cos x}{1 + \cos x}} = \dfrac{1 - \cos x}{\sin x} = \dfrac{\sin x}{1 + \cos x}.$

* The sign in front of radical depends on quadrant in which x falls.

MISCELLANEOUS RELATIONS

$\sin\ x \pm \sin\ y = 2 \sin\ \frac{1}{2}\ (x \pm y)\cdot\cos\ \frac{1}{2}\ (x \mp y).$

$\cos\ x + \cos\ y = 2 \cos\ \frac{1}{2}\ (x + y)\cdot\cos\ \frac{1}{2}\ (x - y).$

$\cos\ x - \cos\ y = - 2 \sin\ \frac{1}{2}\ (x + y)\cdot\sin\ \frac{1}{2}\ (x - y).$

$\tan\ x \pm \tan\ y = \dfrac{\sin\ (x \pm y)}{\cos\ x\cdot\cos\ y}.$ $\qquad \cot x \pm \cot y = \dfrac{\pm\ \sin\ (x \pm y)}{\sin\ x\cdot\sin\ y}.$

$\dfrac{1 + \tan x}{1 - \tan x} = \tan\ (45° + x).$ $\qquad \dfrac{\cot x + 1}{\cot x - 1} = \cot\ (45° - x).$

$\dfrac{\sin\ x \pm \sin\ y}{\cos\ x + \cos\ y} = \tan\ \frac{1}{2}\ (x \pm y).$

$\dfrac{\sin\ x \pm \sin\ y}{\cos\ x - \cos\ y} = - \cot\ \frac{1}{2}\ (x \mp y).$

$\dfrac{\sin\ x + \sin\ y}{\sin\ x - \sin\ y} = \dfrac{\tan\ \frac{1}{2}\ (x + y)}{\tan\ \frac{1}{2}\ (x - y)}.$

$\sin^2 x - \sin^2 y = \sin\ (x + y)\cdot\sin\ (x - y).$

$\cos^2 x - \cos^2 y = - \sin\ (x + y)\ \sin\ (x - y).$

$\cos^2 x - \sin^2 y = \cos\ (x + y)\ \cos\ (x - y).$

INVERSE TRIGONOMETRIC FUNCTIONS

The following table lists each of the six inverse trigonometric functions together with the interval of its principal value:

Function	Interval containing principal value	
	x positive or zero	x negative
$y = \sin^{-1} x$ and $\tan^{-1} x$...........	$0 \leqq y \leqq \pi/2$	$-\pi/2 \leqq y < 0$
$y = \cos^{-1} x$ and $\cot^{-1} x$...........	$0 \leqq y \leqq \pi/2$	$\pi/2 < y \leqq \pi$
$y = \sec^{-1} x$ and $\csc^{-1} x$...........	$0 \leqq y \leqq \pi/2$	$-\pi \leqq y \leqq -\pi/2$

Usually the first letter in "arc" or the name of the inverse trigonometric functions is capitalized if the principal value is desired. Thus

$$\text{Arc sin } \frac{1}{2} = \text{Sin}^{-1}\ \frac{1}{2} = \frac{\pi}{6},$$

while $\qquad \text{arc sin } \dfrac{1}{2} = \dfrac{\pi}{6} + 2\pi n \text{ or } \dfrac{5\pi}{6} + 2\pi n$

In the calculus both for differentiation or integral formulas, capitalization is not adhered to strictly, but principal values are always understood for inverse trigonometric functions when used unless specifically stated otherwise.

TRIGONOMETRY

RELATIONS BETWEEN SIDES AND ANGLES OF ANY PLANE TRIANGLE

In a triangle with angles A, B, and C and sides opposite a, b, and c respectively,

$$\frac{a}{\sin A} = \frac{b}{\sin B} = \frac{c}{\sin C} = \text{diameter of the circumscribed circle.}$$

$$a^2 = b^2 + c^2 - 2bc \cos A.$$

$$a = b \cos C + c \cos B.$$

$$\cos A = \frac{b^2 + c^2 - a^2}{2bc}.$$

$$\tan \frac{A - B}{2} = \frac{a - b}{a + b} \cot \frac{C}{2}.$$

$$\sin A = \frac{2}{bc} \sqrt{s(s - a)(s - b)(s - c)},$$

where $s = \frac{1}{2}(a + b + c)$ and $r = \sqrt{\dfrac{(s - a)(s - b)(s - c)}{s}}.$

$$\sin \frac{A}{2} = \sqrt{\frac{(s - b)(s - c)}{bc}}.$$

$$\cos \frac{A}{2} = \sqrt{\frac{s(s - a)}{bc}}.$$

$$\tan \frac{A}{2} = \sqrt{\frac{(s - b)(s - c)}{s(s - a)}} = \frac{r}{s - a}.$$

$$\frac{a + b}{a - b} = \frac{\sin A + \sin B}{\sin A - \sin B} = \frac{\tan \frac{1}{2}(A + B)}{\tan \frac{1}{2}(A - B)} = \frac{\cot \frac{1}{2} C}{\tan \frac{1}{2}(A - B)}.$$

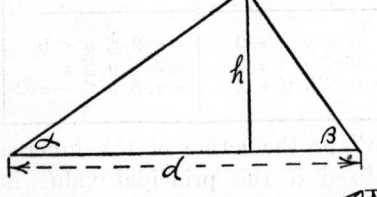

$$h = d \frac{\sin \alpha \sin \beta}{\sin(\alpha + \beta)} = \frac{d}{\cot \alpha + \cot \beta}$$

Similarly

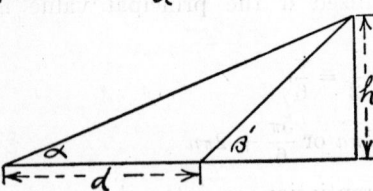

$$h = d \frac{\sin \alpha \sin \beta'}{\sin(\beta' - \alpha)} = \frac{d}{\cot \alpha - \cot \beta'}$$

Fig. 5

RELATIONS IN ANY SPHERICAL TRIANGLE

If A, B and C be the three angles and a, b, and c the opposite sides,

$$\frac{\sin A}{\sin a} = \frac{\sin B}{\sin b} = \frac{\sin C}{\sin c}.$$

$$\cos a = \cos b \cos c + \sin b \sin c \cos A = \frac{\cos b \cos (c \pm \theta)}{\cos \theta}$$

where $\quad \tan \theta = \tan b \cos A.$

$$\cos A = -\cos B \cos C + \sin B \sin C \cos a.$$

$$\sin \tfrac{1}{2} A = \sqrt{\frac{\sin (s - b) \sin (s - c)}{\sin b \sin c}}$$

where $\quad s = \tfrac{1}{2}(a + b + c).$

$$\cos \tfrac{1}{2} A = \sqrt{\frac{\sin s \sin (s - a)}{\sin b \sin c}}.$$

$$\tan \tfrac{1}{2} A = \frac{r}{\sin (s - a)}$$

where $\quad r = \sqrt{\dfrac{\sin (s - a) \sin (s - b) \sin (s - c)}{\sin s}}$

$$\cos \tfrac{1}{2} a = \sqrt{\frac{\cos (S - B) \cos (S - C)}{\sin B \sin C}}$$

where $\quad S = \tfrac{1}{2}(A + B + C).$

$$\sin \tfrac{1}{2} a = \sqrt{-\frac{\cos S \cos (S - A)}{\sin B \sin C}}.$$

$$\tan \tfrac{1}{2} a = R \cos (S - A)$$

where $\quad R = \sqrt{\dfrac{-\cos S}{\cos (S - A) \cos (S - B) \cos (S - C)}}.$

$$\frac{\tan \dfrac{a + b}{2}}{\tan \dfrac{c}{2}} = \frac{\cos \dfrac{A - B}{2}}{\cos \dfrac{A + B}{2}}, \qquad \frac{\tan \dfrac{A + B}{2}}{\cot \dfrac{C}{2}} = \frac{\cos \dfrac{a - b}{2}}{\cos \dfrac{a + b}{2}}.$$

$$\frac{\tan \dfrac{a - b}{2}}{\tan \dfrac{c}{2}} = \frac{\sin \dfrac{A - B}{2}}{\sin \dfrac{A + B}{2}}, \qquad \frac{\tan \dfrac{A - B}{2}}{\cot \dfrac{C}{2}} = \frac{\sin \dfrac{a - b}{2}}{\sin \dfrac{a + b}{2}}.$$

$$\operatorname{hav} a = \operatorname{hav} (b - c) + \sin b \sin c \operatorname{hav} A$$

$$\operatorname{hav} A = \frac{\sqrt{\operatorname{hav} [a + (b - c)] \operatorname{hav} [a - (b - c)]}}{\sin b \sin c}$$

ANALYTICAL GEOMETRY

The distance between two points x_1, y_1, and x_2, y_2, — rectangular coördinates:
$$d = \pm \sqrt{(x_2 - x_1)^2 + (y_2 - y_1)^2}$$
For polar coördinates and points r_1, θ_1, and r_2, θ_2:
$$d = \pm \sqrt{r_1{}^2 + r_2{}^2 - 2r_1 r_2 \cos (\theta_1 - \theta_2)}$$
The area of a triangle whose vertices are x_1, y_1; x_2, y_2, and x_3, y_3:
$$A = \tfrac{1}{2} (x_1 y_2 - x_2 y_1 + x_2 y_3 - x_3 y_2 + x_3 y_1 - x_1 y_3)$$
For polar coördinates and vertices, r_1, θ_1; r_2, θ_2, and r_3, θ_3:
$$A = \tfrac{1}{2} \{ (r_1 r_2 \sin (\theta_2 - \theta_1) + r_2 r_3 \sin (\theta_3 - \theta_2) + r_3 r_1 \sin (\theta_1 - \theta_3) \}$$
The equation of a straight line where m is the tangent of the angle of inclination and c, the distance of intersection with the Y axis from the origin:
$$y = mx + c$$
If a line of slope m passes through the point x_1, y_1, its equation is:
$$y - y_1 = m(x - x_1)$$
The equation of a line through the points x_1, y_1, and x_2, y_2 is:
$$\frac{y - y_1}{y_2 - y_1} = \frac{x - x_1}{x_2 - x_1}$$
If the intercepts on the X and Y axes are a and b respectively, the equation is:
$$\frac{x}{a} + \frac{y}{b} = 1$$
If the length of the perpendicular from the origin is p and its angle of inclination θ the equation is:
$$x \cos \theta + y \sin \theta = p$$
General equation of the straight line:

$Ax + By + C = 0$, where slope $m = \dfrac{-A}{B}$, x-intercept $a = \dfrac{-C}{A}$;

y-intercept $b = \dfrac{-C}{B}$

The equation of a circle whose center is at a, b, and whose radius is c:
$$(x - a)^2 + (y - b)^2 = c^2$$
If the origin is at the center:
$$x^2 + y^2 = c^2$$
The polar equation of a circle with the origin on the circumference and its center at point c, a:
$$r = 2c \cos (\theta - a).$$

If the origin is not on the circumference, the radius a and the center at a point l, a, the equation becomes:

$$a^2 = r^2 + l^2 - 2rl \cos (\theta - a)$$

The equation of a parabola with the origin at the vertex, where f is the distance from the focus to the vertex:

$$y^2 = 4fx$$

If p is the semi-latus rectum $(= 2f)$ the equation is:

$$y^2 = 2px$$

The polar equation, where the pole is at the focus and p the semi-latus rectum is:

$$r = \frac{p}{1 - \cos \theta}$$

If the pole is at the vertex and p as above:

$$r = \frac{2p \cos \theta}{\sin^2 \theta}$$

The equation of the ellipse with the origin at the center and semi-axes a and b:

$$\frac{x^2}{a^2} + \frac{y^2}{b^2} = 1$$

Polar equation where the pole is at the center:

$$r^2 = \frac{a^2b^2}{a^2 \sin^2 \theta + b^2 \cos^2 \theta}$$

The equation of the hyperbola with the origin at the center, semi-axes a and b:

$$\frac{x^2}{a^2} - \frac{y^2}{b^2} = 1$$

Polar equation, pole at center:

$$r^2 = \frac{a^2b^2}{a^2 \sin^2 \theta - b^2 \cos^2 \theta}$$

HYPERBOLIC FUNCTIONS

Definitions

An hyperbolic function represents a relation between the coordinates of a given point on the arc of a rectangular hyperbola.

If O is the center, A the vertex, and P any point of the hyperbola APB,

OM = x,

$\qquad$ MP = y,

$\qquad\qquad$ OA = a.

The function u may be defined by the following relation,

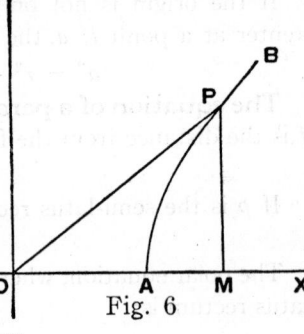

Fig. 6

$$u = \frac{2 \times \text{Area OAP}}{\text{OA}^2}$$

The hyperbolic sine of $u = \sinh u = y/a$.
The hyperbolic cosine of $u = \cosh u = x/a$

Exponential Definitions of Hyperbolic Functions and Their Power Series

$$\sinh u = \frac{e^u - e^{-u}}{2} = \frac{1}{2}(e^u - e^{-u}) = u + \frac{u^3}{3!} + \frac{u^5}{5!} + \cdots$$

$$\cosh u = \frac{e^u + e^{-u}}{2} = \frac{1}{2}(e^u + e^{-u}) = 1 + \frac{u^2}{2!} + \frac{u^4}{4!} + \cdots$$

$$\tanh u = \frac{e^u - e^{-u}}{e^u + e^{-u}} = u - \frac{u^3}{3} + \frac{2u^5}{15} - \frac{17u^7}{315} + \cdots \qquad \left(u^2 < \frac{1}{4}\pi^2\right).$$

$$\sinh^{-1} u = u - \frac{1}{2} \cdot \frac{u^3}{3} + \frac{1 \cdot 3}{2 \cdot 4} \cdot \frac{u^5}{5} - \frac{1 \cdot 3 \cdot 5}{2 \cdot 4 \cdot 6} \cdot \frac{u^7}{7} + \cdots \qquad (u^2 < 1).$$

$$\sinh^{-1} u = \log 2u + \frac{1}{2} \cdot \frac{1}{2u^2} - \frac{1 \cdot 3}{2 \cdot 4} \cdot \frac{1}{4u^4} + \frac{1 \cdot 3 \cdot 5}{2 \cdot 4 \cdot 6} \cdot \frac{1}{6u^6} - \cdots \qquad (u^2 > 1).$$

$$\cosh^{-1} u = \log 2u - \frac{1}{2} \cdot \frac{1}{2u^2} - \frac{1 \cdot 3}{2 \cdot 4} \cdot \frac{1}{4u^4} - \frac{1 \cdot 3 \cdot 5}{2 \cdot 4 \cdot 6} \cdot \frac{1}{6u^6} - \cdots \qquad (u^2 > 1).$$

$$\tanh^{-1} u = u + \frac{u^3}{3} + \frac{u^5}{5} + \frac{u^7}{7} + \cdots \qquad (u^2 < 1).$$

$$\tanh u = \frac{\sinh u}{\cosh u}. \qquad \operatorname{sech} u = \frac{1}{\cosh u}.$$

$$\coth u = \frac{1}{\tanh u}. \qquad \operatorname{csch} u = \frac{1}{\sinh u}.$$

Relations of the Functions

$\sinh x = -\sinh(-x).$ $\qquad\qquad$ $\operatorname{sech} x = \operatorname{sech}(-x).$
$\cosh x = \cosh(-x).$ $\qquad\qquad$ $\operatorname{csch} x = -\operatorname{csch}(-x).$
$\tanh x = -\tanh(-x).$ $\qquad\qquad$ $\coth x = -\coth(-x).$

$$\sinh x = \frac{2 \tanh \frac{1}{2}x}{1 - \tanh^2 \frac{1}{2}x} = \frac{\tanh x}{\sqrt{1 - \tanh^2 x}}.$$

$$\cosh x = \frac{1 + \tanh^2 \frac{1}{2}x}{1 - \tanh^2 \frac{1}{2}x} = \frac{1}{\sqrt{1 - \tanh^2 x}}.$$

$$\cosh^2 x - \sinh^2 x = 1.$$

$$\tanh x = \sqrt{1 - \text{sech}^2 x}. \qquad\qquad \text{sech}\, x = \sqrt{1 - \tanh^2 x}.$$

$$\coth x = \sqrt{\text{csch}^2 x + 1}. \qquad\qquad \text{csch}\, x = \sqrt{\coth^2 x - 1}.$$

$$\sinh \left(\tfrac{1}{2}x\right) = \sqrt{\tfrac{1}{2}(\cosh x - 1)}.$$

$$\cosh \left(\tfrac{1}{2}x\right) = \sqrt{\tfrac{1}{2}(\cosh x + 1)}.$$

$$\tanh \left(\tfrac{1}{2}x\right) = (\cosh x - 1) \div \sinh x = \sinh x \div (\cosh x + 1)$$

$$\sinh (2x) = 2 \sinh x \cosh x.$$

$$\cosh (2x) = \cosh^2 x + \sinh^2 x = 2 \cosh^2 x - 1 = 1 + 2 \sinh^2 x.$$

$$\tanh (2x) = 2 \tanh x \div (1 + \tanh^2 x).$$

$$\sinh 3x = 3 \sinh x + 4 \sinh^3 x.$$

$$\cosh 3x = 4 \cosh^3 x - 3 \cosh x.$$

$$\tanh 3x = (3 \tanh x + \tanh^3 x) \div (1 + 3 \tanh^2 x).$$

$$\sinh (x \pm y) = \sinh x \cdot \cosh y \pm \cosh x \cdot \sinh y.$$

$$\cosh (x \pm y) = \cosh x \cdot \cosh y \pm \sinh x \cdot \sinh y.$$

$$\tanh (x \pm y) = (\tanh x \pm \tanh y) \div (1 \pm \tanh x \cdot \tanh y).$$

$$\sinh x + \sinh y = 2 \sinh \tfrac{1}{2}(x + y) \cdot \cosh \tfrac{1}{2}(x - y).$$

$$\sinh x - \sinh y = 2 \cosh \tfrac{1}{2}(x + y) \cdot \sinh \tfrac{1}{2}(x - y).$$

$$\cosh x + \cosh y = 2 \cosh \tfrac{1}{2}(x + y) \cdot \cosh \tfrac{1}{2}(x - y).$$

$$\cosh x - \cosh y = 2 \sinh \tfrac{1}{2}(x + y) \cdot \sinh \tfrac{1}{2}(x - y).$$

$$\sinh x + \cosh x = \frac{1 + \tanh \frac{1}{2}x}{1 - \tanh \frac{1}{2}x}$$

$$\tanh x \pm \tanh y = \frac{\sinh (x \pm y)}{\cosh x \cosh y}.$$

$$\coth x \pm \coth y = \pm \frac{\sinh (x \pm y)}{\sinh x \sinh y}.$$

Inverse Functions

$$\sinh^{-1} x = \log (x + \sqrt{x^2 + 1}) = \int \frac{dx}{\sqrt{x^2 + 1}} = \cosh^{-1} \sqrt{x^2 + 1}.$$

$$\cosh^{-1} x = \log (x + \sqrt{x^2 - 1}) = \int \frac{dx}{\sqrt{x^2 - 1}} = \sinh^{-1} \sqrt{x^2 - 1}.$$

$$\tanh^{-1} x = \frac{1}{2} \log (1 + x) - \frac{1}{2} \log (1 - x) = \int \frac{dx}{1 - x^2}.$$

$$\coth^{-1} x = \frac{1}{2} \log (1 + x) - \frac{1}{2} \log (x - 1) = \int \frac{dx}{1 - x^2}.$$

$$\text{sech}^{-1} x = \log \left(\frac{1}{x} + \sqrt{\frac{1}{x^2} - 1}\right) = -\int \frac{dx}{x\sqrt{1 - x^2}}.$$

$$\text{csch}^{-1} x = \log \left(\frac{1}{x} + \sqrt{\frac{1}{x^2} + 1}\right) = -\int \frac{dx}{x\sqrt{x^2 + 1}}.$$

HYPERBOLIC FUNCTIONS

Relations to Circular Functions

$\sinh x = -i \sin ix.$ $\qquad$ $\sinh ix = i \sin x.$

$\cosh x = \cos ix.$ $\qquad$ $\cosh ix = \cos x.$

$\tanh x = -i \tan ix.$ $\qquad$ $\tanh ix = i \tan x.$

If $x = \log \tan \left(\dfrac{\pi}{4} + \dfrac{\theta}{2} \right) = \log (\sec \theta + \tan \theta)$,

$\theta = $ the **gudermannian** of $x = $ gd $x.$

$\sinh x = \tan$ gd $x.$ $\qquad$ $\tanh x = \sin$ gd $x.$

$\cosh x = \sec$ gd $x.$ $\qquad$ $\tanh \frac{1}{2} x = \tan \frac{1}{2}$ gd $x.$

$$\frac{d \text{ gd } x}{dx} = \text{sech } x.$$

Differentials

$d \sinh x = \cosh x \cdot dx.$ $\qquad$ $d \coth x = -\text{csch}^2 x \cdot dx.$

$d \cosh x = \sinh x \cdot dx.$ $\qquad$ $d \text{ sech } x = -\text{sech } x \cdot \tanh x \cdot dx.$

$d \tanh x = \text{sech}^2 x \cdot dx.$ $\qquad$ $d \text{ csch } x = -\text{csch } x \cdot \coth x \cdot dx.$

$d \sinh^{-1} x = \dfrac{dx}{\sqrt{1 + x^2}}.$ $\qquad$ $d \coth^{-1} x = -\dfrac{dx}{x^2 - 1}.$

$d \cosh^{-1} x = \dfrac{dx}{\sqrt{x^2 - 1}}.$ $\qquad$ $d \text{ sech}^{-1} x = -\dfrac{dx}{x\sqrt{1 - x^2}}.$

$d \tanh^{-1} x = \dfrac{dx}{1 - x^2}.$ $\qquad$ $d \text{ csch}^{-1} x = -\dfrac{dx}{x\sqrt{x^2 + 1}}.$

Integrals involving the hyperbolic functions will be found in the table of integrals.

ELLIPTIC FUNCTIONS

$$u = F(k, \phi) = \int_0^\phi \frac{d\phi}{\sqrt{1 - k^2 \sin^2 \phi}}, \qquad (k^2 < 1),$$

$= $ elliptic integral of the first kind.

$$u = \int_0^x \frac{dx}{\sqrt{(1 - x^2)(1 - k^2 x^2)}}, \qquad \text{where } x = \sin \phi.$$

ϕ is called the amplitude of u or am u.

k is called the modulus.

$$k' = \sqrt{1 - k^2} = \text{the complementary modulus.}$$

$\sin \phi = $ sn $u = x$ $\qquad$ $\tan \phi = $ tn $u = \dfrac{x}{\sqrt{1 - x^2}}.$

$\cos \phi = $ cn $u = \sqrt{1 - x^2}.$ $\qquad$ $\Delta \phi = $ dn $u = \sqrt{1 - k^2 x^2}.$

am $0 = 0.$ $\qquad$ sn $0 = 0.$

cn $0 = 1.$ $\qquad$ dn $0 = 1.$

am $(-u) = -$am $u.$ $\qquad$ sn $(-u) = -$sn $u.$

cn $(-u) = $ cn $u.$ $\qquad$ dn $(-u) = $ dn $u.$

$\text{tn}\,(-u) = -\text{tn}\,u.$

$\text{sn}^2\,u + \text{cn}^2\,u = 1.$

$\text{dn}^2\,u + k^2\,\text{sn}^2\,u = 1.$

$\text{dn}^2\,u - k^2\,\text{cn}^2\,u = 1 - k^2 = k'^2.$

$$E(\phi, k) = \int_0^\phi \sqrt{1 - k^2 \sin^2 \phi}\; d\phi$$

$$= \int_0^x \frac{\sqrt{1 - k^2 x^2}}{\sqrt{1 - x^2}}\, dx \qquad \text{where } x = \sin\,\phi,$$

$= $ the elliptic integral of the second kind.

Complete Elliptic Integrals

$$K = \int_0^{\pi/2} \frac{d\phi}{\sqrt{1 - k^2 \sin^2 \phi}}.$$

$$E = \int_0^{\pi/2} \sqrt{1 - k^2 \sin^2 \phi}\; d\phi.$$

See tables of values, page 247–249.

INTEREST TABLES

SIMPLE INTEREST

If P is the principal placed at interest at a rate i (expressed as a decimal), for a period of n years

The amount,

$$A = P(1 + ni)$$

Present value,

$$P = \frac{A}{1 + ni}$$

COMPOUND INTEREST

At interest compounded annually the **amount,**—

$$A = P(1 + i)^n$$

At interest compounded q times per year,—

$$A = P\left(1 + \frac{i}{q}\right)^{nq}$$

At interest compounded annually the **present value,**—

$$P = \frac{A}{(1 + i)^n} = A(1 + i)^{-n} = Av^n. \quad v = \frac{1}{1 + i}$$

At interest compounded q times per year,—

$$P = A\left(1 + \frac{i}{q}\right)^{-nq}$$

The amount of an annuity of 1 per annum,—

$$s_{\overline{n}|} \text{ at } i = \frac{(1 + i)^n - 1}{i}$$

The present value of an annuity,—

$$a_{\overline{n}|} \text{ at } i = \frac{1 - (1 + i)^{-n}}{i}$$

The annuity whose present value is 1,—

$$\frac{1}{a_{\overline{n}|} \text{ at } i} = \frac{1}{s_{\overline{n}|}} + i = \frac{i}{(1 - v^n)}$$

Compound amount of 1 for fractional periods,—$(1 + i)^{1/p}$

Nominal rate convertible p times per year equivalent to effective rate i,—

$$j_p = p\left[(1 + i)^{1/p} - 1\right]$$

Amount for year of p deposits of $1/p$, p times per year,—i/j_v

THE NUMBER OF EACH DAY OF THE YEAR

Day of Mo.	Jan.	Feb.	Mar.	Apr.	May	Jun.	Jul.	Aug.	Sep.	Oct.	Nov.	Dec.	Day of Mo.
1	1	32	60	91	121	152	182	213	244	274	305	335	1
2	2	33	61	92	122	153	183	214	245	275	306	336	2
3	3	34	62	93	123	154	184	215	246	276	307	337	3
4	4	35	63	94	124	155	185	216	247	277	308	338	4
5	5	36	64	95	125	156	186	217	248	278	309	339	5
6	6	37	65	96	126	157	187	218	249	279	310	340	6
7	7	38	66	97	127	158	188	219	250	280	311	341	7
8	8	39	67	98	128	159	189	220	251	281	312	342	8
9	9	40	68	99	129	160	190	221	252	282	313	343	9
10	10	41	69	100	130	161	191	222	253	283	314	344	10
11	11	42	70	101	131	162	192	223	254	284	315	345	11
12	12	43	71	102	132	163	193	224	255	285	316	346	12
13	13	44	72	103	133	164	194	225	256	286	317	347	13
14	14	45	73	104	134	165	195	226	257	287	318	348	14
15	15	46	74	105	135	166	196	227	258	288	319	349	15
16	16	47	75	106	136	167	197	228	259	289	320	350	16
17	17	48	76	107	137	168	198	229	260	290	321	351	17
18	18	49	77	108	138	169	199	230	261	291	322	352	18
19	19	50	78	109	139	170	200	231	262	292	323	353	19
20	20	51	79	110	140	171	201	232	263	293	324	354	20
21	21	52	80	111	141	172	202	233	264	294	325	355	21
22	22	53	81	112	142	173	203	234	265	295	326	356	22
23	23	54	82	113	143	174	204	235	266	296	327	357	23
24	24	55	83	114	144	175	205	236	267	297	328	358	24
25	25	56	84	115	145	176	206	237	268	298	329	359	25
26	26	57	85	116	146	177	207	238	269	299	330	360	26
27	27	58	86	117	147	178	208	239	270	300	331	361	27
28	28	59	87	118	148	179	209	240	271	301	332	362	28
29	29	*	88	119	149	180	210	241	272	302	333	363	29
30	30		89	120	150	181	211	242	273	303	334	364	30
31	31		90		151		212	243		304		365	31

* In leap years, after February 28, add 1 to the tabulated number.

AMOUNT AT COMPOUND INTEREST $(1+i)^n$

The following table gives the amount after a term of n years on unit original principal at rate of interest i.

Years	Rate i				
n	.0025 ($\frac{1}{4}\%$)	.004167 ($\frac{5}{12}\%$)	.005 ($\frac{1}{2}\%$)	.005833 ($\frac{7}{12}\%$)	.0075 ($\frac{3}{4}\%$)
1	1.0025 0000	1.0041 6667	1.0050 0000	1.0058 3333	1.0075 0000
2	1.0050 0625	1.0083 5069	1.0100 2500	1.0117 0069	1.0150 5625
3	1.0075 1877	1.0125 5216	1.0150 7513	1.0176 0228	1.0226 6917
4	1.0100 3756	1.0167 7112	1.0201 5050	1.0235 3830	1.0303 3919
5	1.0125 6266	1.0210 0767	1.0252 5125	1.0295 0894	1.0380 6673
6	1.0150 9406	1.0252 6187	1.0303 7751	1.0355 1440	1.0458 5224
7	1.0176 3180	1.0295 3379	1.0355 2940	1.0415 5490	1.0536 9613
8	1.0201 7588	1.0338 2352	1.0407 0704	1.0476 3064	1.0615 9885
9	1.0227 2632	1.0381 3111	1.0459 1058	1.0537 4182	1.0695 6084
10	1.0252 8313	1.0424 5666	1.0511 4013	1.0598 8865	1.0775 8255
11	1.0278 4634	1.0468 0023	1.0563 9583	1.0660 7133	1.0856 6441
12	1.0304 1596	1.0511 6190	1.0616 7781	1.0722 9008	1.0938 0690
13	1.0329 9200	1.0555 4174	1.0669 8620	1.0785 4511	1.1020 1045
14	1.0355 7448	1.0599 3983	1.0723 2113	1.0848 3662	1.1102 7553
15	1.0381 6341	1.0643 5625	1.0776 8274	1.0911 6483	1.1186 0259
16	1.0407 5882	1.0687 9106	1.0830 7115	1.0975 2996	1.1269 9211
17	1.0433 6072	1.0732 4436	1.0884 8651	1.1039 3222	1.1354 4455
18	1.0459 6912	1.0777 1621	1.0939 2894	1.1103 7182	1.1439 6039
19	1.0485 8404	1.0822 0670	1.0993 9858	1.1168 4899	1.1525 4009
20	1.0512 0550	1.0867 1589	1.1048 9558	1.1233 6395	1.1611 8414
21	1.0538 3352	1.0912 4387	1.1104 2006	1.1299 1690	1.1698 9302
22	1.0564 6810	1.0957 9072	1.1159 7216	1.1365 0808	1.1786 6722
23	1.0591 0927	1.1003 5652	1.1215 5202	1.1431 3771	1.1875 0723
24	1.0617 5704	1.1049 4134	1.1271 5978	1.1498 0602	1.1964 1353
25	1.0644 1144	1.1095 4526	1.1327 9558	1.1565 1322	1.2053 8663
26	1.0670 7247	1.1141 6836	1.1384 5955	1.1632 5955	1.2144 2703
27	1.0697 4015	1.1188 1073	1.1441 5185	1.1700 4523	1.2235 3523
28	1.0724 1450	1.1234 7244	1.1498 7261	1.1768 7049	1.2327 1175
29	1.0750 9553	1.1281 5358	1.1556 2197	1.1837 3557	1.2419 5709
30	1.0777 8327	1.1328 5422	1.1614 0008	1.1906 4069	1.2512 7176
31	1.0804 7773	1.1375 7444	1.1672 0708	1.1975 8610	1.2606 5630
32	1.0831 7892	1.1423 1434	1.1730 4312	1.2045 7202	1.2701 1122
33	1.0858 8687	1.1470 7398	1.1789 0833	1.2115 9869	1.2796 3706
34	1.0886 0159	1.1518 5346	1.1848 0288	1.2186 6634	1.2892 3434
35	1.0913 2309	1.1566 5284	1.1907 2689	1.2257 7523	1.2989 0359
36	1.0940 5140	1.1614 7223	1.1966 8052	1.2329 2559	1.3086 4537
37	1.0967 8653	1.1663 1170	1.2026 6393	1.2401 1765	1.3184 6021
38	1.0995 2850	1.1711 7133	1.2086 7725	1.2473 5167	1.3283 4866
39	1.1022 7732	1.1760 5121	1.2147 2063	1.2546 2789	1.3383 1128
40	1.1050 3301	1.1809 5142	1.2207 9424	1.2619 4655	1.3483 4861
41	1.1077 9559	1.1858 7206	1.2268 9821	1.2693 0791	1.3584 6123
42	1.1105 6508	1.1908 1319	1.2330 3270	1.2767 1220	1.3686 4969
43	1.1133 4149	1.1957 7491	1.2391 9786	1.2841 5969	1.3789 1456
44	1.1161 2485	1.2007 5731	1.2453 9385	1.2916 5062	1.3892 5642
45	1.1189 1516	1.2057 6046	1.2516 2082	1.2991 8525	1.3996 7584
46	1.1217 1245	1.2107 8446	1.2578 7892	1.3067 6383	1.4101 7341
47	1.1245 1673	1.2158 2940	1.2641 6832	1.3143 8662	1.4207 4971
48	1.1273 2802	1.2208 9536	1.2704 8916	1.3220 5388	1.4314 0533
49	1.1301 4634	1.2259 8242	1.2768 4161	1.3297 6586	1.4421 4087
50	1.1329 7171	1.2310 9068	1.2832 2581	1.3375 2283	1.4529 5693

AMOUNT AT COMPOUND INTEREST $(1+i)^n$

Years	Rate i				
n	.0025 ($\frac{1}{4}\%$)	.004167 ($\frac{5}{12}\%$)	.005 ($\frac{1}{2}\%$)	.005833 ($\frac{7}{12}\%$)	.0075 ($\frac{3}{4}\%$)
50	1.1329 7171	1.2310 9068	1.2832 2581	1.3375 2283	1.4529 5693
51	1.1358 0414	1.2362 2022	1.2896 4194	1.3453 2504	1.4638 5411
52	1.1386 4365	1.2413 7114	1.2960 9015	1.3531 7277	1.4748 3301
53	1.1414 9026	1.2465 4352	1.3025 7060	1.3610 6628	1.4858 9426
54	1.1443 4398	1.2517 3745	1.3090 8346	1.3690 0583	1.4970 3847
55	1.1472 0484	1.2569 5302	1.3156 2887	1.3769 9170	1.5082 6626
56	1.1500 7285	1.2621 9033	1.3222 0702	1.3850 2415	1.5195 7825
57	1.1529 4804	1.2674 4946	1.3288 1805	1.3931 0346	1.5309 7509
58	1.1558 3041	1.2727 3050	1.3354 6214	1.4012 2990	1.5424 5740
59	1.1587 1998	1.2780 3354	1.3421 3946	1.4094 0374	1.5540 2583
60	1.1616 1678	1.2833 5868	1.3488 5015	1.4176 2526	1.5656 8103
61	1.1645 2082	1.2887 0601	1.3555 9440	1.4258 9474	1.5774 2363
62	1.1674 3213	1.2940 7561	1.3623 7238	1.4342 1246	1.5892 5431
63	1.1703 5071	1.2994 6760	1.3691 8424	1.4425 7870	1.6011 7372
64	1.1732 7658	1.3048 8204	1.3760 3016	1.4509 9374	1.6131 8252
65	1.1762 0977	1.3103 1905	1.3829 1031	1.4594 5787	1.6252 8139
66	1.1791 5030	1.3157 7872	1.3898 2486	1.4679 7138	1.6374 7100
67	1.1820 9817	1.3212 6113	1.3967 7399	1.4765 3454	1.6497 5203
68	1.1850 5342	1.3267 6638	1.4037 5785	1.4851 4766	1.6621 2517
69	1.1880 1605	1.3322 9458	1.4107 7664	1.4938 1102	1.6745 9111
70	1.1909 8609	1.3378 4580	1.4178 3053	1.5025 2492	1.6871 5055
71	1.1939 6356	1.3434 2016	1.4249 1968	1.5112 8965	1.6998 0418
72	1.1969 4847	1.3490 1774	1.4320 4428	1.5201 0550	1.7125 5271
73	1.1999 4084	1.3546 3865	1.4392 0450	1.5289 7279	1.7253 9685
74	1.2029 4069	1.3602 8298	1.4464 0052	1.5378 9179	1.7383 3733
75	1.2059 4804	1.3659 5082	1.4536 3252	1.5468 6283	1.7513 7486
76	1.2089 6291	1.3716 4229	1.4609 0069	1.5558 8620	1.7645 1017
77	1.2119 8532	1.3773 5746	1.4682 0519	1.5649 6220	1.7777 4400
78	1.2150 1528	1.3830 9645	1.4755 4622	1.5740 9115	1.7910 7708
79	1.2180 5282	1.3888 5935	1.4829 2395	1.5832 7334	1.8045 1015
80	1.2210 9795	1.3946 4627	1.4903 3857	1.5925 0910	1.8180 4398
81	1.2241 5070	1.4004 5729	1.4977 9026	1.6017 9874	1.8316 7931
82	1.2272 1108	1.4062 9253	1.5052 7921	1.6111 4257	1.8454 1691
83	1.2302 7910	1.4121 5209	1.5128 0561	1.6205 4090	1.8592 5753
84	1.2333 5480	1.4180 3605	1.5203 6964	1.6299 9405	1.8732 0196
85	1.2364 3819	1.4239 4454	1.5279 7148	1.6395 0235	1.8872 5098
86	1.2395 2928	1.4298 7764	1.5356 1134	1.6490 6612	1.9014 0536
87	1.2426 2811	1.4358 3546	1.5432 8940	1.6586 8567	1.9156 6590
88	1.2457 3468	1.4418 1811	1.5510 0585	1.6683 6134	1.9300 3339
89	1.2488 4901	1.4478 2568	1.5587 6087	1.6780 9344	1.9445 0865
90	1.2519 7114	1.4538 5829	1.5665 5468	1.6878 8232	1.9590 9246
91	1.2551 0106	1.4599 1603	1.5743 8745	1.6977 2830	1.9737 8565
92	1.2582 3882	1.4659 9902	1.5822 5939	1.7076 3172	1.9885 8905
93	1.2613 8441	1.4721 0735	1.5901 7069	1.7175 9290	2.0035 0346
94	1.2645 3787	1.4782 4113	1.5981 2154	1.7276 1219	2.0185 2974
95	1.2676 9922	1.4844 0047	1.6061 1215	1.7376 8993	2.0336 6871
96	1.2708 6847	1.4905 8547	1.6141 4271	1.7478 2646	2.0489 2123
97	1.2740 4564	1.4967 9624	1.6222 1342	1.7580 2211	2.0642 8814
98	1.2772 3075	1.5030 3289	1.6303 2449	1.7682 7724	2.0797 7030
99	1.2804 2383	1.5092 9553	1.6384 7611	1.7785 9219	2.0953 6858
100	1.2836 2489	1.5155 8426	1.6466 6849	1.7889 6731	2.1110 8384

AMOUNT AT COMPOUND INTEREST $(1+i)^n$

Years	Rate i				
n	.01 (1%)	.01125 ($1\frac{1}{8}\%$)	.0125 ($1\frac{1}{4}\%$)	.015 ($1\frac{1}{2}\%$)	.0175 ($1\frac{3}{4}\%$)
1	1.0100 0000	1.0112 5000	1.0125 0000	1.0150 0000	1.0175 0000
2	1.0201 0000	1.0226 2656	1.0251 5625	1.0302 2500	1.0353 0625
3	1.0303 0100	1.0341 3111	1.0379 7070	1.0456 7838	1.0534 2411
4	1.0406 0401	1.0457 6509	1.0509 4534	1.0613 6355	1.0718 5903
5	1.0510 1005	1.0575 2994	1.0640 8215	1.0772 8400	1.0906 1656
6	1.0615 2015	1.0694 2716	1.0773 8318	1.0934 4326	1.1097 0235
7	1.0721 3535	1.0814 5821	1.0908 5047	1.1098 4491	1.1291 2215
8	1.0828 5671	1.0936 2462	1.1044 8610	1.1264 9259	1.1488 8178
9	1.0936 8527	1.1059 2789	1.1182 9218	1.1433 8998	1.1689 8721
10	1.1046 2213	1.1183 6958	1.1322 7083	1.1605 4083	1.1894 4449
11	1.1156 6835	1.1309 5124	1.1464 2422	1.1779 4894	1.2102 5977
12	1.1268 2503	1.1436 7444	1.1607 5452	1.1956 1817	1.2314 3931
13	1.1380 9328	1.1565 4078	1.1752 6395	1.2135 5244	1.2529 8950
14	1.1494 7421	1.1695 5186	1.1899 5475	1.2317 5573	1.2749 1682
15	1.1609 6896	1.1827 0932	1.2048 2918	1.2502 3207	1.2972 2786
16	1.1725 7864	1.1960 1480	1.2198 8955	1.2689 8555	1.3199 2935
17	1.1843 0443	1.2094 6997	1.2351 3817	1.2880 2033	1.3430 2811
18	1.1961 4748	1.2230 7650	1.2505 7739	1.3073 4064	1.3665 3111
19	1.2081 0895	1.2368 3611	1.2662 0961	1.3269 5075	1.3904 4540
20	1.2201 9004	1.2507 5052	1.2820 3723	1.3468 5501	1.4147 7820
21	1.2323 9194	1.2648 2146	1.2980 6270	1.3670 5783	1.4395 3681
22	1.2447 1586	1.2790 5071	1.3142 8848	1.3875 6370	1.4647 2871
23	1.2571 6302	1.2934 4003	1.3307 1709	1.4083 7715	1.4903 6146
24	1.2697 3465	1.3079 9123	1.3473 5105	1.4295 0281	1.5164 4279
25	1.2824 3200	1.3227 0613	1.3641 9294	1.4509 4535	1.5429 8054
26	1.2952 5631	1.3375 8657	1.3812 4535	1.4727 0953	1.5699 8269
27	1.3082 0888	1.3526 3442	1.3985 1092	1.4948 0018	1.5974 5739
28	1.3212 9097	1.3678 5156	1.4159 9230	1.5172 2218	1.6254 1290
29	1.3345 0388	1.3832 3989	1.4336 9221	1.5399 8051	1.6538 5762
30	1.3478 4892	1.3988 0134	1.4516 1336	1.5630 8022	1.6828 0013
31	1.3613 2740	1.4145 3785	1.4697 5853	1.5865 2642	1.7122 4913
32	1.3749 4068	1.4304 5140	1.4881 3051	1.6103 2432	1.7422 1349
33	1.3886 9009	1.4465 4398	1.5067 3214	1.6344 7918	1.7727 0223
34	1.4025 7699	1.4628 1760	1.5255 6629	1.6589 9637	1.8037 2452
35	1.4166 0276	1.4792 7430	1.5446 3587	1.6838 8132	1.8352 8970
36	1.4307 6878	1.4959 1613	1.5639 4382	1.7091 3954	1.8674 0727
37	1.4450 7647	1.5127 4519	1.5834 9312	1.7347 7663	1.9000 8689
38	1.4595 2724	1.5297 6357	1.6032 8678	1.7607 9828	1.9333 3841
39	1.4741 2251	1.5469 7341	1.6233 2787	1.7872 1025	1.9671 7184
40	1.4888 6373	1.5643 7687	1.6436 1946	1.8140 1841	2.0015 9734
41	1.5037 5237	1.5819 7611	1.6641 6471	1.8412 2868	2.0366 2530
42	1.5187 8989	1.5997 7334	1.6849 6677	1.8688 4712	2.0722 6624
43	1.5339 7779	1.6177 7079	1.7060 2885	1.8968 7982	2.1085 3090
44	1.5493 1757	1.6359 7071	1.7273 5421	1.9253 3302	2.1454 3019
45	1.5648 1075	1.6543 7538	1.7489 4614	1.9542 1301	2.1829 7522
46	1.5804 5885	1.6729 8710	1.7708 0797	1.9835 2621	2.2211 7728
47	1.5962 6344	1.6918 0821	1.7929 4306	2.0132 7910	2.2600 4789
48	1.6122 2608	1.7108 4105	1.8153 5485	2.0434 7829	2.2995 9872
49	1.6283 4834	1.7300 8801	1.8380 4679	2.0741 3046	2.3398 4170
50	1.6446 3182	1.7495 5150	1.8610 2237	2.1052 4242	2.3807 8893

AMOUNT AT COMPOUND INTEREST $(1+i)^n$

Years	Rate i				
n	.01 (1%)	.01125 (1⅛%)	.0125 (1¼%)	.015 (1½%)	.0175 (1¾%)
50	1.6446 3182	1.7495 5150	1.8610 2237	2.1052 4242	2.3807 8893
51	1.6610 7814	1.7692 3395	1.8842 8515	2.1368 2106	2.4224 5274
52	1.6776 8892	1.7891 3784	1.9078 3872	2.1688 7337	2.4648 4566
53	1.6944 6581	1.8092 6564	1.9316 8670	2.2014 0647	2.5079 8046
54	1.7114 1047	1.8296 1988	1.9558 3279	2.2344 2757	2.5518 7012
55	1.7285 2457	1.8502 0310	1.9802 8070	2.2679 4398	2.5965 2785
56	1.7458 0982	1.8710 1788	2.0050 3420	2.3019 6314	2.6419 6708
57	1.7632 6792	1.8920 6684	2.0300 9713	2.3364 9259	2.6882 0151
58	1.7809 0060	1.9133 5259	2.0554 7335	2.3715 3998	2.7352 4503
59	1.7987 0960	1.9348 7780	2.0811 6676	2.4071 1308	2.7831 1182
60	1.8166 9670	1.9566 4518	2.1071 8135	2.4432 1978	2.8318 1628
61	1.8348 6367	1.9786 5744	2.1335 2111	2.4798 6807	2.8813 7306
62	1.8532 1230	2.0009 1733	2.1601 9013	2.5170 6609	2.9317 9709
63	1.8717 4443	2.0234 2765	2.1871 9250	2.5548 2208	2.9831 0354
64	1.8904 6187	2.0461 9121	2.2145 3241	2.5931 4442	3.0353 0785
65	1.9093 6649	2.0692 1087	2.2422 1407	2.6320 4158	3.0884 2574
66	1.9284 6015	2.0924 8949	2.2702 4174	2.6715 2221	3.1424 7319
67	1.9477 4475	2.1160 2999	2.2986 1976	2.7115 9504	3.1974 6647
68	1.9672 2220	2.1398 3533	2.3273 5251	2.7522 6896	3.2534 2213
69	1.9868 9442	2.1639 0848	2.3564 4442	2.7935 5300	3.3103 5702
70	2.0067 6337	2.1882 5245	2.3858 9997	2.8354 5629	3.3682 8827
71	2.0268 3100	2.2128 7029	2.4157 2372	2.8779 8814	3.4272 3331
72	2.0470 9931	2.2377 6508	2.4459 2027	2.9211 5796	3.4872 0990
73	2.0675 7031	2.2629 3994	2.4764 9427	2.9649 7533	3.5482 3607
74	2.0882 4601	2.2883 9801	2.5074 5045	3.0094 4996	3.6103 3020
75	2.1091 2847	2.3141 4249	2.5387 9358	3.0545 9171	3.6735 1098
76	2.1302 1975	2.3401 7659	2.5705 2850	3.1004 1059	3.7377 9742
77	2.1515 2195	2.3665 0358	2.6026 6011	3.1469 1674	3.8032 0888
78	2.1730 3717	2.3931 2675	2.6351 9336	3.1941 2050	3.8697 6503
79	2.1947 6754	2.4200 4942	2.6681 3327	3.2420 3230	3.9374 8592
80	2.2167 1522	2.4472 7498	2.7014 8494	3.2906 6279	4.0063 9192
81	2.2388 8237	2.4748 0682	2.7352 5350	3.3400 2273	4.0765 0378
82	2.2612 7119	2.5026 4840	2.7694 4417	3.3901 2307	4.1478 4260
83	2.2838 8390	2.5308 0319	2.8040 6222	3.4409 7492	4.2204 2984
84	2.3067 2274	2.5592 7473	2.8391 1300	3.4925 8954	4.2942 8737
85	2.3297 8997	2.5880 6657	2.8746 0191	3.5449 7838	4.3694 3740
86	2.3530 8787	2.6171 8232	2.9105 3444	3.5981 5306	4.4459 0255
87	2.3766 1875	2.6466 2562	2.9469 1612	3.6521 2535	4.5237 0584
88	2.4003 8494	2.6764 0016	2.9837 5257	3.7069 0723	4.6028 7070
89	2.4243 8879	2.7065 0966	3.0210 4948	3.7625 1084	4.6834 2093
90	2.4486 3267	2.7369 5789	3.0588 1260	3.8189 4851	4.7653 8080
91	2.4731 1900	2.7677 4867	3.0970 4775	3.8762 3273	4.8487 7496
92	2.4978 5019	2.7988 8584	3.1357 6085	3.9343 7622	4.9336 2853
93	2.5228 2869	2.8303 7331	3.1749 5786	3.9933 9187	5.0199 6703
94	2.5480 5698	2.8622 1501	3.2146 4483	4.0532 9275	5.1078 1645
95	2.5735 3755	2.8944 1492	3.2548 2789	4.1140 9214	5.1972 0324
96	2.5992 7293	2.9269 7709	3.2955 1324	4.1758 0352	5.2881 5429
97	2.6252 6565	2.9599 0559	3.3367 0716	4.2384 4057	5.3806 9699
98	2.6515 1831	2.9932 0452	3.3784 1600	4.3020 1718	5.4748 5919
99	2.6780 3349	3.0268 7807	3.4206 4620	4.3665 4744	5.5706 6923
100	2.7048 1383	3.0609 3045	3.4634 0427	4.4320 4565	5.6681 5594

AMOUNT AT COMPOUND INTEREST $(1+i)^n$

Years			Rate i		
n	.02 (2%)	.0225 (2¼%)	.025 (2½%)	.0275 (2¾%)	.03 (3%)
1	1.0200 0000	1.0225 0000	1.0250 0000	1.0275 0000	1.0300 0000
2	1.0404 0000	1.0455 0625	1.0506 2500	1.0557 5625	1.0609 0000
3	1.0612 0800	1.0690 3014	1.0768 9063	1.0847 8955	1.0927 2700
4	1.0824 3216	1.0930 8332	1.1038 1289	1.1146 2126	1.1255 0881
5	1.1040 8080	1.1176 7769	1.1314 0821	1.1452 7334	1.1592 7407
6	1.1261 6242	1.1428 2544	1.1596 9342	1.1767 6836	1.1940 5230
7	1.1486 8567	1.1685 3901	1.1886 8575	1.2091 2949	1.2298 7387
8	1.1716 5938	1.1948 3114	1.2184 0290	1.2423 8055	1.2667 7008
9	1.1950 9257	1.2217 1484	1.2488 6297	1.2765 4602	1.3047 7318
10	1.2189 9442	1.2492 0343	1.2800 8454	1.3116 5103	1.3439 1638
11	1.2433 7431	1.2773 1050	1.3120 8666	1.3477 2144	1.3842 3387
12	1.2682 4179	1.3060 4999	1.3448 8882	1.3847 8378	1.4257 6089
13	1.2936 0663	1.3354 3611	1.3785 1104	1.4228 6533	1.4685 3371
14	1.3194 7876	1.3654 8343	1.4129 7382	1.4619 9413	1.5125 8972
15	1.3458 6834	1.3962 0680	1.4482 9817	1.5021 9896	1.5579 6742
16	1.3727 8571	1.4276 2146	1.4845 0562	1.5435 0944	1.6047 0644
17	1.4002 4142	1.4597 4294	1.5216 1826	1.5859 5595	1.6528 4763
18	1.4282 4625	1.4925 8716	1.5596 5872	1.6295 6973	1.7024 3306
19	1.4568 1117	1.5261 7037	1.5986 5019	1.6743 8290	1.7535 0605
20	1.4859 4740	1.5605 0920	1.6386 1644	1.7204 2843	1.8061 1123
21	1.5156 6634	1.5956 2066	1.6795 8185	1.7677 4021	1.8602 9457
22	1.5459 7967	1.6315 2212	1.7215 7140	1.8163 5307	1.9161 0341
23	1.5768 9926	1.6682 3137	1.7646 1068	1.8663 0278	1.9735 8651
24	1.6084 3725	1.7057 6658	1.8087 2595	1.9176 2610	2.0327 9411
25	1.6406 0599	1.7441 4632	1.8539 4410	1.9703 6082	2.0937 7793
26	1.6734 1811	1.7833 8962	1.9002 9270	2.0245 4575	2.1565 9127
27	1.7068 8648	1.8235 1588	1.9478 0002	2.0802 2075	2.2212 8901
28	1.7410 2421	1.8645 4499	1.9964 9502	2.1374 2682	2.2879 2768
29	1.7758 4469	1.9064 9725	2.0464 0739	2.1962 0606	2.3565 6551
30	1.8113 6158	1.9493 9344	2.0975 6758	2.2566 0173	2.4272 6247
31	1.8475 8882	1.9932 5479	2.1500 0677	2.3186 5828	2.5000 8035
32	1.8845 4059	2.0381 0303	2.2037 5694	2.3824 2138	2.5750 8276
33	1.9222 3140	2.0839 6034	2.2588 5086	2.4479 3797	2.6523 3524
34	1.9606 7603	2.1308 4945	2.3153 2213	2.5152 5626	2.7319 0530
35	1.9998 8955	2.1787 9356	2.3732 0519	2.5844 2581	2.8138 6245
36	2.0398 8734	2.2278 1642	2.4325 3532	2.6554 9752	2.8982 7833
37	2.0806 8509	2.2779 4229	2.4933 4870	2.7285 2370	2.9852 2668
38	2.1222 9879	2.3291 9599	2.5556 8242	2.8035 5810	3.0747 8348
39	2.1647 4477	2.3816 0290	2.6195 7448	2.8806 5595	3.1670 2698
40	2.2080 3966	2.4351 8897	2.6850 6384	2.9598 7399	3.2620 3779
41	2.2522 0046	2.4899 8072	2.7521 9043	3.0412 7052	3.3598 9893
42	2.2972 4447	2.5460 0528	2.8209 9520	3.1249 0546	3.4606 9589
43	2.3431 8936	2.6032 9040	2.8915 2008	3.2108 4036	3.5645 1677
44	2.3900 5314	2.6618 6444	2.9638 0808	3.2991 3847	3.6714 5227
45	2.4378 5421	2.7217 5639	3.0379 0328	3.3898 6478	3.7815 9584
46	2.4866 1129	2.7829 9590	3.1138 5086	3.4830 8606	3.8950 4372
47	2.5363 4352	2.8456 1331	3.1916 9713	3.5788 7093	4.0118 9503
48	2.5870 7039	2.9096 3961	3.2714 8956	3.6772 8988	4.1322 5188
49	2.6388 1179	2.9751 0650	3.3532 7680	3.7784 1535	4.2562 1944
50	2.6915 8803	3.0420 4640	3.4371 0872	3.8823 2177	4.3839 0602

AMOUNT AT COMPOUND INTEREST $(1+i)^n$

Years	Rate i				
n	.02 (2%)	.0225 (2¼%)	.025 (2½%)	.0275 (2¾%)	.03 (3%)
50	2.6915 8803	3.0420 4640	3.4371 0872	3.8823 2177	4.3839 0602
51	2.7454 1979	3.1104 9244	3.5230 3644	3.9890 8562	4.5154 2320
52	2.8003 2819	3.1804 7852	3.6111 1235	4.0987 8547	4.6508 8590
53	2.8563 3475	3.2520 3929	3.7013 9016	4.2115 0208	4.7904 1247
54	2.9134 6144	3.3252 1017	3.7939 2491	4.3273 1838	4.9341 2485
55	2.9717 3067	3.4000 2740	3.8887 7303	4.4463 1964	5.0821 4859
56	3.0311 6529	3.4765 2802	3.9859 9236	4.5685 9343	5.2346 1305
57	3.0917 8859	3.5547 4990	4.0856 4217	4.6942 2975	5.3916 5144
58	3.1536 2436	3.6347 3177	4.1877 8322	4.8233 2107	5.5534 0098
59	3.2166 9685	3.7165 1324	4.2924 7780	4.9559 6239	5.7200 0301
60	3.2810 3079	3.8001 3479	4.3997 8975	5.0922 5136	5.8916 0310
61	3.3466 5140	3.8856 3782	4.5097 8449	5.2322 8827	6.0683 5120
62	3.4135 8443	3.9730 6467	4.6225 2910	5.3761 7620	6.2504 0173
63	3.4818 5612	4.0624 5862	4.7380 9233	5.5240 2105	6.4379 1379
64	3.5514 9324	4.1538 6394	4.8565 4464	5.6759 3162	6.6310 5120
65	3.6225 2311	4.2473 2588	4.9779 5826	5.8320 1974	6.8299 8273
66	3.6949 7357	4.3428 9071	5.1024 0721	5.9924 0029	7.0348 8222
67	3.7688 7304	4.4406 0576	5.2299 6739	6.1571 9130	7.2459 2868
68	3.8442 5050	4.5405 1939	5.3607 1658	6.3265 1406	7.4633 0654
69	3.9211 3551	4.6426 8107	5.4947 3449	6.5004 9319	7.6872 0574
70	3.9995 5822	4.7471 4140	5.6321 0286	6.6792 5676	7.9178 2191
71	4.0795 4939	4.8539 5208	5.7729 0543	6.8629 3632	8.1553 5657
72	4.1611 4038	4.9631 6600	5.9172 2806	7.0516 6706	8.4000 1727
73	4.2443 6318	5.0748 3723	6.0651 5876	7.2455 8791	8.6520 1778
74	4.3292 5045	5.1890 2107	6.2167 8773	7.4448 4158	8.9115 7832
75	4.4158 3546	5.3057 7405	6.3722 0743	7.6495 7472	9.1789 2567
76	4.5041 5216	5.4251 5396	6.5315 1261	7.8599 3802	9.4542 9344
77	4.5942 3521	5.5472 1993	6.6948 0043	8.0760 8632	9.7379 2224
78	4.6861 1991	5.6720 3237	6.8621 7044	8.2981 7869	10.0300 5991
79	4.7798 4231	5.7996 5310	7.0337 2470	8.5263 7861	10.3309 6171
80	4.8754 3916	5.9301 4530	7.2095 6782	8.7608 5402	10.6408 9056
81	4.9729 4794	6.0635 7357	7.3898 0701	9.0017 7751	10.9601 1727
82	5.0724 0690	6.2000 0397	7.5745 5219	9.2493 2639	11.2889 2079
83	5.1738 5504	6.3395 0406	7.7639 1599	9.5036 8286	11.6275 8842
84	5.2773 3214	6.4821 4290	7.9580 1389	9.7650 3414	11.9764 1607
85	5.3828 7878	6.6279 9112	8.1569 6424	10.0335 7258	12.3357 0855
86	5.4905 3636	6.7771 2092	8.3608 8834	10.3094 9583	12.7057 7981
87	5.6003 4708	6.9296 0614	8.5699 1055	10.5930 0696	13.0869 5320
88	5.7123 5402	7.0855 2228	8.7841 5832	10.8843 1465	13.4795 6180
89	5.8266 0110	7.2449 4653	9.0037 6228	11.1836 3331	13.8839 4865
90	5.9431 3313	7.4079 5782	9.2288 5633	11.4911 8322	14.3004 6711
91	6.0619 9579	7.5746 3688	9.4595 7774	11.8071 9076	14.7294 8112
92	6.1832 3570	7.7450 6621	9.6960 6718	12.1318 8851	15.1713 6556
93	6.3069 0042	7.9193 3020	9.9384 6886	12.4655 1544	15.6265 0652
94	6.4330 3843	8.0975 1512	10.1869 3058	12.8083 1711	16.0953 0172
95	6.5616 9920	8.2797 0921	10.4416 0385	13.1605 4584	16.5781 6077
96	6.6929 3318	8.4660 0267	10.7026 4395	13.5224 6085	17.0755 0559
97	6.8267 9184	8.6564 8773	10.9702 1004	13.8943 2852	17.5877 7076
98	6.9633 2768	8.8512 5871	11.2444 6530	14.2764 2255	18.1154 0388
99	7.1025 9423	9.0504 1203	11.5255 7693	14.6690 2417	18.6588 6600
100	7.2446 4612	9.2540 4630	11.8137 1635	15.0724 2234	19.2186 3198

AMOUNT AT COMPOUND INTEREST $(1+i)^n$

Years	Rate i				
n	.035 (3½%)	.04 (4%)	.045 (4½%)	.05 (5%)	.055 (5½%)
1	1.0350 0000	1.0400 0000	1.0450 0000	1.0500 0000	1.0550 0000
2	1.0712 2500	1.0816 0000	1.0920 2500	1.1025 0000	1.1130 2500
3	1.1087 1788	1.1248 6400	1.1411 6613	1.1576 2500	1.1742 4138
4	1.1475 2300	1.1698 5856	1.1925 1860	1.2155 0625	1 2388 2465
5	1.1876 8631	1.2166 5290	1.2461 8194	1.2762 8156	1.3069 6001
6	1.2292 5533	1.2653 1902	1.3022 6012	1.3400 9564	1.3788 4281
7	1.2722 7926	1.3159 3178	1.3608 6183	1.4071 0042	1.4546 7916
8	1.3168 0904	1.3685 6905	1.4221 0061	1.4774 5544	1.5346 8651
9	1.3628 9735	1.4233 1181	1.4860 9514	1.5513 2822	1.6190 9427
10	1.4105 9876	1.4802 4428	1.5529 6942	1.6288 9463	1.7081 4446
11	1.4599 6972	1.5394 5406	1.6228 5305	1.7103 3936	1.8020 9240
12	1.5110 6866	1.6010 3222	1.6958 8143	1.7958 5633	1.9012 0749
13	1.5639 5606	1.6650 7351	1.7721 9610	1.8856 4914	2.0057 7390
14	1.6186 9452	1.7316 7645	1.8519 4492	1.9799 3160	2.1160 9146
15	1.6753 4883	1.8009 4351	1.9352 8244	2.0789 2818	2.2324 7649
16	1.7339 8604	1.8729 8125	2.0223 7015	2.1828 7459	2.3552 6270
17	1.7946 7555	1.9479 0050	2.1133 7681	2.2920 1832	2.4848 0215
18	1.8574 8920	2.0258 1652	2.2084 7877	2.4066 1923	2.6214 6627
19	1.9225 0132	2.1068 4918	2.3078 6031	2.5269 5020	2.7656 4691
20	1.9897 8886	2.1911 2314	2.4117 1402	2.6532 9771	2.9177 5749
21	2.0594 3147	2.2787 6807	2.5202 4116	2.7859 6259	3.0782 3415
22	2.1315 1158	2.3699 1879	2.6336 5201	2.9252 6072	3.2475 3703
23	2.2061 1448	2.4647 1554	2.7521 6635	3.0715 2376	3.4261 5157
24	2.2833 2849	2.5633 0416	2.8760 1383	3.2250 9994	3.6145 8990
25	2.3632 4498	2.6658 3633	3.0054 3446	3.3863 5494	3.8133 9235
26	2.4459 5856	2.7724 6978	3.1406 7901	3.5556 7269	4.0231 2893
27	2.5315 6711	2.8833 6858	3.2820 0956	3.7334 5632	4.2444 0102
28	2.6201 7196	2.9987 0332	3.4296 9999	3.9201 2914	4.4778 4307
29	2.7118 7798	3.1186 5145	3.5840 3649	4.1161 3560	4.7241 2444
30	2.8067 9370	3.2433 9751	3.7453 1813	4.3219 4238	4.9839 5129
31	2.9050 3148	3.3731 3341	3.9138 5745	4.5380 3949	5.2580 6861
32	3.0067 0759	3.5080 5875	4.0899 8104	4.7649 4147	5.5472 6238
33	3.1119 4235	3.6483 8110	4.2740 3018	5.0031 8854	5.8523 6181
34	3.2208 6033	3.7943 1634	4.4663 6154	5.2533 4797	6.1742 4171
35	3.3335 9045	3.9460 8899	4.6673 4781	5.5160 1537	6.5138 2501
36	3.4502 6611	4.1039 3255	4.8773 7846	5.7918 1614	6.8720 8538
37	3.5710 2543	4.2680 8986	5.0968 6049	6.0814 0694	7.2500 5008
38	3.6960 1132	4.4388 1345	5.3262 1921	6.3854 7729	7.6488 0283
39	3.8253 7171	4.6163 6599	5.5658 9908	6.7047 5115	8.0694 8699
40	3.9592 5972	4.8010 2063	5.8163 6454	7.0399 8871	8.5133 0877
41	4.0978 3381	4.9930 6145	6.0781 0094	7.3919 8815	8.9815 4076
42	4.2412 5799	5.1927 8391	6.3516 1548	7.7615 8756	9.4755 2550
43	4.3897 0202	5.4004 9527	6.6374 3818	8.1496 6693	9.9966 7940
44	4.5433 4160	5.6165 1508	6.9361 2290	8.5571 5028	10.5464 9677
45	4.7023 5855	5.8411 7568	7.2482 4843	8.9850 0779	11.1265 5409
46	4.8669 4110	6.0748 2271	7.5744 1961	9.4342 5818	11.7385 1456
47	5.0372 8404	6.3178 1562	7.9152 6849	9.9059 7109	12.3841 3287
48	5.2135 8898	6.5705 2824	8.2714 5557	10.4012 6965	13.0652 6017
49	5.3960 6459	6.8333 4937	8.6436 7107	10.9213 3313	13.7838 4948
50	5.5849 2686	7.1066 8335	9.0326 3627	11.4673 9979	14.5419 6120

AMOUNT AT COMPOUND INTEREST $(1+i)^n$

Years	Rate i				
n	.06 (6%)	.065 (6½%)	.07 (7%)	.075 (7½%)	.08 (8%)
1	1.0600 0000	1.0650 0000	1.0700 0000	1.0750 0000	1.0800 0000
2	1.1236 0000	1.1342 2500	1.1449 0000	1.1556 2500	1.1664 0000
3	1.1910 1600	1.2079 4963	1.2250 4300	1.2422 9688	1.2597 1200
4	1.2624 7696	1.2864 6635	1.3107 9601	1.3354 6914	1.3604 8896
5	1.3382 2558	1.3700 8666	1.4025 5173	1.4356 2933	1.4693 2808
6	1.4185 1911	1.4591 4230	1.5007 3035	1.5433 0153	1.5868 7432
7	1.5036 3026	1.5539 8655	1.6057 8148	1.6590 4914	1.7138 2427
8	1.5938 4807	1.6549 9567	1.7181 8618	1.7834 7783	1.8509 3021
9	1.6894 7896	1.7625 7039	1.8384 5921	1.9172 3866	1.9990 0463
10	1.7908 4770	1.8771 3747	1.9671 5136	2.0610 3156	2.1589 2500
11	1.8982 9856	1.9991 5140	2.1048 5195	2.2156 0893	2.3316 3900
12	2.0121 9647	2.1290 9624	2.2521 9159	2.3817 7960	2.5181 7012
13	2.1329 2826	2.2674 8750	2.4098 4500	2.5604 1307	2.7196 2373
14	2.2609 0396	2.4148 7418	2.5785 3415	2.7524 4405	2.9371 9362
15	2.3965 5819	2.5718 4101	2.7590 3154	2.9588 7735	3.1721 6911
16	2.5403 5168	2.7390 1067	2.9521 6375	3.1807 9315	3.4259 4264
17	2.6927 7279	2.9170 4637	3.1588 1521	3.4193 5264	3.7000 1805
18	2.8543 3915	3.1066 5438	3.3799 3228	3.6758 0409	3.9960 1950
19	3.0255 9950	3.3085 8691	3.6165 2754	3.9514 8940	4.3157 0106
20	3.2071 3547	3.5236 4506	3.8696 8446	4.2478 5110	4.6609 5714
21	3.3995 6360	3.7526 8199	4.1405 6237	4.5664 3993	5.0338 3372
22	3.6035 3742	3.9966 0632	4.4304 0174	4.9089 2293	5.4365 4041
23	3.8197 4966	4.2563 8573	4.7405 2986	5.2770 9215	5.8714 6365
24	4.0489 3464	4.5330 5081	5.0723 6695	5.6728 7406	6.3411 8074
25	4.2918 7072	4.8276 9911	5.4274 3264	6.0983 3961	6.8484 7520
26	4.5493 8296	5.1414 9955	5.8073 5292	6.5557 1508	7.3963 5321
27	4.8223 4594	5.4756 9702	6.2138 6763	7.0473 9371	7.9880 6147
28	5.1116 8670	5.8316 1733	6.6488 3836	7.5759 4824	8.6271 0639
29	5.4183 8790	6.2106 7245	7.1142 5705	8.1441 4436	9.3172 7490
30	5.7434 9117	6.6143 6616	7.6122 5504	8.7549 5519	10.0626 5689
31	6.0881 0064	7.0442 9996	8.1451 1290	9.4115 7683	10.8676 6944
32	6.4533 8668	7.5021 7946	8.7152 7080	10.1174 4509	11.7370 8300
33	6.8405 8988	7.9898 2113	9.3253 3975	10.8762 5347	12.6760 4964
34	7.2510 2528	8.5091 5950	9.9781 1354	11.6919 7248	13.6901 3361
35	7.6860 8679	9.0622 5487	10.6765 8148	12.5688 7042	14.7853 4429
36	8.1472 5200	9.6513 0143	11.4239 4219	13.5115 3570	15.9681 7184
37	8.6360 8712	10.2786 3603	12.2236 1814	14.5249 0088	17.2456 2558
38	9.1542 5235	10.9467 4737	13.0792 7141	15.6142 6844	18.6252 7563
39	9.7035 0749	11.6582 8595	13.9948 2041	16.7853 3858	20.1152 9768
40	10.2857 1794	12.4160 7453	14.9744 5784	18.0442 3897	21.7245 2150
41	10.9028 6101	13.2231 1938	16.0226 6989	19.3975 5689	23.4624 8322
42	11.5570 3267	14.0826 2214	17.1442 5678	20.8523 7366	25.3394 8187
43	12.2504 5463	14.9979 9258	18.3443 5475	22.4163 0168	27.3666 4042
44	12.9854 8191	15.9728 6209	19.6284 5959	24.0975 2431	29.5559 7166
45	13.7646 1083	17.0110 9813	21.0024 5176	25.9048 3863	31.9204 4939
46	14.5904 8748	18.1168 1951	22.4726 2338	27.8477 0153	34.4740 8534
47	15.4659 1673	19.2944 1278	24.0457 0702	29.9362 7915	37.2320 1217
48	16.3938 7173	20.5485 4961	25.7289 0651	32.1815 0008	40.2105 7314
49	17.3775 0403	21.8842 0533	27.5299 2997	34.5951 1259	43.4274 1899
50	18.4201 5427	23.3066 7868	29.4570 2506	37.1897 4603	46.9016 1251

PRESENT VALUE $1/(1+i)^n$

The following table gives the value of unit amount due in n years at rate of interest i, compounded annually, $1/(1 + i)^n = v^n$.

Years	Rate i				
n	.0025 ($\frac{1}{4}\%$)	.004167 ($\frac{5}{12}\%$)	.005 ($\frac{1}{2}\%$)	.005833 ($\frac{7}{12}\%$)	.0075 ($\frac{3}{4}\%$)
1	.9975 0623	.9958 5062	.9950 2488	.9942 0050	.9925 5583
2	.9950 1869	.9917 1846	.9900 7450	.9884 3463	.9851 6708
3	.9925 3734	.9876 0345	.9851 4876	.9827 0220	.9778 3333
4	.9900 6219	.9835 0551	.9802 4752	.9770 0301	.9705 5417
5	.9875 9321	.9794 2457	.9753 7067	.9713 3688	.9633 2920
6	.9851 3038	.9753 6057	.9705 1808	.9657 0361	.9561 5802
7	.9826 7370	.9713 1343	.9656 8963	.9601 0301	.9490 4022
8	.9802 2314	.9672 8308	.9608 8520	.9545 3489	.9419 7540
9	.9777 7869	.9632 6946	.9561 0468	.9489 9906	.9349 6318
10	.9753 4034	.9592 7249	.9513 4794	.9434 9534	.9280 0315
11	.9729 0807	.9552 9211	.9466 1487	.9380 2354	.9210 9494
12	.9704 8187	.9513 2824	.9419 0534	.9325 8347	.9142 3815
13	.9680 6171	.9473 8082	.9372 1924	.9271 7495	.9074 3241
14	.9656 4759	.9434 4978	.9325 5646	.9217 9779	.9006 7733
15	.9632 3949	.9395 3505	.9279 1688	.9164 5182	.8939 7254
16	.9608 3740	.9356 3657	.9233 0037	.9111 3686	.8873 1766
17	.9584 4130	.9317 5426	.9187 0684	.9058 5272	.8807 1231
18	.9560 5117	.9278 8806	.9141 3616	.9005 9922	.8741 5614
19	.9536 6700	.9240 3790	.9095 8822	.8953 7619	.8676 4878
20	.9512 8878	.9202 0372	.9050 6290	.8901 8346	.8611 8985
21	.9489 1649	.9163 8544	.9005 6010	.8850 2084	.8547 7901
22	.9465 5011	.9125 8301	.8960 7971	.8798 8815	.8484 1589
23	.9441 8964	.9087 9636	.8916 2160	.8747 8524	.8421 0014
24	.9418 3505	.9050 2542	.8871 8567	.8697 1192	.8358 3140
25	.9394 8634	.9012 7013	.8827 7181	.8646 6802	.8296 0933
26	.9371 4348	.8975 3042	.8783 7991	.8596 5338	.8234 3358
27	.9348 0646	.8938 0623	.8740 0986	.8546 6782	.8173 0380
28	.9324 7527	.8900 9749	.8696 6155	.8497 1117	.8112 1966
29	.9301 4990	.8864 0414	.8653 3488	.8447 8327	.8051 8080
30	.9278 3032	.8827 2611	.8610 2973	.8398 8394	.7991 8690
31	.9255 1653	.8790 6335	.8567 4600	.8350 1303	.7932 3762
32	.9232 0851	.8754 1578	.8524 8358	.8301 7037	.7873 3262
33	.9209 0624	.8717 8335	.8482 4237	.8253 5580	.7814 7158
34	.9186 0972	.8681 6599	.8440 2226	.8205 6914	.7756 5418
35	.9163 1892	.8645 6365	.8398 2314	.8158 1025	.7698 8008
36	.9140 3384	.8609 7624	.8356 4492	.8110 7896	.7641 4896
37	.9117 5445	.8574 0373	.8314 8748	.8063 7510	.7584 6051
38	.9094 8075	.8538 4604	.8273 5073	.8016 9853	.7528 1440
39	.9072 1272	.8503 0311	.8232 3455	.7970 4907	.7472 1032
40	.9049 5034	.8467 7488	.8191 3886	.7924 2659	.7416 4796
41	.9026 9361	.8432 6129	.8150 6354	.7878 3091	.7361 2701
42	.9004 4250	.8397 6228	.8110 0850	.7832 6188	.7306 4716
43	.8981 9701	.8362 7779	.8069 7363	.7787 1935	.7252 0809
44	.8959 5712	.8328 0776	.8029 5884	.7742 0316	.7198 0952
45	.8937 2281	.8293 5212	.7989 6402	.7697 1317	.7144 5114
46	.8914 9407	.8259 1083	.7949 8907	.7652 4922	.7091 3264
47	.8892 7090	.8224 8381	.7910 3390	.7608 1115	.7038 5374
48	.8870 5326	.8190 7102	.7870 9841	.7563 9883	.6986 1414
49	.8848 4116	.8156 7238	.7831 8250	.7520 1209	.6934 1353
50	.8826 3457	.8122 8785	.7792 8607	.7476 5079	.6882 5165

PRESENT VALUE $1/(1+i)^n$

Years	Rate i				
n	.0025 ($\frac{1}{4}\%$)	.004167 ($\frac{5}{12}\%$)	.005 ($\frac{1}{2}\%$)	.005833 ($\frac{7}{12}\%$)	.0075 ($\frac{3}{4}\%$)
50	.8826 3457	.8122 8785	.7792 8607	.7476 5079	.6882 5165
51	.8804 3349	.8089 1736	.7754 0902	.7433 1479	.6831 2819
52	.8782 3790	.8055 6086	.7715 5127	.7390 0393	.6780 4286
53	.8760 4778	.8022 1828	.7677 1270	.7347 1808	.6729 9540
54	.8738 6312	.7988 8957	.7638 9324	.7304 5708	.6679 8551
55	.8716 8391	.7955 7468	.7600 9077	.7262 2079	.6630 1291
56	.8695 1013	.7922 7354	.7563 1122	.7220 0907	.6580 7733
57	.8673 4178	.7889 8610	.7525 4847	.7178 2178	.6531 7849
58	.8651 7883	.7857 1230	.7488 0445	.7136 5877	.6483 1612
59	.8630 2128	.7824 5208	.7450 7906	.7095 1990	.6434 8995
60	.8608 6911	.7792 0539	.7413 7220	.7054 0504	.6386 9970
61	.8587 2230	.7759 7217	.7376 8378	.7013 1404	.6339 4511
62	.8565 8085	.7727 5237	.7340 1371	.6972 4677	.6292 2592
63	.8544 4474	.7695 4593	.7303 6190	.6932 0308	.6245 4185
64	.8523 1395	.7663 5279	.7267 2826	.6891 8285	.6198 9266
65	.8501 8848	.7631 7291	.7231 1269	.6851 8593	.6152 7807
66	.8480 6831	.7600 0621	.7195 1512	.6812 1219	.6106 9784
67	.8459 5343	.7568 5266	.7159 3544	.6772 6150	.6061 5170
68	.8438 4382	.7537 1219	.7123 7357	.6733 3372	.6016 3940
69	.8417 3947	.7505 8476	.7088 2943	.6694 2872	.5971 6070
70	.8396 4037	.7474 7030	.7053 0291	.6655 4637	.5927 1533
71	.8375 4650	.7443 6876	.7017 9394	.6616 8653	.5883 0306
72	.8354 5786	.7412 8009	.6983 0243	.6578 4908	.5839 2363
73	.8333 7442	.7382 0424	.6948 2829	.6540 3388	.5795 7681
74	.8312 9618	.7351 4115	.6913 7143	.6502 4081	.5752 6234
75	.8292 2312	.7320 9078	.6879 3177	.6464 6973	.5709 7999
76	.8271 5523	.7290 5306	.6845 0923	.6427 2053	.5667 2952
77	.8250 9250	.7260 2794	.6811 0371	.6389 9306	.5625 1069
78	.8230 3491	.7230 1537	.6777 1513	.6352 8723	.5583 2326
79	.8209 8246	.7200 1531	.6743 4342	.6316 0288	.5541 6701
80	.8189 3512	.7170 2770	.6709 8847	.6279 3989	.5500 4170
81	.8168 9289	.7140 5248	.6676 5022	.6242 9816	.5459 4710
82	.8148 5575	.7110 8960	.6643 2858	6206 7754	.5418 8297
83	.8128 2369	.7081 3902	.6610 2346	.6170 7792	.5378 4911
84	.8107 9670	.7052 0069	.6577 3479	.6134 9917	.5338 4527
85	.8087 7476	.7022 7454	.6544 6248	.6099 4118	.5298 7123
86	.8067 5787	.6993 6054	.6512 0644	.6064 0382	.5259 2678
87	.8047 4600	.6964 5863	.6479 6661	.6028 8698	.5220 1169
88	.8027 3915	.6935 6876	.6447 4290	.5993 9054	.5181 2575
89	.8007 3731	.6906 9088	.6415 3522	.5959 1437	.5142 6873
90	.7987 4046	.6878 2495	.6383 4350	.5924 5836	.5104 4043
91	.7967 4859	.6849 7090	.6351 6766	.5890 2240	.5066 4063
92	.7947 6168	.6821 2870	.6320 0763	.5856 0636	.5028 6911
93	.7927 7973	.6792 9829	.6288 6331	.5822 1014	.4991 2567
94	.7908 0273	.6764 7962	.6257 3464	.5788 3361	.4954 1009
95	.7888 3065	.6736 7265	.6226 2153	.5754 7666	.4917 2217
96	.7868 6349	.6708 7733	.6195 2391	.5721 3918	.4880 6171
97	.7849 0124	.6680 9361	.6164 4170	.5688 2106	.4844 2850
98	.7829 4388	.6653 2143	.6133 7483	.5655 2218	.4808 2233
99	.7809 9140	.6625 6076	.6103 2321	.5622 4243	.4772 4301
100	.7790 4379	.6598 1155	.6072 8678	.5589 8171	.4736 9033

PRESENT VALUE $1/(1+i)^n$

Years	Rate i				
n	.01 (1%)	.01125 ($1\frac{1}{8}$%)	.0125 ($1\frac{1}{4}$%)	.015 ($1\frac{1}{2}$%)	.0175 ($1\frac{3}{4}$%)
1	.9900 9901	.9888 7515	.9876 5432	.9852 2167	.9828 0098
2	.9802 9605	.9778 7407	.9754 6106	.9706 6175	.9658 9777
3	.9705 9015	.9669 9537	.9634 1833	.9563 1699	.9492 8528
4	.9609 8034	.9562 3770	.9515 2428	.9421 8423	.9329 5851
5	.9514 6569	.9455 9970	.9397 7706	.9282 6033	.9169 1254
6	.9420 4524	.9350 8005	.9281 7488	.9145 4219	.9011 4254
7	.9327 1805	.9246 7743	.9167 1593	.9010 2679	.8856 4378
8	.9234 8322	.9143 9054	.9053 9845	.8877 1112	.8704 1157
9	.9143 3982	.9042 1808	.8942 2069	.8745 9224	.8554 4135
10	.9052 8695	.8941 5880	.8831 8093	.8616 6723	.8407 2860
11	.8963 2372	.8842 1142	.8722 7746	.8489 3323	.8262 6889
12	.8874 4923	.8743 7470	.8615 0860	.8363 8742	.8120 5788
13	.8786 6260	.8646 4742	.8508 7269	.8240 2702	.7980 9128
14	.8699 6297	.8550 2835	.8403 6809	.8118 4928	.7843 6490
15	.8613 4947	.8455 1629	.8299 9318	.7998 5150	.7708 7459
16	.8528 2126	.8361 1005	.8197 4635	.7880 3104	.7576 1631
17	.8443 7749	.8268 0846	.8096 2602	.7763 8526	.7445 8605
18	.8360 1731	.8176 1034	.7996 3064	.7649 1159	.7317 7990
19	.8277 3992	.8085 1455	.7897 5866	.7536 0747	.7191 9401
20	.8195 4447	.7995 1995	.7800 0855	.7424 7042	.7068 2458
21	.8114 3017	.7906 2542	.7703 7881	.7314 9795	.6946 6789
22	.8033 9621	.7818 2983	.7608 6796	.7206 8763	.6827 2028
23	.7954 4179	.7731 3210	.7514 7453	.7100 3708	.6709 7817
24	.7875 6613	.7645 3112	.7421 9707	.6995 4392	.6594 3800
25	.7797 6844	.7560 2583	.7330 3414	.6892 0583	.6480 9632
26	.7720 4796	.7476 1516	.7239 8434	.6790 2052	.6369 4970
27	.7644 0392	.7392 9806	.7150 4626	.6689 8574	.6259 9479
28	.7568 3557	.7310 7348	.7062 1853	.6590 9925	.6152 2829
29	.7493 4215	.7229 4040	.6974 9978	.6493 5887	.6046 4697
30	.7419 2292	.7148 9780	.6888 8867	.6397 6243	.5942 4764
31	.7345 7715	.7069 4467	.6803 8387	.6303 0781	.5840 2716
32	.7273 0411	.6990 8002	.6719 8407	.6209 9292	.5739 8247
33	.7201 0307	.6913 0287	.6636 8797	.6118 1568	.5641 1053
34	.7129 7334	.6836 1223	.6554 9429	.6027 7407	.5544 0839
35	.7059 1420	.6760 0715	.6474 0177	.5938 6608	.5448 7311
36	.6989 2495	.6684 8667	.6394 0916	.5850 8974	.5355 0183
37	.6920 0490	.6610 4986	.6315 1522	.5764 4309	.5262 9172
38	.6851 5337	.6536 9578	.6237 1873	.5679 2423	.5172 4002
39	.6783 6967	.6464 2352	.6160 1850	.5595 3126	.5083 4400
40	.6716 5314	.6392 3216	.6084 1334	.5512 6232	.4996 0098
41	.6650 0311	.6321 2080	.6009 0206	.5431 1559	.4910 0834
42	.6584 1892	.6250 8855	.5934 8352	.5350 8925	.4825 6348
43	.6518 9992	.6181 3454	.5861 5656	.5271 8153	.4742 6386
44	.6454 4546	.6112 5789	.5789 2006	.5193 9067	.4661 0699
45	.6390 5492	.6044 5774	.5717 7290	.5117 1494	.4580 9040
46	.6327 2764	.5977 3324	.5647 1397	.5041 5265	.4502 1170
47	.6264 6301	.5910 8355	.5577 4219	.4967 0212	.4424 6850
48	.6202 6041	.5845 0784	.5508 5649	.4893 6170	.4348 5848
49	.6141 1921	.5780 0528	.5440 5579	.4821 2975	.4273 7934
50	.6080 3882	.5715 7506	.5373 3905	.4750 0468	.4200 2883

INTEREST TABLES

PRESENT VALUE $1/(1+i)^n$

Years	Rate i				
n	.01 (1%)	.01125 (1⅛%)	.0125 (1¼%)	.015 (1½%)	.0175 (1¾%)
50	.6080 3882	.5715 7506	.5373 3905	.4750 0468	.4200 2883
51	.6020 1864	.5652 1637	.5307 0524	.4679 8491	.4128 0475
52	.5960 5806	.5589 2843	.5241 5332	.4610 6887	.4057 0492
53	.5901 5649	.5527 1044	.5176 8229	.4542 5505	.3987 2719
54	.5843 1336	.5465 6162	.5112 9115	.4475 4192	.3918 6947
55	.5785 2808	.5404 8120	.5049 7892	.4409 2800	.3851 2970
56	.5728 0008	.5344 6843	.4987 4461	.4344 1182	.3785 0585
57	.5671 2879	.5285 2256	.4925 8727	.4279 9194	.3719 9592
58	.5615 1365	.5226 4282	.4865 0594	.4216 6694	.3655 9796
59	.5559 5411	.5168 2850	.4804 9970	.4154 3541	.3593 1003
60	.5504 4962	.5110 7887	.4745 6760	.4092 9597	.3531 3025
61	.5449 9962	.5053 9319	.4687 0874	.4032 4726	.3470 5676
62	.5396 0358	.4997 7077	.4629 2222	.3972 8794	.3410 8772
63	.5342 6097	.4942 1090	.4572 0713	.3914 1669	.3352 2135
64	.5289 7126	.4887 1288	.4515 6259	.3856 3221	.3294 5587
65	.5237 3392	.4832 7602	.4459 8775	.3799 3321	.3237 8956
66	.5185 4844	.4778 9965	.4404 8173	.3743 1843	.3182 2069
67	.5134 1429	.4725 8309	.4350 4368	.3687 8663	.3127 4761
68	.5083 3099	.4673 2568	.4296 7277	.3633 3658	.3073 6866
69	.5032 9801	.4621 2675	.4243 6817	.3579 6708	.3020 8222
70	.4983 1486	.4569 8566	.4191 2905	.3526 7692	.2968 8670
71	.4933 8105	.4519 0177	.4139 5462	.3474 6495	.2917 8054
72	.4884 9609	.4468 7443	.4088 4407	.3423 3000	.2867 6221
73	.4836 5949	.4419 0302	.4037 9661	.3372 7093	.2818 3018
74	.4788 7078	.4369 8692	.3988 1147	.3322 8663	.2769 8298
75	.4741 2949	.4321 2551	.3938 8787	.3273 7599	.2722 1914
76	.4694 3514	.4273 1818	.3890 2506	.3225 3793	.2675 3724
77	.4647 8726	.4225 6433	.3842 2228	.3177 7136	.2629 3586
78	.4601 8541	.4178 6337	.3794 7879	.3130 7523	.2584 1362
79	.4556 2912	.4132 1470	.3747 9387	.3084 4850	.2539 6916
80	.4511 1794	.4086 1775	.3701 6679	.3038 9015	.2496 0114
81	.4466 5142	.4040 7194	.3655 9683	.2993 9916	.2453 0825
82	.4422 2913	.3995 7670	.3610 8329	.2949 7454	.2410 8919
83	.4378 5063	.3951 3148	.3566 2547	.2906 1531	.2369 4269
84	.4335 1547	.3907 3570	.3522 2268	.2863 2050	.2328 6751
85	.4292 2324	.3863 8882	.3478 7426	.2820 8917	.2288 6242
86	.4249 7350	.3820 9031	.3435 7951	.2779 2036	.2249 2621
87	.4207 6585	.3778 3961	.3393 3779	.2738 1316	.2210 5770
88	.4165 9985	.3736 3621	.3351 4843	.2697 6666	.2172 5572
89	.4124 7510	.3694 7956	.3310 1080	.2657 7996	.2135 1914
90	.4083 9119	.3653 6916	.3269 2425	.2618 5218	.2098 4682
91	.4043 4771	.3613 0448	.3228 8814	.2579 8245	.2062 3766
92	.4003 4427	.3572 8503	.3189 0187	.2541 6990	.2026 9057
93	.3963 8046	.3533 1029	.3149 6481	.2504 1369	.1992 0450
94	.3924 5590	.3493 7976	.3110 7636	.2467 1300	.1957 7837
95	.3885 7020	.3454 9297	.3072 3591	.2430 6699	.1924 1118
96	.3847 2297	.3416 4941	.3034 4287	.2394 7487	.1891 0190
97	.3809 1383	.3378 4861	.2996 9666	.2359 3583	.1858 4953
98	.3771 4241	.3340 9010	.2959 9670	.2324 4909	.1826 5310
99	.3734 0832	.3303 7340	.2923 4242	.2290 1389	.1795 1165
100	.3697 1121	.3266 9805	.2887 3326	.2256 2944	.1764 2422

INTEREST TABLES

PRESENT VALUE $1/(1+i)^n$

Years	Rate i				
n	.02 (2%)	.0225 ($2\frac{1}{4}$%)	.025 ($2\frac{1}{2}$%)	.0275 ($2\frac{3}{4}$%)	.03 (3%)
1	.9803 9216	.9779 9511	.9756 0976	.9732 3601	.9708 7379
2	.9611 6878	.9564 7444	.9518 1440	.9471 8833	.9425 9591
3	.9423 2233	.9354 2732	.9285 9941	.9218 3779	.9151 4166
4	.9238 4543	.9148 4335	.9059 5064	.8971 6573	.8884 8705
5	.9057 3081	.8947 1232	.8838 5429	.8731 5400	.8626 0878
6	.8879 7138	.8750 2427	.8622 9687	.8497 8491	.8374 8426
7	.8705 6018	.8557 6946	.8412 6524	.8270 4128	.8130 9151
8	.8534 9037	.8369 3835	.8207 4657	.8049 0635	.7894 0923
9	.8367 5527	.8185 2161	.8007 2836	.7833 6385	.7664 1673
10	.8203 4830	.8005 1013	.7811 9840	.7623 9791	.7440 9391
11	.8042 6304	.7828 9499	.7621 4478	.7419 9310	.7224 2128
12	.7884 9318	.7656 6748	.7435 5589	.7221 3440	.7013 7988
13	.7730 3253	.7488 1905	.7254 2038	.7028 0720	.6809 5134
14	.7578 7502	.7323 4137	.7077 2720	.6839 9728	.6611 1781
15	.7430 1473	.7162 2628	.6904 6556	.6656 9078	.6418 6195
16	.7284 4581	.7004 6580	.6736 2493	.6478 7424	.6231 6694
17	.7141 6256	.6850 5212	.6571 9506	.6305 3454	.6050 1645
18	.7001 5937	.6699 7763	.6411 6591	.6136 5892	.5873 9461
19	.6864 3076	.6552 3484	.6255 2772	.5972 3496	.5702 8603
20	.6729 7133	.6408 1647	.6102 7094	.5812 5057	.5536 7575
21	.6597 7582	.6267 1538	.5953 8629	.5656 9398	.5375 4928
22	.6468 3904	.6129 2457	.5808 6467	.5505 5375	.5218 9250
23	.6341 5592	.5994 3724	.5666 9724	.5358 1874	.5066 9175
24	.6217 2149	.5862 4668	.5528 7535	.5214 7809	.4919 3374
25	.6095 3087	.5733 4639	.5393 9059	.5075 2126	.4776 0557
26	.5975 7928	.5607 2997	.5262 3472	.4939 3796	.4636 9473
27	.5858 6204	.5483 9117	.5133 9973	.4807 1821	.4501 8906
28	.5743 7455	.5363 2388	.5008 7778	.4678 5227	.4370 7675
29	.5631 1231	.5245 2213	.4886 6125	.4553 3068	.4243 4636
30	.5520 7089	.5129 8008	.4767 4594	.4431 4421	.4119 8676
31	.5412 4597	.5016 9201	.4651 1481	.4312 8391	.3999 8715
32	.5306 3330	.4906 5233	.4537 7055	.4197 4103	.3883 3703
33	.5202 2873	.4798 5558	.4427 0298	.4085 0708	.3770 2625
34	.5100 2817	.4692 9641	.4319 0534	.3975 7380	.3660 4490
35	.5000 2761	.4589 6960	.4213 7107	.3869 3314	.3553 8340
36	.4902 2315	.4488 7002	.4110 9372	.3765 7727	.3450 3243
37	.4806 1093	.4389 9268	.4010 6705	.3664 9856	.3349 8294
38	.4711 8719	.4293 3270	.3912 8492	.3566 8959	.3252 2615
39	.4619 4822	.4198 8528	.3817 4139	.3471 4316	.3157 5355
40	.4528 9042	.4106 4575	.3724 3062	.3378 5222	.3065 5684
41	.4440 1021	.4016 0954	.3633 4695	.3288 0995	.2976 2800
42	.4353 0413	.3927 7216	.3544 8483	.3200 0968	.2889 5922
43	.4267 6875	.3841 2925	.3458 3886	.3114 4495	.2805 4294
44	.4184 0074	.3756 7653	.3374 0376	.3031 0944	.2723 7178
45	.4101 9680	.3674 0981	.3291 7440	.2949 9702	.2644 3862
46	.4021 5373	.3593 2500	.3211 4576	.2871 0172	.2567 3653
47	.3942 6836	.3514 1809	.3133 1294	.2794 1773	.2492 5876
48	.3865 3761	.3436 8518	.3056 7116	.2719 3940	.2419 9880
49	.3789 5844	.3361 2242	.2982 1576	.2646 6122	.2349 5029
50	.3715 2788	.3287 2608	.2909 4221	.2575 7783	.2281 0708

PRESENT VALUE $1/(1+i)^n$

Years			Rate i		
n	.02 (2%)	.0225 (2¼%)	.025 (2½%)	.0275 (2¾%)	.03 (3%)
50	.3715 2788	.3287 2608	.2909 4221	.2575 7783	.2281 0708
51	.3642 4302	.3214 9250	.2838 4606	.2506 8402	.2214 6318
52	.3571 0100	.3144 1810	.2769 2298	.2439 7471	.2150 1280
53	.3500 9902	.3074 9936	.2701 6876	.2374 4497	.2087 5029
54	.3432 3433	.3007 3287	.2635 7928	.2310 9000	.2026 7019
55	.3365 0425	.2941 1528	.2571 5052	.2249 0511	.1967 6717
56	.3299 0613	.2876 4330	.2508 7855	.2188 8575	.1910 3609
57	.3234 3738	.2813 1374	.2447 5956	.2130 2749	.1854 7193
58	.3170 9547	.2751 2347	.2387 8982	.2073 2603	.1800 6984
59	.3108 7791	.2690 6940	.2329 6568	.2017 7716	.1748 2508
60	.3047 8227	.2631 4856	.2272 8359	.1963 7679	.1697 3309
61	.2988 0614	.2573 5801	.2217 4009	.1911 2097	.1647 8941
62	.2929 4720	.2516 9487	.2163 3179	.1860 0581	.1599 8972
63	.2872 0314	.2461 5635	.2110 5541	.1810 2755	.1553 2982
64	.2815 7170	.2407 3971	.2059 0771	.1761 8253	.1508 0565
65	.2760 5069	.2354 4226	.2008 8557	.1714 6718	.1464 1325
66	.2706 3793	.2302 6138	.1959 8593	.1668 7804	.1421 4879
67	.2653 3130	.2251 9450	.1912 0578	.1624 1172	.1380 0853
68	.2601 2873	.2202 3912	.1865 4223	.1580 6493	.1339 8887
69	.2550 2817	.2153 9278	.1819 9241	.1538 3448	.1300 8628
70	.2500 2761	.2106 5309	.1775 5358	.1497 1726	.1262 9736
71	.2451 2511	.2060 1769	.1732 2300	.1457 1023	.1226 1880
72	.2403 1874	.2014 8429	.1689 9805	.1418 1044	.1190 4737
73	.2356 0661	.1970 5065	.1648 7615	.1380 1503	.1155 7998
74	.2309 8687	.1927 1458	.1608 5478	.1343 2119	.1122 1357
75	.2264 5771	.1884 7391	.1569 3149	.1307 2622	.1089 4521
76	.2220 1737	.1843 2657	.1531 0389	.1272 2747	.1057 7205
77	.2176 6408	.1802 7048	.1493 6965	.1238 2235	.1026 9131
78	.2133 9616	.1763 0365	.1457 2649	.1205 0837	.0997 0030
79	.2092 1192	.1724 2411	.1421 7218	.1172 8309	.0967 9641
80	.2051 0973	.1686 2993	.1387 0457	.1141 4412	.0939 7710
81	.2010 8797	.1649 1925	.1353 2153	.1110 8917	.0912 3990
82	.1971 4507	.1612 9022	.1320 2101	.1081 1598	.0885 8243
83	.1932 7948	.1577 4105	.1288 0098	.1052 2237	.0860 0236
84	.1894 8968	.1542 6997	.1256 5949	.1024 0620	.0834 9743
85	.1857 7420	.1508 7528	.1225 9463	.0996 6540	.0810 6547
86	.1821 3157	.1475 5528	.1196 0452	.0969 9795	.0787 0434
87	.1785 6036	.1443 0835	.1166 8733	.0944 0190	.0764 1198
88	.1750 5918	.1411 3286	.1138 4130	.0918 7533	.0741 8639
89	.1716 2665	.1380 2724	.1110 6468	.0894 1638	.0720 2562
90	.1682 6142	.1349 8997	.1083 5579	.0870 2324	.0699 2779
91	.1649 6217	.1320 1953	.1057 1296	.0846 9415	.0678 9105
92	.1617 2762	.1291 1445	.1031 3460	.0824 2740	.0659 1364
93	.1585 5649	.1262 7331	.1006 1912	.0802 2131	.0639 9383
94	.1554 4754	.1234 9468	.0981 6500	.0780 7427	.0621 2993
95	.1523 9955	.1207 7719	.0957 7073	.0759 8469	.0603 2032
96	.1494 1132	.1181 1950	.0934 3486	.0739 5104	.0585 6342
97	.1464 8169	.1155 2029	.0911 5596	.0719 7181	.0568 5769
98	.1436 0950	.1129 7828	.0889 3264	.0700 4556	.0552 0164
99	.1407 9363	.1104 9221	.0867 6355	.0681 7086	.0535 9383
100	.1380 3297	.1080 6084	.0846 4737	.0663 4634	.0520 3284

PRESENT VALUE $1/(1+i)^n$

Years		Rate i			
n	.035 (3½%)	.04 (4%)	.045 (4½%)	.05 (5%)	.055 (5½%)
1	.9661 8357	.9615 3846	.9569 3780	.9523 8095	.9478 6730
2	.9335 1070	.9245 5621	.9157 2995	.9070 2948	.8984 5242
3	.9019 4271	.8889 9636	.8762 9660	.8638 3760	.8516 1366
4	.8714 4223	.8548 0419	.8385 6134	.8227 0247	.8072 1674
5	.8419 7317	.8219 2711	.8024 5105	.7835 2617	.7651 3435
6	.8135 0064	.7903 1453	.7678 9574	.7462 1540	.7252 4583
7	.7859 9096	.7599 1781	.7348 2846	.7106 8133	.6874 3681
8	.7594 1156	.7306 9021	.7031 8513	.6768 3936	.6515 9887
9	.7337 3097	.7025 8674	.6729 0443	.6446 0892	.6176 2926
10	.7089 1881	.6755 6417	.6439 2768	.6139 1325	.5854 3058
11	.6849 4571	.6495 8093	.6161 9874	.5846 7929	.5549 1050
12	.6617 8330	.6245 9705	.5896 6386	.5568 3742	.5259 8152
13	.6394 0415	.6005 7409	.5642 7164	.5303 2135	.4985 6068
14	.6177 8179	.5774 7508	.5399 7286	.5050 6795	.4725 6937
15	.5968 9062	.5552 6450	.5167 2044	.4810 1710	.4479 3305
16	.5767 0591	.5339 0818	.4944 6932	.4581 1152	.4245 8109
17	.5572 0378	.5133 7325	.4731 7639	.4362 9669	.4024 4653
18	.5383 6114	.4936 2812	.4528 0037	.4155 2065	.3814 6590
19	.5201 5569	.4746 4242	.4333 0179	.3957 3396	.3615 7906
20	.5025 6588	.4563 8695	.4146 4286	.3768 8948	.3427 2896
21	.4855 7090	.4388 3360	.3967 8743	.3589 4236	.3248 6158
22	.4691 5063	.4219 5539	.3797 0089	.3418 4987	.3079 2567
23	.4532 8563	.4057 2633	.3633 5013	.3255 7131	.2918 7267
24	.4379 5713	.3901 2147	.3477 0347	.3100 6791	.2766 5656
25	.4231 4699	.3751 1680	.3327 3060	.2953 0277	.2622 3370
26	.4088 3767	.3606 8923	.3184 0248	.2812 4073	.2485 6275
27	.3950 1224	.3468 1657	.3046 9137	.2678 4832	.2356 0450
28	.3816 5434	.3334 7747	.2915 7069	.2550 9364	.2233 2181
29	.3687 4815	.3206 5141	.2790 1502	.2429 4632	.2116 7944
30	.3562 7841	.3083 1867	.2670 0002	.2313 7745	.2006 4402
31	.3442 3035	.2964 6026	.2555 0241	.2203 5947	.1901 8390
32	.3325 8971	.2850 5794	.2444 9991	.2098 6617	.1802 6910
33	.3213 4271	.2740 9417	.2339 7121	.1998 7254	.1708 7119
34	.3104 7605	.2635 5209	.2238 9589	.1903 5480	.1619 6321
35	.2999 7686	.2534 1547	.2142 5444	.1812 9029	.1535 1963
36	.2898 3272	.2436 6872	.2050 2817	.1726 5741	.1455 1624
37	.2800 3161	.2342 9685	.1961 9921	.1644 3563	.1379 3008
38	.2705 6194	.2252 8543	.1877 5044	.1566 0536	.1307 3941
39	.2614 1250	.2166 2061	.1796 6549	.1491 4797	.1239 2362
40	.2525 7247	.2082 8904	.1719 2870	.1420 4568	.1174 6314
41	.2440 3137	.2002 7793	.1645 2507	.1352 8160	.1113 3947
42	.2357 7910	.1925 7493	.1574 4026	.1288 3962	.1055 3504
43	.2278 0590	.1851 6820	.1506 6054	.1227 0440	.1000 3322
44	.2201 0231	.1780 4635	.1441 7276	.1168 6133	.0948 1822
45	.2126 5924	.1711 9841	.1379 6437	.1112 9651	.0898 7509
46	.2054 6787	.1646 1386	.1320 2332	.1059 9668	.0851 8965
47	.1985 1968	.1582 8256	.1263 3810	.1009 4921	.0807 4849
48	.1918 0645	.1521 9476	.1208 9771	.0961 4211	.0765 3885
49	.1853 2024	.1463 4112	.1156 9158	.0915 6391	.0725 4867
50	.1790 5337	.1407 1262	.1107 0965	.0872 0373	.0687 6652

PRESENT VALUE $1/(1+i)^n$

Years	Rate i				
n	.06 (6%)	.065 (6½%)	.07 (7%)	.075 (7½%)	.08 (8%)
1	.9433 9623	.9389 6714	.9345 7944	.9302 3256	.9259 2593
2	.8899 9644	.8816 5928	.8734 3873	.8653 3261	.8573 3882
3	.8396 1928	.8278 4909	.8162 9788	.8049 6057	.7938 3224
4	.7920 9366	.7773 2309	.7628 9521	.7488 0053	.7350 2985
5	.7472 5817	.7298 8084	.7129 8618	.6965 5863	.6805 8320
6	.7049 6054	.6853 3412	.6663 4222	.6479 6152	.6301 6963
7	.6650 5711	.6435 0621	.6227 4974	.6027 5490	.5834 9040
8	.6274 1237	.6042 3119	.5820 0910	.5607 0223	.5402 6888
9	.5918 9846	.5673 5323	.5439 3374	.5215 8347	.5002 4897
10	.5583 9478	.5327 2604	.5083 4929	.4851 9393	.4631 9349
11	.5267 8753	.5002 1224	.4750 9280	.4513 4319	.4288 8286
12	.4969 6936	.4696 8285	.4440 1196	.4198 5413	.3971 1376
13	.4688 3902	.4410 1676	.4149 6445	.3905 6198	.3676 9792
14	.4423 0096	.4141 0025	.3878 1724	.3633 1347	.3404 6104
15	.4172 6506	.3888 2652	.3624 4602	.3379 6602	.3152 4170
16	.3936 4628	.3650 9533	.3387 3460	.3143 8699	.2918 9047
17	.3713 6442	.3428 1251	.3165 7439	.2924 5302	.2702 6895
18	.3503 4379	.3218 8969	.2958 6392	.2720 4932	.2502 4903
19	.3305 1301	.3022 4384	.2765 0833	.2530 6913	.2317 1206
20	.3118 0473	.2837 9703	.2584 1900	.2354 1315	.2145 4821
21	.2941 5540	.2664 7608	.2415 1309	.2189 8897	.1986 5575
22	.2775 0510	.2502 1228	.2257 1317	.2037 1067	.1839 4051
23	.2617 9726	.2349 4111	.2109 4688	.1894 9830	.1703 1528
24	.2469 7855	.2206 0198	.1971 4662	.1762 7749	.1576 9934
25	.2329 9863	.2071 3801	.1842 4918	.1639 7906	.1460 1790
26	.2198 1003	.1944 9579	.1721 9549	.1525 3866	.1352 0176
27	.2073 6795	.1826 2515	.1609 3037	.1418 9643	.1251 8682
28	.1956 3014	.1714 7902	.1504 0221	.1319 9668	.1159 1372
29	.1845 5674	.1610 1316	.1405 6282	.1227 8761	.1073 2752
30	.1741 1013	.1511 8607	.1313 6712	.1142 2103	.0993 7733
31	.1642 5484	.1419 5875	.1227 7301	.1062 5212	.0920 1605
32	.1549 5740	.1332 9460	.1147 4113	.0988 3918	.0852 0005
33	.1461 8622	.1251 5925	.1072 3470	.0919 4343	.0788 8893
34	.1379 1153	.1175 2042	.1002 1934	.0855 2877	.0730 4531
35	.1301 0522	.1103 4781	.0936 6294	.0795 6164	.0676 3454
36	.1227 4077	.1036 1297	.0875 3546	.0740 1083	.0626 2458
37	.1157 9318	.0972 8917	.0818 0884	.0688 4729	.0579 8572
38	.1092 3885	.0913 5134	.0764 5686	.0640 4399	.0536 9048
39	.1030 5552	.0857 7590	.0714 5501	.0595 7580	.0497 1341
40	.0972 2219	.0805 4075	.0667 8038	.0554 1935	.0460 3093
41	.0917 1905	.0756 2512	.0624 1157	.0515 5288	.0426 2123
42	.0865 2740	.0710 0950	.0583 2857	.0479 5617	.0394 6411
43	.0816 2962	.0666 7559	.0545 1268	.0446 1039	.0365 4084
44	.0770 0908	.0626 0619	.0509 4643	.0414 9804	.0338 3411
45	.0726 5007	.0587 8515	.0476 1349	.0386 0283	.0313 2788
46	.0685 3781	.0551 9733	.0444 9859	.0359 0961	.0290 0730
47	.0646 5831	.0518 2848	.0415 8747	.0334 0428	.0268 5861
48	.0609 9840	.0486 6524	.0388 6679	.0310 7375	.0248 6908
49	.0575 4566	.0456 9506	.0363 2410	.0289 0582	.0230 2693
50	.0542 8836	.0429 0616	.0339 4776	.0268 8913	.0213 2123

AMOUNT OF ANNUITY $[(1 + i)^n - 1]/i$

The following table gives the amount of an annuity of unit value per period after a term of n periods at rate of interest of i per period; usually indicated as $(s_{\overline{n}|}$ at $i)$.

Years	Rate i				
n	.0025 ($\frac{1}{4}$%)	.004167 ($\frac{1}{12}$%)	.005 ($\frac{1}{2}$%)	.005833 ($\frac{7}{12}$%)	.0075 ($\frac{3}{4}$%)
1	1.0000 0000	1.0000 0000	1.0000 0000	1.0000 0000	1.0000 0000
2	2.0025 0000	2.0041 6667	2.0050 0000	2.0058 3333	2.0075 0000
3	3.0075 0625	3.0125 1736	3.0150 2500	3.0175 3403	3.0225 5625
4	4.0150 2502	4.0250 6952	4.0301 0013	4.0351 3631	4.0452 2542
5	5.0250 6258	5.0418 4064	5.0502 5063	5.0586 7460	5.0755 6461
6	6.0376 2523	6.0628 4831	6.0755 0188	6.0881 8354	6.1136 3135
7	7.0527 1930	7.0881 1018	7.1058 7939	7.1236 9794	7.1594 8358
8	8.0703 5110	8.1176 4397	8.1414 0879	8.1652 5285	8.2131 7971
9	9.0905 2697	9.1514 6749	9.1821 1583	9.2128 8349	9.2747 7856
10	10.1132 5329	10.1895 9860	10.2280 2641	10.2666 2531	10.3443 3940
11	11.1385 3642	11.2320 5526	11.2791 6654	11.3265 1396	11.4219 2194
12	12.1663 8277	12.2788 5549	12.3355 6237	12.3925 8529	12.5075 8636
13	13.1967 9872	13.3300 1739	13.3972 4018	13.4648 7523	13.6013 9325
14	14.2297 9072	14.3855 5913	14.4642 2639	14.5434 2048	14.7034 0370
15	15.2653 6520	15.4454 9896	15.5365 4752	15.6282 5710	15.8136 7923
16	16.3035 2861	16.5098 5520	16.6142 3026	16.7194 2193	16.9322 8183
17	17.3442 8743	17.5786 4627	17.6973 0141	17.8169 5189	18.0592 7394
18	18.3876 4815	18.6518 9063	18.7857 8791	18.9208 8411	19.1947 1849
19	19.4336 1727	19.7296 0684	19.8797 1685	20.0312 5593	20.3386 7888
20	20.4822 0131	20.8118 1353	20.9791 1544	21.1481 0493	21.4912 1897
21	21.5334 0682	21.8985 2942	22.0840 1101	22.2714 6887	22.6524 0312
22	22.5872 4033	22.9897 7330	23.1944 3107	23.4013 8577	23.8222 9614
23	23.6437 0843	24.0855 6402	24.3104 0323	24.5378 9386	25.0009 6336
24	24.7028 1770	25.1859 2053	25.4319 5524	25.6810 3157	26.1884 7059
25	25.7645 7475	26.2908 6187	26.5591 1502	26.8308 3759	27.3848 8411
26	26.8289 8619	27.4004 0713	27.6919 1059	27.9873 5081	28.5902 7075
27	27.8960 5865	28.5145 7549	28.8303 7015	29.1506 1036	29.8046 9778
28	28.9657 9880	29.6333 8622	29.9745 2200	30.3206 5558	31.0282 3301
29	30.0382 1330	30.7568 5866	31.1243 9461	31.4975 2607	32.2609 4476
30	31.1133 0883	31.8850 1224	32.2800 1658	32.6812 6164	33.5029 0184
31	32.1910 9210	33.0178 6646	33.4414 1666	33.8719 0233	34.7541 7361
32	33.2715 6983	34.1554 4090	34.6086 2375	35.0694 8843	36.0148 2991
33	34.3547 4876	35.2977 5524	35.7816 6686	36.2740 6045	37.2849 4113
34	35.4406 3563	36.4448 2922	36.9605 7520	37.4856 5913	38.5645 7819
35	36.5292 3722	37.5966 8268	38.1453 7807	38.7043 2548	39.8538 1253
36	37.6205 6031	38.7533 3552	39.3361 0497	39.9301 0071	41.1527 1612
37	38.7146 1171	39.9148 0775	40.5327 8549	41.1630 2630	42.4613 6149
38	39.8113 9824	41.0811 1945	41.7354 4942	42.4031 4395	43.7798 2170
39	40.9109 2674	42.2522 9078	42.9441 2666	43.6504 9562	45.1081 7037
40	42.0132 0405	43.4283 4199	44.1588 4730	44.9051 2352	46.4464 8164
41	43.1182 3706	44.6092 9342	45.3796 4153	46.1670 7007	47.7948 3026
42	44.2260 3265	45.7951 6547	46.6065 3974	47.4363 7798	49.1532 9148
43	45.3365 9774	46.9859 7866	47.8395 7244	48.7130 9018	50.5219 4117
44	46.4499 3923	48.1817 5357	49.0787 7030	49.9972 4988	51.9008 5573
45	47.5660 6408	49.3825 1088	50.3241 6415	51.2889 0050	53.2901 1215
46	48.6849 7924	50.5882 7134	51.5757 8498	52.5880 8575	54.6897 8799
47	49.8066 9169	51.7990 5581	52.8336 6390	53.8948 4959	56.0999 6140
48	50.9312 0842	53.0148 8521	54.0978 3222	55.2092 3621	57.5207 1111
49	52.0585 3644	54.2357 8056	55.3683 2138	56.5312 9009	58.9521 1644
50	53.1886 8278	55.4617 6298	56.6451 6299	57.8610 5595	60.3942 5732

AMOUNT OF ANNUITY $[(1 + i)^n - 1]/i$

Years	Rate i				
n	.0025 (¼ %)	.004167 (5/12 %)	.005 (½ %)	.005833 (7/12 %)	.0075 (¾ %)
50	53.1886 828	55.4617 630	56.6451 630	57.8610 559	60.3942 573
51	54.3216 545	56.6928 537	57.9283 888	59.1985 788	61.8472 142
52	55.4574 586	57.9290 739	59.2180 307	60.5439 038	63.3110 684
53	56.5961 023	59.1704 450	60.5141 209	61.8970 766	64.7859 014
54	57.7375 925	60.4169 885	61.8166 915	63.2581 429	66.2717 956
55	58.8819 365	61.6687 260	63.1257 750	64.6271 487	67.7688 341
56	60.0291 413	62.9256 790	64.4414 038	66.0041 404	69.2771 003
57	61.1792 142	64.1878 694	65.7636 109	67.3891 646	70.7966 786
58	62.3321 622	65.4553 188	67.0924 289	68.7822 680	72.3276 537
59	63.4879 926	66.7280 493	68.4278 911	70.1834 979	73.8701 111
60	64.6467 126	68.0060 828	69.7700 305	71.5929 016	75.4241 369
61	65.8083 294	69.2894 415	71.1188 807	73.0105 269	76.9898 180
62	66.9728 502	70.5781 475	72.4744 751	74.4364 216	78.5672 416
63	68.1402 824	71.8722 231	73.8368 474	75.8706 341	80.1564 959
64	69.3106 331	73.1716 907	75.2060 317	77.3132 128	81.7576 696
65	70.4839 096	74.4765 728	76.5820 618	78.7642 065	83.3708 521
66	71.6601 194	75.7868 918	77.9649 721	80.2236 644	84.9961 335
67	72.8392 697	77.1026 706	79.3547 970	81.6916 358	86.6336 045
68	74.0213 679	78.4239 317	80.7515 710	83.1681 703	88.2833 566
69	75.2064 213	79.7506 981	82.1553 288	84.6533 180	89.9454 817
70	76.3944 374	81.0829 926	83.5661 055	86.1471 290	91.6200 729
71	77.5854 235	82.4208 384	84.9839 360	87.6496 539	93.3072 234
72	78.7793 870	83.7642 586	86.4088 557	89.1609 436	95.0070 276
73	79.9763 355	85.1132 763	87.8409 000	90.6810 491	96.7195 803
74	81.1762 763	86.4679 150	89.2801 045	92.2100 219	98.4449 771
75	82.3792 170	87.8281 980	90.7265 050	93.7479 137	100.1833 145
76	83.5851 651	89.1941 488	92.1801 375	95.2947 765	101.9346 893
77	84.7941 280	90.5657 911	93.6410 382	96.8506 627	103.6991 995
78	86.0061 133	91.9431 485	95.1092 434	98.4156 249	105.4769 435
79	87.2211 286	93.3262 450	96.5847 896	99.9897 160	107.2680 206
80	88.4391 814	94.7151 044	98.0677 136	101.5729 894	109.0725 307
81	89.6602 793	96.1097 506	99.5580 521	103.1654 985	110.8905 747
82	90.8844 300	97.5102 079	101.0558 424	104.7672 972	112.7222 540
83	92.1116 411	98.9165 004	102.5611 216	106.3784 398	114.5676 709
84	93.3419 202	100.3286 525	104.0739 272	107.9989 807	116.4269 284
85	94.5752 750	101.7466 886	105.5942 969	109.6289 748	118.3001 304
86	95.8117 132	103.1706 331	107.1222 683	111.2684 771	120.1873 814
87	97.0512 425	104.6005 108	108.6578 797	112.9175 432	122.0887 867
88	98.2938 706	106.0363 462	110.2011 691	114.5762 289	124.0044 526
89	99.5396 053	107.4781 643	111.7521 749	116.2445 902	125.9344 860
90	100.7884 543	108.9259 900	113.3109 358	117.9226 837	127.8789 947
91	102.0404 254	110.3798 483	114.8774 905	119.6105 660	129.8380 871
92	103.2955 265	111.8397 643	116.4518 779	121.3082 943	131.8118 728
93	104.5537 653	113.3057 634	118.0341 373	123.0159 260	133.8004 618
94	105.8151 497	114.7778 707	119.6243 080	124.7335 189	135.8039 653
95	107.0796 876	116.2561 118	121.2224 295	126.4611 311	137.8224 951
96	108.3473 868	117.7405 123	122.8285 417	128.1988 210	139.8561 638
97	109.6182 553	119.2310 978	124.4426 844	129.9466 475	141.9050 850
98	110.8923 009	120.7278 940	126.0648 978	131.7046 696	143.9693 731
99	112.1695 317	122.2309 269	127.6952 223	133.4729 468	146.0491 434
100	113.4499 555	123.7402 224	129.3336 984	135.2515 390	148.1445 120

AMOUNT OF ANNUITY $[(1+i)^n-1]/i$

Years	Rate i				
n	.01 (1%)	.01125 ($1\frac{1}{8}$%)	.0125 ($1\frac{1}{4}$%)	.015 ($1\frac{1}{2}$%)	.0175 ($1\frac{3}{4}$%)
1	1.0000 0000	1.0000 0000	1.0000 0000	1.0000 0000	1.0000 0000
2	2.0100 0000	2.0112 5000	2.0125 0000	2.0150 0000	2.0175 0000
3	3.0301 0000	3.0338 7656	3.0376 5625	3.0452 2500	3.0528 0625
4	4.0604 0100	4.0680 0767	4.0756 2695	4.0909 0338	4.1062 3036
5	5.1010 0501	5.1137 7276	5.1265 7229	5.1522 6693	5.1780 8939
6	6.1520 1506	6.1713 0270	6.1906 5444	6.2295 5093	6.2687 0596
7	7.2135 3521	7.2407 2986	7.2680 3762	7.3229 9419	7.3784 0831
8	8.2856 7056	8.3221 8807	8.3588 8809	8.4328 3911	8.5075 3045
9	9.3685 2727	9.4158 1269	9.4633 7420	9.5593 3169	9.6564 1224
10	10.4622 1254	10.5217 4058	10.5816 6637	10.7027 2167	10.8253 9945
11	11.5668 3467	11.6401 1016	11.7139 3720	11.8632 6249	12.0148 4394
12	12.6825 0301	12.7710 6140	12.8603 6142	13.0412 1143	13.2251 0371
13	13.8093 2804	13.9147 3584	14.0211 1594	14.2368 2960	14.4565 4303
14	14.9474 2132	15.0712 7662	15.1963 7988	15.4503 8205	15.7095 3253
15	16.0968 9554	16.2408 2848	16.3863 3463	16.6821 3778	16.9844 4935
16	17.2578 6449	17.4235 3780	17.5911 6382	17.9323 6984	18.2816 7721
17	18.4304 4314	18.6195 5260	18.8110 5336	19.2013 5539	19.6016 0656
18	19.6147 4757	19.8290 2257	20.0461 9153	20.4893 7572	20.9446 3468
19	20.8108 9504	21.0520 9907	21.2967 6893	21.7967 1636	22.3111 6578
20	22.0190 0399	22.2889 3519	22.5629 7854	23.1236 6710	23.7016 1119
21	23.2391 9403	23.5396 8571	23.8450 1577	24.4705 2211	25.1163 8938
22	24.4715 8598	24.8045 0717	25.1430 7847	25.8375 7994	26.5559 2620
23	25.7163 0183	26.0835 5788	26.4573 6695	27.2251 4364	28.0206 5490
24	26.9734 6485	27.3769 9790	27.7880 8403	28.6335 2080	29.5110 1637
25	28.2431 9950	28.6849 8913	29.1354 3508	30.0630 2361	31.0274 5015
26	29.5256 3150	30.0076 9526	30.4996 2802	31.5139 6896	32.5704 3969
27	30.8208 8781	31.3452 8183	31.8808 7337	32.9866 7850	34.1404 2238
28	32.1290 9669	32.6979 1625	33.2793 8429	34.4814 7867	35.7378 7977
29	33.4503 8766	34.0657 6781	34.6953 7659	35.9987 0085	37.3632 9267
30	34.7848 9153	35.4490 0769	36.1290 6880	37.5386 8137	39.0171 5029
31	36.1327 4045	36.8478 0903	37.5806 8216	39.1017 6159	40.6999 5042
32	37.4940 6785	38.2623 4688	39.0504 4069	40.6882 8801	42.4121 9955
33	38.8690 0853	39.6927 9829	40.5385 7120	42.2986 1233	44.1544 1305
34	40.2576 9862	41.1393 4227	42.0453 0334	43.9330 9152	45.9271 1527
35	41.6602 7560	42.6021 5987	43.5708 6963	45.5920 8789	47.7308 3979
36	43.0768 7836	44.0814 3417	45.1155 0550	47.2759 6921	49.5661 2949
37	44.5076 4714	45.5773 5030	46.6794 4932	48.9851 0874	51.4335 3675
38	45.9527 2361	47.0900 9549	48.2629 4243	50.7198 8358	53.3336 2365
39	47.4122 5085	48.6198 5906	49.8662 2921	52.4806 8366	55.2669 6206
40	48.8863 7336	50.1668 3248	51.4895 5708	54.2678 9391	57.2341 3390
41	50.3752 3709	51.7312 0934	53.1331 7654	56.0819 1232	59.2357 3124
42	51.8789 8946	53.3131 8545	54.7973 4125	57.9231 4100	61.2723 5654
43	53.3977 7936	54.9129 5879	56.4823 0801	59.7919 8812	63.3446 2278
44	54.9317 5715	56.5307 2957	58.1883 3686	61.6888 6794	65.4531 5367
45	56.4810 7472	58.1667 0028	59.9156 9108	63.6142 0096	67.5985 8386
46	58.0458 8547	59.8210 7566	61.6646 3721	65.5684 1398	69.7815 5908
47	59.6263 4432	61.4940 6276	63.4354 4518	67.5519 4018	72.0027 3637
48	61.2226 0777	63.1858 7097	65.2283 8824	69.5652 1929	74.2627 8425
49	62.8348 3385	64.8967 1201	67.0437 4310	71.6086 9758	76.5623 8298
50	64.4631 8218	66.6268 0002	68.8817 8989	73.6828 2804	78.9022 2468

AMOUNT OF ANNUITY $[(1 + i)^n - 1]/i$

Years			Rate i		
n	.01 (1 %)	.01125 (1⅛ %)	.0125 (1¼ %)	.015 (1½ %)	.0175 (1¾ %)
50	64.4631 822	66.6268 000	68.8817 899	73.6828 280	78.9022 247
51	66.1078 140	68.3763 515	70.7428 123	75.7880 705	81.2830 136
52	67.7688 921	70.1455 855	72.6270 974	77.9248 915	83.7054 663
53	69.4465 811	71.9347 233	74.5349 361	80.0937 649	86.1703 120
54	71.1410 469	73.7439 890	76.4666 228	82.2951 714	88.6782 925
55	72.8524 573	75.5736 088	78.4224 556	84.5295 989	91.2301 626
56	74.5809 819	77.4238 119	80.4027 363	86.7975 429	93.8266 904
57	76.3267 917	79.2948 298	82.4077 705	89.0995 061	96.4686 575
58	78.0900 597	81.1868 966	84.4378 676	91.4359 987	99.1568 590
59	79.8709 603	83.1002 492	86.4933 410	93.8075 386	101.8921 041
60	81.6696 699	85.0351 270	88.5745 078	96.2146 517	104.6752 159
61	83.4863 666	86.9917 722	90.6816 891	98.6578 715	107.5070 322
62	85.3212 302	88.9704 297	92.8152 102	101.1377 396	110.3884 052
63	87.1744 425	90.9713 470	94.9754 003	103.6548 057	113.3202 023
64	89.0461 869	92.9947 746	97.1625 928	106.2096 277	116.3033 058
65	90.9366 488	95.0409 659	99.3771 253	108.8027 722	119.3386 137
66	92.8460 153	97.1101 767	101.6193 393	111.4348 137	122.4270 394
67	94.7744 755	99.2026 662	103.8895 811	114.1063 359	125.5695 126
68	96.7222 202	101.3186 962	106.1882 008	116.8179 310	128.7669 791
69	98.6894 424	103.4585 315	108.5155 533	119.5701 999	132.0204 012
70	100.6763 368	105.6224 400	110.8719 978	122.3637 529	135.3307 585
71	102.6831 002	107.8106 925	113.2578 977	125.1992 092	138.6990 465
72	104.7099 312	110.0235 628	115.6736 215	128.0771 974	142.1262 798
73	106.7570 305	112.2613 278	118.1195 417	130.9983 553	145.6134 897
74	108.8246 008	114.5242 678	120.5960 360	133.9633 307	149.1617 258
75	110.9128 468	116.8126 658	123.1034 864	136.9727 806	152.7720 560
76	113.0219 753	119.1266 083	125.6422 800	140.0273 723	156.4455 670
77	115.1521 951	121.4669 849	128.2128 085	143.1277 829	160.1833 644
78	117.3037 170	123.8334 885	130.8154 686	146.2746 997	163.9865 733
79	119.4767 542	126.2266 152	133.4506 620	149.4688 202	167.8563 383
80	121.6715 217	128.6466 646	136.1187 953	152.7108 525	171.7938 242
81	123.8882 369	131.0939 396	138.8202 802	156.0015 153	175.8002 162
82	126.1271 193	133.5687 464	141.5555 337	159.3415 380	179.8767 200
83	128.3883 905	136.0713 948	144.3249 779	162.7316 611	184.0245 625
84	130.6722 744	138.6021 980	147.1290 401	166.1726 360	188.2449 924
85	132.9789 971	141.1614 727	149.9681 531	169.6652 255	192.5392 798
86	135.3087 871	143.7495 393	152.8427 550	173.2102 039	196.9087 172
87	137.6618 750	146.3667 216	155.7532 895	176.8083 569	201.3546 197
88	140.0384 937	149.0133 472	158.7002 056	180.4604 823	205.8783 256
89	142.4388 787	151.6897 474	161.6839 581	184.1673 895	210.4811 962
90	144.8632 675	154.3962 571	164.7050 076	187.9299 004	215.1646 172
91	147.3119 001	157.1332 149	167.7638 202	191.7488 489	219.9299 980
92	149.7850 191	159.9009 636	170.8608 680	195.6250 816	224.7787 729
93	152.2828 693	162.6998 495	173.9966 288	199.5594 578	229.7124 015
94	154.8056 980	165.5302 228	177.1715 867	203.5528 497	234.7323 685
95	157.3537 550	168.3924 378	180.3862 315	207.6061 425	239.8401 850
96	159.9272 926	171.2868 527	183.6410 594	211.7202 346	245.0373 882
97	162.5265 655	174.2138 298	186.9305 726	215.8960 381	250.3255 425
98	165.1518 311	177.1737 354	190.2732 798	220.1344 787	255.7062 395
99	167.8033 494	180.1669 399	193.6516 958	224.4364 959	261.1810 987
100	170.4813 829	183.1938 180	197.0723 420	228.8030 433	266.7517 679

AMOUNT OF ANNUITY $[(1+i)^n-1]/i$

Years	Rate i				
n	.02 (2%)	.0225 (2¼%)	.025 (2½%)	.0275 (2¾%)	.03 (3%)
1	1.0000 0000	1.0000 0000	1.0000 0000	1.0000 0000	1.0000 0000
2	2.0200 0000	2.0225 0000	2.0250 0000	2.0275 0000	2.0300 0000
3	3.0604 0000	3.0680 0625	3.0756 2500	3.0832 5625	3.0909 0000
4	4.1216 0800	4.1370 3639	4.1525 1563	4.1680 4580	4.1836 2700
5	5.2040 4016	5.2301 1971	5.2563 2852	5.2826 6706	5.3091 3581
6	6.3081 2096	6.3477 9740	6.3877 3673	6.4279 4040	6.4684 0988
7	7.4342 8338	7.4906 2284	7.5474 3015	7.6047 0876	7.6624 6218
8	8.5829 6905	8.6591 6186	8.7361 1590	8.8138 3825	8.8923 3605
9	9.7546 2843	9.8539 9300	9.9545 1880	10.0562 1880	10.1591 0613
10	10.9497 2100	11.0757 0784	11.2033 8177	11.3327 6482	11.4638 7931
11	12.1687 1542	12.3249 1127	12.4834 6631	12.6444 1585	12.8077 9569
12	13.4120 8973	13.6022 2177	13.7955 5297	13.9921 3729	14.1920 2956
13	14.6803 3152	14.9082 7176	15.1404 4179	15.3769 2107	15.6177 9045
14	15.9739 3815	16.2437 0788	16.5189 5284	16.7997 8639	17.0863 2416
15	17.2934 1692	17.6091 9130	17.9319 2666	18.2617 8052	18.5989 1389
16	18.6392 8525	19.0053 9811	19.3802 2483	19.7639 7948	20.1568 8130
17	20.0120 7096	20.4330 1957	20.8647 3045	21.3074 8892	21.7615 8774
18	21.4123 1238	21.8927 6251	22.3863 4871	22.8934 4487	23.4144 3537
19	22.8405 5863	23.3853 4966	23.9460 0743	24.5230 1460	25.1168 6844
20	24.2973 6980	24.9115 2003	25.5446 5761	26.1973 9750	26.8703 7449
21	25.7833 1719	26.4720 2923	27.1832 7405	27.9178 2593	28.6764 8572
22	27.2989 8354	28.0676 4988	28.8628 5590	29.6855 6615	30.5367 8030
23	28.8449 6321	29.6991 7201	30.5844 2730	31.5019 1921	32.4528 8370
24	30.4218 6247	31.3674 0338	32.3490 3798	33.3682 2199	34.4264 7022
25	32.0302 9972	33.0731 6996	34.1577 6393	35.2858 4810	36.4592 6432
26	33.6709 0572	34.8173 1628	36.0117 0803	37.2562 0892	38.5530 4225
27	35.3443 2383	36.6007 0590	37.9120 0073	39.2807 5467	40.7096 3352
28	37.0512 1031	38.4242 2178	39.8598 0075	41.3609 7542	42.9309 2252
29	38.7922 3451	40.2887 6677	41.8562 9577	43.4984 0224	45.2188 5020
30	40.5680 7921	42.1952 6402	43.9027 0316	45.6946 0831	47.5754 1571
31	42.3794 4079	44.1446 5746	46.0002 7074	47.9512 1003	50.0026 7818
32	44.2270 2961	46.1379 1226	48.1502 7751	50.2698 6831	52.5027 5852
33	46.1115 7020	48.1760 1528	50.3540 3445	52.6522 8969	55.0778 4128
34	48.0338 0160	50.2599 7563	52.6128 8531	55.1002 2765	57.7301 7652
35	49.9944 7763	52.3908 2508	54.9282 0744	57.6154 8391	60.4620 8181
36	51.9943 6719	54.5696 1864	57.3014 1263	60.1999 0972	63.2759 4427
37	54.0342 5453	56.7974 3506	59.7339 4794	62.8554 0724	66.1742 2259
38	56.1149 3962	59.0753 7735	62.2272 9664	65.5839 3094	69.1594 4927
39	58.2372 3841	61.4045 7334	64.7829 7906	68.3874 8904	72.2342 3275
40	60.4019 8318	63.7861 7624	67.4025 5354	71.2681 4499	75.4012 5973
41	62.6100 2284	66.2213 6521	70.0876 1737	74.2280 1898	78.6632 9753
42	64.8622 2330	68.7113 4592	72.8398 0781	77.2692 8950	82.0231 9645
43	67.1594 6777	71.2573 5121	75.6608 0300	80.3941 9496	85.4838 9234
44	69.5026 5712	73.8606 4161	78.5523 2308	83.6050 3532	89.0484 0911
45	71.8927 1027	76.5225 0605	81.5161 3116	86.9041 7379	92.7198 6139
46	74.3305 6447	79.2442 6243	84.5540 3443	90.2940 3857	96.5014 5723
47	76.8171 7576	82.0272 5834	87.6678 8530	93.7771 2463	100.3965 0095
48	79.3535 1928	84.8728 7165	90.8595 8243	97.3559 9556	104.4083 9598
49	81.9405 8966	87.7825 1126	94.1310 7199	101.0332 8544	108.5406 4785
50	84.5794 0145	90.7576 1776	97.4843 4879	104.8117 0079	112.7968 6729

INTEREST TABLES

AMOUNT OF ANNUITY $[(1 + i)^n - 1]/i$

Years			Rate i		
n	.02 (2 %)	.0225 (2¼ %)	.025 (2½ %)	.0275 (2¾ %)	.03 (3 %)
50	84.5794 015	90.7576 178	97.4843 488	104.8117 008	112.7968 673
51	87.2709 895	93.7996 642	100.9214 575	108.6940 226	117.1807 733
52	90.0164 093	96.9101 566	104.4444 939	112.6831 082	121.6961 965
53	92.8167 375	100.0906 351	108.0556 063	116.7818 937	126.3470 824
54	95.6730 722	103.3426 744	111.7569 965	120.9933 957	131.1374 949
55	98.5865 337	106.6678 846	115.5509 214	125.3207 141	136.0716 197
56	101.5582 643	110.0679 120	119.4396 944	129.7670 337	141.1537 683
57	104.5894 296	113.5444 400	123.4256 868	134.3356 272	146.3883 814
58	107.6812 182	117.0991 899	127.5113 289	139.0298 569	151.7800 328
59	110.8348 426	120.7339 217	131.6991 121	143.8531 780	157.3334 338
60	114.0515 394	124.4504 349	135.9915 900	148.8091 404	163.0534 368
61	117.3325 702	128.2505 697	140.3913 797	153.9013 917	168.9450 399
62	120.6792 216	132.1362 075	144.9011 642	159.1336 800	175.0133 911
63	124.0928 060	136.1092 722	149.5236 933	164.5098 562	181.2637 928
64	127.5746 622	140.1717 308	154.2617 856	170.0338 773	187.7017 066
65	131.1261 554	144.3255 948	159.1183 303	175.7098 089	194.3327 578
66	134.7486 785	148.5729 207	164.0962 885	181.5418 286	201.1627 406
67	138.4436 521	152.9158 114	169.1986 957	187.5342 289	208.1976 228
68	142.2125 251	157.3564 171	174.4286 631	193.6914 202	215.4435 515
69	146.0567 756	161.8969 365	179.7893 797	200.0179 343	222.9068 580
70	149.9779 111	166.5396 176	185.2841 142	206.5184 275	230.5940 637
71	153.9774 694	171.2867 590	190.9162 171	213.1976 842	238.5118 856
72	158.0570 188	176.1407 111	196.6891 225	220.0606 205	246.6672 422
73	162.2181 591	181.1038 771	202.6063 506	227.1122 876	255.0672 595
74	166.4625 223	186.1787 143	208.6715 093	234.3578 755	263.7192 773
75	170.7917 728	191.3677 354	214.8882 970	241.8027 171	272.6308 556
76	175.2076 082	196.6735 094	221.2605 045	249.4522 918	281.8097 813
77	179.7117 604	202.0986 634	227.7920 171	257.3122 298	291.2640 747
78	184.3059 956	207.6458 833	234.4868 175	265.3883 162	301.0019 969
79	188.9921 155	213.3179 157	241.3489 880	273.6864 948	311.0320 568
80	193.7719 578	219.1175 688	248.3827 126	282.2128 735	321.3630 185
81	198.6473 970	225.0477 141	255.5922 805	290.9737 275	332.0039 091
82	203.6203 449	231.1112 876	262.9820 875	299.9755 050	342.9640 264
83	208.6927 518	237.3112 916	270.5566 397	309.2248 314	354.2529 472
84	213.8666 068	243.6507 957	278.3205 557	318.7285 142	365.8805 356
85	219.1439 390	250.1329 386	286.2785 695	328.4935 484	377.8569 517
86	224.5268 178	256.7609 297	294.4355 338	338.5271 209	390.1926 602
87	230.0173 541	263.5380 506	302.7964 221	348.8366 168	402.8984 400
88	235.6177 012	270.4676 567	311.3663 327	359.4296 237	415.9853 932
89	241.3300 552	277.5531 790	320.1504 910	370.3139 384	429.4649 550
90	247.1566 563	284.7981 255	329.1542 533	381.4975 717	443.3489 037
91	253.0997 894	292.2060 834	338.3831 096	392.9887 549	457.6493 708
92	259.1617 852	299.7807 202	347.8426 873	404.7959 457	472.3788 519
93	265.3450 209	307.5257 865	357.5387 545	416.9278 342	487.5502 174
94	271.6519 214	315.4451 166	367.4772 234	429.3933 496	503.1767 240
95	278.0849 598	323.5426 318	377.6641 540	442.2016 667	519.2720 257
96	284.6466 590	331.8223 410	388.1057 578	455.3622 126	535.8501 865
97	291.3395 922	340.2883 437	398.8084 018	468.8846 734	552.9256 920
98	298.1663 840	348.9448 314	409.7786 118	482.7790 019	570.5134 628
99	305.1297 117	357.7960 901	421.0230 771	497.0554 245	588.6288 667
100	312.2323 059	366.8465 021	432.5486 540	511.7244 487	607.2877 327

AMOUNT OF ANNUITY $[(1 + i)^n - 1]/i$

Years	Rate i				
n	.035 (3½ %)	.04 (4 %)	.045 (4½ %)	.05 (5 %)	.055 (5½ %)
1	1.0000 000	1.0000 000	1.0000 000	1.0000 000	1.0000 000
2	2.0350 000	2.0400 000	2.0450 000	2.0500 000	2.0550 000
3	3.1062 250	3.1216 000	3.1370 250	3.1525 000	3.1680 250
4	4.2149 429	4.2464 640	4.2781 911	4.3101 250	4.3422 664
5	5.3624 659	5.4163 226	5.4707 097	5.5256 313	5.5810 910
6	6.5501 522	6.6329 755	6.7168 917	6.8019 128	6.8880 510
7	7.7794 075	7.8982 945	8.0191 518	8.1420 085	8.2668 938
8	9.0516 868	9.2142 263	9.3800 136	9.5491 089	9.7215 730
9	10.3684 958	10.5827 953	10.8021 142	11.0265 643	11.2562 595
10	11.7313 932	12.0061 071	12.2882 094	12.5778 925	12.8753 538
11	13.1419 919	13.4863 514	13.8411 788	14.2067 872	14.5834 982
12	14.6019 616	15.0258 055	15.4640 318	15.9171 265	16.3855 907
13	16.1130 303	16.6268 377	17.1599 133	17.7129 828	18.2867 981
14	17.6769 864	18.2919 112	18.9321 094	19.5986 320	20.2925 720
15	19.2956 809	20.0235 876	20.7840 543	21.5785 636	22.4086 635
16	20.9710 297	21.8245 311	22.7193 367	23.6574 918	24.6411 400
17	22.7050 157	23.6975 124	24.7417 069	25.8403 664	26.9964 027
18	24.4996 913	25.6454 129	26.8550 837	28.1323 847	29.4812 048
19	26.3571 805	27.6712 294	29.0635 625	30.5390 039	32.1026 711
20	28.2796 818	29.7780 786	31.3714 228	33.0659 541	34.8683 180
21	30.2694 707	31.9692 017	33.7831 368	35.7192 518	37.7860 755
22	32.3289 022	34.2479 698	36.3033 780	38.5052 144	40.8643 097
23	34.4604 137	36.6178 886	38.9370 300	41.4304 751	44.1118 467
24	36.6665 282	39.0826 041	41.6891 963	44.5019 989	47.5379 983
25	38.9498 567	41.6459 083	44.5652 101	47.7270 988	51.1525 882
26	41.3131 017	44.3117 446	47.5706 446	51.1134 538	54.9659 805
27	43.7590 602	47.0842 144	50.7113 236	54.6691 264	58.9891 094
28	46.2906 273	49.9675 830	53.9933 332	58.4025 828	63.2335 105
29	48.9107 993	52.9662 863	57.4230 332	62.3227 119	67.7113 535
30	51.6226 773	56.0849 378	61.0070 697	66.4388 475	72.4354 780
31	54.4294 710	59.3283 353	64.7523 878	70.7607 899	77.4194 293
32	57.3345 025	62.7014 687	68.6662 452	75.2988 294	82.6774 979
33	60.3412 101	66.2095 274	72.7562 263	80.0637 708	88.2247 603
34	63.4531 524	69.8579 085	77.0302 565	85.0669 594	94.0771 221
35	66.6740 127	73.6522 249	81.4966 180	90.3203 074	100.2513 638
36	70.0076 032	77.5983 138	86.1639 658	95.8363 227	106.7651 888
37	73.4578 693	81.7022 464	91.0413 443	101.6281 389	113.6372 742
38	77.0288 947	85.9703 363	96.1382 048	107.7095 458	120.8873 242
39	80.7249 060	90.4091 497	101.4644 240	114.0950 231	128.5361 271
40	84.5502 777	95.0255 157	107.0303 231	120.7997 742	136.6056 141
41	88.5095 375	99.8265 363	112.8466 876	127.8397 630	145.1189 228
42	92.6073 713	104.8195 978	118.9247 885	135.2317 511	154.1004 636
43	96.8486 293	110.0123 817	125.2764 040	142.9933 387	163.5759 891
44	101.2383 313	115.4128 770	131.9138 422	151.1430 056	173.5726 685
45	105.7816 729	121.0293 920	138.8499 651	159.7001 559	184.1191 653
46	110.4840 314	126.8705 677	146.0982 135	168.6851 637	195.2457 194
47	115.3509 725	132.9453 904	153.6726 331	178.1194 218	206.9842 339
48	120.3882 566	139.2632 060	161.5879 016	188.0253 929	219.3683 668
49	125.6018 456	145.8337 343	169.8593 572	198.4266 626	232.4336 270
50	130.9979 102	152.6670 837	178.5030 283	209.3479 957	246.2174 764

378

AMOUNT OF ANNUITY $[(1 + i)^n - 1]/i$

Years	Rate i				
n	.06 (6 %)	.065 (6½ %)	.07 (7 %)	.075 (7½ %)	.08 (8 %)
1	1.0000 000	1.0000 000	1.0000 000	1.0000 000	1.0000 000
2	2.0600 000	2.0650 000	2.0700 000	2.0750 000	2.0800 000
3	3.1836 000	3.1992 250	3.2149 000	3.2306 250	3.2464 000
4	4.3746 160	4.4071 746	4.4399 430	4.4729 219	4.5061 120
5	5.6370 930	5.6936 410	5.7507 390	5.8083 910	5.8666 010
6	6.9753 185	7.0637 276	7.1532 907	7.2440 203	7.3359 290
7	8.3938 376	8.5228 699	8.6540 211	8.7873 219	8.9228 034
8	9.8974 679	10.0768 565	10.2598 026	10.4463 710	10.6366 276
9	11.4913 160	11.7318 522	11.9779 887	12.2298 488	12.4875 578
10	13.1807 949	13.4944 225	13.8164 480	14.1470 875	14.4865 625
11	14.9716 426	15.3715 600	15.7835 993	16.2081 191	16.6454 875
12	16.8699 412	17.3707 114	17.8884 513	18.4237 280	18.9771 265
13	18.8821 377	19.4998 076	20.1406 429	20.8055 076	21.4952 966
14	21.0150 659	21.7672 951	22.5504 879	23.3659 207	24.2149 203
15	23.2759 699	24.1821 693	25.1290 220	26.1183 647	27.1521 139
16	25.6725 281	26.7540 103	27.8880 536	29.0772 421	30.3242 830
17	28.2128 798	29.4930 210	30.8402 173	32.2580 352	33.7502 257
18	30.9056 525	32.4100 674	33.9990 325	35.6773 879	37.4502 437
19	33.7599 917	35.5167 218	37.3789 648	39.3531 919	41.4462 632
20	36.7855 912	38.8253 087	40.9954 923	43.3046 813	45.7619 643
21	39.9927 267	42.3489 537	44.8651 768	47.5525 324	50.4229 214
22	43.3922 903	46.1016 357	49.0057 392	52.1189 724	55.4567 552
23	46.9958 277	50.0982 420	53.4361 409	57.0278 953	60.8932 956
24	50.8155 774	54.3546 278	58.1766 708	62.3049 874	66.7647 592
25	54.8645 120	58.8876 786	63.2490 377	67.9778 615	73.1059 400
26	59.1563 827	63.7153 777	68.6764 704	74.0762 011	79.9544 151
27	63.7057 657	68.8568 772	74.4838 233	80.6319 162	87.3507 684
28	68.5281 116	74.3325 743	80.6976 909	87.6793 099	95.3388 298
29	73.6397 983	80.1641 916	87.3465 293	95.2552 582	103.9659 362
30	79.0581 862	86.3748 640	94.4607 863	103.3994 025	113.2832 111
31	84.8016 774	92.9892 302	102.0730 414	112.1543 577	123.3458 680
32	90.8897 780	100.0335 302	110.2181 543	121.5659 345	134.2135 374
33	97.3431 647	107.5357 096	118.9334 251	131.6833 796	145.9506 204
34	104.1837 546	115.5255 308	128.2587 648	142.5596 331	158.6266 701
35	111.4347 799	124.0346 903	138.2368 784	154.2516 056	172.3168 037
36	119.1208 667	133.0969 451	148.9134 598	166.8204 760	187.1021 480
37	127.2681 187	142.7482 466	160.3374 020	180.3320 117	203.0703 198
38	135.9042 058	153.0268 826	172.5610 202	194.8569 126	220.3159 454
39	145.0584 581	163.9736 300	185.6402 916	210.4711 810	238.9412 210
40	154.7619 656	175.6319 159	199.6351 120	227.2565 196	259.0565 187
41	165.0476 836	188.0479 904	214.6095 698	245.3007 586	280.7810 402
42	175.9505 446	201.2711 098	230.6322 397	264.6983 155	304.2435 234
43	187.5075 772	215.3537 320	247.7764 965	285.5506 891	329.5830 053
44	199.7580 319	230.3517 245	266.1208 513	307.9669 908	356.9496 457
45	212.7435 138	246.3245 866	285.7493 108	332.0645 151	386.5056 174
46	226.5081 246	263.3356 848	306.7517 626	357.9693 537	418.4260 668
47	241.0986 121	281.4525 043	329.2243 860	385.8170 553	452.9001 521
48	256.5645 288	300.7469 170	353.2700 930	415.7533 344	490.1321 643
49	272.9584 006	321.2954 666	378.9989 995	447.9348 345	530.3427 374
50	290.3359 046	343.1796 720	406.5289 295	482.5299 471	573.7701 564

PRESENT VALUE OF ANNUITY $[1 - (1 + i)^{-n}]/i$

The following table gives the present value of an annuity of unit value per period for a term of n periods at rate of interest i per period; usually indicated as $a_{\overline{n}|}$ at i.

Years	Rate i				
n	.0025 ($\frac{1}{4}$ %)	.004167 ($\frac{1}{12}$ %)	.005 ($\frac{1}{2}$ %)	.005833 ($\frac{7}{12}$ %)	.0075 ($\frac{3}{4}$ %)
1	0.9975 0623	0.9958 5062	0.9950 2488	0.9942 0050	0.9925 5583
2	1.9925 2492	1.9875 6908	1.9850 9938	1.9826 3513	1.9777 2291
3	2.9850 6227	2.9751 7253	2.9702 4814	2.9653 3732	2.9555 5624
4	3.9751 2446	3.9586 7804	3.9504 9566	3.9423 4034	3.9261 1041
5	4.9627 1766	4.9381 0261	4.9258 6633	4.9136 7722	4.8894 3961
6	5.9478 4804	5.9134 6318	5.8963 8441	5.8793 8083	5.8455 9763
7	6.9305 2174	6.8847 7661	6.8620 7404	6.8394 8384	6.7946 3785
8	7.9107 4487	7.8520 5970	7.8229 5924	7.7940 1874	7.7366 1325
9	8.8885 2357	8.8153 2916	8.7790 6392	8.7430 1780	8.6715 7642
10	9.8638 6391	9.7746 0165	9.7304 1186	9.6865 1314	9.5995 7958
11	10.8367 7198	10.7298 9376	10.6770 2673	10.6245 3667	10.5206 7452
12	11.8072 5384	11.6812 2200	11.6189 3207	11.5571 2014	11.4349 1267
13	12.7753 1555	12.6286 0283	12.5561 5131	12.4842 9509	12.3423 4508
14	13.7409 6314	13.5720 5261	13.4887 0777	13.4060 9288	13.2430 2242
15	14.7042 0264	14.5115 8766	14.4166 2465	14.3225 4470	14.1369 9495
16	15.6650 4004	15.4472 2422	15.3399 2502	15.2336 8156	15.0243 1261
17	16.6234 8133	16.3789 7848	16.2586 3186	16.1395 3427	15.9050 2492
18	17.5795 3250	17.3068 6654	17.1727 6802	17.0401 3350	16.7791 8107
19	18.5331 9950	18.2309 0443	18.0823 5624	17.9355 0969	17.6468 2984
20	19.4844 8828	19.1511 0815	18.9874 1915	18.8256 9315	18.5080 1969
21	20.4334 0477	20.0674 9359	19.8879 7925	19.7107 1398	19.3627 9870
22	21.3799 5488	20.9800 7661	20.7840 5896	20.5906 0213	20.2112 1459
23	22.3241 4452	21.8888 7297	21.6756 8055	21.4653 8738	21.0533 1473
24	23.2659 7957	22.7938 9839	22.5628 6622	22.3350 9930	21.8891 4614
25	24.2054 6591	23.6951 6853	23.4456 3803	23.1997 6732	22.7187 5547
26	25.1426 0939	24.5926 9895	24.3240 1794	24.0594 2070	23.5421 8905
27	26.0774 1585	25.4865 0517	25.1980 2780	24.9140 8852	24.3594 9286
28	27.0098 9112	26.3766 0266	26.0676 8936	25.7637 9968	25.1707 1251
29	27.9400 4102	27.2630 0680	26.9330 2424	26.6085 8295	25.9758 9331
30	28.8678 7134	28.1457 3291	27.7940 5397	27.4484 6689	26.7750 8021
31	29.7933 8787	29.0247 9626	28.6507 9997	28.2834 7993	27.5683 1783
32	30.7165 9638	29.9002 1205	29.5032 8355	29.1136 5030	28.3556 5045
33	31.6375 0262	30.7719 9540	30.3515 2592	29.9390 0610	29.1371 2203
34	32.5561 1234	31.6401 6139	31.1955 4818	30.7595 7524	29.9127 7621
35	33.4724 3126	32.5047 2504	32.0353 7132	31.5753 8549	30.6826 5629
36	34.3864 6510	33.3657 0128	32.8710 1624	32.3864 6445	31.4468 0525
37	35.2982 1955	34.2231 0501	33.7025 0372	33.1928 3955	32.2052 6576
38	36.2077 0030	35.0769 5105	34.5298 5445	33.9945 3808	32.9580 8016
39	37.1149 1302	35.9272 5416	35.3530 8900	34.7915 8716	33.7052 9048
40	38.0198 6336	36.7740 2904	36.1722 2786	35.5840 1374	34.4469 3844
41	38.9225 5697	37.6172 9033	36.9872 9141	36.3718 4465	35.1830 6545
42	39.8229 9947	38.4570 5261	37.7982 9991	37.1551 0653	35.9137 1260
43	40.7211 9648	39.2933 3040	38.6052 7354	37.9338 2588	36.6389 2070
44	41.6171 5359	40.1261 3816	39.4082 3238	38.7080 2904	37.3587 3022
45	42.5108 7640	40.9554 9028	40.2071 9640	39.4777 4221	38.0731 8136
46	43.4023 7048	41.7814 0111	41.0021 8547	40.2429 9143	38.7823 1401
47	44.2916 4137	42.6038 8492	41.7932 1937	41.0038 0258	39.4861 6775
48	45.1786 9464	43.4229 5594	42.5803 1778	41.7602 0141	40.1847 8189
49	46.0635 3580	44.2386 2832	43.3635 0028	42.5122 1349	40.8781 9542
50	46.9461 7037	45.0509 1617	44.1427 8635	43.2598 6428	41.5664 4707

PRESENT VALUE OF ANNUITY $[1 - (1 + i)^{-n}]/i$

Years			Rate i		
n	.0025 ($\frac{1}{4}$ %)	.004167 ($\frac{5}{12}$ %)	.005 ($\frac{1}{2}$ %)	.005833 ($\frac{7}{12}$ %)	.0075 ($\frac{3}{4}$ %)
50	46.9461 7037	45.0509 1617	44.1427 8635	43.2598 6428	41.5664 4707
51	47.8266 0386	45.8598 3353	44.9181 9537	44.0031 7907	42.2495 7525
52	48.7048 4176	46.6653 9439	45.6897 4664	44.7421 8301	42.9276 1812
53	49.5808 8953	47.4676 1267	46.4574 5934	45.4769 0108	43.6006 1351
54	50.4547 5265	48.2665 0224	47.2213 5258	46.2073 5816	44.2685 9902
55	51.3264 3656	49.0620 7692	47.9814 4535	46.9335 7895	44.9316 1193
56	52.1959 4669	49.8543 5046	48.7377 5657	47.6555 8802	45.5896 8926
57	53.0632 8847	50.6433 3656	49.4903 0505	48.3734 0980	46.2428 6776
58	53.9284 6730	51.4290 4885	50.2391 0950	49.0870 6856	46.8911 8388
59	54.7914 8858	52.2115 0093	50.9841 8856	49.7965 8846	47.5346 7382
60	55.6523 5769	52.9907 0632	51.7255 6075	50.5019 9350	48.1733 7352
61	56.5110 7999	53.7666 7850	52.4632 4453	51.2033 0754	48.8073 1863
62	57.3676 6083	54.5394 3087	53.1972 5824	51.9005 5431	49.4365 4455
63	58.2221 0557	55.3089 7680	53.9276 2014	52.5937 5739	50.0610 8640
64	59.0744 1952	56.0753 2959	54.6543 4840	53.2829 4024	50.6809 7906
65	59.9246 0800	56.8385 0250	55.3774 6109	53.9681 2617	51.2962 5713
66	60.7726 7631	57.5985 0871	56.0969 7621	54.6493 3836	51.9069 5497
67	61.6186 2974	58.3553 6137	56.8129 1165	55.3265 9986	52.5131 0667
68	62.4624 7355	59.1090 7357	57.5252 8522	55.9999 3358	53.1147 4607
69	63.3042 1302	59.8596 5832	58.2341 1465	56.6693 6230	53.7119 0677
70	64.1438 5339	60.6071 2862	58.9394 1756	57.3349 0867	54.3046 2210
71	64.9813 9989	61.3514 9738	59.6412 1151	57.9965 9520	54.8929 2516
72	65.8168 5774	62.0927 7748	60.3395 1394	58.6544 4427	55.4768 4880
73	66.6502 3216	62.8309 8172	61.0343 4222	59.3084 7815	56.0564 2561
74	67.4815 2834	63.5661 2287	61.7257 1366	59.9587 1896	56.6316 8795
75	68.3107 5146	64.2982 1365	62.4136 4543	60.6051 8869	57.2026 6794
76	69.1379 0670	65.0272 6670	63.0981 5466	61.2479 0922	57.7693 9746
77	69.9629 9920	65.7532 9464	63.7792 5836	61.8869 0229	58.3319 0815
78	70.7860 3411	66.4763 1002	64.4569 7350	62.5221 8952	58.8902 3141
79	71.6070 1657	67.1963 2533	65.1313 1691	63.1537 9239	59.4443 9842
80	72.4259 5169	67.9133 5303	65.8023 0539	63.7817 3229	59.9944 4012
81	73.2428 4458	68.6274 0550	66.4699 5561	64.4060 3044	60.5403 8722
82	74.0577 0033	69.3384 9511	67.1342 8419	65.0267 0798	61.0822 7019
83	74.8705 2402	70.0466 3413	67.7953 0765	65.6437 8590	61.6201 1930
84	75.6813 2072	70.7518 3482	68.4530 4244	66.2572 8507	62.1539 6456
85	76.4900 9548	71.4541 0936	69.1075 0491	66.8672 2625	62.6838 3579
86	77.2968 5335	72.1534 6991	69.7587 1135	67.4736 3007	63.2097 6257
87	78.1015 9935	72.8499 2854	70.4066 7796	68.0765 1706	63.7317 7427
88	78.9043 3850	73.5434 9730	71.0514 2086	68.6759 0759	64.2499 0002
89	79.7050 7581	74.2341 8818	71.6929 5608	69.2718 2197	64.7641 6875
90	80.5038 1627	74.9220 1313	72.3312 9958	69.8642 8033	65.2746 0918
91	81.3005 6486	75.6069 8403	72.9664 6725	70.4533 0273	65.7812 4981
92	82.0953 2654	76.2891 1272	73.5984 7487	71.0389 0910	66.2841 1892
93	82.8881 0628	76.9684 1101	74.2273 3818	71.6211 1923	66.7832 4458
94	83.6789 0901	77.6448 9063	74.8530 7282	72.1999 5284	67.2786 5467
95	84.4677 3966	78.3185 6329	75.4756 9434	72.7754 2950	67.7703 7685
96	85.2546 0315	78.9894 4062	76.0952 1825	73.3475 6869	68.2584 3856
97	86.0395 0439	79.6575 3422	76.7116 5995	73.9163 8975	68.7428 6705
98	86.8224 4827	80.3228 5566	77.3250 3478	74.4819 1193	69.2236 8938
99	87.6034 3967	80.9854 1642	77.9353 5799	75.0441 5436	69.7009 3239
100	88.3824 8346	81.6452 2797	78.5426 4477	75.6031 3607	70.1746 2272

PRESENT VALUE OF ANNUITY $[1-(1+i)^{-n}]/i$

Years			Rate i		
n	.01 (1%)	.01125 (1⅛%)	.0125 (1¼%)	.015 (1½%)	.0175 (1¾%)
1	0.9900 9901	0.9888 7515	0.9876 5432	0.9852 2167	0.9828 0098
2	1.9703 9506	1.9667 4923	1.9631 1538	1.9558 8342	1.9486 9875
3	2.9409 8521	2.9337 4460	2.9265 3371	2.9122 0042	2.8979 8403
4	3.9019 6555	3.8899 8230	3.8780 5798	3.8543 8465	3.8309 4254
5	4.8534 3124	4.8355 8200	4.8178 3504	4.7826 4497	4.7478 5508
6	5.7954 7647	5.7706 6205	5.7460 0992	5.6971 8717	5.6489 9762
7	6.7281 9453	6.6953 3948	6.6627 2585	6.5982 1396	6.5346 4139
8	7.6516 7775	7.6097 3002	7.5681 2429	7.4859 2508	7.4050 5297
9	8.5660 1758	8.5139 4810	8.4623 4498	8.3605 1732	8.2604 9432
10	9.4713 0453	9.4081 0690	9.3455 2591	9.2221 8455	9.1012 2291
11	10.3676 2825	10.2923 1832	10.2178 0337	10.0711 1779	9.9274 9181
12	11.2550 7747	11.1666 9302	11.0793 1197	10.9075 0521	10.7395 4969
13	12.1337 4007	12.0313 4044	11.9301 8466	11.7315 3222	11.5376 4097
14	13.0037 0304	12.8863 6880	12.7705 5275	12.5433 8150	12.3220 0587
15	13.8650 5252	13.7318 8509	13.6005 4592	13.3432 3301	13.0928 8046
16	14.7178 7378	14.5679 9514	14.4202 9227	14.1312 6405	13.8504 9677
17	15.5622 5127	15.3948 0360	15.2299 1829	14.9076 4931	14.5950 8282
18	16.3982 6858	16.2124 1395	16.0295 4893	15.6725 6089	15.3268 6272
19	17.2260 0850	17.0209 2850	16.8193 0759	16.4261 6837	16.0460 5673
20	18.0455 5297	17.8204 4845	17.5993 1613	17.1686 3879	16.7528 8130
21	18.8569 8313	18.6110 7387	18.3696 9495	17.9001 3673	17.4475 4919
22	19.6603 7934	19.3929 0371	19.1305 6291	18.6208 2437	18.1302 6948
23	20.4558 2113	20.1660 3580	19.8820 3744	19.3308 6145	18.8012 4764
24	21.2433 8726	20.9305 6693	20.6242 3451	20.0304 0537	19.4606 8565
25	22.0231 5570	21.6865 9276	21.3572 6865	20.7196 1120	20.1087 8196
26	22.7952 0366	22.4342 0792	22.0812 5299	21.3986 3172	20.7457 3166
27	23.5596 0759	23.1735 0598	22.7962 9925	22.0676 1746	21.3717 2644
28	24.3164 4316	23.9045 7946	23.5025 1778	22.7267 1671	21.9869 5474
29	25.0657 8530	24.6275 1986	24.2000 1756	23.3760 7558	22.5916 0171
30	25.8077 0822	25.3424 1766	24.8889 0623	24.0158 3801	23.1858 4934
31	26.5422 8537	26.0493 6233	25.5692 9010	24.6461 4582	23.7698 7650
32	27.2695 8947	26.7484 4236	26.2412 7418	25.2671 3874	24.3438 5897
33	27.9896 9255	27.4397 4522	26.9049 6215	25.8789 5442	24.9079 6951
34	28.7026 6589	28.1233 5745	27.5604 5644	26.4817 2849	25.4623 7789
35	29.4085 8009	28.7993 6460	28.2078 5822	27.0755 9458	26.0072 5100
36	30.1075 0504	29.4678 5127	28.8472 6737	27.6606 8431	26.5427 5283
37	30.7995 0994	30.1289 0114	29.4787 8259	28.2371 2740	27.0690 4455
38	31.4846 6330	30.7825 9692	30.1025 0133	28.8050 5163	27.5862 8457
39	32.1630 3298	31.4290 2044	30.7185 1983	29.3645 8288	28.0946 2857
40	32.8346 8611	32.0682 5260	31.3269 3316	29.9158 4520	28.5942 2955
41	33.4996 8922	32.7003 7340	31.9278 3522	30.4589 6079	29.0852 3789
42	34.1581 0814	33.3254 6195	32.5213 1874	30.9940 5004	29.5678 0136
43	34.8100 0806	33.9435 9649	33.1074 7530	31.5212 3157	30.0420 6522
44	35.4554 5352	34.5548 5438	33.6863 9536	32.0406 2223	30.5081 7221
45	36.0945 0844	35.1593 1212	34.2581 6825	32.5523 3718	30.9662 6261
46	36.7272 3608	35.7570 4536	34.8228 8222	33.0564 8983	31.4164 7431
47	37.3536 9909	36.3481 2891	35.3806 2442	33.5531 9195	31.8589 4281
48	37.9739 5949	36.9326 3674	35.9314 8091	34.0425 5365	32.2938 0129
49	38.5880 7871	37.5106 4202	36.4755 3670	34.5246 8339	32.7211 8063
50	39.1961 1753	38.0822 1708	37.0128 7575	34.9996 8807	33.1412 0946

PRESENT VALUE OF ANNUITY $[1-(1+i)^{-n}]/i$

Years		Rate i			
n	.01 (1%)	.01125 ($1\frac{1}{8}$%)	.0125 ($1\frac{1}{4}$%)	.015 ($1\frac{1}{2}$%)	.0175 ($1\frac{3}{4}$%)
50	39.1961 1753	38.0822 1708	37.0128 7575	34.9996 8807	33.1412 0946
51	39.7981 3617	38.6474 3345	37.5435 8099	35.4676 7298	33.5540 1421
52	40.3941 9423	39.2063 6188	38.0677 3431	35.9287 4185	33.9597 1913
53	40.9843 5072	39.7590 7232	38.5854 1660	36.3829 9690	34.3584 4632
54	41.5686 6408	40.3056 3394	39.0967 0776	36.8305 3882	34.7503 1579
55	42.1471 9216	40.8461 1514	39.6016 8667	37.2714 6681	35.1354 4550
56	42.7199 9224	41.3805 8358	40.1004 3128	37.7058 7863	35.5139 5135
57	43.2871 2102	41.9091 0613	40.5930 1855	38.1338 7058	35.8859 4727
58	43.8486 3468	42.4317 4896	41.0795 2449	38.5555 3751	36.2515 4523
59	44.4045 8879	42.9485 7746	41.5600 2419	38.9709 7292	36.6108 5526
60	44.9550 3841	43.4596 5633	42.0345 9179	39.3802 6889	36.9639 8552
61	45.5000 3803	43.9650 4952	42.5033 0054	39.7835 1614	37.3110 4228
62	46.0396 4161	44.4648 2029	42.9662 2275	40.1808 0408	37.6521 3000
63	46.5739 0258	44.9590 3119	43.4234 2988	40.5722 2077	37.9873 5135
64	47.1028 7385	45.4477 4407	43.8749 9247	40.9578 5298	38.3168 0723
65	47.6266 0777	45.9310 2009	44.3209 8022	41.3377 8618	38.6405 9678
66	48.1451 5621	46.4089 1975	44.7614 6195	41.7121 0461	38.9588 1748
67	48.6585 7050	46.8815 0284	45.1965 0563	42.0808 9125	39.2715 6509
68	49.1669 0149	47.3488 2852	45.6261 7840	42.4442 2783	39.5789 3375
69	49.6701 9949	47.8109 5527	46.0505 4656	42.8021 9490	39.8810 1597
70	50.1685 1435	48.2679 4094	46.4696 7562	43.1548 7183	40.1779 0267
71	50.6618 9539	48.7198 4270	46.8836 3024	43.5023 3678	40.4696 8321
72	51.1503 9148	49.1667 1714	47.2924 7431	43.8446 6677	40.7564 4542
73	51.6340 5097	49.6086 2016	47.6962 7093	44.1819 3771	41.0382 7560
74	52.1129 2175	50.0456 0708	48.0950 8240	44.5142 2434	41.3152 5857
75	52.5870 5124	50.4777 3259	48.4889 7027	44.8416 0034	41.5874 7771
76	53.0564 8638	50.9050 5027	48.8779 9533	45.1641 3826	41.8550 1495
77	53.5212 7364	51.3276 1510	49.2622 1761	45.4819 0962	42.1179 5081
78	53.9814 5905	51.7454 7847	49.6416 9640	45.7949 8485	42.3763 6443
79	54.4370 8817	52.1586 9317	50.0164 9027	46.1034 3335	42.6303 3359
80	54.8882 0611	52.5673 1092	50.3866 5706	46.4073 2349	42.8799 3474
81	55.3348 5753	52.9713 8286	50.7522 5389	46.7067 2265	43.1252 4298
82	55.7770 8666	53.3709 5957	51.1133 3717	47.0016 9720	43.3663 3217
83	56.2149 3729	53.7660 9104	51.4699 6264	47.2923 1251	43.6032 7486
84	56.6484 5276	54.1568 2674	51.8221 8532	47.5786 3301	43.8361 4237
85	57.0776 7600	54.5432 1557	52.1700 5958	47.8607 2218	44.0650 0479
86	57.5026 4951	54.9253 0588	52.5136 3909	48.1386 4254	44.2899 3099
87	57.9234 1535	55.3031 4549	52.8529 7688	48.4124 5571	44.5109 8869
88	58.3400 1520	55.6767 8169	53.1881 2531	48.6822 2237	44.7282 4441
89	58.7524 9030	56.0462 6126	53.5191 3611	48.9480 0234	44.9417 6355
90	59.1608 8148	56.4116 3041	53.8460 6035	49.2098 5452	45.1516 1037
91	59.5652 2919	56.7729 3490	54.1689 4850	49.4678 3696	45.3578 4803
92	59.9655 7346	57.1302 1992	54.4878 5037	49.7220 0686	45.5605 3860
93	60.3619 5392	57.4835 3021	54.8028 1518	49.9724 2055	45.7597 4310
94	60.7544 0982	57.8329 0997	55.1138 9154	50.2191 3355	45.9555 2147
95	61.1429 8002	58.1784 0294	55.4211 2744	50.4622 0054	46.1479 3265
96	61.5277 0299	58.5200 5235	55.7245 7031	50.7016 7541	46.3370 3455
97	61.9086 1682	58.8579 0096	56.0242 6698	50.9376 1124	46.5228 8408
98	62.2857 5923	59.1919 9106	56.3202 6368	51.1700 6034	46.7055 3718
99	62.6591 6755	59.5223 6446	56.6126 0610	51.3990 7422	46.8850 4882
100	63.0288 7877	59.8490 6251	56.9013 3936	51.6247 0367	47.0614 7304

PRESENT VALUE OF ANNUITY $[1-(1+i)^{-n}]/i$

Years	Rate i				
n	.02 (2%)	.0225 (2¼%)	.025 (2½%)	.0275 (2¾%)	.03 (3%)
1	0.9803 9216	0.9779 9511	0.9756 0976	0.9732 3601	0.9708 7379
2	1.9415 6094	1.9344 6955	1.9274 2415	1.9204 2434	1.9134 6970
3	2.8838 8327	2.8698 9687	2.8560 2356	2.8422 6213	2.8286 1135
4	3.8077 2870	3.7847 4021	3.7619 7421	3.7394 2787	3.7170 9840
5	4.7134 5951	4.6794 5253	4.6458 2850	4.6125 8186	4.5797 0719
6	5.6014 3089	5.5544 7680	5.5081 2536	5.4623 6678	5.4171 9144
7	6.4719 9107	6.4102 4626	6.3493 9060	6.2894 0806	6.2302 8296
8	7.3254 8144	7.2471 8461	7.1701 3717	7.0943 1441	7.0196 9219
9	8.1622 3671	8.0657 0622	7.9708 6553	7.8776 7826	7.7861.0892
10	8.9825 8501	8.8662 1635	8.7520 6393	8.6400 7616	8.5302 0284
11	9.7868 4805	9.6491 1134	9.5142 0871	9.3820 6926	9.2526 2411
12	10.5753 4122	10.4147 7882	10.2577 6460	10.1042 0366	9.9540 0399
13	11.3483 7375	11.1635 9787	10.9831 8497	10.8070 1086	10.6349 5533
14	12.1062 4877	11.8959 3924	11.6909 1217	11.4910 0814	11.2960 7314
15	12.8492 6350	12.6121 6551	12.3813 7773	12.1566 9892	11.9379 3509
16	13.5777 0931	13.3126 3131	13.0550 0266	12.8045 7315	12.5611 0203
17	14.2918 7188	13.9976 8343	13.7121 9772	13.4351 0769	13.1661 1847
18	14.9920 3125	14.6676 6106	14.3533 6363	14.0487 6661	13.7535 1308
19	15.6784 6201	15.3228 9590	14.9788 9134	14.6460 0157	14.3237 9911
20	16.3514 3334	15.9637 1237	15.5891 6229	15.2272 5213	14.8774 7486
21	17.0112 0916	16.5904 2775	16.1845 4857	15.7929 4612	15.4150 2414
22	17.6580 4820	17.2033 5232	16.7654 1324	16.3434 9987	15.9369 1664
23	18.2922 0412	17.8027 8955	17.3321 1048	16.8793 1861	16.4436 0839
24	18.9139 2560	18.3890 3624	17.8849 8583	17.4007 9670	16.9355 4212
25	19.5234 5647	18.9623 8263	18.4243 7642	17.9083 1795	17.4131 4769
26	20.1210 3576	19.5231 1260	18.9506 1114	18.4022 5592	17.8768 4242
27	20.7068 9780	20.0715 0376	19.4640 1087	18.8829 7413	18.3270 3147
28	21.2812 7236	20.6078 2764	19.9648 8866	19.3508 2640	18.7641 0823
29	21.8443 8466	21.1323 4977	20.4535 4991	19.8061 5708	19.1884 5459
30	22.3964 5555	21.6453 2985	20.9302 9259	20.2493 0130	19.6004 4135
31	22.9377 0152	22.1470 2186	21.3954 0741	20.6805 8520	20.0004 2849
32	23.4683 3482	22.6376 7419	21.8491 7796	21.1003 2623	20.3887 6553
33	23.9885 6355	23.1175 2977	22.2918 8094	21.5088 3332	20.7657 9178
34	24.4985 9172	23.5868 2618	22.7237 8628	21.9064 0712	21.1318 3668
35	24.9986 1933	24.0457 9577	23.1451 5734	22.2933 4026	21.4872 2007
36	25.4888 4248	24.4946 6579	23.5562 5107	22.6699 1753	21.8322 5250
37	25.9694 5341	24.9336 5848	23.9573 1812	23.0364 1609	22.1672 3544
38	26.4406 4060	25.3629 9118	24.3486 0304	23.3931 0568	22.4924 6159
39	26.9025 8883	25.7828 7646	24.7303 4443	23.7402 4884	22.8082 1513
40	27.3554 7924	26.1935 2221	25.1027 7505	24.0781 0106	23.1147 7197
41	27.7994 8945	26.5951 3174	25.4661 2200	24.4069 1101	23.4123 9997
42	28.2347 9358	26.9879 0390	25.8206 0683	24.7269 2069	23.7013 5920
43	28.6615 6233	27.3720 3316	26.1664 4569	25.0383 6563	23.9819 0213
44	29.0799 6307	27.7477 0969	26.5038 4945	25.3414 7507	24.2542 7392
45	29.4901 5987	28.1151 1950	26.8330 2386	25.6364 7209	24.5187 1254
46	29.8923 1360	28.4744 4450	27.1541 6962	25.9235 7381	24.7754 4907
47	30.2865 8196	28.8258 6259	27.4674 8255	26.2029 9154	25.0247 0783
48	30.6731 1957	29.1695 4777	27.7731 5371	26.4749 3094	25.2667 0664
49	31.0520 7801	29.5056 7019	28.0713 6947	26.7395 9215	25.5016 5693
50	31.4236 0589	29.8343 9627	28.3623 1168	26.9971 6998	25.7297 6401

PRESENT VALUE OF ANNUITY $[1-(1+i)^{-n}]/i$

Years		Rate i			
n	.02 (2%)	.0225 (2¼%)	.025 (2½%)	.0275 (2¾%)	.03 (3%)
50	31.4236 0589	29.8343 9627	28.3623 1168	26.9971 6998	25.7297 6401
51	31.7878 4892	30.1558 8877	28.6461 5774	27.2478 5400	25.9512 2719
52	32.1449 4992	30.4703 0687	28.9230 8072	27.4918 2871	26.1662 3999
53	32.4950 4894	30.7778 0623	29.1932 4948	27.7292 7368	26.3749 9028
54	32.8382 8327	31.0785 3910	29.4568 2876	27.9603 6368	26.5776 6047
55	33.1747 8752	31.3726 5438	29.7139 7928	28.1852 6879	26.7744 2764
56	33.5046 9365	31.6602 9768	29.9648 5784	28.4041 5454	26.9654 6373
57	33.8281 3103	31.9416 1142	30.2096 1740	28.6171 8203	27.1509 3566
58	34.1452 2650	32.2167 3489	30.4484 0722	28.8245 0806	27.3310 0549
59	34.4561 0441	32.4858 0429	30.6813 7290	29.0262 8522	27.5058 3058
60	34.7608 8668	32.7489 5285	30.9086 5649	29.2226 6201	27.6755 6367
61	35.0596 9282	33.0063 1086	31.1303 9657	29.4137 8298	27.8403 5307
62	35.3526 4002	33.2580 0573	31.3467 2836	29.5997 8879	28.0003 4279
63	35.6398 4316	33.5041 6208	31.5577 8377	29.7808 1634	28.1556 7261
64	35.9214 1486	33.7449 0179	31.7636 9148	29.9569 9887	28.3064 7826
65	36.1974 6555	33.9803 4405	31.9645 7705	30.1284 6605	28.4528 9152
66	36.4681 0348	34.2106 0543	32.1605 6298	30.2953 4409	28.5950 4031
67	36.7334 3478	34.4357 9993	32.3517 6876	30.4577 5581	28.7330 4884
68	36.9935 6351	34.6560 3905	32.5383 1099	30.6158 2074	28.8670 3771
69	37.2485 9168	34.8714 3183	32.7203 0340	30.7696 5522	28.9971 2399
70	37.4986 1929	35.0820 8492	32.8978 5698	30.9193 7247	29.1234 2135
71	37.7437 4441	35.2881 0261	33.0710 7998	31.0650 8270	29.2460 4015
72	37.9840 6314	35.4895 8691	33.2400 7803	31.2068 9314	29.3650 8752
73	38.2196 6975	35.6866 3756	33.4049 5417	31.3449 0816	29.4806 6750
74	38.4506 5662	35.8793 5214	33.5658 0895	31.4792 2936	29.5928 8107
75	38.6771 1433	36.0678 2605	33.7227 4044	31.6099 5558	29.7018 2628
76	38.8991 3170	36.2521 5262	33.8758 4433	31.7371 8304	29.8075 9833
77	39.1167 9578	36.4324 2310	34.0252 1398	31.8610 0540	29.9102 8964
78	39.3301 9194	36.6087 2675	34.1709 4047	31.9815 1377	30.0099 8994
79	39.5394 0386	36.7811 5085	34.3131 1265	32.0987 9685	30.1067 8635
80	39.7445 1359	36.9497 8079	34.4518 1722	32.2129 4098	30.2007 6345
81	39.9456 0156	37.1147 0004	34.5871 3875	32.3240 3015	30.2920 0335
82	40.1427 4663	37.2759 9026	34.7191 5976	32.4321 4613	30.3805 8577
83	40.3360 2611	37.4337 3130	34.8479 6074	32.5373 6850	30.4665 8813
84	40.5255 1579	37.5880 0127	34.9736 2023	32.6397 7469	30.5500 8556
85	40.7112 8999	37.7388 7655	35.0962 1486	32.7394 4009	30.6311 5103
86	40.8934 2156	37.8864 3183	35.2158 1938	32.8364 3804	30.7098 5537
87	41.0719 8192	38.0307 4018	35.3325 0671	32.9308 3994	30.7862 6735
88	41.2470 4110	38.1718 7304	35.4463 4801	33.0227 1527	30.8604 5374
89	41.4186 6774	38.3099 0028	35.5574 1269	33.1121 3165	30.9324 7936
90	41.5869 2916	38.4448 9025	35.6657 6848	33.1991 5489	31.0024 0714
91	41.7518 9133	38.5769 0978	35.7714 8144	33.2838 4905	31.0702 9820
92	41.9136 1895	38.7060 2423	35.8746 1604	33.3662 7644	31.1362 1184
93	42.0721 7545	38.8322 9754	35.9752 3516	33.4464 9776	31.2002 0567
94	42.2276 2299	38.9557 9221	36.0734 0016	33.5245 7202	31.2623 3560
95	42.3800 2254	39.0765 6940	36.1691 7089	33.6005 5671	31.3226 5592
96	42.5294 3386	39.1946 8890	36.2626 0574	33.6745 0775	31.3812 1934
97	42.6759 1555	39.3102 0920	36.3537 6170	33.7464 7956	31.4380 7703
98	42.8195 2505	39.4231 8748	36.4426 9434	33.8165 2512	31.4932 7867
99	42.9603 1867	39.5336 7968	36.5294 5790	33.8846 9598	31.5468 7250
100	43.0983 5164	39.6417 4052	36.6141 0526	33.9510 4232	31.5989 0534

PRESENT VALUE OF ANNUITY $[1-(1+i)^{-n}]/i$

Years	Rate i				
n	.035 (3½%)	.04 (4%)	.045 (4½%)	.05 (5%)	.055 (5½%)
1	0.9661 8357	0.9615 3846	0.9569 3780	0.9523 8095	0.9478 6730
2	1.8996 9428	1.8860 9467	1.8726 6775	1.8594 1043	1.8463 1971
3	2.8016 3698	2.7750 9103	2.7489 6435	2.7232 4803	2.6979 3338
4	3.6730 7921	3.6298 9522	3.5875 2570	3.5459 5050	3.5051 5012
5	4.5150 5238	4.4518 2233	4.3899 7674	4.3294 7667	4.2702 8448
6	5.3285 5302	5.2421 3686	5.1578 7248	5.0756 9207	4.9955 3031
7	6.1145 4398	6.0020 5467	5.8927 0094	5.7863 7340	5.6829 6712
8	6.8739 5554	6.7327 4487	6.5958 8607	6.4632 1276	6.3345 6599
9	7.6076 8651	7.4353 3161	7.2687 9050	7.1078 2168	6.9521 9525
10	8.3166 0532	8.1108 9578	7.9127 1818	7.7217 3493	7.5376 2583
11	9.0015 5104	8.7604 7671	8.5289 1692	8.3064 1422	8.0925 3633
12	9.6633 3433	9.3850 7376	9.1185 8078	8.8632 5164	8.6185 1785
13	10.3027 3849	9.9856 4785	9.6828 5242	9.3935 7299	9.1170 7853
14	10.9205 2028	10.5631 2293	10.2228 2528	9.8986 4094	9.5896 4790
15	11.5174 1090	11.1183 8743	10.7395 4573	10.3796 5804	10.0375 8094
16	12.0941 1681	11.6522 9561	11.2340 1505	10.8377 6956	10.4621 6203
17	12.6513 2059	12.1656 6885	11.7071 9143	11.2740 6625	10.8646 0856
18	13.1896 8173	12.6592 9697	12.1599 9180	11.6895 8690	11.2460 7447
19	13.7098 3742	13.1339 3940	12.5932 9359	12.0853 2086	11.6076 5352
20	14.2124 0330	13.5903 2634	13.0079 3645	12.4622 1034	11.9503 8248
21	14.6979 7420	14.0291 5995	13.4047 2388	12.8211 5271	12.2752 4406
22	15.1671 2484	14.4511 1533	13.7844 2476	13.1630 0258	12.5831 6973
23	15.6204 1047	14.8568 4167	14.1477 7489	13.4885 7388	12.8750 4239
24	16.0583 6760	15.2469 6314	14.4954 7837	13.7986 4179	13.1516 9895
25	16.4815 1459	15.6220 7994	14.8282 0896	14.0939 4457	13.4139 3266
26	16.8903 5226	15.9827 6918	15.1466 1145	14.3751 8530	13.6624 9541
27	17.2853 6451	16.3295 8575	15.4513 0282	14.6430 3362	13.8980 9991
28	17.6670 1885	16.6630 6322	15.7428 7351	14.8981 2726	14.1214 2172
29	18.0357 6700	16.9837 1463	16.0218 8853	15.1410 7358	14.3331 0116
30	18.3920 4541	17.2920 3330	16.2888 8854	15.3724 5103	14.5337 4517
31	18.7362 7576	17.5884 9356	16.5443 9095	15.5928 1050	14.7239 2907
32	19.0688 6547	17.8735 5150	16.7888 9086	15.8026 7667	14.9041 9817
33	19.3902 0818	18.1476 4567	17.0228 6207	16.0025 4921	15.0750 6926
34	19.7006 8423	18.4111 9776	17.2467 5796	16.1929 0401	15.2370 3257
35	20.0006 6110	18.6646 1323	17.4610 1240	16.3741 9429	15.3905 5220
36	20.2904 9381	18.9082 8195	17.6660 4058	16.5468 5171	15.5360 6843
37	20.5705 2542	19.1425 7880	17.8622 3979	16.7112 8734	15.6739 9851
38	20.8410 8736	19.3678 6423	18.0499 9023	16.8678 9271	15.8047 3793
39	21.1024 9987	19.5844 8484	18.2296 5572	17.0170 4067	15.9286 6154
40	21.3550 7234	19.7927 7388	18.4015 8442	17.1590 8635	16.0461 2469
41	21.5991 0371	19.9930 5181	18.5661 0949	17.2943 6796	16.1574 6416
42	21.8348 8281	20.1856 2674	18.7235 4975	17.4232 0758	16.2629 9920
43	22.0626 8870	20.3707 9494	18.8742 1029	17.5459 1198	16.3630 3242
44	22.2827 9102	20.5488 4129	19.0183 8305	17.6627 7331	16.4578 5063
45	22.4954 5026	20.7200 3970	19.1563 4742	17.7740 6982	16.5477 2572
46	22.7009 1813	20.8846 5356	19.2883 7074	17.8800 6650	16.6329 1537
47	22.8994 3780	21.0429 3612	19.4147 0884	17.9810 1571	16.7136 6386
48	23.0912 4425	21.1951 3088	19.5356 0654	18.0771 5782	16.7902 0271
49	23.2765 6450	21.3414 7200	19.6512 9813	18.1687 2173	16.8627 5139
50	23.4556 1787	21.4821 8462	19.7620 0778	18.2559 2546	16.9315 1790

PRESENT VALUE OF ANNUITY $[1-(1+i)^{-n}]/i$

Years		Rate i			
n	.06 (6%)	.065 (6½%)	.07 (7%)	.075 (7½%)	.08 (8%)
1	0.9433 9623	0.9389 6714	0.9345 7944	0.9302 3256	0.9259 2593
2	1.8333 9267	1.8206 2642	1.8080 1817	1.7955 6517	1.7832 6475
3	2.6730 1195	2.6484 7551	2.6243 1604	2.6005 2574	2.5770 9699
4	3.4651 0561	3.4257 9860	3.3872 1126	3.3493 2627	3.3121 2684
5	4.2123 6379	4.1556 7944	4.1001 9744	4.0458 8490	3.9927 1004
6	4.9173 2433	4.8410 1356	4.7665 3966	4.6938 4642	4.6228 7966
7	5.5823 8144	5.4845 1977	5.3892 8940	5.2966 0132	5.2063 7006
8	6.2097 9381	6.0887 5096	5.9712 9851	5.8573 0355	5.7466 3894
9	6.8016 9227	6.6561 0419	6.5152 3225	6.3788 8703	6.2468 8791
10	7.3600 8705	7.1888 3022	7.0235 8154	6.8640 8096	6.7100 8140
11	7.8868 7458	7.6890 4246	7.4986 7434	7.3154 2415	7.1389 6426
12	8.3838 4394	8.1587 2532	7.9426 8630	7.7352 7827	7.5360 7802
13	8.8526 8296	8.5997 4208	8.3576 5074	8.1258 4026	7.9037 7594
14	9.2949 8393	9.0138 4233	8.7454 6799	8.4891 5373	8.2442 3698
15	9.7122 4899	9.4026 6885	9.1079 1401	8.8271 1975	8.5594 7869
16	10.1058 9527	9.7677 6418	9.4466 4860	9.1415 0674	8.8513 6916
17	10.4772 5969	10.1105 7670	9.7632 2299	9.4339 5976	9.1216 3811
18	10.8276 0348	10.4324 6638	10.0590 8691	9.7060 0908	9.3718 8714
19	11.1581 1649	10.7347 1022	10.3355 9524	9.9590 7821	9.6035 9920
20	11.4699 2122	11.0185 0725	10.5940 1425	10.1944 9136	9.8181 4741
21	11.7640 7662	11.2849 8333	10.8355 2733	10.4134 8033	10.0168 0316
22	12.0415 8172	11.5351 9562	11.0612 4050	10.6171 9101	10.2007 4366
23	12.3033 7898	11.7701 3673	11.2721 8738	10.8066 8931	10.3710 5895
24	12.5503 5753	11.9907 3871	11.4693 3400	10.9829 6680	10.5287 5828
25	12.7833 5616	12.1978 7673	11.6535 8318	11.1469 4586	10.6747 7619
26	13.0031 6619	12.3923 7251	11.8257 7867	11.2994 8452	10.8099 7795
27	13.2105 3414	12.5749 9766	11.9867 0904	11.4413 8095	10.9351 6477
28	13.4061 6428	12.7464 7668	12.1371 1125	11.5733 7763	11.0510 7849
29	13.5907 2102	12.9074 8984	12.2776 7407	11.6961 6524	11.1584 0601
30	13.7648 3115	13.0586 7591	12.4090 4118	11.8103 8627	11.2577 8334
31	13.9290 8599	13.2006 3465	12.5318 1419	11.9166 3839	11.3497 9939
32	14.0840 4339	13.3339 2925	12.6465 5532	12.0154 7757	11.4349 9944
33	14.2302 2961	13.4590 8850	12.7537 9002	12.1074 2099	11.5138 8837
34	14.3681 4114	13.5766 0892	12.8540 0936	12.1929 4976	11.5869 3367
35	14.4982 4636	13.6869 5673	12.9476 7230	12.2725 1141	11.6545 6822
36	14.6209 8713	13.7905 6970	13.0352 0776	12.3465 2224	11.7171 9279
37	14.7367 8031	13.8878 5887	13.1170 1660	12.4153 6952	11.7751 7851
38	14.8460 1916	13.9792 1021	13.1934 7345	12.4794 1351	11.8288 6899
39	14.9490 7468	14.0649 8611	13.2649 2846	12.5389 8931	11.8785 8240
40	15.0462 9687	14.1455 2687	13.3317 0884	12.5944 0866	11.9246 1333
41	15.1380 1592	14.2211 5199	13.3941 2041	12.6459 6155	11.9672 3457
42	15.2245 4332	14.2921 6149	13.4524 4898	12.6939 1772	12.0066 9867
43	15.3061 7294	14.3588 3708	13.5069 6167	12.7385 2811	12.0432 3951
44	15.3831 8202	14.4214 4327	13.5579 0810	12.7800 2615	12.0770 7362
45	15.4558 3209	14.4802 2842	13.6055 2159	12.8186 2898	12.1084 0150
46	15.5243 6990	14.5354 2575	13.6500 2018	12.8545 3858	12.1374 0880
47	15.5890 2821	14.5872 5422	13.6916 0764	12.8879 4287	12.1642 6741
48	15.6500 2661	14.6359 1946	13.7304 7443	12.9190 1662	12.1891 3649
49	15.7075 7227	14.6816 1451	13.7667 9853	12.9479 2244	12.2121 6341
50	15.7618 6064	14.7245 2067	13.8007 4629	12.9748 1157	12.2334 8464

INTEREST TABLES

ANNUITY WHOSE PRESENT VALUE IS 1

$$\frac{1}{a_{\overline{n}|}} = a_{\overline{n}|}^{-1} = \frac{i}{1 - (1+i)^{-n}} = \frac{i}{1 - v^n} = s_{\overline{n}|}^{-1} + i$$

Years	Rate i				
n	.0025 ($\frac{1}{4}\%$)	.004167 ($\frac{1}{12}\%$)	.005 ($\frac{1}{2}\%$)	.005833 ($\frac{7}{12}\%$)	.0075 ($\frac{3}{4}\%$)
1	1.0025 0000	1.0041 6667	1.0050 0000	1.0058 3333	1.0075 0000
2	0.5018 7578	0.5031 2717	0.5037 5312	0.5043 7924	0.5056 3200
3	.3350 0139	.3361 1496	.3366 7221	.3372 2976	.3383 4579
4	.2515 6445	.2526 0958	.2531 3279	.2536 5644	.2547 0501
5	.2015 0250	.2025 0693	.2030 0997	.2035 1357	.2045 2242
6	.1681 2803	.1691 0564	.1695 9546	.1700 8594	.1710 6891
7	.1442 8928	.1452 4800	.1457 2854	.1462 0986	.1471 7488
8	.1264 1035	.1273 5512	.1278 2886	.1283 0352	.1292 5552
9	.1125 0462	.1134 3876	.1139 0736	.1143 7698	.1153 1929
10	.1013 8015	.1023 0596	.1027 7057	.1032 3632	.1041 7123
11	.0922 7840	.0931 9757	.0936 5903	.0941 2175	.0950 5094
12	.0846 9370	.0856 0748	.0860 6643	.0865 2675	.0874 5148
13	.0782 7595	.0791 8532	.0796 4224	.0801 0064	.0810 2188
14	.0727 7510	.0736 8082	.0741 3609	.0745 9295	.0755 1146
15	.0680 0777	.0689 1045	.0693 6436	.0698 2000	.0707 3639
16	.0638 3642	.0647 3655	.0651 8937	.0656 4401	.0665 5879
17	.0601 5587	.0610 5387	.0615 0579	.0619 5966	.0628 7321
18	.0568 8433	.0577 8053	.0582 3173	.0586 8499	.0595 9766
19	.0539 5722	.0548 5191	.0553 0253	.0557 5532	.0566 6740
20	.0513 2288	.0522 1630	.0526 6645	.0531 1889	.0540 3063
21	.0489 3947	.0498 3183	.0502 8163	.0507 3383	.0516 4543
22	.0467 7278	.0476 6427	.0481 1380	.0485 6585	.0494 7748
23	.0447 9455	.0456 8531	.0461 3465	.0465 8663	.0474 9846
24	.0429 8121	.0438 7139	.0443 2061	.0447 7258	.0456 8474
25	.0413 1298	.0422 0270	.0426 5186	.0431 0388	.0440 1650
26	.0397 7312	.0406 6247	.0411 1163	.0415 6376	.0424 7693
27	.0383 4736	.0392 3645	.0396 8565	.0401 3793	.0410 5176
28	.0370 2347	.0379 1239	.0383 6167	.0388 1415	.0397 2871
29	.0357 9093	.0366 7974	.0371 2914	.0375 8186	.0384 9723
30	.0346 4059	.0355 2936	.0359 7892	.0364 3191	.0373 4816
31	.0335 6449	.0344 5330	.0349 0304	.0353 5633	.0362 7352
32	.0325 5569	.0334 4458	.0338 9453	.0343 4815	.0352 6634
33	.0316 0806	.0324 9708	.0329 4727	.0334 0124	.0343 2048
34	.0307 1620	.0316 0540	.0320 5586	.0325 1020	.0334 3053
35	.0298 7533	.0307 6476	.0312 1550	.0316 7024	.0325 9170
36	.0290 8121	.0299 7090	.0304 2194	.0308 7710	.0317 9973
37	.0283 3004	.0292 2003	.0296 7139	.0301 2698	.0310 5082
38	.0276 1843	.0285 0875	.0289 6045	.0294 1649	.0303 4157
39	.0269 4335	.0278 3402	.0282 8607	.0287 4258	.0296 6893
40	.0263 0204	.0271 9310	.0276 4552	.0281 0251	.0290 3016
41	.0256 9204	.0265 8352	.0270 3631	.0274 9379	.0284 2276
42	.0251 1112	.0260 0303	.0264 5622	.0269 1420	.0278 4452
43	.0245 5724	.0254 4961	.0259 0320	.0263 6170	.0272 9338
44	.0240 2855	.0249 2141	.0253 7541	.0258 3443	.0267 6751
45	.0235 2339	.0244 1675	.0248 7117	.0253 3073	.0262 6521
46	.0230 4022	.0239 3409	.0243 8894	.0248 4905	.0257 8495
47	.0225 7762	.0234 7204	.0239 2733	.0243 8798	.0253 2532
48	.0221 3433	.0230 2929	.0234 8503	.0239 4624	.0248 8504
49	.0217 0915	.0226 0468	.0230 6087	.0235 2265	.0244 6292
50	.0213 0099	.0221 9711	.0226 5376	.0231 1612	.0240 5787

INTEREST TABLES

ANNUITY WHOSE PRESENT VALUE IS 1

$$a_{\overline{n}|}^{-1} = i/(1 - v^n) = s_{\overline{n}|}^{-1} + i \text{ (Continued)}$$

Years	Rate i				
n	.0025 ($\frac{1}{4}$%)	.004167 ($\frac{5}{12}$%)	.005 ($\frac{1}{2}$%)	.005833 ($\frac{7}{12}$%)	.0075 ($\frac{3}{4}$%)
50	.0213 0099	.0221 9711	.0226 5376	.0231 1612	.0240 5787
51	.0209 0886	.0218 0557	.0222 6269	.0227 2563	.0236 6888
52	.0205 3184	.0214 2916	.0218 8675	.0223 5027	.0232 9503
53	.0201 6906	.0210 6700	.0215 2507	.0219 8919	.0229 3546
54	.0198 1974	.0207 1830	.0211 7686	.0216 4157	.0225 8938
55	.0194 8314	.0203 8234	.0208 4139	.0213 0671	.0222 5605
56	.0191 5858	.0200 5843	.0205 1797	.0209 8390	.0219 3478
57	.0188 4542	.0197 4593	.0202 0598	.0206 7251	.0216 2496
58	.0185 4308	.0194 4426	.0199 0481	.0203 7196	.0213 2597
59	.0182 5101	.0191 5287	.0196 1392	.0200 8170	.0210 3727
60	.0179 6869	.0188 7123	.0193 3280	.0198 0120	.0207 5836
61	.0176 9564	.0185 9888	.0190 6096	.0195 2999	.0204 8873
62	.0174 3142	.0183 3536	.0187 9796	.0192 6762	.0202 2795
63	.0171 7561	.0180 8025	.0185 4337	.0190 1366	.0199 7560
64	.0169 2780	.0178 3315	.0182 9681	.0187 6773	.0197 3127
65	.0166 8764	.0175 9371	.0180 5789	.0185 2946	.0194 9460
66	.0164 5476	.0173 6156	.0178 2627	.0182 9848	.0192 6524
67	.0162 2886	.0171 3639	.0176 0163	.0180 7449	.0190 4286
68	.0160 0961	.0169 1788	.0173 8366	.0178 5716	.0188 2716
69	.0157 9674	.0167 0574	.0171 7206	.0176 4622	.0186 1785
70	.0155 8996	.0164 9971	.0169 6657	.0174 4138	.0184 1464
71	.0153 8902	.0162 9952	.0167 6693	.0172 4239	.0182 1728
72	.0151 9368	.0161 0493	.0165 7289	.0170 4901	.0180 2554
73	.0150 0370	.0159 1572	.0163 8422	.0168 6100	.0178 3917
74	.0148 1887	.0157 3165	.0162 0070	.0166 7814	.0176 5796
75	.0146 3898	.0155 5253	.0160 2214	.0165 0024	.0174 8170
76	.0144 6385	.0153 7816	.0158 4832	.0163 2709	.0173 1020
77	.0142 9327	.0152 0836	.0156 7908	.0161 5851	.0171 4328
78	.0141 2708	.0150 4295	.0155 1423	.0159 9432	.0169 8074
79	.0139 6511	.0148 8177	.0153 5360	.0158 3436	.0168 2244
80	.0138 0721	.0147 2464	.0151 9704	.0156 7847	.0166 6821
81	.0136 5321	.0145 7144	.0150 4439	.0155 2650	.0165 1790
82	.0135 0298	.0144 2200	.0148 9552	.0153 7830	.0163 7136
83	.0133 5639	.0142 7620	.0147 5028	.0152 3373	.0162 2847
84	.0132 1330	.0141 3391	.0146 0855	.0150 9268	.0160 8908
85	.0130 7359	.0139 9500	.0144 7021	.0149 5501	.0159 5308
86	.0129 3714	.0138 5935	.0143 3513	.0148 2060	.0158 2034
87	.0128 0384	.0137 2685	.0142 0320	.0146 8935	.0156 9076
88	.0126 7357	.0135 9740	.0140 7431	.0145 6115	.0155 6423
89	.0125 4625	.0134 7088	.0139 4837	.0144 3588	.0154 4064
90	.0124 2177	.0133 4721	.0138 2527	.0143 1347	.0153 1989
91	.0123 0004	.0132 2629	.0137 0493	.0141 9380	.0152 0190
92	.0121 8096	.0131 0803	.0135 8724	.0140 7679	.0150 8657
93	.0120 6446	.0129 9234	.0134 7213	.0139 6236	.0149 7382
94	.0119 5044	.0128 7915	.0133 5950	.0138 5042	.0148 6356
95	.0118 3884	.0127 6836	.0132 4930	.0137 4090	.0147 5571
96	.0117 2957	.0126 5992	.0131 4143	.0136 3372	.0146 5020
97	.0116 2257	.0125 5374	.0130 3583	.0135 2880	.0145 4696
98	.0115 1776	.0124 4976	.0129 3242	.0134 2608	.0144 4592
99	.0114 1508	.0123 4790	.0128 3115	.0133 2549	.0143 4701
100	.0113 1446	.0122 4811	.0127 3194	.0132 2696	.0142 5017

INTEREST TABLES

ANNUITY WHOSE PRESENT VALUE IS 1

$$a_{\overline{n}|}^{-1} = i/(1 - v^n) = s_{\overline{n}|}^{-1} + i \text{ (Continued)}$$

Years	Rate i				
n	.01 (1%)	.01125 (1⅛%)	.0125 (1¼%)	.015 (1½%)	.0175 (1¾%)
1	1.0100 0000	1.0112 5000	1.0125 0000	1.0150 0000	1.0175 0000
2	0.5075 1244	0.5084 5323	0.5093 9441	0.5112 7792	0.5131 6295
3	.3400 2211	.3408 6130	.3417 0117	.3433 8296	.3450 6746
4	.2562 8109	.2570 7058	.2578 6102	.2594 4479	.2610 3237
5	.2060 3980	.2068 0034	.2075 6211	.2090 8932	.2106 2142
6	.1725 4837	.1732 9034	.1740 3381	.1755 2521	.1770 2256
7	.1486 2828	.1493 5762	.1500 8872	.1515 5616	.1530 3059
8	.1306 9029	.1314 1071	.1321 3314	.1335 8402	.1350 4292
9	.1167 4036	.1174 5432	.1181 7055	.1196 0982	.1210 5813
10	.1055 8208	.1062 9131	.1070 0307	.1084 3418	.1098 7534
11	.0964 5408	.0971 5984	.0978 6839	.0992 9384	.1007 3038
12	.0888 4879	.0895 5203	.0902 5831	.0916 7999	.0931 1377
13	.0824 1482	.0831 1626	.0838 2100	.0852 4036	.0866 7283
14	.0769 0117	.0776 0138	.0783 0515	.0797 2332	.0811 5562
15	.0721 2378	.0728 2321	.0735 2646	.0749 4436	.0763 7739
16	.0679 4460	.0686 4363	.0693 4672	.0707 6508	.0721 9958
17	.0642 5806	.0649 5698	.0656 6023	.0670 7966	.0685 1623
18	.0609 8205	.0616 8113	.0623 8479	.0638 0578	.0652 4492
19	.0580 5175	.0587 5120	.0594 5548	.0608 7847	.0623 2061
20	.0554 1531	.0561 1531	.0568 2039	.0582 4574	.0596 9122
21	.0530 3075	.0537 3145	.0544 3749	.0558 6550	.0573 1464
22	.0508 6372	.0515 6525	.0522 7238	.0537 0332	.0551 5638
23	.0488 8584	.0495 8833	.0502 9666	.0517 3075	.0531 8796
24	.0470 7347	.0477 7701	.0484 8665	.0499 2410	.0513 8565
25	.0454 0675	.0461 1144	.0468 2247	.0482 6345	.0497 2952
26	.0438 6888	.0445 7479	.0452 8729	.0467 3196	.0482 0269
27	.0424 4553	.0431 5273	.0438 6677	.0453 1527	.0467 9079
28	.0411 2444	.0418 3299	.0425 4863	.0440 0108	.0454 8151
29	.0398 9502	.0406 0498	.0413 2228	.0427 7878	.0442 6424
30	.0387 4811	.0394 5953	.0401 7854	.0416 3919	.0431 2975
31	.0376 7573	.0383 8866	.0391 0942	.0405 7430	.0420 7005
32	.0366 7089	.0373 8535	.0381 0791	.0395 7710	.0410 7812
33	.0357 2744	.0364 4349	.0371 6786	.0386 4144	.0401 4779
34	.0348 3997	.0355 5763	.0362 8387	.0377 6189	.0392 7363
35	.0340 0368	.0347 2299	.0354 5111	.0369 3363	.0384 5082
36	.0332 1431	.0339 3529	.0346 6533	.0361 5240	.0376 7507
37	.0324 6805	.0331 9072	.0339 2270	.0354 1437	.0369 4257
38	.0317 6150	.0324 8589	.0332 1983	.0347 1613	.0362 4990
39	.0310 9160	.0318 1773	.0325 5365	.0340 5463	.0355 9399
40	.0304 5560	.0311 8349	.0319 2141	.0334 2710	.0349 7209
41	.0298 5102	.0305 8069	.0313 2063	.0328 3106	.0343 8170
42	.0292 7563	.0300 0709	.0307 4906	.0322 6426	.0338 2057
43	.0287 2737	.0294 6064	.0302 0466	.0317 2465	.0332 8666
44	.0282 0441	.0289 3949	.0296 8557	.0312 1038	.0327 7810
45	.0277 0505	.0284 4197	.0291 9012	.0307 1976	.0322 9321
46	.0272 2775	.0279 6652	.0287 1675	.0302 5125	.0318 3043
47	.0267 7111	.0275 1173	.0282 6406	.0298 0342	.0313 8836
48	.0263 3384	.0270 7632	.0278 3075	.0293 7500	.0309 6569
49	.0259 1474	.0266 5910	.0274 1563	.0289 6478	.0305 6124
50	.0255 1273	.0262 5898	.0270 1763	.0285 7168	.0301 7391

ANNUITY WHOSE PRESENT VALUE IS 1
$$a_{\overline{n}|}^{-1} = i/(1 - v^n) = s_{\overline{n}|}^{-1} + i \text{ (Continued)}$$

Years	Rate i				
n	.01 (1%)	.01125 (1⅛%)	.0125 (1¼%)	.015 (1½%)	.0175 (1¾%)
50	.0255 1273	.0262 5898	.0270 1763	.0285 7168	.0301 7391
51	.0251 2680	.0258 7494	.0266 3571	.0281 9469	.0298 0269
52	.0247 5603	.0255 0606	.0262 6897	.0278 3287	.0294 4665
53	.0243 9956	.0251 5149	.0259 1653	.0274 8537	.0291 0492
54	.0240 5658	.0248 1043	.0255 7760	.0271 5138	.0287 7672
55	.0237 2637	.0244 8213	.0252 5145	.0268 3018	.0284 6129
56	.0234 0824	.0241 6592	.0249 3739	.0265 2106	.0281 5795
57	.0231 0156	.0238 6116	.0246 3478	.0262 2341	.0278 6606
58	.0228 0573	.0235 6726	.0243 4303	.0259 3661	.0275 8503
59	.0225 2020	.0232 8366	.0240 6158	.0256 6012	.0273 1430
60	.0222 4445	.0230 0985	.0237 8993	.0253 9343	.0270 5336
61	.0219 7800	.0227 4534	.0235 2758	.0251 3604	.0268 0172
62	.0217 2041	.0224 8969	.0232 7410	.0248 8751	.0265 5892
63	.0214 7125	.0222 4247	.0230 2904	.0246 4741	.0263 2455
64	.0212 3013	.0220 0329	.0227 9203	.0244 1534	.0260 9821
65	.0209 9667	.0217 7178	.0225 6268	.0241 9094	.0258 7952
66	.0207 7052	.0215 4758	.0223 4065	.0239 7386	.0256 6813
67	.0205 5136	.0213 3037	.0221 2560	.0237 6376	.0254 6372
68	.0203 3889	.0211 1985	.0219 1724	.0235 6033	.0252 6597
69	.0201 3280	.0209 1571	.0217 1527	.0233 6329	.0250 7459
70	.0199 3282	.0207 1769	.0215 1941	.0231 7235	.0248 8930
71	.0197 3870	.0205 2552	.0213 2941	.0229 8727	.0247 0985
72	.0195 5019	.0203 3896	.0211 4501	.0228 0779	.0245 3600
73	.0193 6706	.0201 5779	.0209 6600	.0226 3368	.0243 6750
74	.0191 8910	.0199 8177	.0207 9215	.0224 6473	.0242 0413
75	.0190 1609	.0198 1072	.0206 2325	.0223 0072	.0240 4570
76	.0188 4784	.0196 4442	.0204 5910	.0221 4146	.0238 9200
77	.0186 8416	.0194 8269	.0202 9953	.0219 8676	.0237 4285
78	.0185 2488	.0193 2536	.0201 4436	.0218 3645	.0235 9806
79	.0183 6983	.0191 7226	.0199 9341	.0216 9036	.0234 5748
80	.0182 1885	.0190 2323	.0198 4652	.0215 4832	.0233 2093
81	.0180 7179	.0188 7812	.0197 0356	.0214 1019	.0231 8828
82	.0179 2851	.0187 3678	.0195 6437	.0212 7583	.0230 5936
83	.0177 8887	.0185 9908	.0194 2881	.0211 4509	.0229 3406
84	.0176 5273	.0184 6489	.0192 9675	.0210 1784	.0228 1223
85	.0175 1998	.0183 3409	.0191 6808	.0208 9396	.0226 9375
86	.0173 9050	.0182 0654	.0190 4267	.0207 7333	.0225 7850
87	.0172 6418	.0180 8215	.0139 2041	.0206 5584	.0224 6636
88	.0171 4089	.0179 6081	.0188 0119	.0205 4138	.0223 5724
89	.0170 2056	.0178 4240	.0186 8491	.0204 2984	.0222 5102
90	.0169 0306	.0177 2684	.0185 7146	.0203 2113	.0221 4760
91	.0167 8832	.0176 1403	.0184 6076	.0202 1516	.0220 4690
92	.0166 7624	.0175 0387	.0183 5272	.0201 1182	.0219 4882
93	.0165 6673	.0173 9629	.0182 4724	.0200 1104	.0218 5327
94	.0164 5971	.0172 9119	.0181 4425	.0199 1273	.0217 6017
95	.0163 5511	.0171 8851	.0180 4366	.0198 1681	.0216 6944
96	.0162 5284	.0170 8816	.0179 4541	.0197 2321	.0215 8101
97	.0161 5284	.0169 9007	.0178 4941	.0196 3186	.0214 9480
98	.0160 5503	.0168 9418	.0177 5560	.0195 4268	.0214 1074
99	.0159 5936	.0168 0041	.0176 6391	.0194 5560	.0213 2876
100	.0158 6574	.0167 0870	.0175 7428	.0193 7057	.0212 4880

ANNUITY WHOSE PRESENT VALUE IS 1

$$a_{\overline{n}|}^{-1} = i/(1 - v^n) = s_{\overline{n}|}^{-1} + i \text{ (Continued)}$$

Years	Rate i				
n	.02 (2%)	.0225 (2¼%)	.025 (2½)%	.0275 (2¾%)	.03 (3%)
1	1.0200 0000	1.0225 0000	1.0250 0000	1.0275 0000	1.0300 0000
2	0.5150 4950	0.5169 3758	0.5188 2716	0.5207 1825	0.5226 1084
3	.3467 5467	.3484 4458	.3501 3717	.3518 3243	.3535 3036
4	.2626 2375	.2642 1893	.2658 1788	.2674 2059	.2690 2705
5	.2121 5839	.2137 0021	.2152 4686	.2167 9832	.2183 5457
6	.1785 2581	.1800 3496	.1815 4997	.1830 7083	.1845 9750
7	.1545 1196	.1560 0025	.1574 9543	.1589 9747	.1605 0635
8	.1365 0980	.1379 8462	.1394 6735	.1409 5795	.1424 5639
9	.1225 1544	.1239 8170	.1254 5689	.1269 4095	.1284 3386
10	.1113 2653	.1127 8768	.1142 5876	.1157 3972	.1172 3051
11	.1021 7794	.1036 3649	.1051 0596	.1065 8629	.1080 7745
12	.0945 5960	.0960 1740	.0974 8713	.0989 6871	.1004 6209
13	.0881 1835	.0895 7686	.0910 4827	.0925 3252	.0940 2954
14	.0826 0197	.0840 6230	.0855 3652	.0870 2457	.0885 2634
15	.0778 2547	.0792 8852	.0807 6646	.0822 5917	.0837 6658
16	.0736 5013	.0751 1663	.0765 9899	.0780 9710	.0796 1085
17	.0699 6984	.0714 4039	.0729 2777	.0744 3186	.0759 5253
18	.0667 0210	.0681 7720	.0696 7008	.0711 8063	.0727 0870
19	.0637 8177	.0652 6182	.0667 6062	.0682 7802	.0698 1388
20	.0611 5672	.0626 4207	.0641 4713	.0656 7173	.0672 1571
21	.0587 8477	.0602 7572	.0617 8733	.0633 1941	.0648 7178
22	.0566 3140	.0581 2821	.0596 4661	.0611 8640	.0627 4739
23	.0546 6810	.0561 7097	.0576 9638	.0592 4410	.0608 1390
24	.0528 7110	.0543 8023	.0559 1282	.0574 6863	.0590 4742
25	.0512 2044	.0527 3599	.0542 7592	.0558 3997	.0574 2787
26	.0496 9923	.0512 2134	.0527 6875	.0543 4116	.0559 3829
27	.0482 9309	.0498 2188	.0513 7687	.0529 5776	.0545 6421
28	.0469 8967	.0485 2525	.0500 8793	.0516 7738	.0532 9323
29	.0457 7836	.0473 2081	.0488 9127	.0504 8935	.0521 1467
30	.0446 4992	.0461 9934	.0477 7764	.0493 8442	.0510 1926
31	.0435 9635	.0451 5280	.0467 3900	.0483 5453	.0499 9893
32	.0426 1061	.0441 7415	.0457 6831	.0473 9263	.0490 4662
33	.0416 8653	.0432 5722	.0448 5938	.0464 9253	.0481 5612
34	.0408 1867	.0423 9655	.0440 0675	.0456 4875	.0473 2196
35	.0400 0221	.0415 8731	.0432 0558	.0448 5645	.0465 3929
36	.0392 3285	.0408 2522	.0424 5158	.0441 1132	.0458 0379
37	.0385 0678	.0401 0643	.0417 4090	.0434 0953	.0451 1162
38	.0378 2057	.0394 2753	.0410 7012	.0427 4764	.0444 5934
39	.0371 7114	.0387 8543	.0404 3615	.0421 2256	.0438 4385
40	.0365 5575	.0381 7738	.0398 3623	.0415 3151	.0432 6238
41	.0359 7188	.0376 0087	.0392 6786	.0409 7200	.0427 1241
42	.0354 1729	.0370 5364	.0387 2876	.0404 4175	.0421 9167
43	.0348 8993	.0365 3364	.0382 1688	.0399 3871	.0416 9811
44	.0343 8794	.0360 3901	.0377 3037	.0394 6100	.0412 2985
45	.0339 0962	.0355 6805	.0372 6751	.0390 0693	.0407 8518
46	.0334 5342	.0351 1921	.0368 2676	.0385 7493	.0403 6254
47	.0330 1792	.0346 9107	.0364 0669	.0381 6358	.0399 6051
48	.0326 0184	.0342 8233	.0360 0599	.0377 7158	.0395 7777
49	.0322 0396	.0338 9179	.0356 2348	.0373 9773	.0392 1314
50	.0318 2321	.0335 1836	.0352 5806	.0370 4092	.0388 6549

ANNUITY WHOSE PRESENT VALUE IS 1

$$a_{\overline{n}|}^{-1} = i/(1 - v^n) = s_{\overline{n}|}^{-1} + i \text{ (Continued)}$$

Years	Rate i				
n	.02 (2%)	.0225 (2¼%)	.025 (2½%)	.0275 (2¾%)	.03 (3%)
50	.0318 2321	.0335 1836	.0352 5806	.0370 4092	.0388 6549
51	.0314 5856	.0331 6102	.0349 0870	.0367 0014	.0385 3382
52	.0311 0909	.0328 1884	.0345 7446	.0363 7444	.0382 1718
53	.0307 7392	.0324 9094	.0342 5449	.0360 6297	.0379 1471
54	.0304 5226	.0321 7654	.0339 4799	.0357 6491	.0376 2558
55	.0301 4337	.0318 7489	.0336 5419	.0354 7953	.0373 4907
56	.0298 4656	.0315 8530	.0333 7243	.0352 0612	.0370 8447
57	.0295 6120	.0313 0712	.0331 0204	.0349 4404	.0368 3114
58	.0292 8667	.0310 3977	.0328 4244	.0346 9270	.0365 8848
59	.0290 2243	.0307 8268	.0325 9307	.0344 5153	.0363 5593
60	.0287 6797	.0305 3533	.0323 5340	.0342 2002	.0361 3296
61	.0285 2278	.0302 9724	.0321 2294	.0339 9767	.0359 1908
62	.0282 8643	.0300 6795	.0319 0126	.0337 8402	.0357 1385
63	.0280 5848	.0298 4704	.0316 8790	.0335 7866	.0355 1682
64	.0278 3855	.0296 3411	.0314 8249	.0333 8118	.0353 2760
65	.0276 2624	.0294 2878	.0312 8463	.0331 9120	.0351 4581
66	.0274 2122	.0292 3070	.0310 9398	.0330 0837	.0349 7110
67	.0272 2316	.0290 3955	.0309 1021	.0328 3236	.0348 0313
68	.0270 3173	.0288 5500	.0307 3300	.0326 6285	.0346 4159
69	.0268 4665	.0286 7677	.0305 6206	.0324 9955	.0344 8618
70	.0266 6765	.0285 0458	.0303 9712	.0323 4218	.0343 3663
71	.0264 9446	.0283 3816	.0302 3790	.0321 9048	.0341 9266
72	.0263 2683	.0281 7728	.0300 8417	.0320 4420	.0340 5404
73	.0261 6454	.0280 2169	.0299 3568	.0319 0311	.0339 2053
74	.0260 0736	.0278 7118	.0297 9222	.0317 6698	.0337 9191
75	.0258 5508	.0277 2554	.0296 5358	.0316 3560	.0336 6796
76	.0257 0751	.0275 8457	.0295 1956	.0315 0878	.0335 4849
77	.0255 6447	.0274 4808	.0293 8997	.0313 8633	.0334 3331
78	.0254 2576	.0273 1589	.0292 6463	.0312 6806	.0333 2224
79	.0252 9123	.0271 8784	.0291 4338	.0311 5382	.0332 1510
80	.0251 6071	.0270 6376	.0290 2605	.0310 4342	.0331 1175
81	.0250 3405	.0269 4350	.0289 1248	.0309 3674	.0330 1201
82	.0249 1110	.0268 2692	.0288 0254	.0308 3361	.0329 1576
83	.0247 9173	.0267 1387	.0286 9608	.0307 3389	.0328 2284
84	.0246 7581	.0266 0423	.0285 9298	.0306 3747	.0327 3313
85	.0245 6321	.0264 9787	.0284 9310	.0305 4420	.0326 4650
86	.0244 5381	.0263 9467	.0283 9633	.0304 5397	.0325 6284
87	.0243 4750	.0262 9452	.0283 0255	.0303 6667	.0324 8202
88	.0242 4416	.0261 9730	.0282 1165	.0302 8219	.0324 0393
89	.0241 4370	.0261 0291	.0281 2353	.0302 0041	.0323 2848
90	.0240 4602	.0260 1126	.0280 3809	.0301 2125	.0322 5556
91	.0239 5101	.0259 2224	.0279 5523	.0300 4460	.0321 8508
92	.0238 5859	.0258 3577	.0278 7486	.0299 7038	.0321 1694
93	.0237 6868	.0257 5176	.0277 9690	.0298 9850	.0320 5107
94	.0236 8118	.0256 7012	.0277 2126	.0298 2887	.0319 8737
95	.0235 9602	.0255 9078	.0276 4786	.0297 6141	.0319 2577
96	.0235 1313	.0255 1366	.0275 7662	.0296 9605	.0318 6619
97	.0234 3242	.0254 3868	.0275 0747	.0296 3272	.0318 0856
98	.0233 5383	.0253 6578	.0274 4034	.0295 7134	.0317 5281
99	.0232 7729	.0252 9489	.0273 7517	.0295 1185	.0316 9886
100	.0232 0274	.0252 2594	.0273 1188	.0294 5418	.0316 4667

ANNUITY WHOSE PRESENT VALUE IS 1

$$a_{\overline{n}|}^{-1} = i/(1 - v^n) = s_{\overline{n}|}^{-1} + i \text{ (Continued)}$$

Years	Rate i				
n	.035 (3½%)	.04 (4%)	.045 (4½%)	.05 (5%)	.055 (5½%)
1	1.0350 0000	1.0400 0000	1.0450 0000	1.0500 0000	1.0550 0000
2	0.5264 0049	0.5301 9608	0.5339 9756	0.5378 0488	0.5416 1800
3	.3569 3418	.3603 4854	.3637 7336	.3672 0856	.3706 5407
4	.2722 5114	.2754 9005	.2787 4365	.2820 1183	.2852 9449
5	.2214 8137	.2246 2711	.2277 9164	.2309 7480	.2341 7644
6	.1876 6821	.1907 6190	.1938 7839	.1970 1747	.2001 7895
7	.1635 4449	.1666 0961	.1697 0147	.1728 1982	.1759 6442
8	.1454 7665	.1485 2783	.1516 0965	.1547 2181	.1578 6401
9	.1314 4601	.1344 9299	.1375 7447	.1406 9008	.1438 3946
10	.1202 4137	.1232 9094	.1263 7882	.1295 0457	.1326 6777
11	.1110 9197	.1141 4904	.1172 4818	.1203 8889	.1235 7065
12	.1034 8395	.1065 5217	.1096 6619	.1128 2541	.1160 2923
13	.0970 6157	.1001 4373	.1032 7535	.1064 5577	.1096 8426
14	.0915 7073	.0946 6897	.0978 2032	.1010 2397	.1042 7912
15	.0868 2507	.0899 4110	.0931 1381	.0963 4229	.0996 2560
16	.0826 8483	.0858 2000	.0890 1537	.0922 6991	.0955 8254
17	.0790 4313	.0821 9852	.0854 1758	.0886 9914	.0920 4197
18	.0758 1684	.0789 9333	.0822 3690	.0855 4622	.0889 1992
19	.0729 4033	.0761 3862	.0794 0734	.0827 4501	.0861 5006
20	.0703 6108	.0735 8175	.0768 7614	.0802 4259	.0836 7933
21	.0680 3659	.0712 8011	.0746 0057	.0779 9611	.0814 6478
22	.0659 3207	.0691 9881	.0725 4565	.0759 7051	.0794 7123
23	.0640 1880	.0673 0906	.0706 8249	.0741 3682	.0776 6965
24	.0622 7283	.0655 8683	.0689 8703	.0724 7090	.0760 3580
25	.0606 7404	.0640 1196	.0674 3903	.0709 5246	.0745 4935
26	.0592 0540	.0625 6738	.0660 2137	.0695 6432	.0731 9307
27	.0578 5241	.0612 3854	.0647 1946	.0682 9186	.0719 5228
28	.0566 0265	.0600 1298	.0635 2081	.0671 2253	.0708 1440
29	.0554 4538	.0588 7993	.0624 1461	.0660 4551	.0697 6857
30	.0543 7133	.0578 3010	.0613 9154	.0650 5144	.0688 0539
31	.0533 7240	.0568 5535	.0604 4345	.0641 3212	.0679 1665
32	.0524 4150	.0559 4859	.0595 6320	.0632 8042	.0670 9519
33	.0515 7242	.0551 0357	.0587 4453	.0624 9004	.0663 3469
34	.0507 5966	.0543 1477	.0579 8191	.0617 5545	.0656 2958
35	.0499 9835	.0535 7732	.0572 7045	.0610 7171	.0649 7493
36	.0492 8416	.0528 8688	.0566 0578	.0604 3446	.0643 6635
37	.0486 1325	.0522 3957	.0559 8402	.0598 3979	.0637 9993
38	.0479 8214	.0516 3192	.0554 0169	.0592 8423	.0632 7217
39	.0473 8775	.0510 6083	.0548 5567	.0587 6462	.0627 7991
40	.0468 2728	.0505 2349	.0543 4315	.0582 7816	.0623 2034
41	.0462 9822	.0500 1738	.0538 6158	.0578 2229	.0618 9090
42	.0457 9828	.0495 4020	.0534 0868	.0573 9471	.0614 8927
43	.0453 2539	.0490 8989	.0529 8235	.0569 9333	.0611 1337
44	.0448 7768	.0486 6454	.0525 8071	.0566 1625	.0607 6128
45	.0444 5343	.0482 6246	.0522 0202	.0562 6173	.0604 3127
46	.0440 5108	.0478 8205	.0518 4471	.0559 2820	.0601 2175
47	.0436 6919	.0475 2189	.0515 0734	.0556 1421	.0598 3129
48	.0433 0646	.0471 8065	.0511 8858	.0553 1843	.0595 5854
49	.0429 6167	.0468 5712	.0508 8722	.0550 3965	.0593 0230
50	.0426 3371	.0465 5020	.0506 0215	.0547 7674	.0590 6145

ANNUITY WHOSE PRESENT VALUE IS 1

$$a_{\overline{n}|}^{-1} = i/(1 - v^n) = s_{\overline{n}|}^{-1} + i \text{ (Continued)}$$

Years			Rate i		
n	.06 (6%)	.065 (6½%)	.07 (7%)	.075 (7½%)	.08 (8%)
1	1.0600 0000	1.0650 0000	1.0700 0000	1.0750 0000	1.0800 0000
2	0.5454 3689	0.5492 6150	0.5530 9179	0.5569 2771	0.5607 6923
3	.3741 0981	.3775 7570	.3810 5167	.3845 3763	.3880 3351
4	.2885 9149	.2919 0274	.2952 2812	.2985 6751	.3019 2080
5	.2373 9640	.2406 3454	.2438 9069	.2471 6472	.2504 5645
6	.2033 6263	.2065 6831	.2097 9580	.2130 4489	.2163 1539
7	.1791 3502	.1823 3137	.1855 5322	.1888 0032	.1920 7240
8	.1610 3594	.1642 3730	.1674 6776	.1707 2702	.1740 1476
9	.1470 2224	.1502 3803	.1534 8647	.1567 6716	.1600 7971
10	.1358 6796	.1391 0469	.1423 7750	.1456 8593	.1490 2949
11	.1267 9294	.1300 5521	.1333 5690	.1366 9747	.1400 7634
12	.1192 7703	.1225 6817	.1259 0199	.1292 7783	.1326 9502
13	.1129 6011	.1162 8256	.1196 5085	.1230 6420	.1265 2181
14	.1075 8491	.1109 4048	.1143 4494	.1177 9737	.1212 9685
15	.1029 6276	.1063 5278	.1097 9462	.1132 8724	.1168 2954
16	.0989 5214	.1023 7757	.1058 5765	.1093 9116	.1129 7687
17	.0954 4480	.0989 0633	.1024 2519	.1060 0003	.1096 2943
18	.0923 5654	.0958 5461	.0994 1260	.1030 2896	.1067 0210
19	.0896 2086	.0931 5575	.0967 5301	.1004 1090	.1041 2763
20	.0871 8456	.0907 5640	.0943 9293	.0980 9219	.1018 5221
21	.0850 0455	.0886 1333	.0922 8900	.0960 2937	.0998 3225
22	.0830 4557	.0866 9120	.0904 0577	.0941 8687	.0980 3207
23	.0812 7848	.0849 6078	.0887 1393	.0925 3528	.0964 2217
24	.0796 7900	.0833 9770	.0871 8902	.0910 5008	.0949 7796
25	.0782 2672	.0819 8148	.0858 1052	.0897 1067	.0936 7878
26	.0769 0435	.0806 9480	.0845 6103	.0884 9961	.0925 0713
27	.0756 9717	.0795 2288	.0834 2573	.0874 0204	.0914 4810
28	.0745 9255	.0784 5305	.0823 9193	.0864 0520	.0904 8891
29	.0735 7961	.0774 7440	.0814 4865	.0854 9811	.0896 1854
30	.0726 4891	.0765 7744	.0805 8640	.0846 7124	.0888 2743
31	.0717 9222	.0757 5393	.0797 9691	.0839 1628	.0881 0728
32	.0710 0234	.0749 9665	.0790 7292	.0832 2599	.0874 5081
33	.0702 7293	.0742 9924	.0784 0807	.0825 9397	.0868 5163
34	.0695 9843	.0736 5610	.0777 9674	.0820 1461	.0863 0411
35	.0689 7386	.0730 6226	.0772 3396	.0814 8291	.0858 0326
36	.0683 9483	.0725 1332	.0767 1531	.0809 9447	.0853 4467
37	.0678 5743	.0720 0534	.0762 3685	.0805 4533	.0849 2440
38	.0673 5812	.0715 3480	.0757 9505	.0801 3197	.0845 3894
39	.0668 9377	.0710 9854	.0753 8676	.0797 5124	.0841 8513
40	.0664 6154	.0706 9373	.0750 0914	.0794 0031	.0838 6016
41	.0660 5886	.0703 1779	.0746 5962	.0790 7663	.0835 6149
42	.0656 8342	.0699 6842	.0743 3591	.0787 7789	.0832 8684
43	.0653 3312	.0696 4352	.0740 3590	.0785 0201	.0830 3414
44	.0650 0606	.0693 4119	.0737 5769	.0782 4710	.0828 0152
45	.0647 0050	.0690 5968	.0734 9957	.0780 1146	.0825 8728
46	.0644 1485	.0687 9743	.0732 5996	.0777 9354	.0823 8991
47	.0641 4768	.0685 5300	.0730 3744	.0775 9190	.0822 0799
48	.0638 9765	.0683 2505	.0728 3070	.0774 0527	.0820 4027
49	.0636 6356	.0681 1240	.0726 3853	.0772 3247	.0818 8557
50	.0634 4429	.0679 1393	.0724 5985	.0770 7241	.0817 4286

COMPOUND AMOUNT OF 1 FOR FRACTIONAL PERIODS, $(1+i)^{\frac{1}{p}}$

p	$i = \frac{1}{4}\%$	$\frac{5}{12}$	$\frac{1}{2}$	$\frac{7}{12}$	$\frac{3}{4}$
2	1.0012 492	1.0020 812	1.0024 969	1.0029 124	1.0037 430
3	1.0008 326	1.0013 870	1.0016 639	1.0019 407	1.0024 938
4	1.0006 244	1.0010 400	1.0012 477	1.0014 552	1.0018 697
6	1.0004 162	1.0006 932	1.0008 316	1.0009 699	1.0012 461
12	1.0002 089	1.0003 466	1.0004 157	1.0004 848	1.0006 229
13	1.0001 921	1.0003 199	1.0003 837	1.0004 475	1.0005 749
26	1.0000 960	1.0001 599	1.0001 919	1.0002 237	1.0002 874
52	1.0000 480	1.0000 800	1.0000 959	1.0001 119	1.0001 437
365	1.0000 068	1.0000 114	1.0000 137	1.0000 159	1.0000 205

p	1	$1\frac{1}{8}$	$1\frac{1}{4}$	$1\frac{1}{2}$	$1\frac{3}{4}$
2	1.0049 876	1.0056 093	1.0062 306	1.0074 721	1.0087 121
3	1.0033 223	1.0037 360	1.0041 494	1.0049 752	1.0057 996
4	1.0024 907	1.0028 008	1.0031 105	1.0037 291	1.0043 466
6	1.0016 598	1.0018 663	1.0020 726	1.0024 845	1.0028 956
12	1.0008 295	1.0009 327	1.0010 357	1.0012 415	1.0014 468
13	1.0007 657	1.0008 609	1.0009 560	1.0011 459	1.0013 354
26	1.0003 828	1.0004 304	1.0004 779	1.0005 728	1.0006 675
52	1.0001 914	1.0002 152	1.0002 389	1.0002 864	1.0003 337
365	1.0000 273	1.0000 307	1.0000 340	1.0000 408	1.0000 475

p	2	$2\frac{1}{4}$	$2\frac{1}{2}$	$2\frac{3}{4}$	3
2	1.0099 505	1.0111 874	1.0124 228	1.0136 568	1.0148 892
3	1.0066 227	1.0074 444	1.0082 648	1.0090 839	1.0099 016
4	1.0049 629	1.0055 782	1.0061 922	1.0068 052	1.0074 171
6	1.0033 059	1.0037 153	1.0041 239	1.0045 317	1.0049 386
12	1.0016 516	1.0018 559	1.0020 598	1.0022 633	1.0024 663
13	1.0015 244	1.0017 130	1.0019 012	1.0020 890	1.0022 763
26	1.0007 619	1.0008 562	1.0009 502	1.0010 440	1.0011 375
52	1.0003 809	1.0004 280	1.0004 750	1.0005 218	1.0005 686
365	1.0000 543	1.0000 610	1.0000 676	1.0000 743	1.0000 810

p	$3\frac{1}{2}$	4	$4\frac{1}{2}$	5	$5\frac{1}{2}$
2	1.0173 495	1.0198 039	1.0222 524	1.0246 951	1.0271 319
3	1.0115 331	1.0131 594	1.0147 805	1.0163 964	1.0180 071
4	1.0086 374	1.0098 534	1.0110 650	1.0122 722	1.0134 752
6	1.0057 500	1.0065 582	1.0073 631	1.0081 649	1.0089 634
12	1.0028 709	1.0032 737	1.0036 748	1.0040 741	1.0044 717
13	1.0026 498	1.0030 215	1.0033 916	1.0037 601	1.0041 270
26	1.0013 240	1.0015 096	1.0016 944	1.0018 783	1.0020 614
52	1.0006 618	1.0007 545	1.0008 468	1.0009 387	1.0010 302
365	1.0000 942	1.0001 075	1.0001 206	1.0001 337	1.0001 467

p	6	$6\frac{1}{2}$	7	$7\frac{1}{2}$	8
2	1.0295 630	1.0319 884	1.0344 080	1.0368 221	1.0392 305
3	1.0196 128	1.0212 135	1.0228 091	1.0243 998	1.0259 856
4	1.0146 738	1.0158 683	1.0170 585	1.0182 446	1.0194 265
6	1.0097 588	1.0105 511	1.0113 403	1.0121 264	1.0129 095
12	1.0048 676	1.0052 617	1.0056 541	1.0060 449	1.0064 340
13	1.0044 923	1.0048 560	1.0052 181	1.0055 786	1.0059 376
26	1.0022 436	1.0024 250	1.0026 056	1.0027 854	1.0029 644
52	1.0011 212	1.0012 118	1.0013 020	1.0013 918	1.0014 811
365	1.0001 596	1.0001 726	1.0001 854	1.0001 982	1.0002 109

NOMINAL RATES CONVERTIBLE p TIMES PER YEAR EQUIVALENT TO EFFECTIVE RATE i GIVEN IN HEADING, $j_p = p[(1+i)^{\frac{1}{p}} - 1]$

p	¼	5/12	½	7/12	¾
¼	.0025 094	.0041 928	.0050 376	.0058 846	.0075 848
½	.0025 032	.0041 754	.0050 125	.0058 504	.0075 281
2	.0024 984	.0041 623	.0049 938	.0058 249	.0074 860
4	.0024 977	.0041 602	.0049 907	.0058 206	.0074 790
6	.0024 974	.0041 595	.0049 896	.0058 192	.0074 767
12	.0024 971	.0041 587	.0049 886	.0058 178	.0074 743
13	.0024 971	.0041 587	.0049 885	.0058 177	.0074 742
52	.0024 969	.0041 582	.0049 878	.0058 167	.0074 725
365	.0024 969	.0041 580	.0049 876	.0058 164	.0074 721
∞	.0024 969	.0041 580	.0049 875	.0058 164	.0074 720

p	1	1⅛	1¼	1½	1¾
¼	.0101 510	.0114 413	.0127 363	.0153 409	.0179 648
½	.0100 500	.0113 133	.0125 781	.0151 125	.0176 531
2	.0099 751	.0112 185	.0124 612	.0149 442	.0174 241
4	.0099 627	.0112 029	.0124 418	.0149 164	.0173 863
6	.0099 586	.0111 976	.0124 354	.0149 071	.0173 737
12	.0099 545	.0111 924	.0124 290	.0148 979	.0173 612
13	.0099 541	.0111 920	.0124 285	.0148 971	.0173 602
52	.0099 513	.0111 884	.0124 240	.0148 907	.0173 515
365	.0099 505	.0111 874	.0124 227	.0148 889	.0173 490
∞	.0099 503	.0111 872	.0124 225	.0148 886	.0173 486

p	2	2¼	2½	2¾	3
¼	.0206 080	.0232 708	.0259 532	.0286 553	.0313 772
½	.0202 000	.0227 531	.0253 125	.0278 781	.0304 500
2	.0199 010	.0223 748	.0248 457	.0273 135	.0297 783
4	.0198 517	.0223 126	.0247 690	.0272 209	.0296 683
6	.0198 353	.0222 919	.0247 435	.0271 901	.0296 317
12	.0198 190	.0222 713	.0247 180	.0271 594	.0295 952
13	.0198 177	.0222 697	.0247 161	.0271 570	.0295 924
52	.0198 064	.0222 554	.0246 985	.0271 358	.0295 672
365	.0198 032	.0222 513	.0246 934	.0271 297	.0295 600
∞	.0198 026	.0222 506	.0246 926	.0271 287	.0295 588

p	3½	4	4½	5	5½
¼	.0368 808	.0424 647	.0481 297	.0538 766	.0597 062
½	.0356 125	.0408 000	.0460 125	.0512 500	.0565 125
2	.0346 990	.0396 078	.0445 048	.0493 902	.0542 639
4	.0345 498	.0394 136	.0442 600	.0490 889	.0539 007
6	.0345 002	.0393 492	.0441 787	.0489 891	.0537 804
12	.0344 508	.0392 849	.0440 977	.0488 895	.0536 604
13	.0344 470	.0392 799	.0440 915	.0488 818	.0536 512
52	.0344 128	.0392 355	.0440 355	.0488 131	.0535 683
365	.0344 031	.0392 228	.0440 195	.0487 934	.0535 447
∞	.0344 014	.0392 207	.0440 169	.0487 902	.0535 408

p	6	6½	7	7½	8
¼	.0656 193	.0716 166	.0776 990	.0838 673	.0901 223
½	.0618 000	.0671 125	.0724 500	.0778 125	.0832 000
2	.0591 260	.0639 767	.0688 161	.0736 441	.0784 610
4	.0586 954	.0634 731	.0682 341	.0729 784	.0777 062
6	.0585 528	.0633 064	.0680 416	.0727 583	.0774 567
12	.0584 106	.0631 403	.0678 497	.0725 390	.0772 084
13	.0583 997	.0631 276	.0678 350	.0725 222	.0771 893
52	.0583 016	.0630 129	.0677 027	.0723 710	.0770 180
365	.0582 736	.0629 802	.0676 649	.0723 278	.0769 692
∞	.0582 689	.0629 748	.0676 586	.0723 207	.0769 610

AMOUNT FOR YEAR OF p DEPOSITS of $1/p$, p TIMES PER YEAR, i/j_p

p	$\frac{1}{4}$	$\frac{5}{12}$	$\frac{1}{2}$	$\frac{7}{12}$	$\frac{3}{4}$
$\frac{1}{4}$	0.9962 5	0.9937 717	0.9925 312	0.9912 924	0.9888 201
$\frac{1}{2}$	0.9974 8	0.9979 210	0.9975 062	0.9970 918	0.9962 640
2	1.0006 246	1.0010 406	1.0012 484	1.0014 562	1.0018 715
4	1.0009 370	1.0015 611	1.0018 730	1.0021 848	1.0028 081
6	1.0010 412	1.0017 347	1.0020 813	1.0024 278	1.0031 205
12	1.0011 453	1.0019 083	1.0022 896	1.0026 708	1.0034 329
13	1.0011 533	1.0019 216	1.0023 056	1.0026 895	1.0034 569
52	1.0012 254	1.0020 418	1.0024 498	1.0028 577	1.0036 732
365	1.0012 461	1.0020 762	1.0024 911	1.0029 058	1.0037 351
∞	1.0012 495	1.0020 819	1.0024 979	1.0029 138	1.0037 453

p	1	$1\frac{1}{8}$	$1\frac{1}{4}$	$1\frac{1}{2}$	$1\frac{3}{4}$
$\frac{1}{4}$	0.9851 244	0.9832 823	0.9814 441	0.9777 791	0.9741 295
$\frac{1}{2}$	0.9950 249	0.9944 065	0.9937 888	0.9925 558	0.9913 259
2	1.0024 938	1.0028 046	1.0031 153	1.0037 360	1.0043 618
4	1.0037 422	1.0042 089	1.0046 754	1.0056 076	1.0065 388
6	1.0041 586	1.0046 773	1.0051 958	1.0062 319	1.0072 671
12	1.0045 751	1.0051 458	1.0057 163	1.0068 565	1.0079 957
13	1.0046 071	1.0051 819	1.0057 564	1.0069 046	1.0080 518
52	1.0048 956	1.0055 063	1.0061 169	1.0073 372	1.0085 564
365	1.0049 780	1.0055 991	1.0062 199	1.0074 608	1.0087 007
∞	1.0049 917	1.0056 145	1.0062 371	1.0074 814	1.0087 247

p	2	$2\frac{1}{4}$	$2\frac{1}{2}$	$2\frac{3}{4}$	3
$\frac{1}{4}$	0.9704 950	0.9668 757	0.9632 715	0.9596 824	0.9561 082
$\frac{1}{2}$	0.9900 990	0.9888 752	0.9876 543	0.9864 365	0.9852 217
2	1.0049 752	1.0055 937	1.0062 114	1.0068 284	1.0074 446
4	1.0074 686	1.0083 984	1.0093 268	1.0102 542	1.0111 807
6	1.0083 013	1.0093 344	1.0103 667	1.0113 979	1.0124 282
12	1.0091 339	1.0102 711	1.0114 072	1.0125 424	1.0136 766
13	1.0091 980	1.0103 431	1.0114 873	1.0126 305	1.0137 727
52	1.0097 747	1.0109 919	1.0122 082	1.0134 234	1.0146 376
365	1.0099 396	1.0111 775	1.0124 143	1.0136 502	1.0148 850
∞	1.0099 670	1.0112 083	1 0124 486	1.0136 878	1.0149 261

p	$3\frac{1}{2}$	4	$4\frac{1}{2}$	5	$5\frac{1}{2}$
$\frac{1}{4}$	0.9490 046	0.9419 6	0.9349 7	0.9280 5	0.9211 8
$\frac{1}{2}$	0.9828 010	0.9803 922	0.9779 951	0.9756 098	0.9732 360
2	1.0086 748	1.0099 020	1.0111 262	1.0123 475	1.0135 660
4	1.0130 309	1.0148 774	1.0167 203	1.0185 594	1.0203 950
6	1.0144 858	1.0165 396	1.0185 895	1.0206 357	1.0226 781
12	1.0159 420	1.0182 035	1.0204 611	1.0227 148	1.0249 647
13	1.0160 541	1.0183 316	1.0206 051	1.0228 748	1.0251 407
52	1.0170 632	1.0194 847	1.0219 623	1.0243 160	1.0267 259
365	1.0173 517	1.0198 145	1.0222 733	1.0247 282	1.0271 793
∞	1.0173 997	1.0198 693	1.0223 349	1.0247 967	1 0272 546

p	6	$6\frac{1}{2}$	7	$7\frac{1}{2}$	8
$\frac{1}{4}$	0.9143 7	0.9076 1	0.9009 1	0.8942 7	0.8876 8
$\frac{1}{2}$	0.9708 738	0.9685 230	0.9661 836	0.9638 554	0.9615 385
2	1.0147 815	1.0159 942	1.0172 040	1.0184 110	1.0196 152
4	1.0222 269	1.0240 552	1.0258 800	1.0277 013	1.0295 190
6	1.0247 168	1.0267 517	1.0287 830	1.0308 106	1.0328 346
12	1.0272 107	1.0294 529	1.0316 914	1.0339 262	1.0361 572
13	1.0274 027	1.0296 609	1.0319 154	1.0341 661	1.0364 131
52	1.0291 319	1.0315 340	1.0339 324	1.0363 270	1.0387 179
365	1.0296 265	1.0320 699	1.0345 095	1.0369 453	1.0393 774
∞	1.0297 087	1.0321 589	1.0346 053	1.0370 480	1.0394 870

AMERICAN EXPERIENCE MORTALITY TABLE

Based on 100,000 living at age 10, giving l_x, number of living; d_x, number of deaths; p_x, probability of living; q_x, probability for dying for age x from 10 to 95.

x	l_x	d_x	p_x	q_x	x	l_x	d_x	p_x	q_x
10	100 000	749	.992 510	.007 490	55	64 563	1 199	.981 429	.018 571
11	99 251	746	.992 484	.007 516	56	63 364	1 260	.980 115	.019 885
12	98 505	743	.992 457	.007 543	57	62 104	1 325	.978 665	.021 335
13	97 762	740	.992 431	.007 569	58	60 779	1 394	.977 064	.022 936
14	97 022	737	.992 404	.007 596	59	59 385	1 468	.975 280	.024 720
15	96 285	735	.992 366	.007 634	60	57 917	1 546	.973 307	.026 693
16	95 550	732	.992 339	.007 661	61	56 371	1 628	.971 120	.028 880
17	94 818	729	.992 312	.007 688	62	54 743	1 713	.968 708	.031 292
18	94 089	727	.992 273	.007 727	63	53 030	1 800	.966 057	.033 943
19	93 362	725	.992 235	.007 765	64	51 230	1 889	.963 127	.036 873
20	92 637	723	.992 195	.007 805	65	49 341	1 980	.959 871	.040 129
21	91 914	722	.992 145	.007 855	66	47 361	2 070	.956 293	.043 707
22	91 192	721	.992 094	.007 906	67	45 291	2 158	.952 353	.047 647
23	90 471	720	.992 042	.007 958	68	43 133	2 243	.947 998	.052 002
24	89 751	719	.991 989	.008 011	69	40 890	2 321	.943 238	.056 762
25	89 032	718	.991 935	.008 065	70	38 569	2 391	.938 007	.061 993
26	88 314	718	.991 870	.008 130	71	36 178	2 448	.932 335	.067 665
27	87 596	718	.991 803	.008 197	72	33 730	2 487	.926 267	.073 733
28	86 878	718	.991 736	.008 264	73	31 243	2 505	.919 822	.080 178
29	86 160	719	.991 655	.008 345	74	28 738	2 501	.912 972	.087 028
30	85 441	720	.991 573	.008 427	75	26 237	2 476	.905 629	.094 371
31	84 721	721	.991 490	.008 510	76	23 761	2 431	.897 689	.102 311
32	84 000	723	.991 393	.008 607	77	21 330	2 369	.888 936	.111 064
33	83 277	726	.991 282	.008 718	78	18 961	2 291	.879 173	.120 827
34	82 551	729	.991 169	.008 831	79	16 670	2 196	.868 266	.131 734
35	81 822	732	.991 054	.008 946	80	14 474	2 091	.855 534	.144 466
36	81 090	737	.990 911	.009 089	81	12 383	1 964	.841 395	.158 605
37	80 353	742	.990 766	.009 234	82	10 419	1 816	.825 703	.174 297
38	79 611	749	.990 592	.009 408	83	8 603	1 648	.808 439	.191 561
39	78 862	756	.990 414	.009 586	84	6 955	1 470	.788 641	.211 359
40	78 106	765	.990 206	.009 794	85	5 485	1 292	.764 448	.235 552
41	77 341	774	.989 992	.010 008	86	4 193	1 114	.734 319	.265 681
42	76 567	785	.989 748	.010 252	87	3 079	933	.696 980	.303 020
43	75 782	797	.989 483	.010 517	88	2 146	744	.653 308	.346 692
44	74 985	812	.989 171	.010 829	89	1 402	555	.604 137	.395 863
45	74 173	828	.988 837	.011 163	90	847	385	.545 455	.454 545
46	73 345	848	.988 438	.011 562	91	462	246	.467 532	.532 468
47	72 497	870	.988 000	.012 000	92	216	137	.365 741	.634 259
48	71 627	896	.987 491	.012 509	93	79	58	.265 823	.734 177
49	70 731	927	.986 894	.013 106	94	21	18	.142 857	.857 143
50	69 804	962	.986 219	.013 781	95	3	3	.000 000	1.000 000
51	68 842	1 001	.985 459	.014 541					
52	67 841	1 044	.984 611	.015 389					
53	66 797	1 091	.983 667	.016 333					
54	65 706	1 143	.982 604	.017 396					

*COMMUTATION COLUMNS 3%

$$N_x = D_x + D_{x+1} + D_{x+2} \ldots\ldots + D_{95} \quad M_x = C_x + C_{x+1} + C_{x+2} \ldots\ldots + C_{95}$$

$$1 + a_x = N_x / D_x \quad A_x = M_x / D_x$$

$$D_x = v^x l_x \quad C_x = v^{x+1} d_x$$

x	D_x	N_x	C_x	M_x	$1+a_x$	A_x
10	74409.4	1811 346	541.094	21651.7	24.3430	.290981
11	71701.0	1736 936	523.229	21110.7	24.2247	.294426
12	69089.4	1665 235	505.947	20587.4	24.1026	.297982
13	66571.2	1596 146	489.227	20081.5	23.9765	.301654
14	64143.0	1529 575	473.052	19592.3	23.8463	.305447
15	61801.7	1465 432	458.028	19119.2	23.7118	.309364
16	59543.6	1403 630	442.872	18661.2	23.5731	.313403
17	57366.4	1344 086	428.211	18218.3	23.4298	.317578
18	55267.4	1286 720	414.598	17790.1	23.2817	.321891
19	53243.0	1231 453	401.415	17375.5	23.1289	.326343
20	51290.9	1178 210	388.648	16974.1	22.9711	.330938
21	49408.3	1126 919	376.806	16585.4	22.8083	.335681
22	47592.4	1077 510	365.325	16208.6	22.6404	.340571
23	45840.9	1029 918	354.192	15843.3	22.4672	.345615
24	44151.5	984 077	343.398	15489.1	22.2886	.350817
25	42522.2	939 926	332.933	15145.7	22.1044	.356184
26	40950.7	897 403	323.236	14812.8	21.9142	.361722
27	39434.8	856 453	313.821	14489.5	21.7182	.367431
28	37972.4	817 018	304.681	14175.7	21.5161	.373317
29	36561.7	779 046	296.218	13871.0	21.3077	.379387
30	35200.6	742 484	287.991	13574.8	21.0930	.385642
31	33887.3	707 283	279.991	13286.8	20.8716	.392089
32	32620.3	673 396	272.590	13006.8	20.6435	.398734
33	31397.6	640 776	265.749	12734.2	20.4084	.405580
34	30217.4	609 378	259.074	12468.5	20.1665	.412627
35	29078.2	579 161	252.564	12209.4	19.9174	.419883
36	27978.7	550 082	246.882	11956.9	19.6608	.427356
37	26916.9	522 104	241.318	11710.0	19.3969	.435042
38	25891.6	495 187	236.499	11468.7	19.1254	.442949
39	24901.0	469 295	231.757	11232.2	18.8465	.451073
40	23943.9	444 394	227.685	11000.4	18.5598	.459423
41	23018.8	420 450	223.654	10772.7	18.2655	.467996
42	22124.7	397 432	220.226	10549.1	17.9632	.476799
43	21260.1	375 307	217.080	10328.8	17.6531	.485832
44	20423.8	354 047	214.724	10111.8	17.3350	.495097
45	19614.2	333 623	212.578	9897.03	17.0093	.504585
46	18830.3	314 009	211.371	9684.45	16.6757	.514301
47	18070.5	295 178	210.539	9473.08	16.3348	.524229
48	17333.6	277 108	210.515	9262.54	15.9867	.534368
49	16618.3	259 774	211.455	9052.03	15.6318	.544703
50	15922.8	243 156	213.048	8840.57	15.2709	.555215
51	15246.0	227 233	215.228	8627.53	14.9045	.565889
52	14586.7	211 987	217.935	8412.30	14.5329	.576711

* Based on American Experience Mortality table.

*COMMUTATION COLUMNS 3%

x	D_x	N_x	C_x	M_x	$1+a_x$	A_x
53	13943.9	197401	221.113	8194.36	14.1568	.587667
54	13316.6	183457	224.905	7973.25	13.7765	.598743
55	12703.9	170140	229.052	7748.34	13.3928	.609920
56	12104.8	157436	233.695	7519.29	13.0061	.621182
57	11518.5	145331	238.593	7285.60	12.6172	.632510
58	10944.5	133813	243.706	7047.00	12.2265	.643888
59	10382.0	122868	249.168	6803.30	11.8348	.655298
60	9830.43	112486	254.764	6554.13	11.4427	.666718
61	9289.34	102656	260.463	6299.37	11.0509	.678128
62	8758.32	93366.6	266.080	6038.90	10.6603	.689505
63	8237.14	84608.2	271.450	5772.82	10.2716	.700828
64	7725.77	76371.1	276.575	5501.37	9.88524	.712080
65	7224.18	68645.3	281.455	5224.80	9.50217	.723238
66	6732.31	61421.2	285.678	4943.34	9.12334	.734272
67	6250.54	54688.8	289.148	4657.67	8.74945	.745162
68	5779.34	48438.3	291.784	4368.52	8.38128	.755885
69	5319.23	42659.0	293.136	4076.73	8.01976	.766415
70	4871.16	37339.7	293.182	3783.60	7.66547	.776734
71	4436.10	32468.6	291.428	3490.42	7.31916	.786820
72	4015.47	28032.5	287.447	3198.99	6.98112	.796666
73	3611.07	24017.0	281.095	2911.54	6.65094	.806283
74	3224.79	20405.9	272.472	2630.45	6.32783	.815694
75	2858.40	17181.1	261.892	2357.97	6.01076	.824929
76	2513.25	14322.7	249.643	2096.08	5.69889	.834013
77	2190.41	11809.5	236.190	1846.44	5.39146	.842967
78	1890.42	9619.09	221.761	1610.25	5.08834	.851796
79	1613.60	7728.67	206.374	1388.49	4.78972	.860494
80	1360.22	6115.07	190.783	1182.12	4.49563	.869059
81	1129.82	4754.85	173.976	991.333	4.20849	.877423
82	922.940	3625.02	156.180	817.357	3.92769	.885601
83	739.878	2702.08	137.604	661.177	3.65207	.893629
84	580.725	1962.21	119.166	523.573	3.37889	.901586
85	444.644	1381.48	101.686	404.407	3.10694	.909507
86	330.007	936.837	85.1229	302.721	2.83884	.917315
87	235.272	606.829	69.2159	217.598	2.57926	.924876
88	159.204	371.557	53.5871	148.382	2.33384	.932024
89	100.980	212.353	38.8099	94.7949	2.10292	.938750
90	59.2288	111.373	26.1381	55.9850	1.88039	.945231
91	31.3657	52.1442	16.2148	29.8469	1.66246	.951579
92	14.2373	20.7785	8.76715	13.6321	1.45944	.957492
93	5.05551	6.54120	3.60354	4.86499	1.29388	.962314
94	1.30473	1.48569	1.08577	1.26146	1.13870	.966834
95	0.180961	0.180961	0.175690	0.175690	1.00000	.970874

* Based on American Experience Mortality table.

* COMMUTATION COLUMNS 3½%

$$N_x = D_x + D_{x+1} + D_{x+2} \ldots\ldots + D_{95} \qquad M_x = C_x + C_{x+1} + C_{x+2} \ldots\ldots + C_{95}$$

$$1 + a_x = N_x / D_x \qquad A_x = M_x / D_x$$

x	D_x	N_x	C_x	M_x	$1+a_x$	A_x
10	70891.9	1575 535	513.024	17612.9	22.2245	.248447
11	67981.5	1504 643	493.690	17099.9	22.1331	.251537
12	65189.0	1436 662	475.077	16606.2	22.0384	.254739
13	62509.4	1371 473	457.159	16131.1	21.9403	.258059
14	59938.4	1308 963	439.908	15674.0	21.8385	.261501
15	57471.6	1249 025	423.879	15234.1	21.7329	.265071
16	55104.2	1191 553	407.873	14810.2	21.6236	.268766
17	52832.9	1136 449	392.465	14402.3	21.5102	.272601
18	50653.9	1083 616	378.153	14009.8	21.3926	.276580
19	48562.8	1032 962	364.360	13631.7	21.2707	.280702
20	46556.2	984 400	351.068	13267.3	21.1443	.284974
21	44630.8	937 843	338.727	12916.3	21.0134	.289402
22	42782.8	893 213	326.819	12577.5	20.8779	.293986
23	41009.2	850 430	315.329	12250.7	20.7375	.298731
24	39307.1	809 421	304.243	11935.4	20.5922	.303644
25	37673.6	770 114	293.545	11631.1	20.4417	.308734
26	36106.1	732 440	283.619	11337.6	20.2858	.314008
27	34601.5	696 334	274.028	11054.0	20.1244	.319465
28	33157.4	661 732	264.761	10779.9	19.9573	.325115
29	31771.3	628 575	256.164	10515.2	19.7843	.330964
30	30440.8	596 804	247.846	10259.0	19.6054	.337016
31	29163.5	566 363	239.797	10011.2	19.4202	.343277
32	27937.5	537 199	232.331	9771.37	19.2286	.349758
33	26760.5	509 262	225.406	9539.04	19.0304	.356460
34	25630.1	482 501	218.683	9313.64	18.8256	.363387
35	24544.7	456 871	212.158	9094.96	18.6138	.370547
36	23502.5	432 327	206.383	8882.80	18.3949	.377951
37	22501.4	408 824	200.757	8676.41	18.1688	.385595
38	21539.7	386 323	195.798	8475.66	17.9354	.393490
39	20615.5	364 783	190.945	8279.86	17.6946	.401632
40	19727.4	344 167	186.684	8088.91	17.4461	.410034
41	18873.6	324 440	182.493	7902.23	17.1901	.418692
42	18052.9	305 566	178.828	7719.74	16.9262	.427618
43	17263.6	287 513	175.422	7540.91	16.6543	.436810
44	16504.4	270 250	172.679	7365.49	16.3744	.446275
45	15773.6	253 745	170.127	7192.81	16.0867	.456004
46	15070.0	237 972	168.345	7022.68	15.7911	.466003
47	14392.1	222 902	166.872	6854.34	15.4878	.476258
48	13738.5	208 510	166.047	6687.47	15.1770	.486768
49	13107.9	194 771	165.982	6521.42	14.8591	.497519
50	12498.6	181 663	166.424	6355.44	14.5346	.508490
51	11909.6	169 165	167.315	6189.01	14.2041	.519668
52	11339.5	157 255	168.602	6021.70	13.8679	.531037

* Based on American Experience Mortality table.

*COMMUTATION COLUMNS 3½%

x	D_x	N_x	C_x	M_x	$1+a_x$	A_x
53	10787.4	145916	170.234	5853.09	13.5264	.542584
54	10252.4	135128	172.317	5682.86	13.1801	.554295
55	9733.40	124876	174.646	5510.54	12.8296	.566148
56	9229.60	115142	177.325	5335.90	12.4753	.578129
57	8740.17	105913	180.167	5158.57	12.1179	.590215
58	8264.44	97172.6	183.140	4978.41	11.7579	.602389
59	7801.82	88908.2	186.340	4795.27	11.3958	.614634
60	7351.65	81106.4	189.604	4608.93	11.0324	.626924
61	6913.44	73754.7	192.909	4419.32	10.6683	.639236
62	6486.75	66841.3	196.117	4226.41	10.3043	.651546
63	6071.27	60354.5	199.109	4030.30	9.9410	.663831
64	5666.85	54283.3	201.887	3831.19	9.5791	.676070
65	5273.33	48616.4	204.457	3629.30	9.2193	.688236
66	4890.55	43343.1	206.522	3424.84	8.8626	.700298
67	4518.65	38452.5	208.021	3218.32	8.5097	.712231
68	4157.82	33933.9	208.903	3010.30	8.1615	.724009
69	3808.32	29776.1	208.858	2801.40	7.8187	.735600
70	3470.67	25967.7	207.881	2592.54	7.4820	.746984
71	3145.43	22497.1	205.639	2384.66	7.1523	.758135
72	2833.42	19351.6	201.851	2179.02	6.8298	.769041
73	2535.75	16518.2	196.436	1977.17	6.5141	.779716
74	2253.57	13982.5	189.491	1780.73	6.2046	.790183
75	1987.87	11728.9	181.253	1591.24	5.9002	.800475
76	1739.39	9741.03	171.940	1409.99	5.6002	.810620
77	1508.63	8001.63	161.889	1238.05	5.3039	.820641
78	1295.73	6493.00	151.265	1076.16	5.0111	.830543
79	1100.65	5197.27	140.089	924.894	4.7220	.840318
80	923.338	4096.62	128.880	784.805	4.4368	.849965
81	763.234	3173.29	116.959	655.925	4.1577	.859402
82	620.465	2410.05	104.488	538.966	3.8843	.868648
83	494.995	1789.59	91.6153	434.478	3.6154	.877741
84	386.641	1294.59	78.9564	342.862	3.3483	.886772
85	294.610	907.951	67.0490	263.906	3.0819	.895782
86	217.598	613.342	55.8566	196.857	2.8187	.904682
87	154.383	395.744	45.1992	141.000	2.5634	.913315
88	103.963	241.361	34.8243	95.8011	2.3216	.921492
89	65.6231	137.398	25.0993	60.9768	2.0937	.929197
90	38.3047	71.7747	16.8224	35.8775	1.8738	.936635
91	20.1869	33.4700	10.3854	19.0551	1.6580	.943932
92	9.11888	13.2831	5.58815	8.66969	1.4567	.950741
93	3.22236	4.16421	2.28578	3.08155	1.2923	.956300
94	0.827611	0.941843	0.685392	0.795762	1.1380	.961516
95	0.114232	0.114232	0.110369	0.110369	1.0000	.966184•

* Based on American Experience Mortality table.

*COMMUTATION COLUMNS 4%

$$N_x = D_x + D_{x+1} + D_{x+2} \ldots\ldots + D_{95} \qquad M_x = C_x + C_{x+1} + C_{x+2} \ldots\ldots + C_{95}$$

$$1 + a_x = N_x / D_x \qquad A_x = M_x / D_x$$

x	D_x	N_x	C_x	M_x	$1+a_x$	A_x
10	67556.4	1379 083	486.536	14514.8	20.4138	.214854
11	64471.6	1311 527	465.949	14028.2	20.3427	.217588
12	61525.9	1247 055	446.227	13562.3	20.2688	.220432
13	58713.3	1185 529	427.332	13116.0	20.1918	.223391
14	56027.8	1126 816	409.230	12688.7	20.1117	.226472
15	53463.6	1070 788	392.423	12279.5	20.0283	.229679
16	51014.9	1017 325	375.789	11887.1	19.9417	.233011
17	48677.0	966 310	359.855	11511.3	19.8515	.236483
18	46445.0	917 633	345.065	11151.4	19.7574	.240099
19	44313.6	871 188	330.881	10806.4	19.6596	.243861
20	42278.3	826 874	317.277	10475.5	19.5579	.247774
21	40335.0	784 596	304.652	10158.2	19 4520	.251846
22	38479.0	744 261	292.529	9853.54	19.3420	.256076
23	36706.5	705 782	280.887	9561.01	19.2277	.260472
24	35013.8	669 075	269.709	9280.12	19.1089	.265042
25	33397.4	634 062	258.975	9010.42	18.9854	.269794
26	31853.9	600 664	249.014	8751.44	18.8568	.274737
27	30379.7	568 810	239.437	8502.43	18.7233	.279872
28	28971.9	538 431	230.228	8262.99	18.5846	.285207
29	27627.3	509 459	221.681	8032.76	18.4404	.290754
30	26343.1	481 831	213.451	7811.08	18.2906	.296514
31	25116.4	455 488	205.527	7597.63	18.1351	.302497
32	23944.9	430 372	198.170	7392.10	17.9735	.308713
33	22825.7	406 427	191.339	7193.93	17.8056	.315168
34	21756.5	383 601	184.740	7002.59	17.6316	.321862
35	20735.0	361 845	178.366	6817.85	17.4510	.328810
36	19759.1	341 110	172.677	6639.49	17.2634	.336022
37	18826.5	321 351	167.162	6466.81	17.0691	.343496
38	17935.2	302 524	162.249	6299.65	16.8676	.351245
39	17083.1	284 589	157.467	6137.40	16.6591	.359267
40	16268.6	267 506	153.213	5979.93	16.4431	.367575
41	15489.7	251 237	149.053	5826.72	16.2196	.376168
42	14744.9	235 748	145.357	5677.67	15.9884	.385060
43	14032.4	221 003	141.903	5532.31	15.7494	.394252
44	13350.8	206 970	139.013	5390.41	15.5025	.403752
45	12698.3	193 619	136.300	5251.40	15.2477	.413551
46	12073.6	180 921	134.224	5115.10	14.9849	.423659
47	11475.0	168 848	132.409	4980.87	14.7144	.434063
48	10901.3	157 373	131.122	4848.46	14.4362	.444762
49	10350.9	146 471	130.441	4717.34	14.1507	.455744
50	9822.30	136 120	130.159	4586.90	13.8583	.466988
51	9314.36	126 298	130.227	4456.74	13.5595	.478481
52	8825.89	116 984	130.597	4326.51	13.2546	.490207

* Based on American Experience Mortality table.

*COMMUTATION COLUMNS 4%

x	D_x	N_x	C_x	M_x	$1+a_x$	A_x
53	8355.84	108158	131.227	4195.92	12.9440	.502154
54	7903.23	99802.1	132.194	4064.69	12.6280	.514307
55	7467.07	91898.8	133.337	3932.50	12.3072	.526645
56	7046.53	84431.8	134.732	3799.16	11.9820	.539153
57	6640.78	77385.2	136.233	3664.43	11.6530	.551806
58	6249.13	70744.5	137.815	3528.19	11.3207	.564589
59	5870.97	64495.3	139.549	3390.38	10.9855	.577482
60	5505.61	58624.4	141.311	3250.83	10.6481	.590457
61	5152.55	53118.7	143.083	3109.52	10.3092	.603492
62	4811.29	47966.2	144.763	2966.44	9.96951	.616557
63	4481.48	43154.9	146.264	2821.67	9.62962	.629630
64	4162.85	38673.4	147.593	2675.41	9.29014	.642687
65	3855.15	34510.6	148.753	2527.82	8.95182	.655699
66	3558.12	30655.4	149.533	2379.06	8.61563	.668630
67	3271.74	27097.3	149.894	2229.53	8.28225	.681452
68	2996.01	23825.6	149.806	2079.64	7.95245	.694137
69	2730.97	20829.6	149.053	1929.83	7.62718	.706647
70	2476.88	18098.6	147.643	1780.78	7.30702	.718961
71	2233.97	15621.7	145.349	1633.13	6.99281	.731046
72	2002.70	13387.8	141.985	1487.79	6.68486	.742890
73	1783.69	11385.1	137.512	1345.80	6.38288	.754505
74	1577.57	9601.37	132.012	1208.29	6.08617	.765917
75	1384.89	8023.80	125.666	1076.28	5.79384	.777160
76	1205.95	6638.91	118.636	950.612	5.50511	.788265
77	1040.94	5432.96	111.164	831.975	5.21931	.799257
78	889.735	4392.02	103.369	720.811	4.93633	.810141
79	752.145	3502.29	95.2720	617.442	4.65640	.820908
80	627.945	2750.14	87.2275	522.170	4.37960	.831554
81	516.565	2122.20	78.7785	434.942	4.10829	.841989
82	417.919	1605.63	70.0404	356.164	3.84197	.852232
83	331.805	1187.72	61.1163	286.124	3.57956	.862325
84	257.927	855.910	52.4184	225.007	3.31842	.872368
85	195.588	597.983	44.2991	172.589	3.05736	.882409
86	143.766	402.395	36.7269	128.290	2.79895	.892348
87	101.510	258.629	29.5766	91.5628	2.54781	.902007
88	68.0293	157.118	22.6781	61.9863	2.30957	.911170
89	42.7347	89.0891	16.2664	39.3082	2.08470	.919819
90	24.8246	46.3544	10.8499	23.0418	1.86728	.928182
91	13.0199	21.5298	6.66604	12.1918	1.65361	.936400
92	5.85311	8.50988	3.56960	5.52580	1.45391	.94408
93	2.05838	2.65677	1.45310	1.95620	1.29071	.95036
94	0.52612	0.59839	0.43362	0.50311	1.1374	.9563
95	0.07227	0.07227	0.06949	0.06949	1.0000	.962

* Based on American Experience Mortality table.

* VALUATION COLUMNS 3½%

$$u_x = D_x/D_{x+1} \qquad\qquad k_x = C_x/D_{x+1}$$

x	u_x	k_x	x	u_x	k_x
10	1.042 811	0.007 547	55	1.054 585	0.018 922
11	1.042 838	.007 573	56	1.055 999	.020 289
12	1.042 866	.007 600	57	1.057 563	.021 800
13	1.042 894	.007 627	58	1.059 296	.023 474
14	1.042 922	.007 654	59	1.061 234	.025 347
15	1.042 962	0.007 692	60	1.063 385	0.027 425
16	1.042 990	.007 720	61	1.065 780	.029 739
17	1.043 019	.007 748	62	1.068 433	.032 302
18	1.043 059	.007 787	63	1.071 365	.035 136
19	1.043 100	.007 826	64	1.074 625	.038 285
20	1.043 141	0.007 866	65	1.078 270	0.041 807
21	1.043 194	.007 917	66	1.082 304	.045 704
22	1.043 248	.007 969	67	1.086 782	.050 031
23	1.043 303	.008 022	68	1.091 774	.054 854
24	1.043 358	.008 076	69	1.097 284	.060 178
25	1.043 415	0.008 130	70	1.103 403	0.066 090
26	1.043 484	.008 197	71	1.110 117	.072 576
27	1.043 554	.008 264	72	1.117 388	.079 602
28	1.043 625	.008 333	73	1.125 218	.087 167
29	1.043 710	.008 415	74	1.133 660	.095 323
30	1.043 796	0.008 498	75	1.142 852	0.104 204
31	1.043 884	.008 583	76	1.152 960	.113 971
32	1.043 986	.008 682	77	1.164 314	.124 941
33	1.044 102	.008 795	78	1.177 243	.137 433
34	1.044 221	.008 910	79	1.192 031	.151 720
35	1.044 343	0.009 027	80	1.209 771	0.168 861
36	1.044 493	.009 172	81	1.230 099	.188 502
37	1.044 647	.009 320	82	1.253 477	.211 089
38	1.044 830	.009 498	83	1.280 245	.236 952
39	1.045 018	.009 679	84	1.312 384	.268 004
40	1.045 237	0.009 891	85	1.353 917	0.308 133
41	1.045 463	.010 109	86	1.409 469	.361 806
42	1.045 721	.010 359	87	1.484 979	.434 762
43	1.046 001	.010 629	88	1.584 244	.530 670
44	1.046 331	.010 947	89	1.713 188	.655 254
45	1.046 684	0.011 289	90	1.897 500	0.833 333
46	1.047 106	.011 697	91	2.213 750	1.138 889
47	1.047 571	.012 146	92	2.829 873	1.734 177
48	1.048 111	.012 668	93	3.893 571	2.761 905
49	1.048 745	.013 280	94	7.245 000	6.000 000
50	1.049 463	0.013 974	95		
51	1.050 272	.014 755			
52	1.051 176	.015 629			
53	1.052 185	.016 604			
54	1.053 323	.017 704			

* Based on American Experience Mortality table.

Commissioners 1941 Standard Ordinary Mortality Table*

x	l_x	d_x	p_x	$\overset{\circ}{e}_x$	x	l_x	d_x	p_x	$\overset{\circ}{e}_x$
0	1 023 102	23 102	.977 42	62.33	**50**	810 900	9 990	.987 68	21.37
1	1 000 000	5 770	.994 23	62.76	51	800 910	10 628	.986 73	20.64
2	994 230	4 116	.995 86	62.12	52	790 282	11 301	.985 70	19.91
3	990 114	3 347	.996 62	61.37	53	778 981	12 020	.984 57	19.19
4	986 767	2 950	.997 01	60.58	54	766 961	12 770	.983 35	18.48
5	983 817	2 715	.997 24	59.76	**55**	754 191	13 560	.982 02	17.78
6	981 102	2 561	.997 39	58.92	56	740 631	14 390	.980 57	17.10
7	978 541	2 417	.997 53	58.08	57	726 241	15 251	.979 00	16.43
8	976 124	2 255	.997 69	57.22	58	710 990	16 147	.977 29	15.77
9	973 869	2 065	.997 88	56.35	59	694 843	17 072	.975 43	15.13
10	971 804	1 914	.998 03	55.47	**60**	677 771	18 022	.973 41	14.50
11	969 890	1 852	.998 09	54.58	61	659 749	18 988	.971 22	13.88
12	968 038	1 859	.998 08	53.68	62	640 761	19 979	.968 82	13.27
13	966 179	1 913	.998 02	52.78	63	620 782	20 958	.966 24	12.69
14	964 266	1 996	.997 93	51.89	64	599 824	21 942	.963 42	12.11
15	962 270	2 069	.997 85	50.99	**65**	577 882	22 907	.960 36	11.55
16	960 201	2 103	.997 81	50.10	66	554 975	23 842	.957 04	11.01
17	958 098	2 156	.997 75	49.21	67	531 133	24 730	.953 44	10.48
18	955 942	2 199	.997 70	48.32	68	506 403	25 553	.949 54	9.97
19	953 743	2 260	.997 63	47.43	69	480 850	26 302	.945 30	9.47
20	951 483	2 312	.997 57	46.54	**70**	454 548	26 955	.940 70	8.99
21	949 171	2 382	.997 49	45.66	71	427 593	27 481	.935 73	8.52
22	946 789	2 452	.997 41	44.77	72	400 112	27 872	.930 34	8.08
23	944 337	2 531	.997 32	43.88	73	372 240	28 104	.924 50	7.64
24	941 806	2 609	.997 23	43.00	74	344 136	28 154	.918 19	7.23
25	939 197	2 705	.997 12	42.12	**75**	315 982	28 009	.911 36	6.82
26	936 492	2 800	.997 01	41.24	76	287 973	27 651	.903 98	6.44
27	933 692	2 904	.996 89	40.36	77	260 322	27 071	.896 01	6.07
28	930 788	3 025	.996 75	39.49	78	233 251	26 262	.887 41	5.72
29	927 763	3 154	.996 60	38.61	79	206 989	25 224	.878 14	5.38
30	924 609	3 292	.996 44	37.74	**80**	181 765	23 966	.868 15	5.06
31	921 317	3 437	.996 27	36.88	81	157 799	22 502	.857 40	4.75
32	917 880	3 598	.996 08	36.01	82	135 297	20 857	.845 84	4.46
33	914 282	3 767	.995 88	35.15	83	114 440	19 062	.833 43	4.18
34	910 515	3 961	.995 65	34.29	84	95 378	17 157	.820 12	3.91
35	906 554	4 161	.995 41	33.44	**85**	78 221	15 185	.805 87	3.66
36	902 393	4 386	.995 14	32.59	86	63 036	13 198	.790 63	3.42
37	898 007	4 625	.994 85	31.75	87	49 838	11 245	.774 37	3.19
38	893 382	4 878	.994 54	30.91	88	38 593	9 378	.757 00	2.98
39	888 504	5 162	.994 19	30.08	89	29 215	7 638	.738 56	2.77
40	883 342	5 459	.993 82	29.25	**90**	21 577	6 063	.719 01	2.58
41	877 883	5 785	.993 41	28.43	91	15 514	4 681	.698 27	2.39
42	872 098	6 131	.992 97	27 62	92	10 833	3 506	.676 36	2.21
43	865 967	6 503	.992 49	26.81	93	7 327	2 540	.653 34	2.03
44	859 464	6 910	.991 96	26.01	94	4 787	1 776	.629 00	1.84
45	852 554	7 340	.991 39	25.21	**95**	3 011	1 193	.603 79	1.63
46	845 214	7 801	.990 77	24.43	96	1 818	813	.552 81	1.37
47	837 413	8 299	.990 09	23.65	97	1 005	551	.451 74	1.08
48	829 114	8 822	.989 36	22.88	98	454	329	.275 33	.78
49	820 292	9 392	.988 55	22.12	99	125	125	.000 00	.50

* Reproduced by permission of the Actuarial Society of America.

COMMUTATION COLUMNS 2½%
Commissioners 1941 Standard Ordinary Mortality Table*

x	D_x	N_x	C_x	M_x	$1 + a_x$	A_x
0	1 023 102.00	31 374 230	22 538.536 6	257 876.88	30.665 8	0.252 054
1	975 609.76	30 351 128	5 491.969 1	235 338.35	31.109 9	.241 222
2	946 322.43	29 375 518	3 822.115 2	229 846.38	31.041 8	.242 884
3	919 419.28	28 429 196	3 032.216 8	226 024.26	30.920 8	.245 834
4	893 962.20	27 509 776	2 607.370 2	222 992.05	30.772 9	.249 442
5	869 550.88	26 615 814	2 341.136 0	220 384.68	30.608 7	.253 447
6	846 001.18	25 746 263	2 154.480 3	218 043.54	30.432 9	.257 734
7	823 212.53	24 900 262	1 983.744 5	215 889.06	30.247 7	.262 252
8	801 150.42	24 077 050	1 805.642 5	213 905.32	30.053 1	.266 998
9	779 804.53	23 275 899	1 613.174 7	212 099.67	29.848 4	.271 991
10	759 171.73	22 496 095	1 458.745 1	210 486.50	29.632 4	.277 258
11	739 196.60	21 736 923	1 377.065 5	209 027.75	29.406 1	.282 777
12	719 790.36	20 997 726	1 348.556 5	207 650.69	29.172 0	.288 488
13	700 885.94	20 277 936	1 353.882 1	206 302.13	28.931 9	.294 345
14	682 437.28	19 577 050	1 378.169 3	204 948.25	28.687 0	.300 318
15	664 414.29	18 894 613	1 393.730 0	203 570.08	28.438 0	.306 390
16	646 815.33	18 230 198	1 382.081 2	202 176.35	28.184 5	.312 572
17	629 657.27	17 583 383	1 382.353 7	200 794.27	27.925 3	.318 895
18	612 917.42	16 953 726	1 375.535 5	199 411.91	27.660 7	.325 349
19	596 592.68	16 340 808	1 379.212 3	198 036.38	27.390 2	.331 946
20	580 662.42	15 744 216	1 376.533 1	196 657.17	27.114 2	.338 677
21	565 123.40	15 163 553	1 383.619 6	195 280.63	26.832 3	.345 554
22	549 956.28	14 598 430	1 389.541 6	193 897.01	26.544 7	.352 568
23	535 153.17	14 048 474	1 399.327 5	192 507.47	26.251 3	.359 724
24	520 701.32	13 513 320	1 407.270 0	191 108.14	25.952 2	.367 021
25	506 594.02	12 992 619	1 423.464 9	189 700.88	25.647 0	.374 463
26	492 814.61	12 486 025	1 437.519 2	188 277.41	25.336 2	.382 045
27	479 357.22	11 993 210	1 454.549 1	186 839.89	25.019 4	.389 772
28	466 211.03	11 513 853	1 478.200 3	185 385.34	24.696 7	.397 643
29	453 361.83	11 047 642	1 503.646 4	183 907.14	24.368 3	.405 652
30	440 800.58	10 594 280	1 531.158 0	182 403.50	24.034 2	.413 800
31	428 518.18	10 153 480	1 559.609 4	180 872.34	23.694 4	.422 088
32	416 506.91	9 724 962	1 592.845 3	179 312.73	23.348 9	.430 516
33	404 755.37	9 308 455	1 626.987 4	177 719.88	22.997 7	.439 080
34	393 256.29	8 903 699	1 669.050 8	176 092.90	22.641 0	.447 781
35	381 995.63	8 510 443	1 710.561 0	174 423.84	22.278 9	.456 612
36	370 968.10	8 128 447	1 759.080 1	172 713.28	21.911 4	.465 574
37	360 161.02	7 757 479	1 809.692 8	170 954.20	21.538 9	.474 660
38	349 566.90	7 397 318	1 862.134 5	169 144.51	21.161 4	.483 869
39	339 178.75	7 047 751	1 922.486 9	167 282.38	20.778 9	.493 198
40	328 983.61	6 708 573	1 983.511 0	165 359.89	20.391 8	.502 639
41	318 976.11	6 379 589	2 050.694 7	163 376.38	20.000 2	.512 190
42	309 145.51	6 060 613	2 120.338 1	161 325.68	19.604 4	.521 844
43	299 485.04	5 751 467	2 194.136 7	159 205.35	19.204 5	.531 597
44	289 986.39	5 451 982	2 274.595 1	157 011.21	18.800 8	.541 443
45	280 638.95	5 161 996	2 357.209 9	154 736.61	18.393 7	.551 373
46	271 436.89	4 881 357	2 444.154 2	152 379.40	17.983 4	.561 381
47	262 372.33	4 609 920	2 536.765 0	149 935.25	17.570 1	.571 460
48	253 436.24	4 347 548	2 630.859 4	147 398.48	17.154 4	.581 600
49	244 624.00	4 094 112	2 732.529 2	144 767.62	16.736 3	.591 796
50	235 925.04	3 849 488	2 835.622 1	142 035.10	16.316 6	.602 035

* Reproduced by permission of the Actuarial Society of America.

COMMUTATION COLUMNS 2½%
Commissioners 1941 Standard Ordinary Mortality Table*

x	D_x	N_x	C_x	M_x	a_x	A_x
51	227 335.15	3 613 563	2 943.137 4	139 199.47	15.895 3	.612 310
52	218 847.25	3 386 227	3 053.177 2	136 256.34	15.473 0	.622 609
53	210 456.33	3 167 380	3 168.222 9	133 203.16	15.050 1	.632 925
54	202 155.03	2 956 924	3 283.812 1	130 034.94	14.627 0	.643 244
55	193 940.61	2 754 769	3 401.913 1	126 751.12	14.204 2	.653 556
56	185 808.43	2 560 828	3 522.090 1	123 349.21	13.782 1	.663 852
57	177 754.43	2 375 020	3 641.783 5	119 827.12	13 361 2	.674 116
58	169 777.17	2 197 265	3 761.696 8	116 185.34	12.942 1	.684 340
59	161 874.57	2 027 488	3 880.185 4	112 423.64	12.525 1	.694 511
60	154 046.23	1 865 614	3 996.199 9	108 543.46	12.110 7	.704 616
61	146 292.80	1 711 567	4 107.708 0	104 547.26	11.699 6	.714 644
62	138 616.97	1 565 275	4 216.676 0	100 439.55	11.292 1	.724 583
63	131 019.40	1 426 658	4 315.413 8	96 222.87	10.888 9	.734 417
64	123 508.39	1 295 638	4 407.831 2	91 907.46	10.490 3	.744 139
65	116 088.15	1 172 130	4 489.449 7	87 499.63	10.096 9	.753 734
66	108 767.29	1 056 042	4 558.728 2	83 010.18	9.709 2	.763 191
67	101 555.70	947 274.4	4 613.189 3	78 451.45	9.327 6	.772 497
68	94 465.545	845 718.7	4 650.452 1	73 838.26	8.952 7	.781 642
69	87 511.050	751 253.1	4 670.014 3	69 187.81	8.584 7	.790 618
70	80 706.625	663 742.1	4 669.226 0	64 517.79	8.224 1	.799 411
71	74 068.942	583 035.4	4 644.235 4	59 848.57	7.871 5	.808 012
72	67 618.148	508 966.5	4 595.428 1	55 204.33	7.527 1	.816 413
73	61 373.498	441 348.3	4 520.662 7	50 608.90	7.191 2	.824 605
74	55 355.921	379 974.8	4 418.249.2	46 088.24	6.864 2	.832 580
75	49 587.526	324 618.9	4 288.286 9	41 669.99	6.546 4	.840 332
76	44 089.787	275 031.4	4 130.220 2	37 381.70	6.238 0	.847 854
77	38 884.206	230 941.6	3 944.961 8	33 251.48	5.939 2	.855 141
78	33 990.850	192 057.4	3 733.725 8	29 306.52	5.650 3	.862 189
79	29 428.077	158 066.6	3 498.684 1	25 572.80	5.371 3	.868 993
80	25 211.636	128 638.5	3 243.115 8	22 074.11	5.102 3	.875 553
81	21 353.602	103 426.8	2 970.736 8	18 831.00	4.843 5	.881 865
82	17 862.047	82 073.24	2 686.402 0	15 860.26	4.594 8	.887 931
83	14 739.984	64 211.19	2 395.321 2	13 173.86	4.356 3	.893 750
84	11 985.151	49 471.21	2 103.356 1	10 778.54	4.127 7	.899 324
85	9 589.474 6	37 486.06	1 816.194 6	8 675.180	3.909 1	.904 656
86	7 539.390 5	27 896.58	1 540.039 4	6 858.986	3.700 1	.909 753
87	5 815.463 2	20 357.19	1 280.145 4	5 318.946	3.500 5	.914 621
88	4 393.477 3	14 541.73	1 041.564 6	4 038.801	3.309 8	.919 272
89	3 244.754 6	10 148.25	827.621 52	2 997.236	3.127 6	.923 717
90	2 337.992 9	6 903.496	640.937 68	2 169.615	2.952 7	.927 982
91	1 640.030 9	4 565.503	482.773 06	1 528.677	2.783 8	.932 103
92	✱ 1 117.257 1	2 925.472	352.770 63	1 045.904	2.618 4	.936 136
93	737.236 29	1 808.215	249.339 10	693.133 5	2.452 7	.940 178
94	469.915 86	1 070.979	170.088 82	443.794 4	2.279 1	.944 413
95	288.365 67	601.062 8	111.467 79	273.705 6	2.084 4	.949 162
96	169.864 58	312.697 2	74.109 795	162.237 8	1.840 9	.955 101
97	91.611 740	142.832 6	49.001 885	88.128 0	1.559 1	.961 973
98	40.375 419	51.220 9	28.545 208	39.126 1	1.268 6	.969 058
99	10.845 444	10.845 4	10.580 921	10.580 9	1.000 0	.975 610

* Reproduced by permission of the Actuarial Society of America.

MOMENT OF INERTIA FOR VARIOUS BODIES

The mass of the body is indicated by m.

Body	Axis	Moment of inertia
Uniform thin rod	Normal to the length, at one end	$m\dfrac{l^2}{3}$
Uniform thin rod	Normal to the length, at the center	$m\dfrac{l^2}{12}$
Thin rectangular sheet, sides a and b	Through the center parallel to b	$m\dfrac{a^2}{12}$
Thin rectangular sheet, sides a and b	Through the center perpendicular to the sheet	$m\dfrac{a^2 + b^2}{12}$
Thin circular sheet of radius r	Normal to the plate through the center	$m\dfrac{r^2}{2}$
Thin circular sheet of radius r	Along any diameter	$m\dfrac{r^2}{4}$
Thin circular ring. Radii r_1 and r_2	Through center normal to plane of ring	$m\dfrac{r_1^2 + r_2^2}{2}$
Thin circular ring. Radii r_1 and r_2	Any diameter	$m\dfrac{r_1^2 + r_2^2}{4}$
Rectangular parallelopiped, edges a, b, and c	Through center perpendicular to face ab, (parallel to edge c)	$m\dfrac{a^2 + b^2}{12}$
Sphere, radius r	Any diameter	$m\dfrac{2}{5}r^2$
Spherical shell, external radius, r_1, internal radius r_2	Any diameter	$m\dfrac{2}{5}\dfrac{(r_1^5 - r_2^5)}{(r_1^3 - r_2^3)}$
Spherical shell, very thin, mean radius, r	Any diameter	$m\dfrac{2}{3}r^2$
Right circular cylinder of radius r, length l	The longitudinal axis of the solid	$m\dfrac{r^2}{2}$
Right circular cylinder of radius r, length l	Transverse diameter	$m\left(\dfrac{r^2}{4} + \dfrac{l^2}{12}\right)$
Hollow circular cylinder, length l, radii r_1 and r_2	The longitudinal axis of the figure	$m\dfrac{(r_1^2 + r_2^2)}{2}$
Thin cylindrical shell, length l, mean radius, r	The longitudinal axis of the figure	mr^2
Hollow circular cylinder, length l, radii r_1 and r_2	Transverse diameter	$m\left[\dfrac{r_1^2 + r_2^2}{4} + \dfrac{l^2}{12}\right]$
Hollow circular cylinder, length l, very thin, mean radius	Transverse diameter	$m\left(\dfrac{r^2}{2} + \dfrac{l^2}{12}\right)$
Elliptic cylinder, length l, transverse semiaxes a and b	Longitudinal axis	$m\left(\dfrac{a^2 + b^2}{4}\right)$
Right cone, altitude h, radius of base r	Axis of the figure	$m\dfrac{3}{10}r^2$
Spheroid of revolution, equatorial radius r	Polar axis	$m\dfrac{2r^2}{5}$
Ellipsoid, axes $2a$, $2b$, $2c$	Axis $2a$	$m\dfrac{(b^2 + c^2)}{5}$

MATHEMATICAL SYMBOLS AND ABBREVIATIONS

Symbols and Abbreviations of Commercial Arithmetic

#	Number (if written before a numeral); pounds (weight), lb. (if written after a numeral.)	Apr.	April	Dr.	Debit, debtor, doctor
		a/s	Account sales		
		Aug.	August	ea.	Each
		av.	Average	e.g.	(exempli gratia) for example
		avoir.	Avoirdupois		
		bal.	Balance	etc.	And so forth
@	At, as " @ 5¢ per C," for "at 5 cents per hundred."	bbl. *or* brl.	Barrel	ex.	Example, exercise, express
		bk.	Bank, book	exch.	Exchange
		bl.	Bale	exp.	Expense
		B/L	Bill of lading	F	Fahrenheit
%	Per cent; per hundred.	bu.	Bushel	Feb.	February
		bx.	Box	f.o.b.	Free on board
¢	Cents (placed after figures)	C	(centum) hundred	Fri.	Friday
				frt.	Freight
$	Dollars, (prefixed before figures).	cd.	Cord	ft. *or* f.	Foot
		cg.	Centigram	gal.	Gallon
		ch.	Chain	gi.	Gill
√	Check mark	chg.	Charge	gr.	Grain
&	And, as in "Smith, Jones & Co."	c.i.f.	Carriage and insurance free.	gro.	Gross
				gr. gro.	Great gross
		ck.	Check	guar.	Guarantee
c/o	Care of	cm.	Centimeter	hf.	Half
A	Acre	cml.	Commercial	hhd.	Hogshead
a/c	Account	Co.	Company, county	hr.	Hour
acct.	Account			i.e.	(id est) that is
ad val	(ad valorem), according to value	c.o.d.	Cash on delivery	in.	Inch, inches
		coll.	Collection	ins.	Insurance
		com.	Commission	*inst.*	(instant) the present month
A.M. *or* a.m.	(ante meridiem) in the morning, between midnight and the following noon. 12:00 A.M. is noon, better 12:00 M, 12:01 A.M. is one minute after midnight.	cr.	Credit, creditor, crate		
				int.	Interest
		cs.	Case	inv.	Invoice
		c. *or* ct.	Cent	inv'y	Inventory
		cu.	Cubic	Jan.	January
		cwt.	Hundredweight	kg.	Keg, kilogram
		da.	Day	km.	Kilometer
		Dec.	December	lb., lbs.	Pound, pounds
		dept.	Department	lp	List price
		dft.	Draft	ltd.	Limited
amt.	Amount	disc.	Discount	L.S.	(locus sigillis) place for the seal
ans.	Answer	dm.	Decimeter		
ap.	Apothecaries' weight or measure	do.	Ditto	M	(mille) thousand; meridiem as in 12:00 M
		doz.	Dozen		
		dr.	Dram		

Symbols and Abbreviations of Commercial Arithmetic (Continued)

m.	Mill, meter	P.M.	(post meridiem)	etc.	west, etc.
Mar.	March	*or*	in the after-	Sat.	Saturday
mdse.	Merchandise	p.m.	noon, between	sec.	Second
mi.	Mile		noon and the	sec'y	Secretary
min.	Minute		following mid-	Sept.	September
mm.	Millimeter		night. 12:00	set.	Settlement
mo.	Month		P.M. is mid-	sig.	Signed, signa-
Mon.	Monday		night, 12:01		ture
mortg.	Mortgage		P.M. is one	sq.	Square
N, NE,	North, North-		minute after	stk.	Stock
NW,	east, North-		noon.	Sun.	Sunday
etc.	west, etc.	pp.	Pages	T.	Ton
no. *or*	Number	pr.	Pair	temp.	Temperature
numb.		*prox.*	(proximo) in the	Thu.	Thursday
Nov.	November		following	treas.	Treasurer,
Oct.	October		month		treasury
O.K.	Correct	pt.	Pint, point	Tues.	Tuesday
oz.	Ounce	pwt.	Pennyweight	*ult.*	(ultimo) in the
p.	Page	(*or*			last month
par.	Paragraph	dwt.)		*via*	By way of
pay't	Payment	qr.	Quire	viz.	(videlicet)
pc.	Piece	qt.	Quart		namely
pd.	Paid	rd.	Rod, road	vol.	Volume
per	By, by the, as in	rec'd	Received	Wed.	Wednesday
	"per C," "per	rec't	Receipt	wk.	Week
	M," "per doz."	rm.	Ream	wt.	Weight
pfd.	Preferred	S, SE,	South, South-	yd.	Yard
pk.	Peck, pecks	SW,	east, South-	yr.	Year
pkg.	Package				

Symbols Belonging to Plane Geometry

∠	Angle. Use "rt ∠" not "∟" for "right angle." Write out the word "arc" rather than using "⌒." On ∠ABC, B is the vertex, A, C, points on the sides of the angle.	△	Triangle
		□	Square. Use "rect." not ▭ for "rectangle," and use "trap." not ◹ for trapezoid.
⊥, ⊥s	Perpendicular, perpendiculars.	⊙, ⊙s	Circle, circles. ⊙ A(B) designates the circle with center at A and passing through the point B. ⊙ (ABC), designates the circle passing through given distinct points, A, B, C.
∥, ∥s	Parallel (to), parallel lines.		
▱	Parallelogram (vertices are named in counter-clockwise order, starting at any vertex).		
		≅	(is) congruent (to).
		∼	(is) similar (to).

412

MATHEMATICAL SYMBOLS AND ABBREVIATIONS

Symbols Belonging to Plane Geometry (Continued)

≈	(is) homothetic (to); (is) similar (to) and similarly placed (with).	$\overrightarrow{AB}$	Directed segment, A to B.
#	(is) homothetically congruent (to); or otherwise stated, (is) congruent (to) and similarly placed (with). In case of line segments, this becomes, (is) parallel (with) and congruent (to).	|(AB)	Line (of infinite length) containing points A and B.
		↑(AB)	Directed line (of infinite length) containing points A and B, and in the direction from A to B.
≏	(is) equivalent (to), (in area or volume).	₨	cross-ratio, anharmonic ratio.
$\overline{AB}$	Length of line segment between A and B.	$\overline{\overline{\wedge}}$, $\overline{\overline{\wedge}}$	(is) perspective with, (is) perspective with, from center P.
		$\overline{\wedge}$	(is) projective with.

General Mathematical Symbols and Abbreviations

"Bold-face" type—To indicate vectors. In manuscript and at the blackboard, bold-faced type is variously indicated by wavy underscoring, or enclosure in a circle, or even by wavy overscoring. Some persons use German type.

Half-spaces—In writing numbers with many recorded digits, half-spaces (rather than commas or other marks) may well be used to separate convenient groups of digits. Thus $\pi = 3.14159\ 26536-$.

Superscripts—To indicate: **1.** powers, as in x^2, $(a-x)^n$, etc. In modern practice $a° = 1$ always by definition (even for $a = 0$). Also in ∞', ∞^2, etc., indicating number of degrees of freedom. Wherever the context restricts the value of a to non-negative (real) values and n to positive integers, $a^{1/n}$ means the non-negative (real) nth root of a. For complex numbers, x^y is defined as $e^{y\ (\log x)}$, where the principal value of $\log x$ is to be taken. In tables 0.0^5314 may be used to indicate 0.00000314. Note special use of $\sin^n x$ for $(\sin x)^n$ except for $n = -1$, also for $\cos^n x$, etc. **2.** symbolic powers, or order of iteration, as in T^n or in D^n $(= d^n/dx^n)$, or in inverse functions as in $\sin^{-1}$, $\cos^{-1}$, $\sinh^{-1}$, etc. **3.** order of differentiation, as in y' ("y prime"), y'' ("y second," or "y double prime"), $\cdots$, $y^{(N)}$, $\cdots$. **4.** feet and inches, as in $3'4''$. **5.** degrees, minutes, seconds, as in $34°5'17''$. Do not omit ° for common angles. Write 0°, 30°, 45°, 60°, etc., not 0, 30, 45, 60, etc. Do not use superscript, r, for radians. Write $180° = \pi$ rad, but write $\cos(\pi/3)$ for $\cos 60°$. **6.** days, hours, minutes, seconds, as in $10^d 3^h 27^m 5.3^s$. **7.** degrees of temperature as in 104°. Where C (for Centigrade) or F (for Fahrenheit) is given, recent usage approves the omission of the °, thus 100C = 212F, and −40C = −40F. **8.** For use with integral sign $\int$, and with vertical bar |, see these symbols.

Dot-accents—To indicate derivatives with respect to time, (Newton's notation), as in $\dot{x}$ for x-component of velocity, and $\ddot{x}$ for x-component of acceleration.

Subscripts—To indicate: **1.** position in a sequence, set, or matrix, as in a_1, a_2, a_3, $\cdots a_n$, $\cdots$, or $a_0 x^n + a_1 x^{n-1} + \cdots + a_r x^{n-r} + \cdots a_n$ or in

413

$\begin{pmatrix} a_{11}a_{12}a_{13} \\ a_{21}a_{22}a_{23} \end{pmatrix}$. **2.** general distinguishing mark. Two subscripts may be written adjacently without commas as a_{11} and to be read "a sub one one," not "a sub eleven." A subscript is sometimes enclosed in parentheses as in $F_{(0)1}$ where such distinction seems demanded. For special uses see associated symbols.

Juxtaposition—To indicate: **1.** the algebraic product, as in $2bxy$. **2.** the logical product as in AB where A and B are given classes, and in symbolic logic. Also written with centrally placed dot as $A \cdot B$. **3.** the group product, as in ST (the result of performing first S, then T, or in aH, the co-set consisting for given a of all operations ah, where h is in H. **4.** general operational or functional combination as in dy/dx, $\sin x$, $\log x$, $\max y$, $\lim x_n$, etc. **5.** sequence of points or other elements determining a geometric figure, as line AB, parallelogram $ABCD$, $\angle ABC$, etc. **6.** sum of products (in tensor notation) when index appears as subscript for one factor and superscript for another. Thus $a_i x^i$ means $\Sigma a_i x^i$, in tensor notation.

( )—Parentheses ("round brackets") to indicate: **1.** aggregation, as in $(a + b) \cdot (a - b) = a^2 - b^2$. **2.** argument of function, as in $f(x)$, $g(x,y)$, etc. **3.** sequence or set, as in $a = (a_i)$, $x = (x_{ij})$, (x,y,z), etc. **4.** matrix, as in $\begin{pmatrix} a_{11}a_{12}a_{13} \\ a_{21}a_{22}a_{23} \end{pmatrix}$ also written as $\begin{Vmatrix} a_{11}a_{12}a_{13} \\ a_{21}a_{22}a_{23} \end{Vmatrix}$. **5.** permutation (or substitution) in group theory as in $\begin{pmatrix} a_1 a_2 a_3 \\ b_1 b_2 b_3 \end{pmatrix}$ where a_i is replaced by $b_i (i = 1,2,3)$. **6.** binomial coefficient, as in $\begin{pmatrix} n \\ r \end{pmatrix} = n!/[r!(n-r)!]$. This is also designated by $C_{n,r}$ or $_nC_r$. For n,r, positive integers, $\begin{pmatrix} -n \\ r \end{pmatrix} = (-1)^r \begin{pmatrix} n+r-1 \\ r \end{pmatrix}$, $\begin{pmatrix} n \\ -r \end{pmatrix} = 0$, by definition. **7.** cycle or cylic permutation (in group theory) as in (a_1, a_2, a_3) for $\begin{pmatrix} a_1 a_2 a_3 \\ a_2 a_3 a_1 \end{pmatrix}$. **8.** greatest common divisor, as in $(30,42) = 6$, $(7,5) = 1$. **9.** inner product as in (ab), $= \Sigma_i a_i b_i$. **10.** segment or open interval, as in (a,b), for system of values of x, where $a < x < b$.

Superscript ( )—To indicate: **1.** general index as distinguished from exponent. **2.** index of order of derivative as in y, y', $\cdots$, $y^{(n)}$, $\cdots$. **3.** "factorial," as in $x^{(r)} = x(x - 1) \cdots (x - r + 1)$. By definition $x^{(-r)} = 1/[(x + 1) \cdot (x + 2) \cdots (x + r)]$.

[ ]—Brackets ("square brackets"), to indicate: **1.** aggregation. **2.** argument of function as with ( ). **3.** greatest integer in, as $[2] = 2$, $[-7/3] = -3$. **4.** inner product (for coefficients in normal equations in the method of least squares), as in $[aa]$, $[XY]$, etc. **5.** outer product of vectors. Other notations are $V\,ab$ and $a \times b$. **6.** divided difference (in formal interpolation). $[x_i] = y_i$, $[x_i, x_{i+1}] = (y_{i+1} - y_i)/(x_{i+1} - x_i)$, $\cdots$ $[x_i, x_{i+1}, \cdots, x_{i+r}] = ([x_{i+1}, \cdots, x_{i+r}] - [x_i, \cdots, x_{i+r-1}])/(x_{i+r} - x_i)$. **7.** range of points (in projective geometry) as in $[P]$. **8.** base (basis) of Abelian group, as in $[a,b, \cdots, k]$. **9.** module or ideal, as $[2] = [0, \pm 2, \pm 4, \cdots, \pm 2n, \cdots]$. **10.** Christoffel symbol, as in $\begin{bmatrix} mn \\ p \end{bmatrix} = \frac{1}{2}\left(\frac{\partial g_{pm}}{\partial x^n} + \frac{\partial g_{pn}}{\partial x^m} = \frac{\partial g_{mn}}{\partial x^p} \right)$. **11.** closed interval, as in $[a,b]$ for system of values of x where $a \leqq x \leqq b$.

Subscript—Note. The use of adjacent subscripts, rather than of indices placed directly below is recommended on account of its availability for running text, and its economy of space and of expense in type setting. Thus use

$$\sum_i \text{ rather than } \sum_i, \quad \int_a^b \text{ rather than } \int_a^b, \text{ etc.}$$

{ }—Braces ("curly brackets") to indicate: **1.** aggregation, as in $\{(x-a)(x-b)\}^2$. **2.** class of (in theory of aggregates), where the general element only is mentioned, as in $\{a_i\} = [a_1, a_2, a_3]$, $(i = 1,2,3)$. **3.** Christoffel symbol, as in $\begin{Bmatrix} m\ n \\ p \end{Bmatrix} = g^{rp} \begin{bmatrix} m\ n \\ p \end{bmatrix}$.

< >—Angle brackets to indicate: **1.** aggregation. **2.** closed interval as with [ ].

| |—Vertical bars, to indicate: **1.** absolute value (modulus of complex number), as $|a + ib|^2 = a^2 + b^2$. **2.** magnitude of (for vectors) as $a = |a|$. **3.** determinant, as in $\begin{vmatrix} a & b \\ c & d \end{vmatrix} = ad - bc$. The use of the notation $|a_{ij}|$ for the determinant of the maxtrix (a_{ij}), is common but is ambiguous. The notation det (a_{ij}) may be used for this determinant.

‖ ‖—Double bars, to indicate: **1.** matrix as in $\begin{Vmatrix} a_{11}a_{12}a_{13} \\ a_{21}a_{22}a_{23} \end{Vmatrix}$ or in $\|a_{ij}\|$. **2.** generalized length (for metrical spaces), as in $\|f\|^2 = \int f^2(x)dx$.

(], [).—For intervals, as $(a,b]$, for system of values of x for which $a < x \leq b$, and $[a,b)$, for system of values of x for which $a \leq x < b$. Similarly $(a,b >$, and $< a,b)$ are sometimes used for these respectively.

⊃—**1.** contains (or containing) as proper sub-class. **2.** implies (or implying).

⊇—contains (or containing) as sub-class. (Some writers use, ⊃, for this.)

⊂—(is) contained as proper sub-class within.

⊆—(is) contained as sub-class within. (Some writers use, ⊂, for this.)

≡—**1.** (is) identical with. $\equiv_x$ indicates (is) identical with for all values of x for which both members are defined. **2.** (is) congruent to (with respect to indicated modulus) as in $a \equiv b \pmod{m}$. **3.** (is) equivalent to (in formal logic).

=—(is) equal (to).

<—(is) less than.

>—(is) greater than.

≦ or ≤—(is) less than or equal to. Sometimes read (in the case of real numbers) as "(is) not greater than."

≧ or ≥—(is) greater than or equal to. Sometimes read (in the case of real numbers) as "(is) not less than."

≢—**1.** (is) not identically equal (to). (Not "identically unequal to"), is unequal to for at least one value. **2.** (is) not congruent (to).

≠—(is) not equal (to).

≶—**1.** (is) not equal (to), (for real quantities). **2.** (Sometimes when explained by context) less than or greater than respectively.

∼—**1.** (is) formally, asymptotically, or approximately equal to. (The context should make the meaning specific.) Do not use $\doteq$ for "approximately equal to." **2.** (is) similar (to). **3.** not (in some works on formal logic).

→—**1.** approaches (as a limit), as in $\lim_{x\to a} f(x) = b$, $f(x) \to b$, as $x \to a$, etc. (Do not use $\doteq$). Not usually employed with long expressions. **2.** leads to, validates, implies (in logic). **3.** corresponds to.

↔—**1.** mutually implies (in logic). **2.** in one-to-one correspondence with, corresponds reciprocally to.

Superscript →—directed line as $\overrightarrow{AB}$.

|—Vertical bar, to indicate: **1.** value at, as in $f(x)|_a = f(a)$, or $f(x)|_{x=a} = f(a)$. **2.** value between as in $f(x)|_a^b = f(b) - f(a)$. **3.** is a divisor of, divides (in number theory) as $3|6$, or $(x - a)|(x^2 - a^2)$. **4.** inner product (with parentheses) as $(a|b) = \sum_i a_i b_i$.

\ or /—Stroke, mark of cancellation as in $\not{3}x = \not{6}$, $x + \not{3} = \not{7}$.

/—Solidus, or oblique rule, to indicate: **1.** actual or symbolic division, as in $3/7$, $(x - a)/(x - b)$, d/dx, dy/dx, d^2y/dx^2. Do not write ambiguously $a - b/c - d$, but $(a - b)/(c - d)$ or $a - (b/c) - d$, as may be intended. Do not write a/bc but $(a/b)c$ or $a/(bc)$ as intended. Write a proportion as $a/b = c/d$ not $a:b::c:d$. Where A, B, C, D designate displayed expressions, write the proportion as $\dfrac{A}{B} = \dfrac{C}{D}$. In commercial typing in place of $8\frac{5}{12}$, it is usual to write 8-5/12. The solidus form a/b, adapted to running text should be used where conveniently possible, rather than the displayed form $\dfrac{a}{b}$. **2.** quotient or factor group (in group theory) as G/H, (where H is a normal subgroup of G). **3.** per, as in ft/sec. **4.** discount symbol, as in Cash 6, 4/5, 2/30, n/90 indicating 6 % discount for immediate payment, 4 % discount if paid within 5 days, 2 % discount if paid within 30 days, no discount thereafter, but face amount of bill is due (net) not later than the 90th day. **5.** shilling, (in British currency) as 3/6d, or 10/ —.

Superscript $\overline{}$—Vinculum. This may be regarded as obsolescent for general use as a mark of aggregation due to its unsuitability for monotype setting. In conjunction with the radical sign it is widely used, but may often be avoided. There is little logical or historical basis for using $\sqrt{2}$ rather than $\sqrt{}2$. For a longer expression, one may write $\sqrt{}(x^2 + a^2)$ rather than $\sqrt{x^2 + a^2}$. Instead of $\sqrt{x - a}\,(x - b)$, one might write $(x - b)\sqrt{}(x - a)$. In geometry, the vinculum may be used for line segments as in $\overline{AB}$.

Superscript $\overline{}$—Bar. To indicate: **1.** complex conjugate of, as $\bar{z}$. This is somewhat inconvenient for "upper extended" letters and capitals as, $\bar{b}, \bar{h}, \bar{X}$, etc. Also indicated by *conj*, as *conj* $(x + iy) = x - iy$ or by use of a "star" as in z^*. **2.** arithmetic mean value of, as in $\bar{x}, = \sum_i x_i/n$. **3.** closure of (in topology), as in $\bar{E}$ (the closure of E). **4.** "least upper," as in $\overline{\lim}$, and $\bar{B}$ for least upper limit and least upper bound, respectively. See "sup."

Subscript $\underline{}$—To indicate: **1.** italics (in manuscript). **2.** "greatest lower," as in $\underline{\lim}$, and B, for greatest lower limit, and greatest lower bound respectively. See "inf."

——————horizontal rule, sign of division, as in $\dfrac{x - a}{x + a}$. Ordinarily the solidus form, adapted to running text, is preferred, as in $(x - a)/(x + a)$. When numerator and denominator are both complicated, the displayed form using horizontal rule may be avoided by writing "A/B, where $A = \cdots$, and $B = \cdots$."

$-$ (centrally placed)—Minus sign. To indicate: **1.** subtraction as in $7 - 2 = 5$, $a^2 - b^2 = (a - b)(a + b)$. **2.** overestimate, as in $3.5-$. **3.** approach through negative values as in $-\infty$ and -0. **4.** region where variable indicated by context is negative (in graphs). **5.** logical difference (in theory of classes). **6.** in $(-)^n$, the sign expressed by $(-1)^n$.

. (on line)—**1.** decimal point. In the decimal representation of a number between 0 and 1, the cipher, 0, should (except in tables) appear before the decimal point. Thus 0.314 not .314. Notation by powers of 10, ("scientific notation") is recommended, especially when recording approximate values; thus to four significant figures, 3.140×10^9 and 3.140×10^{-6}. **2.** (sometimes used in quoting bond prices) as in 95.17 for $95\frac{17}{32}$. **3.** (sometimes used in recording mental age) as in 12.3 for 12 yr. 3 mo. **4.** (in symbolic logic) as mark of punctuation separating terms, also as, "and."

:—Colon. To indicate: **1.** hours, in recording time, as in 4:10 p.m. **2.** ratio (an obsolescent form) as in $a:b$. The form a/b is preferred. **3.** (in symbolic logic) as mark of punctuation separating groups of terms, as in $p \cdot p \supset q : \supset : q$.

$\cdot$ (centrally placed)—**1.** mark of algebraic multiplication, particularly where mere juxtaposition would be ambiguous, as in $\overline{AB} \cdot \overline{CD}$. **2.** (for vectors), the mark of inner or dot multiplication as in $\boldsymbol{a} \cdot \boldsymbol{b} = ab \cos < \boldsymbol{ab}$. Other notations are $(\boldsymbol{ab})$ and $S \boldsymbol{ab}$.

$\cdots$ (preferably centrally placed)—"three dots" meaning "and so forth," or "and so forth up to." Particularly in relation to the sequence of natural numbers, as in $1, 2 \cdots, n, \cdots$; or $a_0, a_1, \cdots, a_n, \cdots$, or $1, \cdots, m$.

$\therefore$—hence, therefore.

$\vcentcolon, \Colon, \dblcolon$, etc.—(in symbolic logic), marks of punctuation stronger than $\cdot$ and $:$.

„—ditto.

$+$ plus sign. To indicate: **1.** addition, as in $2 + 3$, $a + b$, 10^{a+1}. **2.** underestimate, as in $3.5+$. **3.** continued fraction as in $a_0 + \dfrac{1}{a_1+} \dfrac{1}{a_2+} \cdots$ for

$a_0 + \cfrac{1}{a_1 + \cfrac{1}{a_2+}}$ **4.** approach through positive values as in $+\infty$, and in $+0$.

5. region where variable indicated by the context is positive, (in graphs). **6.** logical addition (in theory of classes). **7.** " . . or . . or both," (in formal logic). Note: In writing series indicate sign before and after dots of omission, as $a_0 + a_1 + \cdots + a_n$, or $1 - \dfrac{1}{2} + \dfrac{1}{3} + \cdots + (-1)^{n-1}\dfrac{1}{n}$.

8. in abstract group theory a group or co-set may be expressed as the sum of its elements.

$\pm$—**1.** "plus or minus." The repeated appearance of $\pm$ as in $\pm a \pm b \pm c$ is ambiguous. In many cases the sign $\pm$ before a term which appears repeatedly is intended to indicate the systematic use of the positive determination or of the negative determination throughout. Thus one may write $(a \pm b)^3 = a^3 \pm 3a^2b + 3ab^2 \pm b^3$. Where the context restricts the value of a to non-negative (real) values, $\sqrt{a}$ means the non-negative (real) square

root of a. Hence when both signs are desired, write $\pm$ before the radical. For roots of a quadratic equation $ax^2 + bx + c = 0$, use $\pm$ as in $(-b \pm \sqrt{b^2 - 4ac})/(2a)$. **2.** (in theory of observation), "with a probable error of." As in 17.2 ± 0.5 cm.

$\mp$—"minus or plus respectively." Used in context where $\pm$ has appeared previously, as in $(a \pm b)(a^2 \mp ab + b^2) = a^3 \pm b^3$. Here upper signs are to be taken throughout, or else lower signs. The notation $\pm a \mp b \pm c$ is ambiguous, meaning perhaps one of the four values $\pm(a - b) \pm c$, or one of the two values $\pm(a - b + c)$.

$\times$—**1.** times, (sign of algebraic multiplication). Used chiefly in arithmetic, as in $2 \times 2 = 4$, 7.3×10^4. **2.** (for vectors) the sign of outer or cross multiplication. **3.** (for classes) the Cartesian product. Thus $A \times B$ is the class of all ordered pairs (a,b) where a is an element of A, and b of B.

$\div$—sign of division. Used chiefly in arithmetic. Should be replaced by solidus, $/$, where convenient.

$\sqrt{}\ \sqrt[n]{}$—square root of, nth root of. (See discussion under "superscript," and under "vinculum"). By custom, for a positive, $\sqrt{(-a)}$ means usually $i\sqrt{a}$, rather than $-i\sqrt{a}$, but the latter unambiguous forms are preferred.

$!$—"factorial," as in $3! = 1 \cdot 2 \cdot 3 = 6$. $0! = 1$, (by definition). The elementary arithmetic definition of factorial n, may be replaced in favor of the definition as a special case of the Gamma function $\Gamma(x)$. For n a natural number, $n! = \Gamma(n + 1)$, $= \int_0^\infty x^n e^{-x} dx$. For n a large natural number, Stirling's asymptotic formula (extended) yields $n! \sim \sqrt{2n\pi}(n/e)^n\left(1 + \dfrac{1}{12n} + \dfrac{1}{288n^2} - \dfrac{139}{51840n^3} - \cdots\right)$. Note: Do not use the obsolescent form $\lfloor n$ for $n!$

$\int, \int_a^b, \int_a^x, \int\int, \int_c$—Integral signs. (use preferably bold-face type)

$\int_a^b \int_c^d f(x,y)dxdy$ denotes $\int_a^b\left(\int_c^d f(x,y)dx\right)dy$, $= \int_a^b dy \int_c^d dx f(x,y)$.

$\oint$—curvilinear integral over closed path free from singularities. (Use preferably bold-face type.)

§—section, or article.

$\P$ or ¶—paragraph.

$\propto$— varies as. Instead of $y \propto x$ one may write $y = kx$, k being the constant factor of proportionality.

∇—nabla—To indicate: **1.** linear vector operator $\left(\dfrac{\partial}{\partial x}, \dfrac{\partial}{\partial y}, \dfrac{\partial}{\partial z}\right)$ as used also in divergence, gradient, and curl (or rotation). **2.** backward difference (in interpolation theory) $\nabla a_n = a_n - a_{n-1}$.

∇^2—Laplace operator.

$\square$—D'Alembertian operator.

$°, ', '', ''', \cdots$, $(N) \cdots$, (superscript)—superscript numbers. See "superscripts."

∞—infinity. Use $+\infty$ or $-\infty$ respectively, where direction of approach along real numbers is to be indicated. Otherwise use ∞ rather than $\pm\infty$. Note: "$n \to \infty$," may be read "as n increases without bound."

$\aleph$—Aleph (initial Hebrew letter) transfinite cardinal number, in particular that of all real numbers. $\aleph_0$ (aleph null) first transfinite cardinal.

α—Alpha. To indicate: **1.** (in analytic geometry of 3 dimensions), direction angle with X-axis. **2.** angular acceleration. **3.** (in statistics) $\alpha_0 = 1$, $\alpha_1 = 0$, $\alpha_2 = 1$, $\alpha_3 = \mu_3/\sigma^3$, $\alpha_4 = \mu_4/\sigma^4 = \mu_4/\mu_2^2$. **4.** (in mathematical astronomy), right ascension (also indicated by R.A.) **5.** angle of triangle at A, opposite side a. **6.** root of algebraic equation as in $a(x - \alpha)(x - \beta)(x - \gamma) = 0$.

B—(Greek Beta)—$B(m,n) = \Gamma(m)\Gamma(n)/\Gamma(m + n)$, (Eulerian Beta-function).

β—Beta. To indicate: **1.** (in analytic geometry of 3 dimensions), direction angle with Y-axis. **2.** (in statistics), $\beta_1 = \alpha_3^2 = \mu_3^2/\mu_2^3$, $\beta_2 = \alpha_4 = \mu_4/\mu_2^2$ **3.** angle of triangle at B, opposite side b. **4.** root of algebraic equation See α.

Γ—$\Gamma(x)$ Gamma-function. See "!" Among numerous definitions equivalent for positive real values of x, are the two following: (i) $\Gamma(x) = \lim\limits_{n \to \infty}$
$$\frac{1 \cdot 2 \cdots n}{x(x + 1) \cdots (x + n - 1)}n^{x-1}, x > 0. \quad \text{(ii) } \Gamma(x) = \int_0^\infty e^{-t}t^{x-1}dt, R(x) > 0$$

γ—Gamma. To indicate: **1.** (in analytic geometry of 3 dimensions) direction angle with Z-axis. **2.** Euler or Mascheroni constant. (Also indicated by C.) $\gamma = \lim\limits_{n \to \infty} \left(\frac{1}{1} + \frac{1}{2} + \cdots + \frac{1}{n} - \log n\right) = 0.57721\ 56649\ 01532$ $86060\ 65120 \cdots$ **3.** angle of triangle at C, opposite side c. **4.** radius of geodesic curvative. **5.** universal constant of gravitation $= 6.670 \times 10^{-8}$ cm^3/(gm. sec^2). **6.** root of algebraic equation, see α.

Δ—Delta. To indicate: **1.** triangle (in plane geometry). (For right triangle, write rtΔ, not $\varDelta$). Also area of triangle. **2.** increment, as in Δx, Δf, $f(x + \Delta x)$, etc. **3.** forward difference (interpolation theory). $\Delta a_n = a_{n+1} - a_n$. **4.** Laplacian operator $\frac{\partial^2}{\partial x^2} + \frac{\partial^2}{\partial y^2}$, or $\frac{\partial^2}{\partial x^2} + \frac{\partial^2}{\partial y^2} + \frac{\partial^2}{\partial z^2}$ also designated by ∇^2. **5.** selected square root of the discriminant of a given polynomial, as in $\Delta^2 = b^2 - 4ac$ for the polynomial $ax^2 + bx + c$. **6.** triangular number, (of form $(n^2 - n)/2$). **7.** Legendre's radical, $\Delta(\varphi)^2 = 1 - k^2 \sin^2 \varphi$.

δ—Delta. To indicate: **1.** positive constant dependent upon ϵ that may be chosen initially as near to zero as desired. (In theory of limits, of continuity, etc.) **2.** variation of. **3.** (in interpolational theory) central difference $\delta y_{c+i+\frac{1}{2}} = y_{c+i+1} - y_{c+i}$ **4.** (in mathematical astronomy) apparent declination. **5.** number of double points, or nodes (Plücker number). **6.** (in statistics) deviation. **7.** force of interest, $e^\delta = 1 + i$, (in mathematics of finance). **8.** Kronecker Delta, $\delta_{ij} = 0$ for $i \neq j$, $= 1$ for $i = j$. In tensor notation, also $\delta_i{}^j$. One has $\delta_{ij} = \begin{pmatrix} & o \\ i & - j \end{pmatrix}$ or $C_{0,i-j}$. **9.** unit elongation (in strength of materials).

∂—curly d. To indicate: **1.** partial differentiation as in $\partial f(x,y)/\partial x$. **2.** The Jacobian operator, as in $\partial(u,v,w)/\partial(x,y,z)$. This is variously represented, sometimes as $J\left(\dfrac{u,v,w}{x,y,z}\right)$ etc. **3.** a specified square root of the discriminant D. (also sometimes as Δ.)

MATHEMATICAL SYMBOLS AND ABBREVIATIONS

ϵ—Epsilon. To indicate: **1.** positive constant, that may be chosen initially independently as near to zero as desired. (In theory of limits, of continuity, etc.) **2.** primitive root of unity. **3.** (is) member of, (relation of element to containing class). **4.** eccentricity of conic section, usually better designated by e. **5.** (in mathematical astronomy) obliquity of ecliptic. **6.** an ϵ-number is a transfinite ordinal of a certain limiting type. Note: Do not use ϵ or ε for Napierian base except in engineering. See e.

ε—(is not a member of.)

ζ—Zeta. To indicate: **1.** Riemann Zeta-function $\zeta(s) = \Sigma_{n=1}^{\infty} n^{-s}$ (for $s > 1$). **2.** (in statistics) a test of linearity. $\zeta = \eta^2 - r^2$.

η—Eta. To indicate: **1.** general variable or unknown constant, analogous to y as in case of moving system of coordinates, etc. Used in ordered set (ξ, η, ζ). **2.** a confocal coordinate. See ξ. **3.** (in statistics), correlation ratio. **4.** order-type of the aggregate of all rational numbers.

Θ—Theta. To indicate: **1.** Theta-function. See ϑ. **2.** absolute temperature (where t is used for time).

θ—Theta. To indicate: **1.** general angular displacement, (in trigonometry and analytic geometry). **2.** (in plane polar coordinates (r,θ)) angle from initial ray to radius vector, $x = r \cos \theta$, $y = r \sin \theta$. **3.** (in cylindrical coordinates (r,θ,z)) angle from initial radial half-plane to radial half-plane containing radius vector. **4.** (in spherical coordinates (r,θ,φ)) co-latitude (measured from zenith) and (in astronomy) zenith distance. This notation is traditional in mathematical physics. In texts on analytic geometry, usage varies, θ being employed frequently for the longitude. See φ. **5.** Theta-function. See ϑ. **6.** (in formal theory of operations), a displacement operator. **7.** ordinary temperature (when t is used for time).

ϑ—Theta-function. Definitions and notations vary widely. For elliptic Theta-functions the notation here given is that followed by Whittaker and Watson. Here θ_i designates the value of $\vartheta_i(o,q)$, ϑ_i', the value of $d\vartheta_i(z,q)/dz$. $(i = 1,2,3,4)$. These are defined by $\vartheta_1(z,q) = 2q^{\frac{1}{4}} \sin z - 2q^{\frac{9}{4}} \sin 3z + 2q^{\frac{25}{4}}$ $\sin 5z - \cdots \vartheta_2(z,q) = 2q^{\frac{1}{4}} \sin z + 2q^{\frac{9}{4}} \sin 3z + 2q^{\frac{25}{4}} \sin 5z + \cdots \vartheta_3(z,q)$ $= 1 + 2q \cos 2z + 2q^4 \cos 4z + 2q^9 \cos 6z + \cdots \vartheta_4(z,q) = 1 - 2q \cos$ $2z + 2q^4 \cos 4z - 2q^9 \cos 6z + \cdots$.

ι—Iota, number of inflexions (a Plücker number).

$\imath$—inverted Iota, (in formal logic) the unique element fulfilling description stated.

κ—Kappa, number of cusps. (A Plücker number).

Λ—Lambda, sometimes used for null-class.

λ—Lambda. To indicate: **1.** general linear parameter (e.g., in a pencil), as in $F + \lambda G$. **2.** running index, as in $x_\lambda (\lambda = 1, 2, \cdots)$. **3.** longitude (in mathematical astronomy). **4.** characteristic value (as in λ_i) in theory of linear differential equations of second order, linear integral equations, etc. **5.** order-type of the aggregate of all real numbers.

μ—Mu. To indicate: **1.** running index, usually used with λ, as in $x_\lambda y_\mu$. **2.** general linear parameter, when used with λ, as in $\lambda F + \mu G$. **3.** (in statistics) moment, about the arithmetic mean, as in $\mu_k = \Sigma_i f_i(x_i - \bar{x})^k$, $\mu_2 = \sigma^2 = $ variance. **4.** μ_x, force of mortality $= -d (\log_e l_x)/dx$. **5.** (in number theory) inversion function of Moebius and Mertens.

420

ν—Nu. To indicate: **1.** running index, usually with λ and μ. **2.** (in statistics) moment about arbitrary origin A (in "short method") as in $\nu_k = \Sigma_i f_i(x_i - A)^k$.

ξ—Xi. To indicate: **1.** general variable, or unknown constant analogous to x, as in moving systems of coordinates, etc. **2.** a confocal coordinate as in

(i) confocal ellipses and hyperbolas, $\dfrac{x^2}{a^2 - \lambda} + \dfrac{y^2}{b^2 - \lambda} = 1$, $-\infty < \xi < b^2 <$

$\eta < a^2$. (ii) confocal ellipsoids and hyperboloids of revolution, $\dfrac{x^2}{a^2 - \lambda} +$

$\dfrac{y^2 + z^2}{b^2 - \lambda} = 1$, $-\infty < \xi < b^2 < \eta < a^2$. (iii) confocal parabolas, $y^2 + 2\lambda \cdot$

$(x - \lambda) = 0$, $-\infty < \xi < 0 < \eta < +\infty$. (iv) confocal paraboloids of revolution, $y^2 + z^2 + 2\lambda(x - \lambda) = 0$, $-\infty < \xi < 0 < \eta < +\infty$. (v) confocal ellipsoids and hyperboloids, $\dfrac{x^2}{a^2 - \lambda} + \dfrac{y^2}{b^2 - \lambda} + \dfrac{z^2}{c^2 - \lambda} = 1$, $-\infty <$

$\xi < c^2 < \eta < b^2 < \zeta < a^2$. (vi) confocal paraboloids, $\dfrac{x^2}{a^2 - \lambda} + \dfrac{y^2}{b^2 - \lambda} =$

$2z - \lambda$, $-\infty < \xi < b^2 < \eta < a^2 < \zeta < +\infty$.

Π, $\Pi_i \Pi_{i=m}^{n}$, $\Pi_{(R)}$ or Π—**1.** product of terms with index i, or j, etc. ranging from m to n, or over R. Do not use $\underset{i}{\Pi}$, $\underset{i=m}{\overset{n}{\Pi}}$, etc. (Bold-faced type preferred.)

2. (in some formal logical treatments) "for every."

Π_{ij}, Π_{ijk}, $\cdots$ —$\Pi_i\Pi_j$, $\Pi_i\Pi_j\Pi_k$, etc.

π—Pi. **1.** the ratio of the length of circumference of a circle, to the diameter. $\pi = 3.14159\ 26535\ 89793\ 23846 \cdots$ **2.** general notation for plane, projectivity, projective, period, etc.

ρ—Rho. **1.** radius of geodesic curvature. **2.** proportionality factor, as in $\rho X_i = \Sigma_j a_{ij} x_j$.

$\sum$, $\sum_i$, $\sum_{i=m}^{n}$, $\sum_{(R)}$ or $\underset{(R)}{\sum}$—Sigma. **1.** summation, sum of terms of index i,

or j, etc., ranging from m to n, or over range R. Do not use $\underset{i}{\sum}$, $\underset{i=m}{\overset{n}{\sum}}$, etc.

(bold-faced type preferred). **2.** (on some formal logical treatments) "for at least one." **3.** (in number theory) $\Sigma_{d/n}$ summation extended over all divisors of n. **4.** (in mathematical astronomy) Σ-pt is the intersection of the meridian with the equator.

Σ_{ij}, Σ_{ijk} $\cdots$ —$\Sigma_i\Sigma_j$, $\Sigma_i\Sigma_j\Sigma_k$, etc.

σ—Sigma. To indicate: **1.** radius of torsion. **2.** (in statistics) standard deviation $\sigma^2 N = \Sigma_i(x_i - \bar{x})^2 f_i$. **3.** (in number theory), $\sigma_k(n) = $ sum of kth powers of divisors of n. **4.** any one of several analogous Sigma-functions. The simplest elliptic Sigma-function $\sigma(x)$ is related to the Weierstrassian $\wp$ function by $\wp u = -d^2 \log \sigma u / du^2$. One has $\sigma u = u\left\{1 - \dfrac{g_2}{2}\dfrac{u^4}{5!} - \right.$

$\left. 6g_3\dfrac{u^6}{7!} - \dfrac{9}{4}g_2^2\dfrac{u^8}{9!} - 18g_2g_3\dfrac{u^{10}}{11!} - \cdots \right\}$ **5.** proportionality factor, usually used with ρ.

τ—Tau. To indicate: **1.** number of bitangents (a Plücker number). **2.** time (when t is used for temperature). **3.** torsion (of curve in space).

MATHEMATICAL SYMBOLS AND ABBREVIATIONS

ϒ—Upsilon. (In mathematical astronomy) vernal equinox.

φ—Phi. To indicate: **1.** general functional symbol, especially for polynomials. **2.** (in spherical coordinates, (r,θ,φ), longitude from x to y in right-handed system. In some astronomical work the z-axis points to the zenith, θ is the zenith-distance, and φ is the west azimuth. In some works on analytic geometry the roles of θ and φ are interchanged, although the system given is traditional mathematical physics. $x = r \sin\theta \cos\varphi$, $y = r \sin\theta \sin\varphi$, $z = r \cos\theta$. **3.** (in geocentric coordinates, $(r,\varphi,\lambda)\varphi$ = latitude (not co-latitude as with spherical coordinates). **4.** (in plane polar coordinates (r,φ).) Used chiefly as specialized case of spherical coordinates $(r,\pi/2,\varphi)$. See θ. **5.** inclination of plane curve, $\tan\varphi = dy/dx = m$. **6.** (in number theory.) Euler's function or indicatrix. $\varphi(n)$ is the number of positive integers not exceeding n and prime to n. **7.** $\varphi_i(x)$, characteristic function, see λ_i. **8.** argument in Legendre's elliptic integrals. $E(\varphi,k) = \int_0^\varphi \Delta(\varphi)d\varphi$, $F(\varphi_1 k) = \int_0^\varphi d\varphi/\Delta(\varphi)$. **9.** the normal probability function of Laplace and Gauss in the form $\varphi(t) = \dfrac{1}{\sqrt{2\pi}}e^{-t^2/2}$. **10.** $\varphi_n(x)$, sometimes used for Bernoulli polynomial. See $B_n(x)$.

χ—Chi. (In statistical theory) χ^2 is a measure of goodness of fit, devised by Karl Pearson. $\chi^2 = \Sigma(f_i - Np_i)^2/(Np_i)$ for N items, with p_i the probability of appearances and f_i the frequency for items in an ith class.

ψ—Psi. To indicate: **1.** general functional symbol (usually with φ). **2.** angle from radius vector to tangent of plane curve. **3.** (with geocentric coordinates in mathematical astronomy), co-latitude. See φ.

Ω—Omega. To indicate: **1.** a certain annihilator in the theory of binary concomitants. **2.** (with subscript) transfinite ordinals of certain minimal type. **3.** (in geometry of the triangle) Ω,Ω', the Brocard points.

ω—Omega. To indicate: **1.** angular velocity. **2.** first transfinite ordinal, order-type of the aggregate of all natural numbers. **3.** imaginary cube root of unity, related to i, by $\omega = (-1 + i\sqrt{3})/2$. **4.** $\omega_1, \omega_2, \omega_3$, half-periods of Weierstrassian $\wp$-function.

A—**1.** A vertex, and the associated angle of $\triangle ABC$. See α. **2.** A_{ij}, algebraic complement of a_{ij} in determinant, D. $A_{ij} = dD/da_{ij}$. **3.** (in astronomy) azimuth. **4.** (in astronomy) astronomical unit, mean geocentric distance to the sun. **5.** acres. **6.** area.

AM—arithmetic mean. See also superscript ¯.

Ans.—answer.

AP—arithmetic progression.

Ax—axiom.

a—**1.** (in elementray algebra) initial term in arithmetic or geometric progression. **2.** (with subscript) coefficient in Fourier series, $(a_0/2) + \Sigma_{n=1}^{\infty}(a_n \cos nx + b_n \sin nx)$. **3.** (with two indices) element in matrix or determinant, as in $\begin{pmatrix} a_{11} & a_{12} & a_{13} \\ a_{21} & a_{22} & a_{23} \end{pmatrix}$ or $\begin{vmatrix} a_{11} & a_{12} \\ a_{21} & a_{22} \end{vmatrix}$. **4.** (in elementary geometry) apothegm. **5.** (in geometry of triangle) first side-line, also length of first side of the triangle. **6.** (in elementary analytic geometry) x-intercept. **7.** (in elementary analytic geometry) semi-major axis of ellipse or semi-transverse axis of hyperbola,

422

etc. (When equations are in normal form.) For central conics and quadrics the a is usually associated with x, as in $(x^2/a^2) + (y^2/b^2) = 1$, even when a may be less than b, or as in $-(x^2/a^2) + (y^2/b^2) = 1$, where a is the semi-conjugate axis.

abs—absolute value of.

acc—acceleration.

am—amplitude function. $\varphi = \mathrm{am}\ u$, where $u = F = \int_0^\varphi d\varphi / \Delta(\varphi)$.

amp—amplitude of vibration.

approx—approximate(ly).

arc (in "arc sin" etc.)—inverse. Also written $\sin^{-1}$ etc. Do not use "arc" for inverse of hyperbolic functions. Write $\sinh^{-1}$, etc.

arg—argument. For r and θ real, θ is the argument of $re^{i\theta}$.

av—average.

B—1. (With subscripts) Bernoulli numbers and polynomials. To indicate what usage among many is being followed in any given case, authors would do well to list the values of the first few Bernoulli numbers as for example, $B_1 = \frac{1}{2}$, $B_2 = \frac{1}{6}$, $B_3 = 0$, $B_4 = -\frac{1}{30}$, etc. The Bernoulli polynomials, are defined as $B_n(x) = \Sigma_{r=0}^n \binom{n}{r} B_r x^{n-r}$, and satisfy $B_n(x + 1) - B_n(x) = nx^{n-1}$ with the choice of notation for Bernoulli numbers given above. (Also designated by $\varphi_n(x)$.) 2. bound (general symbol). $\bar{B}$, $\underline{B}$ designate least upper, and greatest lower bound respectively. Preferred notations are "sup" and "inf" respectively. 3. a vertex and the associated angle of $\triangle ABC$. See β. 4. (in elementary solid geometry), area of base of a solid.

b—1. (in elementary geometry) length of base of plane figure. b,b', parallel bases of trapezoid. 2. (in elementary analytic geometry) y-intercept. 3. (in elementary analytic geometry) semi-axis. See a. 4. (in geometry of the triangle) second side-line, also length of second side of the triangle.

bei(z)—Thomson-Bessel function, $\mathrm{bei}(z) = \dfrac{(\frac{1}{2}z)^2}{(2!)^2} - \dfrac{(\frac{1}{2}z)^6}{(6!)^2} + \dfrac{(\frac{1}{2}z)^{10}}{(10!)^2} - \cdots$

$\mathrm{ber}(z) \pm i\ \mathrm{bei}(z) = J_0(zi\sqrt{}\ \pm i) = I_0(z\sqrt{}\ \pm i)$.

ber(z)—Thomson-Bessel function. (See bei(z).) $\mathrm{ber}(z) = 1 - \dfrac{(\frac{1}{2}z)^4}{(4!)^2} + \dfrac{(\frac{1}{2}z)^8}{(8!)^2} - \cdots$.

C—1. arbitrary constant of integration. 2. (in elementary geometry) circumference of circle; also, circle. 3. general symbol for curve. 4. (with subscripts) combination, as in $C_{n,r}$ or $_nC_r$, the number of combinations of n things taken r at a time (without repetitions). The form $_nC_r$ or even ^nC_r is widely used but the notation $C_{n,r}$ or $C(n,r)$ or $\binom{n}{r}$ is to be preferred. 5. Roman numeral for "hundred." 6. Euler or Mascheroni constant. Also designated by γ. (See γ.) 7. (chiefly as subscript) contour of integration. 8. Centigrade, degree Centigrade, as $-52C$.

Ci—cosine integral function, $Ci(x) = \int_\infty^x (\cos u/u)du$.

CF—(in elementary differential equations) complementary function.

c—**1.** (in geometry of triangle) third side-line, also length of third side of triangle. **2.** (in elementary analytic geometry), z-intercept. **3.** (in elementary analytic geometry) semi-axis. (See a.)

cis—cis $\theta = \cos \theta + i \sin \theta = e^{i\theta} = exp(i\theta)$. The latter forms preferred.

cls—class, set, or aggregate.

cn—cosine amplitude function. (Jacobian elliptic function.)

colog—cologarithm (of).

conj—(complex) conjugate (of). See superscript $^{-}$.

cos—cosine (of).

$\cos^{-1}$—inverse cosine (of). Also written arc cos.

cosh—hyperbolic cosine (of). Do not write Cos nor $\mathfrak{Cof}$ (in German letters).

$\cosh^{-1}$—inverse hyperbolic cosine of. Do not write arc cosh.

csc—cosecant (of).

$\csc^{-1}$—inverse cosecant (of). Also written arc csc.

ctn—cotangent (of).

ctn^{-1}—inverse cotangent (of). Also written arc ctn.

ctnh—hyperbolic cotangent (of). Do not write Ctn, nor $\mathfrak{Ctn}$ (in German letters).

ctnh^{-1}—inverse hyperbolic cotangent of. Do not write arc ctnh.

cu—cubic.

cum—cumulative

cvrs—coversed sine (of) cvrs $x = 1 - \sin x$.

D—**1.** differential operator, as in $Dy = y'$, $d_x f(x,y) = \partial f/\partial x$. **2.** Roman numeral for "five hundred." **3.** general symbol for denominator, or for determinant. **4.** discriminant of binary form, or of polynomial. **5.** (in statistical theory), (with subscripts 0, 1, $\cdots$, 10), decile marks. **6.** $D(a_1, a_2, \cdots, a_n)$ sometimes designates the Vandermonde determinant

$$\begin{vmatrix} 1 a_1 & \cdots & a_1{}^{n-1} \\ \cdots & \cdots & \cdots \\ 1 a_n & \cdots & a_n{}^{n-1} \end{vmatrix}$$

Def—definition.

Dem—demonstration, proof.

d—**1.** (in elementary algebra), common difference in arithmetic progression. **2.** differential operator, as in d^2y/dx^2. **3.** (in elementary geometry) diameter. **4.** (as superscript) days, as in $2^d 3^h 17^m$. **5.** (British currency) pence.

deg—degree, degrees.

det—determinant of, as in det (a_{ij}).

div—divergence of, also indicated by ∇.

dn—dn(z), a Jacobian elliptic function.

$\exists$—(there) exists.

$\exists|$—there exist uniquely.

E—**1.** E,F,G fundamental differential quantities of first order for surfaces. **2.** $E(\varphi,k)$, Legendre's normal elliptic integral, of the second kind, $E = \int_0^\varphi \Delta(\varphi) d\varphi$. **3.** east. **4.** (in Euler's polyhedral formula) number of edges of polyhedron. **5.** displacement operator, $E(f(x)) = f(x + 1)$. **6.** (in mathematical astronomy) equation of time.

Ei—exponential integral function $Ei(x) = \int_x^\infty du/(ue^u)$.

Eq—equation.

Ex—exercise.

e—**1.** base of natural (or Napierian) logarithms. In place of e^A one may write exp A. $e = 2.71828\ 18284\ 59045\ 23536\ \cdots \log_{10} e = M = 0.43429\ 44819\ 03251\ 82765\ \cdots \log_e 10 = 1/M = 2.30258\ 50929\ 94045\ 68402$. In some engineering work, where e is used otherwise, the base of natural logarithms is designated by ϵ. **2.** eccentricity of a conic. **3.** $e_1 = \wp(\omega_1)$, $e_2 = \wp(\omega_2)$, $e_3 = \wp(\omega_3)$, for Weierstrassian elliptic functions. **4.** (in mathematical astronomy) eccentricity of earth's orbit. **5.** (in elementary solid geometry) length of lateral edge (of right pyramid, prism, etc.).

erf—error function, $\operatorname{erf}(x) = (\sqrt{2/\pi})\int_x^\infty e^{-\frac{1}{2}t^2}dt$.

exp—exponential function of, as in $\exp(a^2 + b^2)$ for $e^{a^2+b^2}$. One could also write this "e^u where $u = a^2 + b^2$."

exsec—exsecant function, $\operatorname{exsec}\theta = \sec\theta - 1$.

F—Force.

F—**1.** general symbol for function or functional. **2.** the second fundamental differential quantity of first order for surfaces. See E. **3.** (in Euler's polyhedral formula) number of faces of polyhedron. **4.** $F(\varphi, k)$, Legendre's normal elliptic integral of the first kind, $F = \int_0^\varphi d\varphi/\Delta(\varphi)$. See Δ and E. φ is here the amplitude of F, $\varphi = \operatorname{am} F$. **5.** $F(a, b; c: x)$, hypergeometric function. **6.** Fahrenheit, degree Fahrenheit, as in 70F.

FS—Fourier series.

Fig.—figure.

Fr—frontier set of.

f—**1.** general symbol for function or functional. **2.** f_i, frequency of X_i in univariate table. **3.** frequency of vibration. **4.** feet as in f/s, feet per second. Preferable ft/sec.

ft—feet. See also f and $'$.

G—**1.** general symbol for group. **2.** the third fundamental differential quantity of first order for surfaces. **3.** $G(x_1, \cdots, x_n; \xi_1, \cdots, \xi_n)$ Green's function for two points in n-space. **4.** (constant) linear group of points on an algebraic curve. See g. **5.** gravitational constant.

G.C.T.—Greenwich civil time.

GCD—greatest common divisor.

GCS—greatest common subgroup.

GF—Galois field, as in GF(p^n).

GM—geometric mean.

GP—geometric progression.

g—**1.** general function symbol, used with f. **2.** (terrestrial) gravitational attraction. **3.** (variable) linear group of points on an algebraic curve. See G. **4.** g_i, frequency of y_i in bivariate table. **5.** general coefficient in tensor, as in $g_{ij}^k x^i y^i z_k$.

gd—Gudermannian. $e^u = \tan\left(\dfrac{\pi}{4} + \dfrac{1}{2}\operatorname{gd} u\right)$.

grad—gradient of. Also written ∇.

H—**1.** general symbol for subgroup, as in G/H, particularly for normal (or self-conjugate) subgroup. **2.** Hessian, as in $H(f) = \det\dfrac{\partial^2 f}{\partial x_i \partial x_j}$. **3.** $H_n(x)$, nth Hermite polynomial, $H_n(x)e^{-x^2/2} = (-1)^n D^n e^{-x^2/2}$. **4.** $H(P_1, P_3; P_2, P_4)$ is the proposition that P_1 and P_3 separate harmonically P_2 and P_4. **5.** orthocenter of triangle. **6.** $H(q_1, \cdots, q_n, t, p_1, \cdots, p_n)$ Hamiltonian function (in mathematical physics). **7.** mean curvature of surface, $H = EG - F^2$. **8.** (in mathematical astronomy) hour-angle. Also designated by t.

HCF—highest common factor.

HM—harmonic mean.

HP—(in elementary algebra) harmonic progression.

Hyp.—hypothesis.

h—**1.** (in interpolation theory), distance, between uniformly spaced ordinates. **2.** class interval, in x. **3.** increment of x. Also Δx. **4.** (as superscript) hours, as in $8^h 15^m$. **5.** (terminal) hyperbolic, as in sinh, $\tanh^{-1}$, etc. **6.** altitude ("height").

hav—haversine (of). hav $x = (\text{vers } x)/2$.

I—**1.** general symbol for interval, and for definite integral. **2.** Roman numeral for "one." Write IV not IIII, IX not VIIII. **3.** $I(\ )$, imaginary part of, also designated by $\mathfrak{T}(\ )$, or $\text{Im}(\ )$. **4.** $I_n(z)$, the Bessel function "of imaginary argument," $I_n(z) = \sum_{m=0}^{\infty} \dfrac{(\frac{1}{2})z^{n+2m}}{m!\,\Gamma(n + m + 1)}$. **5.** (in geometry of triangle) in center. **6.** sometimes used for the identity as an operation in a group.

$\mathfrak{T}$—(Black letter) imaginary part of. See I.

Im—imaginary part of. See I.

i—**1.** running index, as in a_i, $i = 1, \cdots, n$. **2.** one of the two imaginary square roots of -1. (In electrical engineering, when it is used for the current, j is used for this imaginary unit.)

i—i, j, k, unit vectors in a right-handed rectangular system. $i \times j = k$, $j \times k = i$, $k \times i = j$.

inf.—("infimum") greatest lower bound.

J—**1.** Jacobian as in $J\left(\dfrac{u,v,w}{x,y,z}\right)$, also designated by $\partial(u,v,w)/\partial(x,y,z)$. **2.** $J_n(z)$, Bessel coefficient of order n. **3.** Jacobian curve. **4.** Jacobian group of points in a linear series of groups of points on an algebraic curve.

j—**1.** running index, with i. **2.** (sometimes in electrical engineering) $\sqrt{(-1)}$. See i.

j—a unit vector. See i.

K—**1.** specific curvature of surface. **2.** kernel of integral equation, as in $u(x) = f(x) + \lambda \displaystyle\int_a^b K(x,t)u(t)dt$. K_n, the nth iterated kernel is then defined recursively by $K_1 \equiv K$, $K_n(x,y) = \displaystyle\int_a^b K_{n-1}(x,t)K(t,y)dt$. Also designated by $K^{(n)}$. **3.** K, iK', periods for Jacobian elliptic functions. **4.** Symmedian (Lemoine) center of triangle. **5.** $K_n(z)$, the Bessel function ("second solution") $\displaystyle\lim_{\nu \to n} \dfrac{(-1)^n}{2}\left[\dfrac{I_{-\nu}(z) - I_\nu(z)}{\nu - n}\right]$

k—**1.** proportionality factor for variation. Do not use $\dot{y} \propto x$. **2.** running index, used with h. **3.** k,k', modulus and complementary modulus respectively of Jacobian elliptic functions. **4.** class interval, in y. **5.** increment in y. Also Δy.

k—a unit vector. See i.

kei, ker—Bessel functions defined as real for real z and satisfying, ker(z) + i kei$(z) = K_0(z\sqrt{\pm i})$.

L—**1.** general symbol for linear function. **2.** general symbol for linear system, or linear space. **3.** limit, as in $\underset{n\to\infty}{L} e^{-n} = 0$. See "lim." **4.** Roman numeral for "fifty." **5.** length. Also designated by l. **6.** first fundamental differential quantity of second order for surfaces. **7.** Lexis ratio, $\sigma/\sqrt{pq/s}$, for sets of s objects each. **8.** $L_n(x)$, nth Laguerre polynomial, $L_n(x)e^{-x}n! = D^n(e^{-x}x^n)$.

LCD—lowest common denominator.

LCM—lowest (or least) common multiple.

l—**1.** running index. **2.** (in elementary algebra) last term (of arithmetic or geometric progression). **3.** $l = \cos \alpha$, directional cosine, (with x-axis). **4.** length. Also designated by L.

lat.—latitude.

li—logarithmic integral or integral logarithm function, $li(x) = \int_0^x du/\log u$.

lim—limit ( ), $\overline{\lim}$, least upper limit, $\underline{\lim}$, greatest lower limit.

ln—(Sometimes) natural logarithm of.

log—logarithm (of). In theoretical work, the natural base, e, is understood; in numerical computation with tables, the base 10 is understood unless otherwise specified. Some writers use "ln" for natural logarithm of. Where ambiguity is otherwise likely, indicate the base, thus $\log_b x$, $\log_{10} x$, $\log_e x$.

long—longitude.

M—**1.** Roman numeral, thousand. **2.** arithmetic mean. Also designated by superscript bar, as $\bar{X}$, or by AM. **3.** centroid (in geometry of triangle). **4.** second fundamental differential quantity of second order for surfaces.

M.D.—mean deviation.

Md—median.

Mm—mid-mean, arithmetic mean of data in range Q_1 to Q_3.

Mo—mode.

m—**1.** general symbol for natural number, or integer, usually used with n. **2.** slope of line, dy/dx. **3.** $m = \cos \beta$, directional cosine (with y-axis). **4.** m_a, m_b, m_c, median lines, lengths of medians of triangle. **5.** (as subscript) meridian measurement. **6.** class of an algebraic plane curve (a Plücker number). **7.** (superscript) minutes, as in $10^d13^h5^m$. **8.** meters.

max—maximum (of).

meas—measure (of).

mi—miles.

min—**1.** minimum (of). **2.** minutes

mod—**1.** modulus (of), as in mod$(re^{i\theta}) = r$. **2.** modulo as in $7 \equiv -3 \pmod 5$.

N—**1.** third fundamental differential quantity of second order for surfaces. **2.** north. **3.** total frequency in a statistical distribution.

n—**1.** general symbol for natural number or integer. **2.** $n = \cos \gamma$, directional cosine (with z-axis). **3.** order or degree of plane algebraic curve (a Plücker number). **4.** (in elementary algebra) number of terms in finite progression. **5.** (sometimes) total frequency. See N. **6.** outward normal to surface, as in $\cos (\theta, n)$.

O—**1.** origin of coordinates. **2.** circumcenter of triangle. **3.** of comparable order with, as $\Sigma_{n=0}^{N} n = 0(N^2)$.

o—of inferior order to, as $\log n = o(n)$.

ord—order.

P—**1.** general symbol for polynomial, in particular the interpolational polynomial. **2.** product moment. Also expressed by p. **3.** general symbol for point. The common notation indicating the coordinate system used as $P(x,y,z)$, $P(r,\theta,\varphi)$, etc., is not recommended. **4.** general probability distribution function, in particular any one of Pearson's standard types, or Poisson's forms. **5.** $P_n(x)$, Legendre polynomial, $2^n n! P_n(x) = D^n(x^2 - 1)^n$. **6.** total force due to pressure. **7.** function, as in $Pdx + Qdy$, and in $y' + P(x)y = Q(x)$. **8.** $P_{n,r}$ or $_nP_r$, or $P(n,r)$, number of permutations of n distinct things taken r at a time (without repetitions), $= n!/r!$. **9.** general potential due to finite number of particles. In Newtonian case $P = \Sigma_i m_i / r_i$. See U and W. **10.** horizontal parallax. **11.** north celestial pole.

PE—probable error. See $\pm$.

Post.—postulate.

Prob.—**1.** problem. **2.** probability.

Prop.—proposition.

PS—power series.

Pt.—point.

$\wp$—Weierstrassian elliptic function.

p—**1.** general symbol for prime number. **2.** semi-latus rectum. **3.** probability ratio. **4.** genus (or deficiency) or plane algebraic curve (a Plücker number). **5.** perpendicular distance from origin to given line or plane.

6. p_n, numerator of nth convergent of continued fraction $a_0 + \dfrac{1}{a_1+} \dfrac{1}{a_2+}$
$\cdots$ ($p_{-1} = 0$, $p_0 = 1$), $p_1 = a_0$, $p_{n+1} = a_n p_n + p_{n-1}$. **7.** p_{12}, p_{13}, p_{14}, p_{23}, p_{24}, p_{34}, line coordinates (point system). **8.** sometimes "per," as in "rpm," revolutions per second. This use is not recommended. **9.** perimeter. **10.** $p(n)$, total number of partitions of n. **11.** p_i, impulse component.

p.—page.

pos.—positive.

Q—**1.** general symbol for quadratic form or quadratic manifold. **2.** Q_1, Q_3 first and third quartile marks. (Q_2 is the median, Md.) **3.** function, as in $Pdx + Qdy$, and in $y' + P(x)y = Q(x)$. **4.** $Q(P_1, P_2, P_3; P_4, P_5, P_6)$, quadrangular set of six points.

QD—quartile deviation.

Q.E.D.—("Quod erat demonstrandum") which was to be proved.

Q.E.F.—("Quod erat faciendum") which was to be constructed.

q—**1.** complementary probability, $q = 1 - p$. **2.** q_n, denominator of nth convergent of continued fraction, $a_0 + \dfrac{1}{a_1+} \dfrac{1}{a_2+} \cdots$ ($q_0 = 0$), $q_1 = 1$,

$q_{n+1} = a_n q_n + q_{n-1}$. **3.** $q_{12}, q_{13}, q_{14}, q_{23}, q_{24}, q_{34}$, line coordinates (plane system). **4.** q_1, q_2, quartile distances from the median. **5.** q_i, force component.

R—**1.** general symbol for remainder. $R_n(x)$, remainder after n terms in power-series in x. **2.** radius, in particular circumradius of triangle. **3.** real part of. Also indicated by $\mathfrak{R}$ (Black letter), and Re. **4.** general symbol for range of variable, as in $\int_{(R)}$.

$\mathfrak{R}$—(Black letter) real value of. See R.

R. A.—right ascension. Also designated by α.

Re—real value of. See R.

RMS—root-mean-square. $\sqrt{(\Sigma_{i=1}^n x^2/n)}$.

r—**1.** general running index, as in rth term. **2.** radius (see R), in particular in radius of triangle. **3.** coefficient of linear correlation, correlation coefficient. **4.** (in elementary algebra) common ratio between successive terms in a geometric progression. **5.** distance, in polar and in spherical coordinates; projected distances in cylindrical coordinates. **6.** (sometimes) revolutions, as in $r.p.m.$ (revolutions per minute). **7.** (sometimes) (superscript) radians, as in $2\pi^{(r)}$. (This usage is not recommended.)

rad—**1.** radius. **2.** radians. Where no units are indicated angles are measured in radians, sin 30 means "sine of 30 radians," not sin 30°. Do not write $\sin a^r$ or $\sin a^{(r)}$ for $\sin a$ (where a is measured in radians), since superscript r is sometimes interpreted as "revolutions."

rot—rotation or curl of vector. Also designated by $\nabla \times$.

S—**1.** general symbol for space, as S_n, space of n dimension. See L. **2.** general symbol for sum, as in S_n, sum of first n terms of given sequence or series. See s. **3.** south. **4.** standard error of estimate. **5.** radius of spherical curvature of curve.

Si—1st sine-integral function $\text{Si}(x) = \int_0^x (\sin u/u)du$. See si.

S.T.—siderial time.

s.—**1.** general running index. Used with r. **2.** general symbol for sum, as in s_n sum of first n terms of sequence or series. See S. **3.** (in elementary algebra), sum of arithmetic or of geometric progression. **4.** $s_k(n)$, sum of kth powers of first n natural numbers. **5.** s_k, sum of the kth powers of the roots of an algebraic equation. **6.** arc length. **7.** slant height. **8.** (usually as superscript) seconds. **9.** semi-interquartile range. **10.** semi-perimeter of triangle, $s = (a+b+c)/2$. **11.** (sometimes) number of individuals in sample. **12.** root-mean-square deviation about arbitrarily assumed origin, (in "short method").

sec—secant (of).

$\sec^{-1}$—inverse secant (of). Also designated by arc sec.

sech—hyperbolic secant (of). Do not use Sec or $\mathfrak{Sec}$ (in German letters).

sech^{-1}—inverse hyperbolic secant of. Do not use arc sech.

si—2nd sine-integral function, $\beta_i(x) = \int_\infty^x (\sin u/u)du$. See Si.

sgn—(signum) sign (of), more generally for z complex, $\text{sgn}\, z = z/|z|$

sin—sine (of). Do not use Sin.

$\sin^{-1}$—inverse sine (of). Also designated by arc sin.

sinh—hyperbolic sine (of). Do not use Sin, or $\mathfrak{Sin}$ (in German letters).

sinh⁻¹—inverse hyperbolic sine of. Do not use "arc sinh."

sk—skewness of frequency distribution.

sn—(Jacobian elliptic function), sine amplitude.

sq—square.

sup—(supremum) least upper bound. Sometimes designated by L.U.B., or l.u.b.

T—**1.** total time, (as in time of flight of projectile). **2.** clock time. **3.** general symbol for transformation, T^n, nth iterate of T. **4.** tons. **5.** (in logic), true or truth. **6.** absolute temperature.

Th—theorem.

t—**1.** general variable or parameter. **2.** time. See τ. See "dot accent." **3.** ordinary temperature. See T, τ, θ.

tan—tangent (of).

tan⁻¹—inverse tangent (of). Also designated by arc tan.

tanh—hyperbolic tangent (of). Do not use Tan or $\mathfrak{Tan}$ (in German letters).

tanh⁻¹—inverse hyperbolic tangent (of). Do not use arc tanh.

U—general (line surface or volume) potential. In Newtonian case, $U = \int_{(L)} \frac{\mu dL}{r}$ or $\int_{(S)} \frac{\mu dS}{r}$, or $\int_{(V)} \frac{\mu dV}{r}$. See P and W.

u—**1.** general variable, especially dependent variable or real part thereof. See w. **2.** u_n, Lucas' function $u_n = (\alpha^n - \beta^n)/(\alpha - \beta)$, α, β, roots of given quadratic.

V—**1.** Roman numeral, five. **2.** (in Euler's polyhedral formula) number of vertices. **3.** general harmonic function. **4.** volume.

v—(linear) velocity.

v—**1.** general variable, especial dependent variable, used with u, or coefficient of pure imaginary part thereof. See w. **2.** v_n, Lucas' function $\alpha^n + \beta^n$, α, β, roots of given quadratic. See u_n. **3.** speed.

W—**1.** west. **2.** general potential of double layer. In Newtonian case, $W = \int_{(S)} \nu \frac{\partial}{\partial n}\left(\frac{1}{r}\right) dS, = -\int_{(S)} \frac{\nu}{r^2} \cos (r,n)\, dS$. See P and U. **3.** Wronskian,

$$W = \begin{vmatrix} y_1 & y_1' & \cdots & y_1^{(n-1)} \\ \cdots & \cdots & \cdots & \cdots \\ y_n & y_n' & \cdots & y_n^{(n-1)} \end{vmatrix}.$$

4. total weight. Also designated by Wt. **5.** work (or energy). Also designated by Wk.

Wt.—weight. See W.

w—**1.** general symbol for variable, particularly dependent variable. Used with u and v as in $J\left(\frac{u,v,w}{x,y,z}\right)$, etc. **2.** dependent complex variable, $w = u + iv$, or $w(z) = u(x,y) + iv(x,y)$ where $z = x + iy$, x,y,u,v, real.

X—**1.** Roman numeral, ten; as in XCIII, etc. **2.** X_i, original numerical data for x-variates, (previous to change of origin or scale). **3.** general symbol for variable point, particularly on x-axis. **4.** function, as in $X dx + Y dy + Z dz$ or $\frac{dx}{X} = \frac{dy}{Y} = \frac{dz}{Z}$.

x—**1.** general symbol for independent variable or unknown. **2.** first rectangular coordinate. In space a right-handed coordinate system such as indicated

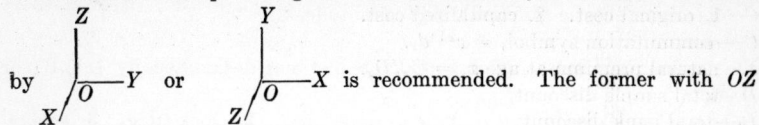

by $\Big/\!\!\!-\!\!O\!-\!Y$ or $\Big/\!\!\!-\!\!O\!-\!X$ is recommended. The former with OZ directed to the zenith is more common. **3.** real part of independent complex variable $z = x + iy$.

Y—**1.** Y_i, original numerical data for y-variates (previous to change of origin or scale). **2.** function as in $Xdx + Ydy + Zdz$, or $\dfrac{dx}{X} = \dfrac{dy}{Y} = \dfrac{dz}{Z}$.

y—**1.** general symbol for dependent (real) variable. **2.** general symbol for second independent variable, r unknown. **3.** second rectangular coordinate. See x. **4.** pure imaginary coefficient, in independent complex variable, $z = x + iy$.

Z—zenith.

Z.T.—zone time.

z—**1.** independent complex variable, $z = x + iy$. **2.** general symbol for third independent variable or unknown. **3.** third rectangular coordinate. See x. **4.** axial coordinate in cylindrical coordinates (r, θ, z). **5.** zenith distance, $(90^0 - h)$.

Selected Symbols Used in Financial and Actuarial Theory

α—net premium in first policy year.

β—net premium in each policy year after the first.

δ—force of interest (and of discount) $e^{\delta} = 1 + i$.

ω—terminal recorded age in mortality table, "limiting" age.

A_x—commutation symbol, present value of net single premium for whole life policy on (x), $= M_x/D_x$.

$a_{\overline{n}|i}$—present value of annuity for unit periodic payment, $= (1 - v^n)/i$.

$a_{\overline{n}|i}^{(p)}$—present value of an annuity of 1 per annum at interest rate i, payable p times a year (in installments of $1/p$ each).

a_x—commutation symbol, present value of (ordinary) whole life annuity on (x) of unit annual payment.

$a_x^{(m)}$—present value of whole life annuity on (x), of unit annual payment, payable m times a year.

$n|a_x$—present value of whole life annuity, on (x), deferred n years for unit annual payment.

$a_{x\overline{n}|}$—present value of temporary life annuity, on (x), for n years, for unit annual payment.

$a_{\infty i}$—present value of perpetuity at rate of interest, i.

$\ddot{a}_{\infty i}$—present value of perpetuity due at rate of interest, i.

$\ddot{a}_x$—commutation symbol present value of whole life annuity due, on (x), of unit annual payment.

$\ddot{a}_{\overline{n}|i}$—present value of an annuity due, for unit periodic payments at interest rate i.

B—book value.

B_k—book value, after k years.

C—1. original cost. 2. capitalized cost.

C_x—commutation symbol, $= v^{x+1}d_x$.

c_x—natural premium at age x, $= C_x/D_x$.

D—total simple discount.

D_b—total bank discount.

D_c—cash discount, where for example, "terms 4/10, 2/30, n/90" designates 4% discount for payment within 10 days, 2% thereafter but within 30 days, payable net in 90 days.

D_t—trade discount.

D_x—commutation symbol, $= v^x l_x$.

d—rate of simple discount, $= 1 - v = 1 - (1 + i)^{-1} = i/(1 + i)$.

d_x—number dying between ages x and $x + 1$, according to mortality table (for 100,000 alive at age 10).

E—present value of expectation.

$_nE_x$—present value of an n-year pure endowment to (x), $= v^n l_{x+n}/l_x$.

e_x—curtate expectation of life for (x), $= (l_x + \cdots + l_\omega)/l_x$.

$\overset{\circ}{e}_x$—complete expectation of life, for (x), $= e_x + \frac{1}{2}$.

F—1. net-cost-rate factor. 2. face value of bond.

I—total interest (ordinary simple).

I'—total interest (exact, simple).

i—rate of interest (effective).

$j_{(p)}$—nominal rate of interest convertible p times a year corresponding to effective annual rate i, $= p[(1 + i)^{1/p} - 1]$.

k_x—valuation symbol, $= C_x/D_{x+1}$.

$_nk_x$—valuation symbol, $= (M_x - M_{x+n})/D_{x+n}$, $[_1k_x = k_x]$, accumulated cost of insurance.

L—1. list price (for trade discount). 2. salvage value.

l_x—number living at age x according to mortality table (for 100,000 alive at age 10).

$\mathbb{N}_x$—("open bar N"), commutation symbol, $= D_x + D_{x+1} + \cdots + D\omega$.

n—number of conversion periods (for compound interest).

P—principal.

P_b—bank proceeds.

P_x—net annual premium for ordinary whole life policy, on (x), for unit annual payment $= A_x/(1 + a_x)$.

$_rP_x$—net annual premium for r-payment life policy, $= M_x/(\mathbb{N}_x - \mathbb{N}_{x+r})$.

p—1. probability of success. 2. interest period/payment interval.

p_x—probability of living for another year for a person of age x (according to mortality table).

$_np_x$—probability that a person aged x will live n years, $= l_{x+n}/l_x$.

p_{xy}—the probability that (x) and (y) will survive jointly for one year.

$_np_{xy}$—the probability that (x) and (y) will survive jointly for n years.

q—probability of failure, $= 1 - p$.

q_x—probability of dying within a year for a person of age x (according to mortality table).

$|_nq_x$—probability that (x) will die within n years.

$_n|q_x$—the probability that (x) will die between ages $x + n$ and $x + n + 1$.

R—**1.** periodic payment or "rent." **2.** replacement cost. **3.** repair charge (annual).

S—amount.

S—**1.** scrap value. **2.** amount of sinking fund. **3.** subscription price. **4.** amount (at simple interest).

s—amount (at compound interest) for unit principal $= (1 + i)^n$.

$s_{\overline{n}|i}$—amount of annuity for unit periodic payment, $= [(1 + i)^n - 1]/i$.

$s_{\infty i}$—amount of perpetuity at interest rate i.

s_∞—amount of perpetuity due.

$s_{\overline{n}|i}$—amount of an annuity due, for unit periodic payments.

$s_{\overline{n}|i}^{(p)}$—amount at end of n years of annuity of 1 per annum at interest rate i, payable p times a year (in installments of $1/p$ each).

u_x—valuation symbol, $= D_x/D_{x+1}$.

$_n u_x$—valuation symbol, $(N_x - N_{x+n})/D_{x+n}$, $[_1 u_x = u_x]$, accumulated value of individual survivors payments.

V—purchase price (of bond).

$_t V_x$—terminal reserve of tth policy year on policy on (x) of unit annual payment.

v—present value (at compound interest) for unit principal, $= (1 + i)^{-1}$.

W—wearing value, $=$ original cost minus scrap value.

x—age of insured (to nearest year).

(x)—a person aged x (for use with mortality table).

$x]$—where $[x] + t$ indicates a life, now aged $x + t$, who was accepted for insurance t years ago at age x.

INDEX

A

INDEX

INDEX

P

INDEX

INDEX